STEAM

ITS GENERATION AND USE

THE BABCOCK & WILCOX COMPANY

NEW YORK

Geo. McKibbin & Son
New York, U. S. A.

THE BABCOCK & WILCOX COMPANY
161 EAST 42ND STREET, NEW YORK 17, N. Y.

WORKS

BARBERTON, O.   BEAVER FALLS, PA.   AUGUSTA, GA.

ALLIANCE, O.   WILMINGTON, N. C.

WEST POINT, MISS.   PARIS, TEX.   BRUNSWICK, GA.

MILWAUKEE, WIS.   LYNCHBURG, VA.

DISTRICT SALES OFFICES AND REPRESENTATIVES

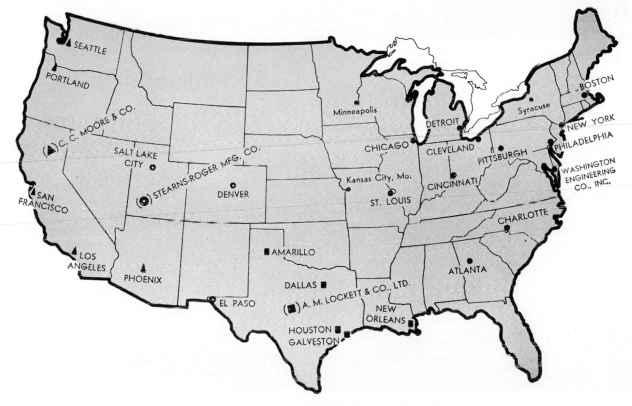

HAWAIIAN ISLANDS—Hawaiian Equipment Co., Ltd.   PHILIPPINE ISLANDS—Earnshaws Docks & Honolulu Iron Works

PUERTO RICO—Portilla Corp.   CUBA—Agencia Macfarlane, S. A.

PLANTS OF THE BABCOCK & WILCOX COMPANY

Main Works, Boiler Division, Barberton, O.

Main Works, Tubular Products Division, Beaver Falls, Pa.

PLANTS OF THE BABCOCK & WILCOX COMPANY

AUGUSTA WORKS, REFRACTORIES DIVISION, AUGUSTA, GA.

RUSH STREET WORKS, BOILER DIVISION, ALLIANCE, O.

PLANTS OF THE BABCOCK & WILCOX COMPANY

WILMINGTON WORKS, BOILER DIVISION, WILMINGTON, N. C.

WEST POINT WORKS, BOILER DIVISION, WEST POINT, MISS.

PLANTS OF THE BABCOCK & WILCOX COMPANY

Paris Works, Boiler Division, Paris, Tex.

Brunswick Works, Boiler Division, Brunswick, Ga.

PLANTS OF THE BABCOCK & WILCOX COMPANY

Nuclear Facilities Plant, Atomic Energy Division, Lynchburg, Va.

Alliance Works, Tubular Products Division, Alliance, O.

PLANTS OF THE BABCOCK & WILCOX COMPANY

Milwaukee Works, Tubular Products Division, Milwaukee, Wis.

Research and Development, Alliance, O.

CONTENTS

Foreword

IN 1867 George H. Babcock and Stephen Wilcox formed a partnership. The present company succeeded it in 1881.

This 37th edition of STEAM—the first appeared in 1879—marks tremendous advances in the production of steam and in the burning of fuels.

Countless improvements have been devised by the ingenuity of man to give him mastery of his environment. Surely some of the greatest are the steam engine and the developments which followed its introduction.

This intensive age depends upon power for convenience and release from physical drudgery and, indeed, for its adequate continuation. Industrial power is still, and will long be, dependent upon the use of fuel for the generation of steam.

The Company gratefully acknowledges the support, cooperation, and loyalty of its patrons and employees, which have made possible its contributions in the field of steam generation. It expresses the hope that this volume may help to stimulate further advances in the art.

CHAIRMAN OF THE BOARD

INTRODUCTION TO STEAM

RECORDS indicate that some knowledge and use of the expansive force of the vapor of water existed before 150 B.C. In the treatise, *Pneumatica*, of about that time, Hero, of Alexandria, described existing devices of his predecessors and contemporaries as well as an invention of his own utilizing the expansive force of steam in raising water above its natural level. He described the use of three properties of steam as a direct source of power; raising water by its elasticity, elevating a weight by its expansive power, and producing a rotary motion by its reaction on the atmosphere. In the last application, known as "Hero's engine," a hollow sphere was supported over a caldron or boiler by two trunnions, one of which was hollow and connected the interior of the sphere with the steam space of the caldron. To provide a connection between the caldron and the atmosphere, two pipes, open at the ends and bent at right angles, were inserted at opposite poles of the sphere. When heat was applied to the caldron, the steam generated passed through the hollow trunnion to the sphere and thence into the atmosphere through the two pipes. The steam, in escaping through these pipes, caused the sphere to rotate as a primitive reaction turbine.

Hero did not suggest the useful application of any of the devices he described. Although these devices were sometimes used for trivial purposes, there is no record of progress until the late sixteenth and early seventeenth centuries.

Early Studies and Applications

Treatises bearing on the generation of steam were published by Matthesius, a German author, in 1571; Besson, a philosopher and mathematician at Orleans, in 1578; Ramelli, in 1588; Battista Della Porta, a Neapolitan mathematician and philosopher, in 1601; De Caus, a French engineer and architect, in 1615; and Branca, an Italian architect, in 1629.

Credit for proposing, if not making, the first useful steam engine is apparently due Edward Somerset, second Marquis of Worcester. In a treatise published in 1663, he described devices for raising water not only by forcing it from two receivers by direct steam pressure but also by a reciprocating piston actuating one end of a lever, the other end operating a pump. His descriptions are rather obscure and there are no drawings. There is no authentic record that any of the devices he described was actually constructed, but it is claimed by many that he did build and operate a steam engine containing pistons.

In 1680 Dr. Denis Papin, a Frenchman, invented a steam digester for culinary purposes, using "a boiler under heavy pressure." To overcome danger from explosion, he added a contrivance which is the first safety valve of record.

First Successful Steam Engine

The first commercially successful steam engine was developed by Thomas Savery. In 1699 Savery exhibited a model steam engine before the Royal Society of England (Sir Isaac Newton was president at the time). This engine consisted of two copper receivers alternately connected, by a three-way hand-operated valve, with a boiler and a source of water supply. When the water in one receiver had been driven out by the steam, cold water was poured over its outside surface, creating a partial vacuum through condensation and causing it to fill again while the water in the other reservoir was being forced out. A number of machines were built on this principle and placed in actual use as mine pumps.

A serious drawback in the use of Savery's engine was that the height to which it could lift water was limited by the pressure the boiler and vessels could bear. Before its eventual displacement by Newcomen's engine, Desaguliers improved the Savery engine by applying the Papin safety valve to the boiler and using a jet within the vessel for condensation in place of surface condensation.

The earliest cylinder and piston steam engine was based on Papin's suggestion, in 1690, that the condensation of steam should be used to make a vacuum beneath a piston after it had been raised by the expansion of steam. Newcomen's atmospheric engine was a practical application of this principle. Papin's first engine was unworkable because the same vessel served as both boiler and cylinder. Heat was applied to a small quantity of water in the bottom of the vessel. After the piston had been raised by the steam generated, the heat was withdrawn and work was done by the piston on its down stroke under pressure of the atmosphere. An improved form of this engine was developed by Papin after hearing of Savery's engine. In Papin's engine of 1705, a floating diaphragm or piston on top of the water in a displacement chamber kept the steam and water from direct contact. The water, delivered to a closed tank by the downward movement of the piston under pressure, flowed in a

Fig. 1. First water-tube boiler. Built by William Blakey and patented by him in 1766

continuous stream against the vanes of a water wheel. When the steam in the displacement chamber had expanded, it was exhausted to the atmosphere through a valve instead of being condensed. The engine was, in fact, a non-condensing, single action steam pump with the steam and pump cylinders in one. A curious feature of this engine was a mass of heated metal placed in the diaphragm to keep the steam dry and so to prevent condensation during expansion. This device might be called the first superheater.

Among the various inventions attributed to Papin was a boiler with an internal firebox, the earliest record of such construction.

Newcomen's Engine for Pumping Water

While Papin neglected his own earlier suggestion of a steam and piston engine to develop Savery's ideas, Thomas Newcomen, with his assistant, John Cawley, adapted Papin's suggestion of 1690 in a practical engine. Steam admitted from the boiler to a cylinder raised a piston by its expansion, assisted by a counterweight on the other end of a beam actuated by the piston. The steam valve was then shut and the steam condensed by a jet of cold water. The piston was then forced downward by atmospheric pressure and did work on a pump. The condensed water in the cylinder was expelled through an escapement valve by the next entry of steam. This engine used steam having a pressure but little, if any, above that of the atmosphere.

In 1711, this engine was introduced into mines for pumping. Whether its action was originally automatic or dependent upon the hand operation of the valves is unknown. The story commonly believed is that a boy, Humphrey Potter, in 1713, whose duty it was to open and shut such valves of an engine he attended, by suitable cords and catches attached to the beam, caused the engine to manipulate these valves automatically. This device was simplified in 1718 by Henry Beighton, who suspended from the beam a rod called the plug-tree, which actuated the valves by tappets. By 1725, this engine was in common use in collieries and was changed but little in the next sixty or seventy years. Since the pressure in the pumps did not depend on the steam pressure, Newcomen's engine was a distinct advance compared with Savery's engine. In common with Savery's engine, the losses from the alternate heating and cooling of the steam cylinder were enormous. Though this engine might have been modified to serve many purposes, its use seems to have been limited almost entirely to the pumping of water.

The rivalry between Savery and Papin stimulated attention to the saving of fuel. In 1730, Dr. John Allen noted that nearly half of the heat of the fire was lost due to the short duration of the contact between the gases and the heating surfaces of the boiler. To overcome this loss, at least partially, he used an internal furnace with a smoke flue winding through the water in the form of a worm in a still. So that the length of passage of the gases might not act as a damper on the fire, he recommended the use of bellows for forcing the gases through

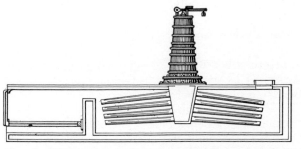

Fig. 2. Water-tube boiler of small tubes connected at one end with a reservoir. John Stevens, 1804

the flue. This is probably the first suggested use of forced draft. In estimating the quantity of fuel lost up the stack, Allen probably made the first boiler test.

Toward the end of the period of use of Newcomen's atmospheric engine, John Smeaton, who, about 1770, built and installed a number of large engines of this type, greatly improved the design in its mechanical details.

Earliest Water-tube Boiler

A patent taken out by William Blakey in 1766, covering an improvement in Savery's engine, included a novel form of steam generator (see Fig. 1). This is probably the first step in the development of the water-tube boiler. Several tubes alternately inclined at opposite angles were arranged in the furnace, the adjacent tube ends being connected by small pipes. The first successful user of water-tube boilers, however, was James Rumsey, an American inventor, celebrated for his early experiments in steam navigation, and it is he who is truly the originator of the water-tube boiler. In 1788, he patented, in England, several forms of boilers, some of which were of the water-tube type. One had a firebox with flat top and sides, with horizontal tubes across the firebox connecting the water spaces. Another had a cylindrical firebox surrounded by an annular water space and a coiled tube was placed within the box, connected at its two ends with the water space. This was the first of the "coil boilers." Another form in the same patent was the vertical tubular boiler, practically as made at the present time.

Great Contributions of James Watt

The improvements in boiler and engine design of Smeaton, Newcomen and their contemporaries, were followed by those of the great engineer, James Watt, an instrument maker of Glasgow. In 1763, while repairing a model of Newcomen's engine, he was impressed by the great waste of steam in the alternate cooling and heating of the engine. His remedy was to maintain the cylinder at the temperature of the entering steam. With this in view, he added a vessel, separate from the cylinder, into which the steam should pass from the cylinder and be condensed, either by the application of cold water outside or by a jet from within. To preserve a vacuum in his condenser, he added an air pump to remove the water of condensation and air brought in with the injection water or due to leakage. As the cylinder no longer acted as a condenser, it could be maintained at a high temperature by covering it with nonconducting material and, in particular, by the use of a steam jacket. Further, and with the same object in view, he covered the top of the cylinder and introduced steam above

Fig. 3. *Water-tube boiler, with tubes connecting water chamber at bottom and steam chamber at top. John Cox Stevens, 1805*

the piston to do the work previously accomplished by atmospheric pressure. After several trials with an experimental apparatus based on these ideas, Watt patented his improvements in 1769.

Though Watt's patent describes a noncondensing engine which would require high pressures, his aversion to such practice was strong. Notwithstanding his knowledge of the advantages through added expansion under high pressure, he continued to use pressures not more than 7 psig. To overcome such pressures, the boilers were fed through a standpipe of sufficient height so that the column of water offset the pressure within the boiler.

In 1782, Watt patented two other features which he had invented as early as 1769. These were the double-acting engine, that is, the use of steam on both sides of the piston; and the use of steam expansively, that is, the shutting off of steam from the cylinder when the piston had made but a portion of its stroke, the power for the completion of the stroke being supplied by the expansive force of the steam already admitted.

He further added a throttle valve for the regulation of steam admission, invented the automatic governor and the steam indicator, a mercury steam gage and a glass water column.

While little is said in the biographies of Watt about the improvement of steam boilers, all the evidence indicates that Boulton and Watt introduced the first "wagon boiler," so called because of its shape. In 1785, Watt took out a number of patents for variations in furnace construction. Because of the low steam pressures used until the early part of the nineteenth century, little attention was given to the form of the boiler for supplying steam to the engines described above.

About 1800, Richard Trevithick, in England, and Oliver Evans, in America, introduced noncondensing, and for that time, high-pressure steam engines. To the initiative of Evans may be attributed the general use of high-pressure steam in the United States, a feature which for many years distinguished

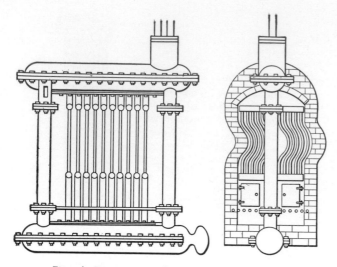

Fig. 4. *First sectional water-tube boiler with well-defined circulation. Joseph Eve, 1825*

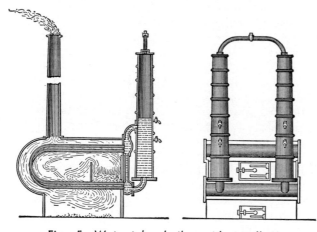

Fig. 5. *Water-tube boiler with small U shaped tubes connected at ends with larger pipes. Goldsworthy Gurney, 1826*

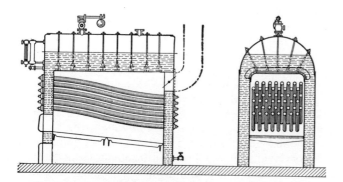

Fig. 6. *Inclined water tubes connecting water spaces at front and rear with steam space above. Stephen Wilcox, 1856*

American from European practice. The demand for light weight and economy of space following the beginning of steam navigation and the invention of the locomotive, required boilers designed and constructed to withstand heavier pressures and forced the adoption of the cylindrical form of boiler, which, as might be expected, varied greatly in detail and principles of operation.

One of the types increasingly used was the plain shell type vessel or the many modifications of the shell type which incorporated a greater or less number of flues conducted across the water space through which the hot gases passed. However, as the number of steam engines and boilers in use continued to multiply due to the intense industrial activity of the middle nineteenth century, the increase in the number and seriousness of shell boiler explosions served to emphasize the inherent safety advantages of the water-tube boiler.

Early American Steam Boilers

The first water-tube boiler made of a combination of small tubes, connected at one end to a reservoir (see Fig. 2) was the invention of an American, John Stevens, in 1804. This boiler was actually used to generate steam for the engine of a steamboat operating on the Hudson river, but like all the "porcupine" boilers, of which type it was the first, it did not have the elements required for continued success. Another form of water-tube boiler was patented in 1805 by John Cox Stevens, a son of John Stevens. This boiler consisted of 20 vertical tubes, 1¼ in. internal diameter and 40½ in. long, arranged in a circle, the outside diameter of which was approximately 12 in., connecting a water chamber at the bottom with a steam chamber at the top. The steam and water chambers were annular spaces of small cross section and contained approximately 33 cu in. The illustration, Fig. 3, shows the cap of the steam chamber secured by bolts. One of these boilers was for a long time at the Stevens Institute of Technology at Hoboken, N. J. and is now in the Smithsonian Institutition at Washington.

About the same time, Arthur Woolf built a boiler of large horizontal tubes, extending across the furnace and connected at the ends to a longitudinal drum above. The first purely sectional water-tube boiler was built by Julius Griffith, in 1821. In this boiler, a number of horizontal water tubes were connected to vertical side pipes, the side pipes were connected to horizontal gathering pipes, and the latter in turn to a steam drum.

In 1822, Jacob Perkins constructed a flash boiler for what was then considered a high pressure. A number of cast iron bars, with 1½ in. annular holes, were arranged in three tiers over the fire, and their outer ends were connected by a series of bent pipes, outside of the furnace walls. The water was fed slowly to the tier by a force pump, and steam in the superheated state was discharged from the lower tiers into a chamber from which it was taken to the engine.

The first sectional water-tube boiler, with a well-defined circulation, was built by Joseph Eve, in 1825 (see Fig. 4). The sections composed of small tubes, practically vertical, but with a slight double curve, were fixed in horizontal headers, which were in turn connected to a steam space above and a water space below formed of larger pipes. The steam and water spaces were connected by outside pipes to secure a circulation of the water up through the sections and down through the external pipes. In the same year, John M'Curdy of New York, built a "Duplex Steam Generator" of "tubes of wrought or cast iron or other material" arranged in several horizontal rows, connected together alternately at the front and rear by return bends. Interior circular vessels closed at the ends were placed in the tubes below the water line, so that a thin sheet of water would be exposed to the action of the fire.

In 1826, Goldsworthy Gurney built a number of boilers, which were used on his steam carriages. A number of small tubes were bent in the shape of a "U" laid sidewise and the ends were connected with larger horizontal pipes (see Fig. 5). These were connected by vertical pipes to permit circulation and also to a vertical cylinder which served as a steam and water reservoir. In 1828, Paul Steenstrup made the first shell boiler with vertical water tubes in the large flues similar to the boiler known as the "Martin," and suggesting the "Galloway."

The first water-tube boiler with fire tubes within water tubes was built in 1830, by Summers & Ogle. Horizontal connections at the top and bottom were connected by a series of vertical water tubes, with fire tubes extending through the water tubes and the horizontal connections. The fire tubes were held in place by nuts, which also served to make the joints.

Early Development of the B&W Boiler

Stephen Wilcox, in 1856, was the first to use inclined water tubes connecting water spaces at the front and rear with a steam space above (see Fig. 6). The first to make such inclined tubes into a sectional form was Twibill, in 1865 (see Fig. 7). He used wrought iron tubes connected at the front and rear with standpipes through intermediate connections. These standpipes carried the steam to a horizontal cross-drum at the top, the entrained water being carried to the rear.

In 1866 George Herman Babcock became associated with Stephen Wilcox and the first Babcock and Wilcox boiler (see Fig. 8) was patented in 1867. The nest of horizontal cast iron tubes at the

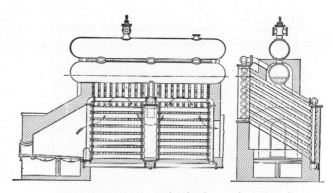

Fig. 7. *First water-tube boiler with inclined tubes in sectional form. Twibill, 1865*

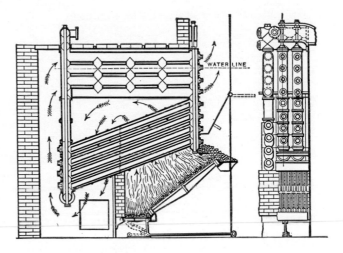

Fig. 8. *First Babcock & Wilcox boiler, patented in 1867*

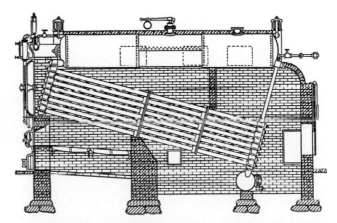

Fig. 9. *Babcock & Wilcox boiler, developed in 1877*

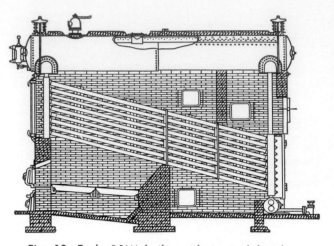

Fig. 10. *Early B&W boiler with vertical headers*

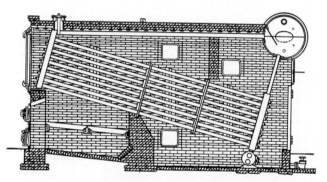

Fig. 11. *Early B&W boiler of cross-drum type*

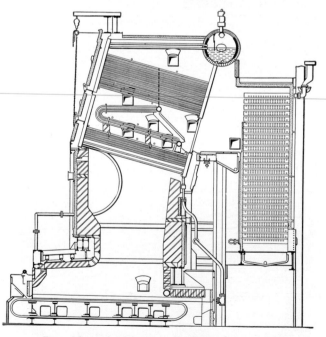

Fig. 12. *B&W boiler for 650 psi working pressure and 750 F total temperature, 1924*

top served in place of a steam and water drum. The inclined steam gathering tubes below, also of cast iron, were placed one above the other in vertical rows, each row and its ends forming a single casting. During the next ten years development of the boiler continued with great vigor. Drums were soon substituted for the nest of cast iron tubes originally used for steam and water storage, and, as might be expected, steel replaced cast iron for the generating tubes. By 1877 the B&W boiler had been modified as shown in Fig. 9. A little later the headers were made of wrought steel to meet the demand for boilers carrying higher pressure. Still later developments are illustrated in Figs. 10 and 11. In these boilers the cast iron drum heads of Fig. 9 had been changed to dished heads of pressed steel.

The following rules, formulated by Stephen Wilcox and originally published in 1875, are of interest since they are quite sound today.

Requirements of a Perfect Steam Boiler

1. Proper workmanship and simple construction, using materials which experience has shown to be the best, thus avoiding the necessity of early repairs.

2. A mud-drum to receive all impurities deposited from the water, and so placed as to be removed from the action of the fire.

3. A steam and water capacity sufficient to prevent any fluctuation in steam pressure or water level.

4. A water surface for the disengagement of the steam from the water, of sufficient extent to prevent foaming.

5. A constant and thorough circulation of water throughout the boiler, so as to maintain all parts at the same temperature.

6. The water space divided into sections so arranged that, should any section fail, no general explosion can occur and the destructive effects will be confined to the escape of the contents. Large and free passages between the different sections to equalize the water line and pressure in all.

7. A great excess of strength over any legitimate strain, the boiler being so constructed as to be free from strains due to unequal expansion, and, if possible, to avoid joints exposed to the direct action of the fire.

8. A combustion chamber so arranged that the combustion of the gases started in the furnace may be completed before the gases escape to the chimney. (Editor's note: Today it is essential that combustion be virtually completed in the furnace.)

9. The heating surface as nearly as possible at right angles to currents of heated gases, so as to break up the currents and extract the entire available heat from the gases.

10. All parts readily accessible for cleaning and

repairs. This is a point of the greatest importance as regards safety and economy.

11. Proportioned for the work to be done, and capable of working to its full rated capacity with the highest economy.

12. Equipped with the very best gages, safety valves, and other fixtures.

Early Central Stations

The plant of the Brush Electric Light Co. in Philadelphia was the first central station in America. Four Babcock & Wilcox boilers of 73 hp each were installed in this plant in 1881. In September of the next year, boilers of similar make were placed in operation at the Pearl Street Station of the Edison Electric Illuminating Co., New York. The Fisk Street Station of Commonwealth Edison Co., Chicago, commenced in 1902 and placed in service in October of 1903, was the first public utility plant exclusively using steam turbines for electrical generation. Ninety-six Babcock & Wilcox boilers of 508 hp each were installed in this plant. The turbines operated at 170 psi with steam at 70 F superheat.

From about 1900 to the period of World War I, steam pressures in the larger central stations were gradually increased. By 1914, 250 to 275 psi and a temperature of 560 F were not uncommon steam conditions at the turbine. In 1921 the North Tees Station of Newcastle Electric Supply Co. (northern England) went into operation at 450 psi and 650 F, with reheat at 500 F and feedwater extraction heating to 300 F. In 1924 the Crawford Avenue Station of Commonwealth Edison Co., Chicago, and the Philo and Twin Branch stations of American Gas and Electric Co. all went into operation with 550 psi and 725 F at the turbine throttle, with reheat at 105 psi and 700 F. Miami Fort Station of Columbia Power Co., Cincinnati, with similar steam conditions, went into operation in 1925. Two turbines each of 50,000 kw and one turbine of 60,000 kw were installed in the Crawford Avenue Station, the largest of these power plants. Steam was supplied to each turbine from four "normal" or "standard" boilers and one reheat boiler—a total of 15 boilers built for a working pressure of 650 psi. Side views of the standard and reheat boilers are shown by Figs. 12 and 13, respectively.

Later Development of B&W Boilers

The really big jump in steam pressure for central stations came in 1924 and 1925 with the design and placing in service of the 1200 psi unit at the Weymouth (later renamed Edgar) Station of Boston Edison Co. The boiler, built to supply steam for the high-pressure, 3150-kw, 3600-rpm turbine, is illustrated by Fig. 14. This boiler was designed to supply 143,000 lb steam per hour at 1200 psi and

a temperature of 700 F. After passing through the high-pressure turbine, the steam was exhausted at 360 psi to the reheater. Here it was reheated to 700 F and was mixed with the steam from other boilers going to the main turbines, where it developed an additional 12,000 kw. This boiler was known as a topping unit, and its turbine as a topping turbine.

Major changes in the production and utilization of steam occurred between 1925 and the early thirties. The design of larger boilers, operating at higher rates of output and particularly with the use of pulverized coal as fuel (then increasing at an exceedingly rapid pace), necessitated the development of the water-cooled furnace. The proportion of boiler surface hitherto arranged in banks could therefore be reduced, since new steam-generating surface was provided in cooling the furnace. Feedwater heating by steam bled from early stages of the turbine had a similar effect. Above all, the increase in steam temperature required for greater turbine efficiency still further served to reduce boiler-bank surface as such, to be replaced by additional superheater surface since, with higher steam pressures and temperatures, it is necessary

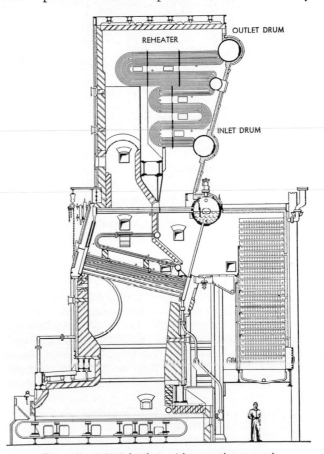

Fig. 13. B&W boiler with superheat and reheat, for 650 psi working pressure, 750 F initial and 725 F reheat temperatures, 1924

cooled surface in the furnace (see Fig. 16).

During the past 20 years boilers and their component equipment have undergone many radical changes. These developments are described in subsequent chapters. The need for larger units, higher pressures and temperatures, and the demand for long periods of uninterrupted service have stimulated design of the drum-and-tube type of boiler. Much work of sound and lasting effect was done during this period in the coordination of fuel burning and combustion control with boiler performance to attain greater efficiency, in the development of pulverized coal, in steam and other fluid measurements, and in the integral-furnace and high-pressure categories.

Steam Production Above Critical Pressure

Studies by the Company to develop a "once-through" design of steam generator for operation at pressures above the critical have been under way

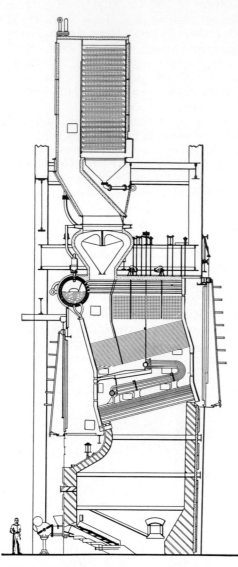

Fig. 14. B&W boiler, 1200 psi working pressure, 700 F initial and reheat temperatures, and reheat pressure at 360 psi, 1924

that a greater proportion of the total heat input be absorbed in the steam after it is produced. Following 1930 and continuing to the present time, the same factors have had an increasing influence on boiler design, particularly in large installations. Thus, for a steam pressure of 2500 psi, steam temperatures of the order of 1050 F, and reheated steam temperatures of 1050 F, the boiler unit consists essentially of drums, furnace water-wall tubes, superheaters, and reheaters, plus such heat-recovery adjuncts as economizers and air heaters (see Fig. 15). Smaller units, built to operate at lower steam pressures and temperatures—in the general pressure region of 1000 psi with moderate superheat—retain a considerable proportion of their total generating surface in tube banks in addition to the water-

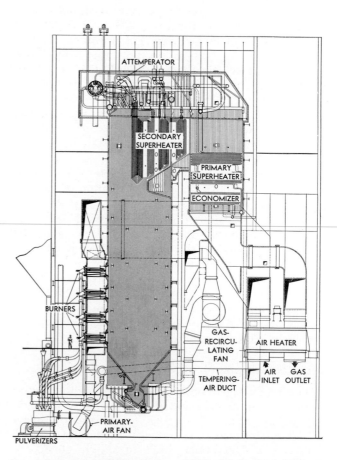

Fig. 15. B&W Radiant boiler, 2500 psi design, 1050 F initial and 1000 F reheat temperatures, generating 2,400,000 lb steam per hr

for some years. A contract for the first commercial installation of this type was concluded in 1953. The unit will supply steam at 4500 psi and 1150 F with two stages of reheat, 1050 F and 1000 F respectively, for a 120,000-kw electric-generating machine. Operation started in 1957, and a new peak in plant thermal efficiency was attained.

The general arrangement of various components is shown diagrammatically by Fig. 17. The working fluid makes one fast uninterrupted trip from the feedwater inlet at 5500 psi, 525 F, to the turbine inlet at 4500 psi, 1150 F. There is no drum. The unit is fired by three 9-ft diameter Cyclone Furnaces, all at the same elevation. There is a relatively small amount of furnace volume and surface and a large convection pass. A wide variety of Eastern Ohio and West Virginia coals will be used. Ash disposal from the Cyclone Furnaces and from the boiler furnace is by the conventional slag-tap method. Gas recirculation, as indicated in the illustration, is used to control ash conditions in the convection tube bank.

In 1956 two additional UP boilers were ordered, each for a capacity of 3,100,000 lb steam per hour, design pressure 4500 psi, initial steam temperature 1050 F, with two stages of reheating to 1050 F at 1265 and 306 psi, respectively. One of these units is Cyclone Furnace fired with slag-tapping, the other pulverized-coal fired with dry-ash removal. Each unit serves a 450,000-kw turbine.

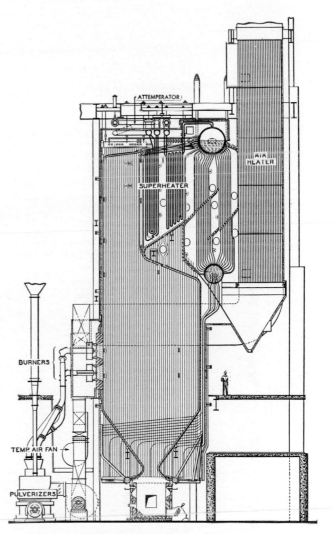

Fig. 16. B&W Stirling boiler, 925 psi working pressure and 900 F steam temperature

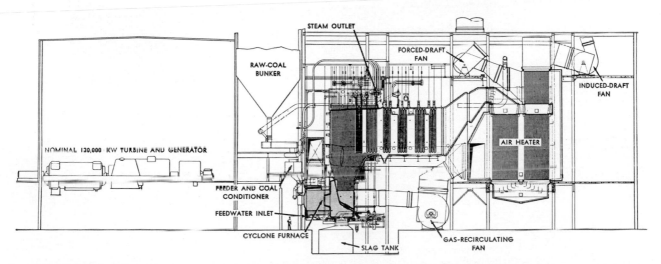

Fig. 17. Diagrammatic arrangement, including 120,000-kw generating unit, of B&W Universal-Pressure (UP) steam generator for operation at 5500-4500 psi, 1150 F, with reheats at 1050 F and 1000 F

Coal — the major source of thermal energy and the most widely used fuel

SOURCES OF HEAT ENERGY—COAL

ALL energy that can be converted to useful purposes is of "atomic origin" by way of the sun, where the "transmutation of hydrogen to helium is believed to produce energy in the form of light with minor supplements of thermal and ultra-violet radiation."

Estimates indicate that only one two-billionths of the sun's energy reaches the earth's atmosphere and that this is 100,000 times the present annual energy requirement of the world. About ½ of this energy is reflected back into interstellar space by the atmosphere, and some of the energy absorbed by the earth by day is lost by radiation at night. The net energy, therefore, theoretically recoverable from this source is estimated to be about 50 times the world requirement.

An estimate of the theoretical heat value at a given time of all vegetation if used directly as fuel, as alcohol or as synthetic gasoline made from vegetation appears in Table 1. Production of vegetation requires CO_2 + sunlight + plant nutrients including moisture. There is an abundance of sunlight and moisture and there seems to be an ample supply of CO_2. Estimates indicate that CO_2 constitutes 0.03 per cent of the atmosphere and 0.0012 per cent of the hydrosphere, or a carbon total of several thousand times as much as the carbon in the coal of the world. However, it would be impossible to use more than a small part of all the vegetation as fuel, since for continued plant growth a large portion of the vegetable matter must be returned to the soil as nutrients. Hence, vegetation cannot be a continuing source of energy in anything like the order indicated in Table 1.

The energy available per year by the better known means of using the continuous energy of the sun is given in Table 2. At present 19 per cent of the energy requirement of the world is obtained from these sources. In 100 years, all the energy (nearly twice the energy required now) might be obtained in this manner. The maximum energy available from these sources is 843.4 times the present annual world requirement, equivalent to 2100 million tons of 13,000 Btu coal.

TABLE 1
Heat Value of All Vegetation

	A	B	C
Fuel (direct)	5800	2.76	5
Alcohol	2940	1.40	32
Gasoline	2450	1.17	17

A = Equivalent million tons coal @ 13,000 Btu/lb
B = Times yearly world requirement
C = Costs in cents per 100,000 Btu

The recoverable reserves in the United States of coal, oil, natural gas and shale as of Jan. 1, 1953, reported by the U. S. Bureau of Mines, are given in Table 3. In equivalent tons of 13,000 Btu coal the total is 1073.5 billion tons. Coal represents 91.88, oil shale 6.72, petroleum 0.67 and natural gas 0.73 per cent. On the basis of the 1951 production of 1,458

TABLE 2
Energy of the Sun Available Per Year
(Equivalent million tons coal @ 13,000 Btu/lb)

	A	B	C
Heat for power	1,700,000	trace	1960
Waterfalls	35,300	98	589
Earth's heat	19,600	trace	trace
Vegetation	5,900	294	980
Peat	4,900	trace	98
Tropical waters	1,960	—	—
Tides	1,272	trace	5
Atmos. electricity	982	—	—
Space heating	882	trace	294
Wind	196	trace	trace
Heat pump	196	trace	20
TOTALS	1,771,188	392	3946

A = Maximum available
B = Used in 1950
C = Possible in 100 years

TABLE 3

United States Reserves and Production of all Fuels
(Coal, billion tons; petroleum and shale oil, billion barrels; natural gas, trillion cu ft)

| | All Mineral Fuels | | Bituminous Coal Equivalent** (13,000 Btu per lb) | | |
| | | | Reserves | | |
	Reserves* Jan. 1, 1952	Annual Production 1951	Billion Tons Jan. 1, 1952	Percent of Total	Annual Production 1951
Coal:					
Anthracite	6.8	.042	6.6	0.62	.041
Low-volatile bituminous	13.9	.104	15.2	1.41	.114
High-volatile bituminous	602.0	.419	602.0	56.08	.419
Subbituminous	233.8	.009	170.9	15.92	.007
Lignite	355.7	.003	191.6	17.85	.002
Total, all ranks	1,212.2	.577	986.3	91.88	.583
Petroleum	32.2	2.48	7.2	0.67	.553
Oil from oil shale	324.0	negligible	72.2	6.72	negligible
Natural gas	193.8	7.97	7.8	0.73	.322
Grand Total, all fuels			1,073.5	100.00	1.458

* The quantities noted under reserves are: *Coal,* recoverable reserves, taken as ½ of the total reserves as estimated by the Geological Survey. *Petroleum,* proved reserves as of Dec. 31, 1951. *Oil from oil shale,* considered to be 60% of the total estimated reserves.
Natural gas, proved reserves as of Dec. 31, 1951.

** Heating value for conversions are: Anthracite, 12,700 Btu/lb; low volatile bituminous coal, 14,200 Btu/lb; high volatile bituminous coal, 13,000 Btu/lb; subbituminous coal, 9,500 Btu/lb; lignite, 7,000 Btu/lb; petroleum and shale oil, 5,800,000 Btu per barrel; natural gas, 1,050 Btu/cu ft.

billion tons of equivalent 13,000 Btu coal, these reserves would last 737 years.

World coal production and coal consumption in 1950, arranged in the order of the ten leading countries in each category are given in Table 4. The total coal reserves of the world are also arranged in the order of quantities for the ten leading geographical

areas. It will be noted that 79 per cent of the total coal reserves is located in the first three countries listed.

United States Reserves and Production

Coal reserves in the United States have been estimated from drillings, out-croppings, gorges cut by

TABLE 4

World Coal Reserves, Production and Consumption by Countries in 1950
(Million Short Tons)

Total Reserves*		%	Production per Year		Consumption per Year	
United States	2,484,639	39.9	United States	560.4	United States	497.5
USSR	1,322,773	21.2	USSR	(291.0)	USSR	—
China	1,114,436	17.9	United Kingdom	242.3	United Kingdom	222.9
Germany	370,679	6.0	Germany	205.7	Germany	127.3
Union of S. Africa	226,409	3.6	Poland	91.3	France	75.4
United Kingdom	189,818	3.0	France	57.8	Poland	56.0
Alaska	107,394	1.7	Czechoslovakia	50.6	Japan	42.7
Canada	98,815	1.6	Japan	43.8	Canada	40.6
Poland	88,205	1.4	China	40.4	China	40.1
India	68,501	1.1	India	36.2	Czechoslovakia	39.4
Others	158,505	2.6	Others	319.5	Others and USSR	599.1
Totals	6,230,174	100.0		1939.0		1741.0

* Approximately ½ of total reserves considered recoverable.

rivers, and explorations for minerals and oil. The distribution of the coal reserves by states, the rank, the amount produced in 1950 and the value per ton f.o.b. mine are given in Table 5.

The eight states with the highest recoverable coal reserves as of Jan. 1, 1951, and the eight states with the highest coal production in 1950 are listed in Table 6.

In the United States the two great coal regions are the Appalachian including the states of Pennsylvania, West Virginia, Ohio, western Maryland, eastern Kentucky, Virginia, Tennessee, and Alabama, and the Central States region including Illinois, Indiana, western Kentucky, Iowa, Missouri, western Kansas, Oklahoma and Arkansas.

However, two-thirds of the coal reserves lie in the Great Plains, the Rocky Mountains and the West.

These coals are sub-bituminous and lignite, and, at some future time, among other uses will very probably serve as a source of synthetic oil. At present, because of distance from industrial areas, these coals are not being used to any extent.

It is estimated that 31 states and Alaska have 340,000 square miles underlain with coal. This represents 11 per cent of the total area of the United States.

Consumption of Coal by Industries

In 1951, as shown in Table 7, the largest consumption of bituminous coal, 25.6 per cent, was in the production of coke, gas and steel, with all "other industries" next, using 25 per cent, and electric utilities third, using 21.4 per cent. The consumption of the latter is increasing each year, and in a few years the

TABLE 5

United States Coal Reserves by States, 1950 Production and Value per Ton
(Million Short Tons)

| State | Estimated Original Reserves* | | | | | Recoverable Reserves† Jan. 1, 1951 | Production 1950 | Dollar/ Ton f.o.b. Mine |
	Bituminous	Sub-Bitum.	Lignite	Anthracite	Total			
Alabama	67,570	0	0	0	67,570	32,949	14.4	5.87
Arkansas	1,396	0	90	230	1,716	765	1.1	7.76
Colorado	213,071	104,175	0	100	317,346	158,198	4.2	5.24
Illinois	171,905	0	0	0	171,905	82,764	56.3	4.05
Indiana	53,051	0	0	0	53,051	25,521	19.9	4.07
Iowa	29,160	0	0	0	29,160	14,235	1.9	3.74
Kansas	18,088	0	0	0	18,088	9,032	2.1	3.96
Kentucky	123,327	0	0	0	123,327	59,633	78.5	4.87
Maryland	8,043	0	0	0	8,043	3,761	.6	4.75
Michigan	297	0	0	0	297	110	.01	—
Missouri	79,362	0	0	0	79,362	39,420	3.0	4.03
Montana	2,363	132,151	87,533	0	222,047	110,864	2.5	2.61
New Mexico	10,948	50,801	0	6	61,755	30,755	.7	5.73
North Dakota	0	0	600,000	0	600,000	299,929	3.3	2.43
Ohio	86,497	0	0	0	86,497	41,516	37.8	3.89
Oklahoma	54,951	0	0	0	54,951	27,314	2.7	6.24
Pennsylvania								
Anthracite	0	0	0	22,805	22,805	6,443	44.0	—
Bituminous	75,093	0	0	0	75,093	30,030	105.8	5.21
South Dakota	0	0	1,020	0	1,020	509	—	—
Tennessee	25,665	0	0	0	25,665	12,503	5.0	5.15
Texas	8,000	0	23,000	0	31,000	15,438	.02	—
Utah	88,184	5,156	0	0	93,340	46,465	6.7	5.46
Virginia	21,149	0	0	500	21,649	10,258	17.7	5.48
Washington	11,413	52,442	0	23	63,878	31,795	.8	7.07
West Virginia	116,618	0	0	0	116,618	53,186	144.1	5.14
Wyoming	13,235	108,319	0	0	121,554	60,408	6.3	4.21
Other States	1,863	15,500	50	0	17,413	8,685	.5	—
U. S. Total	1,281,249	468,544	711,693	23,664	2,485,150	1,212,486	559.93	4.86

* According to estimates by the U. S. Geological Survey, Circular 94, December 1950.
† Assuming 50 per cent recovery.

TABLE 6

Recoverable Coal Reserves, Jan. 1, 1951

(Million Short Tons)
In Eight Leading States

North Dakota	299,929
Colorado	158,198
Montana	110,864
Illinois	82,764
Wyoming	60,408
Kentucky	59,633
West Virginia	53,186
Utah	46,465

Coal Production, 1950

(Million Short Tons)
In Eight Leading States

Pennsylvania	149.8
West Virginia	144.1
Kentucky	78.5
Illinois	56.3
Ohio	37.8
Indiana	19.9
Virginia	17.7
Alabama	14.4

electric utilities will doubtless be the largest consumer. For the electric utilities it is estimated that the coal consumption will increase from 101.8 million tons actually used in 1951 to 146.4 million tons in 1960.

The amount of all fuels used in recent years in electric utilities, the per cent of total, and the per cent of steam and hydro-electric power are given in Table 8.

How Coal Was Formed

The luxurious vegetation of early geological times, produced by the sun's heat, has become the coal of today. Great trees and ferns grew in the hot, humid climate, and successive layers of fallen vegetation, partly decomposed, piled one on the other preventing free access of air. At intervals, wind and water covered this mass with sediment, sand and dirt to form the over-burden now found over coal seams. During millions of years, these layers of vegetation were aged by heat and pressure into coal by converting carbohydrates, $[C_x (H_2O)_y]$, to hydrocarbons (C_xH_y).

The progressive changes were from wood and vegetation to peat, which in turn was changed by heat and pressure to brown coals and lignite, subbituminous, bituminous coals and finally to anthracite and graphite.

Cracks and crevices due to the movement of the earth's crust, filled with mud which left deposits of shale and pyrites to form the extraneous ash found in coal. The intrinsic ash of the coal was largely in the vegetation from the beginning.

It has been estimated that a 9 ft thick seam of bituminous coal was probably formed from 36 ft of solidly packed peat buried millions of years ago. Most of the coal mined in the United States comes from seams 3 to 6 ft thick with an average of 5.41 ft, although one operating seam in Montana is 90 ft thick. The thickest seam in the world, 425 ft, is in Manchuria. The average depth of vertical shafts in the United States is 190 feet.

Coal Analyses

In reporting the components of a coal it is customary to use two different analyses, known as "proximate" and "ultimate." The scope of each is indicated in the analyses of a Virginia coal as noted below. The various values from such analyses are needed to implement the formulas in this chapter and in Chapter 4. Standard laboratory procedures in making these analyses appear in ASTM D271-48.

Coal Analyses

On as Received Basis
(For a Bituminous Coal, Virginia)

Proximate Analysis		Ultimate Analysis	
Component	% By Weight	Component	% By Weight
Moisture	2.90	Carbon, C	80.31
Volatile Matter	22.05	Hydrogen, H_2	4.47
Fixed Carbon	68.50	Sulfur, S	1.54
Ash	6.55	Oxygen, O_2	2.85
Total	100.00	Nitrogen, N_2	1.38
		Moisture, H_2O	2.90
Btu/lb	14,100	Ash	6.55
(heating value)		Total	100.00

Classification by Rank

Coals are classified in an effort to provide the data for predicting their probable performance under given operating conditions. Coal performance, particularly methods and principles of burning, is closely associated with specific types of equipment, and reference should be made to Chapters 4, 15, 16, 17, 18 and 28.

One classification of coal is by rank or age. Volatile matter, fixed carbon, bed moisture, and oxygen are all indicative of rank, but no one item completely defines it. In the ASTM classification, the basic criteria are the fixed carbon and the calorific values calculated on a mineral-matter free basis.

In establishing the rank of coals it is necessary to use criteria which vary appreciably and in order with age. For the older coals a good criterion is the dry, mineral-matter free fixed carbon or volatile. But this criterion is not suitable for designating the rank of the younger coals. A dependable means of classifying the younger coals is the moist, mineral-matter free Btu which varies little for the older coals but appreciably and in order for the younger coals.

By the ASTM standard (see Table 9) for classification according to age, older coals are classified by "dry, mineral-matter free fixed carbon," and younger coals are classified by "moist, mineral-matter free Btu." The Parr formulas, given below, are used for calculating these values from the proximate analysis. The term "moist" refers to bed moisture only and analyses of constituents must be of bed samples collected as prescribed by the ASTM standard D-388-38.

Dry, Mm free FC =

$$\frac{FC - 0.15S}{100 - (M + 1.08A + 0.55S)} \times 100, \text{ per cent} \quad (1)$$

Dry, Mm free VM =

$$100 - \text{Dry Mm free FC, per cent} \quad (2)$$

Moist, Mm free Btu =

$$\frac{Btu - 50S}{100 - (1.08A + 0.55S)} \times 100, \text{ per lb} \quad (3)$$

Or the approximate formulas used to calculate the values given in Table 10.

Dry, Mm free FC =

$$\frac{FC}{100 - (M + 1.1A + 0.1S)} \times 100, \text{ per cent} \quad (4)$$

Dry, Mm free VM =

$$100 - \text{Dry, Mm free FC, per cent} \quad (5)$$

Moist, Mm free Btu =

$$\frac{Btu}{100 - (1.1A + 0.1S)} \times 100, \text{ per lb} \quad (6)$$

Where

Mm = mineral matter
Btu = heating value per lb
FC = fixed carbon, %
VM = volatile matter, %
M = bed moisture, %
A = ash, %
S = sulfur, %
All for coal as received

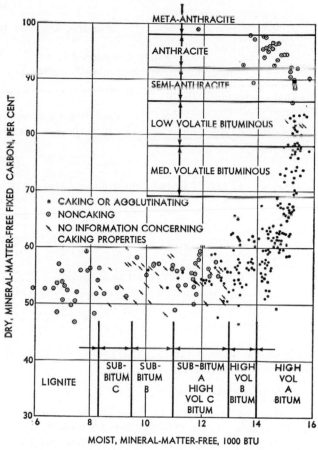

Fig. 1. *Distribution plot for over 300 coals of the United States, illustrating ASTM classification by rank as defined in Table 9.*

In Table 10, seventeen typical United States coals are arranged in the order of the ASTM classification, with the values for the two criteria for the older and younger coals in italics. The bases for the two ASTM classification criteria are shown in Fig. 1 (from U. S. Bureau of Mines, R. I. 3296) for over 300 typical

TABLE 7

United States Coal Consumption by Industries
(Thousand Short Tons)

Year Avg. for Range	Electric Utilities	Coke, Gas and Steel	Other Industries	Retail Dealers	Railroads All Uses	Total Consumption
1935-1939	37,766	73,303	112,057	77,671	85,984	386,781
1940-1944	64,636	108,932	130,508	107,516	115,709	527,301
1945-1950	81,808	107,759	121,009	98,034	96,738	505,348
1951	101,816	121,749	118,917	76,531	57,000	476,013
Per Cent Change To 1951						
From '35-'39	+ 169.6	+ 66.1	+ 0.1	− 1.5	− 33.7	+ 23.1
From '40-'44	+ 57.5	+ 11.8	− 8.9	− 28.8	− 50.7	− 9.7
From '45-'50	+ 24.4	+ 13.0	− 1.7	− 21.9	− 41.1	− 5.8

TABLE 8

Electric Utilities in the United States

	Fuels Consumed Bituminous Coal Equivalent* (1000 Tons)					Kind of Fuel Per Cent of Total				Steam and Hydro Per Cent of Each	
Year	Bitumi-nous	Anthra-cite	Oil	Gas	Total	Bitumi-nous	Anthra-cite	Oil	Gas	All Fuels	Hydro
'35-'39**	37,766	1,907	3,551	6,709	49,933	75.6	3.8	7.1	13.5	62.9	37.1
'40-'44**	64,636	2,833	4,640	10,693	82,802	78.1	3.4	5.6	12.9	67.0	33.0
1945	71,603	3,028	5,187	13,649	93,467	76.6	3.2	5.6	14.6	64.0	36.0
1946	68,743	3,349	9,312	12,843	94,247	72.9	3.6	9.9	13.6	64.9	35.1
1947	86,009	3,416	11,618	15,609	116,652	73.7	2.9	10.0	13.4	69.3	30.7
1948	95,620	3,847	10,935	20,004	130,406	73.3	3.0	8.4	15.3	70.8	29.2
1949	80,610	3,256	17,000	23,018	123,884	65.1	2.6	13.7	18.6	69.2	30.8
1950	88,262	3,504	19,339	26,315	137,420	64.2	2.5	14.1	19.2	70.9	29.1
1951†	101,815	3,754	16,295	31,929	153,793	66.2	2.4	10.6	20.8	—	—

Source of data, Federal Power Commission.

* 3.9 barrels of fuel oil, 23,900 cu ft of gas, 1.03 tons of anthracite, each taken as the equivalent of 1 ton of bituminous coal.

** Average.

† Preliminary.

coals of the United States. The groups of Table 9 are indicated in this figure.

Validity of Other Criteria

It may be of interest to consider the validity of other criteria in the classification of coal by rank. Referring to the ultimate analysis, moisture and ash free basis, Table 11:

For the younger coals, the volatile (VM) either as received (Table 10) or "moisture and ash free" (Table 11) does not line up the coals in anything like the same order as the ASTM method.

Carbon (C), however, does line up the 17 coals in the same order as the ASTM method except for a slight discontinuity between coals 8 and 9, both in the high volatile A group. As a criterion, the carbon content would be quite simple and could undoubtedly be used as a suitable basis for classification.

Hydrogen (H₂) is of no use in classification.

Oxygen (O₂) generally decreases with the age of coals but is not consistent and higher values are indicated for weathered coal.

Nitrogen (N₂) varies little for all ranks.

An ASTM sub-committee on classification of coal by rank has recently been working with European engineers, and it is reported that there is general agreement on three parameters.

(a) Volatile matter of dry ash free coal.

(b) Caking and coking properties.

(c) Calorific value of moist ash free coal.

The first (a) and the third (c) are now in use in the United States, but (b) should eventually provide a valuable additional sub-division of many ranks.

Other criteria for the classification of coal by rank have been proposed by various authorities.

A method of classifying coal by computing the heating value of the residual coal with moisture, ash, and sulfur removed has been used by Lord. This is called the "H" value.

$$\text{"H"} = \frac{\text{Btu} - 4050\text{S}}{100 - (\text{M} + \text{A} + \text{S})} \times 100 \qquad (7)$$

While the "H" values as listed in Table 11 are of interest, they do not arrange the 17 coals in the same order as the ASTM.

Another method of classification has been reported by Perch and Russell based on the following ratio:

$$\text{Ratio} = \frac{\text{Moist Mm free Btu}}{\text{Dry, Mm free VM}} \qquad (8)$$

The values of this ratio for the 17 coals listed in Table 11 arrange these coals in exactly the same order as the ASTM method. It is said that this "ratio" is closely related to the coking properties of coals used in coke oven practice.

Heating Value of the Volatile

Since the quality of the volatile matter in coal is an index of the extent of the conversion of the original carbohydrates to hydrocarbons, studies have been made suggesting that the heating value of the volatile matter will serve as an accurate criterion for classification by rank. This criterion, developed on a "pure coal" basis, is listed under Btu per lb volatile matter (VM), in Table 11, and its derivation is explained below.

Composition of the fixed carbon in all types of coal is substantially all carbon. The variable constituents of coals can, therefore, be considered as concentrated in the volatile matter. One index of the quality of the volatile matter, its heating value, is perhaps the most important property as far as combustion is concerned, and it bears a direct relation to the properties of the pure coals (moisture and mineral matter free). The volatile matter in the coals of lower rank, where the conversion of carbohydrates to hydrocarbons has not progressed far, is relatively high in water and CO_2 and, consequently, low in heating value. In coals of higher rank, the volatile matter is relatively high in hydrocarbons, such as methane (CH_4), and, consequently, relatively high in heating value.

To establish reasonably accurate heating values for the volatile matter, the analyses and heating value of the coal must be converted to the mineral matter free basis. The only difference in the conversion used for this method and the conversion used in the ASTM standard D-388-38 is that half the sul-

TABLE 9

Classification of Coals by Rank,[a] ASTM D 388-38

FC = Fixed Carbon; VM = Volatile Matter; Btu = British Thermal Units

Class	Group	Limits of Fixed Carbon or Btu Mineral Matter Free Basis	Requisite Physical Properties
I Anthracite	1. Meta-anthracite	Dry FC, 98% or more. (Dry VM, 2% or less)	
	2. Anthracite	Dry FC, 92% or more and less than 98%. (Dry VM, 8% or less and more than 2%	
	3. Semi-anthracite	Dry FC, 86% or more and less than 92%. (Dry VM, 14% or less and more than 8%)	Nonagglomerating[b]
II Bituminous[d]	1. Low volatile bituminous	Dry FC, 78% or more and less than 86%. (Dry VM, 22% or less and more than 14%)	
	2. Medium volatile bituminous	Dry FC, 69% or more and less than 78%. (Dry VM, 31% or less and more than 22%)	
	3. High volatile A bituminous	Dry FC, less than 69%. (Dry VM, more than 31%); and moist[c] Btu, 14,000 or more	
	4. High volatile B bituminous	Moist[c] Btu, 13,000 or more and less than 14,000[e]	
	5. High volatile C bituminous	Moist Btu, 11,000 or more and less than 13,000[e]	Either agglomerating or nonweathering[f]
III Sub-bituminous	1. Sub-bituminous A	Moist Btu, 11,000 or more and less than 13,000[e]	Both weathering and nonagglomerating
	2. Sub-bituminous B	Moist Btu, 9,500 or more and less than 11,000[e]	
	3. Sub-bituminous C	Moist Btu, 8,300 or more and less than 9,500[e]	
IV Lignite	1. Lignite	Moist Btu, less than 8,300	Consolidated
	2. Brown coal	Moist Btu, less than 8,300	Unconsolidated

[a]Does not include a few coals of unusual physical and chemical properties which come within the limits of fixed carbon or Btu of the high volatile bituminous and sub-bituminous ranks. [b]If agglomerating, classify in low volatile group of the bituminous class. [c]Moist Btu refers to coal containing only its natural bed moisture. [d]There may be noncaking varieties in each group of the bituminous class. [e]Coals having 69 per cent or more fixed carbon on the dry, mineral matter free basis shall be classified according to fixed carbon regardless of Btu. [f]There are three varieties in the high volatile C bituminous coal group, 1) agglomerating and nonweathering, 2) agglomerating and weathering and, 3) nonagglomerating and nonweathering.

Table 10

Seventeen Typical Coals Arranged in Order of ASTM Classification

No.	Class	Group	State	County	M	VM	FC	A	S	Btu	Dry FC	Moist Btu
Coal Samples Rank Classification					**Coal As Received — Proximate Analysis, %**						**Mm Free**	
1	I	1	Pa.	Schuylkill	2.0	1.76	86.2	10.0	0.79	13,070	99.2	14,720
2	I	2	Pa.	Lackawanna	2.0	6.3	79.7	12.0	0.60	13,000	94.0	15,000
3	I	3	Va.	Montgomery	3.0	10.5	66.5	20.0	0.61	11,800	88.7	15,140
4	II	1	W. Va.	McDowell	3.0	16.3	75.7	5.0	0.73	14,420	82.8	15,250
5	II	1	Pa.	Cambria	4.0	17.0	69.0	10.0	1.63	13,430	*81.1*	15,130
6	II	2	Pa.	Somerset	3.0	20.4	66.6	10.0	1.65	13,520	77.4	15,230
7	II	2	Pa.	Indiana	3.0	23.1	63.9	10.0	2.17	13,600	74.5	15,340
8	II	3	Pa.	Westmoreland	3.0	30.3	55.7	11.0	1.80	13,130	65.4	15,000
9	II	3	Ky.	Letcher; Pike	3.0	34.4	56.6	6.0	0.72	13,800	62.5	14,800
10	II	3	Ohio	Jefferson	6.0	34.8	49.2	10.0	2.44	12,450	59.2	14,030
11	II	4	Ill.	Saline; Perry	10.0	31.7	48.3	10.0	1.60	11,610	61.1	*13,100*
12	II	4	Utah	Carbon; Emery	8.0	36.6	43.4	12.0	0.56	11,480	54.9	*13,230*
13	II	5	Ill.	Sangamon	14.0	34.3	39.7	12.0	4.07	10,470	54.6	*12,100*
14	III	1	Iowa	Polk	13.9	36.9	35.2	14.0	6.15	10,244	50.0	*12,200*
15	III	2	Col.	Weld; Boulder; Sheridan	24.0	30.2	40.8	5.0	0.36	9,200	57.7	*9,750*
16	III	3	Wyo.	Campbell	24.0	30.0	36.0	10.0	0.33	8,450	55.1	*9,500*
17	IV	1	N. D.	McLean; Morton	40.0	27.6	23.4	9.0	1.42	6,330	46.8	*7,040*

NOTES: For definition of Rank Classification according to ASTM requirements, see Table 9.

Data on Coal As Received

M = bed moisture, %; VM = volatile matter, %
FC = fixed carbon, %; A = ash, %; S = sulfur, %
Btu = Btu per lb

Mm-free, dry FC = Dry, mineral-matter-free fixed carbon in %, calculated by formula:

$$\frac{FC \times 100}{100 - (M + 1.1A + 0.1S)}$$

Mm-free, moist Btu = Moist, mineral-matter-free Btu per lb, calculated by formula:

$$\frac{Btu \times 100}{100 - (1.1A + 0.1S)}$$

Values in italics for Mm-free, dry FC and Mm-free, moist Btu are used in ASTM classification by rank.

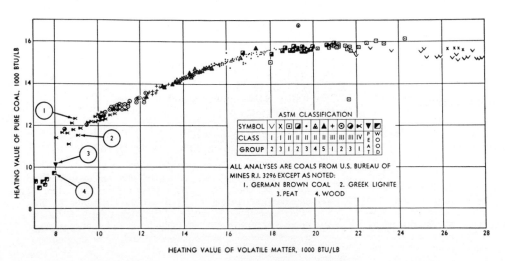

Fig. 2. To illustrate a suggested coal classification using the relationship of the respective heating values of "pure coal" and the volatile matter

fur is assumed to be pyritic and the remainder organic, whereas in the latter, using the Parr formulas, all sulfur in the coal is assumed to be pyritic. The assumption that only half the sulfur is pyritic and the remainder is organic is in closer agreement with the average for a large number of United States coals. The formulas for converting the analyses and coal heating values to the "pure coal" basis and for calculating the heating value of the volatile matter are given below:

$$VM_{pc} = \frac{VM - (0.08A + 0.2S)}{100 - (1.08A + 0.2625S + M)} \times 100, \text{ per cent} \quad (9)$$

$$FC_{pc} = \frac{FC - 0.0625S}{100 - (1.08A + 0.2625S + M)} \times 100, \text{ per cent} \quad (10)$$

$$Btu_{pc} = \frac{Btu - 26.2S}{100 - (1.08A + 0.2625S + M)} \times 100, \text{ per lb} \quad (11)$$

where:

VM, FC, A, S, M, Btu are the same as noted above for the Parr formulas.

Subscript pc denotes "pure coal" basis

Heating Value of Volatile Matter

$$Btu/lb \; VM_{pc} = \frac{Btu_{pc} - \frac{14460}{100} \times FC_{pc}}{VM_{pc}} \times 100 \quad (12)$$

The Btu per lb volatile matter as calculated from the above formulas is given in Table 11 for 16 of the 17 coals listed covering the entire range of rank. It is not given for the first coal listed since this formulation may not be entirely suitable for extremely low-volatile fuels. For only two coals, Nos. 14 and 15, class 3, subbituminous A and B, groups 1 and 2, is the order substantially different from the ASTM arrangement, Table 10. The range of values of Btu per lb volatile matter, from 10,900 to 28,400, is large and should serve as a useful classification.

TABLE 11

Study of the Suitability of Other Criteria in the Classification of Coals

Coals Table 10 No.	Btu Lord's "H" Value	Perch & Russell Ratio	Btu per lb VM_{pc}	From Ultimate Analysis Moisture and Ash Free							Grindability
				VM	FC	C	H_2	O_2	N_2	Btu	
1	15,000	7250	—	2.0	98.0	93.9	2.1	2.3	0.3	14,850	37
2	15,170	2020	28,400	7.3	92.7	93.5	2.6	2.3	0.9	15,100	26
3	15,450	1110	24,700	13.6	86.4	90.7	4.2	3.3	1.0	15,320	83
4	15,800	855	22,000	17.7	82.3	90.4	4.8	2.7	1.3	15,670	100
5	15,870	757	21,750	19.8	80.2	89.4	4.8	2.4	1.5	15,600	112
6	15,750	643	20,000	23.5	76.5	88.6	4.8	3.1	1.6	15,540	105
7	15,950	572	19,850	26.5	73.5	87.6	5.2	3.3	1.4	15,630	95
8	15,580	423	17,350	35.4	64.6	85.0	5.4	5.8	1.7	15,260	88
9	15,290	389	16,650	37.8	62.2	85.2	5.4	7.0	1.6	15,160	56
10	15,180	335	15,800	41.5	58.5	82.2	5.5	7.7	1.7	14,820	61
11	14,750	328	15,140	39.6	60.4	80.6	5.4	10.3	1.7	14,510	66
12	14,470	287	14,550	45.8	54.2	80.3	5.7	11.7	1.6	14,350	45
13	14,850	257	14,550	46.3	53.7	77.5	5.4	10.2	1.4	14,160	60
14	15,150	232	14,640	51.2	48.7	75.8	7.7	26.0	1.2	14,210	62
15	13,000	228	11,000	42.5	57.5	75.0	5.1	17.9	1.5	12,960	58
16	12,890	206	11,100	45.3	54.7	74.1	5.1	18.7	1.3	12,800	55
17	12,740	128	10,900	54.0	46.0	72.4	4.7	18.6	1.5	12,410	—

NOTES:

$$Btu \; \text{"H" value} = \frac{Btu - 4050S}{100 - (M + A + S)} \times 100$$

where Btu, M, A, and S are as given in Table 10 for the coal as received.

$$\text{Perch \& Russell Ratio} = \frac{\text{Moist Mm-free Btu}}{\text{Dry Mm-free VM}}$$

where Moist Mm-free Btu is as given in Table 10. In this formula also, VM on a moisture- and ash-free basis may be used without appreciable error.

$$Btu \; \text{per lb} \; VM_{pc} = \frac{Btu_{pc} - \left\{ \frac{14460}{100} \times FC_{pc} \right\}}{VM_{pc}} \times 100$$

where the subscript pc means on a "pure coal" basis. (See text for conversion of Btu, FC, and VM of coal as received to "pure coal" basis.)

Grindability is determined by the Hardgrove method (see Page 17-15).

The relation of the heating value of the volatile matter and the heating value of the pure coal is shown in Fig. 2 for a large number of coals. It is evident that a fair line could be drawn, without serious error, to indicate the path of this relationship.

A listing of ASTM standards for testing coal will be found in the Appendix under Chapter 2.

Classification of Coal by Grade

In the ASTM standard D389-37 for the classification of coal by grade, the ash, softening temperature, sulfur and Btu are represented by symbols. The classification of a typical coal by grade might be:

(62-146), 4-2 inch 132-A8-F24-S1.6

which would be interpreted as:

High volatile A, bituminous coal having

FC, dry Mm free basis, %	62*
Moist, Mm free Btu/lb	14600**
Size, 80% by wt between	4-2 in†
Btu/lb as received,	13200**
Ash, %, as received, between	6.1-8
Ash, softening temp, F, between	2400-2590
Sulfur, %, as received, between	1.4-1.6

* To nearest whole number
** To nearest 100 Btu
† Round hole screens
See Table 12 for the symbols representing the last three items above.

Commercial Sizes of Coal

Bituminous

Sizes of bituminous coal are not well standardized, but the following sizings are common:

Run of Mine. Run of mine is shipped without screening. It is used for both domestic heating and steam production.

Run of Mine (8 in.). This is run of mine with oversize lumps broken up.

Lump (5 in.). This size will not go through a 5 in. round hole. It is used for hand firing and domestic purposes.

Egg (5 in. × 2 in.). This size goes through 5 in. and is retained on 2 in. round hole screens. It is used for hand firing, gas producers and domestic firing.

Nut (2 in. × 1¼ in.). This size is used for small industrial stokers, gas producers and hand firing.

Stoker Coal (1¼ in. × ¾ in.). This size is used largely for small industrial stokers and domestic firing.

Slack (¾ in. and under). Used for pulverizers and industrial stokers.

Several other sizes of bituminous coal are prepared by different producers, especially for domestic stoker requirements.

TABLE 12

Symbols Used by ASTM for Grading Coal
According to Ash, Ash-Softening Temp and Sulfur
(Analyses Expressed on Basis of the Coal as Sampled)

Ash		Softening Temp of Ash		Sulfur	
Symbol	Per Cent Inclusive	Symbol	F Inclusive	Symbol	Per Cent Inclusive
A4	0.0- 4.0				
A6	4.1- 6.0			S0.7	0.0-0.7
A8	6.1- 8.0	F28	2800 & higher	S1.0	0.8-1.0
A10	8.1-10.0	F26	2600-2790	S1.3	1.1-1.3
A12	10.1-12.0	F24	2400-2590	S1.6	1.4-1.6
A14	12.1-14.0	F22	2200-2390	S2.0	1.7-2.0
A16	14.1-16.0	F20	2000-2190	S3.0	2.1-3.0
A18	16.1-18.0	F20 minus	less than 2000	S5.0	3.1-5.0
A20	18.1-20.0			S5.0 plus	5.1 & higher
A20 plus	20.0 & higher				

Notes:

Ash and sulfur shall be reported to the nearest 0.1 per cent by dropping the second decimal figure when it is 0.04 or less and by increasing the per cent by 0.1 when it is 0.05 or more. For example, 4.85 to 4.94 per cent inclusive shall be taken as 4.9 per cent.

Ash-softening temperatures shall be reported to the nearest 10 F. For example, 2635 to 2644 F, inclusive, shall be taken as 2640 F.

For commercial grading of coals, ranges in the percentage of ash smaller than 2 per cent are commonly used.

Anthracite

Definite sizes of anthracite are standardized as given in Table 13.

TABLE 13
Commercial Sizes of Anthracite
Graded on Round Hole Screens

Trade Name	Diameter of Holes, Inches Through	Retained On
Broken	4⅜	3¼ to 3
Egg	3¼ to 3	2⁷⁄₁₆
Stove	2⁷⁄₁₆	1⅝
Nut	1⅝	1³⁄₁₆
Pea	1³⁄₁₆	⁹⁄₁₀
Buckwheat		
No. 1	⁹⁄₁₆	⁵⁄₁₆
No. 2 (Rice)	⁵⁄₁₆	³⁄₁₆
No. 3 (Barley)	³⁄₁₆	³⁄₃₂
No. 4	³⁄₃₂	³⁄₆₄

The broken, egg, stove, nut and pea sizes are largely used for hand-fired domestic units and gas producers.

Buckwheat No. 1 and No. 2 are used in domestic stokers and hand-fired steam boilers.

Buckwheat No. 3 and No. 4 are used for traveling grate stokers, and No. 4 is also burned in pulverized form.

Sampling of Coal

What is believed to be the first scientific work on sampling coal was published in 1909.[*] The size of the sample that must be taken was based on the ratio of the size to weight of the maximum size lump present in the coal. The rules for reducing the sample to laboratory size were established in the same manner. This principle was widely adopted in Great Britain. And the first ASTM Standard for Sampling Coals (D21-40), used for many years (now obsolete), was based largely on this work. This method was calculated to give an accuracy of 1 per cent ash in the coal in 10,000 samples.

This standard, requiring a fixed size sample, came to be regarded as too laborious, and the ASTM Standard D492-48 (now in use) was developed. In this standard, allowances are made for probable ash content of the coal thus permitting the use of smaller samples for the lower ash coals. Three sizes of samples are specified:

"Commercial Sample." This size will give an accuracy of ± 10 per cent of the ash content in 95 out of 100 samples.

"Special Purpose Sample." This size is 4 times as large as the "commercial sample," and will give an accuracy of ± 5 per cent of the ash content in 95 out of 100 samples.

"Special Purpose Sample." This size is 9 times as large as the "commercial sample," and will give an accuracy of ± 3.33 per cent of the ash content in 95 out of 100 samples.

One or the other of the special purpose samples should generally be used in place of the commercial sample to obtain greater accuracy.

Fusion Temperature of Coal Ash

The procedure for determining the "fusion temperature" of coal ash is given in ASTM Standard D271-48, reprinted in the Appendix for Chapter 18. Small cones of well burned-out ash, held together with a dextrine binder, are heated in a gas-fired furnace (see Fig. 3) until the cone reaches the various stages of fusion.

Tests are run in a reducing atmosphere. If the iron content of the ash is high, tests in an oxidizing

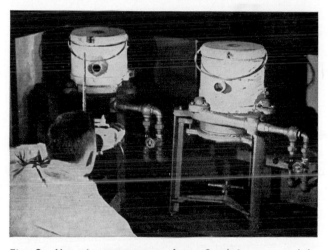

Fig. 3. *Use of pyrometer and gas-fired furnace in laboratory test to determine coal-ash fusion temperatures.*

atmosphere will oxidize the iron and the temperatures will be higher than those obtained in a reducing atmosphere. Actually most boiler furnace operation is only partly oxidizing, and, in applying this data to design, the fusion temperatures for both oxidizing and reducing atmospheres are considered (see Chapter 18).

Viscosity of Coal Ash Slag

The fluid fusion temperature of coal ash is considered a fairly reliable guide to the ease of slag tapping. However, experience with various wet-ash pulverized coal furnaces and Cyclone furnace-fired units indicates that this is not always true, and that the viscosity as well as the fluid temperature of the coal ash is an essential criterion. Even though the necessary margin over the coal ash fluid temperature

[*] E. G. Bailey, in the Journal of Industrial and Engineering Chemistry, March 1909. The name of this publication is now Industrial and Engineering Chemistry.

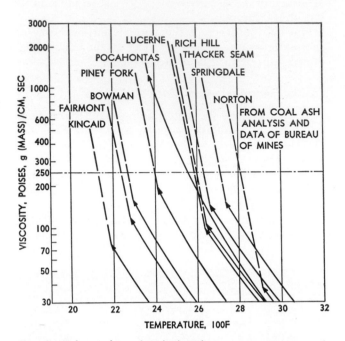

Fig. 4. *Relationship of calculated viscosities (Bureau of Mines method) and temperatures for various coal slags. Below approximately 250 poises the slag tends to flow freely in tapping.*

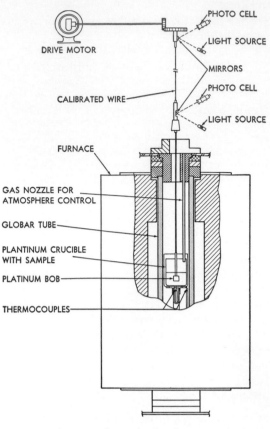

Fig. 6. *Section through the furnace of the high temperature viscometer shown in Fig. 5.*

Fig. 5. *High temperature viscometer for determining actual viscosity of coal-ash in molten state.*

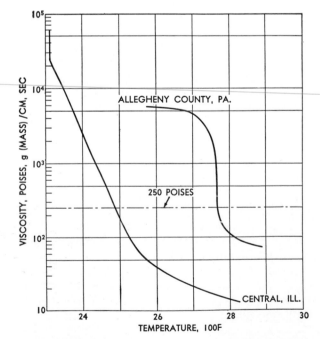

Fig. 7. *Viscosity-temperature relationship for two coal slags of widely differing tapping characteristics.*

is maintained, the slag will not flow freely if the viscosity is too high.

The coal ash viscosities in Fig. 4, calculated from the spectrographic analyses of the ash by the Bureau of Mines, correspond well with the observed tapping characteristics of the coals tested. Difficulty in tapping the slag has been experienced when the calculated coal ash viscosity at 2600F (fluid temperature plus) exceeds 250 poises. Norton, Springdale, and Thacker Seam coal slags, with calculated coal ash viscosities above the 250-poise limit at 2600F, tend to tap rather sluggishly. On the other hand, Kincaid, Fairmont, Bowman, Piney Fork, Pocahontas and Lucerne coal slags, where the viscosities at 2600F are below this limit, tapped easily. It is not yet possible to accept with complete confidence the calculated viscosities for coals of ash composition outside the range covered in the work of the Bureau of Mines.

Viscosity of coal ash slag is actually measured in a high temperature viscometer (Fig. 5). The control panel is at the left and the furnace with its measuring element is at the right. A section through the furnace is shown in Fig. 6. The molten slag sample is placed in a platinum crucible. There is an optical electronic device for measuring the torsional deflection of the calibrated wire. The torque is recorded on a chart. Provision is made for controlling the atmosphere within the furnace.

The viscosities of a Central Illinois and an Allegheny County, Pa., coal ash as measured by the

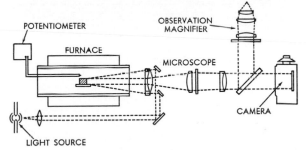

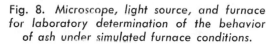

Fig. 8. *Microscope, light source, and furnace for laboratory determination of the behavior of ash under simulated furnace conditions.*

high temperature viscometer are given in Fig. 7. The viscosity of the latter is not only higher than for the Central Illinois slag but it increases rapidly in the plastic range. This may be an undesirable

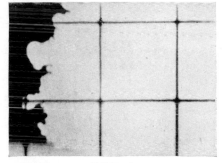

Fig. 9. *Four frames of a motion picture recording the combustion of a coal particle at 2700 F furnace temperature, as obtained with the equipment shown in Fig. 8.*

0.5 SECOND

1 SECOND

2 SECONDS

3 SECONDS

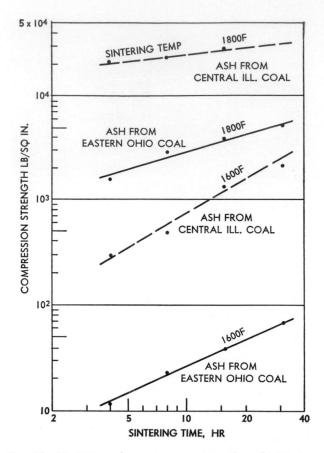

Fig. 10. *Variation of compression strength with sintering time for two fly-ash samples at two sintering temperatures.*

before the coal particle is inserted, the temperature of the furnace is raised to 2700-3000F. The history of burning, which only takes a few seconds, is recorded in a motion picture. Four frames of a motion picture, at intervals of ½, 1, 2, and 3 seconds, taken during the burning are shown in Fig. 9. After ½ second exposure at furnace temperature, swelling of the coal particle and active combustion are well under way. At the end of 2 seconds, small spheroids and cenospheres of fly-ash are formed and carried away by the combustion air. At the end of 3 seconds, large spheroids of ash coalesce to form a completely liquid droplet of slag.

Sintering of Fly-Ash

The combustion of some coals results in troublesome ash deposits which accumulate on furnace walls and convection tube banks. These deposits cannot be accounted for by a comparison of the fusion

characteristic in the operation of a slag-tap furnace if the viscosity is in the medium and high range. The Pennsylvania coal ash taken as an example is definitely in the high range.

By the use of synthetic ash as well as typical coal ash to explore the range of ash composition not covered by the work of the Bureau of Mines, the tapping characteristics of any coal ash can be predicted with fair accuracy from its chemical composition.

Ash Deposition

The Leitz heating microscope, shown in Fig. 8 with diagram, is an aid in studying the ash deposition problem. Components of the instrument are: a furnace capable of maintaining a temperature of 3000F, a 5x microscope, and a light source. The instrument was designed primarily for use in determining the melting behavior of coal ash, clinker and other materials. It is also applied to other phases of this work such as combustion experiments to determine the behavior of ash under simulated furnace conditions. In these experiments a single particle of 18 mesh coal is placed on a platinum stage which can be moved rapidly in or out of the furnace. Just

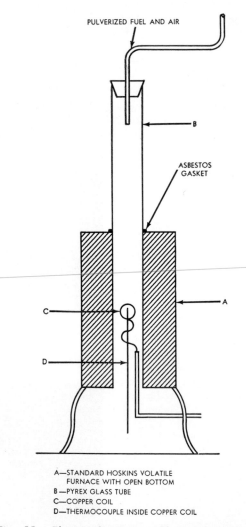

A—STANDARD HOSKINS VOLATILE
　　FURNACE WITH OPEN BOTTOM
B—PYREX GLASS TUBE
C—COPPER COIL
D—THERMOCOUPLE INSIDE COPPER COIL

Fig. 11. *Electric furnace used in laboratory to determine the ignition temperatures of solid fuels.*

temperature of the coal ash and the gas temperature through the tube banks, since they occur in areas where the flue gas temperature is several hundred degrees lower than the fusion temperature. The effect of "sintering" (the forming of a more or less solid mass by heating without thorough melting) on the compression strength of fly-ash from various coals appears to be a rational explanation supported by experience.

It has been established that the compression strength of test pellets of fly-ash from various coals which have been sintered for 24 hr. under conditions similar to those in a superheater, is a good index of fouling tendencies. The compression strength of sintered fly-ash from the Central Illinois coal which causes troublesome ash deposits is ten to thirty times greater than that of sintered fly-ash from an eastern Ohio coal, taken for comparison, which does not produce troublesome slag (see Fig. 10). The compression strength of the fly-ash from both coals increases rapidly with the time and temperature of the sintering treatment.

Bomb Calorimeter

The heating value of coal is determined accurately in an oxygen-bomb submerged in cooling water. Several acceptable makes or types of bomb calorimeters are listed in the ASTM Standards, section D271-48. See also ASME Power Test Codes, part 9, Heat of Combustion. The coal sample is compressed into a hard pellet and ignited by a hot wire. The heating value is determined from the rise in the water temperature.

Grindability of a Coal

Grindability is a term used to measure the ease of pulverizing a coal in comparison with a standard coal chosen as 100 (unity) grindability. A description of the method of testing to determine grindability of a coal in accordance with ASTM Standard D409-51 and an illustration of the machine used in making the test (Fig. 17) appear in Chapter 17. The grindability of 16 of the 17 representative coals in Table 10 is given in the last column of Table 11.

Ignition Test

The temperature at which ignition of coal occurs can be determined by an ignition test, using the electric furnace and components illustrated in Fig. 11. The ignition temperatures established by this test seem to agree with actual results in operation.

The coal sample is pulverized to pass through a

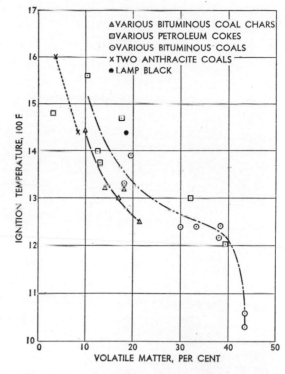

Fig. 12. *Some actual tests indicating the general order of variation of ignition temperatures with volatile matter for several solid fuels.*

44 micron, #325 sieve. A small amount (0.2 gram) is blown into the vertical tube of the electric furnace. The furnace temperature is progressively increased until a small flash or glow indicates that the ignition temperature has been reached. For the ignition temperatures of some United States coals, chars, and petroleum cokes plotted against volatile matter, see Fig. 12.

Moisture Determination

It is preferable to determine the moisture in coal in two steps: 1) prescribed air drying to equilibrium at 10-15C above room temperature, and 2) prescribed oven drying, one hr at 104-110C, after pulverizing. (See also ASTM(D271-48).

The "air dried" component of the total moisture value should be reported separately because this useful information is required in the design and selection of equipment. For efficient pulverizing it is the surface moisture that must be evaporated. Surface moisture, in the range where the bulk density is the lowest (usually 6-8 per cent "air dried" for slack size), is a strong contributing factor in causing hang-ups in bunkers and chutes.

THIS CENTRAL STATION IN CALIFORNIA USES GAS AND OIL AS
FUELS TO GENERATE 2,800,000 POUNDS OF STEAM PER HOUR

3

SOURCES OF HEAT ENERGY — OTHER THAN COAL

ASIDE FROM coal the principal sources* of heat energy are petroleum, natural gas and oil-shale, which, like coal, come from fossil formations, and are nonreplenishable. Vegetation, primarily wood, which is replenishable, is also a minor source (approximately 5 per cent) of heat energy. The use of petroleum and natural gas as sources of heat energy is a comparatively recent development. One half of the cumulative amount of petroleum used in the world has been produced during the past ten years.

While coal in very large quantities is widely distributed throughout the world, the reserves of petroleum and natural gas are very much more limited, and extensive investigations are already underway to improve practical methods of producing oil from coal and oil-shale. The commercial production of liquid fuels from coal has been in successful operation in some parts of the world for several years.

In the United States, during the period of 1899 through 1949, petroleum and natural gas have been used to supply a constantly increasing part of the heat energy requirements, with a corresponding reduction in the use of coal, as indicated in Fig. 1. The annual world production of petroleum increased approximately 75 per cent during the period from 1938 to 1949, while consumption in the United States during the same period increased by 86 per cent.

Availability of Fuels—Other Than Coal

Petroleum. Availability of petroleum is based on the estimated proven reserves in areas where it has actually been found by exploration and drilling. In 1949 the proven reserves of the world were estimated to be about 81 billion barrels. At the rate of consumption in 1949 this quantity would be sufficient for 23 years. The petroleum fields containing these

reserves are located in four great basins: the Eastern Mediterranean Basin; the Caribbean, United States and Canada; the Far Eastern Basin; and the North Polar Basin.

The location of oil reserves in the United States is shown in Fig. 2. The proven petroleum reserves in the United States are presently about 29 billion barrels. The estimate of unproven petroleum reserves in the United States is 50 billion barrels, excluding off-shore reserves which may considerably increase this amount. During recent years the proven reserves have ranged from about 6 to 13 times the annual requirements, and up to the present the rate of development of new reserves has kept pace with the rapidly increasing demand. World production of petroleum in 1948 was of the order of 3.4 billion barrels per year, of which the United States produced 2.1 billion barrels or about 60 per cent. Since

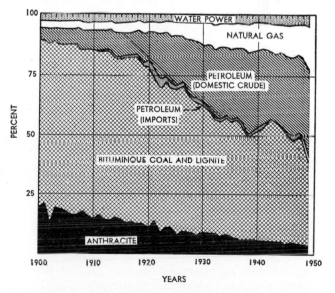

Fig 1 Per cent of total Btu produced each year (1900-1949) from various sources of heat energy in the United States. (Water power converted to Btu equivalent.)

---

*A brief discussion of nuclear energy for power appears in Chapter 27.

the proven reserves of the United States are about 35 per cent of the world total, it appears possible that imports will be needed in the future to supply a substantial portion of the United States requirements. Throughout the years to the end of 1949 the total production of petroleum in the United States was approximately 41 billion barrels. Assuming that the current total petroleum resources in proven and unproven reserves is of the order of 80 billion barrels, approximately ⅓ of the total original oil resources of the United States has been used.

The proportion of petroleum resources actually recovered depends on the rate of withdrawal from existing wells, and the economics of continued exploration and drilling. The number of large fields opened up is likely to diminish, and it will be necessary to drill deeper in less favorable areas. The per cent of dry holes is increasing. In 1938 less than one well in four drilled was dry, while in 1949 the ratio was one in three. The cost of recovering the petroleum from the wells is another economic factor. The 421,000 oil wells in the United States in 1949 produced an average of 12 barrels per well per day, and 89 per cent of the wells required pumps to bring the oil to the surface. In the entire Middle East, 323 wells produced an average of 4600 barrels per day in 1949, and none required pumping. The recovery of petroleum from a field may vary from 25 per cent to 80 per cent depending in large measure on the rate of withdrawal.

Natural Gas. Areas containing petroleum can also be expected to yield natural gas, but there are many natural gas wells that yield no petroleum. The quantity of natural gas reserves of the world is not known. In the United States the proven reserves of natural gas at the end of 1948 were 174 trillion cu ft, the equivalent in heating value of approximately 30 billion barrels of petroleum—about equal to the proven petroleum reserves.

Throughout the years to the end of 1948 the marketed production of natural gas in the United States was of the order of 72 trillion cu ft. A large quantity has also been flared or used in the production of carbon black. It is estimated that in 1944, 30 per cent of the net production of natural gas was so used. The marketed production of natural gas in the United States during 1948 was of the order of 4.5 trillion cu ft. By the end of 1948, assuming reserves of 174 trillion cu ft, which do not include undiscovered resources, about 30 per cent of the total marketed and proven reserves of natural gas in the United States had been consumed. At the 1948 rate of consumption, the present proven reserves will last approximately 40 years.

Oil-Shale. Oil-shale deposits are widely distributed throughout the world. The first commercial extraction of oil from shale was introduced in France about 1839. In 1937 France produced approximately 80,000 barrels of crude oil from shale. Oil reserves of oil-shale in France are of the order of 35 million barrels. In Scotland oil has been produced from shale for many years, reaching a peak in 1914 of 3.3 million barrels. Deposits of oil-shale in Australia amount to approximately 187 million barrels, about 96 per cent evenly divided between New South Wales and Queensland, and the remainder in Tasmania. The largest plant for the extraction of oil from shale was built in Manchuria in 1929. Manchurian reserves are estimated at 250 million barrels. Estonia has estimated reserves of 2.6 billion barrels. Production during World War II was of the order of 1.7 million barrels annually. Sweden has reserves of 1.8 billion barrels. Canada and Brazil have reserves of great magnitude, but lacking sufficient data the quantities cannot be estimated. There has been no commercial exploitation in Brazil. There are also deposits of magnitude in England, Germany, Austria, Bulgaria, Yugoslavia and Russia; and in the Union of South Africa, Peru, Burma and New Zealand.

The principal United States oil-shale reserves are in the Green River formation of Colorado, Wyoming and Utah. These deposits represent approximately 95 per cent of the United States reserves and it is estimated that they contain 100 billion barrels of recoverable oil, a potential supply greater than the petroleum reserves. So far, recovery of oil from this formation has not been carried on commercially. In addition there are deposits in Kentucky and Indiana of Devonian black shale with reserves estimated at 17 billion barrels. There are small deposits

TABLE 1

Forest Areas of the World

Continent	Forest Area Millions of Acres	Per Cent Forest to Total Area
Asia	2096	21.6
South America	2093	44.0
North America	1444	26.8
Africa	797	10.7
Europe	774	31.1
Australia & Oceania	283	15.1
Total	7487	23.6

of cannel shale in West Virginia and Pennsylvania with reserves estimated at 1.6 million barrels.

Wood. In 1923, forest lands of the world were estimated at 7½ billion acres. This is 22 per cent of the land area of the world, exclusive of the polar

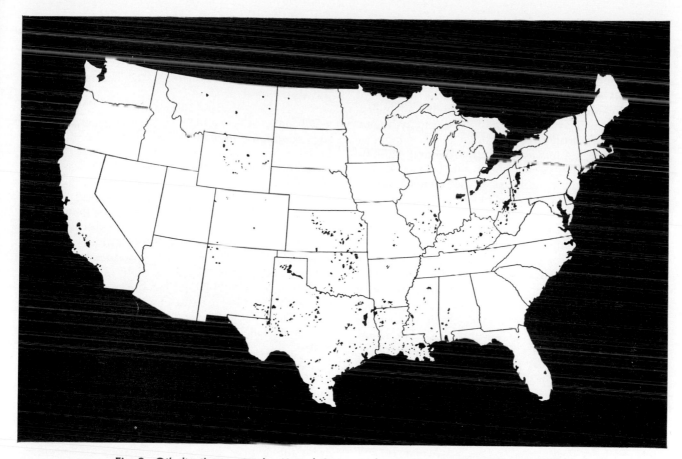

Fig. 2. *Oil distribution in the United States in known or proved producing fields*

regions. Of the forest areas, 5½ billion acres were considered productive. Forest areas of the world by continent are given in Table 1.

Until the latter part of the nineteenth century, when it was replaced by coal, wood supplied the major part of the heat energy requirements. Wood is no longer a major factor as a source of heat energy partly because of the depletion of the forests, the increasing demands for its use as lumber and in the production of paper, plywood, rayon and other products. Today the burning of wood for steam generation is largely confined to locations where it is available as a by-product or waste as in the lumber, furniture, plywood and pulp industries. For instance, in producing lumber from logs half the wood may be discarded as sawdust, bark, shavings, slabs and ends, all of which can be used as fuel. Also waste wood liquors from the pulp industry are burned for the recovery of heat and process chemicals. Various wood wastes are used extensively in other parts of the world, and to a lesser extent in the United States, to produce alcohol as fuel. New methods of barking logs and producing pulp, however, are continually reducing the quantity of wood available as fuel. More profitable end uses, such as the use of bark in the production of roofing ma-

terials, are also reducing the availability of wood for fuel.

Other Vegetation. Numerous other types of vegetation generally in the form of waste or by-products are used for heat energy. In the United States, however, they are an almost negligible factor in the total heat energy requirements. The availability of these wastes or by-products as a source of heat energy is diminishing because, as in the case of wood, more profitable uses are being found for many of them. One of the more common of such wastes is "bagasse" which is the fibrous portion of the cane after the juice has been removed by pressing.

Preparation for Use as Fuel

Petroleum. At the present time petroleum is the most important source of hydrocarbons (compounds of hydrogen and carbon). In crude oil, hydrogen and carbon are combined in various proportions and ways to form an almost limitless number of compounds ranging from methane, CH_4, which is a gas at room temperature, through a wide range of liquids to heavy waxes and asphalts which are solids at room temperature. As recovered, crude oil may contain sufficient water to form an emulsion. Most of this water is removed at the well by electrical or chemical means before delivery to the refinery.

Although small amounts of crude oil are burned without processing, most of the petroleum used has been refined to some extent. Originally, refining crude oil or petroleum was simply the process of separating the lighter compounds, higher in hydrogen, from the heavier compounds, lower in hydrogen, by fractional distillation. Through the development of refining techniques, such as thermal and catalytic cracking and hydrogenation of the heavier hydrocarbons to produce lighter ones, petroleum has now come to be considered as a raw material source of hydrogen and carbon which can be combined as required to meet a variety of specific end uses. Consequently, the characteristics of the portion which is available as fuel oil depend more and more on economic and national security requirements rather than on the nature of the crude oil from which it comes.

The principal volume products obtained from refining petroleum are: (1) gasoline, (2) Diesel oil, (3) fuel oil in various grades including kerosene, (4) lubricating oil, (5) asphalt, wax and grease, (6) synthetic rubber. In addition to the items listed as sources of heat energy, relatively small quantities of refinery gas, acid sludge and petroleum coke are obtained as by-products, and are often consumed as fuels at the refineries or for enriching gases manufactured from coal.

Natural Gas. Since natural gas almost always accompanies petroleum it may well be considered as a part of the petroleum. To reduce the viscosity of the crude oil, to facilitate raising it to the surface and in handling, it is desirable to keep the lighter hydrocarbon compounds in solution by subjecting the oil to pressure. When the pressure is released, the light hydrocarbons such as methane CH_4, ethane, C_2H_6, propane, C_3H_8, butane, C_4H_{10}, and others volatilize as gases or vapors. Propane and butane are often separated from the lighter gases and are widely used as bottle gas. They are distributed and stored under pressure as liquified gas. When the pressure is released the liquid boils, producing gaseous fuel. The portions heavier than butane may be separated and distributed as natural gasoline.

Much of the natural gas produced is suitable for use without further preparation. However, some natural gas may contain enough sand or gaseous sulfur compounds to be obnoxious or troublesome in use. The sand is usually removed at the source. Natural gases containing excessive amounts of sulfur compounds are known as "sour". One authority defines "sour natural gas" as gas containing more than 1½ grains of hydrogen-sulfide or more than 30 grains total sulfur per 100 cu ft of gas. The sulfur compounds are removed before distribution. Where

natural gas is used to replace or supplement manufactured gas, it is sometimes diluted or reformed to bring its heating value in line with the manufactured gas. Natural gas may also be mixed directly with manufactured gas to increase the heating value of the distributed product.

Oil-Shale. On heating, oil-shale, a sedimentary rock containing organic matter, will yield oil. Subsequent refining of the oil is a necessary step in its recovery. Although the recovery of oil from shale has not been done on a commercial basis in the United States, it has been demonstrated in pilot plant operations by the Bureau of Mines that a range of acceptable fuel oils may be produced from shale oil by relatively simple refining techniques and that motor and Diesel fuels can be produced by special refining techniques. Since the yield of oil may be of the order of only 25-30 gal per ton of shale and even less with some lean shales (Swedish shale has about 5 per cent oil) recovery of oil from this source involves a tremendous problem in the disposal of the waste.

Wood. Reduction to convenient size for handling and burning is the primary preparation required when wood is to be used for the generation of steam. The moisture content may also be reduced to improve combustion and efficiency. Bark and slabs from the lumber and pulp industries are often reduced in size by a machine cutter known as a hog. Bark from water-borne logs, bark removed by hydraulic barking methods, and bark from wood stored in the open may contain as much as 60 to 70 per cent moisture by weight. Where such bark is used as a fuel its moisture content is often reduced.

Transportation and Storage

Petroleum. Because of its many non-fuel applications and its high heating value as a fuel, and also because of ease in handling and transportation as a liquid, petroleum and its products are widely distributed throughout the world.

Currently the overall rate of production in the United States is approximately equal to the demand. However, in recent years the production of heavy fuel oils has been of the order of 85 to 88 per cent of the demand, and the balance has been supplied by imports of heavy oils from Venezuela and the Middle East. Lesser quantities have also been received from Mexico, Trinidad, and Canada.

Oil from the Gulf is transported to East Coast refineries by tanker and pipe line. A considerable part of the demand in areas bordering on the Mississippi and its tributaries is supplied from the Gulf by barge shipments. Only a small quantity of oil is shipped from the West Coast to the East Coast. Be-

Table 2

Typical Analyses and Relative Cost of Fuel Oils

Grade of Fuel Oil	No. 1	No. 2	No. 4	No. 5	No. 6
Weight, per cent					
Sulfur	0.1	0.3	0.8	1.0	2.3
Hydrogen	13.8	12.5	—	—	9.7
Carbon	86.1	87.2	—	—	85.6
Nitrogen	—	0.02	—	—	} 2.0
Oxygen	Nil	Nil	—	—	
Ash	Nil	Nil	0.03	0.03	0.12
Gravity					
Deg API	42	32	20	19	—
Specific	0.815	0.865	0.934	0.940	—
Lb per gal	6.79	7.21	7.78	7.83	—
Pour point, F	−35	−5	+20	+30	—
Viscosity					
Centistokes @ 100 F	1.8	2.4	27.5	130	—
SSU @ 100 F	—	34	130	—	—
SSF @ 122 F	—	—	—	30	—
Water & sediment, vol %	Nil	Nil	0.2	0.3	0.74
Heating value					
Btu per lb, gross	19,810	19,430	18,860	18,760	18,300*
Relative cost per Btu	115	100	77	57	44

* Bomb calorimeter determination.

Range of Analyses of Fuel Oils

Grade of Fuel Oil	No. 1	No. 2	No. 4	No. 5	No. 6
Weight, per cent					
Sulfur	0.01-0.5	0.05-1.0	0.2-2.0	0.5-3.0	0.7-3.5
Hydrogen	13.3-14.1	11.8-13.9	(10.6-13.0)*	(10.5-12.0)*	(9.5-12.0)*
Carbon	85.9-86.7	86.1-88.2	(86.5-89.2)*	(86.5-89.2)*	(86.5-90.2)*
Nitrogen	Nil-0.1	Nil-0.1	—	—	—
Oxygen	—	—	—	—	—
Ash	—	—	0-0.10	0-0.10	0.01-0.50
Gravity					
Deg API	40-44	28-40	15-30	14-22	7-22
Specific	0.825-0.806	0.887-0.825	0.966-0.876	0.972-0.922	1.022-0.922
Lb per gal	6.87-6.71	7.39-6.87	8.04-7.30	8.10-7.68	8.51-7.68
Pour point, F	0 to −50	0 to −40	−10 to +50	−10 to +80	+15 to +85
Viscosity					
Centistokes @ 100 F	1.4-2.2	1.9-3.0	10.5-65	65-200	260-750
SSU @ 100 F	—	32-38	60-300	—	—
SSF @ 122 F	—	—	—	20-40	45-300
Water & sediment, vol %	—	0-0.1	tr to 1.0	0.05-1.0	0.05-2.0
Heating value					
Btu per lb, gross (calculated)	19,670-19,860	19,170-19,750	18,280-19,400	18,100-19,020	17,410-18,990

* Estimated.

cause of the relatively higher cost of haulage as compared to water or pipe line transportation comparatively small quantities are shipped overland by rail and truck. The approximate relative costs of shipping petroleum by various means of transportation, although subject to wide variations, are noted in the following tabulation:

Various Transportation Methods	Relative Cost per Ton-Mile
Water	1
Pipe line	9
Railroad	27
Truck	81

To prevent contamination of certain types of crude oil with another, careful precautions must be

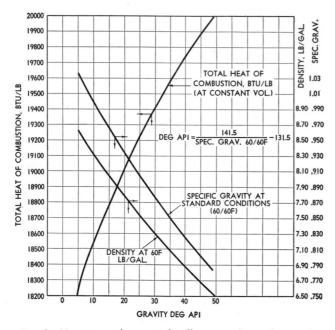

Fig. 3. *Heating value, weight (lb per gal), and specific gravity of fuel oil for a range of API gravities*

taken, such as cleaning the tanks before loading a new shipment. In pipe line transportation this may necessitate the running of parallel lines.

The serious hazard of oil storage tank failure is overcome by storage in underground tanks or by building cofferdams around surface tanks with sufficient capacity to hold the entire contents of the tank. On the West Coast crude oil is commonly stored in huge concrete reservoirs holding several million barrels. In the East oil is usually stored in steel tanks. Steel tanks eliminate evaporation loss and are practically immune to fire hazard created by lightning. A standard set of rules covering the storage and handling of oils, which serves as the basis for many local ordinances and as an excellent guide to safe practices, has been prepared by the National Fire Protection Association. Loss in storage of heavy fuel oils is negligible. Lighter products such as gasoline may volatilize sufficiently in warm weather to cause appreciable loss unless special storage tanks are provided.

It may be necessary to reduce the viscosity of heavy fuel oil by heating before it can be pumped, and consequently transportation and storage facilities are generally provided with heating equipment. Storage tanks, piping and heaters used for heavy oils require cleaning at intervals because of fouling due to sludge formation with certain types of oil or to mixing different types. Various commercial compounds may be helpful in reducing sludge.

Natural Gas. Lacking suitable means of transportation, the use of natural gas would necessarily be limited to areas close to the source. The rapid increase in consumption of natural gas throughout the country and in areas remote from the source is due to the continued extension of a vast system of long distance pipe lines. The distribution of natural gas is subject to some practical limitations because of the energy required for transportation. It is estimated that the energy required to transmit 1 cu ft of gas 1000 miles is of the order of 150 Btu.

In general it is not practical to vary the supply of natural gas to accommodate hourly or daily fluctuations in consumer demand. For economic reasons long distance pipe lines should operate with a high load factor. The rate of withdrawal from the wells may often be limited for conservation reasons, and the cost of the pipe line to provide the peak rate would be prohibitive. Therefore, to meet fluctuations in demand it is usually necessary to provide storage near at hand or briefly to supplement the supply with manufactured gas.

Storage facilities, either above ground or underground are being rapidly increased. Above ground the usual methods of storage are: a) in the familiar large water seal tanks; b) in liquid form in insulated steel tanks; c) in liquid form absorbed in a granular substance, released by passing warm gas over the grains; d) in pipe holders (at or near the surface) of commercial gas line pipe laid parallel and interconnected; e) by using the trunk transmission line as a reservoir by building up the pressure. Because of low cost, underground storage, where the gas is pumped back into depleted or partially depleted gas and oil wells, is the best method for the large storage required to meet seasonal variations in demand. This method is coming more and more into use, and the closer the storage is to the consumer the better, especially for accommodating hourly fluctuations.

Oil-Shale. Because of the low combustible content of oil-shale it appears certain that the oil will be extracted from the shale close to the source.

Commercial use of shale oil will require establishment of distribution storage systems similar to those for petroleum.

Wood. As logged, wood is transported by rail, truck or water. It has not been general practice to transport logs far from the source except by water. The means of water transportation are:

1. Driving: Floating down stream with the current.

2. Towing in Booms: An assembly of floating logs, enclosed within a loop of boom timbers fastened end to end, towed by tug.

3. Towing in Rafts: A number of large logs, arranged several logs deep, chained together, and towed by tug; usually in the open waters along the Pacific Coast.

The logs may or may not be barked at the source depending on the season, the distance of transportation and the destination. To reduce deterioration, it is general practice to remove the bark before storing in piles. If floated to destination, holding areas are generally provided where a large supply of rough logs may be floated until required for use.

In many areas where the weather affects transportation the movement of logs is seasonal. The supply of bark as fuel is therefore seasonal where a year's supply of logs may be received in a few months and barked for storage.

Properties and Utilization

Gasoline and diesel oils produced from petroleum, although very important sources of heat energy, are not normally used for steam generation.

Fuel Oils. In refining petroleum it is common practice to produce fuel oils complying with the several specifications prepared by the ASTM and adopted as a commercial standard by the United States Bureau of Standards. To meet changes in supply and demand these standards have been revised several times in past years, and further changes may be expected. The current standards are tabulated in the appendix. Fuel oils are graded according to gravity and viscosity, the lightest being #1 and the heaviest #6. For satisfactory pumping and burning, grades #5 and #6 generally require heating. Typical analyses, relative cost, and range of analyses and heating values of the different grade fuel oils are given in Table 2.

The gross heating values of various fuel oils of different gravity are noted in Fig. 3. The gross heating values, after correction for the nonhydrocarbon constituents are closely related to the gravity of the oil. The corrected gross heating value in Btu per lb is equal to

$$\frac{Btu \times [100 - (A + B + C)]}{100} + 40.5C$$

Where:
  Btu is taken from Fig. 3
  A = % by weight of water
  B = % by weight of ash
  C = % by weight of sulfur

Where the per cent by weight of water and ash are not known, the per cent by volume of water and sediment can be used without appreciable error.

Fuel oils are generally sold on a volume basis with 60F as the base temperature. To determine what the volume of oil will be at 60F, a correction factor must be applied to the volume at any other temperature. Correction factors, corresponding to temperature and gravity, deg API, are given in Fig. 4 (see Fig. 3 for definition of deg API). Since the

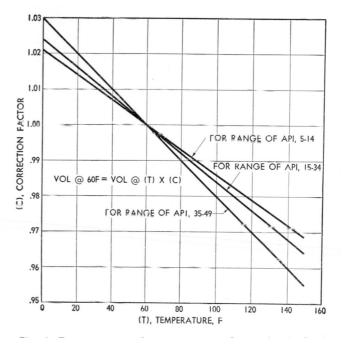

Fig. 4. *Temperature-volume correction factor for fuel oil*

means of handling and particularly the burning equipment are usually designed for oil of a certain maximum viscosity, it is important to know the viscosity characteristics of the fuel oil. In addition, in some instances there are minimum viscosity limitations. To obtain the desired viscosity it may be necessary, because of variations in oil supply, to vary the temperature to which the oil is heated. The viscosity of oil decreases with increase in temperature so that with more viscous oils, higher temperatures are generally required. Also with some oils and certain types of burning equipment it may be necessary to heat the oil to a higher temperature than that required to obtain the desired viscosity in order to obtain satisfactory combustion. It is important to hold the upper limit of the oil temperature below the flash point to prevent carbonization

TABLE 3

Ash Analysis of Some No. 6 Fuel Oils

Column No.*		1	2	3	4	5	6	7
Oil analysis, % by wt								
Ash		0.2	0.14	0.04	0.10	0.11	0.01	0.02
Sulfur		3.0	—	—	2.4	0.90	2.5	3.2
Ash analysis, % by wt								
Silica	as SiO_2	1.8	8.8	24.0	2.3	1.6	—	—
Iron	as Fe_2O_3	3.9	7.6	54.0	1.5	4.3	—	—
Aluminum	as Al_2O_3	3.0	4.1	5.7	0.1	0.1	—	—
Calcium	as CaO	6.0	9.5	3.0	0.1	2.4	—	—
Magnesium	as MgO	1.2	3.3	8.9	1.9	2.0	—	—
Sulfur	as SO_3	45.7	43.3	0.6	13.9	51.8	—	—
Nickel	as NiO	2.1	—	1.0	6.4	1.3	—	—
Vanadium	as V_2O_5	13.0	0.6	—	63.2	0.7	none	39.6
Alkalies	as Na_2O	20.5	23.5	0.6	12.4	30.5	—	—
Cu, Sn, Pb, etc., as oxides		—	—	—	—	0.3	—	—
Undetermined		—	—	—	—	2.9	—	—
Ignition loss @ 900 F, % by wt		—	—	—	2.5	—	—	—
Ash-fusion temperatures, F								
Reducing atm (ASTM)								
Initial deformation		1540	—	—	2880	1550	—	—
Softening		1560	—	—	> 2880	1850	—	—
Fluid		2430	—	—	> 2880	2560	—	—
Oxidizing atmosphere								
Initial deformation		†	—	—	< 1400	1590	—	—
Softening		†	—	—	1400	‡	—	—
Fluid		2720	—	—	1520	2800	—	—

*Col No.	Fuel Oil
1	Source unknown
2	Source unknown
3	Source unknown
4	Venezuelan crude
5	East Texas crude
6	Arabian crude
7	Iranian crude

†Material started to drain out of cone at 1650 F, leaving skeleton cone which started shrinkage at 2250 F.

‡Material drained out of cone.

of the oil, and to avoid possible loss of burner ignition caused by interruption of the flow of oil by vapor binding of pumps when pumping hot oil.

If the viscosity of heavy oils is known at two temperatures, the viscosities at other temperatures can be closely predicted. From a chart (see Fig. 5), standardized by the ASTM, viscosities at various temperatures can be determined with negligible error by drawing a straight line through the plots of the viscosities at two known temperatures. For light oils it is necessary to know the viscosity at only one temperature to determine the viscosities at other temperatures. Using the ASTM standardized chart, Fig. 5, the viscosities of light oils at various temperatures, which fall in the region of the No. 2 fuel oil, can be determined by drawing a line parallel to the viscosity lines for this grade through the plot of the viscosity of the light oil at the known temperature. Copies of this chart may be obtained from the ASTM.

Since the true difference in viscosities is not readily apparent from the Seconds Saybolt Universal values, a more direct comparison of relative viscosities of different oils can be made by converting to kinematic viscosity (centistokes) which very closely represents the true viscosity. A kinematic viscosity of 4.0 centistokes, for instance, is equivalent to a value of 39.1 SSU, while a kinematic viscosity of 2.0 centistokes is equivalent to a value of 32.6 SSU.

Fuel oils, compared to coal, are relatively easy to handle and to burn. Heating is not required for the lighter oils, and even the heavier oils are relatively simple to handle. There is no ash in bulk disposal problem as there is with coal, and there is no objectionable ash discharge from the stack. In most oil burners the oil is atomized to a mist of small particles which mixes with combustion air. In the atomized state oil approaches the characteristics of a gas, and the explosion hazards are of the same order as for gaseous fuels referred to below.

Because of its relatively low cost compared to other weight oils, #6 fuel oil is the most widely used for steam generation. It can be considered a by-product of the refining process. The ash content of #6 fuel oil, ranging from about 0.01 per cent to 0.50 per cent, is exceedingly low compared to coal. The ash, however, despite this low content, is sometimes responsible for a number of serious operating problems. The sulfur contributes to these problems and is itself the cause of others. Among the operating difficulties due to ash and sulfur are:

1. Fluxing of refractory furnace walls.

2. Slagging of high temperature superheater surfaces with deposits not successfully removed by air or steam soot blowers.

3. Attack on steels including high chromium content alloys when the metal temperatures are something above 1200F.

4. Coating of boiler, economizer and air heater surfaces or other heat exchangers.

5. Corrosion and plugging of the cold sections of air heaters.

Experience indicates that the constituents in the ash responsible for the difficulties listed above in items 1 through 4 are sodium or vanadium or both, particularly when the sulfur content is high. Some of the sulfur in the oil combines with the sodium and usually appears in deposits on heating surfaces as sodium sulfate as analyzed.° The vanadium in the oil usually appears in the deposits as V_2O_5 as analyzed.° Since both compounds have low melting points, 1625F for Na_2SO_4 and 1275F for V_2O_5, their presence tends to lower the fusing temperatures of the deposits, the amount depending on the relative quantities of the more refractory materials such as alumina and silica present.

° The actual compounds as they exist in operation are not definitely known.

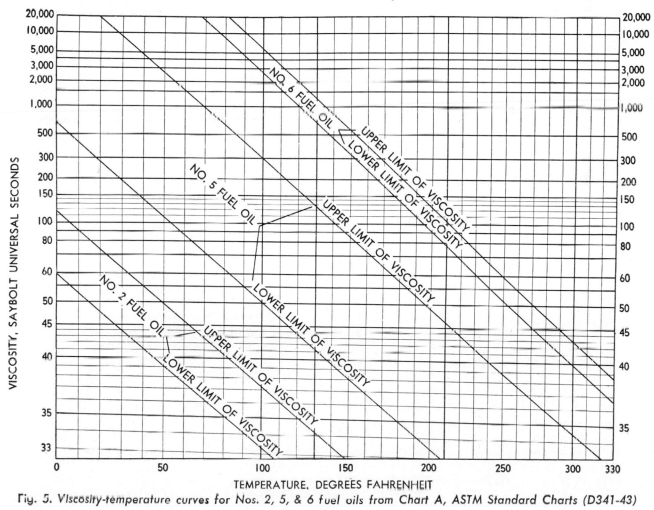

Fig. 5. Viscosity-temperature curves for Nos. 2, 5, & 6 fuel oils from Chart A, ASTM Standard Charts (D341-43)

Typical analyses of oil ash causing the difficulties listed above in items 1, 2 and 3 are given in columns 1 and 2 of Table 3. A typical ash analysis of a trouble-free oil is given in column 3. Oils produced from Venezuelan crudes have a relatively high vanadium content. A typical analysis of an oil ash from a Venezuelan crude is given in column 4. A typical analysis of oil ash from an East Texas crude is given in column 5. Both the Venezuelan and East Texas oils may be expected to be troublesome. Partial analyses of oil ash from an Arabian oil and an Iranian oil are given in columns 6 and 7.

Sulfur from the oil may also appear as sulfuric

TABLE 4

Analysis of Typical Green River Oil-Shale

Physical properties		
Specific gravity, 60F/60F		2.3
Bulk density, 48 mesh, lb/cu ft		67.8
Oil-shale assay*, weight per cent		
Oil		10.3
Gas		2.5
Water		1.4
Organic residue		3.1
Mineral residue		82.7
Yield in oil, gal per ton		26.7
Mineral residue, wt % of raw shale		
Mineral CO_2 evolved		20.0
Mineral analysis of ash		
Silica	as SiO_2	26.4
Calcium	as CaO	17.1
Magnesium	as MgO	5.4
Aluminum	as Al_2O_3	6.6
Alkalies	as Na_2O & K_2O	3.7
Iron	as Fe_2O_3	2.6
Phosphorus & Vanadium	as P_2O_5 & V_2O_5	0.4
Sulfur	as SO_3	0.5

* Modified Fischer assay

acid in the cold sections of the air heater or other components and is responsible for the corrosion mentioned above. Experience indicates that vanadium in the oil increases the amount of plugging and corrosion of air heaters.

Fuel oils generally available on the Eastern seaboard contain varying amounts of Venezuelan and Middle East crudes depending on the relative quantities of shipments and on the blending at the refineries to meet #6 fuel oil viscosity specifications. Fuel oils used on the Gulf Coast are produced largely from domestic crudes, although they may contain some Venezuelan crude. Because of this it is difficult if not impossible to identify the source of fuel oils as fired.

Under certain conditions slagging and fouling in oil firing can be reduced by the addition of simple commercial products to the fuel oil. Actual trials are generally necessary to determine the justification for the use of a product for this purpose. To find economical solutions for the problems inherent in the burning of fuel oils, laboratory and field investigations by oil companies, oil users and equipment manufacturers are continuing at an accelerated rate. See reference in Chapter 18 to the results already achieved in connection with additives to fuel oil.

Natural Gas. Of all fuels, natural gas is considered the most desirable for steam generation. It is piped directly to the consumer, eliminating the need for storage at the consumer's plant. It is substantially free of ash; combustion is smokeless, and, because it is a gas, it mixes easily and intimately with air to give complete combustion with low excess combustion air. Although the total hydrogen content of natural gas is high, the amount of free hydrogen is low. Because of this, natural gas is not as easy to burn as some of the manufactured gases having high free hydrogen contents. As with other gaseous fuels, its ease of mixing with air increases the likelihood of explosion. Great care in the design and operation of gas burning equipment is essential to minimize explosion hazards.

Because of the high hydrogen content of natural gas compared to oil and coal, the water vapor formed in combustion is correspondingly greater which may be reflected in a lower efficiency of the steam generating equipment. This can readily be taken into account in the design of the equipment and evaluated in comparing its cost to other fuels.

Typical analyses of natural gas from several of the United States fields are given in the Appendix.

Oil-Shale. An analysis of a typical Green River oil-shale from the Colorado, Utah, Wyoming area is given in Table 4. Based on this analysis, heavy fuel oils produced from this shale might be expected to have less troublesome ash than many of the fuel oils currently produced from petroleum.

Wood. Typical analyses and heating values of several types of wood (also analyses of wood ash) are given in the Appendix. Wood, in common with all types of vegetation, is composed primarily of carbohydrates and consequently has a relatively low heating value compared to bituminous coal and oil.

Wood bark may pick up impurities during transportation. It is common practice to drag the rough logs to central loading points in the logging area during which the bark will pick up considerable sand. Where the logs are salt water-borne, the bark will absorb a considerable amount of sea water with its included salt. In burning dry bark, combustion temperatures may be high enough so that these impurities will cause fluxing of refractory furnace walls and slagging of boiler heating surfaces unless sufficient furnace cooling surface is provided. Sand passing through the boiler banks may cause erosion of boiler tubes, particularly if the sand loading of the flue gases is increased by the use of cinder catchers for returning collected material to the furnace. To reduce the discharge of incompletely burned bark from the stack to acceptable limits such collectors may be required with some types of bark burning equipment.

As mentioned above under preparation, the moisture content of wood and bark may be quite high. Wood or bark having a moisture content of 50 per cent or less burn quite well; however, as the moisture content increases above this amount, combustion becomes more difficult. With moisture content above 65 per cent a large part of the heat in the wood is required to evaporate the moisture, and little is left over for steam generation. Burning of this wet bark becomes a means of disposal rather than a source of heat energy.

Hogged wood and bark are very bulky and require relatively large handling and storage equipment. Flow from bunkers or bins and through chutes is difficult, and equipment providing uninterrupted flow of bark from the supply point to the furnace without frequent manual attention is the exception rather than the rule.

Bagasse. Mills grinding sugar cane commonly use bagasse for steam production. The mills normally operate 24 hours a day during the grinding season. In mills where refining of the sugar is not done, the supply of bagasse will easily equal that required to meet the plant steam demands. Consequently, where there is no other market for the bagasse, no particular efforts are made to burn the bagasse efficiently, and burning equipment is provided which will burn the bagasse as received from the grinders. In plants where refining is done, supplemental fuels are required to provide the increased steam demands. In these plants greater efforts to obtain higher efficiency are justified. A typical analysis of bagasse as fired is given in the Appendix.

Relative Costs of Fuels

Fuel Oils. As noted above fuel oils are divided into five general classes according to properties, and the relative costs are given in Table 2. These costs are based on prices in the New York area in December 1950. Because of the proportionately great variations over periods of time, and in different localities, these relative costs can only serve as rough approximations. In many parts of the country steam generating equipment is arranged to burn either coal or oil, the fuel selected depending on the relative costs. How these costs have varied in recent years is shown in Fig. 6. These costs were based on a 14,000 Btu/lb coal from the Clearfield district including freight to New York harbor. Oil prices were based on posted prices plus boat freight to the same destination.

Natural Gas. The cost of natural gas in the United States close to the source, is of the order of 6 cents per million Btu and increases up to 30 to 70 cents farther from the source. Since a large per cent of natural gas is used for space heating, the demand

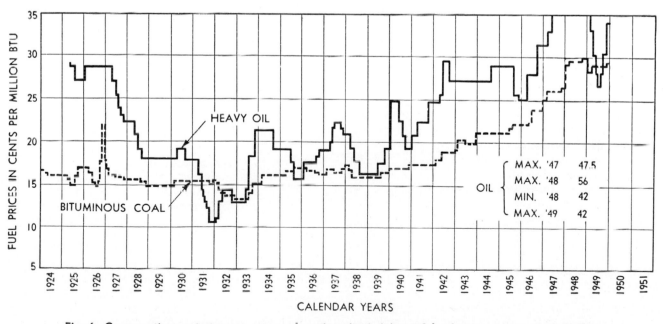

Fig. 6. *Comparative variations in prices of coal and oil delivered by barge at New York harbor*

3-11

for natural gas is considerably higher during the winter months. During summer months natural gas may be available at relatively low cost for steam generation, even in areas a considerable distance from the source. More and more steam plants are being adapted to burn natural gas seasonally. Because the supply of natural gas is much greater than the present pipeline capacity, plants for conversion of natural gas to gasoline are being built. As additional gas is so used and pipeline capacity is increased, the cost of natural gas may approach that of oil and coal, even in areas near its source. A wide range in comparative cost for three different fuels is shown by Fig. 7.

Oil Shale. In the United States, at the prevailing cost of producing oil from petroleum, it has not been commercially attractive to produce oil from oil shale. It is estimated that the cost of producing crude shale oil would be about $2.00 per bbl, including operating costs, depreciation, taxes, and a 6% return on the investment. Continued increase in the cost of oil from petroleum may bring about the commercial production of oil from oil shale in the future.

Other Fuels Sometimes Burned

Among other fuels used, those derived from coal are of the most importance. Combustible by-products or wastes in industries processing woods or vegetation are also used as fuels.

Coke. When coal is heated in the absence of air or with a great deficiency of air, the lighter constituents are volatilized and the heavier hydrocarbons crack, liberating hydrogen and leaving a residue of carbon. Some of the volatilized portions crack on contact with the hot carbon, leaving an additional quantity of carbon. The carbonaceous residue containing the ash and a part of the sulfur of the original coal is called "coke." The amount of sulfur and the amount and nature of the ash in the coke obviously depend in large measure upon the coal from which it is produced and the coking process used. A typical analysis of coke breeze appears in the Appendix. The principal uses for coke are in the production of pig iron in blast furnaces and the charging of iron-foundry cupolas. Because it is smokeless in combustion, considerable quantities are used for space heating.

At the steel mills, undersized coke called "coke breeze," usually passing a ⅝-in. screen, is unsuited for charging blast furnaces and is available for steam generation. Practically all of the coke breeze is consumed at the mills.

Coke production and consumption in millions of tons for the year 1947 are tabulated as follows:

Total coal used for coke production	104.8
Total annual coke production	73.4
Coke breeze produced	5.6
Coke breeze used for steam production	3.5

A portion of the coal tars produced may be burned in equipment similar to that used for heavy petroleum oil.

Gaseous Fuels. A number of gaseous fuels are derived from coal. Typical analyses of some of these are given in the Appendix. The importance of these fuels is diminishing because they have been displaced by natural gas and oil. A description of the gaseous fuels from coal as listed in the table follows:

Coke-Oven Gas. In the production of coke from coal, a considerable portion of the coal is released as gases or vapors. A number of valuable products are recovered from these gaseous portions, including ammonium sulfate, oils, and tars. The noncondensable portion is called "coke-oven gas." Its constituents depend upon the nature of the coal from which the gas is produced and the coke procedure used. A part of the sulfur from the coal may be present as hydrogen sulfide and carbon disulfide gases. These may be removed by scrubbing. Coke-oven gas often contains other impurities which will deposit in lines and burners. To reduce the possibility of trouble from plugging by these deposits, relatively large burner gas-port openings are used, and burners are arranged for easy access for cleaning. Coke-oven gas burns readily because of its high free hydrogen content and, except for the build-up of deposits, presents no problems when used as fuel for steam generation.

Approximately 33% of the coke-oven gas produced is used in firing the coke ovens. Many steel mills have their own coke-producing plants, and, consequently, large quantities of coke-oven gas are available for heating-furnaces and steam generation. Coke-oven gas is also distributed for domestic and industrial use. It is often mixed with other combustible gases before distribution.

Blast-Furnace Gas. The gas discharged from steel mill blast furnaces is used at the mills in heating-furnaces, gas engines, and for steam generation. As shown by the analyses in the Appendix, the gas is quite variable in quality but generally of low heating value and high carbon monoxide content.

The temperature of the gas as discharged from the furnace is around 500 F, and it contains 5 to 7 grains of entrained dust per cu ft. The gas as it comes from the furnace may be burned for steam generation, but at many mills the entrained dust is first removed by washing or by electrostatic precipitation. With many types of washers the wet washed gas will have a dust loading of 0.1 to 0.2

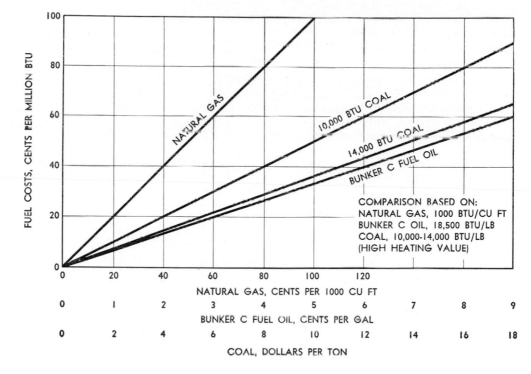

Fig. 7. Comparative fuel costs in cents per million Btu

grains per cu ft, and, with high gas-pressure-drop water scrubbing or cleansing by electrostatic precipitation, the gas may have a dust loading of the order of 0.02 grains per cu ft.

Both the dirty and the wet washed gas cause trouble, when burned for steam generation, by plugging the gas lines and burner port openings and fouling the boiler heating surfaces. Because of the nature of the deposits, wet washed gas is often more troublesome than hot, dry, dirty gas. Electrostatically cleaned gas may or may not cause trouble, depending upon the collector efficiency maintained. Blast-furnace-gas deposits adhere very firmly, and special provisions are required for cleaning the boiler heating surfaces. For blast-furnace-gas firing, means must be provided for access and cleaning of burners.

When blast-furnace gas is used in steam generation, special safety precautions are required because of fluctuation in the gas supply from variations or interruptions in blast-furnace operation. Also, where the steam production rate must be maintained, an alternate fuel must be immediately available.

Water Gas. The gas produced by passing steam through a bed of hot coke is known as water gas. The coke combines with the steam to form hydrogen and carbon monoxide. This is an endothermic reaction which cools the coke bed. To maintain the latter at elevated temperatures, the steam is periodically replaced by air. While the air is passing through the bed, the discharged products of combustion are diverted to the atmosphere to avoid diluting the water gas.

Water gas is often enriched with oil by passing the gas through a checkerwork of hot bricks sprayed with oil which is cracked to a gas by the heat. Refinery gas is also used for enrichment. It may either be mixed with the steam and passed through the coke bed or mixed directly with the water gas. Such enriched water gas is called "carbureted water gas." Water gas is widely used for urban industrial and domestic consumption. In many areas, however, it has been replaced by natural gas. Water gas, like natural gas, is piped directly to the consumer through city mains. Where it is so used, it is cleaned at the source to remove sulfur gases and other impurities.

Producer Gas. When coal or coke is burned with a deficiency of air and a controlled amount of moisture (steam), a gas known as producer gas is obtained. Because of its low heating value, from high nitrogen content, it is used close to the source. Where impurities in the coal prohibit its direct use in firing equipment, producer gas made from this coal may be used to advantage after cleaning to remove entrained ash and sulfur compounds.

A recent experiment has been the underground gasification of coal at Gorgas, Ala., to obtain producer gas for power production at the mine.

Wood Wastes. There are several industries using wood as a raw material where combustible by-products or wastes are available as fuels. The most important of these are the pulp and turpentine industries. The nature and methods of utilization of the combustible by-products from the pulp industry are discussed in Chapter 20.

The residue remaining after the steam distillation of wood stumps for the production of turpentine is usable as a fuel. In the distillation process some of the more easily burned constituents are removed with the result that the residue is somewhat more difficult to burn. Other than this, its properties are much the same as those of the raw wood, and the problems involved in its utilization are similar.

Vegetation Wastes. In the food and related industries there are numerous vegetable wastes which are usable as fuels. They include such materials as grain hulls, the residue from the production of furfural from corn cobs and grain hulls, coffee grounds from the production of instant coffee, tobacco stems etc. The quantity of such fuels is a relatively insignificant part of the total heat energy requirements.

PRINCIPLES OF COMBUSTION

IN the field of power generation useful heat is produced by combustion, which may be defined as the rapid chemical combination of oxygen with the combustible elements of a fuel. The common fuels—coal, oil, gas, wood and their various derivatives—have only three elemental constituents, carbon, hydrogen, and sulfur, which unite with oxygen of the air to produce heat. For most fuels the elemental constituents are carbon and hydrogen, since the per cent of sulfur is so low as to be negligible in producing heat, although some of its compounds can have profound chemical effects (corrosion), which are considered elsewhere (see Chapter 11).

To achieve complete combustion, that is, the combination of the combustible elements and compounds of a fuel with all the oxygen which they can utilize, sufficient space, time, mixing or turbulence, and a temperature high enough to ignite the constituents must be provided.

The combustible elements and their compounds found in fuels used in the commercial generation of heat, as well as their molecular weights and combustion constants, including heat values, are listed in Table 1. The noncombustible elements and compounds involved in combustion are also listed in this table.

Oxygen combines with combustible elements and compounds in accordance with the laws of chemistry, and the various substances involved always combine in fixed proportions by weight. Typical chemical reactions frequently encountered in the commercial production of heat are given in Table 2. These chemical equations are based on the assumption that the reaction is complete and that the exact amount of oxygen required is utilized.

Principles Involved in Combustion

The principles involved in the development of heat by combustion, generally accepted as authoritative, were propounded by Berthelot. His "second law," as applied to combustion in furnace practice, is of particular interest and may be stated as follows:

In a boiler furnace (where no mechanical work is done) the heat energy evolved from the union of combustible elements with oxygen depends upon the ultimate products of combustion and not upon any intermediate combinations that may occur in reaching the final result.

A simple demonstration of this law is the union of 1 lb of carbon with oxygen to produce a specific amount of heat (about 14,100 Btu, Table 1). The union may be in one step to form the gaseous product of combustion, CO_2. Under certain suitable conditions the union may be in two steps, first, to form CO, producing a much smaller amount of heat (about 4000 Btu) and, second, the union of the CO so obtained to form CO_2, releasing 10,100[*] Btu. However, the sum of the heats released in these two steps equals the 14,100 Btu evolved when carbon is burned in one step to form CO_2 as the final product.

That carbon may enter into these two combinations with oxygen is of utmost importance in the design of combustion equipment. Firing methods must assure proper and complete mixture of the fuel and the oxygen. Failure to meet this requirement will result in appreciable losses in combustion efficiency and heat potentials because of unburned combustibles.

Measurement of the Heat of Combustion

In boiler practice the heat of combustion of a fuel, or the calorific value frequently referred to as the "fuel Btu value," is the amount of heat, expressed in Btu, generated by the complete combustion, or oxidation, of a unit weight (1 lb in the United States) of the fuel. The amount of heat so generated is a

---

[*] The National Bureau of Standards, Bulletin No. 500, gives 10,096 Btu per lb for graphite C at 78 F burned from CO to CO_2.

TABLE 1

Combustion Constants

No.	Substance	Formula	Molecular Weight	Lb per Cu Ft	Cu Ft per Lb	Sp Gr Air = 1.0000	Heat of Combustion — Btu per Cu Ft Gross (High)	Btu per Cu Ft Net (Low)	Btu per Lb Gross (High)	Btu per Lb Net (Low)	For 100% Total Air — Moles per mole of Combustible or Cu Ft per Cu Ft of Combustible — Required for Combustion O2	N2	Air	Flue Products CO2	H2O	N2	For 100% Total Air — Lb per Lb of Combustible — Required for Combustion O2	N2	Air	Flue Products CO2	H2O	N2
1	Carbon*	C	12.01	......	......	......	...	...	14,093	14,093	1.0	3.76	4.76	1.0	...	3.76	2.66	8.86	11.53	3.66	...	8.86
2	Hydrogen	H2	2.016	0.0053	187.723	0.0696	325	275	61,100	51,623	0.5	1.88	2.38	...	1.0	1.88	7.94	26.41	34.34	...	8.94	26.41
3	Oxygen	O2	32.000	0.0846	11.819	1.1053	...	...	.....	.....	...	...	...	...	...	...	...	...	...	...	...	...
4	Nitrogen (atm)	N2	28.016	0.0744	13.443	0.9718	...	...	.....	.....	...	...	...	...	...	...	...	...	...	...	...	...
5	Carbon monoxide	CO	28.01	0.0740	13.506	0.9672	322	322	4,347	4,347	0.5	1.88	2.38	1.0	...	1.88	0.57	1.90	2.47	1.57	...	1.90
6	Carbon dioxide	CO2	44.01	0.1170	8.548	1.5282	...	...	.....	.....	...	...	...	...	...	...	...	...	...	...	...	...
	Paraffin series																					
7	Methane	CH4	16.041	0.0424	23.565	0.5543	1013	913	23,879	21,520	2.0	7.53	9.53	1.0	2.0	7.53	3.99	13.28	17.27	2.74	2.25	13.28
8	Ethane	C2H6	30.067	0.0803	12.455	1.0488	1792	1641	22,320	20,432	3.5	13.18	16.68	2.0	3.0	13.18	3.73	12.39	16.12	2.93	1.80	12.39
9	Propane	C3H8	44.092	0.1196	8.365	1.5617	2590	2385	21,661	19,944	5.0	18.82	23.82	3.0	4.0	18.82	3.63	12.07	15.70	2.99	1.63	12.07
10	n-Butane	C4H10	58.118	0.1582	6.321	2.0665	3370	3113	21,308	19,680	6.5	24.47	30.97	4.0	5.0	24.47	3.58	11.91	15.49	3.03	1.55	11.91
11	Isobutane	C4H10	58.118	0.1582	6.321	2.0665	3363	3105	21,257	19,629	6.5	24.47	30.97	4.0	5.0	24.47	3.58	11.91	15.49	3.03	1.55	11.91
12	n-Pentane	C5H12	72.144	0.1904	5.252	2.4872	4016	3709	21,091	19,517	8.0	30.11	38.11	5.0	6.0	30.11	3.55	11.81	15.35	3.05	1.50	11.81
13	Isopentane	C5H12	72.144	0.1904	5.252	2.4872	4008	3716	21,052	19,478	8.0	30.11	38.11	5.0	6.0	30.11	3.55	11.81	15.35	3.05	1.50	11.81
14	Neopentane	C5H12	72.144	0.1904	5.252	2.4872	3993	3693	20,970	19,396	8.0	30.11	38.11	5.0	6.0	30.11	3.55	11.81	15.35	3.05	1.50	11.81
15	n-Hexane	C6H14	86.169	0.2274	4.398	2.9704	4762	4412	20,940	19,403	9.5	35.76	45.26	6.0	7.0	35.76	3.53	11.74	15.27	3.06	1.46	11.74
	Olefin series																					
16	Ethylene	C2H4	28.051	0.0746	13.412	0.9740	1614	1513	21,644	20,295	3.0	11.29	14.29	2.0	2.0	11.29	3.42	11.39	14.81	3.14	1.29	11.39
17	Propylene	C3H6	42.077	0.1110	9.007	1.4504	2336	2186	21,041	19,691	4.5	16.94	21.44	3.0	3.0	16.94	3.42	11.39	14.81	3.14	1.29	11.39
18	n-Butene	C4H8	56.102	0.1480	6.756	1.9336	3084	2885	20,840	19,496	6.0	22.59	28.59	4.0	4.0	22.59	3.42	11.39	14.81	3.14	1.29	11.39
19	Isobutene	C4H8	56.102	0.1480	6.756	1.9336	3068	2869	20,730	19,382	6.0	22.59	28.59	4.0	4.0	22.59	3.42	11.39	14.81	3.14	1.29	11.39
20	n-Pentene	C5H10	70.128	0.1852	5.400	2.4190	3836	3586	20,712	19,363	7.5	28.23	35.73	5.0	5.0	28.23	3.42	11.39	14.81	3.14	1.29	11.39
	Aromatic series																					
21	Benzene	C6H6	78.107	0.2060	4.852	2.6920	3751	3601	18,210	17,480	7.5	28.23	35.73	6.0	3.0	28.23	3.07	10.22	13.30	3.38	0.69	10.22
22	Toluene	C7H8	92.132	0.2431	4.113	3.1760	4484	4284	18,440	17,620	9.0	33.88	42.88	7.0	4.0	33.88	3.13	10.40	13.53	3.34	0.78	10.40
23	Xylene	C8H10	106.158	0.2803	3.567	3.6618	5230	4980	18,650	17,760	10.5	39.52	50.02	8.0	5.0	39.52	3.17	10.53	13.70	3.32	0.85	10.53
	Miscellaneous gases																					
24	Acetylene	C2H2	26.036	0.0697	14.344	0.9107	1499	1448	21,500	20,776	2.5	9.41	11.91	2.0	1.0	9.41	3.07	10.22	13.30	3.38	0.69	10.22
25	Naphthalene	C10H8	128.162	0.3384	2.955	4.4208	5854	5654	17,298	16,708	12.0	45.17	57.17	10.0	4.0	45.17	3.00	9.97	12.96	3.43	0.56	9.97
26	Methyl alcohol	CH3OH	32.041	0.0846	11.820	1.1052	868	768	10,259	9,078	1.5	5.65	7.15	1.0	2.0	5.65	1.50	4.98	6.48	1.37	1.13	4.98
27	Ethyl alcohol	C2H5OH	46.067	0.1216	8.221	1.5890	1600	1451	13,161	11,929	3.0	11.29	14.29	2.0	3.0	11.29	2.08	6.93	9.02	1.92	1.17	6.93
28	Ammonia	NH3	17.031	0.0456	21.914	0.5961	441	365	9,668	8,001	0.75	2.82	3.57	...	1.5	3.32	1.41	4.69	6.10	...	1.59	5.51
29	Sulfur*	S	32.06	......	......	......	...	...	3,983	3,983	1.0	3.76	4.76	SO2 1.0	...	3.76	1.00	3.29	4.29	SO2 2.00	...	3.29
30	Hydrogen sulfide	H2S	34.076	0.0911	10.979	1.1898	647	596	7,100	6,545	1.5	5.65	7.15	1.0	1.0	5.65	1.41	4.69	6.10	1.88	0.53	4.69
31	Sulfur dioxide	SO2	64.06	0.1733	5.770	2.2640	...	...	.....	.....	...	...	...	...	...	...	...	...	...	...	...	...
32	Water vapor	H2O	18.016	0.0476	21.017	0.6215	...	...	.....	.....	...	...	...	...	...	...	...	...	...	...	...	...
33	Air	.....	28.9	0.0766	13.063	1.0000	...	...	.....	.....	...	...	...	...	...	...	...	...	...	...	...	...

*Carbon and sulfur are considered as gases for molal calculations only.

Note: This table is reprinted from *Fuel Flue Gases*, 1941 Edition, courtesy of American Gas Association.

All gas volumes corrected to 60 F and 30 in. Hg dry.

constant for any given combination of combustible elements and compounds and, in accordance with Berthelot's second law, is not affected by the manner in which combustion takes place, providing it is complete.[*]

TABLE 2

Common Chemical Reactions of Combustion

Combustible	Reaction
Carbon (to CO)	$2C + O_2 = 2CO + \triangle Q$
Carbon (to CO_2)	$C + O_2 = CO_2 + \triangle Q$
Carbon monoxide	$2CO + O_2 = 2CO_2 + \triangle Q$
Hydrogen	$2H_2 + O_2 = 2H_2O + \triangle Q$
Sulfur (to SO_2)	$S + O_2 = SO_2 + \triangle Q$
Sulfur (to SO_3)	$2S + 3O_2 = 2SO_3 + \triangle Q$
Methane	$CH_4 + 2O_2 = CO_2 + 2H_2O + \triangle Q$
Acetylene	$2C_2H_2 + 5O_2 = 4CO_2 + 2H_2O + \triangle Q$
Ethylene	$C_2H_4 + 3O_2 = 2CO_2 + 2H_2O + \triangle Q$
Ethane	$2C_2H_6 + 7O_2 = 4CO_2 + 6H_2O + \triangle Q$
Hydrogen sulfide	$2H_2S + 3O_2 = 2SO_2 + 2H_2O + \triangle Q$

where $\triangle Q$ = the heat of reaction

To determine the calorific value of any fuel, the most satisfactory and universally adopted method is by direct measurement, in a calorimeter, of the heat evolved during combustion. Fuel calorimeters and the methods of operation are described in detail by numerous authorities.

For solid fuels and most liquid fuels, calorimeters of the "bomb" types in which combustible substances are burned in a constant volume of oxygen, give the most satisfactory results. With bomb calorimeters, properly operated, combustion is complete, all of the heat generated is absorbed and measured, and heat from external sources can be excluded or proper corrections applied.

For gaseous fuels, calorimeters of the continuous, or constant-flow, type are ordinarily accepted as standard.

The accuracy of the determination of the heat value of a fuel by calorimeter, largely a question of the personal equation, depends upon careful manipulation of the instrument. With proper care the results should be accurate to within a fraction of 1%. In addition to the calorific value, it is customary (necessary for heat balance calculations) to report the ultimate or the proximate analysis of the fuel.

For solid and liquid fuels, separate determinations of the calorific value of each specific fuel are necessary. For the calorific values of some solid and liquid

fuels, refer to Chapters 2 and 3. For elements and combustible compounds comprising gaseous fuels, the heats of reaction have been determined by so many authorities that established values may be accepted as correct without determination. For gaseous fuels and various substances frequently encountered in combustion work, see Table 1.

While it is preferable, for accuracy, to determine the heat value of a fuel by actual test in a calorimeter, approximate heat values may be determined by computation from the ultimate chemical analysis of certain fuels. Dulong's formula, below, in general use as a routine check of values determined by calorimeter, gives reasonably accurate results (within 2 or 3%) for most coals:

$$Btu/lb = 14,544 \; C + 62,028 \; \left(H_2 - \frac{O_2}{8}\right) + 4050 \; S \quad (1)$$

In this formula, the symbols represent the proportionate parts by weight of the constituents of the fuel—carbon, hydrogen, oxygen, and sulfur—as established by an ultimate analysis (as-fired or other basis); the coefficients represent the approximate heating values of the constituents in Btu per lb. The term $\frac{O_2}{8}$ is a correction applied to the hydrogen in the fuel to account for the hydrogen already combined with oxygen in the form of moisture. The formula is not generally suitable for calculating the Btu values of gaseous fuels.

In the case of gaseous mixtures where the proportionate parts by volume or weight are readily available, the heating value may be accurately computed from a table of the heat values of individual constituents, which values have been definitely fixed by numerous calorimetric experiments, as noted above.

High and Low Heat Values

Most commercial fuels contain hydrogen as one of the constituents, and water, H_2O, is formed as a product of combustion when the hydrogen is burned in air. This water may remain in the vapor state, or it may be condensed to the liquid state, giving a substantial difference in the heat value. In determining the heat given up by a unit of such fuel, two values may be reported—the high, or gross, heat value and the low, or net, heat value. For the high, or gross, heat value, it is assumed that any water vapor formed by the burning of the hydrogen constituent is all condensed and cooled to the initial temperature in the calorimeter at the start of the test. The heat of vaporization is therefore present in the reported value. For the low, or net, heat value, it is assumed that none of the water vapor condenses and that all of the products of combustion remain in a gaseous state.

---

[*] Actually, when substances react to form other substances, a definite amount of heat is either evolved or absorbed. The reaction of C with H_2O to form CO and H_2, in which about 5900 Btu per lb C is absorbed, is an example of heat absorption. Boiler practice in general, however, is concerned with combinations involving the evolution of heat.

The high, or gross, heat value is given directly and accurately by proper and well-defined (ASTM) laboratory procedure, using prescribed equipment. Direct determination of the low heat value is difficult, and the low heat value, where this value is to be used, is usually calculated from the high heat value, thus:

$$Q_L = Q_H - 1040 \; w \qquad (2)$$

where:

Q_L = low heat value of the fuel, Btu per lb
Q_H = high heat value of the fuel, Btu per lb
w = lb water formed per lb of fuel
1040 = a factor commonly used to reduce high heat value at 80 F and constant volume to low heat value at constant pressure

In the United States the practice in boiler combustion calculations is to use the high heat values, since these values are available directly from calorimeter determinations and also because of the established custom of buying fuel on a Btu, high heat value, basis. In Europe generally, low heat values are used.

Oxygen and Nitrogen in Air

Theoretically, it is easy to assume that sufficient oxygen is present for combination with the combustibles and that the temperature required to bring about the chemical reactions of combustion can be attained. However, even with proper temperature conditions, the most important and difficult problem in the burning of all fuels is the manner of the physical introduction of oxygen to the combustible substances to effect complete oxidation and at the same time to assure the utilization of all or a maximum proportion of the oxygen supplied.

Usually, in the generation of heat, the oxygen required for combustion is supplied by using air, and the other constituents of the air act as diluents. However, in certain instances, particularly when the products of combustion must be minimized because of disposal problems, pure or slightly diluted oxygen is used. In these designs the heat potentials are exceptionally high, since all of the heat of combustion is transferred to a greatly reduced quantity of combustion products.

Atmospheric air is a mixture—as distinguished from a chemical compound—of oxygen, nitrogen, and small amounts of carbon dioxide, water vapor, argon, and other inert gases. If N'_2 is taken to represent the aggregate of nitrogen (N_2) and the small amounts of CO_2, argon, and other inert gases, then air may be considered to be 23.15% O_2 and 76.85% N'_2 by weight. Since in most combustion work the rare inert gases are negligible in effect, it is sufficient to consider N'_2 as consisting wholly of nitrogen, N_2. Usually accepted values of O_2 and N_2 in air are given in Table 3.

TABLE 3

Per Cent Oxygen and Nitrogen in Air
(Rare inert gases included as N_2)

	Per Cent by Weight	Per Cent by Volume
Oxygen, O_2	23.15	21.0
Nitrogen, N_2	76.85	79.0

Because of the proportionate parts by weight of oxygen and nitrogen, 0.2315 and 0.7685, respectively, to supply 1 lb of oxygen for combustion it is necessary to supply 1/0.2315 = 4.32 lb of air, and in this amount of air there are $4.32 \times 0.7685 = 3.32$ lb of nitrogen, which do not enter directly into the combustion process but remain present nevertheless.

Oxygen, with its strong affinity for the combustible constituents of the fuel under proper conditions of temperature, is separated from the oxygen-nitrogen mixture (air) and joins the combustible in chemical combination to form, with the nitrogen, the products of combustion. The heat liberated by combustion is transferred by radiation, convection, and conduction to the heat-exchange apparatus, and ultimately on leaving, the combustion products carry heat to waste (the stack). The quantity of heat so wasted is directly proportional to the temperature and the amount, at exit, of the products of combustion (commonly called flue gas at this point). Hence, the air used in modern combustion practice is generally as carefully measured as the fuel, and great care is taken to effect a tight setting to prevent the admission of air except in the zone where it unites with the fuel.

Ignition Temperatures

Every combustible substance has a minimum ignition temperature, which must be attained or exceeded, in the presence of oxygen, if combustion is to ensue under given conditions. This ignition temperature may be defined as the temperature at which more heat is generated by the reaction than is lost to the surroundings, and combustion thus becomes self-sustaining. Ignition temperatures depend to a considerable extent upon the surrounding conditions, such as pressure (generally lower as pressure increases). The term usually applies to rapid combustion in air at atmospheric pressure.

The ignition temperatures of combustible substances vary greatly, as indicated in Table 4, in which minimum temperatures and temperature ranges in air are given for fuels and for the combustible constituents of fuels commonly used in the commercial generation of heat.

The ignition temperatures of the gases of a coal vary considerably and are appreciably higher than the ignition temperatures of the fixed carbon of the coal. However, the ignition temperature of coal may be considered as the ignition temperature of its fixed carbon content, since the gaseous constituents are usually distilled off, but not ignited, before this temperature is attained.

TABLE 4
Ignition Temperature in Air[a]
(At Pressure of One Atmosphere)

Combustible	Formula	Temperature, F
Sulfur	S	470
Charcoal	C	650
Fixed carbon (bituminous coal)	C	765
Fixed carbon (semibituminous coal)	C	870
Fixed carbon (anthracite)	C	840-1115
Acetylene	C_2H_2	580-825
Ethane	C_2H_6	880-1165
Ethylene	C_2H_4	900-1020
Hydrogen	H_2	1065-1095
Methane	CH_4	1170-1380
Carbon monoxide	CO	1130-1215
Kerosene	—	490-560
Gasoline	—	500-800

[a] Rounded-out values and ranges from various sources; a guide only.

The chemical combinations resulting from the union of oxygen with the combustible elements and compounds of some fuels commonly used in the generation of heat are given in Table 2. From the chemical combinations for these and many other fuels used in the generation of heat (not listed in Table 2) and the use of the molecular weights and volumes of the elements and compounds involved, their proportionate parts by weight and volume in the reactions as well as the weight and volume of the products of combustion (flue products or "flue gases") have been computed as listed in Table 1. The amount of air required to supply the oxygen is also included in this table. Since the oxygen comes from the air, the amount of air and accordingly the amount of nitrogen are fixed when the amount of oxygen has been established. Computations may be demonstrated by the following examples with atmospheric air as the oxidant.

Oxygen Required for Combustion

From the second reaction in Table 2, it is evident that one molecule of carbon combines with one molecule of oxygen to form one molecule of carbon dioxide:

$$C + O_2 = CO_2$$

Using molecular weights, this reaction is represented by:

$$12 + 32 = 44$$

That is, when burning carbon to carbon dioxide, 12 parts by weight of carbon (the approximate molecular weight of C) combine with 32 parts by weight of oxygen (the molecular weight of O_2) to form 44 parts by weight of carbon dioxide (the approximate molecular weight of CO_2). By simple division, 1 lb of carbon plus 2.66 lb of oxygen yield 3.66 lb of carbon dioxide.

The equation, $C + O_2 = CO_2$, also fixes the proportions by volume of the elements and compound in this reaction, represented by the coefficients (1 in this case) of each chemical symbol. However, all the constituents must be considered as gaseous; hence, in the case of carbon (a solid) the fact is of academic interest only at this point. More suitable illustrations may be given:

$$2H_2 + O_2 = 2H_2O$$

where 2 volumes of hydrogen plus 1 volume of oxygen combine to form 2 volumes of water vapor. Also,

$$CH_4 + 2O_2 = CO_2 + 2H_2O$$

where 1 volume of methane plus 2 volumes of oxygen combine to form 1 volume of carbon dioxide and 2 volumes of water vapor.

Another example may be given:

$$2C_2H_2 + 5O_2 = 4CO_2 + 2H_2O$$

where 2 volumes of acetylene plus 5 volumes of oxygen combine to yield 4 volumes of carbon dioxide and 2 volumes of water vapor.

For the volume relationship to hold, all the gases involved must be at the same conditions of temperature and pressure.

It may be noted in the three illustrations above that in the first and third the volumes of the final products of combustion are less than the volumes of the original constituents and that in the second the volume of the final products of combustion is the same as the volume of the original constituents.

The Mole in Combustion Calculations

The volume relationship of gaseous combustion constituents is particularly important in calculations on the "mole" basis (see below) since, for the same conditions of temperature and pressure, the volume of the mole is constant for all so-called perfect gases. Hence, as noted in Table 1, the ratios of the elements and compounds to the combustibles in the reactions are numerically equal, whether expressed as cu ft per cu ft of combustible or as moles per mole of combustible.

Combustion calculations involving gaseous mixtures can be simplified by the use of the pound-mole unit of weight, generally known as the mole.* Since, from the fundamental gas laws, equal volumes of gases at any given pressure and temperature contain the same number of molecules, the weights of equal volumes of gases are proportional to their molecular weights. If M is the molecular weight of the gas, 1 mole equals M lb (or M grams, depending upon the system of units). For instance:

$$1 \text{ mole } \quad O_2 = 32 \text{ lb } O_2$$
$$1 \text{ mole } \quad H_2 = 2 \text{ lb } H_2$$
$$1 \text{ mole } CH_4 = 16 \text{ lb } CH_4$$

That the volume of 1 mole at a given pressure and temperature is approximately fixed and independent of the kind of gas may be demonstrated as follows (see Table 1):

At 60 F and atmospheric pressure (14.7 psia) the specific volume of oxygen is 11.819 cu ft per lb. Therefore, 1 mole of oxygen has a volume of $32 \times 11.819 = 379$ cu ft. Similarly, at 60 F and atmospheric pressure, the specific volume of hydrogen is 187.723 cu ft per lb, and 1 mole has a volume of $2.016 \times 187.723 = 379$ cu ft. This volume, 379 cu ft, therefore approximates the volume of 1 mole of any gas at the assumed standard pressure and temperature. The volume of the mole at atmospheric pressure is in direct proportion to the absolute temperature.

As noted above, molal ratios and volume ratios (gaseous) are numerically equal. By volume (see Table 3), air consists of 21 parts O_2 and 79 parts N_2. This relationship can be expressed as 21 volumes O_2 and 79 volumes N_2 per 100 volumes air or as 21 moles O_2 and 79 moles N_2 per 100 moles air.

As indicated by the following example for a fuel gas, molal calculations have a simple and direct application to gaseous fuels, where the analyses are usually reported in per cent on a volume basis.

Fuel Gas
Analysis by Volume
in Per Cent

CH_4	85.3
C_2H_6	12.6
CO_2	0.1
N_2	1.7
O_2	0.3
Total	100.0

This analysis may also be expressed as 85.3 moles of CH_4 per 100 moles of fuel; 12.6 moles of C_2H_6 per 100 moles of fuel; etc.

*The validity of this method depends upon the fact that most gases follow rather closely the fundamental laws for so-called perfect gases.

Keeping in mind that the molecular form is taken as unity, the elemental breakdown of each constituent may also be designated in moles per 100 moles of fuel, as indicated in the following tabulation for the above analysis:

$$\text{C in } CH_4 = 85.3 \times 1 = 85.3 \text{ moles}$$
$$\text{C in } C_2H_6 = 12.6 \times 2 = 25.2 \text{ moles}$$
$$\text{C in } CO_2 = 0.1 \times 1 = 0.1 \text{ moles}$$

Total C per 100 moles fuel = 110.6 moles

$$\text{H}_2 \text{ in } CH_4 = 85.3 \times 2 = 170.6 \text{ moles}$$
$$\text{H}_2 \text{ in } C_2H_6 = 12.6 \times 3 = 37.8 \text{ moles}$$

Total H_2 per 100 moles fuel = 208.4 moles

$$N_2 \text{ per 100 moles fuel} = 1.7 \times 1 = 1.7 \text{ moles}$$
$$O_2 \text{ per 100 moles fuel} = 0.3 \times 1 = 0.3 \text{ moles}$$

In general, for each mole of C, H_2, and S burned, one mole of CO_2, H_2O, and SO_2, respectively, will be formed.

An analysis of the flue gas (always made on a volume basis, dry, by Orsat or other gas analyzers) produced by burning a gas fuel of the composition given above will be, say, in per cent, 10.4 CO_2, 2.8 O_2, and 86.8 N_2. These percentages may also be expressed as 10.4 moles CO_2, 2.8 moles O_2, and 86.8 moles N_2, each per 100 moles of flue gas. Since, from the fuel analysis (above), there are 110.6 moles C per 100 moles fuel, the same number of moles CO_2 will be formed by the combustion of the 100 moles of fuel. Hence, the moles of flue gas per mole of CO_2 will be $100 \div 10.4 = 9.62$. Therefore, the 100 moles of fuel will yield $110.6 \times 9.62 = 1064$ moles of dry flue gas. Thus by the application of the mole method, an important value has been quickly determined through knowing only the flue gas analysis and fuel analysis. Assuming the molecular weight of flue gas to be approximately 30 (air is 29), the weight of 1064 moles of flue gas is approximately $1064 \times 30 = 31,920$ lb per 100 moles of fuel. The weight of 100 moles of the gas fuel is the sum of the products of the moles of each constituent in the fuel and its molecular weight. The weight of dry flue gas produced per lb of fuel can be determined by dividing the weight of 100 moles of flue gas by the weight of 100 moles of fuel.

For complete applications of the mole method in combustion calculations, including an exact evaluation of the molecular weight of flue gas and other quantity determinations, reference should be made to the examples in the Appendix.

Combustion Calculations—General

The purpose of combustion calculations is to determine a) the quantities of the constituents involved in the chemistry of combustion, b) the heat thus released, and c) the efficiency of the combustion process under ideal and under practical conditions. The results of these calculations are necessary for the determination of heat transfer and performance of heat transfer equipment, such as boilers and their related component parts (see Chapters 7 and 11).

The determination of the quantities of the constituents involved in combustion is necessary to establish the size and performance characteristics of equipment, such as fuel pumps or feeders, and fans and ducts for both air and combustion gases. The necessity of knowing the amount of heat released per unit of fuel or per unit of time is apparent.

The heat input and the losses in burning fuel in air must be determined and segregated by combustion calculations in order to establish the efficiency of heat transfer to the heat exchanger. Knowing the amounts of each of the various losses is particularly helpful in deciding how efficiency may be improved through the possible reduction of certain of the losses. For instance, only enough excess air should be supplied completely to burn the fuel, since more than this amount increases the heat rejected to the stack. A portion of the stack loss is, therefore, a controllable loss and should be held to a minimum by close control of excess air.

Another prime factor affecting efficiency and losses is, of course, temperature, particularly the temperature of combustion gases finally rejected to the stack. The temperatures throughout the boiler or heat exchange unit depend closely upon the manner of heat transfer, discussed in the above references (Chapters 7 and 11), and, therefore, combustion calculations are not generally concerned with these temperatures.

However, the adiabatic, or "theoretical," temperature (without gain or loss of heat), that might conceivably be attained in burning a fuel under certain conditions, is sometimes calculated. Even though this temperature never exists in actual practice, it is of value in estimating furnace temperatures and furnace heat absorption.

The theoretical, or adiabatic, temperature is the maximum gas temperature that can be obtained under certain conditions. With less excess air or higher air preheat temperature, the gas temperature will be higher. If the gas temperature exceeds about 3200 F, a phenomenon occurs in which the CO_2 and H_2O constituents of the combustion gases tend to split into their component parts. This process is called gas dissociation. The effect of this reversal in the combustion process is to reduce the availability of the heat of combustion and thereby reduce the heat producing high temperatures. However, since the furnace exit temperatures are usually not high enough to be affected by this phenomenon, gas dissociation is seldom considered in boiler combustion calculations.

Calculations by Weight and Mole Methods

The detailed steps in the solution of combustion problems are best illustrated by working examples. Four simple examples involving both solid and gaseous fuels are presented (see below) to show how calculations are made using the weight and the mole methods, respectively. It should be noted that in these examples the amount of moisture in the combustion air is taken as 0.0132 lb per lb of dry air, corresponding to conditions of 60% relative humidity and 80 F dry-bulb temperature. This value is often used as standard in combustion calculations.

The values in examples 1 to 4 were generally developed from the data in Table 1, and the procedure followed is apparent from the execution. The results are limited to the determination of the quantities of fuel and air constituents involved, and heat balances are not included in these examples. See *Combustion Air, Btu Method* below and the examples of combustion calculations appearing in the Appendix for suitable methods in heat balance determinations.

EXAMPLE 1
Weight Method — Solid Fuel — Standard Air*
(Complete Combustion Assumed)
See Table 1 for Multipliers

Ultimate Analysis, lb/lb Fuel As Fired		Required for Combustion, lb/lb Fuel @ 100% Total Air	
		O_2	Dry Air
C	$0.728 \times 2.66; 11.53$	1.936	8.394
H_2	$0.048 \times 7.94; 34.34$	0.381	1.648
O_2	0.062	---	---
N_2	0.015	---	---
S	$0.022 \times 1.00; 4.29$	0.022	0.094
H_2O	0.035	---	---
Ash	0.090	---	---
Sum	1.000	2.339	10.136
Less O_2 in fuel (deduct)		−0.062	−0.268†
Required (at 100% Total Air)		2.277	9.868

† Air equivalent of O_2 in fuel.

	Required for Combustion, lb/lb Fuel @ 125% Total Air	
	O_2	Dry Air
O_2 and Air $\times$ 125/100, total	2.846	12.335
Excess air $= 12.335 - 9.868$	---	2.467
Excess $O_2 = 2.846 - 2.277$	0.569	---

Products of Combustion

		lb/lb Fuel @ 125% Total Air
CO_2	0.728×366	2.664
H_2O	$0.048 \times 8.94 + 0.035 + 0.0132 \times 12.335$	0.624
SO_2	0.022×2.00	0.044
O_2	(excess)	0.569
N_2	$12.335 \times 0.7685 + 0.015$	9.494
Weight, wet		13.395
Weight, dry $= 13.395 - 0.624$		12.771

* Air at 60% relative humidity and 80 F dry bulb, or 0.0132 lb of moisture per lb dry air.

EXAMPLE 2

Weight Method — Gaseous Fuel — Standard Air
(Complete Combustion Assumed)
See Table 1 for lb/cu ft and Multipliers

Fuel Analysis, % by Vol As Fired	lb/lb Fuel	Required for Combustion, lb/lb Fuel @ 100% Total Air	
		O_2	Dry Air
CH₄ 90.0	0.832 × 3.99; 17.27	3.320	14.370
C₂H₆ 5.0	0.087 × 3.73; 16.12	0.324	1.402
N₂ 5.0	0.081	———	———
Sum 100.0	1.000	3.644	15.772
Required (at 100% Total Air)		3.644	15.772

	Required for Combustion, lb/lb Fuel @ 115% Total Air	
	O_2	Dry Air
O_2 and Air × 115/100, total	4.191	18.138
Excess air = 18.138 − 15.772	———	2.366
Excess O_2 = 4.191 − 3.644	0.547	———

Products of Combustion

	lb/lb Fuel @ 115% Total Air
CO₂ 0.832 × 2.74 + 0.087 × 2.93	2.535
H₂O 0.832 × 2.25 + 0.087 × 1.80	
+ 0.0132 × 18.138	2.265
O_2 (excess)	0.547
N₂ 18.138 × 0.7685 + 0.081	14.020
Weight, wet	19.367
Weight, dry = 19.367 − 2.265	17.102

EXAMPLE 3

Mole Method — Solid Fuel — Standard Air
(Complete Combustion Assumed)
See Table 1 for Mol. Wt and Multipliers

Ultimate Analysis, lb/100 lb Fuel AF	Moles per 100 lb Fuel	Required for Combustion, Moles/100 lb Fuel @ 100% Total Air	
		O_2	Dry Air
C 72.8	6.07 × 1.00; 4.76	6.07	28.89
H₂ 4.8	2.38 × 0.5; 2.38	1.19	5.66
O₂ 6.2	0.19	——	——
N₂ 1.5	0.05	——	——
S 2.2	0.07 × 1.00; 4.76	0.07	0.33
H₂O 3.5	0.19	——	——
Ash 9.0	——	——	——
Sum 100.0	8.95	7.33	34.88
Less O_2 in fuel (deduct)		−0.19	−0.90*
Required (at 100% Total Air)		7.14	33.98

*Air equivalent of O_2 in fuel.

	Required for Combustion, Moles/100 lb Fuel @ 125% Total Air	
	O_2	Dry Air
O_2 and Air × 125/100, total	8.93	42.48
Excess air = 42.48 − 33.98	——	8.50
Excess O_2 = 8.93 − 7.14	1.79	——

Products of Combustion

		Moles/100 lb Fuel	% by Vol, Dry Basis
CO₂	6.07 × 1	6.07	14.60
H₂O	2.38 × 1 + 42.48 × 0.021†		
	+ 0.19	3.46	———
SO₂	0.07 × 1	0.07	0.17
N₂	42.48 × 0.79	33.56	80.91
O_2	(excess)	1.79	4.32
Wet		44.95	100.00
Dry = 44.95 − 3.46		41.49	

†0.021 = (29 ÷ 18) × 0.0132

EXAMPLE 4

Mole Method — Gaseous Fuel — Standard Air
(Complete Combustion Assumed)
See Table 1 for Multipliers

Fuel Analysis, % by Vol As Fired	Moles per 100 Moles Fuel	Required for Combustion, Moles/100 Moles Fuel @ 100% Total Air	
		O_2	Dry Air
CH₄ 90.0	90.0 × 2.0; 9.53	180.0	857.7
C₂H₆ 5.0	5.0 × 3.5; 16.68	17.5	83.4
N₂ 5.0	5.0	——	——
Sum 100.0	100.0	197.5	941.1
Required (at 100% Total Air)		197.5	941.1

	Required for Combustion, Moles/100 Moles Fuel @ 115% Total Air	
	O_2	Dry Air
O_2 and Air × 115/100, total	227.1	1082.3
Excess air = 1082.3 − 941.1	———	141.2
Excess O_2 = 227.1 − 197.5	29.6	———

Products of Combustion

		Moles/100 Moles Fuel @ 115% Total Air	% by Vol, Dry Basis
CO₂	90 × 1 + 5 × 2.0	100.0	10.11
H₂O	90 × 2 + 5 × 3		
	+ 1082.3 × 0.021‡	217.7	——
N₂	1082.3 × 0.79 + 5.0	860.0	86.90
O_2	(excess)	29.6	2.99
Wet		1207.3	100.00
Dry = 1207.3 − 217.7		989.6	

‡0.021 = (29 ÷ 18) × 0.0132

For more complete combustion calculations involving heat balances, reference should be made to calculations on the mole basis (5 cases) and on the Btu basis (2 cases) in the Appendix. Reference curves of molal specific heats (Fig. 1) and enthalpies of flue gas and air (Figs. 2 and 3) for use with the calculations on the mole and Btu bases, respectively, will also be found in the Appendix.

General Formulas — Combustion Air

Since carbon, hydrogen, and sulfur are the only combustible elements found in the fuels used for commercial steam generation, the lb of air (for zero excess air, 100 per cent total air) theoretically required for the complete combustion of 1 lb of fuel is:

$$11.53 \ C + 34.34 \ (H_2 - O_2/8) + 4.29 \ S \qquad (3)$$

where C, H_2, O_2, and S represent the proportionate parts by weight of carbon, hydrogen, oxygen, and sulfur, and the constants are those given in Table 1. The factor $O_2/8$ in the term $(H_2 - O_2/8)$ is a correction for the hydrogen already combined with the O_2 in the fuel to form water vapor.

With gaseous fuels, instead of breaking down the hydrocarbons into their constituent elements, it is simpler to use the amount of air for the various compounds directly as given in Table 1. For instance, for a gaseous fuel containing the combustible gases indicated in the expression below, the lb of air required per lb of fuel for complete combustion with theoretical air will be:

$$2.47 \ CO + 34.34 \ H_2 + 17.27 \ CH_4 + 13.30 \ C_2H_2 + $$
$$14.81 \ C_2H_4 + 16.12 \ C_2H_6 + 6.10 \ H_2S - 4.32 \ O_2 \qquad (4)$$

Again, the molecular symbols represent the proportionate parts by weight of the gaseous compounds and elements.

If, as is the usual custom, the analyses of gaseous fuels are given on a volumetric basis, the cu ft of combustion air required as given in Table 1 should be used. Thus, for a gaseous fuel containing the combustible gases indicated in the following expression, the cu ft of theoretical air required per cu ft of fuel for complete combustion will be:

$$2.38 \ (CO + H_2) + 9.53 \ CH_4 + 11.91 \ C_2H_2 + $$
$$14.29 \ C_2H_4 + 16.68 \ C_2H_6 - 4.76 \ O_2 \qquad (5)$$

where the molecular symbols represent the proportionate parts by volume of the gaseous compounds and elements.

It should be noted that the total air requirement will be reduced if oxygen is one of the constituents of the fuel.

The products of combustion can also be determined from the data given in Table 1. Assuming complete combustion with theoretical air of the fuels ordinarily used for commercial steam generation, the products of combustion in lb (including the nitrogen carried with the combustion air) per lb of fuel are:

$$CO_2 = 3.66 \ C$$
$$H_2O = 8.94 \ (H_2 - O_2/8) + H_2O^*$$
$$SO_2 = 2.00 \ S$$
$$N_2 = 8.86 \ C + 26.41 \ H_2 + 3.29 \ S + N_2†$$

* Proportional weight of H_2O in the fuel as moisture.
† Proportional weight of N_2 in the fuel as nitrogen.

To this must be added the moisture carried in with the combustion air, to obtain the total weight of combustion products. The molecular symbols represent the proportionate parts by weight of the constituents in the fuel.

Combustion Air, Btu Method

In many combustion calculations the air required per lb of fuel can be established by using a convenient working tool, the theoretical air required per 10,000 Btu heat value of the fuel. The established values for the air requirements on this basis vary slightly for each particular fuel. Accurate values may be obtained from the formula:

$$\text{Lb theoretical air/lb fuel} = \frac{\text{Btu/lb fuel, as fired}}{10,000}$$
$$\times \text{(values from Fig. 4 or Table 5 or 6)} \qquad (6)^*$$

* Approximate formulas sometimes used:
$$\text{Lb theoretical air/lb fuel} = \frac{\text{Btu/lb fuel, as fired}}{1300}$$
$$\text{Cu ft air (@ 60 F \& 29.92 in. Hg)/lb fuel} = \frac{\text{Btu/lb fuel, as fired}}{100}$$

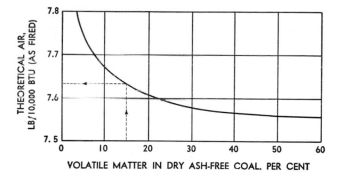

Fig. 4. Theoretical air in lb per 10,000 Btu released, for coal with a range of volatile

For a typical heavy fuel oil† and a Texas natural gas‡, the theoretical air required and the moisture in the products of combustion in lb per 10,000 Btu (as-fired basis) are given in Table 5.

†Per Cent by Wt		‡Per Cent by Vol	
S	1.16	CH_4	84.10
H_2	10.33	C_2H_6	6.70
C	87.87	CO_2	0.80
N_2	0.14	N_2	8.40
O_2	0.50	Sp gr	0.630
Btu/lb		Btu/cu ft	
as fired, 18,400		as fired, 974	

TABLE 5

Theoretical Air, Fuel, and Resulting Moisture Per 10,000 Btu As Fired

Fuel	Theoretical Air§, lb/10kB	Fuel, lb/10kB	Moisture, lb/10kB
Fuel oil	7.46	0.544	0.51
Natural gas	7.19	0.496	0.93
Coal (prox anal.)	See Fig. 4	—	—
Coal (ult anal.)	See Table 6	—	—

§ Dry air. To obtain wt of wet air required, moisture in air at standard conditions (0.0132 lb per lb dry air @ 60% relative humidity and 80 F dry bulb) must be added.

The theoretical air requirements by the Btu method can be determined from Fig. 4 for coal if the proximate analysis is known and from Table 6 for any fuel if the ultimate analysis is available.

TABLE 6

Formula for Calculating Theoretical Air*

In lb per 10,000 Btu of Fuel As Fired
Ultimate Analysis of Fuel on As-Fired Basis,
Per Cent by Weight

C = Carbon
H_2 = Hydrogen
O_2 = Oxygen
S = Sulfur
Btu/lb = Heat value of fuel

$$\text{Theoretical Air†, lb} = 144 \times \frac{8C + 24\left\{H_2 - \dfrac{O_2}{8}\right\} + 3S}{\text{Btu/lb}}$$
(per 10kB)

* This formula should be used only when the exact ultimate analysis and the correct heating value are given for the fuel.

† Dry air. To obtain wt of wet air required, moisture in air at standard conditions (0.0132 lb per lb dry air @ 60% relative humidity and 80 F dry bulb) must be added.

The following two simple examples illustrate the use of the Btu method to determine the amount of air required:

Bituminous Coal

Proximate Analysis As Fired, % by Wt

Moisture	12.0
Volatile matter	25.8
Fixed carbon	46.2
Ash	16.0
Btu/lb	10,900

From this analysis, the volatile matter on a dry ash-free basis is $25.8 \times 100 \div (25.8 + 46.2) = 35.8\%$. Entering Fig. 4 with 35.8, the theoretical air in lb per 10,000 Btu as fired is 7.57, and the required total dry air (for 20% excess air) = $7.57 \times 120/100 \times 10,900/10,000 = 9.90$ lb per lb of fuel.

From Table 5, for a heavy fuel oil of 18,400 Btu/lb, the theoretical air in lb/10,000 Btu as fired is 7.46, and the required total dry air (for 18% excess air) = $7.46 \times 118/100 \times 18,400/10,000 = 16.19$ lb per lb of fuel.

The Btu method is entirely suitable for the rapid determination of complete heat balances and other data in combustion calculations, as will be noted by reference to the outline and examples in the Appendix.

Excess Air Held at a Minimum

As noted before and indicated in the preceding examples, it is necessary to use more than the theoretical air requirements to assure sufficient oxygen for complete combustion. Excess air would not be required if it were possible to have an ideally perfect union of the air and the fuel, and it must be held at a practical minimum to reduce the stack heat losses. Realistic values of excess air to the fuel-burning equipment (based on experience) required for burning various fuels are given in Table 7.

In most furnaces operating under suction there is also some leakage of air into the setting, and consequently the excess air leaving the furnace is greater than that entering the furnace as intended. This is not so in a pressure-fired unit.

Inherent and Avoidable Heat Losses

In the combustion of fuel for the commercial generation of heat, there are certain inherent heat losses over which no control is possible, as well as other heat losses which are subject to some control.

The inherent, or unavoidable, heat losses are the

TABLE 7

Usual Amount Excess Air Supplied to Fuel-burning Equipment

Fuel	Type of Furnace or Burners	Excess Air, % by Wt
Pulverized coal	Completely water-cooled furnace for slag-tap or dry-ash-removal	15-20
	Partially water-cooled furnace for dry-ash-removal	15-40
Crushed coal	Cyclone Furnace—pressure or suction	10-15
Coal	Stoker-fired, forced-draft, B&W chain-grate	15-50
	Stoker-fired, forced-draft, underfeed	20-50
	Stoker-fired, natural-draft	50-65
Fuel oil	Oil burners, register-type	5-10
	Multifuel burners and flat-flame	10-20
Acid sludge	Cone- and flat-flame-type burners, steam-atomized	10-15
Natural, Coke-oven, & Refinery gas	Register-type burners	5-10
	Multifuel burners	7-12
Blast-furnace gas	Intertube nozzle-type burners	15-18
Wood	Dutch-oven (10-23% through grates) and Hofft-type	20-25
Bagasse	All furnaces	25-35
Black liquor	Recovery furnaces for kraft and soda-pulping processes	5-7

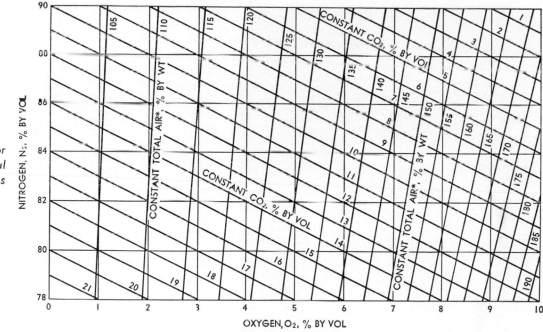

Fig. 5. Chart for approximating total air from flue gas analysis

OXYGEN, O_2, % BY VOL

*TOTAL AIR = 100 + % EXCESS AIR BY WT

result of 1) the discharge of the products of combustion at a temperature higher than the temperature of the fuel, and 2) the moisture content of the fuel plus the combination of some of the hydrogen with the oxygen in the fuel.

The avoidable heat losses, or those which can be controlled to some extent by good design and careful operation, can be minimized by:

1. Careful control of excess air.
2. Tolerating virtually no unburned solid combustible matter in ash and refuse.
3. Permitting no unburned gaseous combustibles in the exit gases.
4. A well-insulated setting for the boiler and heat exchanger components to reduce radiation.

The efficiency of combustion in a heat exchanger (boiler) is 100 minus the sum of the heat losses in per cent. This calculation is known as a heat balance and is illustrated in the combustion calculation examples in the Appendix.

Measurement of Total or Excess Air

To accomplish effective control over avoidable heat losses, the continuous measurement of the air used is a necessity in modern practice. The amount of air used can be determined by a) continuously indicated or recorded flue gas analysis and b) metering the combustion air or the flue gas.

Flue Gas Analysis

In the continuously recording or indicating flue gas analyzer, gas is continuously drawn from a selected location, and samples are analyzed at intervals of 1 minute or longer. Both the performance of the analysis and the indication or record of the results are automatic. Depending upon the type of instrument, the analysis may or may not include all the constituents of the products of combustion. Many of the continuously recording instruments give the per cent of CO_2 only; others only the per cent of O_2; and still others the per cent of unburned gases. Unburned gases, however, should not be present with proper combustion in the field of heat production.

The amount of O_2 in the flue gases is significant in defining the status of the combustion process. Its presence always means that more oxygen (excess air) is being introduced than is being used. Assuming complete combustion, low values of O_2 in the flue gases reflect moderate (nearly correct) excess air and reduced heat losses to the stack, while higher values of O_2 mean needlessly higher stack losses. The quantitative determination of total air (total air = 100 + per cent excess air) admitted to an actual combustion process requires a complete flue gas analysis for CO_2, O_2, CO, and N_2 (by difference) or the direct measurement of the air supplied by a suitable fluid meter (see below).

The approximate per cent total air from flue gas analyses may be determined from the curves of Fig. 5. A formula that has long been used for approximating the per cent excess air from an Orsat analysis is:

$$\% \text{ Excess Air} = 100 \times \frac{O_2 - CO/2}{0.264N_2 - (O_2 - CO/2)}$$

Fig. 6. Boiler Meter for indicating and recording ratio of air used to Btu input

The results are reasonably close for flue gases from hydrocarbon fuels of low nitrogen content; the error increases with increase in the per cent nitrogen in the fuel.

Flue Gas Sampling. Great care should be taken to secure truly representative samples of the gas for analysis. The usual practice for a manually operated gas analyzer is to take successive samples from a number of points, laid out in "checkerboard" fashion over a cross section of the flue or area traversed by the gas. The number of sampling points and their position are best determined by preliminary trial analyses of gas samples from tentative locations. If the values from point to point vary widely, more sampling locations across the plane should be used.

Gas samples should be drawn at regular intervals over a relatively long period (during the entire period of a formal test). Unless operating conditions are exceptionally uniform, which is unlikely, a few samples drawn at irregular intervals are of little use in obtaining a true analysis.

Fixed-position samplers of the branched-pipe type, extending into the flue area, are likely to give mis-leading results, since the proportion of gas drawn into each branch may or may not correspond to the flows over the flue cross section. A better arrangement is to insert a single sampling element in the flue, at a location established by thorough preliminary analyses, from which samples can be drawn representing a fair average. Samples for the automatic mechanical gas analyzers are frequently drawn through a single sampling pipe carefully located in this manner.

When the temperatures exceed about 900 F, gas samples should be drawn through a water-cooled pipe to avoid the loss of O_2 from oxidation of pipe material at about this temperature. Noncooled pipes of special steels have been used with fair success, but there is still the uncertainty of the loss of some O_2 to the metal. A properly designed water-cooled sampler can be safely used to obtain gas samples from the hottest regions of a furnace (3000 F and above). The completeness of combustion progressively through the furnace is sometimes determined by the analyses of samples taken in this manner. Construction of a water-cooled sampler suitable for this duty is similar to that of the water-cooled portions of the HVT probe illustrated in Chapter 6.

Metering Combustion Air

Another method of establishing the amount of total air used in a boiler or other similar combustion heat exchanger is to meter the flow of air or the flow of combustion gases through the unit. Furthermore, for a given total air, the flow so measured has a nearly straight-line relationship to the Btu input. In a steam boiler, the steam output (and consequently the Btu output) bears a nearly constant relation to the Btu input. Metered steam is, therefore, a suitable index of Btu input, and the operator may thus proportion the combustion air to the fuel at any rate of steam output.

As a necessary adjunct to obtaining good boiler efficiency, instruments recording the air flow-steam flow relationship are included in most modern boiler installations. The instrument in general use for this function is illustrated by Fig. 6 and is known as the Boiler Meter. Since the air quantity can be adjusted to the fuel quantity in the proper proportion at all times, manually by the operator or by automatic combustion-control equipment, it is not necessary to take and analyze flue gas samples in regular operation. In the initial setting of the Boiler Meter, however, it is necessary to take and to analyze such samples, and most boiler rooms are equipped to make periodical checks with an Orsat analyzer.

5

FANS AND DRAFT

ATMOSPHERIC air is a mechanical mixture of gases. Its constituents are oxygen, nitrogen, and small amounts of carbon dioxide, water vapor, argon, and other inert gases. In steam boiler work, the "trace" gases in air usually are included in the nitrogen content. On this basis, the generally accepted values are: (a) by volume: oxygen 21.0 per cent, nitrogen 79.0 per cent; (b) by weight: oxygen 23.15 per cent, nitrogen 76.85 per cent. Based on the molecular weights of oxygen and nitrogen in the proportions by weight just noted, the equivalent molecular weight for air, as though it were a true gas, is, therefore, commonly accepted as 28.9 or simply as 29.

From the established gas laws, the relationship between pressure, volume, and temperature of any weight of a "perfect" gas is expressed by:

$$pV_t = w_t RT \tag{1}$$

hence
$$pV = RT \tag{2}$$

and
$$pmV = mRT \tag{3}$$

where:

p = absolute pressure, lb/ft^2
V_t = total volume of the gas, ft^3, at p and T conditions
w_t = total weight of gas, lb
T = absolute temperature, R = F + 460
R = specific gas constant, peculiar to each gas
V = specific volume of the gas, ft^3/lb at p and T conditions
m = molecular weight of the gas

In (3), mV = a constant, approx 379 cu ft at 60 F and 14.7 psia (the volume of 1 mole of any gas at these p and T conditions, see Chapter 4)

and mR = a constant (the "universal gas constant")

From (3) $mR = \dfrac{pmV}{T} = 1544$, approximately (4)

For any gas (closely obeying the gas laws), close values of R, the specific gas constant, may be computed from equation (4):

$$R = \frac{1544}{m} \tag{5}$$

For practical purposes, within the range of ordinary pressures and temperatures used, air may be considered as obeying the established gas laws.

Since the volume of a gas is a function of both temperature and pressure, it is necessary, as a suitable basis for comparison, to refer volumes to a standard set of conditions, now ordinarily accepted as an absolute pressure of 14.7 psia and variously at temperatures of 32 F, 60 F, 70 F, 80 F, and others depending upon the field of application. The specific volume and the specific weight of air at atmospheric pressure and varying temperatures are given in Table 1. The specific gravities of the gases in boiler flue products are given in Table 1, Chapter 4.

The Flow of Air and Gases

In nature, a force varying from a light breeze to a gale or hurricane moves very large quantities of air with velocities up to 150 mph. This force is caused by the earth's rotation and by differences in atmospheric pressures in different locations on the earth's surface and in the stratosphere. Differences in pressures are caused primarily by temperature and moisture in the atmosphere. These unrestricted movements of the earth's atmosphere represent the expenditure of tremendous amounts of energy, but at relatively low level.

On the other hand, in steam power boilers the flow of air and combustion gases is confined to ducts, boiler settings, flues, and stacks. To supply the correct amount of air for combustion and to remove the gases from the boiler setting, this flow must be established and controlled. This can be done by using a stack by which temperature differences are set up as in nature, or by mechanically driven fans which act as air pumps. Either the stack or fans, or a combination of stack and fans produce a difference in pressure causing gas flow through the boiler unit.

Draft. Draft is the difference in pressure that is available for producing a flow of the gases. If the gases within a stack are heated, each cu ft will expand, and the weight of the expanded gas per cu ft will be less than that of a cu ft of the cool air outside the stack. Therefore, the unit pressure at the base of the stack due to the weight of the column of heated gas will be less than that due to a column of cool air. This difference in pressure will cause a flow of the gases into the base of the stack. The cool air on its way to the stack must pass through the furnace or furnaces of the boilers connected to the stack, and it in turn becomes heated. This newly heated gas will be displaced by more incoming cool air and the action will be continuous.

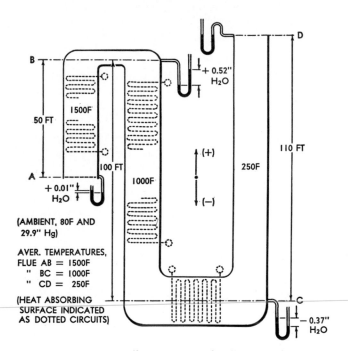

Fig. 1. *Diagram illustrating stack effect or chimney action in three vertical gas passes arranged in series*

Gases always press or push and never pull. To avoid confusion of terms, as applied to the subject of this chapter, the value of drafts or draft pressures is referred to atmospheric pressure at the same level as the base and the plus or minus sign is used to designate whether the value is above or below this base. A draft differential is the difference between draft pressures measured at two points, using atmospheric pressure as the base for each measurement. Draft readings in absolute pressure do not throw any more light upon the flow of gases than do readings taken with atmospheric pressure as the base, and as a practical matter they do not readily disclose whether leakage is into or out of a gas passage.

Balanced Draft. Balanced draft is a useful term in referring to draft conditions at a particular location in the furnace where the pressure is equal to atmospheric. Usually in boiler operation the furnace normally is operated at slightly less than atmospheric pressure. However, in recent practice furnaces have been designed to operate under pressure greater than atmospheric (see below).

Velocity Pressure. The pressure corresponding to the velocity of flow is known as the velocity pressure and is a measure of the kinetic energy in the fluid. It is equivalent to the dynamic head or the pressure producing the flow as it would be measured by a pitot tube placed in the path of the gas. The relation of velocity of flow to the dynamic head is expressed, as in Chapter 8, by the fundamental formulas of fluid flow:

$$v = \sqrt{2gH} \qquad (6)$$

$$\text{and} \qquad H = \frac{v^2}{2g} \qquad (7)$$

Where

$v =$ velocity of the fluid in ft per sec

$H =$ head in ft of fluid causing flow; (at the same temperature as the fluid)

$g =$ the gravitational constant, taken as 32.2 ft/sec^2

It is necessary clearly to understand the meaning of "H" in equations (6) and (7). It is helpful to visualize this "H" or head in feet of fluid causing flow by recalling that the pressure exerted by a stream of water, moving at a velocity of v, on the open end of a pitot tube will support a column of water of a height in ft equal to the "H" in equations (6) and (7). Similarly, the pressure exerted by a stream of mercury, for instance, moving at a velocity of v, on the open end of a pitot tube will support a column of mercury of a height in feet equal to "H" in equation (6) or (7). If the velocity of the stream is the same then the height "H" of the supported column will be the same whether the fluid is water or mercury.

While it is not so easy to visualize, the pressure exerted on the open end of a pitot tube inserted in a moving stream of air will also support a similar column of air, of the same height "H" as the supported columns of water or mercury if the velocity of the stream is the same in each case. For a velocity of 10 ft per sec, for instance, it is evident from equation (7) that $H = \dfrac{100}{64.4}$ or 1.55 ft of the fluid causing the flow, whether that fluid is water, mercury or air. Thus if "H" in equation (6) or (7) is always considered as of the same physical composition as the corresponding moving fluid, it will not be difficult correctly to apply these fundamental formulas.

In the case of air, or gases generally, it is impractical to observe or read "H" in feet of gas. The head, however, may be easily observed as the equivalent height in inches of a column of visible liquid as in the common U tube or draft gage. If water is used as the visible liquid the following relation[*] applies:

$$H_w = 12H \times \frac{\delta_t}{\delta_w} \qquad (8)$$

where:

  H_w = head in in. of water

  H = as in equations (6) and (7)

  δ_t = sp wt of the gas or liquid flowing, lb/cu ft

  δ_w = sp wt of water, lb/cu ft, at the temperature of the U tube (usually taken as 62.31 lb cu ft)

Air flow or gas flow as used in boiler practice is the actual quantity of material flowing through an enclosure. The term is usually expressed either as pounds per hour or cubic feet per minute. Flow is produced by a differential draft or pressure, but a differential draft does not necessarily produce a flow (as in a boiler setting closed against entrance of air but connected to an operating stack).

Air flow is related to velocity by the following expression:

$$Q = A \, v_m \qquad (9)$$

where:

  Q = quantity flow rate in cfm

  A = cross-sectional area of flow channel, sq ft

  v_m = velocity in fpm

Draft Loss. The term "draft loss" is commonly applied to note an energy or friction loss caused by gas flow between any two points in a boiler setting. Gas flow in closed conduits always involves or is accompanied by draft loss.

Draft Differential. Draft differential on the other hand is a more inclusive term. It is simply a difference in pressure between two points. It may be used to note a draft loss caused by flow or to note the difference in pressure between two points because of their relative position above a certain datum. (See *Stack Effect* below.) It may also be used to note the difference in pressure between two points caused by a combination of draft loss and stack effect. Draft measurements in boiler work cannot be taken without realizing what the final readings will mean.

Stack Effect. Stack effect, or chimney action, is the draft or pressure difference, exclusive of flow losses, available for producing flow in vertical ducts or passages conveying heated gases. The intensity and distribution of this draft or pressure depend upon the vertical height and arrangement of the various ducts or passages and on the gas temperature in each. Stack effect is of particular significance in a series of boiler passes and flues, with the direction of gas flow variously up and down. To determine stack effect accurately it must be calculated, since simple draft gage readings always indicate the combined values of stack effect and friction flow losses. The diagrammatic sketch, Fig. 1, indicates the general method of its determination. Three passages, of heights AB, BC and CD, are shown. The passages may contain heat-absorbing surface. Gases, at different average temperatures as indicated, are assumed to be momentarily brought to rest as by a closure at A. The top of passage CD at D is in a region of atmospheric pressure.

In analyzing the stack effect for the arrangement shown in Fig. 1, it is best to establish the effect in each passage separately and in succession, assigning minus values when proceeding downward and plus values when proceeding upward. Thus, for the conditions indicated in the sketch and using the values in Table 2 for an ambient temperature of 80 F, the stack effect in in. of water, referred to atmosphere, in each component is as follows:

  Stack effect, D→C = 110 x 0.0034 = −0.37

  Stack effect, C→B = 100 x 0.0089 = +0.89

  Stack effect, B→A = 50 x 0.0102 = −0.51

If hypothetical draft gages, one end open to atmosphere, were placed as indicated at A, B, and C, the theoretical zero-flow draft readings in in. of water would be:

  Draft at A = −0.37 + 0.89 −0.51 = +0.01

  Draft at B = draft at A, + A→B,

  = +0.01 + 0.51 = +0.52

  Draft at C = draft at B, + D→C,

  = +0.52 − 0.89 = −0.37

For the conditions in the above example, there is no net head available to produce flow up the component CD even though the outlet lies above all parts of the arrangement. The net stack effect of the system reduces rather than increases the draft in the unit. Fans or stack height must, therefore, be selected not only to provide the necessary draft to overcome friction losses through the unit but also to allow for the stack effect of the system.

In some boiler settings, gases leak from the upper portions into the boiler room when the unit is operating at very low rates of output or is taken out of service, even though the outlet flue may show a substantial negative draft. The reason is evident from the above example, where there is a plus pressure of 0.52 in. at B and a negative pressure of 0.37 in. at C.

Barometric Pressure. Barometric pressure is the total deadweight of a unit column of air of the earth's atmosphere from the point of measurement extending out to the limit of the atmosphere. At sea level and 60 F temperature, the normal barometric pressure is 29.92 in. of mercury, or 33.9 ft of water, or 14.7 psia. Values for barometric pressure at various elevations above sea level are given in Table 3.

Pressure. Air or gas pressure usually means the

---

*See also Chapter 8.

pressure in in. of water of the parts of the air or gas system which are higher than atmospheric pressure rather than below.

The Chimney or Stack

All the early boilers operated with natural draft. The draft necessary to produce the required air flow was provided by use of stacks. Smaller modern boilers may also use natural draft. However, for larger boilers equipped with superheaters, economizers and air heaters, where the total draft loss is large, it is not practical or economical to obtain sufficient induced draft by use of a stack alone. In these units the stack serves as an aid to a mechanically driven induced draft fan.

The required height and diameter of a chimney or stack for natural draft boilers depend on:

1) Draft loss through the boiler from the point of balanced draft to the gas entrance to the stack. For natural draft units (without forced draft fan) the entire unit will be under suction or induced draft.

2) The temperature of the gases passing up the stack and the temperature of the surrounding atmosphere.

3) The quantity of gases carried by the stack.

4) The altitude of the plant above sea level—barometric pressure.

There is no satisfactory formula covering all of the many factors involved in the determination of the height and diameter of the stack. For all prac-

tical purposes, however, a sufficiently comprehensive and accurate method has been developed which covers the most important factors affecting stack draft: (a) temperature of the surrounding atmosphere and the temperature of gases entering the stack; (b) the drop in temperature of gases within the stack due to heat loss to atmosphere and air infiltration; and (c) the stack draft loss due to friction and stack exit loss.

TABLE 2

Stack Effect or Pressure Difference, In. of Water

For Each Foot of Vertical Height
(Barometer = 29.92 in. Hg)

Average Temp in Flue, F	Temp of Air Outside Flue, F			
	40	60	80	100
250	.0045	.0039	.0034	.0029
500	.0073	.0067	.0061	.0056
1000	.0101	.0095	.0089	.0084
1500	.0114	.0108	.0102	.0097
2000	.0122	.0116	.0110	.0105
2500	.0127	.0121	.0115	.0110

(a) *Theoretical Draft Due to Temperature.* The intensity of the draft, or differential pressure, usually is measured in inches of water. As an example, if the atmospheric temperature is 60F and the average temperature of the gases in the chimney is 500F, the difference between the weights of the external

TABLE I

Specific Volume and Weight of Air
At Atmospheric Pressure

Temp F	Cu Ft per lb	Lb per cu ft	Temp F	Cu Ft per lb	Lb per cu ft	Temp F	Cu Ft per lb	Lb per cu ft
32	12.36	.0809	160	15.58	.0642	425	22.24	.0450
35	12.44	.0804	170	15.83	.0632	450	22.87	.0437
40	12.56	.0796	180	16.08	.0622	475	23.50	.0425
45	12.69	.0788	190	16.33	.0612	500	24.13	.0415
50	12.81	.0781	200	16.58	.0603	525	24.75	.0404
55	12.94	.0773	210	16.84	.0594	550	25.38	.0394
60	13.06	.0766	220	17.09	.0585	575	26.01	.0385
65	13.19	.0758	230	17.34	.0577	600	26.64	.0376
70	13.32	.0752	240	17.59	.0568	625	27.27	.0367
75	13.44	.0744	250	17.84	.0561	650	27.90	.0359
80	13.57	.0737	260	18.09	.0553	675	28.53	.0351
85	13.69	.0730	270	18.34	.0545	700	29.15	.0343
90	13.82	.0724	280	18.60	.0538	725	29.78	.0336
95	13.94	.0717	290	18.85	.0531	750	30.40	.0329
100	14.07	.0711	300	19.10	.0524	775	31.04	.0322
110	14.32	.0699	320	19.60	.0510	800	31.67	.0316
120	14.57	.0686	340	20.10	.0498	825	32.30	.0310
130	14.82	.0675	360	20.61	.0485	850	32.93	.0304
140	15.08	.0664	380	21.11	.0474	875	33.55	.0298
150	15.32	.0653	400	21.61	.0463	900	34.18	.0293

air and the internal flue per cu ft is:

Weight of a cu ft of air at 60 F $= 0.0766$ lb

Weight of a cu ft of gases at 500 F $= 0.0415$ lb

Difference $= 0.0351$ lb

If the stack is 100 ft high, the pressure exerted at the base is $0.0351 \times 100 = 3.51$ lb per sq ft. One lb per sq ft is equivalent to 0.192 in. of water. Under the above temperature conditions, the 100-ft stack would, therefore, show a theoretical draft of $3.51 \times 0.192 = 0.674$ in. of water.

From the principles outlined above, the following formula may be derived:

$$\text{Stack draft} = 0.192H \ (\delta_a - \delta_g) \qquad (10)$$

Since the weight per cu ft of air (gas) varies inversely as the absolute temperature, the equation may also be written:

$$\text{Stack draft} = 0.52H \times p \left\{ \frac{1}{T_a} - \frac{1}{T_g} \right\} \qquad (11)$$

where:

Stack draft $=$ induced draft in in. of water

$\delta_a =$ sp wt of outside air, lb/cu ft

$\delta_g =$ sp wt of stack gases, lb/cu ft

$H =$ height of stack above gas entrance, ft

$p =$ atmospheric pressure, psia

$T_a =$ temperature (absolute) of outside air, R $=$ F $+ 460$

$T_g =$ average temperature (absolute) of stack gases, R $=$ F $+ 460$

Because the atmospheric or barometric pressure is usually listed in in. of mercury, the stack draft formulas may be written:

$$\text{Stack draft, in. } H_2O = 0.256 \times Hp' \left\{ \frac{1}{T_a} - \frac{1}{T_g} \right\} \ (12)$$

where:

$p' =$ atmospheric pressure in in. of mercury

In developing formulas (11) and (12), as a simplification the density of the flue gases is taken as equal to that of air at the same temperature, without appreciable error.

Under the temperature conditions of the preceding example, the 100-ft stack at an atmospheric pressure of 22.22 in. of mercury, corresponding to an altitude of 8000 ft above sea level, would produce a theoretical draft of:

$$\text{Stack draft} = 0.256 \times 100 \times 22.22 \left\{ \frac{1}{520} - \frac{1}{960} \right\}$$

Stack draft $= 0.50$ in. of water

(b) *Average Stack Temperature.* The stack temperature used in the above example is an arithmetic average of the temperatures entering and leaving the stack. Gases passing through a stack lose some heat through the shell of the stack to the outside atmosphere. By the infiltration of cold air, stack temperatures may be lowered an appreciable amount. The loss in temperature depends upon the

TABLE 3

Barometric Pressure

(Effect of Altitude)

Ft Above Sea Level	Pressure,* In. Hg
0	29.92
1000	28.86
2000	27.82
3000	26.81
4000	25.84
5000	24.89
6000	23.98
7000	23.09
8000	22.22
9000	21.38
10000	20.58

*Values from Bulletin No. 110, 1952 National Association of Fan Manufacturers. Temperature $= 60$ F.

type of stack, stack diameter and its height, and a number of variables influencing the outside atmosphere. The approximate temperature change for stacks is indicated by the curves in Fig. 2.

(c) *Stack Flow Loss.* In the flow of gases up the stack there are friction and stack exit losses. Obviously, the available induced draft is the difference between the theoretical draft as determined by the draft formula and the flow loss in the stack proper. The friction loss from flow may be determined by the first term of the formula given below, which is based on the Fanning equation. The second term of the formula represents the exit loss.

$$\text{Stack flow loss} = 0.0942 \, f \, T_g \frac{H}{D^5} \left\{ \frac{W}{100,000} \right\}^2 +$$

$$\frac{0.0942 T_g}{D^4} \left\{ \frac{W}{100,000} \right\}^2 \qquad (13)$$

$$\text{Stack flow loss} = 0.0942 \frac{T_g}{D^4} \left\{ \frac{W}{100,000} \right\}^2 \left\{ 1 + \frac{fH}{D} \right\} \qquad (14)$$

where:

Stack flow loss is measured in in. of water

$W =$ weight flow of gases, lb/hr

$D =$ diameter of stack, ft

$H =$ height of stack above gas entrance, ft

$f =$ friction factor from Fig. 3

$T_g =$ average gas absolute temp, R $=$ F $+ 460$

The available draft is the theoretical draft (equation 12) minus the stack flow loss (equation 14). The total stack flow loss is usually less than 4 per cent of the calculated draft. Of the total stack flow loss, the stack exit loss is much greater than the loss from friction—in the order of 3 to 7 times, depending upon the height and diameter of the stack.

Selection of Stack Size

In selecting a stack suitable for the requirements of

a particular installation it should be kept in mind that the construction cost for some one combination of diameter and height will be less than for any other combination, and the builder of stacks should be consulted before these dimensions are fixed. For convenience in making a tentative selection of optimum stack dimensions the necessary data is given graphically in Fig. 2, Fig. 4, and Fig. 5 for sea level and 80F atmosphere. The use of these graphs to establish stack dimensions may be illustrated by the following example:

Known Data

1) Steam generated per hr, lb   360,000

Type of Firing	Approx. Gas wt per lb of Steam per hour
(a) Oil or gas	1.15
(b) Pulverized coal	1.25
(c) Stoker	1.50
(d) Hand-fired	1.75

2) Stack gas flow from 1)(b), lb/hr   450,000
3) Stack inlet gas temperature, F   550
4) Stack exit gas temperature (assumed), F 450
5) Stack draft required, in. of water   1.0
   (from point of balance to stack gas-entrance)
6) Stack located at sea level

Find Economical Dimensions of Stack
1) Diameter of stack to nearest 6 in. increment, in.
2) Active height of stack, ft
3) Total height of stack (add to item 2 as required), ft
4) Stack exit gas temperature, F

Diameter. Enter graph, Fig. 5 with a stack gas flow of 450,000 lb per hr. This will give a stack diameter (to nearest 6 in. increment) of 14 ft 6 in. or 174 inches.

Height (approximate). Enter graph, Fig. 4, with the required stack draft of 1 in. of water and an average gas temperature of $\frac{550 + 450}{2} = 500F$. This will give an approximate stack height of 160 ft.

Exit Gas Temperature. Enter graph, Fig. 2, with the approximate stack height of 160 ft and the diameter of 174 inches. This will give a stack exit temperature of 436F, and the average stack temperature will be $\frac{550 + 436}{2} = 493F$.

Height (actual). Enter graph, Fig. 4, with the stack draft required increased by 10 per cent as a factor of safety, and, using the average stack temperature of 493F determine a new stack height based on zero stack flow loss = 177 feet. For a stack flow loss taken at the usual arbitrary value of 5 per cent, the final actual stack height = 177 ÷ .95 = 186 ft.

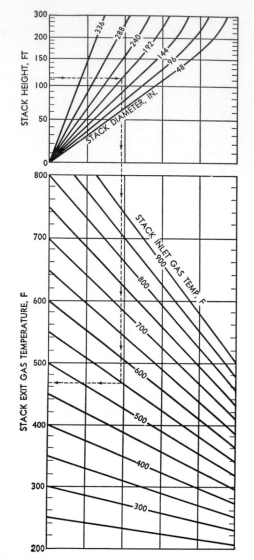

Fig. 2. *Stack exit gas temperature—its approximate relationship to stack diameter and height*

(active height above flue entrance; to which must be added any inactive section required from foundation to flue entrance).

The stack flow loss may be checked by using the above values for diameter, height, average gas temperature and gas flow in equation (14). A check of the net draft available by using equations (12) and (14) indicates that the 1 in. draft requirement is amply met. For economical reasons the stack flow loss should be about 5 per cent of the available draft and the diameter as the dominating factor in this loss may be modified as necessary to suit this condition.

If the plant is not located at sea level the stack draft required should be increased by the altitude factor $\frac{30}{B}$, where B equals the normal barometer read-

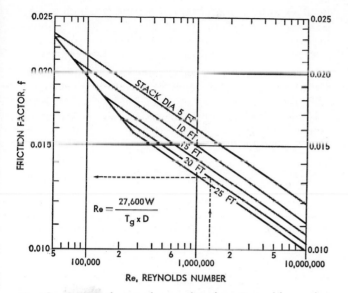

Fig. 3. *Friction factor, f, as related to Reynolds number and stack diameter, for use in equations (13) or (14)*

ing, in in. of mercury, at the boiler site.

Normally a stack is thought of merely as a long cylinder extending high into the air, although there are other forms with which improved performance is sometimes possible in specific applications. In the évasé stack, a venturi design, a part of the velocity or kinetic energy of the gases is recovered before discharge into the atmosphere. In another type of stack a fan is used as an integral part of the évasé feature to discharge air or gases at high velocity into the

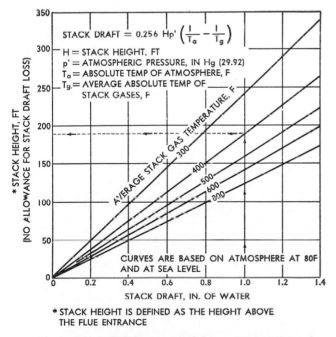

* STACK HEIGHT IS DEFINED AS THE HEIGHT ABOVE THE FLUE ENTRANCE

Fig. 4. *Stack height required for a range of stack drafts and average stack gas temperatures*

throat of the venturi section. In this way the gases are withdrawn from the setting by jet action. Depending on the application, the fan handles only a portion of the gases. For steam locomotives the required induced draft is supplied by the jet action of exhaust steam.

As one of the esential elements of any steam power plant the stack is a symbol of industry. As noted, it may be used for moving the air for combustion through the boiler. In every instance it is used to convey the flue gases to the atmosphere, and in many locations one of its purposes is to discharge the flue gases at a sufficient height for dispersion and dilution.

While the stack is used successfully for dispersing the suspended dust particles over a large area, never-

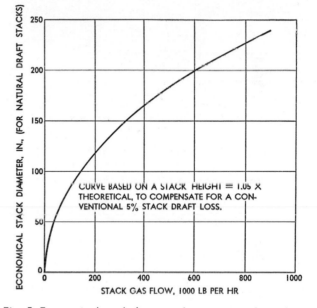

Fig. 5. *Economical stack diameter for a range of gas flows.*

theless, in locations where there is a concentration of industry the atmosphere will often be overloaded with the discharge from many stacks. The effect is particularly objectionable on damp, foggy days when the combination of smoke and fog blankets the area. In the interest of comfort and health many cities have established civic ordinances to restrict pollution of the atmosphere by requiring industrial furnaces and power plants to meet rigid specifications controlling the quantity and size of dust particles emitted from the stack. To comply with such regulations, dust collectors or precipitators are usually installed for coal fired units. Some rather wide differences still exist in the requirements of the ordinances in different cities. An interim guide is the Example Sections for a Smoke Regulating Ordinance appearing in the ASME Information Bulletin, May 1949. A continuing committee of the ASME is working on

Fig. 6. Example of fan with backward-curved blades and vane-control inlet. Suitable for forced draft, handling room air

a final code similar in purpose, in its field, to the Boiler Construction Code.

Some power plants, located near airports, are prohibited from using stacks sufficiently high to discharge the gases for proper dispersion to eliminate excessive pollution. To approximate the dispersive effect of a higher stack, the stack may be necked down at the top to increase the discharge velocity. When this is done, the discharge velocity in ft per sec from the stack equals roughly the height in ft which would have to be added to the stack to obtain the same dispersive effect. This rule of thumb applies with a 10 mph wind at the top of the stack. If the wind velocity increases, the effect of the high stack-discharge velocity will decrease. Naturally, necking down the stack adds an appreciable amount of stack resistance and can only be used in connection with a mechanical induced-draft system.

Fans—Air Horsepower

A fan is a "pump" or volumetric machine which can move a quantity of air or gas by imparting to it enough energy to set it into motion and to overcome all resistance to flow in its path. The fan usually consists of a bladed impeller or rotor which does the actual work and a housing which collects and directs the air discharged by the impeller. The power expended on the gas by the fan depends upon the volume moved and the total head against which it is pumped. It is usually expressed as air horsepower.

The numerical expression for air horsepower can be developed as follows:

$$hp = \frac{\text{ft-lb per min}}{33000}$$

$$\text{Air hp} = \frac{\text{lb of air per min} \times H_t}{33000}$$

$$= \frac{\text{cfm} \times \delta_a \times H_t}{33000}$$

where:

δ_a = density of air, lb/cu ft

cfm = volume flow of air, cu ft/min

H_t = total head imparted to fluid flowing, ft = (velocity head + pressure head at fan discharge) − (velocity head + pressure head at fan inlet)

Since head is normally measured in in. of water, total head, H_t, can be calculated as follows:

$$H_t = \frac{H_w}{12} \times \frac{\text{sp wt of water at 70 F}}{\delta_a} = \frac{H_w}{12} \times \frac{62.31}{\delta_a}$$

where:

H_w = head in in. of water @ standard conditions (70 F, 14.7 psia)

Therefore, $\text{Air hp} = \dfrac{\text{cfm} \times \delta_a \times H_w \times 62.31}{33000 \times 12 \times \delta_a}$

$$\text{Air hp} = \frac{62.31}{33000 \times 12} \times \text{cfm} \times H_w \quad (15)$$

$$\text{Air hp} = 0.0001573 \times \text{cfm} \times H_w \quad (16)^*$$

according to Standard Test Code (NAFM Bulletin No. 110, 1952).

---

* To obtain horsepower input to fan, value from equation (16) must be divided by the fan efficiency expressed as a decimal.

Fig. 7. Example of fan with radial-tip blades and double inlet. Arranged for induced-draft service

Energy is imparted by a fan to the gas in two forms — kinetic or velocity energy, and potential or pressure energy. Either one of these forms can be converted to the other by a gradual change in the area of the channel through which the gas is flowing. Therefore, if the characteristics of a fan are such that the impeller discharges the gas at a velocity higher than that required for flow through the discharge duct and at a pressure lower than that required to overcome the system resistance, some of the velocity energy may be converted to pressure energy after the air leaves the impeller.

Fans—Performance

Stacks frequently cannot provide the draft needed by modern boilers. The draft may range to 30 or 50 in. of water, as with the Cyclone furnace. Centrif-

Fig. 8. *Multi-bladed fan arranged for handling hot air or gases. Double inlet with louver damper control shown*

ugal or axial flow fans are generally used to supply the required mechanical draft. Fans are built in the widest assortment of designs and types so that the user has adequate selection opportunity. All fans are basically fluid acceleration devices. Their performance can be altered by changing one or many of a multitude of design variables. The details of such variations, and the underlying theory, are not properly subjects for treatment in this book. The reader can find ample treatment in standard references. Here, the objective is better to acquaint the boiler user with those features of the fan art which are particularly pertinent to the generation of steam. Some of the types of fans in use are illustrated by Figs. 6, 7 and 8.

Two essentially different kinds of fans are distinguishable:

1) The centrifugal fan, in which a fluid is ac-

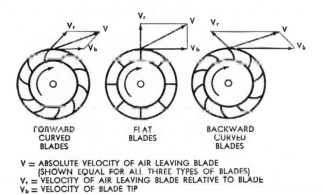

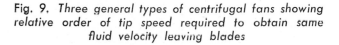

V = ABSOLUTE VELOCITY OF AIR LEAVING BLADE
(SHOWN EQUAL FOR ALL THREE TYPES OF BLADES)
V_r = VELOCITY OF AIR LEAVING BLADE RELATIVE TO BLADE
V_b = VELOCITY OF BLADE TIP

Fig. 9. *Three general types of centrifugal fans showing relative order of tip speed required to obtain same fluid velocity leaving blades*

celerated radially outward in a rotor from the heel to the tip of the blades and delivered to a surrounding scroll casing (Fig. 9).

2) The axial flow fan (fluid accelerated parallel to fan axis) is not unlike the customary desk fan but with a casing added for development of static pressure (Fig. 10).

The performance of a fan is a complicated functional relationship which is best expressed in graphical form, as in Fig. 11. These graphs are called the characteristic curves. In the figure, the capacity, cfm, is plotted horizontally as the independent variable, and the head (static pressure), the shaft horsepower, and the efficiency are plotted vertically as the dependent variables. The rotative speed, rpm, is constant. The basic significance of the characteristic curves must be appreciated. They rigorously and exactly define the performance, at which the fan must operate. If the head for a given capacity is less than that indicated on the fan characteristic curve, additional system resistance, such as a damper, to

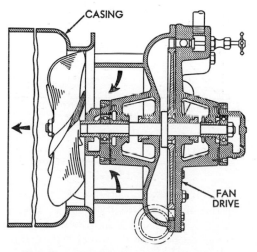

Fig. 10. *Simple type of axial flow fan*

serve as a throttle, must be interposed. If this increase in resistance to flow is not interposed, the fan will supply additional air until the flow rate establishes a system resistance which complies with some point on the characteristic curve. There is no alter-

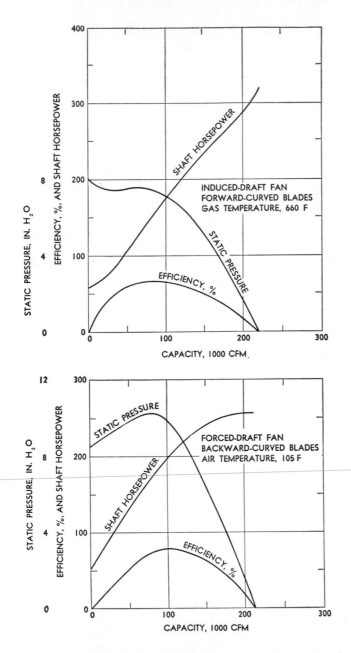

Fig. 11. *Characteristic curves for two types of centrifugal fans in typical service, operating at 5500 ft elevation and 965 rpm*

native; the fan must operate at a point on the characteristic where a balance is established. This concept is fundamental to an appreciation of the performance of fans and all other fluid-acceleration machines.

For a given fan, the numerical performance values

of the characteristics can be changed by varying the operating speed, rpm, to yield a nest of curves as shown in Fig. 12. The nature of these curves remains, however, substantially unaltered. The performance at the different speeds can be related, for the same point on the efficiency curve, by the rules:

1. Capacity is directly proportional to speed (rpm).
2. Head is directly proportional to speed squared (rpm)².
3. Power input is directly proportional to speed cubed (rpm)³.

Fan performance is based on standard air at 70 F and with a density of 0.075 lb per cu ft, which corresponds to dry air at 29.92 in. Hg absolute pressure. If a gas at some other density is to be handled, the performance can be estimated by using the characteristic curves as plotted. For any given volume, the head, measured in in. of water, and the horsepower will each change directly with the density. The fan develops head in feet of fluid, but a scale in in. of water is used for convenience.

System resistance may be plotted on the same graph as the characteristic curves of the fan, as shown in Fig. 12. If the fan runs at constant speed, then, for any output less than that shown as at the intercepts (system resistance and rpm curves), the excess head must be throttled. If variable speed can be used, then the waste of energy by throttling is avoided.

Variations in the designs of fans are indicated by the diversity of characteristics which are available in the market. By plotting characteristics on a percentage basis, some of these variations are shown in Fig. 24, Chapter 10. The rating point is taken for the conditions prevailing at the point of maximum efficiency. Some fans give steep head characteristics, others give flat head characteristics. Some horsepower characteristics are concave upward; others are concave downward. The latter have the advantage of being self-limiting, so that there is little danger of burning out the driver or little need for the alternative of overmotoring. The power requirement, however, at lighter loads is greater than for the horsepower characteristic with concavity upward.

The steep head characteristic has merit in that there is less possibility of error in the selection and a better opportunity to assure equalization of load in parallel operation. Those fans, on the other hand, which offer the flat head characteristic have the merit of handling larger volumes for a given head and are usually identified as volume fans. The fans with steep head characteristics are the high-speed designs calling for the maximum speeds in the generation of a specified head. In the selection of centrifugal fans for draft service, it is customary to find the backward-curved blade designs used for forced draft and the radial tip or forward-curved blade designs preferred for induced draft. The steel plate types are sometimes used for induced draft when there are heavy dust loadings in the gas. Likewise, exhausters for pulverizing mills are generally of the steel-plate type. The axial-flow fan or the vane-axial designs are found in forced-draft service where maximum speed and minimum bulk are prime objectives, as is the case with marine applications.

Fan Testing. It is difficult to obtain consistent results from field tests of fans installed in duct systems. For air measurement in the field there is seldom available a straight section of duct in the system long enough to eliminate the effect of bends or dampers before entering or after leaving the section. Structural arrangements at the fan entrance and discharge will also materially affect the results of field tests of fans. Fans are, therefore, guaranteed by the manufacturer only on the basis of a factory test on a "test block."

In the factory test setup there is a long straight section of duct at the fan discharge, with a throttling device at the end of the duct to vary the output. The long duct permits optimum recovery of the fan's kinetic energy, whereas in most commercial installations a bend or an increase in cross section is usually too close to the fan to allow the uneven velocity distribution at its discharge to even out before the air enters the modified section. The characteristics of fan performance established by tests under ideal conditions are known as "test block specifications." When ordering a fan on the basis of its test block specifications, adequate allowance must be made for the effect of field conditions on fan performance, and the guidance of the manufacturer should be followed because deviations can be severe.

Control of Fan Output

Very few applications permit the fan to operate at constant pressure and volume output at all times. Therefore, to meet the requirements of the system, some convenient means of varying the fan output is necessary. The common ways of controlling fan output are:

Outlet-Damper Control. A damper placed at the fan discharge is a simple control. It acts as a throttle valve, introducing enough resistance into the system to restrict the fan output to any desired quantity. Damper control, however, is wasteful because the fan develops excess pressure energy which must be dissipated by throttling.

The advantages of damper control are:
1. Lowest first cost of all types of control.
2. Ease with which it can be operated or adapted to automatic control.
3. The least expensive type of fan drive, a con-

stant-speed induction-type a-c motor, can be used.

4. It is a continuous rather than a step type of control and is therefore effective throughout the entire range of fan operation.

Variable-Speed Control. The most efficient way of controlling output, as far as power consumption of the fan is concerned, is by varying the speed. From the relationship of speed to capacity, pressure, and power, noted above, it follows that if the speed is cut to ½, the output of the fan will be cut to ½, the pressure to ¼, and the horsepower to ⅛. In using speed control there is some loss in efficiency, since no variable-speed driver is as efficient throughout the entire fan-load range as a direct-connected constant-speed a-c motor. The amount of the loss in effectiveness depends upon the type of speed variation selected.

A number of commonly used variable-speed arrangements are: a) magnetic coupling; b) hydraulic coupling; c) special mechanical drives; d) variable-speed d-c motor; e) variable-speed a-c motor; and f) variable-speed steam turbine. The magnetic coupling consists of two windings in a

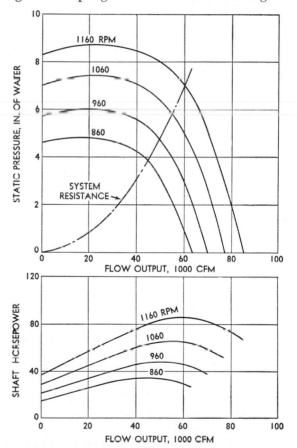

Fig. 12. *Illustrating how desired output and static pressure can be obtained economically by varying fan speed to avoid large throttling losses*

housing with a variable field. A change in field strength varies the slip and consequently the speed of the fan. A hydraulic coupling is illustrated in Fig. 13. Among the special mechanical drives are the variable pitch v-belt and the variable speed planetary transmission. In general all of these methods of speed variation are more expensive than the less efficient damper control. An economic balance of first cost and power consumption must, therefore, be effected in reaching a decision on the type of drive to be selected.

Two Speed A-C Motors. Two-speed a-c motors are often used to supplement damper control. A two-speed motor is less expensive than the variable speed arrangements with a-c drives, and will give an improvement in the fan efficiency with simple damper control. The spread between upper and lower speeds should not be too great. Thus, if the top speed is

Fig. 13. *Hydraulic coupling installed between motor and fan to obtain wide variation in speed, using constant speed driver*

1200 rpm the second speed should not be less than 900, and if the top speed is 900 the lower speed may be 720 rpm.

Inlet Vane Control. The inlet vane control method is more efficient than outlet damper control in regulating the airflow through a fan. The inlet vanes (see Fig. 14) give the air a varying degree of spin, and the greater the spin, the less will be the volume output of the fan. Inlet vane control is more expensive than outlet damper control but less expensive than speed variation. It is most effective for a moderate degree of change at high fan output, but offers some saving in efficiency over damper control throughout its entire range.

Vane leakage often makes it difficult to reduce the airflow below ¼ of full fan output when a single speed motor is used for the fan drive. Therefore, when vane control is used for mechanical draft fans,

and where a wide load range is required, it is advisable to use a two-speed drive motor or a supplementary outlet damper to increase the control range of the vanes.

The effect upon the power input required by the fan drives for various types of fan control is indicated by the curves in Fig. 15.

Fan Drives

Electric motors are normally used for fan drives because, when properly selected, they are less expensive and more efficient than any other type of drive. For fans of over a few horsepower, squirrel cage induction motors are the usual choice. This type of motor is relatively inexpensive, reliable, and high in efficiency over a wide load range. In large sizes it is frequently used in conjunction with a magnetic or hydraulic coupling where variable speed is required. For some variable speed installations, particularly in the smaller sizes, wound rotor ("slip ring") induction motors are used. If a d-c motor is required the compound type is usually selected. For fan drives, the steam turbine is more expensive than a squirrel cage motor, but it is generally less expensive than any of the variable speed electric motor arrangements in sizes over 50 hp. The steam turbine is used where a constant supply of electricity is not assured. This type of drive may prove more economical than the electric drive in plants where the exhaust may be used for process work.

The Forced Draft Fan

Fan Capacity. In an ordinary boiler installation the forced draft fan pushes the air through the combustion air supply system to the furnace. It should have a discharge pressure high enough to equal the total resistance of the air ducts, air heater, burners or fuel bed, and any other resistance between the fan discharge and the furnace. This makes the furnace the point of balanced draft since, when the air reaches it, the pressure should have dropped to zero. The volume output of the fan must equal the total quantity of air required for combustion. In some cases, of course, more than one forced draft fan is needed. When this is so, the output of each fan may be made equal to about ⅔ of the full load requirements to permit operation of the boiler at a substantial load when one fan is out of service.

To establish the characteristics of the forced draft fan, the system resistance from fan to furnace is calculated for the actual weight of air required by the combustion equipment plus the expected leakage from the air to the gas side of the air heater. For calculation purposes in boiler work, the air temperature entering the fan is usually taken as 80F. Having thus established the net characteristics of the fan, the required test block specifications are arrived at

Fig. 14. *Application of inlet-vane method to control output of a forced draft fan handling room air*

by adding factors of safety to the weight, total head and temperature. These factors are in the order of 15-20 per cent, 15-25 per cent and 25F respectively. It is necessary to use these factors of safety because ideal test block conditions do not prevail in practice, and they forestall any likelihood of the fan capacity setting a limit to peak boiler output. The safety factors also anticipate possible loss of air from the system due to duct or air heater leakage not already accounted for; duct resistance due to field changes made to the original design; additional combustion air required due to some unexpected falling off in the performance of the fuel burning equipment; and higher than expected resistance of the fuel burning equipment caused, for instance, by a change in the coal size used for a stoker.

Fan Requirements. A forced draft fan for boiler service must operate under far more stringent conditions than an ordinary ventilating fan. The important requirements for a forced draft fan are listed below:

Utmost reliability is a prime requirement. Modern boilers must operate continuously for long periods (up to 18 months in some instances) without shutdown for repairs or maintenance. To satisfy this condition the fan must have a rugged rotor and housing and conservatively loaded bearings. The fan must also be well balanced and the blades should be

shaped so that they are not likely to collect dirt to disturb this balance.

Since many boilers are operated under varying load conditions it is important that the fan should have a high efficiency over a wide range of output.

Fan pressure should vary uniformly with output giving a smooth curve over the range of capacity. This will permit easy application of damper control and will assure minimum disturbance of air flow when the system resistance changes due to minor adjustments to the fuel burning equipment.

When two or more fans are to operate in parallel the pressure to output curves should drop off at a constant rate from near the shutoff condition, so that each fan will share the load equally.

If the fan is driven by a direct-connected motor, it should have a "self limiting" horsepower characteristic so that the driving motor cannot be overloaded. This means that the horsepower should reach a peak and then drop off near the full load fan output.

To reduce space requirements, since relatively clean air is handled, a high speed type of forced draft fan may be used.

In general, the requirements noted above for a forced draft fan are best satisfied by the backward curved centrifugal designs. For small boiler units, however, a single propeller type fan mounted directly upon the burner windbox is frequently used because of its low cost and economy of space. Vane-axial fans have been used for some special high pressure forced draft applications.

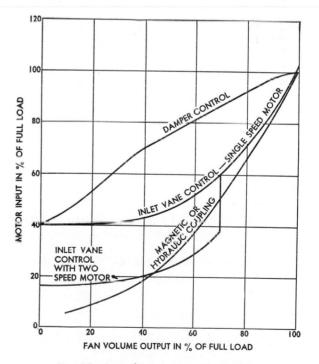

Fig. 15. *Fan drive power required for several types of volume control*

The Induced-Draft Fan

Fan Capacity. The induced-draft fan must have the capacity to set up a sufficient pressure differential to cause the required quantity of gas at full load to pass through the boiler against the draft loss caused by flow over all the heating surface and through the gas passages between the furnace and the fan. Normally the gases pass into a stack or discharge from the fan at substantially atmospheric pressure.

The weight of gas used to calculate the draft loss is equal to the weight of the combustion gases plus the weight of air infiltration to the boiler setting from the room and from the air side to the gas side of the air heater. The gas temperature used in arriving at the fan size is the temperature calculated for estimating boiler performance. To establish the test block specifications for the fan required, safety factors similar to those used for forced-draft fans are added to the calculated quantities (see above). These factors allow for the possibility of an excessive accumulation of surface dirt as well as the other items noted for forced-draft fans.

Fan Requirements. The requirements for induced-draft fans are the same as for forced-draft fans except that they must handle a larger volume of hot, dirty, and often erosive gas. Flat, forward-curved and backward-curved blades are variously used. If backward-curved blades are used, the curvature generally is less than in forced-draft fans. The lesser curvature blade, by the reduction in rotative speed, tends to diminish the erosive effect of the ash particles, and, because of the shape, the deposit of dirt upon the back of the blades is reduced. In handling particularly dirty or erosive gases, a flat-bladed centrifugal fan of lower speed may be used. To avoid excessive maintenance from fly-ash erosion, the casing and blades may be protected by replaceable wear strips. Bearings are usually water cooled and have radiation shields on the shaft between the fan and bearing to avoid overheating the bearing lubricant by the hot gases within the fan.

Fan Selection

The following example shows the method of establishing the characteristics of fans suitable for a boiler, based on data obtained from the calculated performance of the oil-fired unit of Fig. 16.

Data, Assigned or From Calculated Performance Boiler Unit Illustrated in Fig. 16

Steam flow, lb per hr @ 920 psi and 905 F	325,000
Output at station bus, from 325,000 lb steam per hr, kw	40,000
Input to furnace, Btu per hr	416,000,000
Air flow through unit, lb per hr	
Theoretical air for combustion	315,000

Excess air required at burner, 5%	15,750
*Leakage, furnace and boiler, 10%	31,500
*Leakage from air to gas, air heater, 2%	6,300
Fuel consumption, lb per hr	22,500
Temperatures, F	
Air entering air heater	80
Gas leaving air heater	335
Atmospheric pressure, in. of mercury	29.9
†Air resistance, in. of water	
Air heater	2.84
Ducts	0.86
Burners and windbox	3.15
Total air resistance	6.85
†Draft loss, in. of water	
Furnace	0.10
Boiler and superheater	5.10
Air heater	2.08
Flues	0.40
Total draft loss	7.68

* Determined empirically.

† Assigned or calculated by methods outlined in Chapters 8 and 11. The net stack effect within the setting has been included.

Selection of Forced-Draft Fan

(a) Weight of air to be handled by fan, lb per hr

Theoretical air for combustion	315,000
Excess air required at burner	15,750
Leakage, air to gas in air heater	6,300
Total net fan requirement	337,050
Add 20% safety factor	67,410
Test block requirement	404,460

(b) Static pressure at fan discharge, in. of water

Total air resistance, fan to burner

Air resistance in air heater	2.84
Air resistance in ducts	0.86
Air resistance in burners and windbox	3.15
Total net requirement	6.85
Add 25% safety factor	1.71
Test block requirement	8.56

(c) Temperature of air to be handled by fan, F

Net requirement, air temperature at fan	80
Safety factor	25
Test block requirement	105

Selection of Induced-Draft Fan

(a) Weight of gas to be handled by fan, lb per hr

Theoretical air for combustion	315,000
Excess air required at burner	15,750
Leakage, furnace and boiler	31,500
Leakage, air to gas in air heater	6,300
Fuel—assume no ash—all in flue gases	22,500
Total net fan requirement	391,050
Add 18% safety factor	70,390
Test block requirement	461,440

(b) Draft to be provided by fan, in. of water
Total draft loss

Draft loss in furnace	0.10
Draft loss in boiler and superheater	5.10
Draft loss in air heater	2.08
Draft loss in flues	0.40
Total net requirement	7.68
Add 25% safety factor	1.92
Test block requirement	9.60

(c) Temperature of gas to be handled by fan, F

Net requirement, gas leaving air heater	335
Safety factor	25
Test block requirement	360

Pressure Settings

In a number of large steam-generating units, the induced-draft fan has been omitted and the entire boiler setting is under positive pressure. To prevent the escape of noxious gases into the boiler room, it is essential that the leakage, normally expected in a conventional setting, be completely eliminated. In a pressure setting, all the work of creating gas flow through the unit is done by the forced-draft fan,

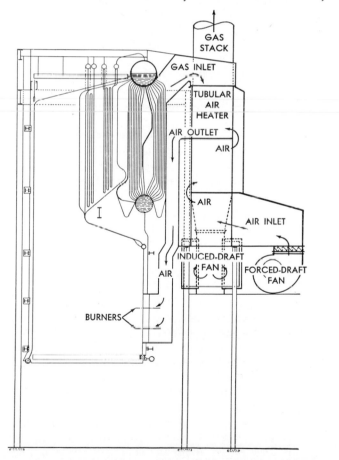

Fig. 16. *Diagrammatic arrangement of forced- and induced-draft fans and stacks for 325,000 lb steam per hr boiler unit*

and operating cost is reduced in two ways:

1. Since there is no air infiltration into the setting to increase the stack loss, the boiler efficiency may be improved by 0.25 to 0.75 per cent. A mean value of 0.50 per cent may be used in most calculations.

2. There is no air leakage into the boiler setting, and the forced-draft fan handles a lesser weight of cool air at smaller volume and higher efficiency than in handling hot gases.

In the following example, to illustrate the saving in net fan power, a comparison is made of the fan power required for the boiler unit in Fig. 16 with a conventional fan arrangement and with a pressure setting. An over-all efficiency of 70 per cent is used for fan and motor.

1) Conventional Arrangement
(a) Forced-draft fan

Air weight, lb per hr	337,050
Air temperature, F	80
Air density at 80 F, lb per cu ft	0.0737
Air volume, cfm $= \dfrac{337{,}050}{0.0737 \times 60}$	76,221
Static pressure, H_w, in. of water	6.85
Air horsepower, equation (16), hp $=$ 0.0001573 $\times$ 76,221 $\times$ 6.85	82.1
Motor input, hp (combined efficiency, 70%) $= \dfrac{82.1}{0.70}$	118
Motor input, kw $= 118 \times 0.746$	88

(b) Induced-draft fan

Gas weight, lb per hr	391,050
Gas temperature, F	335
Gas density at 335 F, lb per cu ft	0.0501
Gas volume, cfm $= \dfrac{391{,}050}{0.0501 \times 60}$	130,090
Static pressure, H_w, in. of water	7.68
Air horsepower, hp $=$ 0.0001573 $\times$ 130,090 $\times$ 7.68	157
Motor input, hp (combined efficiency, 70%) $= \dfrac{157}{0.70}$	225
Motor input, kw $= 225 \times 0.746$	168

(c) Total fan power required, forced draft + induced draft

Total motor input, hp $= 118 + 225$	343
Total motor input, kw $= 88 + 168$	256

2) Pressure-Setting Arrangement
(a) Forced-draft fan only

Air weight, lb per hr	337,050
Air temperature, F	80
Air density at 80 F, lb per cu ft	0.0737
Air volume, cfm $= \dfrac{337{,}050}{0.0737 \times 60}$	76,221
Static pressure, H_w, in. of water (see below)	13.76

Air horsepower, hp =
$0.0001573 \times 76,221 \times 13.76$ 165

Motor input, hp $= \dfrac{165}{0.70}$ 236

Motor input, kw $= 236 \times 0.746$ 176

3) Saving of Pressure Setting over Forced- and Induced-Draft Fan Arrangement

Fan power saving, kw $= 256 - 176$ 80

Fan power saving, % of output =
$80 \times 100/40,000$ 0.2

Total saving

Improved boiler efficiency, % (0.5% less fuel burned, see 1. under *Pressure Settings* above)   0.5

Fan power saving, % (0.2% more salable power)   0.2

Approximate total gain, %   0.7

In the pressure-setting arrangement with no leakage from the room into the setting, the calculations (see Chapter 8) to determine the gas pressure drop through the unit are based on the following gas weights (lb per hr), differing somewhat from those used in determining the draft loss for the conventional arrangement:

Theoretical air for combustion	315,000
Fuel (100% into flue gases)	22,500
Excess air at burners	15,750
Gas through boiler and superheater, lb per hr	353,250
Gas through boiler and superheater	353,250
Leakage of air to gas side of air heater	6,300
Gas through air heater, lb per hr	359,550

The calculated pressure drop (in. of water) through the unit with a pressure setting, used above as the required static pressure at the fan discharge, may be recapitulated as follows:

Air resistance, fan to furnace	6.85
Furnace (assumed)	0.10
Boiler and superheater	4.56
Air heater	1.87
Flues	0.38
Total net head on fan, in. of water	13.76

It will be noted that the decrease in operating cost of the unit because of a pressure setting is substantial. There is an added saving from the elimination of the maintenance of the induced-draft fan which must handle hot and frequently erosive and corrosive gases. The increased cost of a completely airtight boiler setting must be weighed against these savings.

Operation and Maintenance

Stacks. All idle entrances leading to the stack should be tightly sealed to prevent cold-air leakage to the base. Cold-air leakage not only lowers the stack temperature, which adversely affects draft, but it also increases the mass of gas flow that the stack must handle. Some plants find it expedient to dispose of factory wastes into the boiler stack for dispersion high into the atmosphere. Careful consideration should be given to such use of the stack since it may increase maintenance cost.

The stack is subject to the erosive action of ash in the flue gases, to acid corrosion by sulfur products, and to the corrosion and deterioration incident to the continuous exposure of any equipment to the weather. The erosion or wastage of the stack material normally occurs at stack entrance or at throats and necked-down sections where there is a change in the direction of gas flow. These sections may require replacements at long period intervals. The reduction in maintenance will usually offset the original use of premium-priced abrasive-resistant materials.

Low temperatures are the cause of the corrosion of steel stacks or steel-lined stacks. The moisture formed by the low temperatures absorbs the sulfur fumes from the gases to form a dilute sulfuric acid. Acid corrosion may destroy a steel stack in a few years or even a few months. Corrosion-resistant metals, refractory coatings, and high-temperature acid-resisting paints are used to prolong the life of steel stacks. Refractory stacks are subject to deterioration from the chemicals and water vapor in the gases. Long exposure in wet weather, during out of service periods, and insufficient drying on starting-up contribute to higher maintenance cost.

Fans. The service of fans as components of a boiler unit is a fairly simple and light duty, but their operation, like all running equipment, requires frequent observation to detect and correct irregularities that might cause trouble. The period of continuous operation of fans should be long compared with other power plant equipment. To assure this continuity of operation, proper lubrication and cooling of fan shafts, couplings, and bearings are essential.

Fan bearings and couplings must be carefully aligned with the driving equipment. Proper allowance should be made for the small vertical movement of the fan rotor caused by temperature rise of the bearing supports from cold to running conditions. Additional end clearances must be provided for oil slingers at the floating bearing and at the coupling to compensate for the increase in length of the shaft from heat conduction. At each revolution, the bumping action caused by poor alignment is progressive and will soon hammer the bearing to destruction.

To assure smooth and lasting service, the fan should be properly balanced — both statically and dynamically. The weight of the rotor should be equally distributed about the center of rotation, and the load should be equally distributed around the fan rotor and uniformly outward from the shaft. The balance should be checked after each shutdown for maintenance by running the fan, at full speed, (1) with no air flow and (2) with full air flow. A skillful mechanic can usually balance the fan rotor by trial and error methods. Special instruments may be used, especially with larger fans, to establish the amount and location of weight to be added for static balance. Fans in operation are frequently thrown out of balance temporarily by the uneven shedding of fly-ash deposits from the blades. This condition is usually self correcting, but, to guard against serious mechanical damage to the equipment, operation, while out of balance, should be under careful observation.

In fans handling gases with entrained abrasive dust particles the blades and the housing near the discharge are subject to erosion. Abrasive resistant materials and liners are used to reduce such wear. Some operators apply beads of welding to repair and to lengthen the life of fan blades of induced draft fans subject to erosion.

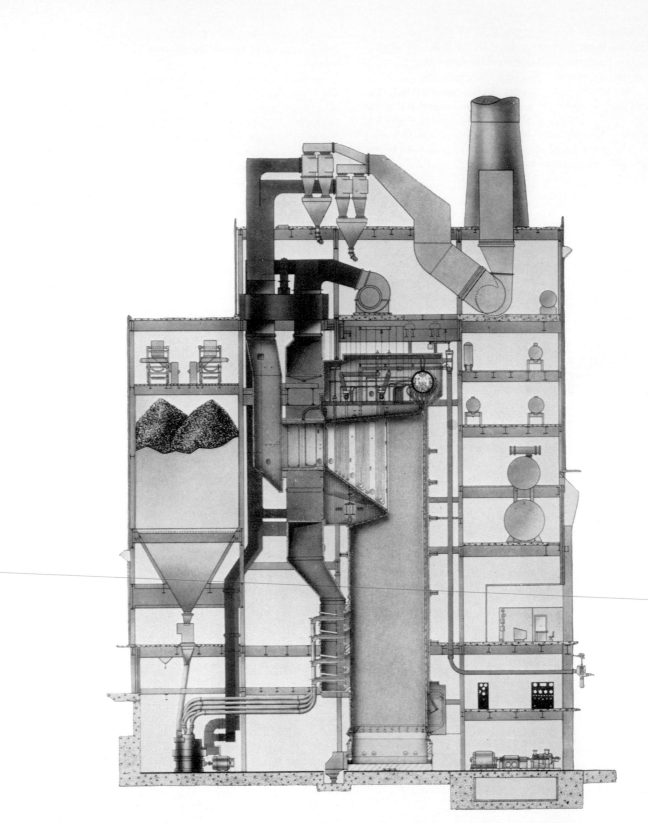

A LARGE BOILER UNIT WHICH UTILIZES THE MOST MODERN OPERATING TECHNIQUES

TEMPERATURE MEASUREMENT

EARLY in life everyone learns to distinguish between hot and cold. This sensory experience, supplemented by familiarity with such phenomena as the freezing and boiling of water, the cooking of food and the glow of hot metals, gives rise to a general concept of temperature, but does not provide any quantitative measure of degree of hotness—in other words, a scale of temperature. One of the great contributions of thermodynamics was the establishment of a usable theoretical temperature scale (thermodynamic scale), completely independent of any actual substance, which forms the basis of scales of temperature used in the quantitative measurement of degree of hotness.

Temperature Scales

Before the theory of temperature had been fully developed various arbitrary temperature scales were devised. Two of these, Fahrenheit and Celsius (centigrade) are firmly established. The Fahrenheit scale is fixed by the freezing point (32F) and the boiling point (212F) of water at standard atmospheric pressure, with 180 equal degrees between the boiling and freezing points. The centigrade scale is based on the same freezing point (zero C) and boiling point (100C) of water at standard atmospheric pressure, with 100 equal degrees between. In the conversion from one to the other, $F = (C \times 9/5) + 32$, and $C = (F-32) \times 5/9$.

Whenever heat is added to a substance the molecular energy is increased, causing temperature rise, melting, or vaporization. Similarly, when heat is removed the decrease in molecular energy causes lowering of temperature, freezing, or condensation. Applying this principle, the thermodynamic scale, in which equal temperature intervals correspond to equal changes in heat energy, is based on the behavior of a theoretically perfect gas, which would have properties similar to those of ordinary gases but which would not condense or freeze at low temperatures. The point at which all heat has been abstracted from the perfect gas and all molecular motion has ceased is the lowest conceivable temperature; this point is called absolute zero, and corresponds to $-273.2C$ or $-459.7F$.

Two additional scales useful in scientific work are the absolute temperature scales starting at absolute zero. The absolute scale using centigrade degrees as the temperature interval is called the Kelvin scale (K); the absolute scale using Fahrenheit degrees is called the Rankine scale (R). For engineering work, using round figures for absolute zero, the values of K and R and the conversion from one to the other are: $K = C + 273 = R/1.8$ and $R = F + 460 = 1.8K$.

For the purpose of calibrating thermometers the fusion or vaporization temperatures of various pure substances have been carefully determined, and are known as "fixed points." Six fixed points form the basis of the International Temperature Scale. These, all at atmospheric pressure of 29.92 in. Hg, are:

Oxygen boiling	— 182.97C	— 297.35F
Water freezing	0.00C*	+ 32.00F*
Water boiling	+ 100.00C*	+ 212.00F*
Sulfur boiling	+ 444.60C	+ 832.28F
Silver melting	+ 960.8 C	+1761.4 F
Gold melting	+1063 C	+1945 F

*Exact, by definition

Importance of Temperature Determination

Heat exchange, heat balances, and a multitude of other problems involving temperature are important in all phases of power generation. Means of indicating, recording, and controlling temperatures are important in design, fabrication, operation, and testing power generating and utilizing equipment and associated apparatus. Methods of measuring temperatures accurately are therefore of prime interest to power engineers. Great strides have been made in the past in developing suitable instruments, and progress is continuing. Both test and commercial operating instruments are being constantly improved and simplified. In recent years thermocouples have found widespread acceptance and are extensively used in the power-generating field.

Methods of Measuring Temperature

Many properties of substances affected by heat, such as change of state, thermal expansion, radiation, and electrical effects, have been applied to temperature indicators suitable for commercial use. Instruments of this kind, usually of a high order of accuracy, are available for a great variety of applications. Accuracy in temperature measurement will depend upon care in application and an appreciation of the limitations of the instrument used. Before readings are taken, it is the engineer's responsibility to make certain that every application is correct and that the results are not affected by any extraneous factors.

Changes of State

Fusion. For a pure chemical element or compound such as mercury or water, fusion, or change of state from solid to liquid, occurs at a fixed temperature. The melting points of such materials are therefore suitable fixed points for temperature scales.

The fusion of pyrometric cones is widely used in the ceramic industry as a method of measuring high temperatures in refractory heating furnaces. These cones, small pyramids about 2 in. high, are made of selected mixtures of oxides and glass which soften and melt at established temperatures. In the power industry, use of the pyrometric cone is generally limited to the laboratory and is suitable for a temperature range from 1100 F to 3600 F.

Fusion pyrometers are also made in the form of crayon, paint, and pellets, which indicate a range of established temperatures up to 2000 F. When the crayon or paint is applied to a cold surface, a dull-finish mark is made which melts and changes to a glossy finish as the surface is heated to the specified temperature. These marks, therefore, indicate whether or not the surface temperature has reached or exceeded a selected value. The pellets begin to melt at specified temperatures when in contact with a surface.

Vaporization. The vapor pressure of a liquid depends upon its temperature. When the liquid is heated to the boiling temperature, the vapor pressure is equal to the total pressure above the liquid surface. Therefore, the boiling points of various pure chemical elements or compounds at standard atmospheric pressure (29.92 in. Hg) can be used as thermometric fixed points.

The change of vapor pressure with temperature is utilized in the vapor pressure thermometer, illustrated schematically in Fig. 1, which consists of a bulb, partially filled with liquid, and a capillary tube leading from the bulb to a pressure gage calibrated to read temperature directly. If the space between the liquid and the pressure gage is filled only with vapor from the liquid, the pressure will vary directly with the temperature of the liquid in the bulb. The capillary tube may be of considerable length, and its temperature does not affect the reading, but the accuracy of the instrument is affected by variations in atmospheric pressure and by elevation of the bulb above or below the gage. The temperature scale is nonuniform. To prevent partial and indeterminate condensation of the vapor in the capillary, the bulb temperature must be somewhat above or below that of the capillary. The working range of a given instrument is limited to several hundred degrees and usually lies between minus 20 F and plus 700 F.

Expansion Properties

Most substances expand when heated, and in many cases the amount of expansion is almost directly proportional to the change in temperature. This effect is utilized in various types of thermometers using gases, solids, or liquids.

Gases. The expansion of gases follows the relationship:

$$PV = RT/M$$

where:

P = absolute pressure, lb per sq ft
V = specific volume, cu ft per lb
R = universal gas constant, 1544
T = absolute temperature, deg
   Rankine = F + 460
M = molecular weight of the gas

At high pressures or near the condensation point gases deviate considerably from this relationship. Under other conditions, however, the deviation is small.

Two types of gas thermometers are based on this relationship. In one a constant gas volume is maintained, and changes in pressure are used to measure changes in temperature. In the other a constant pressure is maintained, and changes in volume are used to measure changes in temperature. Instruments of this type, of highest accuracy, have been developed for laboratory work. The constant volume type is widely used commercially.

Nitrogen is commonly used for the gas-filled thermometer in industrial application. It is suitable for a temperature range of minus 60 F to plus 1000 F. Except that the system is filled with nitrogen gas instead of liquid and vapor, the construction is similar to the vapor pressure pyrometer shown in Fig. 1. Expansion of the heated nitrogen in the bulb increases the pressure in the system and actuates the temperature indicator or recorder. The temperature scale is uniform, and the capillary tube may be of any length. Changes in temperature of the capillary tubing will introduce small errors.

Liquids. The expansion of liquids is used in a thermometer similar in design to the vapor pressure instrument shown in Fig. 1, except that the bulb and capillary tube are completely filled with liquid. Mercury is suitable for a temperature range of minus 38F to plus 1000F; and alcohol may be used for a range of minus 50F to plus 300F. The readings of instruments of this type are subject to error if the capillary tubing is affected by temperature changes.

Liquid-in-glass thermometers, also based on the expansion of liquids, are so widely used that they are discussed in a separate section.

Solids. The actuating medium in thermometers based on the expansion of solids when heated is the bimetallic strip. Flat ribbons of two different metals, having different coefficients of thermal expansion, are joined face to face by riveting or welding to form a bimetallic strip. When the strip is heated, the expansion is greater for one side of the double layer than for the other, and the strip bends, if originally flat, or, changes its curvature if initially in the spiral form frequently used. Bimetallic strips are seldom used in power plant thermometers, but are widely used in inexpensive household thermometers, many designs of thermostats, and a variety of temperature control and regulating equipment. They are particularly useful for automatic temperature-compensation in the mechanisms of other instruments.

Radiation Properties

All solid bodies emit radiation. The amount is very small at low temperatures and large at high temperatures. The values for radiation may be calculated by the following formula, developed by Stefan-Boltzmann:

$$W = \sigma \epsilon T^4$$

Where:

W — radiant energy per unit of time per unit area, Btu/sq ft hr

σ = Stefan-Boltzmann constant, 1.73×10^{-9} Btu/sq ft hr (deg R)^4

ϵ = Emissivity of the surface, a dimensionless number between 0 and 1 (usually about 0.90 for steel)

T = absolute temperature, deg R

At low temperatures the radiation is chiefly in the infra-red range, invisible to the human eye. As the temperature rises an increasing proportion of the radiation is in shorter wavelengths, becoming visible as the dull red glow of bodies at about 1000F and passing through yellow toward white at higher temperatures. The temperature of hot metals (above 1000F) can be estimated by their color. For iron or steel the color scale is roughly as follows:

Dark red	1000F
Medium cherry red	1250F
Orange	1650F
Yellow	1850F
White	2200F

Two types of temperature measuring instruments, the optical pyrometer and the radiation pyrometer, are based upon the radiating properties of materials.

Optical. By sighting an optical pyrometer on a hot object brightness of the latter can be compared visually with the brightness of a calibrated source of radiation within the instrument, usually an electrically heated tungsten filament. A red filter may be

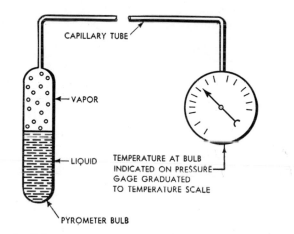

Fig. 1. *Schematic assembly—vapor pressure pyrometer*

used to restrict the comparison to a particular wavelength. This instrument is designed for measuring the temperature of surfaces with an emissivity of 1.0, known in heat transfer parlance as "black bodies."* When accurately calibrated it will give excellent results above 1500F, provided its use is restricted to the application for which it is designed. Measurement of the temperature of the interior of a uniformly heated enclosure, such as a muffle furnace, is such an application. When used to measure the temperature of a hot object in the open the optical pyrometer will always read low, the error being small (20F) for high-emissivity bodies such as steel ingots, and considerable (200F to 300F) for unoxidized liquid steel or iron surfaces.

The optical pyrometer has a wide field of application for temperature measurements in heating

---

* By definition a "black body" absorbs all radiation falling upon it, reflecting none and transmitting none. (See Chapter 7, Heat Transfer.)

furnaces, and around steel mills and iron foundries. It is of no value for the commercial measurement of gas temperatures, since clean gases do not radiate in the visible range.

Radiation. In the radiation pyrometer, all radiation from the hot body, regardless of wavelength, is absorbed by the instrument. The heat absorption is measured by the temperature rise of a delicate thermocouple within the instrument, calibrated to indicate the temperature of the hot surface at which the pyrometer is sighted, assuming that the surface emissivity equals 1.0. The hot surface must fill the entire field of view of the instrument.

The radiation pyrometer has been developed into a laboratory research instrument of extreme sensitivity and high precision over a wide range of temperature. The usual industrial type instrument gives good results above 1000F when used to measure temperatures of high-emissivity bodies, such as the interiors of uniformly heated enclosures. Since its operation is independent of human judgment, the radiation pyrometer may be used as remotely-operated indicators or recorders, or in automatic control systems. Errors in measuring the temperatures of hot bodies with emissivities of less than 1.0, especially if they are in the open, are extremely large. The radiation pyrometer is not suitable for the commercial measurement of gas temperatures.

Electrical Properties

Two classes of widely used temperature measurement instruments, the thermocouple and the electrical resistance thermometer, are based on the relation of temperature to the electrical properties of metals.

Because of its versatility, convenience and ruggedness, the thermocouple is of particular importance in power plant temperature measurements. A discussion of the thermocouple and its application will be found in separate sections.

Electrical Resistance. The electrical resistance thermometer, used over a range of temperature from minus 400F to plus 1800F, is based on the increase in electrical resistance of metals with increase in temperature, and almost in direct proportion. Therefore, if the electrical resistance of a wire of known and calibrated material is measured (by a Wheatstone bridge or other device) the temperature of the wire can be determined.

In the simplest form of this instrument, shown in sketch (a) Fig. 2, the readings would be the sum of the resistances of the calibrated wire and the leads connecting this wire to the Wheatstone bridge. These readings would be subject to error due to temperature changes of the leads. By using a slightly more complicated circuit, shown in sketch (b) Fig. 2, the resistance of the leads can be eliminated from

the instrument reading. In order to localize the point of temperature measurement the resistance wire may be made in the form of a small coil. From room temperature to 250F commercial instruments usually have resistance coils of nickel or copper. Platinum is used for higher temperatures, and in many high-precision laboratory instruments over a wide range of temperatures.

The electrical resistance thermometer does not require human judgment, and can therefore be used for the remote operation of indicating, recording, or automatic control instruments. If proper precautions are taken in its use it is stable and accurate.

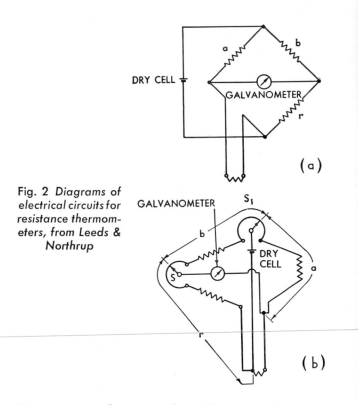

Fig. 2 *Diagrams of electrical circuits for resistance thermometers, from Leeds & Northrup*

However, it is less rugged and less versatile than a thermocouple.

Other Properties

There are other properties of materials which vary with temperatures and which could be used as the basis of temperature-measuring instruments. For example, the velocity of sound in a gas varies directly as the square root of the absolute temperature. While this phenomenon has been used in research it has not been commercially applied due to difficulties in instrumentation. By using the flow of gas through two orifices in series a method has been developed for measuring gas temperatures up to 2000F commercially, and up to 4500F in the laboratory. Temperatures in the range from absolute zero to 5000F have been determined with considerable accuracy by the use of an electronic laboratory instrument which measures the motion of electrons. High temperature research has been stimulated by gas turbine and jet propulsion problems, and the development of new and improved temperature measuring instruments is to be expected.

Liquid-in-Glass Thermometers

The liquid-in-glass thermometer is a simple, direct reading, and conveniently portable instrument, widely used in many activities requiring the determination of temperature. Low precision thermometers are inexpensive, and instruments of moderate precision are available for laboratory use.

This type of thermometer is usually made with a reservoir of liquid in a glass bulb connected directly to a glass capillary tube with graduated markings or with a scale attached. Mercury, the most commonly used liquid, is satisfactory from minus 38F, its freezing point, up to about 600F if the capillary space above the mercury is evacuated, or up to 900F or higher if this space is filled with nitrogen under pressure. In the range from minus 100F to plus 250F alcohol may be used, and in the range from minus 300F to plus 70F pentane has been found suitable.

Use of unprotected glass thermometers is restricted to laboratory or field research applications. For more rugged service there are various designs of "industrial" thermometers, with the bulb and stem protected by a metal casing, and usually arranged for screwing into a thermometer well. Obviously, the accuracy of this type is not as high as that of the unprotected laboratory-type instrument, and there is a greater time lag if temperatures are changing.

Correction of Errors

When high precision is desired correction must be made for several possible sources of instrument error, which may be outlined as follows:

If the capillary bore is not uniform, equal increments of temperature will produce unequal changes in the length of the liquid column, and, hence the readings will not represent the true temperature.

The markings of the fixed and intermediate points on the scale may be in error.

The temperature readings will be slightly different when taken in the vertical and in the horizontal position of the thermometer because of the change in volume of the bulb due to the hydrostatic pressure of the liquid column. Any change in the volume of the bulb due to external pressure will also, of course, affect the readings.

When the temperature of a thermometer is changed over a wide range the glass will slowly "creep." This is known as thermal hysteresis. It may take a day to attain equilibrium.

A correction is required for the portion of the stem of the thermometer not exposed to the temperature being measured. This is known as the emergent stem correction. Many laboratory thermometers are calibrated with the entire thermometer at uniform temperature (total immersion). If a total immersion thermometer is only partially immersed in a hot fluid, with a portion of the stem exposed to the atmosphere, some of the liquid in the capillary will be at a reduced temperature and will expand less than for total immersion. A correction for partial immersion may be made by using an auxiliary thermometer affixed to the first so that the bulb of the auxiliary thermometer is next to the emergent stem of the first thermometer one-fourth of the way up between the liquid surface and the top of the liquid column in the first thermometer. The correction factor for mercury in glass thermometers will then be:

$$K = 0.00009 \ D \ (t_1 - t_2)$$

Where:

K = correction, deg F, to be added when the stem is cooler than the bulb.

D = number of degrees on scale of first thermometer not immersed.

t_1 = temperature, deg F, indicated by the partially immersed thermometer.

t_2 = temperature, deg F, indicated by the auxiliary thermometer.

Some thermometers are calibrated for partial immersion to a specified point which is marked on the stem.

If a separation appears in the liquid column in the capillary the column should be reunited before the thermometer is used. This is usually done by cooling the bulb to a very low temperature and shaking or rapping the thermometer so that the separated sections of the column rejoin the main body of the liquid.

When the temperature of the thermometer surroundings is changed, readings should not be taken until thermal equilibrium has been re-established.

Thermometers used at high temperature (over 300F) may undergo permanent change of bulb volume and, therefore, require recalibration.

In reading the instrument care must be taken to avoid the error due to parallax (viewing the scale at an angle).

In industrial measurements the largest source of error is usually due to the difficulty of keeping the immersed portion of the thermometer at the same temperature as the fluid in which it is immersed. Cooling or heating effects of conduction or radiation from nearby materials must be eliminated or mini-

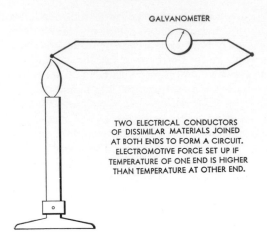

GALVANOMETER

TWO ELECTRICAL CONDUCTORS OF DISSIMILAR MATERIALS JOINED AT BOTH ENDS TO FORM A CIRCUIT. ELECTROMOTIVE FORCE SET UP IF TEMPERATURE OF ONE END IS HIGHER THAN TEMPERATURE AT OTHER END.

Fig. 3. *Principle of the thermocouple illustrated*

mized if accurate results are to be achieved. It is also well to bear in mind that a strong source of illumination near the thermometer may change its temperature due to radiation.

The Thermocouple

The principal advantages of the thermocouple in measuring temperatures are: (a) versatility of application; (b) rapidity of response through wide ranges of temperature; (c) high degree of accuracy; (d) durability; (e) accurate reproducibility at relatively low cost; (f) convenience of centralized reading or recording from one or many remote points; (g) simplicity of application to equipment for control and regulation of temperature.

The operation of a thermocouple is based on the following phenomenon:

If two electrical conductors of dissimilar materials are joined at both ends to form a circuit and one of the junctions is maintained at a temperature higher than that of the other junction, an electromotive force is set up which will produce a flow of current through the circuit (see Fig. 3). The magnitude of the net electromotive force depends upon the magnitude of the difference between the temperatures of the two junctions and the materials used for the conductors. No unbalanced or net electromotive force will be set up if the two junctions of dissimilar materials are at the same temperature, nor with conductors of the same material even though the two junctions are at different temperatures. If one junction, of dissimilar materials which have been calibrated, is maintained at a known temperature, the temperature of the other junction can be determined by measuring the net electromotive force produced, since this force is proportional (almost directly) to the difference in temperature of the two junctions.

Temperature Measurement

As a temperature measuring device, within its use limits, a thermocouple will accurately indicate the temperature at any accessible point, since the net or unbalanced emf developed in two dissimilar electrical conductors when joined together at both ends is proportional to the difference in temperature between the point of application ("hot junction") and the "cold junction," or "reference junction" of the circuit, which would be at some point of known temperature, as the room or area where the reading is taken. A commonly used and generally accurate method is illustrated diagrammatically in Fig. 5.

The relationship between the electrical unit (mv) for emf and the equivalent corresponding temperature difference (between the two junctions) has been carefully established by laboratory tests throughout the temperature range limits for various thermocouple conductors in common use.* The electrical readings are therefore readily converted to the equivalent temperature. For example, assume that A represents the unknown temperature at the point of application ("hot junction") and B the known temperature at the "cold junction" from which the leads are taken to the point of reading, and that the thermocouple conductors are copper to constantan, then by reference to the table for these conductors: if the electrical reading is 14.71 mv, and the temperature at B is 80F corresponding to 1.73 mv, the mv corresponding to the difference in temperature from zero to A will be 14.71 + 1.73 or 16.44 mv, equivalent to a temperature of 600F for A. To make direct readings possible the electrical instruments now usually have scales in degrees of temperature calibrated for the various thermocouple conductors commonly used.

---

* Tables covering this data, with zero F "reference" or cold junction temperature, as prepared by the Leeds and Northrup Co. will be found in the Appendix.

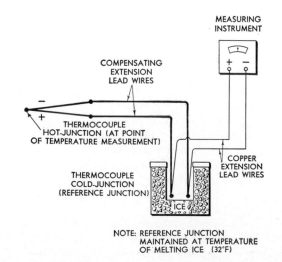

MEASURING INSTRUMENT

COMPENSATING EXTENSION LEAD WIRES

THERMOCOUPLE HOT-JUNCTION (AT POINT OF TEMPERATURE MEASUREMENT)

THERMOCOUPLE COLD-JUNCTION (REFERENCE JUNCTION)

COPPER EXTENSION LEAD WIRES

ICE

NOTE: REFERENCE JUNCTION MAINTAINED AT TEMPERATURE OF MELTING ICE (32°F)

Fig. 4. *Simple thermocouple circuit and extension leads*

In considering the temperature-emf characteristics of different pairs of materials, one conductor is said to be positive to the other when the emf at its cold junction terminal is electrically positive to that of the companion material at its cold junction terminal. In referring to thermocouple pairs it is customary to mention the positive conductor first. The relationship between various materials throughout a suitable range of temperature is conveniently demonstrated by individual reference to platinum as the companion conductor, as shown in Fig. 6.

Reference Junction. For precise laboratory work, or where exacting accuracy is required, it is customary to maintain the cold junction (or "reference junction") at a controlled temperature such as the fixed point of melting ice (0C or 32F). For less exacting work, the temperature of the reference junction may be measured by an auxiliary thermocouple or thermometer and the potentiometer readings corrected accordingly, or the instrument may be adjusted to give the true readings direct. Many popular types of indicating or recording potentiometers are equipped with compensating coils which, by a change of resistance with temperature, automatically adjust the readings to suit any variation from the cold junction temperature at which the materials of the thermocouple are calibrated.

Measuring Circuits. In the simple thermocouple circuits illustrated in Fig. 4 and 5, the thermocouple wires of dissimilar materials extend without inter-

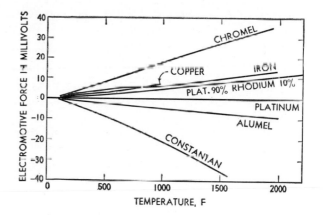

Fig. 6. *Electromotive force (emf) of various metals (thermocouple grade) referred to platinum*

ruption from the hot junction to the cold junction (or reference junction) terminals. In the potentiometer circuit, copper leads may be run from the reference junction terminals to the measuring instrument without affecting the net emf of the thermocouple. The pair of similar copper leads act merely as electrical connectors to transfer the emf from the reference junction to the copper terminals of the potentiometer. If the instrument is at a uniform temperature throughout, no emf is set up between the copper conductors and slide wire materials of different composition within the potentiometer itself. However, if temperature differences do exist within the instrument there will be disturbing emfs in the circuit and the readings will be affected.

Multiple Circuits. If two or more thermocouples are connected in series, the total net emf at the outside terminals is equal to the sum of the emf developed by the individual couples. Where all of the individual hot junctions and all of the individual cold junctions are maintained at the same respective temperatures, as in the device known as the "thermopile," this multiplied value of emf makes it possible to detect and measure extremely small variations in temperature of the hot junctions.

In a similar series connection, if the individual hot junctions are at different temperatures, for example when located at several points of a gas stream or of an object that is not uniform in temperature, while the cold junctions are maintained at a constant temperature, the total net emf will likewise be the sum of the individual emfs. The total net emf divided by the number of thermocouples in the series connection will give an arithmetical mean of the temperature of the gas stream or object. Use of the series circuit for measurement of average temperature is usually impractical because the multiplied value of emf at the terminals is likely to be beyond the range of the instrument normally available for measurement of data from single thermocouples.

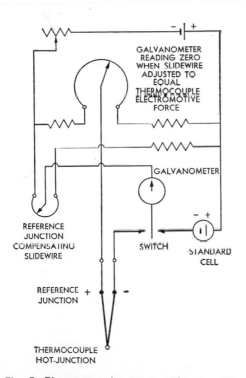

Fig. 5. *Thermocouple circuit with manually adjusted reference junction compensation*

Two or more thermocouples may be connected in parallel for the purpose of obtaining a single reading of average temperature. In this case the resistance of leads of all individual thermocouples must be equal. The emf across the terminals of such a circuit is the average of all the individual emfs and may be read on a potentiometer normally used for single thermocouples.

Two thermocouples may be connected in series with opposed or "bucking" polarity to measure the difference in temperature between their hot junction contacts. It is advisable in this case to provide leads for the measurement of both individual temperatures, as well as the differential, in order to establish the proper range of emf-per-degree characteristics of the conductors employed.

To prevent short circuit or current flow between points of differing potential when two or more thermocouples are connected in series or parallel, it is important that both the hot junction and cold junction terminals of the individual couples be electrically insulated from one another. Also, for multiple type circuits the simple conversion of average emf to temperature equivalent is strictly true only if the emf-per-degree for the thermocouple materials is constant through the range of temperature of all thermocouple positions.

General Principles of Application

For successful use of thermocouples in practical application certain general principles and their corollaries, as outlined below, must be kept in mind.

There may be a difference between the temperature of the hot junction and the temperature of the object or substance under investigation. This may be caused by inadequate thermal contact between thermocouple and object, by localized conduction of heat to or from the hot junction resulting from exposure of the thermocouple wires to media of higher or lower temperature, or by radiation effects of surrounding objects. The application of the thermocouple itself may in some cases distort the normal conditions of heat flow or temperature pattern within the object being studied. These factors should be minimized as far as possible by means that become apparent on consideration of the problem. Beyond that, the readings may sometimes be corrected by evaluating the possible errors by calculation or by reasonable estimate and comparison with correlated data.

If the composition of the thermocouple conductors is not homogeneous or a third material is present in the circuit, then, if there is also a temperature difference in the region of these conditions, the emf at the terminals will be affected. Intermediate or parasitic couples will be set up within the circuit which may raise or lower the net emf developed by the primary couple. It is, therefore, clear that the use of brazing or soldering material as a bond between two thermocouple wires at the hot junction, or their separate attachment, in close proximity to one another, to the object of which the temperature is to be measured, to form the hot junction, would affect the readings if they are nonuniform in temperature but would not alter the net thermal emf at the cold junction terminals, provided this third material at each point of contact with the conductors is at the same temperature. By similar reasoning, it is wrong to assume that the structural parts of a boiler and its supports may be utilized without error as a common iron conductor, as is sometimes done for connecting a group of iron to constantan couples to a multiple point recorder or selector switch.

Faulty readings may be obtained from a portable potentiometer when it is taken from cold surroundings into a warm room or vice versa and used for temperature measurements before all parts of its circuit have reached a uniform temperature.

Spurious emfs may be developed in the thermocouple circuit by inductive effects of unshielded a-c power leads, by electrolytic activity in damp insulation, or (damp) deposits in contact with the conductors. Similarly, the terminal emf may be affected by short circuit of the conductors caused by deterioration of insulation and physical contact of lead wires or deposited material.

The service life of a thermocouple can be no greater than the endurance of any of its several components, from hot junction contact, through lead wire and splices, to contacts and proper functioning of the measuring instrument. Much useful data is lost through careless or unimaginative installation of lead wire which fails to provide adequate support and protection against chafing, expansion strains, or local exposure to extreme temperature.

The emf developed by a thermocouple is independent of wire size, and is independent of change in size of conductors between the measuring junction and recorder terminals. Use of smaller wires at the hot junction will give a more rapid response to change of temperature because of the lesser mass of the hot junction. Their use also minimizes the disturbing effects of heat conduction in the wires adjacent to the hot junction. Offsetting these advantages, however, are the greater vulnerability of the smaller wires to physical damage, and the shorter service life if subjected to oxidation at high temperature or to corrosive atmospheres. Also, in using smaller wires, if long leads are employed, it is more difficult to balance the potentiometer because of the reduced sensitivity of the thermocouple-potentiometer assembly, since the current flow for a given emf is less due to the increased electrical resistance.

Practical Use of Thermocouples

Selection of Materials. While many combinations of dissimilar metals might be employed to form thermocouple pairs, it is important for satisfactory use in temperature measurement that they have the following characteristics: a thermal emf which increases continuously and uniformly with increase in temperature, and is of sufficient magnitude to be measured with accuracy; physical strength; resistance to oxidation or corrosive attack; availability in wire form; composition or emf characteristics unaffected by fabrication or by reaction with atmospheres and contact with other materials.

Combinations of metals and alloys most frequently used for thermocouples are listed in Table I, with their general characteristics and useful temperature range. Selection depends largely on ability to withstand oxidation attack at the maximum service temperatures expected. Durability will depend on size of wire, use or omission of protection tubes and nature of the atmosphere. For heavy duty service #8 B&S gage (0.128 in. diameter) wire is generally used. Smaller diameters, also available, are more convenient for test work and cost less.

service life may be extended, with a sacrifice of rapidity of response to temperature changes, by using closed-end protection tubes of alloy or ceramic material. The arrangement should permit removal of the thermocouple from the protection tube for calibration, and renewal when necessary. For duty during short periods of time as in some test work, protection tubes may be omitted if calibration is frequent so that the data may be corrected as required. For normal duty within the useful range of the thermocouple selected, the correction due to change of calibration is usually negligible.

Thermocouple and Lead Wire. There are two classes of wire for thermocouples, the closely standardized and matched "thermocouple wire," and the less accurate "compensating lead wire." For thermocouples of noble metal, extension leads of copper and cop-

TABLE I

Types of Thermocouples in General Use

Type of Thermocouple*	Useful Temp Range F	Maximum Temp F	Millivolts at 500F**	Suitable Atmosphere	Magnetic Wire
(+) Copper to Constantan (−)	−300 to 650	1100	13.24	Oxid. or Reduc.	-----
(+) Iron to Constantan (−)	−300 to 1500	1800	18.08	Oxid. or Reduc.	Iron (+)
(+) Chromel to Alumel (−)	−300 to 2200	2500	13.53	Oxidizing	Alumel (−)
(+) 90% Plat. 10% Rhodium to Platinum (−)	900 to 2600	3190***	2.048	Oxidizing	-----

*Nominal composition: constantan, 55% Cu, 45% Ni; chromel, 90% Ni, 10% Cr; alumel, 95% Ni, 5% Al, Si, Mn.

**Reference junction, zero F.

***Melting point.

All thermocouple materials will deteriorate when exposed at the higher temperatures of their useful range to air or other atmospheres, and to contact with other materials. Platinum in particular is affected by metallic oxides, and by carbon and hydrocarbon gases when used at temperatures above 1000F and, in the course of time, is subject to calibration drift. From Table I it will be noted that the upper limit of the useful range in temperature for all thermocouple materials listed is far below the maximum temperature at which rapid deterioration sets in.

For high temperature duty in a permanent installation, or where destructive contact is extreme,

per-nickel alloy, which have an emf characteristic near that of the noble metal pair, are used to save cost. For thermocouples of base metal, the extension leads in general use, while of the same nominal composition as the thermocouple wires, are less expensive since the control in manufacture and in subsequent calibration and matching of pairs need not be as rigorous.

Wires of these two classes are made by several manufacturers, in a variety of sizes, with insulating coverings of various materials in both the single conductor and "duplex" arrangement of paired wires.

For accuracy the matched "thermocouple wire" should be used at the hot junction and continued through the zone of greatest temperature gradient to a point substantially at room temperature where "compensating lead wire" may be spliced on for extension to the reference junction. The reference junction is usually located at the recorder or central point of observation, but where a number of ther-

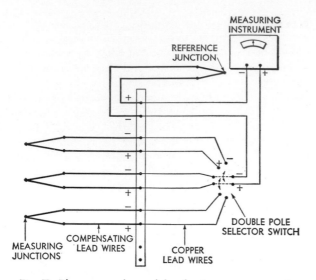

Fig. 7. *Thermocouple and lead wire arrangement to measuring instrument through selector switch*

mocouples are used it is sometimes economical to establish a "zone box" (see Fig. 7) from which copper conductors of lower cost are extended to the recorder panel.

Splicing of extension lead wires may be done by twisting the ends of the wires together or by the use of screw clamp connectors, or by fusion welding, soldering or brazing. The wire ends should be thoroughly cleaned to provide good electrical contact.

Care should be taken to maintain correct polarity by joining together wires of the same composition. Polarity is usually identified by color code or tracers in the wire covering. Where one wire of a thermocouple is magnetic the correct polarity may be confirmed by using a magnet to detect the magnetic wire of the pair. As a check, the completed thermocouple should be connected to a potentiometer circuit and each of the intermediate junctions should be heated. If the wires are correctly paired the galvanometer will not indicate any deflection

unless the thermocouple hot junction is heated.

Upon completing an installation of thermocouples and extension leads, each circuit may be checked for poor contact in splices and broken or grounded conductors by measuring its overall electrical resistance, using a portable ohm-meter. This record will also serve as a reference in subsequent checking when deterioration of junctions may be suspected. Normal resistance of various thermocouples wires are shown in Table 2.

Application of Hot Junction

A number of practical applications of the hot junction of a thermocouple are illustrated in Figs. 8 to 13.

Welded Bead Junction. Wire and pipe type elements may be purchased commercially or may be made from stock thermocouple-wire as shown in Fig. 8. These types are useful for direct immersion in a gas stream, for insertion into thermometer wells or for thermal contact with solid surfaces. The junction contact between wires is preferably made by fusion welding in a carbon arc, or, for base metal couples, in a neutral to oxidizing flame, with sparing use of borax or other flux suited to the material. If the ends of very fine wires (28 gage) are joined by a short twist, a welded bead may be formed by making arc contact with mercury as an electrode, submerged in silicone or mineral oil to prevent oxidation. Where temperature and other limitations permit, the junction may be soldered or brazed.

The effective hot junction occurs where the conductors make electrical contact (nearest to the potentiometer), which may be in advance of the terminal weld. If the entire twist and bead are at uniform temperature no error is introduced. Precautions should be taken to prevent a temperature gradient in the vicinity of the measuring junction.

Peened Junction. One of the most useful and versatile types of hot junction, where the temperature of a metallic surface is to be measured, is formed by peening the wires separately into holes

TABLE 2

Thermocouple Wire Resistance

Ohms per ft at 68F

B&S Gage	Iron	Constantan	Copper	Chromel	Alumel	Plat.	90Pt-10Rh
8	0.00461	0.0185	0.000637	0.026	0.0104	0.0041	0.0081
14	0.0186	0.0745	0.00253	0.104	0.0432	0.0165	0.0328
16	0.0295	0.118	0.00402	0.165	0.0685	0.0262	0.0519
20	0.0745	0.299	0.0102	0.417	0.1730	0.066	0.131
22	0.119	0.476	0.0161	0.660	0.277	0.105	0.208
24	0.189	0.758	0.0257	1.048	0.440	0.167	0.332
28	0.476	1.91	0.0649	2.64	1.108	0.422	0.840

drilled into the surface of the metal. Steps in the procedure for making this type of junction are illustrated in Fig. 9. It has the advantage of being completely mechanical in application, with tight and remarkably strong attachment, and with minimum interference to the normal temperature of the object. The temperature indicated is essentially that of the metallic surface, which is the first point of contact with the conductors. The depth of the drilled hole has no effect other than for mechanical strength. The points of junction contact are subject to the effects of thermal conduction in the wires, and where this type of error is significant precautions should be taken to prevent temperature gradient in the wires. Drilled holes for reception of the wire ends should allow for a snug fit before peening. The wire ends should be thoroughly cleaned, and dressed to a flat end by filing.

The mechanics of forming the peened hot junction lend themselves to making a convenient type of anchorage, referred to as the "peened staple" for giving physical support to thermocouple and lead wires along a metal surface. The peened staple is illustrated in Fig. 9.

Millivolt Potentiometer

The temperature-emf relationships of standardized thermocouple wires, as established by the Leeds & Northrup Co., for the four thermocouple pairs in Table I, are given in tables in the Appendix. By the use of these tables, readings taken on a millivolt potentiometer may be converted to values of equivalent temperature. Tabulated values represent the net emf impressed on the potentiometer terminals when the reference junction is at zero F and the measuring junction is at the temperature shown. The millivolt potentiometer may be employed with any type of thermocouple and is frequently used in practice when several different types of couples are installed in the test set up.

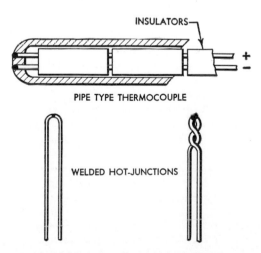

Fig. 8. *Thermocouple elements and hot junctions*

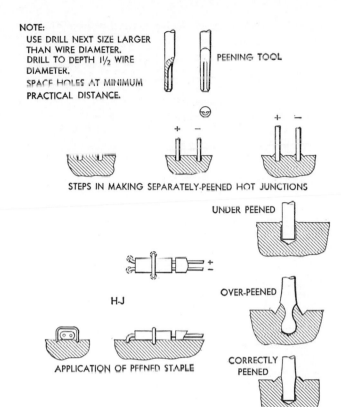

Fig. 9. *Application of thermocouple by drilling hole for and peening each wire separately to form hot junction*

It is, of course, impractical to maintain the reference junction at zero F while taking readings. Correction for any reference junction temperature can be made by adding to each observed reading of emf the value of the emf corresponding to the temperature of the reference junction, and then, by entering the table with this sum, find the equivalent temperature of the measuring junction. Most millivolt potentiometers are equipped with a compensator which may be adjusted to correct for the actual reference junction temperature by setting the compensator at the value of emf from the table corresponding to the actual temperature of the reference junction. Direct readings will then conform to the values in the table. Even when this is so the previous method is recommended and may be followed by setting the compensator at zero; this method is preferable since it is simpler and eliminates the possibility of incorrect compensator setting. Also, in using this method, compensation may be made at a later time under good working conditions and can be independently checked by others at any time.

Direct Reading Potentiometer

When calibrated for use with specific types of thermocouples, a potentiometer may be graduated to read directly in terms of temperature of the hot junction instead of millivolts. In this case the reference junction temperature is usually compensated automatically by resistor coils, built into the instrument circuit, which respond to deviations from a standard room temperature basis. It is, of course, necessary that compensating lead wires, or their equivalent, be extended to the instrument terminals, so that the reference junction is located at, or is at the same temperature as the instrument. Characteristics of the compensating coils are specifically adapted to the type of thermocouple material for which the potentiometer is calibrated.

While not recommended as good practice, circumstances sometimes make it expedient to use a direct reading potentiometer, calibrated for one type of couple, in combination with thermocouples of different emf characteristics. Equivalent corrected temperatures may be determined by conversion of scale readings, through use of the tables previously mentioned, with proper recognition of the effect of automatic reference junction compensation. The following example of such conversion may serve as a pattern for the procedure for other combinations of types.

Assuming an I-C (iron to constantan) thermocouple connected to a potentiometer calibrated for a C-A (chromel to alumel) thermocouple:

(1) Read the potentiometer scale in F.

(2) Measure reference junction temperature in F.

(3) From the table for C-A take the mv corresponding to the temperature in (1).

(4) From the table for C-A take the mv corresponding to reference junction temperature in (2).

(5) Subtract (4) from (3)

(6) From the table for I-C take the mv corresponding to reference junction temperature in (2).

(7) Add (5) and (6)

(8) In the table for I-C the temperature corresponding to (7) will be the measuring junction temperature.

Temperature Recorders

In the temperature recorders a power operated mechanism adjusts the slide wire of a potentiometer circuit to balance the impulse received from the thermocouple. The action of the slide wire is coordinated with the movement of a recording pen or print wheel that is drawn over or impressed on a temperature graduated chart that moves at a speed proportional to time.

In the earlier types of recorders, (many are still in use) the deflection of a moving galvanometer coil (and its stylus), which receives the primary impulse of a change in thermocouple emf, monitors the independently driven power mechanism that adjusts the slide wire until the emf is balanced and the galvanometer is restored to neutral or null position. In this type of recorder the only load imposed upon the feeble impulse of the thermocouple is that of deflecting the galvanometer, and at the null or balanced position this load is essentially zero. To insure sensitivity, the galvanometer coil and its suspensions are necessarily light, and require accurate mechanical balancing. Some provision is also usually made for cushion mounting of the recorder to minimize disturbances due to mechanical shock or vibration, which might cause deflection of the coil.

The more recent type of recorder has a completely electrically balanced circuit, and is therefore not subject to the limitations imposed by the moving galvanometer. In this circuit a change of thermocouple emf sets up an electrical unbalance which, upon being amplified, is used to drive a reversing motor that adjusts the slide wire in the proper direction to restore the circuit to balance. Response to electrical unbalance is immediate, and extremely fast action of the driving mechanism is possible, so that an essentially continuous record may be traced for one thermocouple, or a rapid scanning of many thermocouples may be recorded.

Checking Recorder Calibration. Compared to the manually operated potentiometer, all recorders are inherently less accurate due to wear and lost motion in driving gears, shrinkage or printing inaccuracies of paper and chart scales, and, in the case of the moving galvanometer type, some lag in reaching exact balance because of diminishing impulse as this point is approached. Use of extremely long or unduly small gage lead wires aggravates the lag. This is particularly so for the galvanometer type of instrument because of the very small current flow as the unbalanced emf is reduced to zero. The resistance of long leads is of much less consequence where the energy of unbalance is amplified, as in the electronic type recorder. However, the accuracy of recorders is sufficient for most commercial purposes, and may be enhanced by the use of double or multiple-range circuits which in effect increase the chart scale dimensions to any desired extent.

Calibration and adjustment of recorders may be checked by means of a portable potentiometer of known accuracy. In this operation the thermocouple terminals of the potentiometer should be connected, by compensating lead wires, to the same polarity thermocouple terminals of the recorder from which the thermocouple has been disconnected. After checking both instruments for standard cell adjustment, the recorder should be started, the slide wire of the portable instrument set on some desired reading, and the thermocouple switch engaged. The recorder will then operate to balance the emf imposed on it by the service cell of the portable potentiometer, and if it is in correct adjustment, the printed record will correspond to the reading set manually on the scale of the portable instrument.

Temperature of Fluids Inside Pipes

The temperature of a fluid (liquid, vapor, or gas) flowing under pressure through a pipe is usually measured by a glass thermometer, electric resistance thermometer, or thermocouple inserted in a thermometer well projecting into the fluid, or by a thermocouple attached to the outside of the pipe wall. While the latter will give accurate results if all the necessary precautions are observed, the thermometer well is generally preferred, since the likelihood of error is less.

A metal tube closed at one end, screwed or welded into a pipe wall and projecting into the fluid, serves as a thermometer well (see Fig. 10). It must have the mechanical strength and rigidity to withstand hydrostatic pressure, bending caused by its resistance to fluid flow, and vibration. To minimize conduction of heat to the surroundings and to give rapid response to temperature changes the dimensions of the well should be as small as compatible with the strength requirements. The part outside the pipe should be as small as possible. The material of the well must resist the erosive or corrosive action of the fluid. Since the temperature may be locally depressed due to acceleration through a constriction in a pipe carrying a compressible fluid, the well should not be placed near a constriction. Projecting parts of the thermometer well, and the pipe wall for some distance from the well, should be thoroughly insulated against heat loss. The space between the outer end of the well and the thermal element should be tightly packed with insulating material so that there can be no circulation of air into the well; omission of this packing may introduce a substantial error.

The details of thermometer well designs vary. If the fluid is a liquid or a saturated vapor, good heat transfer is assured and a plain well is satisfactory. If the fluid is a gas or superheated vapor, a finned well is sometimes used. The method of attachment to the pipe wall, either by screwing into the wall or a boss, or by welding or brazing, is optional with the designer provided safety code requirements are met.

The thermometer well will tend to give an average temperature, even if there is temperature stratification in the fluid, since thermal conduction along the well will serve to equalize the temperature.

Thermocouples may be attached to the outside of pipes by brazing, welding, or peening. Peening the thermocouple wires into holes drilled in the surface of the pipe is preferred as an easy and reliable method of installation. The thermocouple readings will give the temperature of the pipe wall at the exact point of contact with the wires, and any factor which

causes the pipe wall temperature at that point to differ from the temperature of the fluid inside the pipe will introduce an error.

Heat flow from the fluid to the surroundings will cause a temperature drop through the fluid film inside the pipe and through the pipe wall. Conversely, a temperature rise will occur if heat flows from the surroundings through the pipe wall to the fluid. If the pipe is not insulated these temperature differences will usually be great enough to give incorrect read-

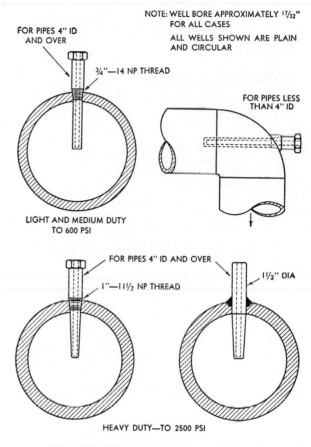

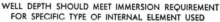

Fig. 10. *Thermometer wells and method of installation*

ings for the fluid temperature. However, if the pipe is properly insulated such changes in temperature will be negligible, and the readings will accurately indicate the temperature of the fluid. Insulation restricted to the immediate vicinity of the thermocouple, with the remainder of the pipe bare, is not sufficient, since thermal conduction along the pipe wall will affect the readings.

Conduction of heat along the thermocouple wires is an important source of possible error. This can be prevented if the thermocouple wires are wrapped once or twice tightly around the pipe, and held in place, before the pipe insulation is applied. In this way the wires are brought to pipe-wall temperature in the region of the thermocouple junction and heat equilibrium is established. Extending the wires back and forth against the pipe wall will accomplish the same result. Both methods are illustrated in Fig. 11. In either case, fine wire will permit less heat conduction than heavy wire.

An additional source of error is the influence of "through steel"—uninsulated connections or valves which extend through the insulation and cause local cooling of the pipe wall. Locations remote from "through steel" should therefore be selected for the installation of thermocouples to determine the temperature of fluids inside pipes.

Tube Temperature Measurement

In steam boiler practice it is frequently desirable to know accurately the metal temperature of tubes in different classes of service, such, for example, as furnace wall or boiler generating tubes that are cooled by water and steam at saturation temperature, economizer tubes cooled by water below the tem-

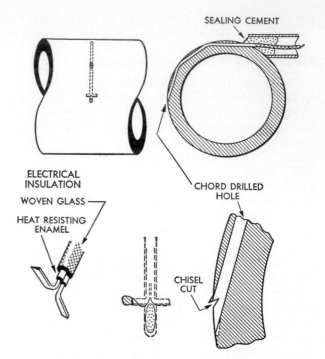

Fig. 12. *Thermocouple wires extending from hot junction through chord-drilled holes in tube wall*

perature of saturation, or superheater and reheater tubes cooled by steam above saturation temperature. Such measurements may be for the purpose of determining the safety of pressure parts, for determining uniformity or unbalanced condition among tubes in parallel flow circuits, for measurement of temperature increase of the fluid between inlet and outlet conditions, or for similar functional problems. In determining the temperature of the tube wall metal itself, measurement by thermocouple is a very practical and reliable method and is now used almost exclusively.

The peened type of hot junction as illustrated in Fig. 9 is satisfactory in many cases, and is probably the simplest form of thermocouple application. This couple measures essentiailly the temperature of the tube metal surface, subject to errors caused by thermal conduction in the thermocouple wires to or from the junction contact. Conduction errors may be minimized as previously described, and by shielding the wires from heat input or loss by wrapping with asbestos or other insulating material.

Furnace Wall Tubes

For satisfactory results and durability of the thermocouple, special protection is obviously necessary in the determination of the temperature of water-cooled furnace wall tubes which are exposed to extremely high temperatures, the deposit and shedding of ash or slag, and the effect of destructive atmospheres. If a simple peened couple is used the results

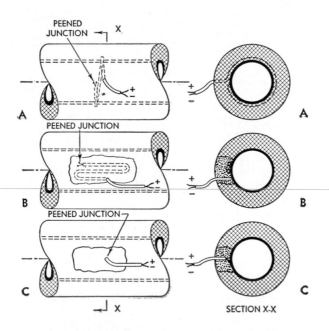

A   GOOD PRACTICE—THERMOCOUPLE WIRE WRAPPED AROUND PIPE UNDERNEATH PIPE INSULATION

B   GOOD PRACTICE—THERMOCOUPLE WIRE LAID ALONG PIPE WALL BEFORE REINSULATION

C   BAD PRACTICE—THERMOCOUPLE WIRE LED DIRECTLY TO OUTSIDE

NOTE: ANY OPENING MADE IN PIPE INSULATION FOR ACCESS TO PIPE WALL FOR INSTALLATION OF THERMOCOUPLE MUST BE CAREFULLY REINSULATED WITH DRY INSULATION FIRMLY HELD IN PLACE.

Fig. 11. *Thermocouple wires extending from hot junction disposed on pipe wall before leading outside*

are likely to be of doubtful accuracy because of error due to conduction, and in most cases the service life would be short due to physical damage or deterioration of the wires by overheating. Cover plates, welded to the tubes, have been used to protect the wires; but these plates interfere with the normal heat flow, and may be the cause of local ash deposits which will create abnormal conditions at the point of temperature measurement.

The use of chord-drilled holes in the tube metal, through which the thermocouple wires are laced as shown in Fig. 12 was developed by B&W, and has been found to be a very satisfactory method of application for furnace wall tubes. The tube surface is free from projections, the wires are protected, and the effect of thermal conduction at the hot junction is minimized because the wires pass through an essentially isothermal zone before emerging into cooler surroundings at the rear of the tube. To minimize the effect on the heat flow pattern within the tube metal the chord-drilled holes should be as small as possible. The effect of these holes upon the strength of the tube is small. It is least in the critical direction of hoopstress, and is readily tolerated in the direction of longitudinal stress. Use of chord-drilled holes in the thicker wall tubes for high steam pressure is, therefore, justified and practicable.

Gradient Thermocouples. To measure the temperature gradient in the tube metal and for the determination of the heat flow rate or the thermal resistance caused by internal scale deposit, two thermocouples may be applied within the thickness of the tube wall spaced at different depths below the tube surface.

The chord holes for the thermocouples are spaced at a nominal distance from one another along the length of the tube to avoid physical or thermal interferences. As a check and to detect the possible presence of localized or nonuniform external ash deposits that might cause individual gradient couples to vary, it is advisable to provide two sets of each type of couple. In practice couples of this type may be applied to a separate short section of tube which may then be welded into a furnace tube at the desired location.

This type of gradient couple is shown in Fig. 13 and characteristic data obtained from its use is shown in Fig. 14.

When heat is conducted radially through a cylindrical wall the heat flow area decreases as the inside of the wall is approached. Consequently the temperature does not vary in proportion to the actual thickness alone since there is a change in area, and a plot of temperature against wall thickness will not be a straight line. In analyzing test data from tube wall thermocouples it is convenient to make use of an "equivalent thickness," as shown in the illustration, which is defined by the equation:

$$Le = R_2 \log_e (R_2/R_1)$$

Where:

Le = equivalent thickness, inches

R_2 = radius from tube centerline to outside of tube wall, inches

R_1 = radius from tube centerline to tube wall thermocouple, inches.

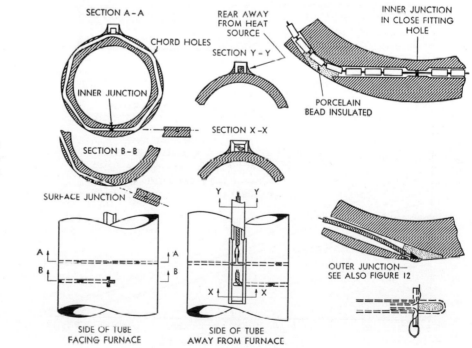

Fig. 13. *Thermocouples in chord-drilled holes for determining temperature gradient through tube wall*

When temperature is plotted against equivalent thickness the points lie on a straight line which may be extended to the tube wall surfaces.

Lead Wire Protection. If proper care is taken, thermocouples may be placed on steam generating tubes completely exposed to high temperature gas flow, as in a furnace screen or boiler tube bank. Lead wires of suitably small dimension, having high-temperature fiberglass covering or porcelain insulators, may be protected by extending them through steel channel conduit attached by continuous welding along the length of the water-cooled tube to a suitable point of exit from the furnace. Lead wires and channel are maintained within safe temperature limits by good thermal contact with the water-cooled tube, and, in most cases, obtain further shielding or protection by the accumulation of external slag or ash coating.

Superheater Tubes

Application of thermocouples to superheater tubes in active heat transfer zones is one of the most difficult problems of tube temperature measurement. This is true primarily because of the difficulty in protecting lead wires from excessive temperature in passing from the hot junction to a convenient exit from the boiler setting. Since the superheater tubes are essentially at higher temperatures than the water-cooled generating tubes, less cooling is available for the protecting channels. Continuous welding of these channels is usually not permissible because of

thermal expansion stresses set up in the tube. Short channel sections with intermittent welds have sometimes been used with success.

In several instances, where the effort has been justified by the importance of tube temperature measurement, the method illustrated in Fig. 15 has been used with good results. A tube of small dimensions, extending through the interior of the superheater tube and attached at each end to the wall of the tube with pressure tight welds, serves as a conduit for the thermocouple wires. Chord-drilled holes at the hot junction end provide thermal and physical protection of the wires, and the wires emerge outside of the gas flow zone where the extension lead wires may be spliced on without difficulty. In passing through the coolest medium (steam) the thermocouple wires are given the maximum possible protection. To avoid excessive stresses at the terminal welds due to differential temperature expansion between the materials of conduit and superheater tube, care must be taken to make the conduit sufficiently flexible. Careful attention should also be given to the metallurgical and welding problems involved in making these attachments.

Gas Temperature Measurement

Gas temperature is one of the most important items of the data required in testing or recording the performance of steam generating units. It is also of equal importance in safe and efficient operation. In

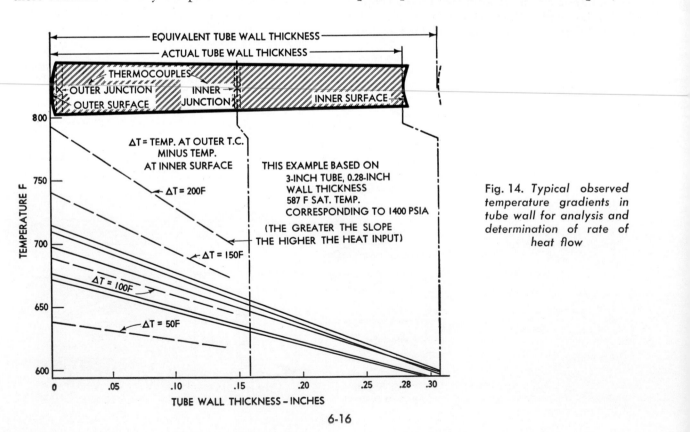

Fig. 14. *Typical observed temperature gradients in tube wall for analysis and determination of rate of heat flow*

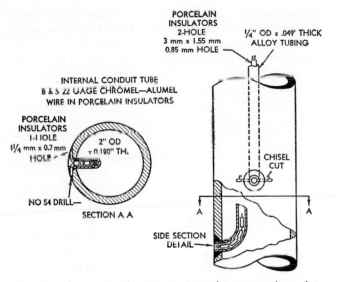

PORCELAIN INSULATORS 2-HOLE
3 mm x 1.55 mm
0.85 mm HOLE

¼" OD x .049' THICK ALLOY TUBING

INTERNAL CONDUIT TUBE
B & S 22 GAGE CHROMEL—ALUMEL
WIRE IN PORCELAIN INSULATORS

PORCELAIN INSULATORS I-I HOLE
1¼ mm x 0.7 mm
HOLE

2" OD x 0.190" TH.

CHISEL CUT

NO 54 DRILL

SECTION A A

A   A

SIDE SECTION DETAIL

Fig. 15. *Thermocouple wire protected in internal conduit. Somtimes used in high temperature service*

the measurement of gas temperature, therefore, care must be taken, first, to make certain that the instrument used indicates the temperature correctly, and, second, to interpret the temperature readings to give a true average temperature of the gas stream which is usually not uniform.

In all cases of gas temperature measurement the temperature-sensitive element approaches a temperature in equilibrium with the conditions of its environment. While it receives heat primarily by convection transfer from the hot gases in which it is immersed, it is also subject to heat exchange by radiation to and from surrounding surfaces, and by conduction through the instrument itself, which should be reduced to negligible values. If the temperature of the surrounding surfaces do not differ from that of the gas (air flowing through an insulated duct) the temperature indicated by the instrument should represent quite accurately the temperature of the gas. If the temperature of the surrounding surfaces is higher than that of the gas, the temperature indicated by the instrument will be higher than the temperature of the gas, and conversely, if the temperature of the surrounding surfaces is lower than that of the gas, the temperature indicated by the instrument will be lower than the temperature of the gas.

The amount of variation from the true temperature of the gas depends upon the temperature and velocity of the gas, the temperature of the surroundings, the size of the temperature-measurement element, and the physical construction of the element and its supports. To correct for the errors in temperature due to the surroundings in any particular installation, it is best to calibrate the instrument against a known and reliable determination of the gas temperature.

When gas temperatures below 1000F are to be measured a bare thermocouple, resistance pyrometer, mercury-in-glass thermometer, or one of the various bulb-type pyrometers may be used.

The average error, due to surroundings colder than the gas, in using a 22 gage bare thermocouple with exposed leads to measure gas temperatures in boiler, economizer, and air heater cavities, shown in Fig. 16, indicates the magnitude to be expected.

If gas temperatures exceed 1000F the errors mentioned above become more pronounced. The high-velocity and multiple-shield high-velocity thermocouples (see below) developed to correct these errors are the best instruments available for the measurement of high gas temperature in colder surroundings or low gas temperature in hotter surroundings. A comparison of the readings between the high-velocity and the multiple-shield high-velocity thermocouples in typical boiler furnaces and cavities is shown in Fig. 16. The optical pyrometer and the radiation pyrometer are not designed to measure gas temperatures, and should not be used for this purpose, since the result may be extremely misleading.

High Velocity Thermocouple

Since transfer of heat to the thermocouple by convection is proportional to a power of gas mass flow, and to the first power of the temperature difference between gas and thermocouple, while transfer of

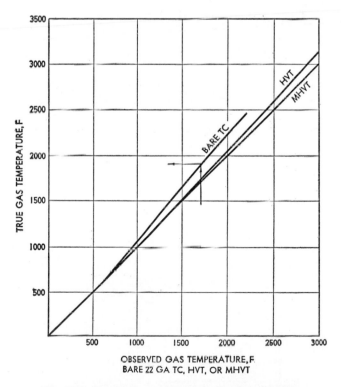

Fig. 16. *General magnitude of error in the observed readings when measuring temperature of gas in boiler cavities with thermocouples*

heat by radiation is proportional to surface area, emissivity and the difference of the fourth powers of absolute temperature of source and receiver, it follows (the gases being considered as nominally transparent to the passage of radiant energy) that the effects of radiation increase as the temperature difference between the thermocouple hot junction and surrounding surfaces increases. It also follows that the temperature of the junction may be brought more nearly to the true temperature of the gas by increasing the rate of mass flow and convection transfer, while shielding the junction from the influence of radiation transfer.

A "high-velocity thermocouple" (HVT) for measuring high gas temperatures in boiler units is illustrated in the sketch, Fig. 17. This portable assembly is used primarily for making test traverses in high duty zones by insertion through inspection doors or other test openings in the setting.

The thermocouple is supported by a water-cooled holder consisting of concentric tubes of suitable length to span the traverse distance. The measuring junction is surrounded by a porcelain tube or radiation shield, through which gas flow is induced at high velocity by an aspirator attached to the external connections. The gas aspiration rate over the thermocouple can be checked by measuring the gas drawn through the probe by an orifice incorporated with the aspirator and connected to the probe by a length of hose. The gas-mass-flow over the thermocouples junction should be not less than 15,000 lb per sq ft per hour (see Fig. 18). Heat transfer to junction and shield by convection is simultaneous so that both approach the temperature of the gas stream, and radiation transfer at the junction is diminished due to the shield. However, since the shield is exposed externally to the radiation effect of the surroundings it may gain or lose heat and thus its temperature may be somewhat different from that of the junction.

Recommended sizes for water-cooled high-velocity thermocouples are noted in Table 3. The fittings indicated in the sketch, Fig. 17, (preferably of brass though malleable iron can be used) for water outlet and inlet, the aspirator suction, and the bushings, terminating in a packed gland, are of standard commercial size suitable for machining to telescope over and seal the tubing as shown.

TABLE 3

Recommended Sizes for Water-cooled HVT
(See Fig. 17)

Nominal Probe Size	Tubing Sizes Stainless Steel or Brass	Water Flow Annulus Area Sq In.	
		Outside	Inside
(1) 1 in.	1 in. OD x 18 BWG		
	¾ in. OD x 20 BWG	0.20	0.17
	½ in. OD x 20 BWG		
(2) 1¼ in.	1¼ in. OD x 18 BWG		
	1 in. OD x 20 BWG	0.26	0.37
	⅝ in. OD x 20 BWG		
(3) 1¾ in.	1¾ in. OD x 18 BWG		
	1¼ in. OD x 20 BWG	0.91	0.79
	⅝ in. OD x 20 BWG		

(1) Seldom used over 12 ft long, and at this length subject to overheating above 2200 F.
(2) Best for all-round use for lengths to 15 ft except in primary furnaces.
(3) Used for primary furnaces or lengths to 20 ft.

By using multiple shields around the junction, all of which receive heat by convection induced by the high rate of gas flow, successive effects of the transfer of heat by radiation are so reduced that there is virtually no exchange of heat between junction and innermost shield. Measurements with the "multiple-shield high-velocity thermocouple" (MHVT) will closely approach the true temperature of the gas. Cross sections through single and multiple-shield high-velocity thermocouples developed for use in

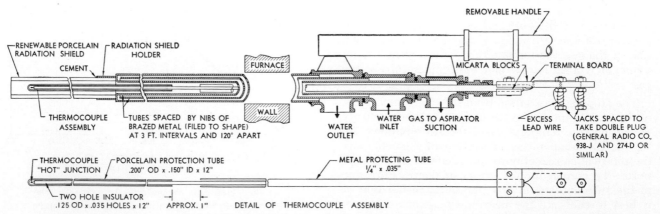

Fig. 17. *Rugged water-cooled high-velocity thermocouple (HVT) for determination of high gas temperature*

boiler testing are shown in Fig. 19. Because of the small flow areas, which rapidly become clogged by ash, practical use of the MHVT is limited to clean gas condition.

The surfaces (water-cooled walls, superheater or boiler tube banks, etc.) surrounding the usual location of a gas traverse, are cooler than the gases. Consequently, the readings from a bare unshielded thermocouple will indicate lower temperature than those obtained with a single-shield HVT. For the same reason a single shield HVT will generally indicate lower values than a MHVT. Where traverses are taken in dust or slag laden gases, it is usually necessary to use the single-shield HVT, and to correct the readings by comparison with the results from aMHVT obtained under clean gas conditions. The magnitude of these corrections is indicated in Fig. 16.

For temperatures exceeding 2200F, noble metal thermocouples are required, and it is important to protect the couple from contamination by the gases or entrained ash. The porcelain tube covering shown in the sketch, Fig. 17, provides some protection for the wires, and especially so when fouling occurs from molten slag at temperatures above 2400F. When platinum couples are used in gases ranging from 2600F to 3000F or higher, appreciable calibration drift may occur while taking measurements requiring only several minutes of exposure time. Under those conditions, the thermocouple elements should be checked periodically and corrections should be applied to the observed readings. When the magnitude of error reaches 40F to 60F, the contaminated end of the couple should be removed and a new junction of the sound portion of the wire should be made. Calibration of the service couple may be checked by comparing its readings with those from a standard couple of the same material, when both couples, bound together, are inserted in a specially arranged tubular resistance-wound electric furnace; taking care that the temperature gradient from the hot junction to the sound section of the service couple is the same as during its use.

Evaluation of Gas Temperatures

If the entire gas stream is at a uniform temperature a single temperature reading at any point in the stream will be representative. However, such a condition is unusual, and it is generally necessary to make a traverse, taking readings at a number of points distributed across the gas stream. In order to properly evaluate the temperature readings it is necessary to know, or to estimate, the direction and velocity of the gas flow at the various points in the gas stream where the temperatures are measured. Sometimes the gas velocity will be constant at all points, but there will be temperature stratification in the gas stream. More frequently, both gas tem-

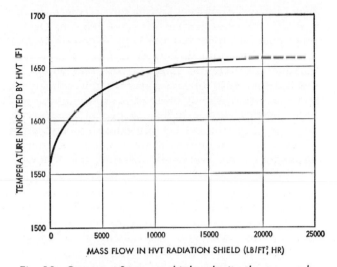

Fig. 18. *Gas mass flow over high-velocity thermocouple junction greatly affects indicated temperature*

perature and gas velocity will be stratified. Occasionally there is recirculation, with some of the gas flowing through the traverse plane in one direction and some in the opposite direction.

The degree of accuracy required in the determination of the temperature of the gas at any location in the unit will depend upon the use to which the data is to be applied. For instance, an arithmetical average of the gas temperatures in the region of the soot

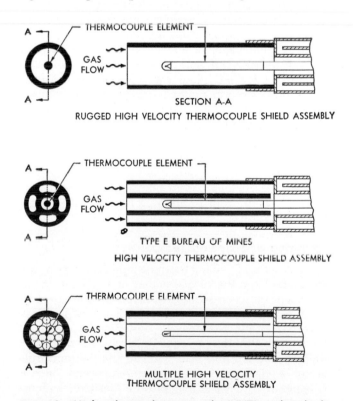

Fig. 19. *High velocity thermocouple (HVT) and multiple high velocity thermocouple (MHVT) shield assemblies*

blower may be entirely satisfactory as the basis for a study of the service life of a soot blower. On the other hand, if a heat balance is to be determined for a section of the unit such as the furnace, the average temperature required must be the one which, in combination with the total gas weight, will give a true measure of the quantity of heat leaving the section. In this case a higher degree of accuracy is necessary, and the correct procedure (though often in practice it can be only approximated) for the determination of an average temperature is as follows:

Select an arbitrary imaginary surface (a surface in one plane is often, but not always, the most convenient), in which the temperature and gas velocity traverses are to be made. Measure gas temperature, gas flow direction, and gas velocity at a sufficient number of points of this surface for a comprehensive coverage. Divide the surface into a convenient number of small areas (which may be unequal). From the measurements taken establish the gas temperature, gas flow direction, and gas flow velocity representative of each of the small areas. Next, calculate the vector component of gas velocity normal to the surface of each small area. If there is recirculation, some of these vector components will be negative. For each small area set down separately the product of temperature, area, and component of velocity, and the product of area and component of velocity. To obtain the true average temperature divide the sum of the first set of products by the sum of the second set of products. Should the gas temperature vary over so wide a range that the assumption of a constant average value of specific heat for all parts of the gas stream is not warranted, gas enthalpy must be substituted for gas temperature. This procedure is based on a general mathematical theorem (Gauss's theorem) which finds wide application in various branches of physics.

When bulb-type or resistance pyrometers are installed permanently to measure gas temperature in a flue or duct it is common practice to extend the bulb or resistance element from one side of the gas pass to the other in order to obtain a representative average temperature.

Insulation and Casing Temperature

Inner Surfaces. The thermocouple is particularly well suited for the measurement of temperatures at interfaces between successive layers of insulation, or at other points inside insulation. The temperature-sensitive hot junction may be buried out of sight and the temperature may be read remotely. Furthermore, the hot junction and lead wires of the thermocouple are of small dimensions, which is important since it is imperative that the temperature-sensitive elements should be accurately located because of the steep temperature gradient through insulation.

Because of its low thermal conductivity, the rate of heat transfer through insulating material is low. This accentuates the effect of any heat conduction along the thermocouple lead wires, which is therefore a potential source of large error. To minimize or to eliminate this conduction error the leads must extend for some distance in a constant temperature zone, and small diameter wire should be used. If, for instance, in a composite wall, the temperature of the interface between high-temperature block and 85% magnesia block is to be determined, the hot junction should be located between the layers of block, and the lead wires should be extended at least one foot between the layers before being brought to the outside (see Fig. 20). Since mechanical support is assured, fine wire (#22 or #28 B&S gage) may be used. The block surfaces should be grooved sufficiently to accommodate the wire without being separated by it.

Outer Surfaces. To avoid errors of considerable magnitude in the measurement of the temperature of the outer surface of insulation, thoughtful attention and careful workmanship are essential. Portable contact thermocouple instruments, designed to be pressed against a surface to measure its temperature, are unsatisfactory for this case and will not read correctly when applied to hot uncased insulation. Such instruments cool the surface at the point of contact, and the low rate of heat transfer through the insulating material prevents the restoration of normal surface temperature by heat flow from the surrounding areas.

For satisfactory results, the means of attachment of the thermocouple at the surface of the insulation must not appreciably alter the normal rate of heat transmission through the insulation and from the surface of the insulation to the surroundings. If serious errors due to conduction are to be avoided, it is essential that the lead wires be maintained at the temperature of the surface. Fine wires can be attached more easily than heavy wires. If the insulation is plastic at the time of application it may be possible to press the thermocouple junction and several feet of lead wires into the very surface of the insulation with assurance that the thermocouple will adhere when the insulation hardens. If the insulation is already hard and dry it may be possible to cement the junction and lead wires to the surface, using a minimum amount of cement (see Fig. 20). Fastening the wires to the surface with staples introduces conduction errors; covering the wires with scotch tape or friction tape changes the heat transfer characteristics of the surface and imposes an undesirable insulation layer between the wires and the ambient air. Each specific installation will tax the ingenuity and heat transfer knowledge of the test engineer.

Steel Casings. The temperatures of steel casings of boilers may be measured with greater ease and accuracy. Portable contact thermocouple instruments give good results, since lateral heat flow from adjoining metal areas quickly compensates for the small quantity of heat drawn by the instrument from the point of contact. Thermocouple wire may be peened into or fused onto the metal surface to form the hot junction, and leads may be cemented to the surface for several feet. The best possible thermal contact between the lead wires and the surface, and the least possible covering of the wire or disturbance of heat transfer from the surface to the ambient air, are desirable.

Approximate surface temperatures may be conveniently measured with the fusion paints or crayons mentioned earlier in this chapter.

In power plants thermometers are sometimes fastened to metal surfaces by wads of putty. This method of measuring temperatures gives a reliable approximate surface temperature indication if the metal is massive and not far from room temperature. It is not recommended for boiler casing temperature measurement, and is completely unsatisfactory for insulation surface temperature measurements.

"Through steel," such as metal ribs imbedded in insulation, studs or door frames extending through insulation, etc., causes considerable local upsets in surface temperatures, and its influence may spread laterally for some distance along a metal casing. These effects must be given careful consideration in the planning and interpretation of surface temperature measurement.

Miscellaneous Applications

It is apparent that the several features of the thermocouple may be combined to advantage in numerous unique applications in the measurement of temperature. Two of these are mentioned below to illustrate the peculiar appropriateness of the thermocouple for special applications.

Coal Pile Temperatures. Raw coal in storage undergoes slow oxidation which may develop zones of elevated temperature and spontaneous combustion. As the coal storage pile is being laid, thermocouples may be placed at strategic points with lead wires extended to the border of the pile. Thus a check may be maintained of the trend of temperature to give a timely warning of dangerous conditions. Exploratory readings of temperature in a coal pile or bunker may

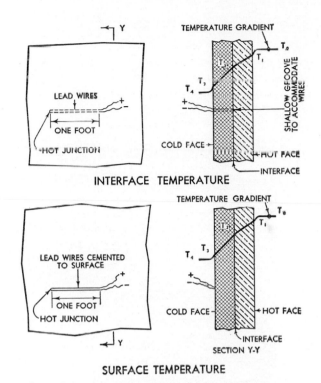

INTERFACE TEMPERATURE

SURFACE TEMPERATURE

Fig. 20. *Thermocouples for measuring surface or interface temperature of insulation*

be taken by probing with a thermocouple lance. For this service, the pipe type thermocouple is sufficiently sensitive and may be made very rugged for driving into the pile, or other rough handling.

Stoker Link Temperatures. The extreme temperature conditions to which the moving links of a chain grate stoker are sometimes subjected cause decrease of stoker service life and increase in the cost of maintenance. By charting the temperature history of chain grate links during the travel through the furnace much useful information can be obtained about fuel bed conditions and the proper adjustment of zoning dampers for different types of coal. A thermocouple may be peened to the end of a stoker link as it passes around the feed-end sprocket, and by marking off the lead wire to correspond to linear distances of travel, temperature readings may be made at successive positions of the junction. As the stoker moves around the sprocket the lead wire is guided into the clearance spaces between adjacent links. When the cycle of chain travel is completed, the leads may be detached and the procedure may be repeated for check readings in several successive cycles until the couple is damaged.

CALCULATIONS OF HEAT TRANSFER IN STEAM-GENERATING UNITS
CALL FOR THE SKILLFUL USE OF THE TOOLS OF SCIENCE AND TECHNOLOGY

HEAT TRANSFER

EAT TRANSFER is a subject which deals with the transmission of thermal energy, the source of which may be the combustion of fuels, the fissioning of material, or the inevitable losses, such as pressure drop and friction, encountered in the transmission or the transformation of other types of energy. Heat transfer is demonstrated in countless aspects of everyday life, as in cooking, heating, refrigeration, and clothing.

While the fundamentals of heat transfer are simple, practical applications may become extremely complicated because of irregular configurations of equipment, simultaneous operation of several different modes of heat transfer, and changes in conditions from moment to moment. In the applications of heat transfer it is, therefore, necessary to combine basic scientific principles with empirical information derived from experience.

Application of heat transfer data to the design of boiler surface, economizers, superheaters, and air heaters is covered by specific examples in Chapter 11. Making due allowance for the great value of the theoretical and practical concepts of heat transfer, it is clear from these examples that the exercise of judgment based on experience is paramount for successful results.

Three Usual Modes of Heat Transfer

There are three usual modes of heat transfer—conduction, radiation, and convection. One or another or a combination of these modes enters into all the many varied phases of heat transfer. The three modes of heat transfer may be defined as follows:

Conduction. The transfer of heat from one part of a body to another part of the same body, or from one body to another in physical contact, without appreciable displacement of the particles of the body or bodies.

Radiation. The transfer of energy between bodies by electromagnetic vibrations without dependence

upon the presence of matter in the intervening space. Thermal radiation is the transfer of heat by radiation. All matter radiates, and the transfer of heat is one important manifestation of this phenomenon. The intensity of the emission and the distribution among various wave lengths depend upon the temperature and the nature of the matter. When radiation impinges on a body, some of it may be reflected, some of it may be transmitted through the body, and the remainder will be absorbed. The portion absorbed is commonly converted into heat.

Convection. The transfer of heat within a fluid (gas or liquid) from one point to another by the mixing of one part with another through the movement of the fluid, or between one fluid and another by the mixing of the fluids, or between a fluid and a solid through relative motion between them.

(a) It is called natural or free convection where the movement of the fluid or fluids is caused solely by

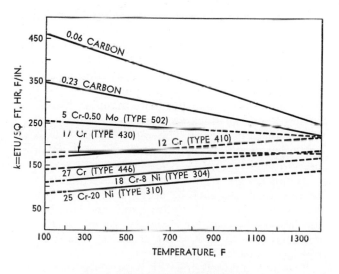

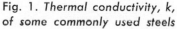

Fig. 1. *Thermal conductivity, k, of some commonly used steels*

differences in density resulting from differences in temperature within the fluid or fluids.

(b) It is called forced convection where mechanical force, density difference from change of state of the fluid, or stack induction is used to give motion to the fluid.

Over-all or Combined Conductance

Actual transfer of heat energy usually involves more than one of these modes. When two modes of heat transfer occur simultaneously and independently, such as radiation and convection, the combined conductance, U, is the sum of the individual conductances U_r and U_c, which in effect are in parallel. When the heat flow paths are in series, the resistances, not the conductances, are additive. In all cases the potential force causing the transfer is a temperature difference.

The general equation for heat flow rate by these modes, singly or in combination, may be written in the form:

$$q = U S \triangle t = \frac{S \triangle t}{R} \qquad (1)$$

where:

q = rate of heat flow, Btu/hr
U = over-all or combined conductance, Btu/sq ft, hr, F
S = surface involved in the heat transfer, sq ft
$\triangle t$ = temp difference causing heat flow, F
$R = \dfrac{1}{U}$ = combined resistance of the heat flow path, sq ft, hr, F/Btu

In the following, each mode of heat transfer is treated separately.

Heat Transfer by Conduction

If a flat plate is heated on one side and cooled on the other, heat will flow across the plate from the hot side to the cold side. To determine the rate of heat flow per unit of surface area of the plate it is necessary to know: 1) the temperature difference, $\triangle t$, between the two sides of the plate, F; 2) the thermal conductivity, k, of the plate material, Btu per sq ft, hr, F per in. thickness; and 3) the thickness, l, of the plate in inches. The rate of heat flow is directly proportional to 1) and 2) and inversely proportional to 3).

Metals are good conductors and have high conductivities; materials such as asbestos are poor conductors with low conductivities and are suitable for insulation. Typical approximate values of thermal conductivities of various materials at room temperature are given in Table 1.

Thermal conductivities of most pure metals decrease with increase in temperature, while conductivities of alloys may either increase or decrease.

Thermal conductivities of various steels are shown in Fig. 1. Thermal conductivities of insulating materials generally increase with increasing temperature, as shown in Fig. 19, Chapter 14.

TABLE 1
Thermal Conductivity, k
(Btu/sq ft, hr, F/in. thickness)

Material	k^*
Silver	2880
Copper	2640
Carbon steel	312
Alloy steel, 18% Cr-8% Ni	108
First-quality firebrick	4.5
Insulating firebrick	0.8
85% Magnesia block	0.5

* At room temperature.

In the case of a simple plate heated on one side and cooled on the other, the distribution of temperature will be as shown in Fig. 2, heat flowing from the higher temperature to the lower. If the thermal conductivity of the material does not change with change in temperature, the temperature gradient will be a straight line; if the conductivity increases with increase in temperature, the temperature gradient will be convex; if the conductivity decreases with increase in temperature, the gradient will be concave. In most cases it is satisfactory to assume a constant conductivity at the average temperature of the material.

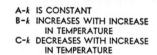

A-k IS CONSTANT
B-k INCREASES WITH INCREASE IN TEMPERATURE
C-k DECREASES WITH INCREASE IN TEMPERATURE

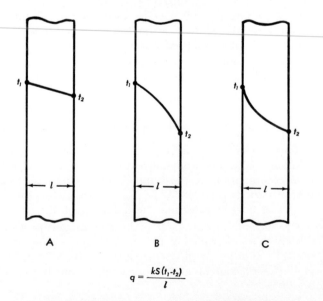

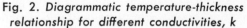

$$q = \frac{kS(t_1 - t_2)}{l}$$

Fig. 2. *Diagrammatic temperature-thickness relationship for different conductivities, k*

In the case of heat transfer by conduction only, the general equation (1) is expressed as:

$$q = U_d S \, \triangle t = \frac{S \, \triangle t}{R} = \frac{kS \, \triangle t}{l} \qquad (2)$$

where:

U_d = combined conduction conductance, Btu/sq ft, hr, F

k = conductivity of the material, Btu/sq ft, hr, F/in.

l = length of heat flow path (thickness of material), in.

R = combined resistance of heat flow path as in equation (1) = $1/U_d = R_1 + R_2 + R_3$, etc., = $l_1/k_1 + l_2/k_2 + l_3/k_3$, etc., for a series of resistances

In the simple example, Fig. 2, for a flat steel plate ¼ in. thick, 1 sq ft in area, and $t_1 - t_2 = \triangle t = 25$ F, the combined conductance, U_d, is the single conductance through the steel plate and is equal to the conductivity, k, of steel (312, from Table 1) divided by the thickness of the plate. Therefore in equation (2):

$$q = \frac{312 \times 1 \times 25}{0.25} = 31,200 \text{ Btu/hr}$$

Equation (1) is used for the composite example, Fig. 3, which may be the wall of a flue conveying hot gases. In this case U, the combined conductance, is not a single conductance but is the combination of incremental conductances in series through the fluid films and the various layers of materials, and R, the combined resistance, is equal to the sum of the incremental resistances, thus:

$$R = R_{01} + R_{12} + R_{23} + R_{34} + R_{45}$$

$$= R_{01} + \frac{l_{12}}{k_{12}} + \frac{l_{23}}{k_{23}} + \frac{l_{34}}{k_{34}} + R_{45}$$

For this example the assigned numerical values are:

S = 600 sq ft, wall surface

t_o = 1080 F, temp hot gases

t_5 = 80 F, temp room air

$\triangle t = t_o - t_5 = 1000$ F, temp difference

k_{12} = 1.08, for insulating firebrick

k_{23} = 300, for steel (trial value)

k_{34} = 0.5, for insulation

l_{12}, l_{23}, l_{34} = 4 in., ¼ in., and 3 in., respective thicknesses

U_{01}, U_{45} = 5.0, 2.0, respective film conductances

R_{01}, R_{45} = 1/5, 1/2, respective film resistances

The film conductances, U_{01} and U_{45}, depend upon a variety of factors, chiefly velocity or mass flow of the fluids giving up and receiving heat, and the temperatures of the fluids (see below, also Chapter 11).

Using the above assigned values in equation (1) for the composite wall,* illustrated in Fig. 3:

* See Chapter 14, Fig. 21, for a similar example.

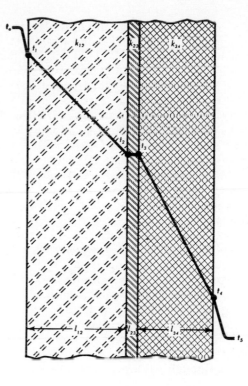

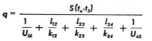

$$q = \frac{S(t_o - t_5)}{\frac{1}{U_{01}} + \frac{l_{12}}{k_{12}} + \frac{l_{23}}{k_{23}} + \frac{l_{34}}{k_{34}} + \frac{1}{U_{45}}}$$

Fig. 3. *Temperature distribution in composite wall (fluid films included)*

$$q = \frac{600 \times 1000}{\frac{1}{5} + \frac{4}{1.08} + \frac{0.25}{300} + \frac{3}{0.5} + \frac{1}{2}}$$

$$= 57,600 \text{ Btu/hr}$$

and $\dfrac{q}{S} = \dfrac{57,600}{600} = 96$ Btu/sq ft, hr

Since the heat flow rate through each resistance is the same and in series, the face and interface temperatures may be determined:

In equation (1) $q = \dfrac{S \triangle t}{R}$ and $\triangle t = \dfrac{q}{S} \times R$

$t_o - t_1 = \dfrac{q}{S} \times R_{01}$ or $1080 - t_1 = 96 \times \dfrac{1}{5}$ and $t_1 = 1061$ F

$t_1 - t_2 = \dfrac{q}{S} \times \dfrac{l_{12}}{k_{12}}$ or $1061 - t_2 = 96 \times \dfrac{4}{1.08}$ and $t_2 = 705$ F

$t_2 - t_3 = \dfrac{q}{S} \times \dfrac{l_{23}}{k_{23}}$ or $705 - t_3 = 96 \times \dfrac{0.25}{300}$ and $t_3 = 705$ F

$t_3 - t_4 = \dfrac{q}{S} \times \dfrac{l_{34}}{k_{34}}$ or $705 - t_4 = 96 \times \dfrac{3}{0.5}$ and $t_4 = 129$ F

Equation (2) can be developed mathematically

to take account of heat flow in all directions instead of only one and can be further developed to take account of heat flow where the temperatures not only vary from point to point but also vary with time. However, the fundamental principles outlined above form the basis of the whole theory of heat conduction, either in the steady state (temperatures do not vary with time, and heat flow is constant) or in the unsteady state (temperatures vary with time, and heat flow is variable). Heat conduction and electrical conduction are analogous and follow the same laws, temperature difference corresponding to voltage difference and heat flow rate to electrical current. This important analogy permits the use of electrical models and combinations of electrical circuits for the solution of heat conduction problems which are too complex for mathematical analysis.

The expression k/l in the formulas above is characteristic of any area of the plate, and it is found useful to give this characteristic a special name, conductance, which has the dimensions Btu/sq ft, hr, F. The reciprocal of conductance is resistance, $R =$ sq ft, hr, F/Btu $= l/k$. For any case in which heat flows through successive flat layers of material, the reciprocal of the over-all conductance equals the sum of the reciprocals of the individual conductances, and the total resistance equals the sum of the individual resistances. If the successive layers of material do not make good thermal contact with each other, there will be interface resistances from air or oxide films, etc. These resistances may be neglected in composite walls of insulating materials but become important and must be included in calculations if the resistances of the layers are small in comparison with the interface resistances.

When heat is conducted radially through a cylindrical wall, as in heat flow through the wall of a steam line from the inside to the outside of the pipe (Fig. 4), the flat-plate formula must be modified, since the heat-flow surface area, S, is no longer a constant but increases as the distance from the center of the pipe increases. If the outside surface area of the pipe is used for the value of S, then it can be shown that the thickness of the pipe wall, corresponding to length l in the flat-plate formula, must be replaced by the equivalent (thickness) length, l_e, given by the equation:

$$l_e = 0.5 \, d_o \log_e (d_o/d_i) \qquad (3)$$

where:
  $l_e =$ equivalent length, in.
  $d_o =$ outside pipe diameter, in.
  $d_i =$ inside pipe diameter, in.

The equation for heat flow through a cylindrical wall thus becomes:

$$q = \frac{kS\,(t_1-t_2)}{l_e} = \frac{2kS\,(t_1-t_2)}{d_o \log_e (d_o/d_i)} \qquad (4)$$

If the heat flows through two successive cylindrical walls, as in an insulated steam pipe, and if the film conductances (see below under convection) U_{o1} of the steam and U_{34} of the air outside the insulation (Fig. 5) are included, the formula becomes:

$$q = \frac{S\,(t_o-t_i)}{\dfrac{d_3}{d_1}\dfrac{1}{U_{o1}} + \dfrac{d_3}{2k_{12}}\log_e \dfrac{(d_2)}{(d_1)} + \dfrac{d_3}{2k_{23}}\log_e \dfrac{(d_3)}{(d_2)} + \dfrac{1}{U_{34}}} \qquad (5)$$

where:
  $d_3 =$ outside diameter of insulation, in.
  $S =$ outside surface area of insulation, sq ft

Many problems of heat transfer in the power field involve conduction through plane or cylindrical walls and can be treated by the methods outlined. For other geometrical shapes, such as thick-wall rectangles, ribbed construction, etc., special treatment is required.

Conduction in Fluids

Conduction in fluids (liquids and gases) follows the same laws as conduction through solids. In engineering practice, heat transfer by conduction through fluids is small in comparison with convection. However, the thermal conductivities of fluids and solids enter into convection heat transfer. The thermal conductivity of water ranges from about 3.8 Btu/sq ft, hr, F/in. at 32 F to about 4.8 at 260 F. Most of the other nonmetallic liquids have conductivities between 0.60 and 1.80 Btu/sq ft, hr, F/in. The thermal conductivities of gases are independent of pressure* but increase with increasing temperature, the higher values being associated with the lighter and smaller molecules (see Table 2). The relatively high

* At low pressures.

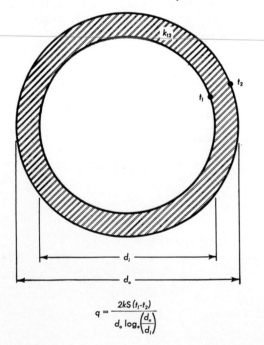

$$q = \frac{2kS\,(t_1 - t_2)}{d_o \log_e \left(\frac{d_o}{d_i}\right)}$$

Fig. 4. Heat flow through cylindrical wall (see formula)

conductivity of hydrogen is utilized in hydrogen-cooled generators.

Thermal Conductivity, k
(Btu/sq ft, hr, F/in. thickness)
Water and Steam Vapor

Temp, F	Sat. Liquid, k	Sat. Vapor, k
35	3.840	0.108
100	4.368	0.132
200	4.728	0.156
300	4.740	0.204
400	4.584	0.300
500	4.176	0.420
600	3.504	0.576
650	2.940	0.744
700	1.8	1.2
705.4	1.5	1.5

Gases

Temp, F	Air, k	CO₂, k	O₂, k	N₂, k	H₂, k
0	0.168	0.096	0.156	0.168	1.080
500	0.300	0.252	0.312	0.264	2.004
1000	0.408	0.384	0.444	0.336	2.724
1500	0.480	0.516	0.564	0.408	3.360
2000	0.564	0.624	0.672	0.468	3.924
2500	0.636	0.720	0.792	0.528	4.464
3000	0.696	0.804	0.912	—	5.004

Flue Gases

Temp, F	*Nat Gas, k	*Fuel Oil, k	†Coal, k
0	—	—	—
500	0.264	0.264	0.264
1000	0.360	0.348	0.348
1500	0.444	0.432	0.432
2000	0.528	0.516	0.516
2500	0.612	0.588	0.600

*For 115% total air.
†For 120% total air.

Unsteady-State Conduction

Thus far the discussion has been limited to steady-state conduction, where temperatures vary from point to point but do not change with time. Unsteady-state conduction is involved in heating or cooling processes where temperatures change with time, as in heating of billets, regenerative heaters, raising of pressure in a boiler, quenching of steel, and warming up and cooling down of steam lines and turbines. With the introduction of time as an additional variable, the problems of conduction become much more complicated. In this difficult field, electrical analogy models are particularly applicable.

All unsteady-state conduction involves heat storage. For instance, in heating up a furnace enough heat must be supplied to bring the walls to the operating temperature and also to make up for the steady-state

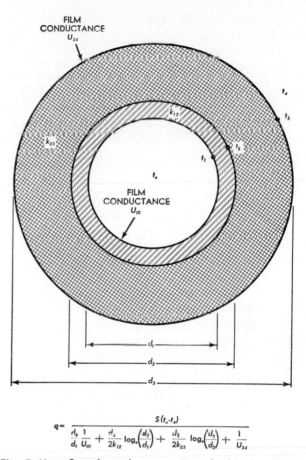

$$q = \frac{S(t_o - t_4)}{\dfrac{d_4}{d_1}\dfrac{1}{U_{01}} + \dfrac{d_3}{2k_{12}}\log_e\left(\dfrac{d_2}{d_1}\right) + \dfrac{d_3}{2k_{23}}\log_e\left(\dfrac{d_3}{d_2}\right) + \dfrac{1}{U_{34}}}$$

Fig. 5. Heat flow through composite cylindrical wall (pipe and insulation) with fluid films included (see formula)

losses of normal operation. In large power boilers which run for long periods of time, heat storage in the walls and boiler metal is an insignificant fraction of the total heat input. In small boilers with refractory settings which are operated only a part of each day or in heating furnaces which are frequently heated and cooled in batch process work, heat storage in the walls during start-up may be a considerable proportion of the total heat input. Often in equipment of this type, the use of insulating firebrick of low heat-storage capacity instead of standard firebrick, even though the initial expense may be somewhat greater, is warranted by substantial savings in fuel cost and in the time required for start-up.

Unsteady-state conduction is important in the equalization of temperatures in boiler drums during pressure-raising and -reducing periods. When pressure is raised in a boiler, the water temperature increases. The inner surface of the steam drum is heated by contact with the water below the waterline and by the condensation of steam above the waterline. The temperatures of the inside and outside of the drum are raised by unsteady-state conduction. Heat flow takes time, however, and it is necessary to restrict the rate of pressure rise in thick boiler drums to keep from exceeding allowable stresses in the drum metal caused by differential expansion resulting from excessive temperature differences. During pressure-reducing periods the inside of the drum below the waterline is cooled by water. The top of the drum is cooled only by radiation to the water and by unsteady-state conduction through the metal walls of the drum. The rate of pressure reduction must therefore also be limited (see Chapter 21).

Heat Transfer by Radiation

The fractions of radiation reflected, transmitted, and absorbed by a surface are known respectively as the reflectivity, ρ, transmissivity, τ, and absorptivity, α, of the body. The sum of these fractions equals one:

$$\rho + \tau + \alpha = 1$$

Bodies that are good absorbers are equally good emitters of radiation, and it can be shown that at thermal equilibrium their emissivities are equal to their absorptivities. A blackbody is defined as one which absorbs all the radiant energy incident upon it, reflecting and transmitting none; the absorptivity and emissivity of a blackbody are each equal to one. The word "black" as used in radiation is a technical heat transfer term for a surface which neither reflects nor transmits radiant energy and has unit absorptivity and emissivity. It does not necessarily mean that the body appears black to the eye. Snow, for instance, absorbs only a few per cent of visible light falling upon it, but to the longer wavelengths (the bulk of thermal radiation) snow is almost a blackbody. A blackbody at a temperature of 2000 F will glow brightly, since part of its radiation is in the visible range. No actual bodies are completely black, but a hole through the wall of a large enclosure approximates blackbody conditions, since radiation entering the hole will undergo multiple reflections and absorptions inside the enclosure and will, so to speak, be unable to find its way out.

The radiation emitted by a blackbody depends upon its surface area and temperature and follows a relationship known as the Stefan-Boltzmann law:

$$q = \sigma S T^4 \tag{6}$$

where:

q = rate of heat flow, Btu/hr
σ = Stefan-Boltzmann constant, 1.73×10^{-9} Btu/sq ft, hr, T^4
S = surface area of body, sq ft
T = absolute temperature, R = F + 460

The above formula is based on the emissivity (equal to 1) of a blackbody and must be modified as indicated to account for the emissivity of an actual body.

$$q = \sigma \, \epsilon S T^4 \tag{7}$$

where ϵ, emissivity, is the ratio of the energies radiated, respectively, by an actual body and a blackbody at the same absolute temperature.

The radiation from a blackbody extends over the whole range of wavelengths, although the bulk of it is concentrated in a moderately narrow band. The wavelength at which the maximum radiation intensity occurs is inversely proportional to the absolute temperature of the body. Fortunately many commercial surfaces, particularly at high temperatures, have emissivities of 0.80 to 0.95 and behave very much

TABLE 3

* Normal Emissivities, ϵ, For Various Surfaces

Material	Emissivity, ϵ	Temp, F	Description
Aluminum	0.055	78	Rough plate
Brass	0.22	120-660	Dull plate
Copper	0.16-0.13	1970-2330	Molten
Copper	0.023	242	Polished
Copper oxide	0.66-0.54	1470-2010	
Iron	0.21	392	Polished, cast
Iron	0.55-0.60	1650-1900	Smooth sheet
Iron	0.242	68	Fresh emeried
Iron oxide	0.85-0.89	930-2190	
Steel	0.79	390-1110	Oxidized at 1100 F
Steel	0.657	70	Rolled sheet
Steel	0.28	2910-3270	Molten
Steel (Cr-Ni)	0.44-0.36	420-914	"18-8" Rough, after heating
Steel (Cr-Ni)	0.90-0.97	420-980	"25-20" Oxidized in service
Brick, red	0.93	70	Rough
Brick, silica	0.80	1832	Rough, unglazed
Brick, refractory	0.80-0.90	1110-1830	Various, good radiators
Carbon, lamp black	0.945	100-700	0.003" or thicker
Water	0.95-0.963	32-212	

* From Hottel.

like blackbodies. Typical emissivity values are noted in Table 3.

The emission of radiant energy described above depends solely on the temperature and emissivity of the surface of the body and is independent of any other heat exchange, whether by conduction, radiation, or convection, which may be occurring at the same time.

When two blackbody surfaces are arranged so that all the radiant energy emitted by one falls upon the other (as, for example, two infinite parallel planes), the net rate of heat exchange between the hot surface 1 and the cold surface 2 is:

$$q_{12} = \sigma S (T_1^4 - T_2^4) \qquad (8)$$

where:

q_{12} = Btu/hr
$\sigma = 1.73 \times 10^{-9}$ Btu/sq ft, hr, T^4
S = surface area of one plane, sq ft
T_1, T_2 = absolute temperatures of surfaces 1 and 2, R = F + 460

If the two blackbodies are arranged so that all the radiation emitted by one does not fall on the other, it is necessary to introduce an angle factor, F_{12} (less than one), into the equation, which then becomes:

$$q_{12} = F_{12} \sigma S_1 (T_1^4 - T_2^4) \qquad (8a)$$

The angle factor depends upon the geometry of the situation and the body used to define S_1.

If the emissivity of a surface is less than one but is independent of wavelength, the surface is termed a nonselective radiator, or "gray" surface; if the emissivity depends upon wavelength, the surface is termed a selective radiator. Exact allowance for the departure of surfaces from black or ideal radiating characteristics is in general too complicated for engineering use. However, if the assumption that all surfaces are gray is permitted, a simpler treatment is possible. This involves introducing an emissivity factor, F_ϵ, which depends upon the geometry, the emissivities involved, and the surface area selected for use as S in the formulas. Two special cases are of interest:

1) Where one body is completely surrounded by a much larger body (e.g., a steam pipe in a large room), the general equation for the net rate of heat exchange between one surface and another becomes:

$$q_{12} = \sigma \epsilon_1 S_1 (T_1^4 - T_2^4) \qquad (9)$$

where:

q_{12} = Btu/hr
$\sigma = 1.73 \times 10^{-9}$ Btu/sq ft, hr, T^4
ϵ_1 = emissivity of smaller surface $1 - F_\epsilon$
S_1 = area of smaller surface 1, sq ft
T_1 = absolute temperature of smaller surface 1, R = F + 460
T_2 = absolute temperature of larger surface 2, R = F + 460

2) For the heat exchange between two small gray bodies at considerable distance from one another, the general equation for the net rate of heat exchange between one surface and another becomes:

$$q_{12} = \sigma \epsilon_1 \epsilon_2 (\omega/2\pi) S_1 (T_1^4 - T_2^4) \qquad (10)$$

where:

q_{12} = Btu/hr
$\sigma = 1.73 \times 10^{-9}$ Btu/sq ft, hr, T^4
ϵ_1, ϵ_2 = emissivities of surfaces 1 and 2
$\epsilon_1 \epsilon_2$ = emissivity factor, F_ϵ
S_1 = area of surface 1, sq ft
ω = solid angle intercepted by body 2 as seen from body 1, steradians*
π = 3.1416
$\omega/2\pi$ = angle factor, F_{12}
T_1, T_2 = absolute temperatures of surfaces 1 and 2, R = F + 460

* 2π steradians comprise a hemispherical solid angle about a point.

Since the solid angle intercepted by body 2, at a distance from body 1, is something less than 2π steradians, the factor $\omega/2\pi$ is less than unity, and the effective surface area of body 1 becomes $(\omega/2\pi) S_1$.

A complicated case of intersolid radiation is encountered in flames made luminous by particles, such as pulverized coal, averaging about 0.001 in. in diameter, or by soot formed by the thermal decomposition of hydrocarbons, having particle diameters of about 0.00001 inch. The treatment of radiation from luminous flames is beyond the scope of this chapter.

Radiation From and To Gases

Although many gases, such as oxygen and nitrogen, do not appreciably absorb or emit radiation, some others, such as water vapor, carbon dioxide, sulfur dioxide, and carbon monoxide, both absorb and emit. Water vapor and carbon dioxide are important because they are found in considerable quantities in the products of combustion of hydrocarbon fuels. These gases are selective radiators which emit and absorb radiation only in certain wavelength bands which lie outside of the visible range. Their radiation, therefore, cannot be seen and is termed nonluminous gas radiation. Whereas solid radiation is a surface phenomenon, a gas both radiates and absorbs (within its absorption bands) at every point throughout the gas body. Furthermore, the emissivity of a gas changes with temperature, and the presence of one radiating gas has an effect on the radiating characteristics of another radiating gas with which it is mixed. The amount of radiant energy emitted by a radiating gaseous mixture depends upon the temperature of the mixture, the partial pressures of the gaseous radiating constituents, and the shape and dimensions of the gas body. The fraction of radiant energy emitted by the surroundings, which is absorbed by the gas, depends upon the temperature and surface of the surroundings as well as upon the foregoing.

Heat Transfer by Convection

Heat transfer by convection between a fluid (gas or liquid) and a solid, such as a boiler tube, is expressed in the basic equation:

$$q_c = U_c S \triangle t \tag{11}$$

where:

q_c = rate of heat flow by convection, Btu/hr

U_c = convection film conductance, Btu/sq ft, hr, F

S = heat transfer surface normal to heat flow, sq ft

$\triangle t = (t-t_s)$ or (t_s-t), depending upon direction of transfer

t = fluid temperature, F

t_s = surface temperature, F

From this formula it is evident that heat flux density, the quantity of heat (Btu) transferred per sq ft, hr, depends upon the film conductance and the difference between the surface temperature and the fluid temperature. For the same difference in temperatures, heat flux densities are, therefore, proportional to the film conductances. In general, film conductance must be determined experimentally by painstaking test procedures involving precise measurements of surface temperatures and fluid temperatures. For the effect of film conductance, see example above of composite heat flow path (Fig. 3) and also Chapter 11.

Free Convection

The quantity of heat transfer by convection is vitally affected by the type of motion within a fluid. A fluid at rest, exposed to a heated surface, will be at a higher temperature adjacent to the surface than elsewhere. The difference in specific weights of the particles of the fluid because of this difference in temperature will cause the fluid to circulate, thus carrying heat from one place to another. Heat transfer in this manner is known as free or natural convection, as differentiated from forced convection, where outside mechanical force, change of state of the fluid, or stack induction is used to circulate the fluid. The relationships of the numerous variables affecting the free-convection heat transfer conductance for different media are fully discussed in texts on the subject. In the power field, however, air and flue gases at atmospheric pressure are the most important natural-convection heat transfer media, and in this case the following formula is applicable:

$$U_{fc} = C(\triangle t)^{0.25} \tag{12}$$

where:

U_{fc} = free-convection film conductance, Btu/sq ft, hr, F

C = coefficient, characteristic of shape and position of heat transfer surface

$\triangle t$ = difference in temperature between the surface and the air or gas, F

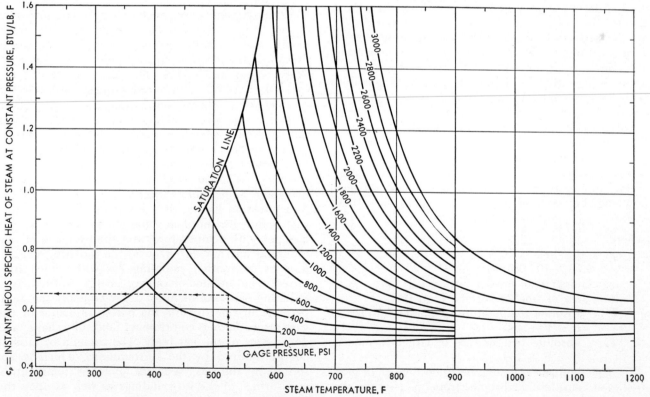

Fig. 6. *Instantaneous specific heat of steam at constant pressure*

Values of C for various surfaces are listed below:

Horizontal plates facing upward   0.38
Horizontal plates facing downward   0.20
Vertical plates more than 1 ft high   0.27

Vertical plates less than 1 ft high $\dfrac{0.28}{L^{0.25}}$

Vertical pipes more than 1 ft high $\dfrac{0.27}{D_o^{0.25}}$

Horizontal pipes $\dfrac{0.27}{D_o^{0.25}}$

where:

L = height of plate, ft
D_o = outside diam of pipe, ft

The flow resulting from the boiling of a liquid at a heating surface should be differentiated from free convection. Whereas the free-convection film conductance for water is in the order of 25-50 Btu/sq ft, hr, F, the heat transfer conductance for boiling water may vary between very wide limits (see below and Chapters 21 and 29) depending upon the rate of heat input and other factors.

Forced Convection

Forced-convection heat transfer depends upon mechanically imposed fluid flow or equivalent. The mechanisms and types of fluid flow are described in Chapter 8. In subsections a) through e) which follow, radiation which may be occurring simultaneously is intentionally omitted.

a) Streamline Flow Inside Tubes

In streamline or laminar flow, the elements or layers of the fluid flow parallel to the axis of the channel, with no appreciable lateral disturbance. For heating or cooling viscous liquids in the streamline flow region inside horizontal or vertical tubes, the film conductance between fluid and surface, based on the arithmetic mean temperature difference, can be determined by the following empirical equation from McAdams:

$$U_{cl} = 1.86 \frac{k}{D_i}\left\{\frac{\mu}{\mu_s}\right\}^{0.14}\left\{\frac{GD_i}{\mu}\frac{c_p\mu}{k}\frac{D_i}{L}\right\}^{1/3} \qquad (13)$$

U_{cl} = convection film conductance in long flow, Btu/sq ft, hr, F
D_i = inside tube diameter, ft
k = conductivity of fluid within tube, Btu/sq ft, hr, F/ft
G = mass velocity, or mass flow, of fluid within tube, lb/ hr, sq ft of cross section
c_p = specific heat at constant pressure, Btu/lb, F (see Fig. 6 for steam)
L = heated length of straight tube, ft
μ = absolute fluid viscosity at bulk temperature, lb/ft, hr
μ_s = absolute fluid viscosity at surface temperature, lb/ft, hr

In the case of low-viscosity fluids, such as water and gases, a more complex equation is required to allow for the effects of natural convection at the heat transfer surface. This refinement is of little interest in industrial practice since, generally, it is impractical to use water and gases in streamline flow.

b) Turbulent Flow

In turbulent flow, the fluid elements move radially as well as axially. The combination of radial and axial components of flow sets up an eddy motion, which increases the activity within the body of the fluid. Consequently, there is a considerable increase in the convection heat transfer as compared with streamline flow.

Studies of the velocity gradient across a fluid indicate that in turbulent flow the velocity at the heat transfer surface is zero. In the zone immediately adjacent to the surface, known as the sublaminar layer, the flow is streamline, and the heat leaving or approaching the surface travels by conduction. In the next zone, known as the buffer layer, where the motion is a mixture of streamline and turbulent flow, the heat is transferred partly by convection and partly by conduction. Heat is transferred mainly by convection in the bulk of the stream cross section, known as the turbulent zone, or turbulent core in the case of flow inside pipes or tubes.

The streamline flow in the sublaminar layer and the streamline component in the buffer layer act as a barrier to the convection transfer of heat to or from the surface. This barrier may be likened to a film, the thickness of which depends, to a certain extent, upon the velocity of the fluid. By increasing the velocity, a part of this film can be swept away, thus decreasing its thickness and reducing the resistance to heat transfer by conduction.

c) Reynolds Number and Others

It was only after the important variables were arranged in a number of so-called dimensionless groups that the data from the earlier research of various investigators in convection heat transfer could be plotted and compared in an orderly manner. In correlating and using forced-convection heat transfer information, the best method is to compare fluid flow, temperature, and heat transfer characteristics for geometrically similar systems. Geometrical similarity is a familiar concept, frequently encountered in the scale model, where size is changed but relative physical proportions remain constant.

A familiar example of dimensionless groups of factors is the Reynolds number, $\rho VD/\mu$, which is used as a criterion of fluid-flow similarity in pipes flowing full. This number represents the ratio of the inertial forces, F_I, to the viscous forces, F_μ as shown below:

$$F_I = ma = \rho L^3 V^2/L = \rho L^2 V^2$$
$$F_\mu = \mu AV/L = \mu L^2 V/L = \mu LV$$
$$F_I/F_\mu = \rho L^2 V^2/\mu LV = \rho LV/\mu$$

where:

ρ = density of fluid, lb (mass)/cu ft

V = mean velocity of fluid, ft/hr

μ = viscosity of fluid, lb (mass)/ft, hr

L = characteristic lineal dimension, ft

For fluid flowing full in closed conduits, the characteristic lineal dimension is the internal diameter for pipe flow or the equivalent diameter for conduits of noncircular cross section. It can be demonstrated mathematically that, for dynamically similar fluid motion in geometrically similar systems of different size, $\rho_1 V_1 D_1 / \mu_1$ for one system is equal to $\rho_2 V_2 D_2 / \mu_2$ for another system. The flow pattern in geometrically similar systems is therefore determined by the variables ρ, V, D, and μ.

In the derivation of the dimensionless expression $\rho V D / \mu$, it is assumed that the fluid is a continuous medium filling its conduit and that the gravitational and elastic forces are negligible compared with the inertial and viscous forces.

Where the velocity of the fluid is high and the viscosity is low, as in water flowing rapidly through a pipe (high Reynolds number), the inertial forces are predominant, and the flow will be turbulent.

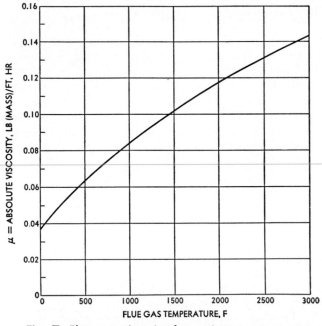

Fig. 7. Flue gas viscosity for various temperatures

Where the velocity is low and the viscosity is high, as in the flow of heavy oil in a pipe (low Reynolds number), the viscous forces predominate, and the tendency is for the flow to be laminar.

Another dimensionless group of factors known as the Prandtl number, $c_p \mu / k$, serves as a criterion of temperature gradient similarity. This group can be considered as specific heat, c_p, divided by the ratio of

thermal conductivity to viscosity, k/μ. The numerator, c_p, is a measure of the temperature rise of a given mass of fluid for a given heat energy input. The denominator, k/μ, is a measure of the ease of heat transmission through the fluid, since high conductivity or low viscosity stimulates heat transmission.

The dimensionless group known as the Nusselt number, $U_c D / k$, is a criterion of heat transfer similarity and can be considered as a ratio of the size factor, D, to the thickness of the boundary layer of the fluid, expressed as k/U_c.

The dimensionless group known as the Stanton number, $U_c / \rho V c_p$, is the ratio of the conductance to the product of the mass flow and the specific heat at constant pressure, which is the ratio of the heat absorbed to that available for absorption. It is used in the following expression as a designating function.

The Nusselt number can be expressed as the product of the Stanton, Reynolds, and Prandtl numbers:

$$\frac{U_c D}{k} = \left\{ \frac{U_c}{\rho V c_p} \right\} \left\{ \frac{\rho V D}{\mu} \right\} \left\{ \frac{c_p \mu}{k} \right\} \qquad (14)$$

where:

$\dfrac{U_c D}{k}$ = Nusselt number, dimensionless

$\dfrac{U_c}{\rho V c_p} = \dfrac{U_c}{G c_p}$ = Stanton number, dimensionless

$\dfrac{\rho V D}{\mu} = \dfrac{G D}{\mu}$ = Reynolds number, dimensionless

$\dfrac{c_p \mu}{k}$ = Prandtl number, dimensionless

d) Turbulent Flow Inside Pipes or Tubes

By applying these ratios, extensive research data on gases and liquids of low viscosity in turbulent flow through long tubes have been correlated to give the following equation:

$$\frac{U_{ci} D_i}{k} = 0.023 \left[\frac{G D_i}{\mu} \right]^{0.8} \left[\frac{c_p \mu}{k} \right]^{0.4} \left[\frac{T_b}{T_f} \right]^{0.8} \qquad (15)$$

$$U_{ci} = 0.023 \frac{G^{0.8} c_p^{0.4} k^{0.6}}{D_i^{0.2} \mu^{0.4}} \frac{T_b^{0.8}}{T_f^{0.8}} \qquad (16)$$

where:

U_{ci} = convection film conductance in long flow, Btu/sq ft, hr, F

T_b = avg bulk absolute temp, R = F + 460

T_f = avg film absolute temp

$\quad = \dfrac{\text{surface abs temp} + T_b}{2}$, R = F + 460

Equation (16) applies to both the heating and the cooling of fluids flowing inside clean conduits. For convenience in use, equation (16) is presented in the form:

$$U_{ci} = U'_{ci} F_{pp} F_T \qquad (17)$$

where:

U'_{ci} = basic convection conductance in long flow
$\quad = 0.023 \, G^{0.8} / D^{0.2}$, Btu/sq ft, hr, F (Fig. 31, Chapter 11)

F_{pp} = physical properties factor evaluated at t_f for $c_p^{0.4} \, k^{0.6}/\mu^{0.4}$ (Figs. 32 and 33, Chapter 11)

F_T = temperature factor = $(T_b/T_f)^{0.8}$ (Fig. 34, Chapter 11)

t_f = avg film temperature

= $\dfrac{\text{avg surface temp} + \text{avg bulk temp}}{2}$, F

Charts for evaluating the several factors for convection conductance in longitudinal flow appear in Chapter 11, as does also an empirical equation for determining the steam film conductance (see superheater example).

e) Turbulent Flow Outside Pipes or Tubes

In the steam boiler, the most important application of convection is in the transfer of heat from hot combustion gases to the various heat-absorbing tubular surfaces. Compared with the extensive research on heat transfer for fluids flowing inside tubes, little has been done to establish convection heat transfer coefficients for crossflow over tube banks. Perhaps the most authoritative and complete data on crossflow heat transfer are those obtained as part of a B&W research program. The following equation was developed from the correlation of these data:

$$\frac{U_{cc} D_o}{k} = 0.287 \left\{ \frac{G D_o}{\mu} \right\}^{0.61} \left\{ \frac{c_p \mu}{k} \right\}^{0.33} F_a \quad (18)$$

$$U_{cc} = 0.287 \frac{G^{0.61} \, c_p^{0.33} \, k^{0.67}}{D_o^{0.39} \, \mu^{0.28}} F_a \quad (19)$$

where:

U_{cc} = convection film conductance in crossflow, Btu/sq ft, hr, F

F_a = arrangement factor which corrects for difference in geometric configuration from base arrangement

Equation (19) applies to both the heating and the cooling of fluids flowing outside clean tubes in crossflow. For convenience in use, equation (19) is presented in the form:

$$U_{cc} = U'_{cc} F_{pp} F_a F_d \quad (20)$$

where:

U'_{cc} = basic convection conductance in crossflow
= $0.287 \, G^{0.61}/D^{0.39}$, Btu/sq ft, hr, F (Fig. 35, Chapter 11)

F_{pp} = physical properties factor evaluated at t_f for $c_p^{0.33} k^{0.67}/\mu^{0.28}$ (Figs. 36 and 37, Chapter 11)

F_a = arrangement factor (Fig. 38, Chapter 11)

F_d = depth factor (Fig. 8)

t_f = avg film temperature

= $\dfrac{\text{avg surface temp} + \text{avg bulk temp}}{2}$, F

Charts for evaluating U'_{cc}, F_{pp}, and F_a will be found in Chapter 11.

The arrangement factor, F_a, depends upon the tube arrangement, the ratios of tube spacing to tube diameter, and the Reynolds number. Values for F_a are given in Fig. 38, Chapter 11, for various conditions. The mass flow factor, G, in equation (19) and in the Reynolds numbers for the curves in the figure just mentioned, is based on the minimum free area available for fluid flow, which may occur either in the transverse or in the diagonal openings.

The value of the film conductance, U_{cc}, in equation (19) applies to banks of tubes which are 10 or more rows deep in the direction of gas flow. Tests confirm the assumption that the heat transfer coefficient increases beyond the first row because of increased turbulence. However, in banks of ten or more rows of tubes, the effect of the relatively low conductance in the first row, because of undisturbed flow, is negligible. For undisturbed flow* approaching a bank of less than 10 rows, the film conductance, U_{cc}, must be multiplied by a correction factor, F_d, known as the depth factor, given in Fig. 8. Factor F_d should be taken as unity when the tube bank is preceded by a bend, screen, or damper.

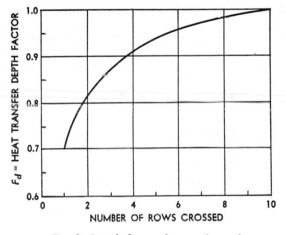

Fig 8. Depth factor for number of tube rows crossed in convection banks

Although equations (16) and (17) were developed for flow inside tubes, the same equations can also be developed by correlating the limited data available for flow of gases longitudinally over the outside of tubular surfaces, except that an equivalent diameter must be substituted for the tube diameter. The equivalent diameter is defined as 4 times the area of the flow cross section divided by the contact perimeter. For flow along banks of circular tubes arranged in rectangular spacing, the equivalent diameter is:

$$D_e = \frac{4 \times (L_1 \times L_2 - 0.785 \, D_o^2)}{\pi D_o} \quad (21)$$

---

* Flow is considered undisturbed when it is straight and uninterrupted for at least 4 ft before entering a tube bank.

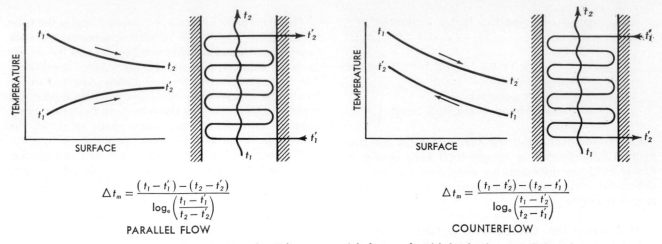

$$\Delta t_m = \frac{(t_1 - t_1') - (t_2 - t_2')}{\log_e \left(\frac{t_1 - t_1'}{t_2 - t_2'} \right)}$$

PARALLEL FLOW

$$\Delta t_m = \frac{(t_1 - t_2') - (t_2 - t_1')}{\log_e \left(\frac{t_1 - t_2'}{t_2 - t_1'} \right)}$$

COUNTERFLOW

Fig. 9. Temperature relationship (diagrammatic), hot and cold fluids, for parallel and counterflow, with corresponding formulas for logarithmic mean temperature difference

where:

D_e = equivalent diameter, ft
D_o = tube outside diameter, ft
L_1 and L_2 are tube pitches, ft

f) Temperature Difference

The temperature difference indicated in equation (11) applies to that existing between a fluid and a solid at any point. In the transfer of heat between two fluids, which is the usual case, the temperatures of both fluids may change as they traverse the heat transfer surface (see Fig. 9). It then becomes necessary to modify equation (11) by an integrating process to obtain a mean effective temperature difference for the surface swept. This difference is known as the logarithmic mean temperature difference, Δt_m, a general expression for which follows:

$$*\Delta t_m = \frac{\Delta t_1 - \Delta t_2}{\log_e \frac{\Delta t_1}{\Delta t_2}} = \frac{\Delta t_1 - \Delta t_2}{2.3 \log_{10} \frac{\Delta t_1}{\Delta t_2}} \quad (22)$$

where:

Δt_1 = initial temp difference
Δt_2 = final temp difference

For practical design purposes, where the value of the ratio $\frac{\Delta t_1}{\Delta t_2}$ in equation (22) is not over 1.5, the arithmetic mean of the temperature differences may be used as a reasonably close approximation.

The logarithmic mean temperature difference applies to the over-all heat transfer between two fluids when the specific heats and the local heat transfer coefficients are constant, that is, when these values are relatively unaffected by the temperature change along the surface. This is the condition in the majority of convection heat transfer applications in the

*See Fig. 23, Chapter 11, for Δt_m of specific arrangements.

generation of steam. Where either or both the local heat transfer conductance and the specific heat vary along the heat transfer surface, special treatment is required.

Combinations of Heat Transfer Mechanisms

In a practical heat exchanger the transfer of heat usually depends upon the operation of a combination of at least two of the three fundamental mechanisms of heat transfer, conduction, convection, and radiation. For instance, in a tube wall separating two fluids, the convection conductances for each of the two fluid streams as well as the conduction through the tube wall must be evaluated. These conductances are combined into a single over-all conductance.

As noted above in the section on *Conduction*, there is an analogy between heat conduction and electrical conduction. By this analogy any resistance to heat flow may be treated as an equivalent resistance in an electrical circuit. The resistance to heat flow can be defined as the reciprocal of the conductance, or $R = \frac{1}{U}$, where U is the unit for conductance, Btu/sq ft, hr, F.

a) Convection and Conduction Through Tube Wall

In Fig. 10 a tube wall separates two fluids with temperature t_o for the outside fluid and temperature t_i for the inside fluid. The over-all resistance is $R = R_{ab} + R_{bc} + R_{cd}$. Where D_o and D_i are respectively the outside and the inside diameters and k and l_e respectively the conductivity and the equivalent thickness of the tube wall, the conductance per sq ft of outside surface area per hr per F is: U_{oo} through the outside film, $\frac{k}{l_e}$ through the tube wall, and

$U_{ei} \dfrac{D_i}{D_o}$ through the inside film, all referred to the outside surface. If the over-all heat conductance is U, then by substituting the reciprocals of the total and individual conductances for the total and individual resistances the expression becomes:

$$\frac{1}{U} = \frac{1}{U_{oo}} + \frac{l_o}{k} + \frac{1}{U_{ei}} \frac{D_o}{D_i} \qquad (23)$$

For heat transfer between gases or superheated vapors separated by a tube wall, the resistances to heat flow in the films are generally many times greater than the resistance in the metal of the tube. In the evaluation of the over-all coefficient, the metal conductance may, therefore, be neglected without serious error. If the metal conductance is omitted and U_{eo} and U_{ei} are based upon the same surface, equation (23) can be rearranged to read:

$$U = \frac{U_{eo} \times U_{ei}}{U_{eo} + U_{ei}} \qquad (24)$$

This is the general equation for the over-all conductance between two fluids, where the resistance to heat flow of the metal separating them is negligible. In this instance the combination of two convection conductances has been analyzed.

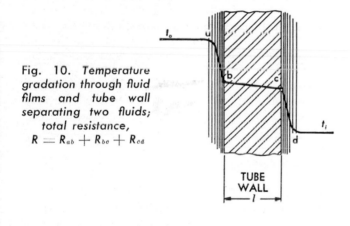

Fig. 10. *Temperature gradation through fluid films and tube wall separating two fluids; total resistance,*
$R = R_{ab} + R_{bc} + R_{cd}$

b) Convection and Radiation in Tube Banks

Carbon dioxide and water vapor, which are found in considerable quantities in the products of combustion of hydrocarbon fuels, absorb and emit radiant energy or heat. In tube banks, therefore, heat is transferred by radiation as well as by convection. Since the resistance of circuits in parallel is the reciprocal of the sum of the reciprocals of the resistance of each circuit, heat transfer resistance, by analogy to electrical resistance, can be expressed as follows:

$$R = \frac{1}{\dfrac{1}{R_{rg}} + \dfrac{1}{R_{cg}}} + R_{tw} + R_{cs} \qquad (25)$$

where:

R_{rg} = resistance of gas film (the hotter fluid) to radiant heat flow

R_{cg} = resistance of gas film (the hotter fluid) to convection heat flow

R_{tw} = resistance of tube wall to conduction heat flow

R_{cs} = resistance of the other fluid film (the colder fluid) to convection heat flow

Neglecting the tube wall resistance, assuming that all conductances are based on the same surface, and substituting the reciprocals of the total and individual conductances for the total and individual resistances in the analogy to the electrical expression:

$$\frac{1}{U} = \frac{1}{U_{rg} + U_{cg}} + \frac{1}{U_{cs}}$$

and by rearranging:

$$U = \frac{(U_{rg} + U_{cg}) \times U_{cs}}{U_{rg} + U_{cg} + U_{cs}} \qquad (26)$$

where:

U_{rg} = intertube radiation conductance, Btu/sq ft, hr, F

U_{cg} = hotter fluid convection conductance, Btu/sq ft, hr, F

U_{cs} = colder fluid convection conductance, Btu/sq ft, hr, F

In equation (26), U represents the combined conductance for most boiler, economizer, superheater, and air heater heat transfer problems, where the resistance to heat flow through metal (such as tube walls) is small and may be neglected. This usually is so where the quantities of heat transferred and the resulting temperatures of the hotter and colder fluids are to be determined. However, where metal temperatures must be accurately established, conductance through the metal must be included.

The combined conductance, U, from equation (26) can now be used in the general equation for heat flow, $q = U S \triangle t_m$, which is identical with equation (1) with $\triangle t_m$ substituted for $\triangle t$ as the mean temperature difference.

An exact evaluation of intertube radiation is too cumbersome for engineering calculations. An approximate value can be obtained by applying the data for cavity radiation to the space bounded by a characteristic cluster of tubes (see Chapter 11).

c) Heat Transfer in Porous Materials

It is well known that porosity is an important factor in the effectiveness of materials as insulation in reducing heat losses. When so used in boiler work, porous materials are backed up by solid walls or casings, so that there is no appreciable flow through the pores of the material.

In porous insulating materials, heat flow is by conduction through the material itself and by the combination of conduction, convection, and radiation across the gas-filled voids in the material. The relative magnitudes of heat flow from these various mechanisms of heat transfer depend upon such variables as porosity of the material, the type of porosity (cellular or otherwise), the type of material, the composition and density of gas filling the voids, the temperature gradient through the material, and the absolute temperature of the material.

The analytical evaluation of the separate mechanisms of heat transfer in porous materials is extremely difficult. Some experimental work, however, has been done to establish an over-all conductivity (see Fig. 19, Chapter 14). Using the factor $k = $ Btu/sq ft, hr, F/in. as over-all conductivity, the expression for the quantity of heat flowing through a porous material per unit of time then becomes similar to the expression for conduction of heat through a homogeneous substance. The effect on thermal conductivity of varying the pore size while maintaining a constant density of the material is shown by Fig. 11. The effect of other variables can be determined in a similar manner.

In high-temperature applications, the principal means of heat transfer across the voids is by radiation. Consequently for good insulation, the mean radiating path in the direction of heat flow should be as disrupted as possible. In low-temperature applications, heat flow by conduction and convection across the voids approaches the order of magnitude of heat flow by radiation. It is therefore important not only that the radiation path should be disrupted but also that the pores should cause the pools or pockets of fluid to be nearly stagnant, so that heat flow by free convection will also be restricted.

An important recent development in the use of porous material is in what is called "transpiration" or "sweat" cooling. This extremely effective method of cooling is currently used for the protection of parts of gas turbines and rocket motors exposed to high gas temperatures, in the order of 3000 to 6000 F and even higher. The part to be cooled is constructed of a porous material consisting of metal particles having a high degree of structural interconnection. The particle interconnections in a porous metal part of this type are obtained by pressing powdered metal in a forming die, followed by heating ("sintering") in an inert atmosphere.

A cooling fluid, either liquid or gas, passes through the porous walls of the part to the surfaces exposed to heat. On leaving this exposed surface, the coolant passes through the adjacent laminar layer of gases in a direction opposite to the flow of heat by conduction through the layer. This opposite flow creates an effective barrier against convection heat transfer to the exposed surface. Heat reaching the surface by radiation or other means travels a short distance (1/32 to 1/16 in.) into the material by thermal conduction through the interconnected metal particles forming the part. The internal pore surface in this thin layer of material into which the heat penetrates is several times greater than the external surface exposed to the heat, and this very effective internal "extended" surface is cooled by the fluid (coolant) flowing through the material. The thermal conductance between the cooling fluid and the internal surface of the material is extremely high. For air at atmospheric pressure and 80 F as the coolant, this conductance will be in the order of 200 to 1000 Btu/sq ft, hr, F, depending upon pore size (inversely).

d) Heat Exchange

Porous material is also used effectively in various types of regenerative heat exchangers, where a fluid is made to flow through or over the material. A very high ratio of heat exchange surface to volume is possible by this means. Typical of well-known regenerative heat exchangers are: 1) the heating of combustion air for blast furnaces and open-hearth furnaces by passing the air through chambers of brick checkerwork which have been heated by furnace gases and 2) the pebble air heater (see Chapter 11) developed by B&W, where the air is heated by passing it through a heated mass of nonagglomerating solid particles in a moving bed.

A modern technique for regenerative heat exchange, utilizing what is called a "fluidized bed," has been developed in connection with hydrocarbon synthesis, coal gasification, and other chemical processes. The bed of finely pulverized nonagglomerating material is held in suspension (fluidized) by an

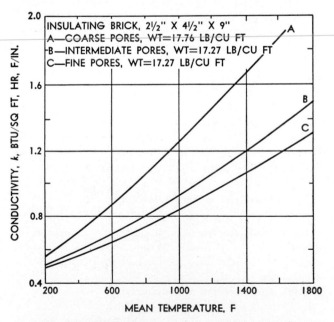

Fig. 11. *Effect of pore size on conductivity, k, of a porous insulating brick*

upward stream of gas. The gas is evenly distributed by a perforated distributing plate at the base of the bed. The very effective transfer of heat to surfaces immersed in the bed results from the high ratio of heat exchange surface to volume of the suspended particles, the high rate of heat transfer between fluid (gas) and particles, and the rapid and thorough intermixing of particles in the fluidized bed.

In some applications of this process, heat is supplied by the combustion of fluidizing air and fuel within the bed itself, and the excess heat is removed by a tubular heat exchanger immersed in the bed. When combustion or other chemical reaction is made to take place in the fluidized bed, the fluidizing gas is not recirculated through the bed. However, almost all of the bed particles in the leaving gas are extracted by a cyclone separator and returned to the bed.

Other Forms of Heat Transfer

Condensation—Film Type

When a pure saturated vapor strikes a surface of lower temperature, the vapor condenses, and a film is formed on the surface. If it is assumed that the condensate film flows along the surface because of gravity alone and a condition of streamline flow exists throughout the film thickness, then heat transfer through this film is by conduction only.

Since the heat exchange is by conduction, the thickness of the condensate film has a direct effect on the quantity of heat transferred. The thickness of the film, in turn, depends upon the rate at which the condensate is removed. On a vertical surface, because of drainage, the thickness of the film at the bottom will be greater than at the top. The thickness of the film will increase as a plate is inclined from the vertical position.

An increase in the film temperature, which is the mean of the surface and vapor temperatures, decreases the film thickness, since the drainage velocity increases with the decrease in viscosity. The film thickness is affected by an appreciable velocity of the vapor because of the frictional drag between the vapor and the condensate. The preferable arrangement of the surface, therefore, is such that the vapor flows in the same direction (downward) as the condensate. As heat transfer increases with an increase in the temperature difference between the vapor and the surface, the thickness of the condensate film also increases. The surface conductance of heat transfer, therefore, decreases with an increase in temperature difference, which is an unusual relationship.

The theoretical equations for the conductance of heat transfer for film condensation involve the thermal conductivity, viscosity, and density of the condensate, the temperature difference between the vapor and the surface, and certain dimensions of the surface, such as height for vertical surfaces and diameter for horizontal tubes.

Dropwise Condensation

Steam will condense in drops, rather than as a film, on a surface contaminated with a substance which prevents the condensate from wetting the surface. Under these conditions a large part of the surface, not covered by an insulating film, is free for unobstructed heat transfer. This is known as dropwise condensation. The data of several investigators indicate that conductances for dropwise condensation are 4 to 8 times as high as the conductances for film condensation.

Mass Transfer and Diffusion

There are two related phenomena involved in some types of condensation. When a mixture of condensable vapor and a noncondensable gas is in contact with a surface which is below the dewpoint of the mixture, some condensation occurs, and a film of liquid is formed on the surface. A common example of this phenomenon is the condensation of water vapor on the outside of a glass of iced tea.

The mixture of vapor and noncondensable gas adjacent to the condensate film contains a lower proportion of vapor than the main body of the mixture, since some of the vapor has been removed as condensate. As vapor from the main body of the mixture diffuses through the vapor-lean layer, it is condensed on the cold surface. The rate of condensation is thus governed by the laws of gas diffusion, while the sensible heat transmission is controlled by the laws of heat conduction and convection. This mode of heat transfer is important in the design of cooling towers, humidifiers, etc., where mixtures of vapors and noncondensable gases are encountered.

Evaporation or Boiling

The boiling point of a liquid may be defined as the temperature at which its vapor pressure is equal to the total pressure above its free surface. Under special conditions the liquid may be heated until the vapor pressure is considerably higher than the total pressure, without the formation of bubbles as a visible indication of "boiling." When a liquid is heated to a temperature above its boiling point, it is said to be superheated.

A liquid must be superheated to start bubble formation (for temperatures below the "critical"), because more thermal energy is required to free an escaping molecule from a small concave surface than from a plane surface. This concept is based on the molecular action at the interface between a liquid and its vapor. Molecules of the liquid continually leave the surface and are projected into space. This space, however, is not empty but is occupied by rapidly moving vapor and gaseous molecules which are farther apart than the molecules escaping from the liquid. Some of the vapor molecules are continually entering the liquid. When the rate at which molecules escape from the liquid to the vapor equals the rate at which molecules from the vapor enter the liquid, a condition of equilibrium exists, and there is no net interchange of material between liquid and vapor phases. When heat is added to the liquid, its temperature and the corresponding kinetic energy of its molecules increase, with the result that molecules escape from the liquid surface at a faster rate than molecules from the vapor enter the liquid. This is the process known as evaporation.

Escaping molecules from a flat liquid surface collide only with the vapor and gaseous molecules above this surface, but when the liquid surface is in hollow or concave form, the escaping molecules occasionally collide with one another. Such collisions increase in frequency as the curvature of the surface increases, and they reach a maximum when the surface returns upon itself like the inside of a hollow sphere or bubble, where the opposing walls tend to cancel each other's efforts to eject molecules into space. It follows that a smaller number of the vapor and gaseous molecules are required within the bubble to prevent additional molecules from permanently escaping from the liquid. This means that the pressure within the bubble is lower than the pressure above a flat liquid surface or, conversely, that the superheat in the

liquid must be higher around a bubble than at a flat liquid surface. If the diameter of the bubble is infinitely small, the superheat has to be infinitely high, so, theoretically, in an absolutely pure liquid a bubble cannot be started, and boiling below the liquid surface cannot be initiated.

Water can be evaporated without considerable superheating because of the presence in the liquid of small curved surfaces which tend to initiate bubble formation. This condition is caused in part by the roughness of the heating surface and by the presence of dissolved gases or small particles which act as nuclei for the formation of bubbles. Heat transfer from a heating surface to a vapor bubble may be divided into two parts: 1) from the heating surface to the boiling liquid and 2) from the liquid to the bubble.

At high temperature differences, the conductance reaches a maximum and then decreases with a further increase in temperature difference. This is because of the formation of a continuous vapor film at the surface, which insulates the surface from the liquid. The surface becomes so hot that the liquid no longer wets it, as in the case of a drop of water rolling on the cover of a hot stove.

The temperature difference between the surface and the liquid for maximum heat transfer varies but is usually in the order of 40 to 80 F. Maximum film conductance for boiling water at atmospheric pres-

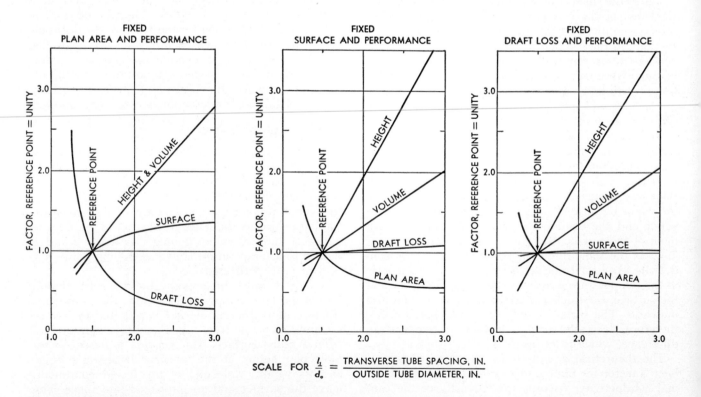

Fig. 12. General effect of convection tube arrangement on volume occupied, amount of surface, draft loss, and floor area for selected conditions fixed. Based on tubes in line and longitudinal spacing, $l_{\parallel} = 2 \times$ tube OD

sure is approximately 10,000 Btu/sq ft, hr, F. Field tests of boilers, however, have indicated film conductances in the order of 20,000 Btu/sq ft, hr, F. The boiling-water film conductance is so high that this conductance is not a limiting factor and may be ignored in evaluating surface requirements.

It is apparent that with boiling liquids, forced circulation of the liquids or the gases is not necessary to obtain very high film conductances. There has been intensive research in connection with the possible use of this method of heat transfer in rocket- and jet-engine cooling and in removing heat from nuclear piles.

Heat Transfer Applications

Convection Banks

In applying the theoretical relationships of heat transfer by convection to the design of practical convection banks in boilers, many other factors must be considered, which will usually require a compromise in selecting the optimum characteristics. Among these factors, the effects of which on freedom of design are covered in detail in Chapters 11 and 12, are:

1. Available space in a plant.
2. Type of fuel, firing rates, and feedwater conditions.
3. Maintenance and operating costs.
4. Allowable metal temperatures and drum- or header-wall thicknesses.
5. Manufacturing standards set up by boiler manufacturers for a range of tube sizes and arrangements based on operating experience.

a) Tube Spacing and Arrangement

The more important factors, other than heat absorption and resistance to gas flow, to be considered in establishing the optimum tube spacing and arrangement for a convection surface are slagging or fouling of surfaces, accessibility for cleaning, and space occupied. However, within these limitations, an optimum transverse spacing for in-line or staggered banks should be selected. A large longitudinal spacing ($l_{||}$) in relation to the transverse spacing ($l_\perp$) is usually undesirable, since the length of flow path for the calculated surface may be excessive.

The effect on design of various ratios of transverse tube spacing to outside tube diameter is plotted in Fig. 12 for in-line tube banks and longitudinal spacing equal to two tube diameters. By entering the curves with calculated values for draft loss, heating surface, and space occupied based on an assumed tube diameter and transverse spacing, a pattern best suited to the requirements of the unit can be selected. Similar curves can be plotted for staggered arrangements with a fixed back pitch.

b) Tube Diameter

For turbulent flow, the heat transfer conductance is inversely proportional to some power of the tube diameter (see equations (16) and (19) above). The exponent for longitudinal flow is 0.20 and for cross-flow, 0.39. For most effective heat transfer, therefore, it is desirable to hold the tube diameter to a minimum. An optimum tube diameter for this purpose, however, may require an arrangement that is expensive to fabricate and difficult to install and maintain in operating condition, thus increasing the initial and maintenance costs. A compromise between heat transfer effectiveness and manufacturing, erection, and service limitations is, therefore, always necessary in the selection of tube diameter.

In oil-fired boilers of high rating for marine service, tubes of 1-in. OD are used in the boiler bank beyond the screen tubes. Because of the higher heat absorption rates, which necessitate an increase in the quantity of circulating water, the screen tubes and water-wall tubes are usually 1½-in. OD (see Chapter 11 for tube sizes in other applications).

c) Penetration of Radiation

A convection bank or banks of tubes bordering a furnace or a cavity act as blackbodies in absorbing radiant heat. Some of this heat, however, radiates through the spaces between the tubes of the first row and sometimes penetrates beyond the fourth row. The quantity of radiant heat penetration can be established by geometric or analytical methods. The effect of this penetration is especially important in establishing tube temperatures for superheaters located fairly close to a furnace or a high-temperature cavity (see Chapter 11).

d) Effect of Lanes

Lanes in tube banks, formed by the omission of a row of tubes, may decrease the heat absorption considerably, since, in effect, these passages act as by-passes for the hot gases through the banks. Although the over-all efficiency will decrease, the high mass flow and greater gas weight through the lanes will increase the absorption rates of the adjacent tubes and may develop critical tube temperatures in superheaters or steaming conditions in economizers. Whenever possible, therefore, lanes should be eliminated both within tube banks and between tube banks and walls. Lanes, however, are unavoidable under certain conditions. In installing superheaters, for instance, space must be allowed for additional surface to satisfy future specified increases in superheated steam temperature. A calculation for the lanes, taking into account the increased gas weight and mass flow, is therefore necessary.

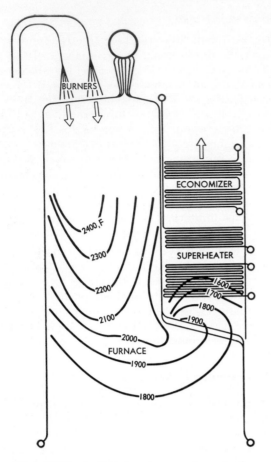

Fig. 13. *Typical temperature contours in the furnace of a down-fired Radiant boiler*

e) Heat Transfer to Water

Water Film Conductance. In boiler design practice, the film conductance for water in economizers is so much higher than the gas-side conductance that it is neglected in evaluating economizer surface.

Boiling-Water Conductance. In boiler practice the combined gas-side conductance (convection plus intertube radiation) seldom exceeds 30 Btu/sq ft, hr, F. In estimating the resistance to heat flow, the film conductance for boiling water is therefore neglected, since its reciprocal (the resistance to heat flow) is so very small compared to the gas-side resistance.

Effect of Oil or Scale. Scale deposits interpose a high resistance to the flow of heat, and the additional temperature drop required to maintain a given fluid temperature inside the tube as the thickness of the scale increases will necessitate a dangerously high metal temperature, which will eventually cause failure. With the high heat absorption rates to which furnace-row tubes of high-capacity boilers are exposed, it is therefore essential entirely to prevent the formation of scale (see Fig. 16, Chapter 29). The formation of scale and the deposit of oil, also a factor in resistance to the flow of heat, can be prevented by proper feedwater treatment and careful operation.

f) Heat Transfer to Steam

In the design of superheaters, the steam film constitutes a significant resistance to the flow of heat, and although this resistance is many times lower than the gas-side resistance, it cannot be neglected in computing the over-all resistance to heat flow or the heat transfer rate. It is particularly significant in estimating superheater tube temperatures, since the temperature of the inside wall is equal to the steam temperature plus the temperature drop through the steam film. If the steam film conductance is designated as U_s, the film temperature drop will be $q/S \div U_s$, where q/S and U_s are expressed in Btu/sq ft, hr, and Btu/sq ft, hr, F, respectively, using the outside surface area of the tube as the base in each expression.

Because of the relative magnitude of the resistance to heat flow in the steam film and the elevated temperatures at which superheater tubes operate, it is imperative that scale deposits be prevented in superheater tubes. Even an extremely thin layer of scale forms an objectionable insulating barrier, which together with the steam film will be sufficient to cause overheating and ultimate failure of a tube.

Furnaces

An analytical solution of the problem of heat transfer in the furnace of a steam-generating unit is extremely complex, and it is impossible to calculate furnace outlet temperatures by theoretical methods alone. Nevertheless, the furnace outlet temperature must be predicted correctly since, in a large measure, this temperature determines the design of the remainder of the unit, particularly the superheater.

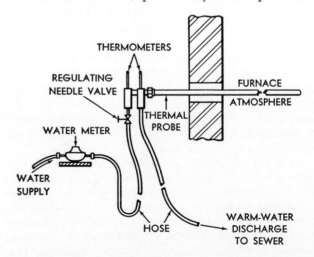

Fig. 14. *Special thermal probe or calorimeter (diagrammatic) sometimes used to establish the heat absorption rates of surfaces throughout a furnace*

An attempt will therefore be made to outline the complexities of the problem and its practical solution.

In the furnace of a steam-generating unit, all of the principal mechanisms of heat transfer take place simultaneously. These mechanisms are: intersolid radiation between solids in fuel beds or pulverized-coal particles and tubes and refractory materials; nonluminous gas radiation from the products of combustion; convection from the furnace gases to the furnace walls; and conduction through ash deposits on tubes.

Temperature varies throughout the furnace (see Fig. 13 for typical furnace-temperature contours). Fuel and air enter at relatively low temperatures, reach a high temperature during combustion, and cool again as the products of combustion give up heat to the furnace enclosure. Water-cooled surface is at a relatively low temperature, while deposits on tubes and refractory in the furnace walls are at high temperatures. All of these temperatures change with load, excess air, burner adjustment, and other operating conditions. A special water-cooled calorimeter, the thermal probe illustrated in Fig. 14 (as well as the high-velocity thermocouple, see Chapter 6), is a useful tool for establishing the order of heat absorption in a furnace. Variations in heat absorption in a primary slag-tap furnace of a steam-generating unit are shown in Fig. 15.

Furnace geometry is complex. Furnaces vary in shape and size, in the location and spacing of burners, in the size of fuel beds, in the disposition of cooling surface, in the spacing of tubes in tube-and-refractory walls, and in the arrangement of arches and hoppers. Flame shape and length affect the geometry of radiation in the furnace.

Surface characteristics vary. The enclosing furnace walls may include any combination of fuel bed, refractory material, studded tubes, water-cooled cast-iron blocks, spaced tubes backed by refractory, close-spaced tubes, or tube banks. Emissivities of flames and various types of surfaces are different. The water-cooled surface may be covered with fluid slag or dry ash in any thickness, or it may be clean. Heat-absorbing surface in a furnace may, when clean, show absorption rates of 175,000 Btu/sq ft, hr, or even higher. When slag accumulations reach equilibrium, the absorption rate may be reduced to 50,000 Btu/sq ft, hr, or even lower.

Fuel variation is significant. Not only are there important differences inherent in the use of different fuels and in the manner in which they are burned, as in stoker, pulverized-coal, gas, oil, or waste-fuel firing, but there are also differences caused by the use of different types of the same fuel. Coal, for example, may be high volatile or low volatile, may have much or little ash, and the ash may fuse at high or low temperature, varying considerably or very little with the oxidizing properties of the furnace atmosphere.

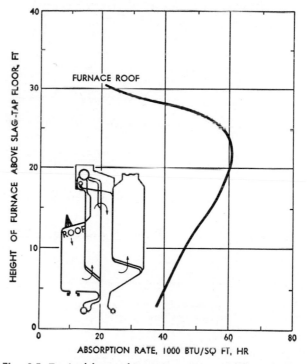

Fig. 15. *Typical heat absorption rates at different elevations in a furnace of type indicated, at maximum output*

Since furnace outlet temperatures cannot be calculated by theoretical heat transfer methods alone, it is necessary to use an empirical approach. Calculations are based on test results from similar types of units, supplemented by data accumulated from operating experience and by judgment based on a knowledge of heat transfer principles and the characteristics of fuels and slags. To acquire the necessary basic information on furnace outlet temperature, B&W pioneered in the development of the high-velocity thermocouple and conducted an extensive program of field tests for measuring gas temperatures in furnaces of operating units. A similar program has been undertaken by a special research committee of the ASME on furnace performance factors.

In setting up an empirical method of furnace temperature calculation, stoker, waste-fuel, pulverized-coal, natural gas, and oil firing must be considered separately. For simplification, the problem is divided into several classes, the number of variables is reduced by disregarding those of lesser importance, and other separate factors are combined into single variables, concentrating on the variables of greatest influence.

In the absorption of radiant heat, the effectiveness of tubes spaced other than touching and backed by refractory as compared with completely water-cooled surface (touching tubes or equivalent*) is shown in Fig. 16. The effectiveness of block-covered or stud-

* A wall of flat-stud tubes is considered completely water cooled.

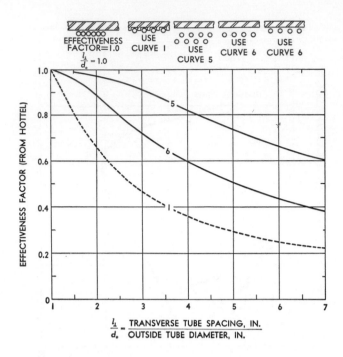

Fig. 16. *Furnace-wall area-effectiveness factor (1.0 for completely water-cooled surface). A reduced area (effective-cold surface) is determined from these curves for walls not completely water cooled ($l_1/d_o > 1$)*

ded-tube surface and its expected ash covering, as compared with completely water-cooled surface, can also be estimated. The entire furnace envelope can then be evaluated in terms of effective-cold surface.

The heat energy supplied by the fuel and by the preheated combustion air, corrected for minor items such as unburned combustible loss, may be combined into a single variable known as heat available (see examples, Chapter 4, Appendix, for calculated values of heat available). For correlating furnace outlet gas temperature and heat available, the Btu per sq ft of absorbing surface is a better basis than Btu per cu ft of furnace volume. Experience has shown that the outlet temperature of a given furnace burning a given fuel in suspension varies approximately as the logarithm of the heat available per hr per sq ft of effective-cold surface.

Assuming typical ratios between effective-cold surface and total furnace envelope, the approximate furnace outlet gas temperature will be of the order shown in Fig. 17. The curve shown for pulverized coal is for a dry-ash-removal furnace with fairly clean walls.

The furnace outlet temperatures and the heat absorption rates for heat available (heat input) rates of most pulverized-coal-fired furnaces lie within the shaded bands shown in Figs. 18 and 19, respectively. The limits indicated are intended to serve only as a general guide. The horizontal scale in each case is

heat available in thousand Btu per hr per sq ft of water-cooled surface, excluding the floors of slag-tap furnaces. The bands for dry-ash and for slag-tap overlap between 100,000 and 150,000 heat available rates, but not with the same coal. Within this range, the coal used in the slag-tap furnace should have a relatively low ash-fluid temperature, and the coal used in the dry-ash furnace should have ash with a very high initial-deformation temperature. In the overlapping range, dry-ash and slag-tap each have about the same rate of heat absorption, as shown in Fig. 19, or the same "dirtiness" factor. Both bands may seem rather broad, but they cover a wide range of ash characteristics, considerable diversity in type of water-wall construction, and, in some cases, a difference in dirtiness as a result of difference in cleaning, load factor, etc.

The quantity of heat leaving the furnace can be calculated from the gas weight leaving the furnace, the composition of the gas, and the furnace outlet gas temperature, using gas enthalpy values given in Chapter 4 (Appendix). The quantity of heat absorbed in the furnace is the difference between the quantity of heat leaving the furnace and the quantity of heat supplied by the preheated combustion air and by the combustion of the fuel fired.

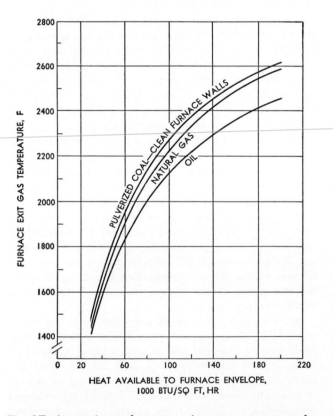

Fig. 17. *Approximate furnace outlet gas temperature for different fuels at different rates of heat available to water-cooled furnace surface*

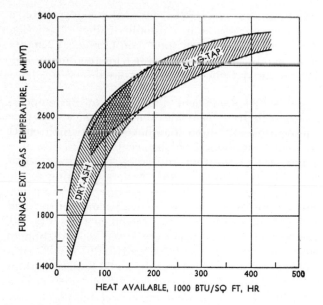

Fig. 18. *General range of furnace exit gas temperature for dry-ash and slag-tap pulverized-coal firing*

Cavities

In designing steam-generating units, it is necessary to provide cavities between tube banks for access, for soot blowers, or for the installation of additional surface as required. However, heat transfer from hot flue gas to heat-absorbing surface surrounding cavities does take place. The gas loses heat by radiation to the surroundings while passing through the cavity. Though the procedure for calculating the quantity of heat transferred in a particular case is too complex for treatment here, cavity radiation can be calculated by using methods applying to nonluminous radiation developed by authorities on heat transfer. It may be of interest, however, to discuss briefly some of the factors which affect heat transfer by nonluminous gas radiation in cavities.

Temperature Level. Radiation from nonluminous gases to the boundary surfaces and radiation to the gas by the surroundings increase approximately as the fourth powers of their respective absolute temperatures.

Composition of the Gas. In steam-generating units, the only normal constituents of flue gas which contribute importantly to nonluminous gas radiation are carbon dioxide and water vapor. The concentrations of these constituents depend upon the fuel burned and the excess air; the amount of radiation depends upon these concentrations.

Particles in the Gas. The particles carried by dust-laden gases receive heat from the gas by radiation,

convection, and conduction and radiate by intersolid radiation to the surroundings.

Size of Cavity. The quantity of heat transferred per unit of time increases as the size of the cavity increases. Thick layers of gas radiate more vigorously than thin layers. The shape of the cavity also has a complicated effect upon heat transfer.

Receiving Surface. Refractory surface forming part of a cavity boundary will reach a fairly high temperature by convection and radiation from the flue gas and will reradiate to the gas and to the other walls of the enclosure. Reradiation from clean heat-absorbing surface is small unless the surface temperature is high, as it may be in superheaters and reheaters. Deposits of ash or slag on the tubes reduce heat absorption and increase reradiation.

In boiler design there are two effects of cavity radiation which are important. The temperature of flue gas will drop, sometimes as much as 100 F, in passing across a cavity. This is a significant fact in design calculations. Gas radiation also increases the heat absorption rates for the tubes forming the cavity boundaries. This effect is often important in high-temperature superheaters, where absorption rates strongly influence tube temperatures and the selection of alloys.

Insulation

The calculation of heat transfer through insulation follows the principles outlined for conduction through a composite wall. A number of practical matters must also be considered in the design of insulation. These will be briefly discussed. The reader is

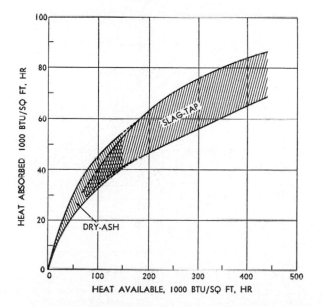

Fig. 19. *General range of furnace heat absorption in dry-ash and slag-tap pulverized-coal-fired furnaces*

referred to Chapter 14 for detail information, including properties of insulating materials, the mechanics of application, and a sample calculation of heat flow through a tube-and-brick wall covered with insulation.

Hot-Face Temperature. In a boiler furnace with tube-to-tube walls, the hot-face temperature of the insulation may be taken as saturation temperature of the water in the tubes. If the inner face of the furnace wall is refractory, with or without cooling by spaced tubes, the hot-face temperature of the insulation must be calculated or estimated from a knowledge of conditions on the gas side of the furnace wall, based on radiation and convection heat transfer and empirical data. Fortunately, for a considerable error in the hot-face temperature of the insulation, the corresponding error in cold-surface temperature is much smaller, and the effect on total heat loss from the unit is not important, although it may be misleading in the selection of materials.

Heat Loss and Cold-Face Temperature. The heat loss to the surroundings and the cold-surface temperature decrease as the thickness of the insulation increases. A cold-face temperature of 130 to 160 F is usually considered satisfactory for a boiler room. When the insulation is thick, the change in cold-surface temperature for increase in thickness is small, whereas the cost of the insulation increases steadily with thickness (see Chapter 14). Standard commercial thicknesses of insulating materials should be used in the composite wall.

The detailed calculation of over-all heat loss by radiation and convection from the surfaces of a steam-generating unit (usually called "radiation loss") is tedious and time consuming. A simple approximate method is provided by the chart (Fig. 20) prepared from the ABAI original.

Ambient Air Conditions. Low ambient air temperature and high air velocities tend to reduce cold-face temperature, although they have only a small effect on total heat loss, since surface film resistance is a minor part of the total insulation resistance to heat flow. The proximity of other boilers radiating to the first will increase cold-face temperature. Surface film conductances for various wall temperatures and ambient air conditions may be taken from Fig. 20, Chapter 14. These curves are based on radiation to 80 F surroundings, using an emissivity of 0.95, plus natural-convection heat transfer to 80 F air at various velocities. The effect of surface conductance on heat loss through casings and on casing temperature is illustrated in Fig. 22, Chapter 14.

Temperature-Use Limits and Conductivities. Refractory or insulation material suitable for high-temperature applications is usually more expensive and less effective as insulation than low-temperature materials. It is therefore customary to use several layers of insulation, the lowest cost and most effective insulation in the cool zones and the higher cost material only where the temperature exceeds the permissible operating limits for low-temperature materials. Typical temperature-use limits and thermal conductivities are shown in Fig. 19, Chapter 14.

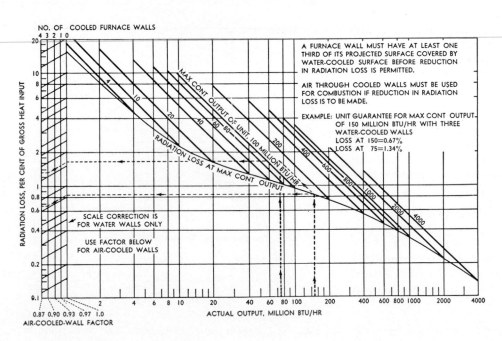

Fig. 20. *Radiation loss (ABAI) in per cent of gross heat input*

FLUID DYNAMICS

IN THE production and utilization of steam there are many problems involving the flow of fluids. The broad subject of fluid mechanics must be culled for those elements which are of particular significance in the field of steam. These would include the flow of steam and water in pipes, fittings, valves, and tube bundles; the flow of air and gases through ducts and tube banks; the convection flow and circulation of water and steam; the convection flow of gases for draft effect; the flow of water and steam through nozzles, orifices, and venturi tubes; the throttling calorimeter; and the separation of liquids, vapors, and solid particles from flowing streams. The fluids-in-motion, or fluid dynamic aspects of these phenomena are more important in practice than fluid statics.

Determination of the velocity, v, at which the fluid moves is a prime requirement in the study of the effects produced by fluid motion. To evaluate the quantity of flow, friction losses, viscosity forces, particle separation, heat absorption and fluid flow paths it is first necessary to know the fluid velocity.

Energy Equation Applied to Fluid Flow

The basic theoretical relationships involving all fluid flow stem from the fundamental general energy equation of Chapter 10. Thus if a fluid moves through a system (an orifice or a pipe line), no heat is added or abstracted ($\triangle Q = 0$), no work is done ($\triangle W = 0$), the general energy equation can be reduced to the form:

$$\frac{v_2^2 - v_1^2}{2g} = (p_1 V_1 + u_1) - (p_2 V_2 + u_2) + (Z_1 - Z_2) \tag{1}$$

Where:

v_1 and v_2 = fluid velocities, @ stations (1) and (2) respectively, ft/sec

g = gravitational constant, 32.2 ft/sec²

p_1 and p_2 = static pressures @ respective stations, lb/sq ft

V_1 and V_2 = specific volumes @ respective stations, cu ft/lb

u_1 and u_2 = internal energy of fluid @ respective stations, Btu/lb

Z_1 and Z_2 = elevation above datum @ respective stations, ft

Where there is no difference in elevation at the initial and subsequent stations (1) and (2), $Z_1 = Z_2$, and where the initial velocity of the fluid, v_1, often referred to as the velocity of approach, is zero or negligibly small, equation (1) for the gain in kinetic energy becomes:

$$\frac{v_2^2}{2g} = (p_1 V_1 + u_1) - (p_2 V_2 + u_2) \tag{2}$$

Since the energies represented by ($p_1 V_1 + u_1$) and ($p_2 V_2 + u_2$) are equal to the energies represented by the enthalpy h_1 and h_2 of the fluid at the respective stations, equation (2) for the gain in kinetic energy becomes:

$$\frac{v_2^2}{2g} = (h_1 - h_2) \tag{3}$$

If enthalpy is measured in Btu per lb, as is generally the case, equation (3) for the gain in kinetic energy becomes:

$$\frac{v_2^2}{2g} = 778^* (h_1 - h_2), \text{ ft lb/lb.} \tag{4}$$

* Exact value = 778.26

Solving equation (4) for velocity

$$v_2 = 223.7 \sqrt{h_1 - h_2}, \text{ ft/sec, jet velocity} \tag{5}$$

For steam as the fluid, the enthalpy drop may be determined from the Mollier chart (see Chapter 10, Appendix). Where a Mollier chart is not available, and if the perfect gas laws are applicable, the velocity can be computed with the following equation:

$$v_2 = 8.02 \sqrt{\frac{k}{k-1} \times p_1 V_1 \left[1 - \left\{ \frac{p_2}{p_1} \right\}^{\frac{k-1}{k}} \right]}$$

ft/sec, jet velocity   (6)

where:

$k = C_p/C_v$, ratio of specific heats @ constant pressure and constant volume

Equations (1) through (5) apply to all fluids, equation (6) to fluids that follow the perfect-gas laws. For an incompressible fluid, where the specific volume does not change ($V_1 = V_2$) and where, with frictionless flow, the internal energies u_1 and u_2 are equal, equation (1) for the gain in kinetic energy becomes:

$$\frac{v_2{}^2 - v_1{}^2}{2g} = (p_1 - p_2) V + (Z_1 - Z_2)$$
$$= H_{\Delta p} + H_{\Delta z} = H, \text{ ft-lb/lb} = \text{ft} \quad (7)$$

where:

$H_{\Delta p}$ = head from pV difference between 1 and 2, feet of fluid

$H_{\Delta z}$ = head from difference in elevation between 1 and 2, ft of fluid

$H = H_{\Delta p} + H_{\Delta z}$ = net head causing flow, ft

$V = V_1 = V_2$, specific volume of fluid, cu ft/lb

If the velocity of approach, initial velocity, v_1, is zero or negligibly small, equation (7) for the gain in kinetic energy becomes:

$$\frac{v_2{}^2}{2g} = H, \text{ ft head of fluid (velocity head)} \quad (8)$$

Solving equation (8) for velocity:

$$v_2 = 8.02 \sqrt{H}, \text{ ft/sec, jet velocity} \quad (9)$$

In establishing the head, H, in ft of fluid, the following conversions are helpful:

$$H, \text{ ft of fluid} = \frac{\Delta p \text{ in psi} \times 144}{\text{specific weight of fluid}} \quad (10)$$

Or use Fig. 21, Chapter 10 (for water)

$$H, \text{ ft of gas} = \frac{\text{head in in. of water}}{12} \times \frac{\text{specific weight of water}}{\text{specific weight of gas}} \quad (11)$$

For the conversion of manometer readings to head, H, in ft of fluid flowing:

$$H, \text{ ft of fluid} = \text{manometer scale, ft} \times \frac{\delta_{mf} - \delta_{sf}}{\delta_{ff}}$$
$$(11a)$$

where:

δ_{mf} = specific weight of manometer fluid

δ_{sf} = specific weight of superposed fluid

δ_{ff} = specific weight of fluid flowing

Where the superposed fluid is air or gas, the value of δ_{sf} is negligibly small and need not be considered.

From equation (9) it is evident that, for frictionless flow of a nonexpansive fluid with a negligible velocity of approach ($v_1 = 0$), the velocity of a free-spouting jet is determined solely by the pressure or head, H, in ft of fluid causing the flow and that the velocity of the jet is independent of the density of the fluid.

To determine the velocity for expansive fluids where the pressure drop is small, as in many metering nozzles or the flow of air in fan and draft systems, equation (5) or (6) cannot be used with reliability because of the difficulty in accurately evaluating the factors involved. In such cases, where the difference in specific weight of the fluid upstream and downstream is small, $\frac{V_2 - V_1}{V_2} < 0.05$, the fluid may be considered practically nonexpansive, and equation (9) can be used to determine the velocity.

The example below will serve to illustrate an application of equation (5) to a simple case of an expansive fluid in motion:

Example 1

To find the velocity of steam flowing from a header through a well-insulated horizontal pipe, using the Mollier chart to determine the enthalpy of the steam at stations 1 and 2 for the conditions given:

Station 1 in header	$v_1 = 0$
Steam pressure	207 psia
Steam temperature	469 F
Enthalpy, h_1	1250 Btu/lb

Station 2 in pipe	v_2 to be determined
Steam pressure	118 psia
Steam temperature	380 F
Enthalpy, h_2	1214 Btu/lb

Substituting values of h_1 and h_2 in equation (5):

$$v_2 = 223.7 \sqrt{1250 - 1214} = 1342 \text{ ft/sec}$$

The observed value of h_2 reflects the effect of pipe friction on the steam, tending to raise the value of h_2 and thus decrease the value of v_2. Had the flow in the pipe to station 2 been assumed to encounter less friction, the observed hypothetical values of pressure and temperature might have been 120 psia and 358 F ($h_2 = 1200$ Btu), giving a velocity of:

$$v_2 = 223.7 \sqrt{1250 - 1200} = 1582 \text{ ft/sec}$$

Flow from well-formed nozzles and thin-plate orifices closely approaches the frictionless condition (constant entropy). Flow through rough pipes or labyrinthine channels, such as turbine shaft seals, is far removed from the frictionless condition.

Loss From Friction

To express the effect of friction on a nonexpansive fluid (or where the change in specific volume, V, is negligible) flowing between two points at the same elevation, equation (1) becomes:

$$p_1 V + \frac{v_1{}^2}{2g} = p_2 V + \frac{v_2{}^2}{2g} + (u_2 - u_1) \quad (12)$$

Where: $u_2 - u_1 =$ change in internal energy due to friction

or

$$p_1V + \frac{v_1^2}{2g} = p_2V + \frac{v_2^2}{2g} + H_F \qquad (13)$$

and

$$H_F = (p_1 - p_2)V + \frac{v_1^2}{2g} - \frac{v_2^2}{2g} \qquad (14)$$

Where: $H_F =$ head loss due to friction, ft of fluid flowing, equal in energy to $u_2 - u_1$, the change in internal energy due to friction

If $v_1 = 0$, equation (14) becomes

$$H_F = (p_1 - p_2)V - \frac{v_2^2}{2g}, \text{ ft of fluid} \qquad (15)$$

If $v_1 = v_2$,

$$H_F = (p_1 - p_2)V, \text{ ft of fluid} \qquad (16)$$

Since head loss due to friction is a function of velocity squared, it is frequently given as a loss of so many velocity heads (head loss due to friction $\div$ the velocity head, $\frac{v^2}{2g}$, in the conduit).

The simple example (Fig. 1) will serve to demonstrate a typical application of equation (16) where the over-all friction loss, including entrance and exit losses, is to be determined for a portion of a flow circuit in which the elevation, $Z_1 = Z_2$, and the difference in specific volume is negligible.

The velocity head, $\frac{v^2}{2g} = H$, ft of fluid flowing, for the tube in the flow circuit is determined by the proper conversion of the reading of a manometer connected to a pitot tube suitably inserted in the stream of the moving fluid.

To find the friction loss, the pressure drop, $(p_1 - p_2)V$, is determined by a proper conversion of the reading of a U tube manometer connected to indicate the difference in static pressure at the two points.

Weight and Volume Flow

The velocity of a free spouting jet as determined variously by the use of equations (5), (6) and (9) can be combined with the cross-sectional area of the flow path (conduit, nozzle or aperture) to give the continuity equations for volume and weight flow:

$$Q = Av \qquad (17)$$
$$W = Av\delta \qquad (18)$$

Where:
$Q =$ volume flow, cu ft/sec
$A =$ cross-sectional flow area, sq ft
$v =$ flow velocity, ft/sec
$W =$ weight flow, lb/sec
$\delta =$ fluid density, lb/cu ft
    $=$ reciprocal of specific volume, cu ft/lb

Equations (9), (17) and (18) applied to cold water flowing through a nozzle of 1 sq in. area give ideal flow velocities and quantities as shown in Fig. 2. The flow velocity, the volume flow, and the weight flow all increase as the square root of the head.

With an expansive fluid, such as steam or air, the flow relationships are not as simple as for water. The results seem to be contrary to expectation. It is possible rationally to interpret the observed facts only after careful analysis and study. The complication stems from the change in specific volume and temperature which accompanies a drop in pressure and an increase in velocity. The flow relationships of an expansive fluid may be demonstrated by considering a nozzle in which the initial pressure, p_1, is constant and the back pressure, p_2, is variable. In this case, for dry saturated steam where the initial pressure is fixed as 100 psia and the back pressure ranges from 100 psia downward, the ideal weight flow is as shown in Fig. 3.

The unique feature of this graph is the rapid increase in the weight flow as the pressure difference increases until it reaches a value of 45.6 psia. The

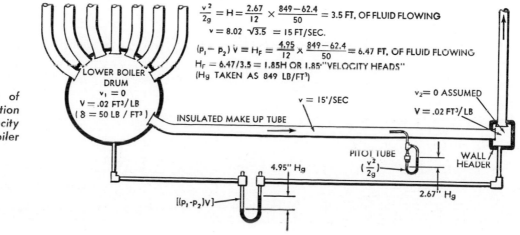

Fig. 1. Determination of flow velocity, and friction losses, in terms of velocity heads, in a simple boiler circuit

$\frac{v^2}{2g} = H = \frac{2.67}{12} \times \frac{849 - 62.4}{50} = 3.5$ FT. OF FLUID FLOWING

$v = 8.02 \sqrt{3.5} = 15$ FT/SEC.

$(p_1 - p_2)V = H_F = \frac{4.95}{12} \times \frac{849 - 62.4}{50} = 6.47$ FT. OF FLUID FLOWING

$H_F = 6.47/3.5 = 1.85H$ OR 1.85 "VELOCITY HEADS"
(H_g TAKEN AS 849 LB/FT³)

LOWER BOILER DRUM
$v_1 = 0$
$V = .02$ FT³/LB
($\delta = 50$ LB/FT³)

INSULATED MAKE UP TUBE

$v = 15'$/SEC

$v_2 = 0$ ASSUMED
$V = .02$ FT³/LB

PITOT TUBE
$\left(\frac{v^2}{2g}\right)$

WALL/HEADER

4.95" Hg

2.67" Hg

$[(p_1 - p_2)V]$

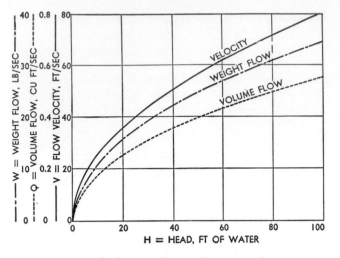

Fig. 2. *Ideal water flow velocities and quantities through a 1 sq in. (throat) nozzle*

weight flow will not increase for any further decrease in the back pressure, i.e., for any further increase in the pressure drop across the nozzle. This limitation of the value of the weight flow is a critical condition, characteristic of expansive fluids, and is most conveniently measured in terms of a critical pressure, p_c. The critical pressure is usually expressed as a fraction of the initial pressure, p_1, and has a value between 0.5 and 0.6 for all gases and vapors. For fixed gases it is defined by the equation:

$$\text{Critical pressure ratio, } \frac{p_c}{p_1} = \left\{ \frac{2}{k+1} \right\}^{\frac{k}{k-1}} \ (19)$$

Where:

$$k = \frac{\text{specific heat @ constant pressure}}{\text{specific heat @ constant volume}}$$

Typical values for k and the critical pressure ratio are given in Table 1.

TABLE 1

Substance	k	p_c/p_1
Air	1.40	0.528
Superheated steam		
$p_1 = 100$ psia $T_1 = 400F$	1.31	0.544
$p_1 = 500$ psia $T_1 = 900F$	1.28	0.549
$p_1 = 1000$ psia $T_1 = 1000F$ $p_1 = 1500$ psia $T_1 = 1050F$	1.27	0.551
Dry saturated steam		
$p_1 = 100$ psia	1.31	0.544
$p_1 = 500$ psia	1.28	0.549
$p_1 = 1000$ psia	1.26	0.553

The maximum weight flow is fixed by the acoustic velocity developed in the throat of the nozzle and

the density of the fluid at the critical condition. This critical phenomenon can be illustrated most effectively in a graph, as in Fig. 4, plotted as in Fig. 3 except that the ratio (p_2/p_1) is substituted for the pressure drop $(p_1 - p_2)$. If the initial pressure, p_1, is constant on the nozzle and the back pressure, p_2, is variable, the typical graph for weight flow can be plotted as in diagram (a) in Fig. 4. On the other hand, if the back pressure, p_2, is constant and the initial pressure, p_1, is variable, the typical graph for weight flow can be plotted as in diagram (b) in Fig. 4.

Where the initial pressure, p_1, is constant and the back pressure, p_2, is variable (diagram (a) Fig. 4) is will be noted, as the back pressure decreases, that the weight flow increases rapidly, reaching a maximum when the back pressure is equal to the critical pressure, p_c, i.e., when p_2/p_1 is equal to the critical pressure ratio, p_c/p_1. Any further reduction in back pressure will not increase the weight flow, since the critical pressure, p_c, a constant for this condition, serves as a barrier and limits expansion in the nozzle to that pressure. The weight flow from this point to the lowest value of the back pressure is, therefore, constant. For the condition where the initial pressure, p_1, is variable and the back pressure, p_2, is constant (diagram (b) Fig. 4), the critical pressure, p_c, increases as the initial pressure increases, since the critical pressure ratio, p_c/p_1, is a constant. Up to and including the point where the critical pressure, p_c, becomes equal to the constant back pressure, p_2, i.e., where $p_c/p_1 = p_2/p_1$, the velocity for calculating weight flow is based on complete expansion from the initial pressure, p_1, to the constant back pressure, p_2. From this point, as the initial pressure increases,

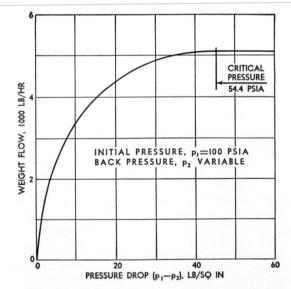

Fig. 3. *Ideal weight flow of dry saturated steam through a 1 sq in. (throat) nozzle*

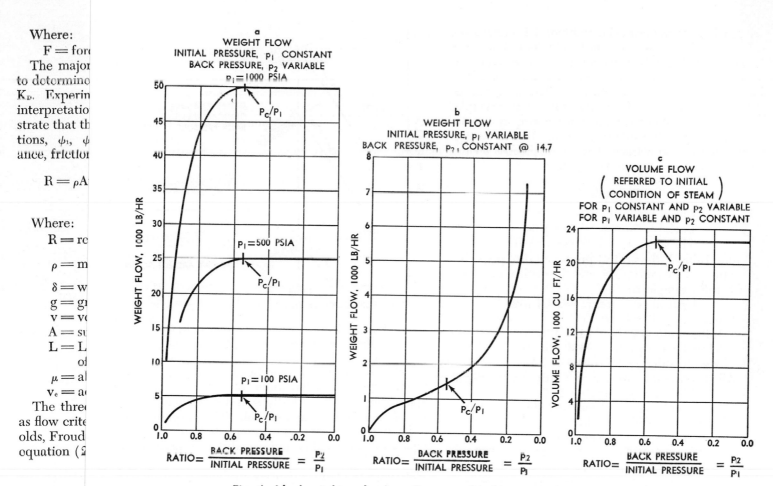

a

WEIGHT FLOW
INITIAL PRESSURE, p_1 CONSTANT
BACK PRESSURE, p_2 VARIABLE
p_1 = 1000 PSIA

WEIGHT FLOW, 1000 LB/HR

P_c/P_1

P_1 = 500 PSIA

P_c/P_1

P_1 = 100 PSIA

P_c/P_1

$$RATIO = \frac{BACK\ PRESSURE}{INITIAL\ PRESSURE} = \frac{P_2}{P_1}$$

b

WEIGHT FLOW
INITIAL PRESSURE, p_1 VARIABLE
BACK PRESSURE, p_2, CONSTANT @ 14.7

WEIGHT FLOW, 1000 LB/HR

P_c/P_1

$$RATIO = \frac{BACK\ PRESSURE}{INITIAL\ PRESSURE} = \frac{P_2}{P_1}$$

c

VOLUME FLOW
(REFERRED TO INITIAL
CONDITION OF STEAM)
FOR p_1 CONSTANT AND p_2 VARIABLE
FOR p_1 VARIABLE AND p_2 CONSTANT

VOLUME FLOW, 1000 CU FT/HR

P_c/P_1

$$RATIO = \frac{BACK\ PRESSURE}{INITIAL\ PRESSURE} = \frac{P_2}{P_1}$$

Fig. 4. Ideal weight and volume flow rates for dry saturated steam through a
1 sq in. (throat) nozzle with different initial and back pressure conditions

the corresponding increase in the critical pressure limits the expansion from the initial pressure to the critical pressure and, thus, while the weight flow continues to increase rapidly, the critical pressures serve as barriers to complete expansion to the back pressure.

It is interesting to note that the volume flow indicated in diagram (c) Fig. 4 at the various ratios of p_2/p_1 is constant for all initial pressures if the critical pressure ratio is rounded out at an average (see Table 1) for the gas concerned. The difference, using the particular values of p_c/p_1 for various values of p_1 is negligible. Also, there is no change in volume flow at various ratios of p_2/p_1 whether the initial pressure is constant and the back pressure is variable or the reverse. In other words, for the various conditions of weight flow shown, the volume flow does not change for the same size nozzle opening.

Because of the limitation on weight flow through nozzles with large pressure drops, and since the acoustic velocity in a gaseous substance does not change materially with pressure but only with temperature, it is possible and convenient to develop

simple, rational equations for weight flow, as given below:

Weight Flow, W, lb per sec
Through 1 in. sq Nozzle

For dry saturated steam

$$W = \frac{p_1^{0.97}}{60} \qquad (20)$$

For superheated steam

$$W = \frac{p_1^{0.97}}{60\ (1 + 0.00065F\ superheat)} \qquad (21)$$

For wet steam

$$W = \frac{p_1^{0.97}}{60\ \sqrt{dryness\ fraction}} \qquad (22)$$

For air
Where $p_1 > 2$ atmospheres, and $p_2 \leqslant 1$ atmosphere

$$W = \frac{p_1}{1.9\ \sqrt{T_1}} \qquad (23)$$

Where p_1 = initial pressure, psia; and T_1 = initial temp, deg R

To find the velocity, in order to determine the

in the supersonic region, for velocities above the critical. Consequently, for fluids such as steam and water moving through pipe lines flowing full, it is only necessary to define the Reynolds criterion for relating flow pattern of model and prototype.

Flow Coefficients for Nozzles and Orifices

The actual velocity, with a free-spouting jet of fluid issuing from a nozzle or orifice, is related to the ideal velocity from equations (5), (6), and (9) by using a velocity coefficient, C_v, defined as:

$$C_v = \frac{\text{actual jet velocity, } v_a, \text{ ft/sec}}{\text{ideal jet velocity, } v_i, \text{ ft/sec}} \qquad (27)$$

The velocity coefficient, C_v, is related to the flow resistance coefficient, C_{Drag}, by equation (28)

$$C_v = \sqrt{1 - C_{Drag}} \qquad (28)$$

The jet will not necessarily fill the entire physical area of the orifice, A, at the point where the jet velocity is measured, i.e., the vena contracta. This difference in area is expressed by a contraction coefficient, C_c, defined as:

$$C_c = \frac{\text{actual area of jet, } A_a, \text{ sq ft}}{\text{cross-sectional area of orifice, } A, \text{ sq ft}} \qquad (29)$$

From equation (17), $Q = Av$, the product of the velocity coefficient, C_v, and the contraction coefficient, C_c, can be defined as the over-all discharge coefficient, C_d (or C_{do} where the velocity of approach is zero), expressed as:

$$C_d \text{ (or } C_{do}) = C_v \times C_c \qquad (30)$$

and:

$$\text{actual flow} = \text{ideal flow} \times C_d \text{ (or } C_{do}) \qquad (31)$$

Numerical values of C_{do} and C_d are given in Fig. 6, derived from data published in ASME Research Publication on *Fluid Meters* (1937). Values for over-all discharge coefficients are in general determined from actual test flow measurements and are related to the Reynolds number. Values of C_v and C_c are not easily determined by direct measurement. However, the square-edge thin-plate orifice, the bell-mouth streamlined flow nozzle, and the venturi nozzle all offer very little resistance to flow, and the value of C_v usually is taken at between 0.98 and 0.99. The relatively low discharge coefficient of the orifice reflects a low contraction coefficient.

The two examples below show the use of the above data in calculating the flow through orifices and nozzles.

Example 3

Water under 100-ft head flows through a 1-sq in. aperture in (a) a square-edge orifice, and (b) a bell-mouth flow nozzle. Velocity of approach is zero. To find the velocity and the volume of discharge in each case:

(a) Square-edge orifice

Ideal velocity, $v_i = 8.02 \sqrt{100} = 80.2$ ft/sec, from Eq (9)

Discharge coefficient, $C_{do} = 0.6$ (approximate), from Fig. 6

Actual flow, $Q = 0.6 \times \frac{1}{144} \times 80.2$

$= 0.334$ cu ft/sec, from Eq (17)

Velocity coefficient, $C_v = 0.98$

Actual jet velocity, $v_a = 0.98 \times 80.2$
$= 78.6$ ft/sec, from Eq (27)

(b) Bell-mouth flow nozzle

Ideal velocity, $v_i = 8.02 \sqrt{100} = 80.2$ ft/sec

Discharge coefficient, $C_{do} = 0.98$ (approximate), from Fig. 6

Actual flow, $Q = 0.98 \times \frac{1}{144} \times 80.2$

$= 0.547$ cu ft/sec

Velocity coefficient, $C_v = 0.99$

Actual jet velocity, $v_a = 0.99 \times 80.2$
$= 79.4$ ft/sec

If the orifice, nozzle, or venturi is installed in a pipe, the velocity of approach must be considered, and the over-all discharge coefficient, C_d, should be used instead of C_{do}.

Example 4

Dry saturated steam at 100 psi is escaping from a safety valve where the diameter is 3 in. and the lift is ⅜ in. The discharge coefficient, C_d, is 0.74 by test on this type of valve. To find the relieving capacity of the safety valve:

Area of the annulus $= 3 \times 3.14 \times ⅜ = 3.53$ sq in.

Ideal flow $= \frac{114.7^{0.97}}{60} \times 3.53 = 5.86$ lb/sec, from Eq (20)

Actual flow $= 5.86 \times 0.74 = 4.34$ lb/sec, from Eq (31) $= 15,620$ lb/hr relieving capacity

Actual Flow in Pipes and Ducts

The flow of steam and water through pipes, the flow of air and gases through ducts, and the flow of fluids through valves, fittings, tubes, and tube bundles are all problems of immediate concern to the boiler user and the boiler designer. These are all classified as flow through closed conduit systems. Many experimental data on these phenomena have been accumulated, which permit use of the principles developed as equations (25) and (26). Before attempting to analyze this experimental evidence, it is well to recognize that the friction loss in a closed conduit system will appear as a heating effect. If, as is usual, the transfer of heat to the surroundings is negligibly small, then this entire friction loss must manifest itself as a change in internal energy or a rise in the fluid temperature and a change in volume. This means that for real flow of a nonexpansive fluid, with friction, the ideal equation (1) must include the internal energy term. It is not practical to measure the friction loss by a thermometer but nevertheless that loss is relatable to the loss reflected in equations (25) and (26). The drag coefficient, K_D, actually measures that loss.

For a pipe of circular cross-section, equation (25) can be resolved to a more useful form, as follows:

By the geometry, the surface is

$$A = \pi DL, \text{ sq ft}$$

Where:

D = diameter of the pipe, ft
L = length of pipe, ft

and:

Resistance to flow, $F = K_D \, \rho v^2 \, \pi DL, \text{ lb}$ (32)

It is not very useful to measure this resistance to flow in a pipe as a force in pounds. It is better to express the resistance to flow as pressure drop in lb per sq ft or lb per sq in.; or as head loss in feet of fluid. Since the cross-sectional area of a circular pipe or duct is $\frac{\pi D^2}{4}$, the pressure drop, $\triangle P$, in lb per sq ft is

$$\triangle P = K_D \, \rho v^2 \times \frac{\pi LD}{\dfrac{\pi D^2}{4}}$$

$$\triangle P = K_D \times \frac{4\rho v^2 L}{D}, \text{ lb/sq ft} \quad (33)$$

Or expressed as pressure drop, $\triangle P$, in lb per sq in.

$$\triangle P = K_D \times \frac{4\rho v^2 L}{144 D}, \text{ lb/sq in.} \quad (34)$$

Or expressed as head loss due to friction, H_f, in ft of fluid

Since density of fluid, lb/cu ft $= \delta = \rho g$

$$H_f = K_D \times \frac{4\rho v^2 L}{D} \div \rho g$$

$$H_f = K_D \times \frac{4 L v^2}{g D}, \text{ ft of fluid} \quad (35)$$

If the duct is noncircular in cross-section, equations (33), (34), and (35) must be modified to account for the cross-sectional perimeter of the duct ("wetted perimeter") and the corresponding equivalent diameter $4d_m$, in which:

$$d_m = \frac{\text{cross-sectional area of duct}}{\text{cross-sectional perimeter of duct}} \quad (36)$$

Related to the diameter, D, of a circular duct

$$d_m = \frac{\pi D^2}{4} \div \pi D = \frac{D}{4}$$

and

$$4d_m = D$$

For a noncircular duct, therefore, D must be replaced by $4d_m$, where d_m is determined from equation (36). Substituting $4d_m$ for D in equation (35) the expression for friction loss in ft of fluid in a noncircular duct becomes:

$$H_f = K_D \times \frac{L v^2}{g d_m}, \text{ ft of fluid} \quad (37)$$

The several equations above, for determining fluid friction loss, are variously attributed to Chezy, D'Arcy, or Fanning. A consistent system of units, such as (a) ft, lb, sec, or (b) ft, lb, hr should be used in applying these equations. Care should be taken in the manipulation of the basic data to avoid errors due to improper selection of units. Since the ft, lb, hr system is most conveniently applicable to calculations involving boilers, these units have been selected.

Careful attention is required in the selection of the proper numerical value for the friction or drag coefficient, K_D, for the flow circumstances at hand. Much experimental data is available for this purpose. The most rational data is based on the Reynolds number criterion for defining the flow pattern. The Reynolds number is the function, ϕ_1, of equation (26). Experimental data on friction factors using this basis is correlated in Fig. 7.

In the calculation of these quantities as applied to boilers the time interval of the hour, instead of the second is used, and the preceding data and equations can be rearranged accordingly so that the following symbols and units apply.

$\triangle P$ = pressure drop, lb per sq in.
L = length of flow path, ft
d = equivalent diameter, in.
v' = velocity, ft per hr
g' = gravitational acceleration, ft per hr^2
     $= 4.17 \times 10^8$
V = specific volume, cu ft per lb
G = mass flow, lb per sq ft, hr
μ = absolute viscosity, lb (mass) per ft, hr
R_e = Reynolds number $= \dfrac{dG}{12\mu}$
f = friction factor $= K_D$, drag coefficient

When these definitions and units are substituted in equation (34) the equation for pressure drop becomes:

$$\triangle P = \frac{f L V}{d} \left\{ \frac{G}{100,000} \right\}^2, \text{ lb per sq in.} \quad (38)$$

Realistic values of flow velocity, based on the experience of practice, for an assortment of piping and duct systems are given in Table 2. The densities of liquids and gases in Tables 3 and 4, respectively, and the steam tables in the Appendix (for Chapter 10) will also prove useful in calculating mass flows.

The friction factor, f, for an assortment of pipe and duct flow patterns can be determined from Fig. 7. This graph shows a possible range of numerical values from 0.01 to 0.054, for the friction factor. For

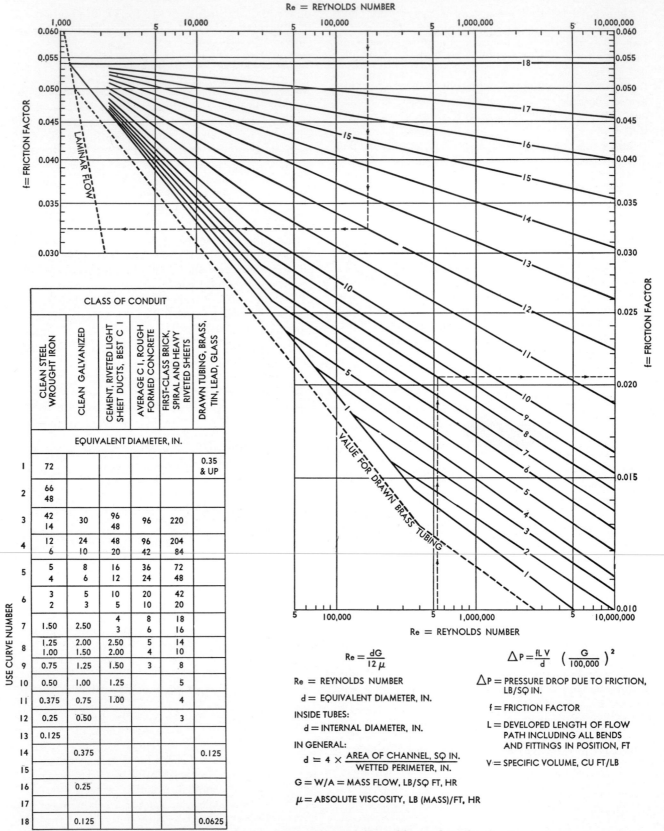

Fig. 7. Friction factor, f, as related to Reynolds number, for use in equation (38) to determine the pressure drop in pipe and ducts

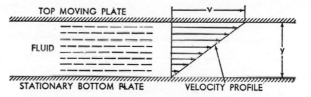

Fig. 8. *Diagram illustrating viscosity as a drag reaction between successive fluid layers*

TABLE 2

Range of Allowable Velocities in Duct and Piping Systems

Nature of Service	Velocity Ft/min
Steam lines	
high pressure	8,000-12,000
low pressure	12,000-15,000
vacuum	20,000-40,000
Superheater tubes, steam	2,000-5,000
Compressed air lines	1,500-2,000
Natural gas lines (large trans-continent)	100-150
Forced draft ducts	1,500-3,600
Forced draft ducts, entrance to burners	1,500-2,000
Induced draft flues and breeching	2,000-3,500
Stacks and chimneys	2,000-5,000
*Boiler gas passes	3,000-6,000
Coal-and-air lines, pulverized coal	3,000-4,500
Air heater, gas and air sides	1,000-5,000
Ventilating ducts	1,000-3,000
Register grills	300-600
Water lines	500-750
Economizer tubes, water	150-300
Crude oil lines (6″ to 30″)	60-360
Boiler circulation	70-700

* See also Tables 4 and 5, Chapter 18.

correct results it is essential to select the friction factor by entering the graph with the Reynolds number, $R_e = \dfrac{\rho v D}{\mu}$, evaluated in units of the tabulation above, by the expression

$$R_e = \frac{dG}{12\mu} \qquad (39)$$

Viscosity

In the solution of equation (38), the absolute viscosity, μ, must be correctly evaluated, which can be troublesome, usually because of confusion about the units. See Table 5 for the relationship between various units of viscosity. Viscosity measures the internal fluid friction or the resistance of a fluid to the relative motion of its parts. The significance of viscosity can be illustrated, as in Fig. 8 where two flat plates are separated by a layer of fluid of thickness, y. If the bottom plate is stationary and the top plate moves at a velocity, v, the fluid layer in contact with the top plate, because of adhesion, moves with the same velocity as the plate and the fluid layer in contact with the bottom plate, for the same reason, is stationary. At intermediate distances between the two plates, the velocity of the fluid is proportional to the distance from the bottom plate. Because of internal fluid friction each layer of fluid exerts a drag on the more rapidly moving layer above, and the topmost layer exerts a drag on the moving plate. The resistance to motion at each layer is the same. A force is, therefore, required to maintain the motion of the top plate. In derivations relating viscous phenomena, absolute viscosity is measured either as lb (force) hr per sq ft or lb (mass) per ft, hr.

TABLE 3

Physical Properties of Liquids
(at 14.7 psia)

Liquid	Temp, F	Density, lb/cu ft	Specific Volume cu ft/lb	Sp Heat, C_p
Water	70	62.4	0.0160	1.000
	212	59.9	0.0167	1.000
Automotive oil	70			
SAE 10		55-57	0.0182-0.0175	0.435
SAE 50		57-59	0.0175-0.0170	0.425
Mercury	70	846	0.0018	0.033
Fuel oil, #6	70	60-65	0.0167-0.0154	0.40
	180	60-65	0.0167-0.0154	0.46
Kerosene	70	50-51	0.0200-0.0196	0.47

Table 4

Physical Properties of Gases
(at 14.7 psia)

Gas	Temp, F	Density, lb/cu ft	Spec. Vol. cu ft/lb	Specific Heat (instantaneous values) C_p	C_v	k, C_p/C_v
Air	70	0.0751	13.32	0.241	0.172	1.40
	200	0.0603	16.58	0.242	0.173	1.40
	500	0.0415	24.10	0.248	0.180	1.38
	1000	0.0273	36.63	0.265	0.197	1.34
CO_2	70	0.1148	8.71	0.202	0.155	1.30
	200	0.0922	10.85	0.216	0.170	1.27
	500	0.0634	15.77	0.247	0.202	1.22
	1000	0.0417	23.98	0.280	0.235	1.19
H_2	70	0.0052	191.2	3.440	2.440	1.41
	200	0.0042	238.0	3.480	2.490	1.40
	500	0.0029	345.0	3.500	2.515	1.39
	1000	0.0019	526.3	3.540	2.560	1.38
Flue gas*	70	0.0836	11.96	0.253	0.187	1.35
	200	0.0776	12.88	0.255	0.189	1.35
	500	0.0428	23.38	0.265	0.199	1.33
	1000	0.0282	35.48	0.283	0.217	1.30
Methane	70	0.0416	24.05	0.530	0.406	1.30
	200	0.0334	29.95	0.575	0.451	1.27
	500	0.0230	43.50	0.720	0.596	1.21
	1000	0.0151	66.22	0.960	0.836	1.15

* From coal, 120% total air. Flue gas molecular wt taken as 30.

Table 5

Relationship Between Various Units of Viscosity

Absolute (Dynamic) Viscosity Values					Kinematic Viscosity Values		
Metric Units		English Units			Metric Units		English Unit
Centipoise	Poise	————	————	————	Centistoke	Stoke	————
0.01 Poise	$\frac{g(mass)}{cm, sec}$	$\frac{lb(mass)}{ft, sec}$	$\frac{lb(mass)}{ft, hr}$	$\frac{lb(force), sec}{ft^2}$	0.01 stoke	$\frac{cm^2}{sec}$	$\frac{ft^2}{sec}$
1.0	0.01	0.000672	2.42	0.0000209	0.016δ	0.00016δ	0.00000017δ
100	**1.0**	0.0672	242	0.00209	1.6δ	0.016δ	0.000017δ
1,488	14.88	**1.0**	3600	0.0311	23.8δ	0.238δ	0.000256δ
0.413	0.00413	0.000278	**1.0**	0.0000086	0.0066δ	0.000066δ	0.00000007δ
47,900	479	32.2	115,900	**1.0**	767δ	7.67δ	0.00826δ
62.4/δ	0.624/δ	0.042/δ	151/δ	0.0013/δ	**1.0**	0.01	0.0000108
6240/δ	62.4/δ	4.2/δ	15,100/δ	0.13/δ	100	**1.0**	0.00108
5,800,000/δ	58,000/δ	3,900/δ	14,040,000/δ	121/δ	92,900	929	**1.0**

δ = density, lb/ft³

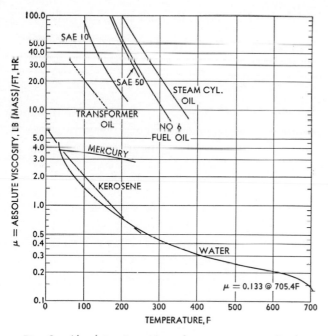

Fig. 9. *Absolute viscosities of some common fluids*

Some numerical values of viscosity for selected liquids, gases and vapors are given in Figs. 9, 10 and 11. The independent variable in all of these plots is temperature, and it will be noted that there is a very material change in viscosity with change in temperature. For liquids (Fig. 9) the fluid viscosity decreases substantially as the temperature is raised. On the other hand, for gases and vapors (Figs. 10 and 11) there is an increase in viscosity as the fluid temperature increases. These opposite effects are the consequence of cohesion and diffusivity in fluids. As the temperature of a liquid increases, the cohesive forces are lowered more than the diffusivity is increased, and consequently the viscosity decreases. For gases and vapors there is a lack of cohesive forces, and consequently the viscosity increases with rising temperature because of the increased diffusivity. That there is also some change in viscosity with pressure, is indicated in Fig. 11 for steam.

Flow in Valves and Fittings

Pipe lines and duct systems contain many valves and fittings to make a working entity of the assembly. Unless the lines are used for transporting fluid long distances as in the distribution of process steam at a factory or for the cross-country transmission of oil or gas, the straight runs of pipe or duct are relatively short. Usually, the water, steam, air, and gas lines in a power plant have relatively short runs of straight pipe with many valves and fittings. Consequently the resistance to flow offered by the valves and fittings is a large, if not a major, part of the total

resistance. The methods outlined above are helpful in the exact evaluation of fluid pressure for straight run pipes and ducts. The data available for estimating the frictional resistance to flow in valves and fittings is much less exact since basic difficulties practically preclude the correlation of experimental data on a solid and rational foundation. It is customary to express pressure drop for valves and fittings either (a) on the basis of equivalent lengths of straight pipe in ft, or (b) on the basis of the number of equivalent velocity heads in ft of fluid. This pressure drop for valves and fittings, in one or the other valuation, is furnished by the manufacturers. Where this pressure drop is expressed in lengths of straight pipe, the friction loss for the system is found by equation (38). Where it is expressed in velocity heads, the friction loss for the system is found by using equation (38) for the straight length of pipe, and the velocity head, equation (8), for the valves and fittings, by expressing this part of the loss as:

$$\text{Friction loss} = y \times \frac{v^2}{2g}, \text{ ft head of fluid} \quad (40)$$

Where:

y = number of velocity heads

v = nominal fluid velocity, ft/sec, ft/min, or ft/hr

g = gravitational acceleration, 32.2 ft/sec², 1.16 × 10⁵ ft/min², or 4.17 × 10⁸ ft/hr²

The range in pressure drop through an assortment

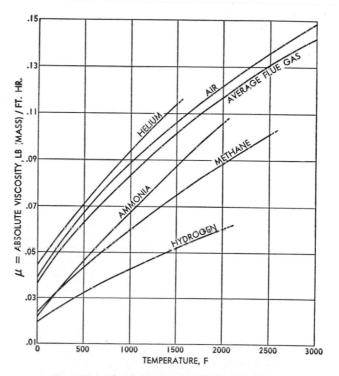

Fig. 10. *Absolute viscosities of some common gaseous fluids at atmospheric pressure*

of commercial fittings is given in Table 6 in equivalent velocity heads. As noted, pressure drop through fittings may also be expressed as the loss in equivalent lengths of straight pipe.

Two examples are given to show the use of the above data in estimating the pressure drop (1) in a steam pipe line, and (2) in a forced draft duct system, as follows:

Example 5

A steam pipe system, of 200 ft straight pipe, three long sweep elbows and two gate valves, to deliver 10,000 lb per hr of steam @ 100 psi, dry and saturated:

To find:
  (1) Nearest commercial nominal pipe size, in.
  (2) $\triangle P$, pressure drop due to friction, lb/sq in.
If $v =$ approximately 200 ft/sec
  From equation (17) and for specific volume,
    $V = 3.9$

$$Q = Av = \frac{10,000 \times 3.9}{3600} = 10.83 \text{ cu ft/sec}$$

$$A = \frac{10.83}{200} = 0.054 \text{ sq ft} = 7.8 \text{ sq in.}$$

$$d = 3.15 \text{ in.}$$

Nearest nominal pipe size, 3 in., where $d = 3.068$ in.
    $= 0.256$ ft (See Table 7 for pipe sizes)
    $A = 0.0515$ sq ft

$$v = \frac{10.83}{0.0515} = 210 \text{ ft/sec}$$

In equation (38), for pressure drop in straight pipe

$$\triangle P = \frac{fLV}{d} \left\{ \frac{G}{100,000} \right\}^2, \text{ lb/sq in.}$$

$$G = \frac{10,000}{0.0515} = 194,300$$

$$d = 3.068$$
    $\mu = 0.0405$ from Fig. 11 for sat steam @ 114.7 psia

In equation (39)
$$R_e = \frac{dG}{12\mu} = \frac{3.068 \times 194,300}{12 \times 0.0405} = 1,227,000$$

    $f = 0.0168$ from Fig. 7 for $d = 3.068$ in. & $R_e = 1,227,000$

For $\triangle P$ in 200 ft of straight pipe
$$\triangle P = \frac{0.0168 \times 200 \times 3.9}{3.068} \times$$
$$\left\{ \frac{194,300}{100,000} \right\}^2 = 16.13, \text{ lb/sq in.}$$

From Table 6:
  Loss of pressure through one elbow $= 0.3$ velocity head

Loss of pressure through one gate valve $= 0.2$ velocity head

In equation (40), friction loss in fittings:

$$= y \times \frac{v^2}{2g}$$

One velocity head $= \frac{v^2}{2g} = \frac{210^2}{64.4} = 685$ ft of fluid

$$= \frac{685}{V} = \frac{685}{3.9} = 175.3 \text{ lb/sq ft} = 1.22 \text{ lb/sq in.}$$

Loss of pressure through elbows and valves
$= (3 \times 0.3 + 2 \times 0.2) 1.22 = 1.59$ lb/sq in.
Estimated total loss of pressure for entire system
$= 16.13 + 1.59 = 17.72$ lb/sq in.

Example 6

A forced draft duct (depth limited to 2 ft) of 100 ft straight run and four elbows, with square outside corner (see sketch (a), Fig. 15), to deliver air at 300 F at a rate of 60,000 cu ft per minute.

To find:
  (1) Dimension of duct system
  (2) $\triangle P$, pressure drop due to friction, in. wg

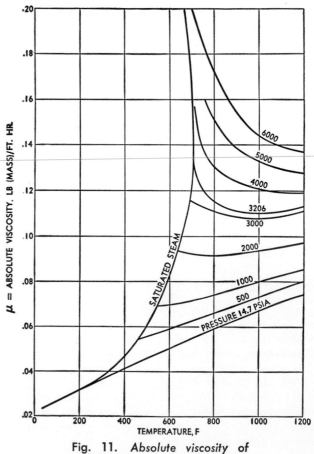

Fig. 11. Absolute viscosity of saturated and superheated steam

$v = 3600$ ft/min $= 60$ ft/sec (from Table 2)

From equation (17)

$Q = Av - A \times 60 - 1000$ cu ft/sec

$A = 16.7$ sq ft

Dimensions of duct system required

2 ft $\times$ 8.35 ft

Equivalent diameter, d, from equation, Fig. 7

$$d = 4 \times \frac{16.7 \times 144}{(2 \times 8.35 + 2 \times 2) \, 12} = 38.7 \text{ in.}$$

In equation (38), friction loss in straight duct

$$\Delta P = \frac{fLV}{d} \left\{ \frac{G}{100,000} \right\}^2$$

Density of air @ 300 F $= 0.0751 \times \dfrac{530}{760}$

$\qquad = 0.0523$ lb/cu ft

Sp. vol, $V = \dfrac{1}{0.0523} = 19.1$ cu ft/lb

$$G = \frac{60,000 \times 60 \times 0.0523}{16.7} = 11,270 \text{ lb/sq ft, hr}$$

$d = 38.7$, in.

$\mu = 0.057$, absolute viscosity, lb (mass)/ft, hr (from Fig. 10 for air @ 300 F)

In equation (39)

$$R_e = \frac{dG}{12\mu} = \frac{38.7 \times 11,270}{12 \times 0.057} = 637,600$$

$f = 0.015$ from Fig. 7 for $d = 38.7$ and R_e
$\qquad = 637,600$

$$\Delta P = \frac{0.015 \times 100 \times 19.1}{38.7} \left\{ \frac{11,270}{100,000} \right\}^2$$

$\qquad = 0.00945$ lb/sq in.

$\Delta P = 0.26$ in. of water

In equation (40), friction loss in elbow (90° bend)

$$= y \times \frac{v^2}{2g}$$

Width of duct, W $- 8.35$ ft, depth of duct, d $= 2$ ft
(see above and Fig. 15)

Aspect ratio $=$ W $\div$ d $= 8.35 \div 2 = 4.17$

Radius ratio $=$ r $\div$ d $= 3 \div 2 = 1.5$

For the above aspect and radius ratios:

Loss of head in one elbow
$\qquad = 0.25 \times$ velocity head
$\qquad = 0.25 \times \dfrac{60^2}{64.4} = 14$ ft head of fluid

Loss of head in 4 elbows $- 56$ ft of fluid

$\qquad 56 \times 12 \times \dfrac{0.0523}{62.4} = 0.56$ in. water

Head loss for system

In straight duct $= 0.26$
In four elbows $\ = 0.56$

$\qquad\qquad$ Total $\quad \overline{0.82}$ in. water

TABLE 6

Resistance to Flow of Fluids Through Commercial Fittings*

Fitting	Loss in Velocity Heads
Ell, 90° standard sweep	0.3-0.7
Ell, 90° long sweep	0.2-0.5
Tee, flow through run	0.15-0.5
Tee, flow 90° through branch	0.6-1.6
Return bend, close	0.6-1.7
Gate valve, open	0.1-0.2
Globe valve, open	5.0-15.0
Angle valve, 90° open	3.0-7.0
Boiler non-return, open	1.0-3.0

* See Fig. 13 for loss in velocity heads in flow of fluids through pipe bends.

Fluid Flow in Boilers and Tube Banks

The above data is usually adequate for estimating fluid dynamic performance values in nozzles, orifices, piping, and duct systems. However, for estimating fluid flow performance values in a boiler as on the gas side, more exact and more elaborate data is generally desirable. While it is not within the scope of this chapter to provide an exhaustive review, the following data and equations will indicate the nature of the problem (see also Chapter 11). The problem is complicated by the presence of not only viscous or skin friction losses, but also losses due to shock and impact caused by changes in the direction of flow and changes in the cross-sectional area available for flow.

The shock or impact losses are represented by the loss of energy due to the formation of eddies and swirls when fluid particles, moving at different velocities, come into contact. Such losses can be conveniently expressed in terms of the velocity head of the flowing fluid. Another method in common use is to consider these losses as equivalent to the viscous loss in the flow through a certain length of straight conduit. The latter method is not as accurate as the former since the coefficient of friction for straight conduit resistance varies with the surface roughness and the Reynolds number, and is inversely proportional to the fifth power of the diameter, whereas impact losses are inversely proportional to the fourth power of the diameter.

Effect of Contraction and Enlargement

The simplest sectional change is where the boundaries converge. There is no shock when pressure is converted to kinetic energy if the shape of the converging section approximates natural stream lines, as in a flow nozzle, or if the stream is constricted by a gradually converging section terminating tangentially in the smaller downstream section. Converging boundaries have a tendency to steady the flow. If the included angle of the converging boundaries is less than 45° and the terminal junction is smooth, the loss of energy is due to skin friction only and is approximately 0.05 of the velocity head based on the smaller (downstream) section. Identifying the upstream and downstream sections by the subscripts 1 and 2, respectively, and applying equation (1) where

$$\triangle u = 0, \quad \triangle Z = 0, \quad V_1 = \frac{1}{\delta_1}, \text{ and } V_2 = \frac{1}{\delta_2}, \text{ the differ-}$$

ence in pressure due to a gradual contraction in a horizontal conduit is determined as follows:

$$\frac{p_1}{\delta_1} + \frac{v_1^2}{2g} = \frac{p_2}{\delta_2} + \frac{v_2^2}{2g} + \frac{0.05v_2^2}{2g}$$

and if the fluid is treated as incompressible and δ is taken as the average specific wt or weight density,

$$\frac{\triangle p}{\delta} = \frac{p_1 - p_2}{\delta} = \frac{1.05v_2^2 - v_1^2}{2g}$$

from equation (17)

$$Q = A_1 v_1 = A_2 v_2$$

$$v_1 = \frac{A_2 v_2}{A_1}$$

then the static pressure difference in terms of velocity heads for the smaller section becomes,

$$\frac{\triangle p}{\delta} = \frac{1.05v_2^2 - \left\{ \dfrac{A_2 v_2}{A_1} \right\}^2}{2g} \qquad (41)$$

$$= \frac{\left\{ 1.05 - \left\{ \dfrac{A_2}{A_1} \right\}^2 \right\} v_2^2}{2g}, \text{ ft of fluid} \qquad (42)$$

TABLE 7

Nominal Wall Thickness of Welded and Seamless Steel Pipe, Inches

Nominal Pipe Size, in.	Outside Diameter in.	Schedule Numbers									
		10	20	30	40	60	80	100	120	140	160
⅛	0.405	—	—	—	0.068	—	0.095	—	—	—	—
¼	0.540	—	—	—	0.088	—	0.119	—	—	—	—
⅜	0.675	—	—	—	0.091	—	0.126	—	—	—	—
½	0.840	—	—	—	0.109	—	0.147	—	—	—	0.187
¾	1.050	—	—	—	0.113	—	0.154	—	—	—	0.218
1	1.315	—	—	—	0.133	—	0.179	—	—	—	0.250
1¼	1.660	—	—	—	0.140	—	0.191	—	—	—	0.250
1½	1.900	—	—	—	0.145	—	0.200	—	—	—	0.281
2	2.375	—	—	—	0.154	—	0.218	—	—	—	0.343
2½	2.875	—	—	—	0.203	—	0.276	—	—	—	0.375
3	3.5	—	—	—	0.216	—	0.300	—	—	—	0.437
3½	4.0	—	—	—	0.226	—	0.318	—	—	—	—
4	4.5	—	—	—	0.237	—	0.337	—	0.437	—	0.531
5	5.563	—	—	—	0.258	—	0.375	—	0.500	—	0.625
6	6.625	—	—	—	0.280	—	0.432	—	0.562	—	0.718
8	8.625	—	0.250	0.277	0.322	0.406	0.500	0.593	0.718	0.812	0.906
10	10.75	—	0.250	0.307	0.365	0.500	0.593	0.718	0.843	1.000	1.125
12	12.75	—	0.250	0.330	0.406	0.562	0.687	0.843	1.000	1.125	1.312
14	14.0	0.250	0.312	0.375	0.437	0.593	0.750	0.937	1.062	1.250	1.406
16	16.0	0.250	0.312	0.375	0.500	0.656	0.843	1.031	1.218	1.437	1.562
18	18.0	0.250	0.312	0.437	0.562	0.718	0.937	1.156	1.343	1.562	1.750
20	20.0	0.250	0.375	0.500	0.593	0.812	1.031	1.250	1.500	1.750	1.937
24	24.0	0.250	0.375	0.562	0.687	0.937	1.218	1.500	1.750	2.062	2.312
30	30.0	0.312	0.500	0.625	—	—	—	—	—	—	—

NOTE: Values in italics in schedules 30 and 40 are identical with the old "standard weight" pipe.
Values in italics in schedules 60 and 80 are identical with the old "extra-heavy" pipe.

When the change of section is a sudden contraction, energy is lost in eddies at the corners of the larger section, in the orifice effect due to the coefficients of velocity and contraction, and in the expansion of the fluid from the vena contracta to the downstream pipe area. Since the major part of this loss is due to the last item, the loss caused by a sudden contraction is approximately:

$$(v_c - v_2)^2/2g \qquad (43)$$
$$= (1/C_c - 1)^2 \, v_2^2/2g \qquad (44)$$

Where
$v_c =$ velocity at the vena contracta
$C_c =$ coefficient of contraction
$$v_c = \frac{v_2}{C_c}$$

Calling $(1/C_c - 1)^2 = K$, then K will vary with the sectional area ratio, $\dfrac{A_2}{A_1}$, (small to large) as given in Table 8.

TABLE 8

Values of K Corresponding to Area Ratios
For Sudden Contraction

$\frac{A_2}{A_1} =$	0.1	0.2	0.3	0.4	0.5	0.6	0.7	0.8	0.9	1.0
$K =$	0.47	0.43	0.39	0.34	0.30	0.26	0.21	0.16	0.08	0

Applying the relationship, $\dfrac{p_1}{\delta_1} + \dfrac{v_1^2}{2g} = \dfrac{p_2}{\delta_2} + \dfrac{v^2}{2g} + \dfrac{Kv_2^2}{2g}$, as before, the static pressure difference becomes:

$$\frac{\Delta p}{\delta} = \frac{\left\{1 + K - \left\{\frac{A_2}{A_1}\right\}^2\right\} v_2^2}{2g}, \text{ ft of fluid} \qquad (45)$$

When there is a sudden enlargement of the conduit section, the rapidly moving particles impinging upon the slowly moving particles cause an eddy formation in the downstream section (2), and the energy lost is:

$$(v_1 - v_2)^2/2g$$

Applying the relationship as before to determine the pressure difference:

$$\frac{p_1}{\delta_1} + \frac{v_1^2}{2g} = \frac{p_2}{\delta_2} + \frac{v_2^2}{2g} + \frac{(v_1 - v_2)^2}{2g}$$

The static pressure difference in terms of the velocity head for the smaller section (1) becomes:

$$\Delta p/\delta = 2 \frac{A_1}{A_2}\left\{\frac{A_1}{A_2} - 1\right\} v_1^2/2g, \text{ ft of fluid} \qquad (46)$$

For sudden enlargement it is evident that the static pressure $\dfrac{p_2}{\delta_2}$ downstream will always be larger than the static pressure $\dfrac{p_1}{\delta_1}$ upstream ahead of the enlarge-

ment if $\dfrac{v_2^2}{2g} + \dfrac{(v_1 - v_2)^2}{2g}$ is less than $\dfrac{v_1^2}{2g}$. This is true for all area ratios greater than 0 and less than 1.0. Where $v_2 = 0$ as in discharging into a large tank, it is also evident that $\dfrac{p_2}{\delta_2}$, the static pressure downstream, will equal $\dfrac{p_1}{\delta_1}$, the static pressure upstream, and that the energy lost is $v_1^2/2g$.

When there is a gradual enlargement of the conduit section, the fluid has a tendency to leave the walls, eddies are formed and energy is lost, the amount depending upon the size of the included angle. The energy loss may be expressed as $K(v_1 - v_2)^2/2g$, with average values for K as given in Table 9.

TABLE 9

Values of K Corresponding to Included Angle
For Gradual Enlargement

Included angle, degrees	6	10	20	40	60	(180)
K		0.14	0.18	0.44	0.85	1.10	(1.00)

The value of K rises rapidly with increase of in-

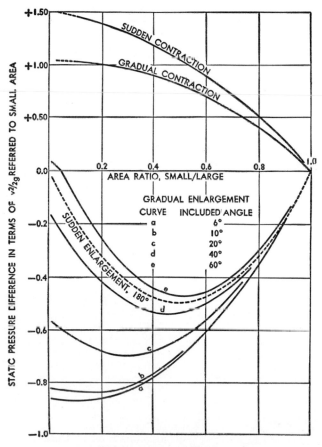

Fig. 12. *Static pressure difference due to sudden and gradual change in section*

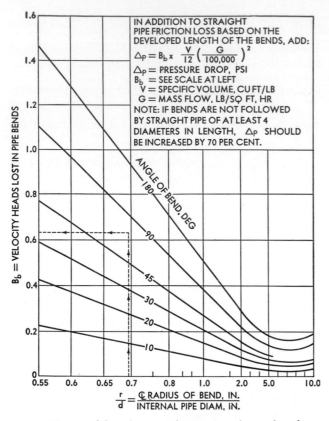

Fig. 13. *Bend loss for round pipe in velocity heads*

change in section decreases the velocity in the direction of motion the fluid becomes detached from the boundaries and energy is dissipated in eddies. Static pressure differences, in terms of the velocity head at the small area, corresponding to the section area ratios are plotted in Fig. 12.

Losses of energy due to impact or shock are caused by changes in direction, such as bends in a pipe line or duct system. The tendency of the fluid to leave

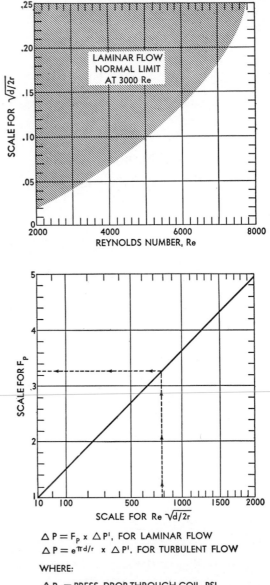

cluded angle until at 50 degrees the loss of energy is the same as for a sudden enlargement, or an included angle of 180 degrees. Applying the relationship as before to determine the static pressure difference due to a gradual enlargement in terms of the velocity head at the smaller section:

$$\frac{p_1}{\delta_1} + \frac{v_1^2}{2g} = \frac{p_2}{\delta_2} + \frac{v_2^2}{2g} + \frac{K(v_1 - v_2)^2}{2g}$$

or

$$\frac{\triangle p}{\delta} = \left\{ \left\{ \frac{A_1}{A_2} \right\}^2 - 1 + K \left\{ 1 - \frac{A_1}{A_2} \right\}^2 \right\} v_1^2/2g,$$

ft of fluid (47)

For gradual enlargement it is evident that the static pressure $\frac{p_2}{\delta_2}$, downstream will always be larger than the static pressure, $\frac{p_1}{\delta_1}$, upstream ahead of the enlargement if $\frac{v_2^2}{2g} + \frac{K(v_1 - v_2)^2}{2g}$ is less than $\frac{v_1^2}{2g}$. This is true except where the area ratio, $\frac{A_1}{A_2}$, is less than 0.05 and the included angle is 60°.

When a conduit section is changed so that the velocity increases gradually in the direction of motion the fluid adheres to the boundaries, but when a

$\triangle P = F_p \times \triangle P^1$, FOR LAMINAR FLOW
$\triangle P = e^{\pi d/r} \times \triangle P^1$, FOR TURBULENT FLOW

WHERE:

$\triangle P$ = PRESS. DROP THROUGH COIL, PSI
$\triangle P^1$ = STRAIGHT FLOW PRESS. DROP THROUGH DEVELOPED LENGTH OF COIL, PSI
Re = REYNOLDS NUMBER
d = INSIDE DIAMETER OF TUBING, IN.
r = CENTERLINE RADIUS OF COIL, IN.
e = 2.718, NAPIERIAN LOG BASE

Fig. 14. *Pressure drop for laminar and turbulent flow in coils*

Table 10

Static Pressure Difference, Velocity Heads
Through 90° Angle of Bend in Pipe

Radius ratio, r/d	0.5	0.75	1.0	2.0	3.0	4.0	5.0	6.0	7.0
Velocity heads, $v^2/2g$*	1.24	0.60	0.38	0.23	0.19	0.16	0.14	0.12	0.11
Degree of bend	15	30		45	60		90	135	180
Factor**	0.31	0.53		0.69	0.81		1.00	1.21	1.34

* These values are the mean of experimental results for rough and smooth pipe bends, and apply only where the bend is followed by at least 4 diameters of straight pipe.

** To be applied to the velocity heads above for other than 90° angles of bend.

the wall which curves away from the direction of flow depends upon the sharpness of the curvature and the angle through which the stream is deflected. The inertia of the main stream causes it to impinge on the wall which curves into the direction of flow. This sets up a secondary flow at the walls directed toward the center of curvature, and, by continuity, a flow toward the outer wall in the body of the stream. A straight length of conduit beyond the bend is required to equalize the unequal velocity distribution caused by a change of direction. Since the entire energy loss is not concentrated within the bend, the most satisfactory method of evaluating the loss is to express it as an addition to the friction loss through a straight pipe of equal length.

Static pressure differences for bends in round pipe expressed in terms of velocity heads in excess of straight pipe friction vary slightly with Reynolds numbers below 150,000. For Reynolds numbers above this value they are reasonably constant, and depend solely on the dimensionless radius ratio, r/d, defined as the ratio of the center-line radius of the bend to the internal diameter of the pipe. For commercial pipe, where the angle of bend is 90° and where the bend is followed by at least 4 diameters of straight pipe, the values of the static pressure difference in velocity heads for various radius ratios, r/d, as given in Table 10, are recommended for practical use. The combined effect of radius ratio and angle of bend is shown in Fig. 13 in terms of velocity heads.

Flow Through Coils

A convenient method for calculating the pressure drop in flow through coils is to apply a factor to the drop through an equivalent length of straight pipe. This factor depends upon the type of flow, laminar or turbulent, and the radius of the coil. The type of flow, and the factors for laminar and turbulent flow can be determined from the curves and formulas in Fig. 14.

Flow Through Rectangular Ducts

The loss of energy due to a change of direction in a rectangular duct system is similar to that for

cylindrical pipe. However, an additional factor, the shape of the duct in relation to the direction of bend, must be taken into account. This is known as the aspect ratio, defined as the ratio of the width and depth of the duct. The width of the duct is always

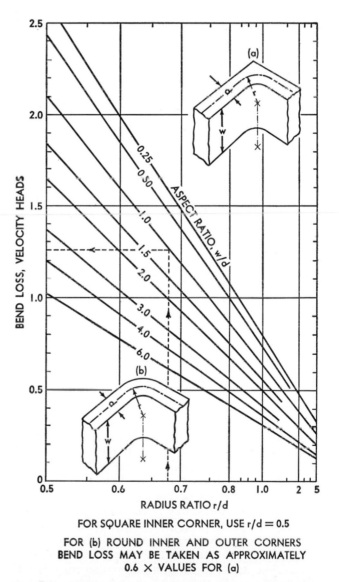

FOR SQUARE INNER CORNER, USE $r/d = 0.5$

FOR (b) ROUND INNER AND OUTER CORNERS
BEND LOSS MAY BE TAKEN AS APPROXIMATELY
0.6 × VALUES FOR (a)

Fig. 15. Friction loss in rectangular ducts, 90° bends

considered to be the dimension of the sides which curve into and away from the direction of flow (see Fig. 15). The bend loss for the same radius ratio will decrease as the aspect ratio increases. This is due to the smaller proportionate influence of the secondary flow on the stream as a whole. The combined effect of radius and aspect ratios on 90° duct bends with a square outer corner is given in terms of velocity heads in Fig. 15. Losses for bends other than 90° can be taken as proportional to the angle of bend. It is apparent that bend losses in rectangular ducts can be reduced by the use of splitters, which increase both the aspect ratio and the average radius ratio. See example 6, above.

A convenient chart for the calculation of draft loss due to impact losses in duct systems conveying flue gas or air is shown in Fig. 16. Knowing the mass flow and temperature, a base velocity head in inches of water at sea level can be obtained. This is subject to an altitude correction if such applies.

Flow Through Valves

The flow resistance of valves is due to the shape and condition of the valve and the extent and shape of the valve opening. The resistance coefficients for valves and special fittings should be obtained from the manufacturers (see Table 6).

Flow of Gases Over Tube Banks

Resistance to the transverse flow of gases over tube banks, when the tubes are in line, is an example of more or less extreme sectional changes, and when the tubes are staggered, both sectional and directional changes affect the resistance. Experimental results and the analytical conclusions of an extended research by B&W, using the orifice formula as a basis, indicate that three principal variables affect resistance to the transverse flow of gases over tube banks. The primary variable is the number of major restrictions. The second variable is the so-called friction factor, relatable to the Reynolds number based on the tube diameter, and the tube pitch and pattern, in-line or staggered. The third variable is the depth factor applicable to banks of a depth less than 10 rows.

The product of the friction factors and the number of major restrictions is, in effect, the summation of the velocity head losses in the flow of fluids through apparatus when the major resistance is due to impact losses. This fact can be applied in establishing procedures for the calculation of draft loss through units of a fixed type or design. In units of this type the ratio of the length of flow path and the equivalent diameter of any longitudinal flow section remains unchanged, as does the ratio of heating surface and free-flow area. In calculating the draft loss through

units of this type the procedure is resolved into the three factors, temperature, type, and loading. The physical properties of the fluid, such as density and viscosity, vary with temperature and are accounted for by the temperature factor. The type factor accounts for the geometric pattern of the design. The loading factor accounts for the rate of driving and is proportional to the gas weight per sq ft of surface area raised to a power. The product of these three factors is the base draft loss subject to the applicable stack effect corrected for altitude (see Chapter 5). A further correction is required when the gas or air outlet is above or below the inlet. This correction is additive if the hot gases are forced to flow downward against their natural tendency to rise in relation to the cooler ambient air, and is subtractive when the hot gas outlet is above the hotter gas inlet. Examples of draft loss calculations for simple tube bank arrangements appear in Chapter 11.

Stacks and Chimneys

At the base of a stack or chimney the pressure inside is less than the pressure outside because of the difference in fluid densities of the hot gases within and the cooler atmospheric air outside. This difference in pressure, called the theoretic draft, can be expressed by the following equation:

$$\text{Theoretic draft} = \frac{\text{Height of stack, in.}}{62.4} (\delta_a - \delta_g), \text{ in. of water} \tag{48}$$

Where:

62.4 = specific wt of water
δ_a = specific wt of surrounding air
δ_g = specific wt of hot gases inside

If an opening were made at the base of the stack, the total head available for causing flow would be as in equation (48). As soon as flow is established the net draft which can be utilized in overcoming resistance, such as offered by a fuel bed or a tube bank, is less than this theoretic value by the amount of the velocity head and the frictional resistance in the stack. The net or actual draft can be expressed as follows:

$$\text{Actual draft} = \text{Theoretic draft} - v^2/2g - \text{frictional resistance} \tag{49}$$

For computing the velocity head, $v^2/2g$, the usual maximum value of velocity for stacks is in the order of 40 to 50 ft per second. To establish the frictional resistance see above and Chapter 5.

In the calculation of draft for boilers the height of the stack is generally limited to some practical value, less than 200 feet. The structure of tall stacks should be designed with care, since the trailing vortices of even light winds can cause appreciable crosswind vibrations. Stack temperatures seldom exceed 500 F and are usually in the order of 300 F or less for high efficiency installations. With these values for temperature and practical limits on height, stacks are inadequate for the high drafts needed for modern boilers. Natural draft must, therefore, be supplemented, if not entirely superseded by, mechanical draft.

Boiler Circulation

The fluid mechanics of water circulation in a boiler is similar in principle to draft in a stack. Two columns of equal vertical height are connected at the bottom, as illustrated in Chapter 9. One column is filled with liquid water, the other column is filled with a mixture of steam bubbles and water. The fluid in the latter column is of lower specific gravity than the fluid in the former. Consequently for a given height, H, there is a difference in pressure at the base of the two columns. This difference in pressure can be calculated by methods outlined in Chapters 9 and 29.

However, since the difference in density of the fluids is not uniform throughout the height of the two vertical columns, the calculation of the head and flow rate (see above references) is not as simple as for stack draft. The added steam formation for each ft of height can be calculated for a given rate of heat transfer. Having established this cumulative formation of steam, the average density of the fluid in the rising column can be determined. Usual circulation velocities are of the order of 5 to 10 ft per second. This velocity must be high enough to scrub the steam bubbles from the surface as they are formed. Expressed on a mass flow basis, the flow through usual circulatory systems, in natural circulation boilers, ranges from 5 to 10 times the rate of steam output of the boiler.

Throttling Calorimeter

The throttling calorimeter is used for the determination of the quality and the enthalpy of wet steam. As shown in Fig. 17, steam taken from the header in a sampling tube passes through a valve where it is throttled to a lower pressure. The kinetic energy of the high velocity steam is all returned as reheat in the fluid when it is brought to rest in the low pressure, downstream calorimeter chamber. The expansion, thermodynamically and fluid dynamically, is, therefore, at constant enthalpy. This was first recognized by Joule in his porous plug experiments. The phenomenon can be defined in mathematical terms by reference to the general energy equation in the reduced form of equation (1), applicable to fluid flow. Since there is no change, over-all, in the elevational head, Z, and velocity, v (see above), equation (1) can be reduced to the form:

$$p_1 V_1 + u_1 = p_2 V_2 + u_2 \qquad (50)$$

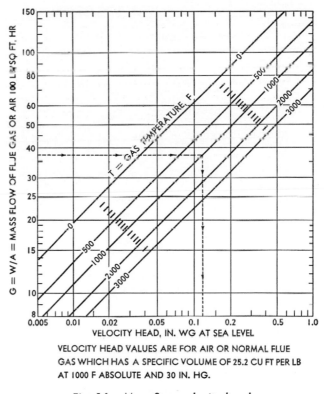

G = W/A = MASS FLOW OF FLUE GAS OR AIR 100 LB/SQ FT, HR

VELOCITY HEAD, IN. WG AT SEA LEVEL

VELOCITY HEAD VALUES ARE FOR AIR OR NORMAL FLUE GAS WHICH HAS A SPECIFIC VOLUME OF 25.2 CU FT PER LB AT 1000 F ABSOLUTE AND 30 IN. HG.

Fig. 16. *Mass flow-velocity head relationship for flue gas or air*

and since $h = pV + u$
where h = enthalpy, Btu per lb
$$h_1 = h_2 \qquad (51)$$

That $h_1 = h_2$ can be verified by equation (26), Chapter 10, since no work is done.

In the operation of the throttling calorimeter, the temperature and pressure are taken in the low pressure chamber. The readings can be used only if there is superheat at this point. Use of the calorimeter can be demonstrated by the following examples in finding the quality of steam:

Example 7

For Steam in Header

Pressure	100 psi (114.7 psia)
Temperature	338 F

The steam tables show that these readings apply to:
1) dry saturated steam
2) saturated water
3) wet steam

There is, however, a vast difference in the quality (0 to 100% dryness) and in the enthalpy, h, (309 to 1189 Btu/lb) implicit in these readings, and they give no information on whether the fluid in the header is water, steam, or a mixture.

By expanding a sample of the steam from the header through the needle valve of a throttling calorimeter:

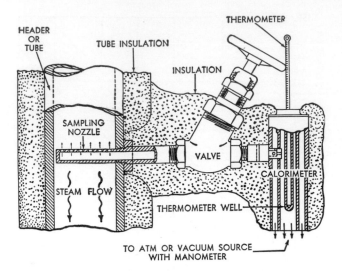

Fig. 17. *Throttling calorimeter, showing sampling nozzle installed in steam header or tube*

Steam in Calorimeter Chamber

Pressure   14.7 psia
Temperature   262 F
Enthalpy, h_2,   1175 Btu/lb
                (from steam tables)

Since the saturation temperature at 14.7 psia is 212 F, the steam in the calorimeter chamber has 50 degrees of superheat. On the Mollier chart, if the reading for the steam in the calorimeter chamber, represented by point 2 in Fig. 18, is projected horizontally to the left at constant enthalpy of 1175 Btu/lb in accordance with equation (51) the moisture of the steam at 114.7 psia (the pressure in the header) is 1.6% and the quality is 98.4% at point 1.

If no superheat appears in the calorimeter chamber at atmospheric pressure it is often possible to extend the range by connecting the chamber to a vacuum source, and thus operate at negative pressure. The following example will serve to demonstrate this condition:

Example 8
For Steam in Header

Pressure   100 psi (114.7 psia)
Temperature   338 F
      Steam in Calorimeter Chamber
Pressure   14.7 psia
Temperature   212 F

If the calorimeter chamber is connected to a vacuum source:

      Steam in Calorimeter Chamber
Pressure   25 in. vacuum
                (4.92 in. Hg abs)
Temperature   180 F
Enthalpy, h_3,   1141 Btu/lb
                (from steam tables)

Since saturation temperature at a pressure of 4.92 in. Hg abs is 133 F, the steam in the calorimeter chamber has 47 degrees of superheat. On the Mollier chart, if the reading for the steam in the calorimeter chamber (connected to a vacuum source), represented by point 3 in Fig. 18, is projected horizontally to the left at constant enthalpy of 1141 Btu/lb, the moisture content of the steam for 114.7 psia (the pressure in the header) is 5.5% (94.5% quality) at point 1'. This reading as shown by point 3' will give 212 F with 1% moisture in the calorimeter chamber when operated at atmospheric pressure (14.7 psia).

To measure steam quality beyond the range of the throttling calorimeter, a device, like a separating calorimeter, must be used in which the liquid is physically separated from the vapor and measured—a trying operation, at best.

Entrainment by Fluid Flow

Collecting or transporting solid particles or a second fluid by the flow of a primary fluid at high velocity is known as entrainment. This is usually done by jets using a small quantity of high-pressure fluid to carry along large quantities of another fluid or of solid particles. The pressure energy of the high-pressure fluid is converted into kinetic energy by nozzles, with a consequent reduction of pressure. The material to be transported is drawn in at the low-pressure zone where it meets the high velocity jet and is carried along by it. Usually the jet is followed by a parallel throat section to equalize the velocity profile before the fluid with its entrained substance enters a diverging section in which kinetic energy is partially reconverted into pressure energy. The chief loss of energy is due to impact or shock.

Entrainment is a very useful means of performing certain functions. The injector is a jet pump that

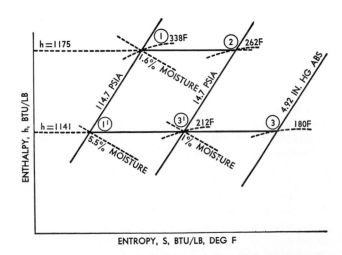

Fig. 18. *Trace of Mollier chart for determining steam quality with throttling calorimeter*

uses steam as the high-pressure fluid to entrain low-pressure water for delivery against a back pressure higher than the pressure of the actuating fluid. The ejector, similar to the injector, is designed to entrain gases, liquids, or even mixtures of solids and liquids for delivery against a pressure less than the pressure of the primary fluid. In a water-jet aspirator, water is used to entrain air to obtain a fair vacuum. In the Bunsen burner, a jet of gas issuing from a small orifice entrains air for combustion. In a carburetor the air entrains liquid fuel to provide a flammable mixture. Steam-jet blowers are used in the base of locomotive stacks and also in the stacks of small natural-draft boiler plants to increase the draft for short peak loads.

In several instances entrainment is a source of trouble in the operation of steam boilers. Particles of ash entrained by the products of combustion, when deposited on heating surfaces reduce thermal conductance, when passing through fans erode the blades, and when discharged into the atmosphere are sometimes a public nuisance. Moisture, carrying solids either in suspension or in solution, is entrained in the steam, and these solids may be carried through to the turbine and deposited on the blades, increasing the back pressure and decreasing the turbine efficiency. In downcomers or supply tubes, steam bubbles are entrained in the water when the drag on the bubbles is greater than the buoyant force, causing a reduced density in the pumping columns of natural-circulation boilers. See reference to cyclone separator, Chapter 9.

Separation

In the boiler field there are two clearly recognizable separation problems concerned with the removal of solid or liquid particles from a flowing gas or vapor stream. The elimination of dust and fly-ash from the products of combustion and the separation of water or moisture from steam vapor as it leaves the boiler drum are common boiler problems. In the case of dust and fly-ash several different principles of separation are employed, to wit:

1) Entrainment in another fluid, as with washing by water sprays,

2) Filtration in which the dust-laden gases are passed through fiber filters where the small openings serve to catch the solid particles,

3) Ionization in which the dust particles are given an electrostatic charge and withdrawn from the gas stream by the attraction of a charged electrode,

4) Inertia which utilizes an abrupt change in the direction of the flow path,

5) Gravitation in which there is a sudden reduction in the flow velocity, and

6) Centrifugal force as with the whirling action of a cyclone separator.

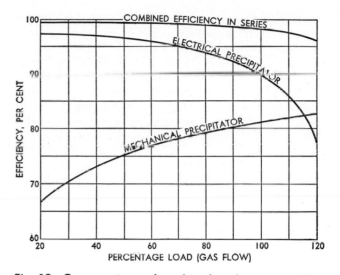

Fig. 19. *Comparative and combined performance of flue gas dust collectors. Typical for pulverized coal fired boiler practice*

Some of the principles of separation listed above are essentially fluid dynamic and are applicable both to the separation of solid particles and liquid drops. In an understanding of these principles it is necessary to recognize that (1) the inertia of the solid particle or liquid drop, is a function of its volume (for a given density), and (2) the resistance to flow of the particle or drop through a gaseous or vapor medium is a function of the exterior surface of the particle or drop. With a spherical configuration for the particle or drop this means that its inertia is proportional to the cube of its diameter while the flow resistance is proportional to the square of its diameter. By Newton's law of motion a particle or drop, entrained in a flowing stream, will continue to move in a straight line unless acted upon by an external force. That continuance of motion in a straight line is a function of the inertia. Opposing the motion is the fluid resistance. If separation is then attempted by fluid dynamic means, in which the direction of the flowing stream is altered, the solid or liquid particles will, by virtue of this inertia, tend to continue moving in their original direction. They will not follow the altered direction of the general gas stream. The particles will move across that stream but energy will be dissipated by fluid friction and ultimately the particles conform to the pattern of the gas stream. The greater the particle mass and size, the greater will be the inertia effects and the consequent effectiveness of the separation of the particle from the general gas stream.

The inertia principle is employed in a wide variety of devices, of which the B&W cyclone steam separator, illustrated in Chapters 9 and 29, is one of the most prominent. Here the bulk of the physically entrained water is removed from the steam in a series of cyclones that communicate with a girth compartment into which the steam-and-water mixture from the risers is discharged. From the cyclone steam separators the steam passes through scrubber baffles for final drying. The scrubber baffles are made of a number of corrugated plates, closely nested so that a large surface is available for collecting moisture as the steam, at relatively low velocity, continually changes direction through the tortuous passages between the baffles.

Eliminating the discharge of steam from the risers below the free surface of the water and thorough removal of water from the steam in the cyclone steam separators insure the densest fluid to the downcomers and, consequently, a maximum differential head for circulation. The high quality of the steam delivered, after passing through the cyclone steam separators and scrubber baffles, is indicated by a solids carry-over of only 0.3 to 0.6 parts per million. This freedom from scale-forming material permits long periods of continuous trouble-free operation of both superheater and turbine.

These fluid dynamic principles are used also in the separation of dust, fly-ash, and cinders from flue gases. Because of the inertia and fluid-resistance aspects considered above, it is found that mechanical dust separators are more effective (1) when dealing with large and dense solid particles, rather than with small and flocculent solids, (2) when operating with higher rather than lower fluid velocities, (3) when running at full load rather than at part load, and (4) when operating with heavy, rather than light, dust loadings.

It should be noted that these results are quite the opposite from experience with electrostatic dust precipitators, which are more effective for light and small particles, low velocities, and partial loads.

The performance of typical flue gas dust separators as applied to boilers is shown in Fig. 19. For most complete dust elimination, one of the best methods is to use mechanical and electrostatic precipitators in series. The changes in efficiency with load for the two components are largely offset, and a high sustained over-all efficiency is maintained over the entire range of load, equivalent to the sum of the two component efficiencies minus one hundredth of their product.

Despite all the efforts made to separate fly-ash and

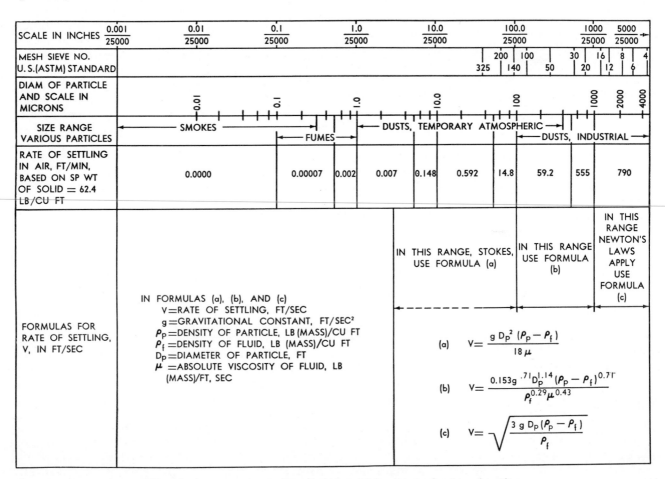

Fig. 20. Comparative scales of dust particle size and rates of settling

cinders from flue gas, additional precautions are necessary to reduce the nuisance of dust to a satisfactory minimum. Basically any small particles (from 100 to 30 microns sometimes extended to as low as 3 microns) discharged from a stack will settle in still air according to Stokes. The results of applying this and similar rules to various particle sizes, and the applicable formulas for rate of settling, are given in Fig. 20. High stacks or a high issuing velocity up to about 100 ft per sec, contribute greatly to the satisfactory dissemination of dust particles. The dust deposit rate per sq ft is reduced in proportion to the cube of the stack height. Wind velocity upsets these calculations and by its turbulent effects cause the deposition of dust particles in close proximity to the stack. Deflecting and baffle effects of adjacent structures or ground contours also introduce great turbulence.

SUFFICIENT STEAM IS SUPPLIED BY THE BOILERS OF THIS PLANT TO GENERATE
THE ELECTRICITY FOR A COMMUNITY OF NEARLY 2,000,000 PEOPLE

STEAM GENERATION AND BOILER CIRCULATION

THE process of generating steam by boiling water at pressures below the critical is a familiar phenomenon. The terms *boiling, saturation, liquid, water, vapor, steam, mixture, heat of vaporization,* and *superheat*, all relevant to this process, define the physical states or properties of the working substance. Thermodynamically, boiling may be considered a special case of adding heat to the working substance in a constant-pressure constant-temperature process.

On the other hand, when the working substance (H_2O) is compressed to and above the critical pressure, 3206.2 psia, and the temperature is increased to and above 705.4 F, the above terms no longer have their former significance. As the pressure and temperature of the working substance approach the critical, the value of the heat of vaporization (h_{fg} of the steam tables) decreases rapidly and finally at the critical condition (3206.2 psia and 705.4 F) becomes zero and remains zero above this point.

Heat added in increments to the working substance at the critical pressure or any pressure above produces gradual changes in temperature, specific heat, viscosity, conductivity, specific volume, and all other known properties. In each case the relationship proceeds smoothly without discontinuities.

Since a definitive point on any particular function curve-trace indicating a change of state cannot be assigned from the various properties, it is misleading to apply the term *vapor* to the working substance in the region above the critical. The "vapor dome" of the familiar p-V and T-s diagrams is not involved when operating above the critical point. The lines of constant pressure, from 3206.2 psia upward, lie in a region outside the dome, as illustrated in the T-s diagram in the steam tables. Similarly, lines of constant temperature above 705.4 F lie outside the dome in a p-V diagram, but the direction of slope is different.

When heat is added at or above the critical pressure, the term *fluid* may be used to describe the working substance in its continuous passage from the cold to the hot end of the circuit. Unlike the practice in the subcritical region, attempts to define the *state* of the working substance at a particular point in the circuit are generally unsatisfactory and unnecessary.

In the heat-power field the range of steam operating pressures has gradually increased at the upper end to within 500 to 600 psi of the critical. For many years, tenuous excursions have been conducted experimentally into the region of supercritical pressure operation, and recently energy conversion (fuel to kwhr) by this mode has been inaugurated on a large commercial scale. Further extension may be expected currently and in the future.

For the moment, however, much of what follows is concerned with the phenomena attending boiling and with steam production in boilers within the more usual subcritical pressure ranges.

Types of Boiling

The change from liquid to vapor occurs both at a solid-liquid interface, as at the inside tube surface of a water-tube boiler, and at a liquid-vapor interface, as with water surrounding a steam bubble. It has been observed that two distinct types of boiling, known as nucleate boiling and film boiling, occur at a solid-liquid interface. Nucleate boiling is characterized by the formation and release of steam bubbles at the interface with the water still wetting the surface, while in film boiling this surface is covered by a film of steam. To transfer heat from the surface to the fluid, a temperature gradient ($\triangle T$) is necessary. The magnitude of this gradient depends mainly upon whether nucleate or film boiling is taking place and, to a lesser extent, upon the pressure, the surface material, and the condition of the surface.

Conservative boiler design for subcritical pressures should stay within nucleate boiling conditions, where

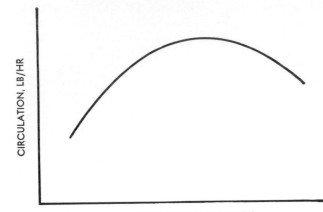

Fig. 1. *Typical relationship between circulation in a boiler circuit (at a given pressure) and amount of steam produced (scale arbitrary)*

the water still wets the tube surfaces and the $\triangle T$ values are low. For a given pressure under the condition of nucleate boiling, incremental increases in $\triangle T$ produce quite uniform increases in conductance, Btu per sq ft, hr, F. Beyond this condition there is a sharp decrease in conductance for further increase in $\triangle T$. This limit marks the transition from nucleate to partial nucleate partial steam-film boiling, and the tube wall is no longer continuously wetted.

In a boiler unit, if the heat-absorbing surfaces are vertical, the mass flow and velocity of water and steam through the tubes seem to have little effect on the temperature difference, $\triangle T$, and velocities over a relatively wide range (1 to 10 ft/sec) are variously encountered. For horizontal surfaces or sloping surfaces, mass flow and velocity must be sufficient to maintain the wetted condition. Entering velocities to circuits of this nature are conventionally in the upper half of the above range, depending upon heat absorption rate, direction of heat application, and degree of slope.

Types of Circulation

An adequate flow of water and water-steam mixture, necessary to the proper performance of all the circuits of a steam-generating unit, may be produced naturally by the action of the force of gravity, mechanically by means of pumps, or by a combination of the two.

In natural circulation the force of gravity available to produce flow comes from the difference between the specific weights (lb/cu ft) of the fluids in the downcomer (down-flow) and riser (up-flow) circuits. Ideally, the fluid in the downcomer is water at or slightly below saturation temperature and uncontaminated by steam bubbles (see *Steam Separation*

and Purity below). Heat-absorbing up-flow circuits, at saturation temperature, convey to the boiler drum a water-steam mixture of lesser density than the water in the down-flow circuits, thus establishing the force available for circulation. Natural circulation is commonly used in all parts of the world for operating steam pressures less than 100 psi up to as high as 2650 psi.

Forced Circulation

In boiler units designed for forced circulation at subcritical pressures), the flow in the various circuits is produced by a pump or pumps. This system is used to a limited extent in Europe (and to an even lesser extent in the United States). There are two general types of forced circulation:

a) In the "once-through" forced-circulation type, water from the feed supply is pumped to the inlet end or ends of the heat-absorbing circuits. Evaporation or change of state gradually takes place along the length of the circuit, and when change of state is complete, further progress of the fluid through the heated circuits results in superheating the vapor. The pounds of steam produced are numerically equal to the pounds of water supplied. Conventionally this type of forced circulation requires no steam-and-water drum.

b) In the "recirculating" forced-circulation type, the water supplied to the circuits by a separate circulating pump is in excess of the steam produced. A steam-and-water drum is required (as in a natural-circulation boiler) in which steam separation takes place. The separated water together with feedwater from the feed pump is returned through down-comer circuits to the circulating pump for another "round trip."

In the recirculating type of forced circulation there is a net thermal loss for the boiler unit because of the separate circulating pump. While practically all of the energy put into the pump reappears in the pumped water as added enthalpy, the energy came originally from the fuel pile at a conversion-to-useful-energy-factor of less than 1.00. If an electric motor is used to drive the pump, the net energy loss referred to the fuel pile is in the order of double the energy supplied to the pump motor (based on a plant thermal efficiency of 0.33).

Natural Circulation

In any given natural-circulation system the circulation will increase with increased heat input (and increased steam output) until a maximum value is reached, after which further increase in heat absorption will result in a decrease in flow. The general form of the curve is shown in Fig. 1. Two opposing forces are present: The increase in flow results from the increase in the difference of the densities of the respective fluids in downcomers and risers caused by the increase in heat absorption. However, at the same time the friction and impact losses (see Chapter 8) in both downcomers and risers are increasing. When the sum of the losses becomes greater than the gain from increase in the density differentials, the flow rate will begin to drop. A proper objective, therefore, is always to design all the circuits to operate in the region of the rising part of the curve.

Because of the above, a natural-circulation boiler tends to be self-compensating for the numerous variations in heat-absorption conditions usual in an operating unit. Some of these are: sudden overloads, change in heat-absorbing-surface cleanliness, non-uniform fuel bed or burner conditions, and even the inability to forecast precisely the actual conditions over the operating lifetime.

No similar compensating effect is inherent in a forced-circulation unit operating at subcritical pressures, since a large part of the total resistance of the riser circuits is caused by flow-distribution devices required at the circuit inlets. Under these conditions an increase in heat absorption to an individual circuit or group of circuits changes the flow rate only a little because of the disproportionately large resistance of the distributors.

The method of producing flow in boiler circuits, whether natural or mechanical, has virtually no bearing on the effectiveness of heat-absorbing surface with nucleate boiling. The prime requirement is that the inside surface should be wetted at all times by the water in a water-steam mixture of suitable quality for the given conditions (see above and Fig. 2). Having met this fundamental requirement, the water film resistance to heat flow is negligibly small (see Chapter 11), and the over-all heat conductance depends upon gas-film and tube-wall resistances. Any departure from this sound practice means the introduction of a steam-film resistance—a truly contradictory situation in the satisfactory operation of any boiler surface under saturated water conditions. In other words, boiler heat-absorbing surface in the furnace or convection portion of the unit will absorb substantially the same amount of heat per sq ft, whether the circulating flow is produced by natural methods or by pumps.

Forced or Natural Circulation

Under certain conditions forced circulation can be usefully applied to steam generation. Mechanical means to move the fluid within the circuits are employed for boilers designed to operate above or near the critical pressure (3206.2 psia). There are instances, also, in the process and waste-heat field where temperature control or consolidating heat pick-up from widely separated points can be economically effected by circuits activated by pumps. The conditions where forced circulation can be applied to advantage are quite specific. In the usual field of boiler design, however, experience has shown that there is little purely physical reason for the use of forced circulation below an operating pressure of at least 2700 psi. The differential in specific weights of steam and water available to overcome friction and produce flow for the range of 14.7 to 3206.2 psia is given in Fig. 3. It will be noted that a substantial differential persists well up toward the critical. As long as this differential is maintained by the effective separation of the steam from the water in the circulating system, as with the use of the cyclone separator (see below), mechanical aid to circulation should not be necessary below the operating pressure noted. Very large boiler units are operating successfully with natural circulation at 2050 to 2650 psi, with no indication that the final limit has been reached.

Circulation Design Criteria

Rational design of boiler circuits to insure the necessary movement (circulation) of the contained

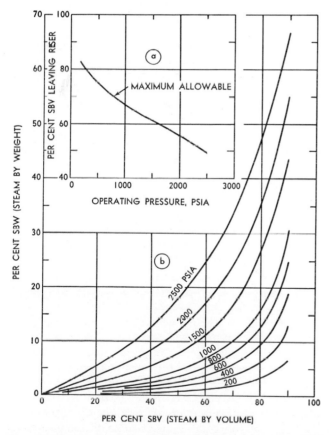

Fig. 2. Diagram a, maximum allowable per cent SBV leaving riser, at various pressures. Diagram b, per cent SBW corresponding to per cent SBV for various pressures

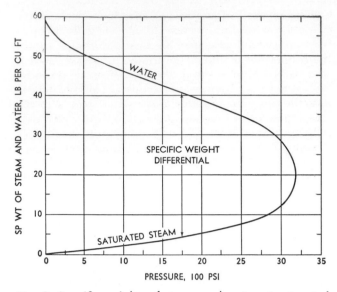

Fig. 3. *Specific weights of steam and water at saturated steam temperature for pressures from atmospheric to critical*

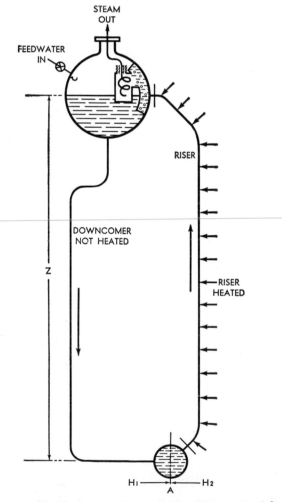

Fig. 4. *Simple hypothetical circuit (diagrammatic) including primary steam separator in drum*

fluid requires the evaluation of a number of variables. In establishing these variables, use is made of accumulated data on limiting values and design criteria derived largely from experience. The riser circuits usually are fixed by arrangement to provide the required heat absorption or to act as an enclosure. The arrangement of downcomer circuits usually is not as rigidly prescribed as that of the risers. Determination of flow areas in various parts of the system, particularly in the downcomer (supply) circuits, usually is the end result of the design calculations.

One design criterion is the maximum allowable per cent steam by volume (% SBV), or the corresponding per cent steam by weight (% SBW), leaving a heat-absorbing riser circuit. Typical values (intended as a guide only) for this criterion are given in Fig. 2 for a range of operating pressures.

The quality of the mixture is not, however, the only criterion of proper conditions within the tubes or flow path. Minimum allowable velocities inside tubes are another important criterion. These values vary widely with the heat-absorption rate, manner of heat application, and arrangement of tubes in the circuit. If the tubes are only slightly inclined from the horizontal and heat is absorbed on the top side, as in a furnace floor, relatively high velocities entering the heat-absorption zone, of the order of 5 to 10 ft per sec, must be maintained. On the other hand, if the riser circuit is substantially vertical, with heat applied on one side or all around the tubes, the minimum allowable entering velocity may be relatively low, of the order of 1 to 5 ft per second. The specific criteria that shall govern involve too many factors for a thorough discussion here.

The rate of heat absorption must be evaluated from fuel combustion data and from knowledge, based on experience, of the probable performance of the specific arrangement of the heat-absorbing surface. In practice, the heat input pattern is rarely uniform along the length of the heat-absorbing path, and integrated values of the instantaneous density-height relationship are required to permit precise determination of mean fluid densities.

Analyses of downcomer circuits as compared with riser circuits are less involved. The specific weight of the fluid in the downcomer (preferably all in the liquid phase) is readily determined, since it is at a temperature related to the feedwater and saturation. Steam bubbles in the downcomer circuit seriously affect the head available for natural circulation (see *Steam Separation and Purity* below).

In the simple circulation calculation example to follow, the application of all refinements is beyond the scope of the treatment. It must be emphasized that the number of possible arrangements of boiler circuits is almost endless, with parallel and series circuits inevitably present. To establish a circulation balance in a complete system is an exceedingly involved problem, and, while the principles of equations (1), (2), (3) and (4) given below apply, the procedure for a thorough solution requires experience in this field, and the application of knowledgeable and expeditious methods.

Principles of Natural Circulation

The elementary circuit shown in Fig. 4 and the basic relationships noted may be used to demonstrate the principles of natural circulation, simple in conception but somewhat tedious in application.

For stabilized flow (system in equilibrium), the quantity of flow in the downcomer must equal the quantity of flow in the riser. Also, the net pressure, at A in Fig. 4, of the fluid in the downcomer must be balanced by the net pressure of the fluid in the riser; that is, the net head in the downcomer, H_1, must equal the net head in the riser, H_2.

Referring to Fig. 4:

$Z =$ difference in elevation, lineal ft
$\rho_1 =$ mean density, downcomer fluid, lb/cu ft
$\rho_{ex} =$ mixture density, leaving riser, lb/cu ft
$\rho_m =$ mean density, riser fluid, lb/cu ft
$Z\rho_1/62.4 =$ downcomer gravity head, ft of std water
$Z\rho_m/62.4 =$ riser gravity head, ft of std water
$F_d =$ sum of downcomer losses; ft of std water (friction, entrance, exit, bend, change of section)
$F_r =$ sum of riser losses; ft of std water (friction, entrance, exit, bend, change of section, separator)

$$H_1 = H_2 \tag{1}$$

$$H_1 = Z\rho_1/62.4 - F_d = \text{downcomer net head, ft of std water} \tag{2}$$

$$H_2 = Z\rho_m/62.4 + F_r = \text{riser net head, ft of std water} \tag{3}$$

$$Z(\rho_1 - \rho_m)/62.4 = F_d + F_r, \text{ from equations (1), (2) and (3)} \tag{4}$$

The term "std water" refers to water at density $= 62.4$ lb/cu ft.

From equation (4) it is evident that the difference in gravity heads, in downcomer and riser, is equal to the sum of the circulation losses in the system. The latter, as noted above, include entrance, exit and bend losses, change of section losses, head losses through baffles and steam separating devices, as well as friction losses along the straight flow paths.

In general, therefore, the losses in the riser portions of the circuit are:
$F_r = \triangle H_L + \triangle H_b + \triangle H_{en} + \triangle H_{ex} + \triangle H_k + \triangle H_s$
and similarly for the downcomer circuit,
$F_d = \triangle H_L + \triangle H_b + \triangle H_{en} + \triangle H_{ex} + \triangle H_k$
Each $\triangle H$ increment represents the various circulation losses in the riser and downcomer portions of the circuit as enumerated above. The flow path friction, $\triangle H_L$, may be expressed by a form of the Fanning equation. The bend loss, $\triangle H_b$, entrance loss, $\triangle H_{en}$, and exit loss, $\triangle H_{ex}$, change of section loss, $\triangle H_k$, and the steam separator loss, $\triangle H_s$, being shock losses (see Chapter 8), are best expressed in "velocity heads." All incremental losses are converted to ft head of standard water.

Specifically:

$$\triangle H_L \text{ (downcomer)} = \frac{2.31fL}{d\rho_1}\left\{\frac{G}{100,000}\right\}^2, \text{ ft of std water} \tag{5}$$

$$\triangle H_L \text{ (riser)} = \frac{2.31fL}{d\rho_m}\left\{\frac{G}{100,000}\right\}^2, \text{ ft of std water} \tag{6}$$

$$\triangle H_b = \frac{N_b}{5.2 \times \rho}\left\{\frac{G}{100,000}\right\}^2, \text{ ft of std water} \tag{7}$$

$$\triangle H_{en}, \triangle H_{ex} \text{ and } \triangle H_k = N_v \times \frac{v^2}{2g} \times \frac{\rho}{62.4}, \text{ ft of std water} \tag{8}$$

$\triangle H_s =$ value depends upon separator type (from manufacturer), ft of std water

In the above equations (5), (6), (7), (8):
$f =$ friction factor, from Fig. 7, Chapter 8
$L =$ length of flow path, ft
$d =$ equivalent diameter (usually ID of tube), in.
$\rho =$ fluid density at region considered, lb/cu ft
$N_b =$ factor (number of velocity heads), from Fig. 13, Chapter 8
$v =$ fluid velocity at region considered, ft/sec
$N_v = 0.5$ and 1.0 commonly used for $\triangle H_{en}$ and $\triangle H_{ex}$, respectively
$G =$ mass flow, lb fluid/sq ft, hr

The following additional definitions and relationships are helpful in circulation analyses:

$$\rho_{mix} = \frac{\% SBV \times \rho_g}{\% SBW}, \text{ lb/cu ft} \tag{9}$$

$$\rho_{mix} = \rho_f - \frac{\% SBV(\rho_f - \rho_g)}{100}, \text{ lb/cu ft} \tag{10}$$

Where:
$\% SBV =$ per cent steam by volume
$\% SBW =$ per cent steam by weight
$\rho_f =$ density of saturated water, lb/cu ft
$\rho_g =$ density of saturated steam, lb/cu ft
$\rho_{mix} =$ density of mixture, lb/cu ft

Example

A simple example using the above relationships for a natural circulation hypothetical circuit, similar to the one shown in Fig. 4, follows:

Conditions

Operating pressure = 600 psia

Feedwater temperature = 486.2 F

$\rho_f = 1/sp\ vol = 49.8$ lb/cu ft, from steam tables

$\rho_g = 1/sp\ vol = 1.3$ lb/cu ft, from steam tables

$h_{fg} = 731.6$ Btu/lb water, heat added, from steam tables

Z = 23 ft, difference in elevation

$L_r = 25$ ft, length of riser circuit

$L_d = 28$ ft, length of downcomer circuit

Heat input = 70,000 Btu/sq ft, hr, of projected riser area (uniform along L_r for simplicity)

Riser circuit arrangement:

   30, 3-in. OD × 2.67-in. ID vertical tubes (touching)

   3, 45° bends @ 18-in. radius

Downcomer circuit:

   Size and number of tubes to be determined

   3, 90° bends @ 18-in. radius

Bend loss factors, from Fig. 13, Chapter 8

$\triangle H_s = 1.10$ ft std water, steam separator loss (from manufacturer for the conditions)

Procedure

Riser, projected area $= \dfrac{30 \times 3 \times 25}{12} = 187.5$

   sq ft

Riser, flow area $= 30 \times \dfrac{(2.67)^2}{144} \times 0.7854 = 1.167$

   sq ft

Steam, total produced $= \dfrac{70,000 \times 187.5}{731.6}$

   $= 17,950$ lb/hr

%SBV leaving riser, max allowable = 73, from Fig. 2

%SBW leaving riser = 6.6, from Fig. 2

Steam/lb mixture, leaving riser = 0.066 lb

Circulation ratio $= \dfrac{1}{0.066} = 15.1$ lb mixture/lb

   steam produced

Flow in circuit, total $= 17,950 \times 15.1 = 271,000$ lb/hr

$\rho_1 = \rho_f = 49.8$ lb/cu ft, mean sp wt in downcomer

$\rho_{ex} = \dfrac{73 \times 1.3}{6.6} = 14.38$ lb/cu ft, sp wt @ riser exit, from equation (9)

$\rho_m = \dfrac{49.8 + 14.38}{2} = 32.09$ lb/cu ft, mean sp wt in riser*

---

*An approximate method; an integrated value should be used for most actual calculations.

%SBV in riser, mean $= \dfrac{100\,(49.8 - 32.09)}{49.8 - 1.3}$

   $= 36.5$, from equation (10)

Cu ft of steam/cu ft of mixture in riser = 0.365

Riser Incremental Losses

The viscosity, μ, of the mixture in the riser at mean density may be taken as approximately proportional to the steam and water by volume, using μ values for the steam and water components from Figs. 11 and 9, Chapter 8.

Hence this example:

μ, mixture, mean $= 0.365 \times 0.058 + 0.635 \times 0.255 = 0.18$ lb(mass)/ft, hr

G, mass flow, riser $= \dfrac{271,000}{1.167}$

   $= 232,000$ lb/sq ft, hr

Re, Reynolds number $= \dfrac{2.67 \times 232,000}{12 \times 0.18}$

   $= 287,000$

f, friction factor, riser = 0.020, from Fig. 7, Chapter 8

Velocity, entering riser $= \dfrac{271,000}{49.8 \times 3600 \times 1.167}$

   $= 1.29$ ft/sec

Velocity, leaving riser $= \dfrac{271,000}{14.38 \times 3600 \times 1.167}$

   $= 4.50$ ft/sec

$\triangle H_L$, riser $= \dfrac{2.31 \times 0.020 \times 25}{2.67 \times 32.09}\left\{\dfrac{232,000}{100,000}\right\}^2$

   $= 0.73$ ft, std water

$\triangle H_{en}$, riser $= 0.5\,\dfrac{(1.29)^2}{64.4} \times \dfrac{49.8}{62.4} = 0.010$ ft, std water

$\triangle H_{ex}$, riser $= 1.0\,\dfrac{(4.50)^2}{64.4} \times \dfrac{14.38}{62.4} = 0.072$ ft, std water

Bend factor for 45° bends, 2.67-in. ID @ 18-in. radius = 0.10, from Fig. 13, Chapter 8

$\triangle H_b$, riser, lower $= 1.0 \times \dfrac{0.10}{5.2 \times 49.8} \times$

   $\left\{\dfrac{232,000}{100,000}\right\}^2 = 0.002$ ft, std water

$\triangle H_b$, riser, upper $= 2.0 \times \dfrac{0.10}{5.2 \times 14.38} \times$

   $\left\{\dfrac{232,000}{100,000}\right\}^2 = 0.015$ ft, std water

$\triangle H_k$, riser, no change in section, $\triangle H_k = 0.0$

$\triangle H_s = 1.10$ ft, std water, from manufacturer

$F_r = $ sum $\triangle H$ riser $= 0.73 + 0.01 + 0.072 + 0.002 + 0.015 + 1.10 = 1.93$ ft, std water

$\dfrac{23(49.8 - 32.09)}{62.4} = F_d + 1.93$, from equation (4)

$F_d = 6.53 - 1.93 = 4.60$ ft, std water

To effect a balance in the circuit the flow area of the downcomer should be selected so that F_d, the total incremental losses $= 4.60$ ft, std water.

Downcomer Incremental Losses

Downcomer tube size is selected by trial and error. For this example, tentative preliminary trials are omitted. Four, 3 in. OD $\times$ 2.67 in. ID tubes will produce a balance, and the evaluation of the incremental downcomer losses follows:

Downcomer flow area $= 4 \times 0.0389 = 0.1556$ sq ft

$$G, \text{ mass flow} = \frac{271,000}{0.1556} = 1,740,000 \text{ lb/sq ft, hr}$$

$$Re, \text{ Reynolds number} = \frac{2.67 \times 1,740,000}{12 \times 0.255}$$
$$= 1,520,000$$

f, friction factor, downcomer $= 0.0162$

Velocity, entering and leaving downcomer,

$$V_{en} = V_{ex} = \frac{271,000}{49.8 \times 3600 \times 0.1556} = 9.73 \text{ ft/sec}$$

$$\triangle H_L = \frac{2.31 \times 0.0162 \times 28}{2.67 \times 49.8} \left\{ \frac{1,740,000}{100,000} \right\}^2 = 2.39$$
ft, std water

$$\triangle H_{en} + \triangle H_{ex} = (0.5 + 1.0)\frac{(9.73)^2}{64.4} \times \frac{49.8}{62.4}$$
$$= 1.76 \text{ ft, std water}$$

Bend factor for 90° bends, 2.67 in. @ 18 in. radius $= 0.12$

$$\triangle H_b = 3 \times \frac{2.31 \times 0.12}{12 \times 49.8} \left\{ \frac{1,740,000}{100,000} \right\}^2 = 0.42 \text{ ft,}$$
std water

$\triangle H_x$, downcomer, no change in section,
$$\triangle H_x = 0.0$$

$F_d = $ sum $\triangle H$ losses, calculated $= 2.39 + 1.76 + 0.42 = 4.57$ ft, std water

As calculated, the total of the downcomer incremental losses, $F_d = 4.57$ ft, standard water, is in substantial agreement with the allowable value of 4.60 ft, standard water, set by equation (4). The sum of the calculated losses should not exceed the allowable losses as derived by the equation, since, if it does, the allowable per cent SBV, one of the criteria imposed, will be exceeded.

Multiple Circuits in Parallel

Parallel riser circuits are frequently used in boiler arrangements. Detail examples of such arrangements are not within the scope of this chapter, but the general approach may be as follows:

A hypothetical multiple circuit with three heated riser components, c, b, a, and a downcomer is illustrated diagrammatically in Fig. 5. In the diagram, Fig. 6, the flow in each of these riser components

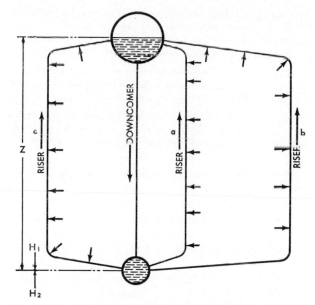

Fig. 5. Hypothetical multiple circuit (diagrammatic) with three heated riser components

PROCEDURE

FOR HEAT INPUT PERTINENT TO EACH RISER

1. CALCULATE POSITION OF POINTS ⊙ AT MAXIMUM ALLOWABLE VALUE FOR PER CENT STEAM BY VOLUME

2. CALCULATE POSITION OF POINTS ⊗ FOR VALUES GREATER THAN THE MAXIMUM ALLOWABLE PER CENT STEAM BY VOLUME.

3. CALCULATE POSITION OF POINTS X FOR VALUES LESS THAN THE MAXIMUM ALLOWABLE PER CENT STEAM BY VOLUME

4. DRAW TRACES THROUGH POINTS ⊙·⊗·X AND FOR THE TOTAL FLOW (ADDITIVE)

5. DRAW LINE m-n THROUGH THE LOWEST POINT ⊙; THE INTERCEPTS DETERMINE THE FLOW IN EACH RISER AND THE TOTAL FLOW

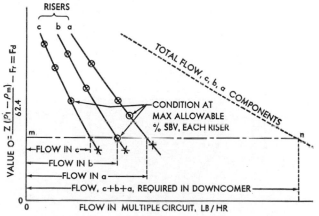

Fig. 6. Method of establishing a circulation balance for a multiple parallel circuit (see Fig. 5). The flow in each riser component and the allowable downcomer loss (at m intercept) are determined for a specified heat input to each riser, using the % SBV criterion

and the total flow in all are evaluated horizontally, while the downcomer losses in terms of F_d from equation (4) are evaluated vertically.

The initial point for each curve in Fig. 6 is established from the criteria set for the particular riser component, usually quality of the mixture, allowable per cent SBV, leaving the heat absorbing region. (Such a point was determined in the above example for a 30-tube riser where $F_d = 4.60$ ft, standard water for a flow of 271,000 lb per hour.) Additional values for F_d corresponding to flow are then calculated for each riser component, using the original value of heat input or lb steam produced, but with other hypothetical values for the quality of the mixture both above and below the maximum allowable. Traces through the points so determined will be of the general form shown in Fig. 6. The lowest point for the group, designating the allowable criterion assigned to the particular riser component, thus establishes the position of a horizontal line, m-n, as indicated. The intercept of this line with the curve

for each riser defines the flow in that particular component. The sum of all the riser component flows establishes, as at n, the total flow in the downcomer, for which the flow area and loss in head are to be determined. The intercept of the horizontal line with the ordinate representing the F_d values fixes the losses permissible in the downcomer for a circulation balance.

It is clear from Fig. 6 that once the position of the horizontal line is fixed (at the low value of F_d) for maximum allowable per cent SBV (when used as a criterion) in the controlling riser component, the per cent SBV and the flow in the other riser components are both inexorably set by the intercepts.

Steam Separation and Purity

In the usual form of steam boilers operating at pressures below the critical the steam drum is important functionally. Feedwater is added here and the saturated steam is separated from the mixture before the steam enters the main line to point of use, or the superheater portion of the unit as in most boilers. Boiler water treatment by chemicals may take place in the drum. Any necessary blowdown for reduction of boiler water concentration is usually from the drum. Further, it is from the drum that the water separated from the mixture, together with feedwater, must be recirculated, preferably in all-liquid phase, to the heat absorbing surfaces.

In a modern boiler drum, the separation of steam from the mixture delivered by the riser portions of the circuit usually takes place in two steps. The "primary" separation removes nearly all the water from the mixture so that, in effect, no steam is recirculated through the circuits.

After the primary separation the steam may still contain contaminants which must be removed, or reduced in amount, before the steam is sufficiently pure for use in high pressure turbines. This step is called "secondary" separation or "steam scrubbing." Both steps are usually accomplished in one steam drum.

A part of the contamination of the steam is caused by dissolved solids contained in tiny droplets that may remain after primary separation. The rest of the contamination appears to be silica, either in solution in vapor phase steam or in vaporized form. This type of contaminant cannot be mechanically removed by primary separation, and washing or scrubbing is necessary for its dilution or complete removal.

Other instances of steam contamination are possible. Gross impurities in the steam may be caused by periods of abnormally high water level, due to operational upsets, in which the separating equipment is submerged, allowing the water to be carried over in gulps. This action may be called "priming." Another type of gross carry-over may occur if the boiler

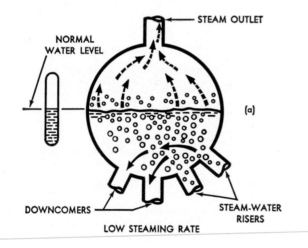

NORMAL WATER LEVEL

STEAM OUTLET

(a)

DOWNCOMERS

STEAM-WATER RISERS

LOW STEAMING RATE

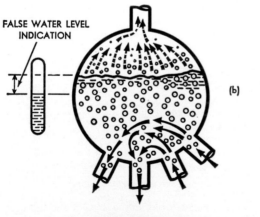

FALSE WATER LEVEL INDICATION

(b)

HIGH STEAMING RATE

Fig. 7. Effect of rate of steam generation on steam separation in an open boiler drum

water used causes excessive foam in the drum. This action, known as "foam-over" and also as "priming," may be severe enough to render the separating devices ineffective. Priming and foam-over are comparatively rare occurrences in the modern boiler equipped with proper water level regulation and control of boiler water quality by chemical methods.

Factors Affecting Steam Separation

Separation of the steam from the steam-water mixture discharged into the drum from the riser circuits is related to both design and operating factors, which may be listed as follows:

Design Factors

1. Operating pressure.
2. Rate of steam generation.
3. Rate of water circulation (the circulation ratio).
4. Arrangement of downcomer and riser circuits in the drum.
5. Size of the steam drum.

Operating Factors

1. Boiler water analysis.
2. Type of steam load.
3. Water level carried.

In steam drums without separation devices, where separation is by gravity only, the manner in which some of the above items affect separation is indicated in simplified form in Figs. 7 and 8.

For a low rate of steam generation (up to something in the order of 3 ft per sec velocity of steam leaving the water surface) there is sufficient time for the steam bubbles to separate from the mixture by gravity without being drawn into the downcomers and without carrying entrained water droplets into the steam outlet (see diagram a, Fig. 7). However, for this same arrangement at a higher rate of steam generation (diagram b, Fig. 7) the time is insufficient to attain either of these desirable results. Moreover, the dense upward traffic of steam bubbles in the mixture may cause a false water level, as indicated.

The effect of the location of the riser circuits in relation to the water level is illustrated in diagrams a and b, Fig. 8. Neither arrangement is likely to yield desirable results in a drum where gravity alone is used for separation.

It is apparent from the above that separation by the action of gravity alone is possible if the velocity of either the mixture or the steam bubbles within the mixture is sufficiently low, but the arrangement may be uneconomical. For gravity separation in a single drum, the steam generated per ft length of drum must be kept extremely low. A single drum under these conditions is generally uneconomical except for small low-duty boilers. Using multiple drums of reasonable size in series, as in diagram a, Fig. 10, somewhat higher steam outputs per ft length of drum are possible with gravity separation.

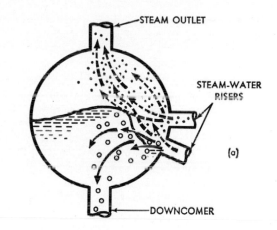

DISCHARGE TUBES NEAR DRUM CENTERLINE

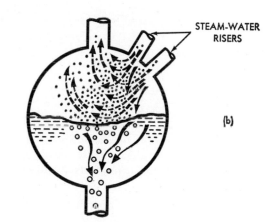

DISCHARGE TUBES ABOVE DRUM CENTERLINE

Fig. 8. *Effect of location of discharge from risers on steam separation in an open boiler drum*

Operating pressure has an effect on the natural tendency of steam and water to separate. The relationship shown in Fig. 3 between pressure and the differential in the specific weights of water and steam is indicative of this effect. In the separation of steam and water, the limiting velocity of a water particle conveyed in steam and the force of gravity both vary directly with the differential in the specific weights of the water and the steam (Stokes law, see Chapter 8). Hence, as the sp wt differential diminishes with increase in operating pressure, so does the force of gravity available for separation. The effect of increasing operating pressure (above 300 psi for comparison) on steam flow (per unit of flow area), on steam velocity (above the drum water level), and on the force of gravity for separation is typically shown in Fig. 9. It will be noted that the percentage drop in gravity-separating force closely follows the drop in limiting velocity.

As steam pressure increases, sp wt of steam in-

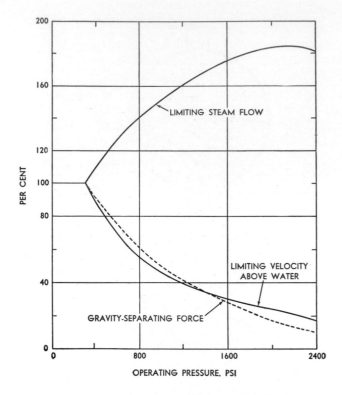

Fig. 9. *Typical effect of increase in operating pressure (above 300 psi for comparison) on 1) limiting steam flow (per unit of flow area), 2) limiting velocity (above water), and 3) gravity-separating force—steam and water*

creases, and the size of steam bubbles in the mixture decreases. Consequently, the velocity of the mixture leaving the riser circuits is reduced, which justifies a higher duty per ft of drum length for a given size of drum, or the use of a smaller drum.

Boiler Water Characteristics

Steam contamination (solid particles in the super-heated steam) comes from the boiler water largely in the carry-over of water droplets. Therefore, in general, as boiler water concentration increases, steam contamination may be expected to increase. The tendency to foam formation also increases with boiler water high in dissolved solids, but a strict correlation of this tendency with specific boiler water analyses is not yet available despite extensive research.

The need for extreme purity of steam for use in high-pressure turbines has prompted the development of highly satisfactory devices for separating steam and water in a boiler drum. Consequently, steam contamination has been steadily reduced. Troublesome deposits on turbine blades may occur with surprisingly low (0.6 ppm) total solids contamination in steam. In the 500 to 900 psi range these deposits are usually water soluble and can be removed by periodic washing. In the 1000 to 1500 psi range, however, silica deposits predominate, and these deposits are not easily removed by water washing. With operating pressures of 2000 psi and above, insoluble deposits appear to diminish. In some instances soluble deposits do occur, which may be controlled by water washing at intervals.

With a rapid increase in boiler load, steam pressure usually starts to decrease as the firing rate is increased. The volume of steam throughout the boiler is increased, and the resulting "swell" raises the water level in the drum. The amount of the increase in water level depends upon the rate of load change and its magnitude. Where rapid load changes are anticipated, the steam drums should be large enough to prevent carry-over from this action.

When there is a foam layer in the steam drum, the steam space available for gravity steam separation is decreased, and separation is adversely affected. Priming may occur. Judicious lowering of the normal water level may relieve the tendency to moisture carry-over.

Mechanical Steam Separators for Drums

As noted above, gravity steam separation alone is generally unsatisfactory for boilers in the usual sizes and required duties. Most steam drums, therefore,

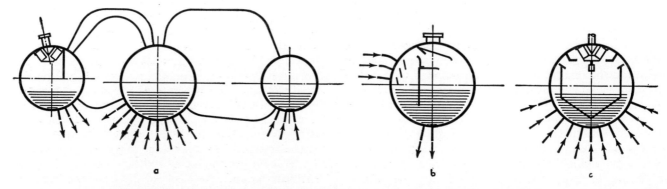

Fig. 10. *Simple types of primary steam separators in boiler drums: a) deflector baffle, b) another arrangement of deflector baffle, and c) compartment baffle*

are fitted with some form of primary separator. Simple types of primary separators are illustrated in Fig. 10. These facilitate or supplement gravity separation. The extent and arrangement of the various baffles and deflectors should always allow for entry into and internal inspection of the drums.

In the B&W cyclone separator shown in Figs. 11 and 12, centrifugal force, at many times the force of gravity, is used to separate the steam and water. Cyclones, essentially cylindrical in form, and corrugated scrubbers are the basic components of this type of separator.

A number of cylinders are arranged inside along the length of the drum, and the steam-water mixture is admitted tangentially. The water forms a layer against the cylinder walls, and the steam (of less density) moves to the core of the cylinder and then upward. The water flows downward in the cylinder and is discharged through an annulus at the bottom, below the drum water level. Thus, with the water returning from drum storage to the downcomers virtually free of steam bubbles, maximum net head is available for producing flow in the circuits, which is the important factor in the successful use of natural circulation, as previously noted. The steam moving upward from the cylinder passes through a small corrugated scrubber at the top of the cyclone (see Figs. 11 and 12) for additional separation. Under many conditions of operation no further refinement in separation is required, although the cyclone separator is considered only as a primary separator.

When wide load fluctuations and variations in water analyses are expected, large corrugated scrub-

Fig. 11. *Double-row arrangement of cyclone-type primary steam separators, with scrubber elements at top of drum for secondary separation*

bers may be installed at the top of the drum (also shown in Figs. 11 and 12) to provide nearly perfect steam separation. These scrubbers may be termed secondary separators. They provide a large surface which intercepts water particles as the steam flows

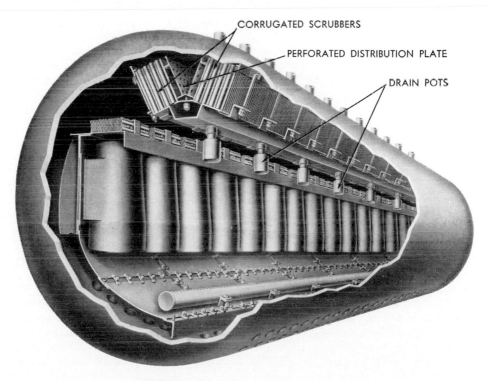

Fig. 12. *Single-row arrangement of cyclone steam separators with scrubbers*

CORRUGATED SCRUBBERS

PERFORATED DISTRIBUTION PLATE

DRAIN POTS

sinuously between the closely fitted plates. Steam velocity through the corrugated-plate assembly is very low, and thus re-entrainment of water is avoided. The collected water is drained from the bottom of the scrubber assembly to the water below.

Single or double rows of cyclone separators are installed in boiler drums, with ample room for access. For smaller boilers (FH and Two-Drum Stirling) at lower pressures (100 psi), the separation of clean steam (see below) with single and double rows of cyclone separators is in the order of 4000 and 6000 lb, respectively, per hr per ft of drum length and, at pressures around 1050 psi, increases to 9000 and 15,000 lb, respectively, per hr per ft of drum length. For large utility boilers (RB and OP) at pressures to 2000 psi and above, separation with single and double rows of cyclone separators is in the order of 15,000 and 30,000 lb, respectively, per hr per ft of drum length.

The combination of cyclone separators and scrubbers described above provides the means for obtaining, under a wide variation in operating conditions, steam purity in the order of less than 1.0 ppm solids content, a result that is commercially quite acceptable. However, further refinement in steam purification is required to remove boiler water salts, such as silica, which are entrained in the steam by vaporization or solution mechanism. Washing the steam with condensate or feedwater of acceptable purity may be used for this purpose.

Steam Washing

For any given operating condition, silica is distributed between boiler water and steam in a definite ratio, commonly referred to as the distribution ratio. As illustrated in Fig. 13, the value of the distribution ratio increases rapidly with increasing pressure. For example, if operating pressure is doubled from 1300 to 2600 psi, the distribution ratio increases tenfold. Experience has indicated that troublesome silica deposits will not form in condensing turbines if the silica concentration in the steam does not exceed approximately 0.025 ppm. By assuming an allowable silica concentration in the steam of 0.025 ppm and using the distribution ratios of Fig. 13, we find that above 2000 psi, the silica content in the boiler water must be kept well below 1 ppm if turbine fouling is to be avoided. Since it is often impractical to maintain boiler water concentrations of silica sufficiently low to prevent turbine fouling, other measures such as steam washing must be used to control this type of steam contamination.

Steam washing is an absorption process by which vaporous silica is absorbed from steam by wash water. A net transfer of silica takes place when the ratio of silica concentration in steam to that in the wash water differs from the distribution ratio. For

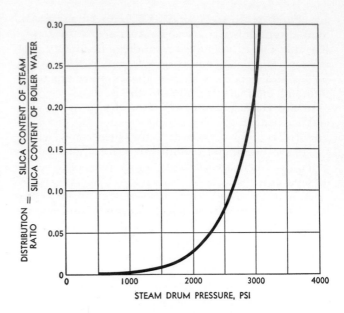

Fig. 13. *Effect of pressure on silica distribution ratio*

example, if pure steam is in contact with water of high silica content, silica will transfer from the water to the steam. This action will continue until the distribution ratio has been established. In steam washing, silica-laden steam is brought into intimate contact with relatively pure wash water, such as condensate or feedwater, and silica is absorbed from the steam by the wash water. The actual amount of silica transferred, and therefore the final silica concentrations of the steam and wash water, will depend upon the relative amounts of steam and water present, the degree of mixing, and the time of contact. In practice, neither the contact area between the steam and the water nor the contact time is sufficiently great to permit a complete interchange of silica from steam to water. As a result, the ratio of the silica concentration of the washed steam to the wash water does not quite reach theoretical equilibrium.

A typical steam drum arrangement employing steam washing is shown in Fig. 14. This drum is equipped with primary mechanical separators of the centrifugal type and primary scrubbers. The steam leaving the primary separators flows to a steam washer arranged in the top of the steam drum. This washer consists of a rectangular column approximately the length of the steam drum. The steam passes vertically upward through a perforated plate, a pack of stainless steel wire mesh, a second perforated plate, and finally a corrugated scrubber element. Wash water enters the drum through a nozzle and flows downward through the washer counterflow to the steam. The steam velocity through the tray perforations maintains, above each tray, a layer of wash water which is kept in violent agitation by the steam. The wire mesh provides a large surface area for achieving intimate contact between the steam and the wash water.

In many installations in which it is impractical to maintain the silica content of the boiler water low enough to prevent turbine deposits, the use of steam washers will eliminate these deposits. In other cases, where it is now possible to prevent turbine deposits by large blowdown rates with resultant low silica content in the boiler water, the use of steam washers will permit lower blowdown rates and higher boiler water silica content.

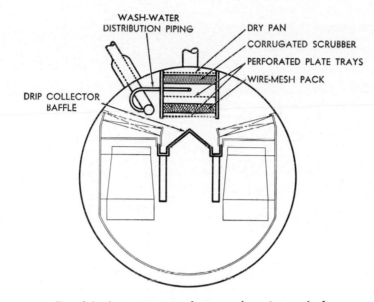

Fig. 14. *Arrangement of steam drum internals for washing silica-laden steam*

First commercial supercritical pressure unit in the
U. S. gives unrivalled thermal performance at this
Ohio station

STEAM AND OTHER ENERGY CYCLES

S TEAM is generated in power boilers for use (1) in a prime mover for the development of mechanical work, (2) to provide process heat, or (3) in a combination of (1) and (2). The central station public utility or a steamship is an example of its use for the development of mechanical work. A building heating system is an example of its use to provide process heat. A plant for a paper mill or a chemical factory is an example of its use in a combination of the two.

Steam is particularly favored for many heating operations because vapor pressure is an ideal thermostat. This fact, coupled with high latent heat, reasonable density and reasonable pressure all combine to make steam the prevalent economical process fluid. The steam tables (in the Appendix) give the physical properties of steam. The first two columns constitute the vapor tension relationship for water and exactly define the vapor pressure which must be established for equilibrium between the liquid and vapor phases for any specified temperature. Steam may be heated beyond this saturation condition to any desired higher value of temperature. The properties for this superheated condition are given in the Appendix.

The steam tables also contain data on specific volume, sensible heat and latent heat which is essential for determination of the suitability of steam for heat purposes. There is also other data, the significance of which is developed below in a consideration of the thermodynamic aspects of the problem.

Laws of Thermodynamics

Thermodynamics is concerned with the mechanics of heat and especially with the conversion of heat into work. There are two basic principles involved which have become firmly established in the scientific field as the first and second laws of thermodynamics. These principles can be variously stated, and the reader should consult any standard book on thermodynamics for a complete statement.

According to the law of the conservation of energy or the first law of thermodynamics, energy can be neither created nor destroyed. Thus in any device or system into which energy is put and out of which some energy is taken, this principle means that an exact balance must prevail among the positive and negative quantities. There can be no excess or no deficiency. Energy may be converted within the device from one form to another, such as heat or work, but there must be complete conservation of the aggregate. This law can be expressed in symbols as in equation (1) and diagrammatically as in Fig. 1. To account for the energy flow, in at (1) and out at (2), in Fig. 1, representing a boiler or a turbine or a compressor or any thermodynamic system or device, assuming for convenience that 1 lb of working fluid moves through, an equation can be written, as follows:

$$Z_1 + \frac{v_1^2}{2g} + p_1 V_1 + u_1 \pm \triangle W \pm \triangle Q = Z_2 + \frac{v_2^2}{2g}$$
$$+ p_2 V_2 + u_2 \qquad (1)$$

Where, in this, the "general energy equation"

Z = the elevational head (potential energy), ft lb per lb

v = the flow velocity through the intake and discharge pipes, ft per sec

g = gravitational acceleration, ft per sec²

$\frac{v^2}{2g}$ = the kinetic energy, ft lb per lb

p = the static pressure under which the fluid exists at the inlet and outlet pipes, lb per ft²

V = the specific volume of the fluid, cu ft per lb

pV = the flow work, ft lb per lb

u = the internal or intrinsic energy of the fluid, Btu per lb

$\triangle W$ = work done on or by the fluid while it is in the device, ft lb per lb

$\triangle Q$ = heat added to or abstracted from the fluid while it is in the device, Btu per lb

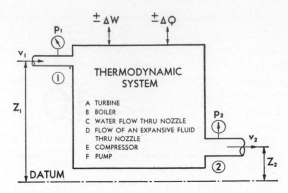

Fig. 1. *Diagram to illustrate the application of the general energy equation to thermodynamic systems*

In using the general energy equation (1) it is essential that all terms be expressed in a consistent system of units. It is not customary to measure all the energy items in the same units, hence the diversity in equation (1). Thus elevation head, Z, is measured in ft; the kinetic energy, $\frac{v^2}{2g}$, the flow work, pV, and the work done, $\triangle$W, are usually all measured in ft lb. On the other hand the intrinsic energy, u, and the heat added, $\triangle$Q, are generally measured in Btu. Joule's experiments based on the law of the conservation of energy give the mechanical equivalent of heat. The heat unit which is in use today is the international Btu. This is defined rigorously in terms of the electrical unit of the watt hour so that the exact conversion is given by the relation

$$1 \text{ Btu} = 778.26 \text{ ft lb} \qquad (2)$$

This conversion factor (usually taken as 778 in engineering work) will serve to give the necessary consistency in the use of equation (1) which may be rewritten as

$$\frac{Z_1}{778} + \frac{v_1^2}{2g \times 778} + \frac{p_1 V_1}{778} + u_1 \pm \frac{\triangle W}{778} \pm \triangle Q = \frac{Z_2}{778}$$
$$+ \frac{v_2^2}{2g \times 778} + \frac{p_2 V_2}{778} + u_2 \qquad (3)$$

The terms u and pV, representing, respectively, the intrinsic energy and the flow work of a fluid, can be treated conveniently as a group. They are then usually expressed as a single symbol, h, called enthalpy, thus

$$h = u + \frac{pV}{778}, \text{ Btu per lb} \qquad (4)$$

Enthalpy values for water and steam are given in the steam tables (see Appendix).

The general energy equation can be applied to specific equipment examples (see Fig. 1), as follows, in each case considering the performance to be for a theoretically perfect machine.

(A) Steam Turbine

The change in elevational head $\triangle$Z, the change in flow velocity, $\triangle$v, from throttle, 1, to exhaust, 2, and the heat transferred to the surroundings, $\triangle$Q, are all zero. Hence, energy equation (3) reduces to

$$\frac{p_1 V_1}{778} + u_1 = \frac{p_2 V_2}{778} + u_2 + \frac{\triangle W}{778}$$

or

$$h_1 = h_2 + \frac{\triangle W}{778}$$

or

$$\frac{\triangle W}{778} = h_1 - h_2 \qquad (5)$$

From equation (5) it is evident that the work done, $\frac{\triangle W}{778}$, for an ideal steam turbine is equal to the difference between the enthalpy, h_1, of the steam entering and the enthalpy, h_2, of the steam leaving.

(B) Steam Boiler

The change in elevational head, $\triangle$Z, the change in flow velocity, $\triangle$v, from feed introduction, 1, to steam takeoff, 2, and the work done, $\triangle$W, are all zero. The energy equation (3) therefore reduces to

$$\frac{p_1 V_1}{778} + u_1 + \triangle Q = \frac{p_2 V_2}{778} + u_2$$

or

$$h_1 + \triangle Q = h_2$$

or

$$\triangle Q = h_2 - h_1 \qquad (6)$$

From equation (6) it is evident that the heat added, $\triangle$Q, for the conversion of water into steam in a boiler, is equal to the difference between the enthalpy, h_2, of the steam leaving the boiler, and the enthalpy, h_1, of the feedwater entering the boiler.

(C) Water Flow Through a Nozzle

For water flowing through a nozzle, the change in elevational head, $\triangle$Z, the change in specific volume, $\triangle$V, the change in intrinsic energy, $\triangle$u, the work done, $\triangle$W, and the heat added, $\triangle$Q, are all zero. Energy equation (3) therefore reduces to

$$\frac{v_1^2}{2g \times 778} + \frac{p_1 V}{778} = \frac{v_2^2}{2g \times 778} + \frac{p_2 V}{778}$$

or

$$\frac{v_2^2}{2g} - \frac{v_1^2}{2g} = (p_1 - p_2) V \qquad (7)$$

The increase in kinetic energy, or the acceleration, of the fluid is given in equation (7). If the velocity of approach, v_1, is zero, then equation (7) can be rewritten

$$\frac{v_2^2}{2g} = (p_1 - p_2) V$$

or

$$v_2 = \sqrt{2g (p_1 - p_2) V} \qquad (8)$$

But $(p_1 - p_2)$ is the difference in the static pressure, upstream and downstream, which when multiplied by the specific volume, V, gives the static head, H

$$(p_1 - p_2) V = H \qquad (9)$$

where H is measured in ft lb per lb or ft. The velocity

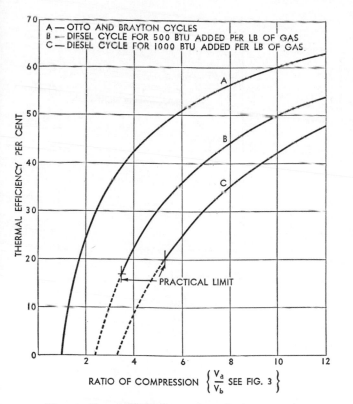

A — OTTO AND BRAYTON CYCLES
B — DIESEL CYCLE FOR 500 BTU ADDED PER LB OF GAS
C — DIESEL CYCLE FOR 1000 BTU ADDED PER LB OF GAS

THERMAL EFFICIENCY PER CENT

PRACTICAL LIMIT

RATIO OF COMPRESSION $\left\{\dfrac{V_a}{V_b} \text{ SEE FIG. 3}\right\}$

Fig. 4. Thermal efficiencies of ideal gas cycles

$$\text{Thermal efficiency} = \frac{T_1 - T_2}{T_1} \quad (20)$$

The value of efficiency given by equation (20) is a rigorous maximum limit imposed by the second law of thermodynamics. No cycle can have a better efficiency between specified temperature limits, than the value given for the Carnot cycle. Other cycles may equal it, but none can exceed it.

Because the atmosphere is the usual thermodynamic sink and its temperature is of the order of 500 deg R, it is evident from equation (20) that the conversion efficiency of heat into work is substantially less than 100 per cent. By what extent it is less is measured by the heat which must be thrown away as heat. This is the unavailable portion which cannot be converted into work. The entropy, S_r or S_d in Fig. 2, is the practical measure of this unavailability.

In the cycles of real thermal power plants there is practically only one source, T_1, of heat - fuel, and one sink, T_2,—the atmosphere—to which the residue must be discarded. As an example, these temperatures can be taken as of the order of 3000 deg R and 500 deg R, respectively. Any ideal heat engine working between these temperatures will then have a limiting thermal efficiency as set by the Carnot cycle. From equation (20), this is

$$\text{Thermal efficiency} = \frac{3000 - 500}{3000} = 0.83. \quad (21)$$

No power plant actually even approaches this value.

The best steam plants and gines give thermal efficienc overall. These are the bes tice, and the average are

Using the temperatures Carnot cycle, where a fi working fluid, is plotted planes as shown in di cycle there are two is processes. This cycle h real engine using a fi Isothermal compressi realized in practice. T effective pressure, w

mep

The Otto, Diese overcome the prac cycle and are rep practice by the g the gas turbine. "B," "C," and " limits set in th

The ratio

is the sole el fluences the Fig. 3) and the Diesel c bustion line ond variabl Otto, Bray standard a the first t Th eff, O

$$1 - \frac{T_a}{T_b}$$

of a free spouting jet is then by substitution in Eq. (8)

$$\text{Velocity ft/sec} = \sqrt{2g\,H} = 8.02\sqrt{H} \quad (10)$$

(D) Flow of an Expansive Fluid Through a Nozzle

If steam, air, or any other expansive fluid is substituted for the flow conditions given under (C), the change in the specific volume, ΔV, and in the intrinsic energy, Δu, are no longer zero so that energy equation (3) becomes

$$\frac{v_1^2}{2g \times 778} + \frac{p_1 V_1}{778} + u_1 = \frac{v_2^2}{2g \times 778} + \frac{p_2 V_2}{778} + u_2$$

or

$$\frac{v_1^2}{2g \times 778} + h_1 = \frac{v_2^2}{2g \times 778} + h_2$$

or

$$\frac{v_2^2}{2g \times 778} - \frac{v_1^2}{2g \times 778} = h_1 - h_2 \quad (11)$$

If the velocity of approach, v_1, is zero then

$$\frac{v_2^2}{2g \times 778} = h_1 - h_2$$

or

$$v_2 = \sqrt{2g \times 778\,(h_1 - h_2)} \quad (12)$$

From equation (12) it is evident that the velocity of a free spouting jet of an expansive fluid, such as steam or air, is a function of the enthalpies (h_1 and h_2) of the fluid entering and leaving the nozzle. This equation may be reduced to

$$\text{Velocity, ft per sec} = 223.7\sqrt{(h_1 - h_2)} \quad (13)$$

(E) Compressor

If an expansive fluid moves through a compressor, well insulated, then the change in elevational head, ΔZ, the change in velocity, Δv, from inlet, 1, to discharge, 2, and the heat transferred to the surroundings, ΔQ, are all zero, and energy equation (3) reduces to

$$\frac{p_1 V_1}{778} + u_1 + \frac{\Delta W}{778} = \frac{p_2 V_2}{778} + u_2$$

or

$$h_1 + \frac{\Delta W}{778} = h_2$$

or

$$\frac{\Delta W}{778} = h_2 - h_1 \quad (14)$$

From equation (14) it is evident that the work done, $\dfrac{\Delta W}{778}$, by the ideal compressor is equal to the difference in the enthalpies of the fluid entering and leaving the unit (h_2 and h_1)

(F) Pump

When a nonexpansive fluid, such as water, is substituted in (E) then the change in specific volume, ΔV, and in intrinsic energy, Δu, become zero and energy equation (3) reduces to

$$\frac{p_1 V}{778} + \frac{\Delta W}{778} = \frac{p_2 V}{778}$$

or

$$\Delta W = (p_2 - p_1)\,V \quad (15)$$

but $(p_2 - p_1)\,V = H$, the static head, in ft of fluid, so that equation (15) becomes

$$\Delta W = H \quad (16)$$

Equation (16) is a rigorous demonstration that in pumping a truly noncompressible fluid all the energy added as work goes ideally to raising the static head. There is no change in temperature.

Second Law of Thermodynamics

The examples (A) to (F) noted above, represent some of the basic manipulations which can be made in applying the general energy equation to specific apparatuses. The great significance of the property of enthalpy is amply demonstrated by the examples cited. All of these manipulations are based on the first law of thermodynamics. They account for all energy added or abstracted and the conclusions satisfy the requirement for an exact balance (heat balance) of the energy supplied to a system and of the energy rejected.

The general energy equation, however, has one very serious shortcoming—it tells practically nothing of the possible extent of conversion of one form of energy into another in the many kinds of apparatus found in practice. Thus, if 100 heat units were added to a system how much could be converted into work? According to the first law, not more than the 100 units could be converted but nothing is said about how much less than the 100 units can be converted. The basic purpose of the second law of thermodynamics is rigorously to define the extent of possible conversion of heat into work. This concept is very broad, very tantalizing, and yet most useful in all fuel burning power plants whether steam, internal combustion, gas turbine, or nuclear.

Therefore, to define the extent of the possible conversion of heat energy into work, the first law of thermodynamics and the general energy equation must be supplemented by the second law. By using the concept of entropy it is possible to represent heat

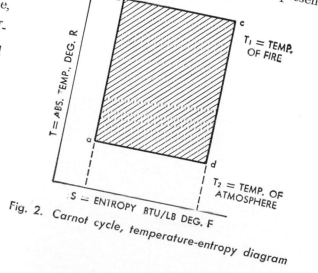

Fig. 2. Carnot cycle, temperature-entropy diagram

added (+) or heat rejected (−) as areas and so demonstrate the extent of this possible conversion. For ideal processes this property (entropy) is defined mathematically (assuming unit mass of the substance) as:

$$ds = \frac{dQ}{T} \tag{17}$$

where:

ds = entropy change, Btu per lb, F
dQ = heat added, Btu per lb
T = absolute temperature at which heat is added, R = F + 460

where R = degrees Rankine (the absolute Fahrenheit temperature scale)

Entropy can be more generally defined as the property which measures that portion of the heat added which cannot be converted into work no matter how nearly perfect the operation may be. Or expressed in another way, it is the measure of unavailability.

The limitations imposed by the second law are perhaps best illustrated by considering the temperature-entropy (T-S) diagram, Fig. 2, where absolute

temperature is plott
tally, and areas rep
jected (−). Consid
T₁, which might be
heat source), and
tical purposes is
by atmospheric te
ciple the maximu
the T-S diagram
the rectangle as
represents the
under T₁ repre
and the area
to the sink. Th
is defined as:

The

but by the f

Thermal

For the C

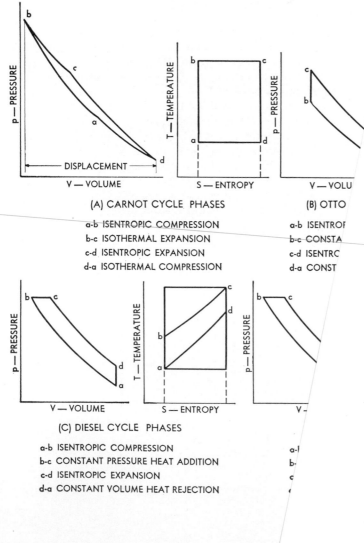

(A) CARNOT CYCLE PHASES

a-b ISENTROPIC COMPRESSION
b-c ISOTHERMAL EXPANSION
c-d ISENTROPIC EXPANSION
d-a ISOTHERMAL COMPRESSION

(B) OTTO

a-b ISENTROP
b-c CONSTA
c-d ISENTRC
d-a CONST

(C) DIESEL CYCLE PHASES

a-b ISENTROPIC COMPRESSION
b-c CONSTANT PRESSURE HEAT ADDITION
c-d ISENTROPIC EXPANSION
d-a CONSTANT VOLUME HEAT REJECTION

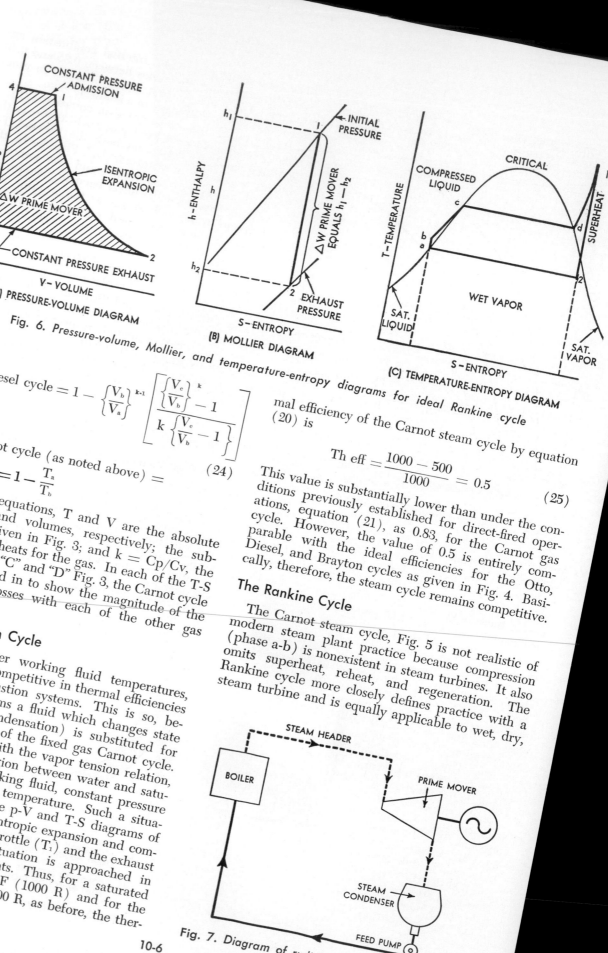

Fig. 6. Pressure-volume, Mollier, and temperature-entropy diagrams for ideal Rankine cycle

$$\text{Th eff, Diesel cycle} = 1 - \left\{\frac{V_b}{V_a}\right\}^{k-1} \left[\frac{\left\{\frac{V_e}{V_b}\right\}^{k} - 1}{k\left\{\frac{V_e}{V_b}\right\} - 1}\right]$$

$$\text{Th eff, Carnot cycle (as noted above)} = \frac{T_b - T_a}{T_b} = 1 - \frac{T_a}{T_b} \tag{24}$$

In the above equations, T and V are the absolute temperatures and volumes, respectively; the subscripts are as given in Fig. 3; and k = Cp/Cv, the ratio of specific heats for the gas. In each of the T-S diagrams of "B," "C" and "D" Fig. 3, the Carnot cycle has been sketched in to show the magnitude of the deviations and losses with each of the other gas cycles.

The Carnot Steam Cycle

Despite the lower working fluid temperatures, steam systems are competitive in thermal efficiencies with internal combustion systems. This is so, because in steam systems a fluid which changes state (evaporation and condensation) is substituted for the isothermal phases of the fixed gas Carnot cycle. Thus, in accordance with the vapor tension relation, if steam, in the wet region between water and saturated vapor, is the working fluid, constant temperature is represented in the p-V and T-S diagrams of Fig. 5. Such a situation is approached in pression connecting the throttle (T₁) and the exhaust (T₂) conditions. This situation is approached in Uniflow steam engine plants. Thus, for a saturated steam temperature of 540 F (1000 R) and for the same sink temperature of 500 R, as before, the ther-

mal efficiency of the Carnot steam cycle by equation (20) is

$$\text{Th eff} = \frac{1000 - 500}{1000} = 0.5 \tag{25}$$

This value is substantially lower than under the conditions previously established for direct-fired operations, equation (21), as 0.83, for the Carnot gas cycle. However, the value of 0.5 is entirely comparable with the ideal efficiencies for the Otto, Diesel, and Brayton cycles as given in Fig. 4. Basically, therefore, the steam cycle remains competitive.

The Rankine Cycle

The Carnot steam cycle, Fig. 5 is not realistic of modern steam plant practice because compression (phase a-b) is nonexistent in steam turbines. It also omits superheat, reheat, and regeneration. The Rankine cycle more closely defines practice with a steam turbine and is equally applicable to wet, dry,

Fig. 7. Diagram of

or superheated steam. This cycle is shown schematically in Fig. 6 where in the p-V diagram the two constant pressure phases of admission (4-1) and exhaust (2-3) are connected by an isentropic expansion phase (1-2). The work of this cycle, shown in the designated area of Fig. 6 is most conveniently evaluated by thermal methods, using the properties of steam (from the steam tables), the Mollier chart for steam (see Appendix), and general energy equation (3). It was demonstrated in the derivation of equation (5) that the work of the ideal prime mover (diagram "A") Fig. 6) is found exactly as

$$\frac{\triangle W}{778}, \text{ Prime mover} = (h_1 - h_2), \text{ Btu per lb} \quad (26)$$

where h_1 and h_2 are the initial and final enthalpies of the steam entering and leaving the prime mover, expressed in Btu per lb. The isentropic relationship between h_1 and h_2, most conveniently manipulated by using a vertical line on the Mollier chart, is shown

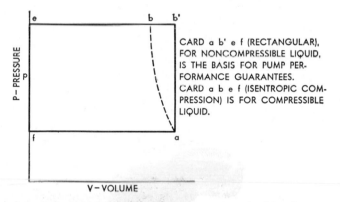

CARD a b' e f (RECTANGULAR), FOR NONCOMPRESSIBLE LIQUID, IS THE BASIS FOR PUMP PERFORMANCE GUARANTEES.
CARD a b e f (ISENTROPIC COMPRESSION) IS FOR COMPRESSIBLE LIQUID.

Fig. 8. *Indicator card or p-V diagram for ideal feed pump*

in diagram "B" Fig. 6. The water rate or steam rate (WR) of the prime mover follows from the value of work, equation (26), and the mechanical equivalents of kw hr (3412.75 Btu) and hp hr (2545 Btu), thus

$$WR = \frac{3412.75 \times 778}{\triangle W}, \text{ lb per kw hr} \quad (27)$$

$$\text{or} \quad WR = \frac{2545 \times 778}{\triangle W}, \text{ lb per hp hr} \quad (28)$$

Equations 26, 27 and 28 are most useful in the calculation of work and water rate but these values must be related to the heat supplied ($\triangle Q$ added), in order to determine thermal performance. This goes far beyond the prime mover and requires the inclusion of accessory equipment in the steam plant. The arrangement of equipment in a rudimentary condensing steam power plant is shown schematically in Fig. 7. In addition to the prime mover there is the boiler, the condenser, and the feed pump. The functional elements of boiler, prime mover, condenser,

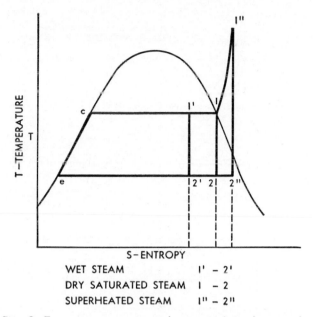

Fig. 9. *Temperature-entropy diagram of Rankine cycle, using wet, dry saturated, and superheated steam*

WET STEAM   1' — 2'
DRY SATURATED STEAM   1 — 2
SUPERHEATED STEAM   1" — 2"

and feed pump are essential for a workable steam plant which complies with the basic thermodynamic cycle.

The T—S diagram, "C," Fig. 6, again serves to show the nature of the entire operation. This diagram must contain, in graphical form, the properties for liquid, wet vapor, and superheat as taken from the steam tables. The Rankine cycle can then be superimposed, as shown, where the heat added ($\triangle Q$ added) is the area under the irregular line b-c-d-1; the heat rejected, ($\triangle Q$ rejected to the condenser) is the area under the line 2-a; the isentropic expansion in the prime mover is the vertical line 1 to 2; and the isentropic compression in the feed pump is the vertical line ab. Usually the compression phase is so small as to be negligible, and the points a and b can, therefore, be considered as the single point, saturated liquid at the exhaust pressure. The compressed liquid phase need only be recognized for pressures higher than 1000 psi. The feed pump p-V diagram or indicator card is substantially a rectangle as shown in Fig. 8. The net work of the Rankine cycle for the complete power plant of Fig. 7 is then

Net work of cycle =
     Prime mover work — Feed pump work   (29)

$$\text{Net work} = (h_1 - h_2) - \frac{\triangle W}{778} \text{ (FP)} \quad (30)$$

The heat supplied ($\triangle Q$ added), to make steam is the difference in the enthalpy, h_b, of the feed entering the boiler, and the enthalpy, h_1, of the steam leaving the boiler (diagram "C" Fig. 6). The value, h_b, is for compressed liquid and is most conveniently found by using the saturated liquid value, h_a (called h_{liq} hereafter) from the steam tables and adding to

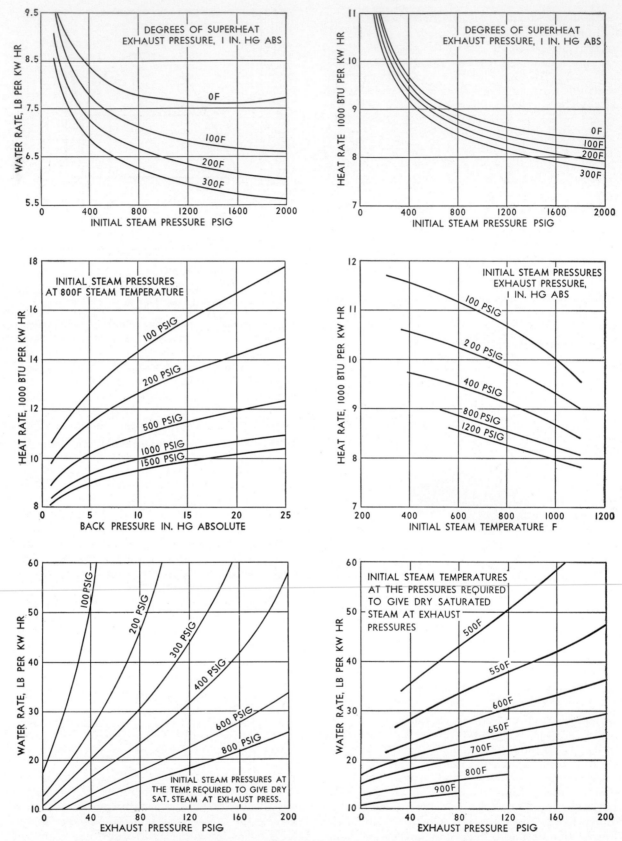

Fig. 10. *Diagrams showing effect of change in steam pressure, steam temperature, and exhaust pressure on ideal Rankine cycle performance*

10-8

it the feed pump work, $\triangle W_{FP}$, or

$$\triangle Q \text{ added} = h_1 - h_b \qquad (31)$$

$$= (h_1 - h_a) - \frac{\triangle W_{FP}}{778} \qquad (32)$$

$$- (h_1 \quad h_{11q}) \quad \frac{\triangle W_{FP}}{778} \qquad (33)$$

The thermal efficiency of the Rankine cycle is then from equations (18), (30) and (33).

$$\text{Th eff, Rankine cycle} = \frac{(h_1 - h_2) - \dfrac{\triangle W_{FP}}{778}}{(h_1 - h_{11q}) - \dfrac{\triangle W_{FP}}{778}} \quad (34)$$

As explained above, if steam pressures are not higher than 1000 lb, equation (34) may be simplified to the approximate form

$$\text{Approx th eff, Rankine cycle} = \frac{(h_1 - h_2)}{(h_1 - h_{11q})} \quad (35)$$

The heat rate, which is the heat supplied per unit of power output, is generally preferred to thermal efficiency because it is more directly applicable to fuel performance. It is defined as

$$\text{HR, Heat rate} = \frac{3412.75}{\text{Th eff}}, \text{ Btu per kw hr} (36)$$

and on the horsepower basis

$$\text{HR, Heat rate} = \frac{2545}{\text{Th eff}}, \text{ Btu per hp hr} \quad (37)$$

These several equations for the Rankine cycle are equally applicable to steam which is wet, dry, or superheated. The influence of steam quality (wet, dry, and superheated) is evident from the several Rankine cycle diagrams drawn in Fig. 9. It will be noted that the shape of the Rankine cycle diagram is greatly altered by shifting point 1 from its position for dry steam to the positions 1' for wet steam or 1'' for superheated steam.

The effect of changes in superheat, steam pressure

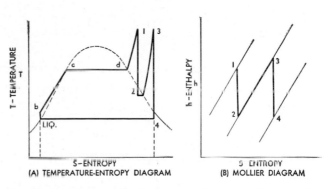

Fig. 11. *Illustrating effect of resuperheat on steam cycle*

and exhaust pressure on the performance of the ideal Rankine cycle are shown graphically in Fig. 10.

The Resuperheat Cycle

The resuperheat cycle is a modification of the simple Rankine cycle which latter is limited by practical considerations to something in the order of 1000 F for maximum steam temperatures. As shown in Fig. 11, expansion proceeds from 1 to 2 at an intermediate pressure; the steam is then reheated to an elevated temperature 3, approximately equal to the value at 1, and expansion proceeds isentropically from 3 to the exhaust pressure at 4. The work of the complete cycle is found by use of the Mollier chart, and is the sum of two Rankine cycle values, equation (26), or

$$\frac{\triangle W \text{ Prime mover}}{778}$$

$$= (h_1 - h_2) + (h_3 - h_4), \text{ Btu per lb} \quad (38)$$

$$\frac{\triangle W}{778} \text{ Resuperheat cycle, Btu/lb} =$$

$$(h_1 - h_2) + (h_3 - h_4) - \frac{\triangle W_{FP}}{778} \quad (39)$$

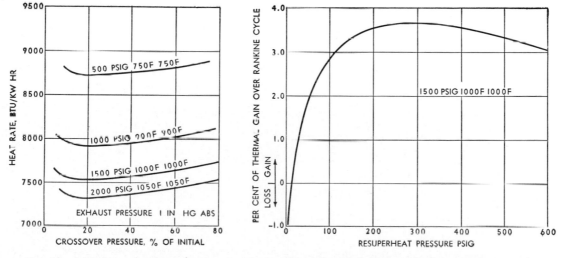

Fig. 12. *Influence of resuperheat pressure on thermal gains of the ideal resuperheat cycle*

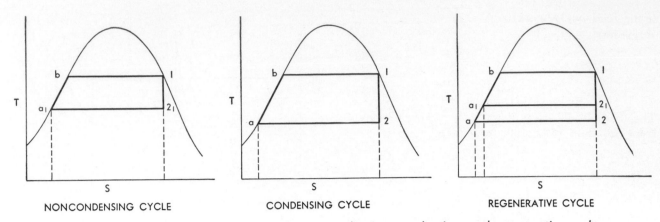

Fig. 13. *Temperature-entropy diagrams for noncondensing, condensing, and regenerative cycles*

The heat added, $\triangle Q$, is the sum of the two components, primary and reheat, or:

$$\triangle Q, \text{Btu/lb} = (h_1 - h_b) + (h_3 - h_2) \qquad (40)$$

$$\triangle Q, \text{Btu/lb} = (h_1 - h_{11q}) + (h_3 - h_2) - \frac{\triangle W_{FP}}{778} \qquad (41)$$

The thermal efficiency and heat rate are then, respectively:

Thermal eff, Resuperheat cycle =

$$\frac{(h_1 - h_2) + (h_3 - h_4) - \dfrac{\triangle W_{FP}}{778}}{(h_1 - h_{11q}) + (h_3 - h_2) - \dfrac{\triangle W_{FP}}{778}} \qquad (42)$$

Heat rate, Resuperheat cycle, =

$$\frac{3412.75}{\text{Thermal eff}}, \text{Btu/kwhr} \qquad (43)$$

Some of the implications of the influence of resuperheat pressure on the thermal performance of reheat cycles are shown in Fig. 12. In fact, resuperheating gains are so vitally affected by reheat pressure that it is entirely possible to show a loss in heat rate as compared with the simple Rankine cycle, as indicated at the right-hand diagram of Fig. 12.

The Regenerative Cycle

No practical steam plant operates without a feedwater heater. For every 10 degrees rise in feed temperature, there is an approximate reduction of 1 per

TABLE 1

Performance of Three Steam Cycles Compared
(See Figs. 13 and 14)

Cycle	1 Non- condensing	2 Condensing	3 Combining 1 & 2
Initial Conditions			
Pressure, psia	115	115	115
Temperature, F	338	338	338
Quality, % dryness	100	100	100
Enthalpy, h_1, Btu/lb	1190	1190	1190
Exhaust Conditions			
Pressure, psia and in. Hg	14.7 psia	1.0 in. Hg	—
Temperature, F	212	79	—
Enthalpy, h_2, Btu/lb	1040	855	—
Rankine Cycle Work			
$W = (h_1 - h_2)$, Btu/lb	150	335	—
Enthalpy of Liquid at			
Exhaust, h_{11q}, Btu/lb	180	47	—
Heat Added to Make Steam			
$(h_1 - h_{11q})$, Btu/lb	1010	1143	—
Rankine Cycle			
Water rate, lb/kwhr	22.8	10.2	11.0
Thermal efficiency	0.148	0.293	0.307
Heat rate, Btu/kwhr	23,000	11,630	11,113
Power taken out, Btu/kwhr	3,413	3,413	3,413
Heat rejected, Btu/kwhr	19,587	8,217	7,700

cent in the heat that must be added to make steam. However, this heating must be done by utilizing some otherwise waste-heat source, or in the language of thermodynamics, it must be done regeneratively. Thus a feedwater heater serves regeneratively to raise the temperature of the feed above the saturated liquid condition for the back pressure, as contained in the Rankine cycle specification (see Fig. 11). Much could be written and many formulas could be developed about the theoretical calculations involving regenerative feed-heating. Real cycles, however, are so divergent from theory that only a brief treatment on the theoretical aspects is given here, followed by elaboration of the practical aspects of actual cycles for power plants.

Consider two steam cycles, each supplied with steam at the same pressure, say 115 psia dry and saturated, $h_1 = 1190$ Btu/lb, one exhausting to the atmosphere at 14.7 psia and the other exhausting to a condenser in which a vacuum of 1 in. mercury absolute is maintained. The evaluation of the performance of these two cycles (Fig. 13) as given in Table 1 can be determined by applying the basic equations (27), substituting $(h_1 - h_2) \times 778$ for $\triangle W$, (35), and (36).

Regenerative principles can be demonstrated by combining these cycles as shown in Figs. 13 and 14 (with performance given in Table 1). If the exhaust from the noncondensing cycle is used regeneratively to heat the feedwater coming from the hot well of the condenser, then in Fig. 13 it is necessary that the area under (a-a₁), the heat per lb required to raise the temperature of the condensate multiplied by the weight of the condensate, must equal the area under (2₁-a₁), the heat available per lb in the noncondensing cycle exhaust multiplied by the weight of the noncondensing exhaust used. This equality can be established only by adjusting the weights of steam supplied to the condensing and noncondensing cycles, respectively. To heat 1 lb of condensate, only a fraction of a lb of steam is required. For the ex-

ample given in Table 1, the balance is effected with
$$\frac{(212 - 79) \times 10.2}{860} = 1.577 \text{ lb of 14.7 psia exhaust}$$
steam to heat 10.2 lb of condensate. The aggregate generation is then, for steam flow rates of 10.2 lb and 1.577 lb per hr, as follows:

Condensing cycle, $\dfrac{10.2}{10.2} = 1.000$ kw

Noncondensing cycle, $\dfrac{1.577}{22.8} = 0.069$ kw

Total $= 1.069$ kw

The combined performance of the two cycles, or of the regenerative cycle of Fig. 14, is then:
Total throttle flow $= 10.2 + 1.577 = 11.777$ lb per hr

Water rate (WR), throttle $= \dfrac{11.777}{1.069}$

$= 11.00$ lb per kwhr

Water rate (WR), condenser $= \dfrac{10.2}{1.069}$

$= 9.55$ lb per kwhr

Heat rate (HR), throttle =
11.00 (1190 — 180) = 11,113 Btu per kwhr
Heat rate (HR), condenser =
9.55 (855 — 47) = 7,700 Btu per kwhr
Power taken out = 3,413 Btu per kwhr

Comparing these values with the corresponding values in Table 1 for the condensing cycle, it is evident that the throttle WR is greater (11.0 vs 10.2) and the condenser WR is less (9.55 vs 10.2) for the regenerative cycle. Despite this water rate situation, the throttle heat rate, 11,113 Btu per kwhr (and therefore the thermal efficiency) is best of all for the regenerative cycle. This superior thermal performance results from the reduction, through regeneration, of the heat rejected to the condenser to the minimum value of 7700 Btu per kwhr.

This example, confined to one feed temperature and one stage of heating, serves to demonstrate the principle of regenerative feedwater heating. Different feed temperatures (from hot well to boiler saturation) and various numbers of stages of heating (from zero to infinity) will alter the thermal improvement. The effect of feed temperature and number of stages of heating on the gain in thermal efficiency, with ideal regenerative cycles, is indicated in Fig. 15. The multistage regenerative heating cycles shown are all based on the thermodynamic desirability of equal temperature rises in all stages. There is also the basic implication that maximum work has been obtained from a lb of steam before that steam is used for feed heating. In other words, no thermodynamic gain is possible by using live steam to heat feedwater, because steam so used does no work.

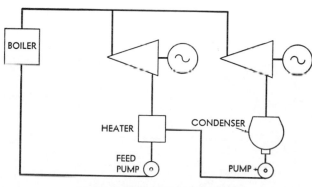

SINGLE-STAGE REGENERATIVE CYCLE

Fig. 14. *Single-stage regenerative cycle—a combination of the noncondensing and condensing cycles*

Heat Balances and Real Steam Cycles

The discussion above is primarily concerned with ideal thermodynamic conditions, and is useful in establishing the solid foundation on which to build the performance of real steam plants. Flow diagrams, cycle diagrams, or heat balance diagrams are useful in showing schematically the performance of real plants. They include numerical data on size, quantity, pressure, temperature, enthalpy, power and the like for each component piece of apparatus used in the plant. Being real they must contain all necessary allowances for the actual performance of each component. The heat balance data can be no more exact than the understanding, interpretation, and correctness of the equipment performance data which is used. Some useful performance data, not treated elsewhere, is given below.

Steam Turbines

Engine efficiency. The actual work obtained per lb of steam in real turbines is less than the theoretical Rankine cycle value from equation (5) or (26). Engine efficiency, a measure of this reduction in value, is defined as

$$\text{Engine efficiency} = \frac{\text{Actual work}}{\text{Rankine cycle work}} \quad (44)$$

Representative values of efficiency for different classes and sizes of turbines are given in Fig. 16. Marine turbines, because of larger clearances, are usually less efficient than shore turbines by some 2 to 5 per cent. Engine inefficiency is manifest in raising point 2 on the Mollier diagrams, "B" Fig. 6 and Fig. 17, to a new and larger value of enthalpy and entropy at point 2'. The losses which occur in a turbine appear as reheat in the exhaust so that the result when plotted on the Mollier diagram (Fig. 17) is a curved or inclined line, as shown, called the condition curve or state line.

The values of engine efficiency at part load can be estimated from the percentage Willans' lines of Fig. 18 or other more exact data. Throttle losses are less than 2 per cent on the pressure drop basis and gland leakages on well maintained turbines seldom exceed 0.5 to 1 per cent of full load throttle flow for each positive pressure external gland. The pressures in the stages of a turbine are a function of the flow below that stage, so that the absolute pressure is substantially directly proportional to the weight flow. Thus if the pressure is known for any stage at a particular flow the pressure for any other flow can be estimated by direct proportionality. The enthalpy, in turn, can be read from the appropriate state line or condition curve, Fig. 17. The exhaust from a tur-

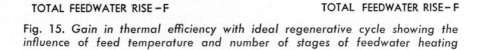

Fig. 15. *Gain in thermal efficiency with ideal regenerative cycle showing the influence of feed temperature and number of stages of feedwater heating*

terminal temperature difference. Deaerating
usually are specified for a minimum temperat
of 25 to 30 F to assure effective degasificatio
feedwater. Drain coolers and heat exchang
selected for 10 to 20 F terminal temperature
ence.

Pumps

Except in the smallest sizes, when they
reciprocating, pumps are of centrifugal or, i
rare instances, of axial flow type. This pern
use of direct-connected high-speed drivers wit
mum weight and space requirements. The
ary drive is the constant speed induction moto
economics may dictate the use of variable spe
tor, hydraulic coupling, magnetic coupling,
turbine, or internal combustion engine. Stea
iliary drive, while giving good reliability,
poses the problem of absorbing the heat of
haust regeneratively at all loads.

The performance of pumps is based on ha
cold water (85 F max) which is considered
truly noncompressible (see Fig. 8). Thus th
retic water horsepower (whp) is given by the
ing equation

$$\text{whp} = \frac{\text{gpm} \times \text{head in ft} \times \text{sp gr}}{3960}$$

or $$\text{whp} = \frac{\text{lb per min} \times \text{head in ft}}{33{,}000}$$

The efficiency of a pump is defined as the ra
the theoretic water horsepower, whp, to the
horsepower input, shp, or

$$\text{Pump efficiency} = \frac{\text{whp}}{\text{shp}}$$

Centrifugal and axial flow pumps show peak ef
cies which range from 50 to 90 per cent; the
values for larger pumps, lower heads, or fewer
The impact of high steam pressures has m
necessary to recognize that large amounts of e
are imparted to the feedwater through the
shaft. In this connection it is customary to co

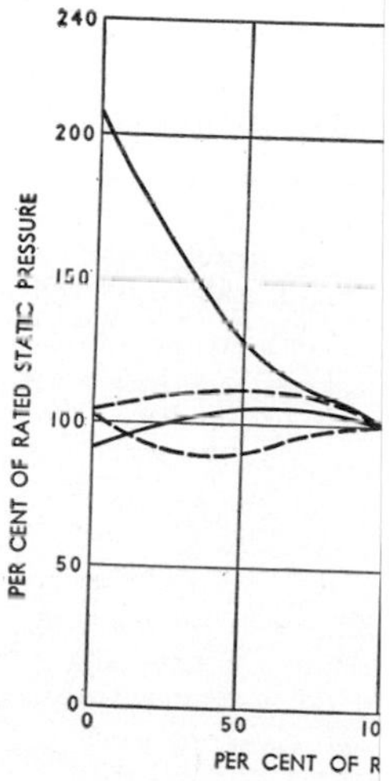

Fig. 24. *Centrifugal and axial flow fan characteristic curves — percentage basis*

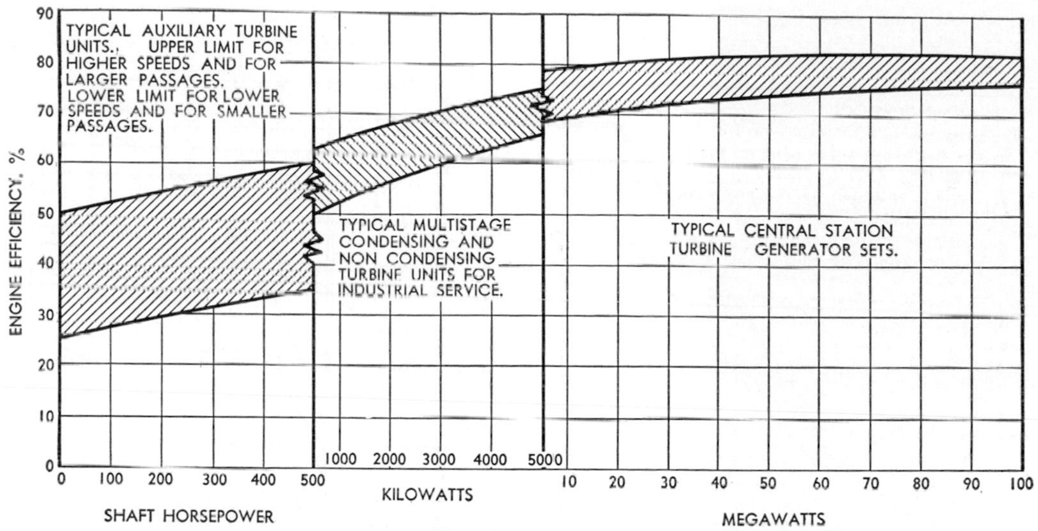

Fig. 16. *Representative engine efficiencies for typical steam turbine units*

bine contains residual, unabsorbed, kinetic energy. There is thus an exhaust or leaving loss which varies with the flow and the blading size, shown typically in Fig. 19. Generator, mechanical and electrical, losses are of the order of 1 or 2 per cent for large units, and seldom exceed 5 per cent in any case.

Steam Condensers

Representative condenser performance can be computed from the basic data of the Heat Exchange Institute, New York. Water velocities seldom exceed 7 ft per sec in practice and cleanliness factor of 0.7 to 0.9 is usually applied to the data. Circulating water requirements are limited generally to a temperature rise at full load of 5 to 10 F for single pass and 10 to 20 F for two pass condensers. Steam jet air ejectors require 300 to 600 lb of steam per hr per element and the heat is usually recovered in the condensate.

Feedwater Heaters

Heat transfer rates are given by the data of Fig. 20. Selection of the suitable size of heater usually resolves itself into an allowable terminal temperature difference of from 3 to 8 F at full load and pressure drops of less than 25 psi. If the terminal temperature difference is desired at some other load it can be approximated by the relation

$$\text{TTD} \propto (\text{Water flow rate})^{0.8} \qquad (45)$$

Open, contact, and deaerating heaters give zero

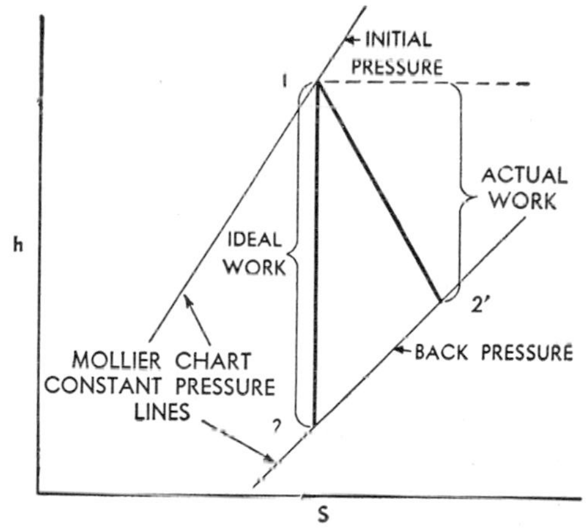

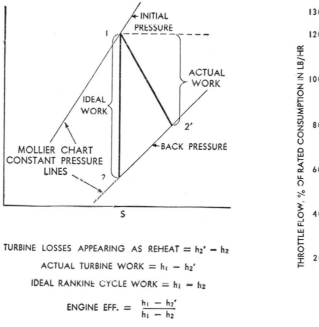

TURBINE LOSSES APPEARING AS REHEAT $= h_2' - h_2$

ACTUAL TURBINE WORK $= h_1 - h_2'$

IDEAL RANKINE CYCLE WORK $= h_1 - h_2$

$$\text{ENGINE EFF.} = \frac{h_1 - h_2'}{h_1 - h_2}$$

Fig. 17. *Condition curve or state line of steam turbine*

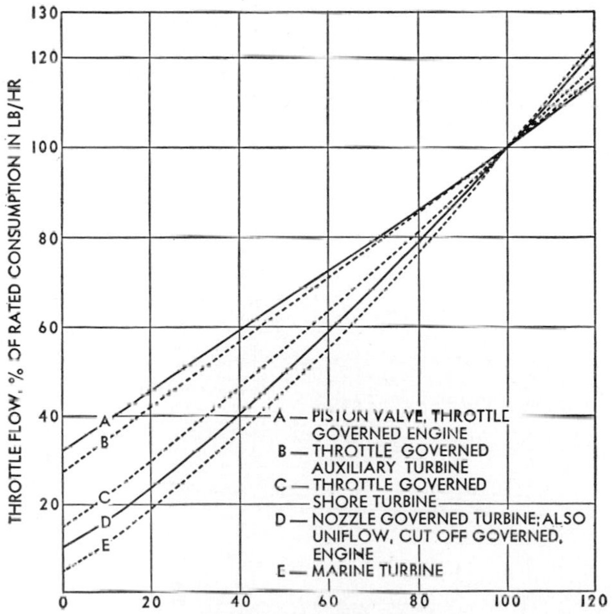

Fig. 18. *Willans lines for steam engines and turbines*

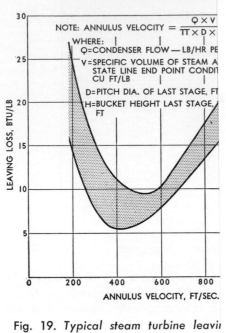

Fig. 19. *Typical steam turbine leavi*

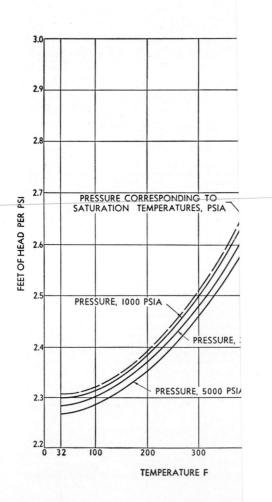

TABLE 2

Heat Balance Calculations for Cycle Shown in Fig. 26

(10,000 Kw Condensing Unit)

	Full Throttle	Part Throttle		Full Throttle	Part Throttle
Turbine			**4th Stage Extraction Heater (cont'd)**		
Steam flow, lb/hr	117,000	85,000	Heater sat. temp., F	323	299
Pressure, psia	440	440	Terminal temp., diff., F	4	2
Total temperature, F	800	800	Water temp. out, F	319	297
Condenser			Water enthalpy out, Btu/lb	289	267
Steam flow, lb/hr	92,200	68,300	Water enthalpy in, Btu/lb	211	192
Pressure, in. Hg abs	1	1	Enthalpy rise of water, Btu/lb	78	75
Hot well temperature, F	79	79	Heat required, Btu/hr	8,500,000	5,925,000
Hot well enthalpy, Btu/lb	47	47	Extraction enthalpy, Btu/lb	1287	1264
11th Stage Extraction Heater			Drip enthalpy, Btu/lb	293	269
°Water flow to heater, lb/hr	92,200	68,300	Heat avail. in extraction, Btu/lb	994	995
Turbine stage press., psia	7.0	5.1	Extraction required, lb/hr	8,550	6,000
Press. drop to heater, psia	0.7	0.5	Boiler feed, lb/hr	117,000	85,000
Heater shell press., psia	6.3	4.6	**Turbine Generator**		
Heater sat. temp, F	172	159	Enthalpy at throttle, Btu/lb	1414	1414
Terminal temp. diff., F	4	2	Work up to 4th stage, Btu/lb	127	150
Water temp. out, F	168	157	Work up to 8th stage, Btu/lb	226	245
Water temp. in, F	79	79	Work up to 11th stage, Btu/lb	312	327
Water temp. rise, F	89	78	Expansion line end point, Btu/lb	979	981
Heat required, Btu/hr	8,206,000	5,320,000	Leaving loss, Btu/lb	16	9
Extraction enthalpy, Btu/lb	1102	1087	Exhaust enthalpy, Btu/lb	995	990
Drip enthalpy, Btu/lb	140	127	Work up to exhaust, Btu/lb	419	424
Heat avail. in extraction, Btu/lb	962	960	**Internal Generation up to:**		
Extraction required, lb/hr	8,520	5,600	4th stage, kw	318	264
8th Stage Extraction Heater			8th stage, kw	513	366
Water flow to heater, lb/hr	100,720	73,900	11th stage, kw	780	536
Turbine stage press., psia	29.0	20.5	Exhaust, kw	11,340	8,485
Press. drop to heater, psi	2.9	2.0	Total generation, kw	12,951	9,651
Heater shell press., psia	26.1	18.5	Generator losses, mechanical plus electrical, kw	398	385
Heater sat. temp., F	243	224	Gross load, gen. terminals, kw	12,553	9,266
Terminal temp. diff., F	0	0	**Boiler**		
Water temp. out, F	243	224	Enthalpy of steam, Btu/lb	1414	1414
Water enthalpy out, Btu/lb	211	192	Enthalpy of feed, Btu/lb	289	267
Water enthalpy in, Btu/lb	136	125	Heat added to steam, Btu/lb	1125	1147
Enthalpy rise of water, Btu/lb	75	67	Heat added to steam, 10^6 Btu/hr	131.6	97.5
Heat required, Btu/hr	7,555,000	4,960,000	Boiler efficiency, %	83.6	84.4
Extraction enthalpy, Btu/lb	1188	1169	Heat in fuel to attain above efficiency, 10^6 Btu/hr	157.4	115.5
Drip enthalpy, Btu/lb	211	192	**Plant Performance**		
Heat avail. in extraction, Btu/lb	977	977	Auxiliary power use, %	4.0	4.5
Extraction required, lb/hr	7,730	5,100	Auxiliary power use, kw	503	417
4th Stage Extraction Heater			Net plant send out, kw	12,050	8,849
Water flow to heater, lb/hr	108,450	79,000	°°Plant realization ratio	0.95	0.94
Turbine stage press., psia	103	73	Plant heat supplied, 10^6 Btu/hr	165.7	122.9
Press. drop to heater, psi	10	7	Overall plant heat rate, Btu/kwhr	13,750	13,900
Heater shell press., psia	93	66			

°The water flow from the condenser to the last stage extraction feedwater heater can be approximated by a trial estimate of the total extraction required, which can be computed from its simple relation to the total rise in temperature from hot well to boiler feed. Trial values can then be adjusted as necessary to achieve an overall balance.

°°An overall ratio to cover all losses not included in the heat balance, such as soot blowing, blowdown, makeup, radiation, gland leakage, steam driven auxiliaries, and banking.

that all the losses, as well as the theoretic work, will appear as a change in the enthalpy of the water as it passes through the pump. This effect can be calculated by the expression

$$\text{Enthalpy increase through pump, Btu per lb} = \frac{\text{Head developed by pump in ft of fluid}}{\text{Pump eff} \times 778}$$

$$(49)$$

The calculation of the head in ft of fluid is facilitated by the data plotted in Fig. 21. If the temperature of the compressed liquid is desired, the enthalpy increase from equation (49) can be added to the saturated liquid value from the steam tables and the resulting compressed liquid enthalpy can be used to get the liquid temperature.

Centrifugal and axial flow pump performance is best shown through the medium of characteristic curves. These are generally plotted with capacity, (gpm), horizontally and head, shaft horsepower, and efficiency vertically, all at constant speed. These characteristics are exact in their definition of the performance of fluid acceleration machinery. If performance characteristics at other speeds are sought they can be evaluated by applying the following basic laws at a given point on the efficiency curve, or

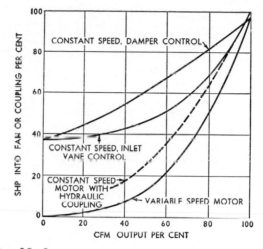

Fig. 25. Power comparison for centrifugal fan at constant speed, variable speed, and vane control

Capacity, gpm, varies as the rpm   (50)
Head, ft, varies as the $(\text{rpm})^2$ (51)
Power, shp, varies as the $(\text{rpm})^3$ (52)

The curves can be plotted on a percentage basis as in Fig. 22 where the rating (100 per cent) is defined as the performance at the point of maximum effi-

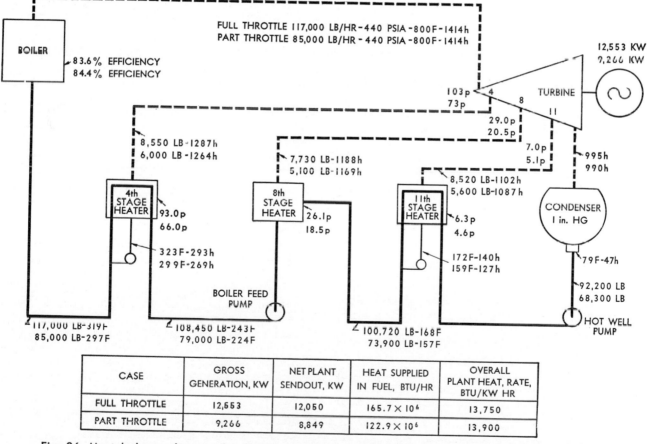

CASE	GROSS GENERATION, KW	NET PLANT SENDOUT, KW	HEAT SUPPLIED IN FUEL, BTU/HR	OVERALL PLANT HEAT, RATE, BTU/KW HR
FULL THROTTLE	12,553	12,050	165.7×10^6	13,750
PART THROTTLE	9,266	8,849	122.9×10^6	13,900

Fig. 26. Heat balance diagram for 10,000 kw steam power plant. Calculations shown in Table 2

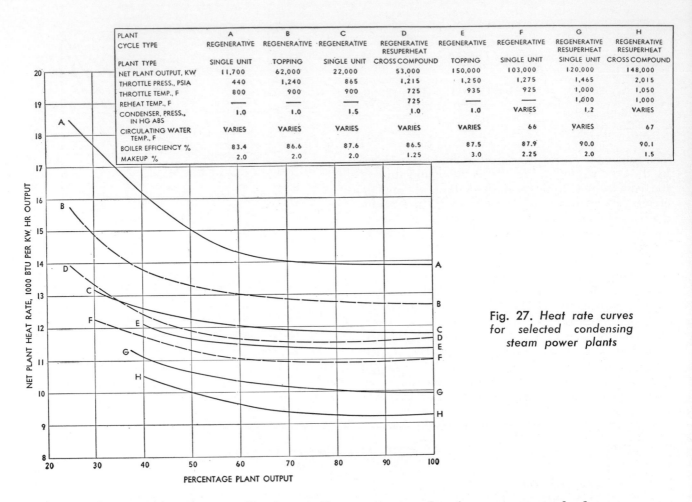

PLANT	A	B	C	D	E	F	G	H
CYCLE TYPE	REGENERATIVE	REGENERATIVE	REGENERATIVE	REGENERATIVE RESUPERHEAT	REGENERATIVE	REGENERATIVE	REGENERATIVE RESUPERHEAT	REGENERATIVE RESUPERHEAT
PLANT TYPE	SINGLE UNIT	TOPPING	SINGLE UNIT	CROSS COMPOUND	TOPPING	SINGLE UNIT	SINGLE UNIT	CROSS COMPOUND
NET PLANT OUTPUT, KW	11,700	62,000	22,000	53,000	150,000	103,000	120,000	148,000
THROTTLE PRESS., PSIA	440	1,240	865	1,215	1,250	1,275	1,465	2,015
THROTTLE TEMP., F	800	900	900	725	935	925	1,000	1,050
REHEAT TEMP., F	—	—	—	725	—	—	1,000	1,000
CONDENSER, PRESS., IN HG ABS	1.0	1.0	1.5	1.0	1.0	VARIES	1.2	VARIES
CIRCULATING WATER TEMP., F	VARIES	VARIES	VARIES	VARIES	VARIES	66	VARIES	67
BOILER EFFICIENCY %	83.4	86.6	87.6	86.5	87.5	87.9	90.0	90.1
MAKEUP %	2.0	2.0	2.0	1.25	3.0	2.25	2.0	1.5

Fig. 27. Heat rate curves for selected condensing steam power plants

ciency. These percentage curves apply substantially to all pumps of an homologous series at all usual speeds. In Fig. 22 data is shown for the performance of representative pumps and they should facilitate estimates of performance at part loads.

In the specification of pump head and capacity requirements a system resistance curve should be plotted as in Fig. 23. This should include allowances for all such items as elevational head between pump and delivery point; pressure drop through piping, heaters, economizers, superheaters; margins for the operation of flow regulators and safety valves. Pump head characteristics must be matched against the system resistance curve for proper selection.

Fans

Fans, fluid dynamically, are like pumps in their behavior. Representative characteristic curves, on the percentage basis, are shown in Fig. 24 for different types of fans. Part load performance can be appreciably improved by the use of variable speed or by the use of adjustable inlet guide vanes with constant speed (see Fig. 25). In the specification of fan requirements the system resistance curves, like those for pumps (Fig. 23) should be constructed. For forced and induced draft service with boilers, allowances should be included for unusual fuel or firing conditions, worn blades, plugged or dirty passages, and leakage (see Chapter 5).

Circulating Water Reclamation Systems

It has been found necessary in an increasing num-

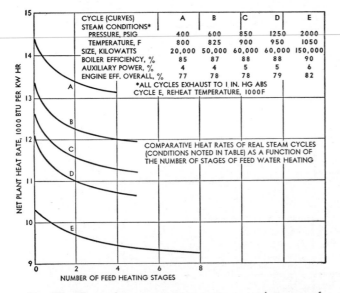

CYCLE (CURVES) STEAM CONDITIONS*	A	B	C	D	E
PRESSURE, PSIG	400	600	850	1250	2000
TEMPERATURE, F	800	825	900	950	1050
SIZE, KILOWATTS	20,000	50,000	60,000	60,000	150,000
BOILER EFFICIENCY, %	85	87	88	88	90
AUXILIARY POWER, %	4	4	5	5	6
ENGINE EFF. OVERALL, %	77	78	78	79	82

*ALL CYCLES EXHAUST TO 1 IN. HG ABS
CYCLE E, REHEAT TEMPERATURE, 1000F

COMPARATIVE HEAT RATES OF REAL STEAM CYCLES (CONDITIONS NOTED IN TABLE) AS A FUNCTION OF THE NUMBER OF STAGES OF FEED WATER HEATING

Fig. 28. Effect of pressure, temperature, and stages of feedwater heating on performance of steam cycles

ber of steam plants to reclaim circulating water by the use of spray ponds or cooling towers. These installations all utilize the evaporative effect for cooling purposes. Thus the heat which is contained in the exhaust of the prime mover must ultimately be delivered to the atmosphere by the evaporation of some of the circulating water. Theoretically, the amount of the evaporation loss will at least equal the weight of the steam flow to the exhaust. To this must be added the drift which can vary from 10 to 100 per cent of the theoretic loss, depending on equipment type, and wind conditions. Cooling towers can be generally selected to give a 10-20 F range in the cooling of the water and to approach to within 10-15 F of the wet bulb temperature. The summer wet bulb temperature will be crucial in the selection, size, and performance of evaporative reclaiming equipment.

Makeup Requirements

In condensing plants the water required for makeup seldom exceeds a maximum value of 1 to 2 per cent of full load steam output. This makeup must be pure. Chemical treatment, demineralization, compression distillation, or an evaporator will give the degree of purity required. To conserve the heat needed for distillation, the evaporator is included in the heat balance for the plant cycle.

Auxiliary Power

The power used for driving the auxiliaries of a condensing steam plant lies between 4 and 7 per cent of the gross generation at full load. For part load the auxiliary power may be estimated by using a straight line relationship in which, at no load, it is approximately one half the requirement at full load.

Realization Ratio

Since no heat balance calculation can include allowance for all losses which occur in a real plant,

such as soot blowing, blowdown, makeup, gland leakage, steam driven auxiliaries and banking, it is necessary to apply an overall realization ratio to the computed figures. This ratio may range from 0.90 to 0.98.

Heat Balance Calculations

To show the applicability of the above data, a typical heat balance is worked out for the following conditions in a 10,000 kw condensing unit.

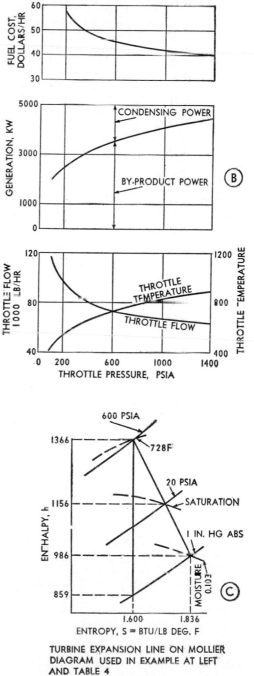

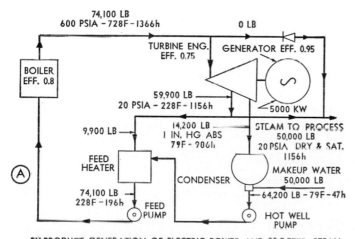

BY-PRODUCT GENERATION OF ELECTRIC POWER AND PROCESS STEAM
NET ELECTRIC SENDOUT 4650 KW PROCESS STEAM 50,000 LB/HR (SEE TABLE 4)

TURBINE EXPANSION LINE ON MOLLIER DIAGRAM USED IN EXAMPLE AT LEFT AND TABLE 4

Fig. 29. *Diagrams "A" and "C" show the conditions for the heat balance calculations, Table 4. The effect of change in throttle pressure and temperature on by-product power and fuel cost is indicated in diagram "B"*

TABLE 3

Typical Approximate Correction Factors
For Condensing Steam Plants

Initial Conditions					
Pressure, psig	400	600	850	1250	2000
Temperature, F	800	825	900	950	1050
Reheat temp., F	–	–	–	–	1000
Corrections for					
Pressure, Btu/psi	3.3	2.3	0.7	0.55	0.3
Initial temp., Btu/F	4.3	3.8	3.0	3.0	1.3
Reheat temp., Btu/F	–	–	–	–	1.2
Vacuum, Btu/in. Hg	320	220	200	200	200
Feed temp., Btu/F	1.5*	1.4*	1.1*	0.8*	1.5**

*Change in boiler efficiency is not included.
**Change in boiler efficiency is included.
Note:
Corrections represent the change in net plant heat rate (Btu per net kw hr) per unit change in variable.

TABLE 4

Heat Balance Calculations for By-product Power Cycle
(See "A," and "C" Fig. 29)

Requirements		Total internal generation, kw	5,270
Gross load generator terminals, kw	5,000	Generator efficiency	0.95
Process steam, lb/hr @ 20 psia, dry & sat	50,000	Electrical and mechanical losses, kw	270
		Gross load, generator terminals, kw	5,000
Throttle Conditions		Throttle water rate, lb per kw hr	14.8
Pressure, psia	600	Condenser water rate, lb per kw hr	2.84
Temperature, F	728	**Boiler**	
Steam flow, lb per hr	74,100	Enthalpy at superheater outlet, Btu per lb	1,366
		Enthalpy at feed, Btu per lb	196
Condenser		Heat added to steam, Btu per lb	1,170
Steam flow, lb per hr	14,200	Heat added to steam, 10^6 Btu per hr	86.7
Pressure, in. Hg abs	1	Boiler efficiency	0.8
Hot-well temperature, F	79	Heat supplied in fuel, 10^6 Btu per hr	108
Hot-well enthalpy, Btu per lb	47	**Plant Performance**	
Makeup water flow, lb per hr	50,000	Auxiliary power	0.07
Water flow out, lb per hr	64,200	Auxiliary power, kw	350
Feed Heater		Net plant electric sendout, kw	4,650
Heater pressure, psia	20	Plant realization ratio	0.95
Heater saturation temperature, F	228	Net plant heat supplied, 10^6 Btu per hr	114
Enthalpy, water in, Btu per lb	47	Fuel price, ¢ per million Btu	40
Enthalpy, water out, Btu per lb	196	Fuel cost per hr	$45.60
Heat added to water, Btu per hr	149	**Allocation of Heat Charges**	
Heat added to water, 10^6 Btu per lb	9.5	Steam flow, lb per hr	50,000
Bleed enthalpy, Btu per lb	1,156	Enthalpy of steam, Btu per lb	1,156
Heat available from bleed, Btu per lb	960	Enthalpy of makeup, Btu per lb	47
Extraction required, lb per hr	9,900	Heat to process, Btu per lb	1,109
Boiler feed, lb per hr	74,100	Heat to process, 10^6 Btu per hr	55.4
Turbine Generator		Heat to power (balance) 10^6 Btu per hr	31.3
Enthalpy at throttle, Btu per lb	1,366	Fraction chargeable to process	0.64
Enthalpy at bleed point, Btu per lb	1,156	Fraction chargeable to power	0.36
Enthalpy drop to bleed point, Btu per lb	210	Fuel cost, process steam, per hr	$29.20
Extraction, lb per hr	59,900	Fuel cost, power, per hr	$16.40
Internal generation by extracted steam, kw	3,690	Fuel cost, process steam, ¢ per M lb	58.4
Enthalpy at exhaust, Btu per lb	986	Fuel cost, power, mills per net kw hr	3.53
Enthalpy drop to exhaust, Btu per lb	380	Net plant heat rate chargeable to power,	
Condenser flow, lb per hr	14,200	Btu per net kw hr	8,800
Internal generation by condenser flow, kw	1,580		

BOILERS, ECONOMIZERS, AND AIR HEATERS

IN a natural-circulation unit, boiler heating surface may be defined as those parts of shells, drums, or tubes which are a part of the boiler circulatory system and which are in contact with the hot gases on one side and water or a mixture of water and steam on the other side. By convention, the economizer is not considered a part of the boiler heating surface. In some types of forced-circulation boilers, the amount of water-wetted heating surface in a given unit is not constant but varies with operating procedure, and an exact designation is not practical. For other types of forced-circulation boilers, the definition given above for natural-circulation boilers will apply. Heat from the hot gases flows through the confining walls of these pressure parts to the water on the opposite side. The heat so transmitted, after raising the temperature of the water in the boiler to the boiling point, produces steam at a greater or lesser rate, depending upon the rate of heat input. Boilers may be broadly classified in three types: (a) shell, (b) fire-tube, and (c) water-tube.

Shell-Type Boiler

The shell boiler may be defined simply as a closed vessel containing water, with a portion of the shell exposed to a source of heat, such as a fire burning under it. However, it is now used chiefly in such modern adaptations as the electric boiler and the accumulator. The water in the former is heated by electrodes and in the latter by steam from an outside source. In neither case is the shell exposed to the source of heat. In the early shell boilers externally fired, the vessel was given a cylindrical form in order to withstand the steam pressure and to provide heating surface along the length of the bottom of the shell. The steam capacity and efficiency of this simple shell-type boiler set over a fire were both very low because of the relatively small area of boiler heating surface. Only the lower part of the shell and one end of the cylinder absorbed heat from the

gases, chiefly by radiation, with very little heat transfer by convection.

Fire-Tube Boiler

The heating surface of the shell-type boiler was increased by passing the hot gases from the fire through the inside of tubes located within the shell. This was the beginning of the type known as the fire-tube boiler. The inner surfaces of the tubes absorbed heat from the gases by convection and radiation. Because heat is absorbed by the tubes as well as by the shell, the efficiency of the fire-tube is much higher than that of the simple shell-type boiler. This made it possible to reduce fuel consumption and to increase capacities for the same over-all dimensions of the boiler. Under favorable conditions of fuel and at a rating not exceeding 100%, the efficiency is of the order of 70%. Since the fire-tube boiler is not well suited for superheat, the better economy with superheated steam is not available.

Many arrangements of the fire-tube boiler have been developed. Tubes have been placed in horizontal, vertical, or inclined positions, with one or more gas passes. The simplest and usual arrangement is the horizontal-return-tubular boiler shown in Fig. 1. In this boiler the furnace and grates are located directly below the front end of the shell. The gases pass over the bridge wall and horizontally along the bottom of the shell to the rear of the boiler and then return through horizontal tubes to the front of the boiler and stack—hence the name horizontal-return-tubular (HRT) boiler.

In a fire-tube boiler, known as the firebox class, the firebox or furnace as well as the fire tubes is located within the shell. A well-known example is the Scotch marine boiler (see Fig. 2). Combustion takes place within one or more cylindrical water-cooled chambers, with the gases leaving the chambers toward the rear and returning through the fire

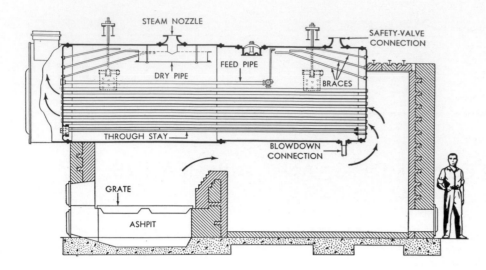

Fig. 1. *Early horizontal-return-tube boiler set for hand firing*

tubes to the stack at the front of the boiler. Compared with the horizontal-return-tubular boiler, the firebox type is self-contained and compact. The Scotch marine boiler, however, is limited in steam output since the diameter seldom exceeds 14 ft. A greater diameter tends to require an excessive plate thickness. Within this limiting diameter of shell, the maximum grate surface that can be installed (with a four-furnace arrangement) is of the order of 100 sq ft. The steam output is accordingly limited to approximately 25,000 lb of steam per hr for the larger sizes.

Many types of fire-tube boilers are in use, but, as a class, the fire-tube boiler is confined to relatively small capacities and low steam pressures. It is, however, extensively used to supply steam for space heating and is still used to some extent in the railroad locomotive in steam outputs to 4000 bhp or more.

A fire-tube type of boiler, known as the gas-tube

boiler, developed by B&W for utilizing the heat in waste gases, has been in use for many years. This boiler is described and illustrated in Chapter 19.

Water-Tube Boiler

As the requirements for steam capacity and pressure increased, the shell diameter of the fire-tube boiler became very large, and it was necessary to use thick plates to withstand the high stresses. Furthermore, these early fire-tube boilers were subjected to stresses of high and indeterminate magnitude because of the differences in temperature in the various parts. The combined effect of the known pressure stresses and the indeterminate thermal stresses, aggravated by scale deposits from hard water, caused many boiler explosions. The water-tube boiler then being developed had the advantage, in this respect, of lower stresses from pressure and temperature differentials, since its components were relatively much smaller in diameter and were

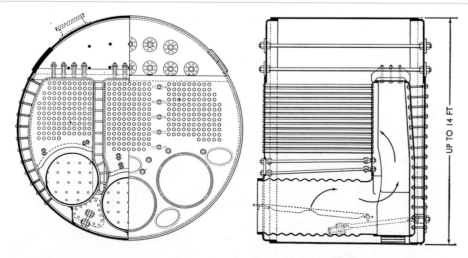

Fig. 2. *Scotch marine boiler, fitted for coal firing*

arranged to accommodate the expansions caused by differences in temperature. It was apparent, because of the lower stresses inherent in its design, that the water-tube boiler was much more suitable for larger capacities and higher pressures while still maintaining a high margin of safety.

In principle, the water-tube boiler is the reverse of the fire-tube boiler. The hot gases are in contact with the outside surface of the tubes, and the boiler water and steam are in contact with the inside surface of the tubes. The term "water-tube" is, therefore, universally recognized as descriptive of this type of boiler.

Straight-Tube Boiler

All B&W straight-tube boilers (see Figs. 3 and 4) are made up of sections of staggered tubes, inclined at an angle of 15° and expanded at the ends into vertical headers. The area of the heating surface is varied by changing the length of the tubes, the number of tubes high, and the number of sections wide. Each section is made up of a downtake header supplying water to the tubes and an uptake header discharging water and steam from the tubes. Sections may be single deck, with a single downtake and a single uptake header, or double or triple deck using more than one downtake and more than one uptake header connected by expanded nipples. The lower ends of the downtake headers are connected by nipples into a small (7¼-in. sq or 10¾-in. round) header, known as a mud drum. The mud drum, as its name implies, serves as a collecting chamber for the sediment, solids, or mud in the boiler water. This

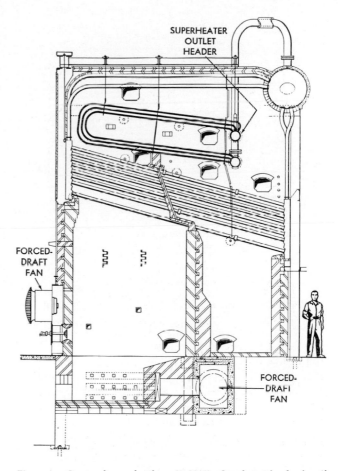

Fig. 4. Cross-drum boiler (B&W) fired with fuel oil and cottonseed hulls. Design pressure 400 psi; steam temperature 790 F; maximum steam output 16,500 lb/hr

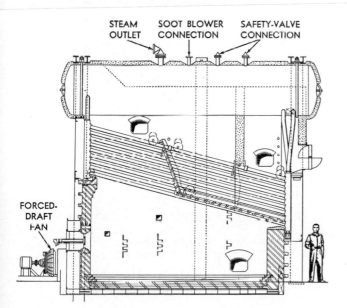

Fig. 3. Long-drum boiler (B&W) installed in Brazilian rubber-processing plant. Design pressure 250 psi; steam output 18,000 lb/hr

header is provided with a blowoff connection which also serves as a boiler drain.

The generating tubes are usually 4-in. or 3¼-in. OD spaced on 7-in., 7¾-in., 8¼-in., or 8¾-in. centers horizontally, depending upon the design pressure. As the design pressure increases, the header thickness increases, and consequently the horizontal tube spacing increases. Tube rows are spaced vertically on 6-in. centers (or at 12-in. for some lower rows where a slag screen is desired).

In the headers, opposite each tube end, there is a handhole of sufficient size to permit removal or renewal of the tube. These handholes can also be used for turbining and cleaning the inside of the tubes.

Vertical or slightly inclined gas baffles are arranged for two or three gas passes across the tubes. The arrangement of gas baffling depends upon many factors, including acceptable draft loss, size and arrangement of boiler heating surface, and position of gas outlet. Sometimes a straight-tube boiler is designed without baffles, and the gases make a single pass across the tubes.

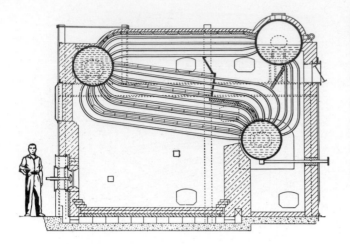

Fig. 5. Type H Stirling boiler (B & W). Particularly suitable for low headroom. Fired with fuel oil, gas, and coal (stoker or hand firing)

In the long-drum boiler, usually of one bank of tubes and three gas passes, the steam drum is placed longitudinally in relation to the boiler tubes, as indicated in Fig. 3. The steam and water circulating tubes are connected to the steam drum in circumferential rows. This limits the number of sections that can be connected to a single drum. Obviously, the maximum number of sections wide per drum depends upon the drum diameter. A 48-in. diameter steam drum can accommodate as many as 14 sections in width. For wider long-drum boilers more than one steam drum must be used. Because of the limitations in the amount of heating surface with one steam drum, the long-drum boiler is economically suitable only for small units and low pressures which require relatively large steam-release areas. Heating surface ranges from about 1000 to 10,000 sq ft per boiler. Capacities range from 5000 to 80,000 lb of steam per hr per boiler. Design pressures range from 160 to 325 psi. Comparatively few long-drum boilers are being built today.

As indicated in Fig. 4, the steam drum of a cross-drum boiler is placed across or at right angles to the tube bank, and there may be one or more banks of boiler tubes with one or more gas passes across the tubes. The steam and water circulating tubes are connected to the steam drum in longitudinal rows. In contrast to the long-drum boiler, the single drum of the cross-drum boiler is not limited in the number of sections, since the length of the drum can be increased to suit the increase in width required for additional sections. The cross-drum boiler has a wide field of application. Boiler heating surfaces range from about 1000 to 25,000 sq ft. Capacities range from 5000 lb of steam per hr upward. The largest boiler unit of this type has a capacity of 525,000 lb of steam per hr. Design pressures range from 160 to 1450 psi. This design provides flexibility in the amount and disposition of heating surfaces to suit specific requirements of capacity, efficiency, draft loss, over-all dimensions, position of gas outlet, and space for superheater, reheater, and gas by-pass.

As mentioned above in reference to long-drum boilers, very few cross-drum straight-tube boilers are being built today, the preference being for water-tube boilers of the bent-tube designs.

Bent-Tube Boiler — General Classification

Many important modern designs of boilers, such as the type H Stirling, the Two-Drum Stirling, the Integral-Furnace, the Open-Pass, and the Radiant, are included in this general classification. The main elements of these water-tube boilers (also many subordinate designs) are essentially drums or drums and headers connected by bent tubes. Furthermore, the water-cooled furnace, of bent tubes suitably connected to the circulatory system to form a furnace enclosure, is an integral part of the boiler unit. The principal designs referred to are illustrated in Figs. 6, 7, 8, 9, 10, 11, and 12.

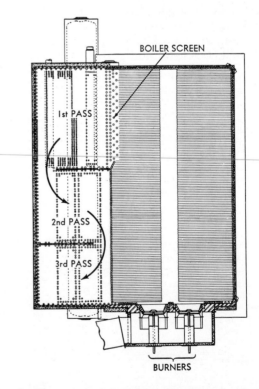

Fig. 6. Plan section through generating banks of type FH Integral-Furnace boiler (B & W) illustrated in Fig. 6, Chapter 21

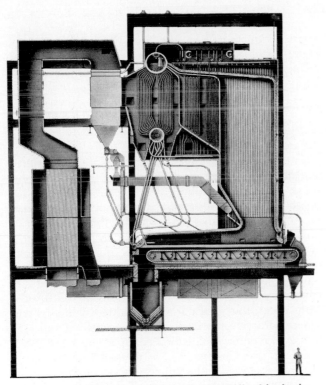

Fig. 10. *Stirling Two-Drum boiler (B&W) with single gas pass; 220,000 lb steam per hr, arranged for chain-grate-stoker firing*

6¾-in. centers to permit tube renewal without disturbing adjacent tubes. To increase gas velocities along the tubes, the front-to-back spacing of the tubes in the section is about 4 in. on centers.

The size and capacity of these boilers are varied by changing the length of the tubes and the number of sections wide. The size varies over a considerable range. This type of boiler is particularly well suited for rapidly fluctuating loads and where water conditions may not be maintained at high quality.

Although there are many Stirling Four-Drum boilers in operation, this design has been superseded, for economic and other reasons, by the simpler Stirling Two-Drum boiler.

Stirling Two-Drum Boiler (B&W). The simple arrangement possible for the connecting tubes, with one upper steam-and-water drum directly over one lower drum, led to the development of a series of designs known as the Stirling Two-Drum boiler. The most important unit of the series, generally superseding earlier designs, is the single-gas-pass arrangement, illustrated in Fig. 10, where the tubes in the generating banks, of 2½-in. OD swaged to 2-in. entering the drums, are side-spaced on 3⅞₆-in. centers and the front-to-back spacing is 4 in. on centers.

Superheaters usually are fitted for steam temperatures to 1000 F or even more. As indicated in the

For the best and simplest connection of tubes to drums, the tubes must enter the shell radially, hence all or almost all of the tubes so connected are bent. A common classification of bent-tube boilers is by the number of drums per boiler: two-, three-, and four-drum boilers. Gas baffles are arranged in many different patterns with gas flowing across and along the tubes in one or more passes.

Type H Stirling Boiler (B&W). One of the types of bent-tube three-drum boilers for low headroom, widely used in smaller sizes, is the H-type boiler illustrated in Fig. 5. Two drums are completely filled with boiler water, and the third drum, with feed inlet and steam outlet connections, is a steam-and-water drum. Boiler water circulates from the steam drum down to the lower drum, up through the inclined bank of generating tubes to the intermediate drum, and horizontally back to the steam drum, where the steam and water are separated. The steam passes through the steam outlet, and the separated water mixed with the incoming feed continues to circulate through the boiler. The hot gases make three passes over the boiler heating surface.

Boiler tubes, 3¼-in. OD spaced on 6-in. centers, are arranged vertically over each other to constitute a section. The horizontal or side spacing of sections is alternately on 5¼-in. and 6¾-in. centers to permit tube renewal at any point within the tube bank without disturbing adjacent tubes.

The size and capacity of the H-type boiler are varied by changing the length of the tubes and the number of sections wide.

Integral-Furnace Boilers

In the earlier stages of development, boilers were set over brick or refractory furnaces, and all of the heat-absorbing surface was in the boiler. As the units increased in size, furnace temperatures increased, and brick maintenance became excessive, particularly for pulverized-coal firing. The higher gas temperatures also resulted in increased slagging or fouling of the boiler surface. To overcome these difficulties, the furnaces were first partly and later completely water cooled. Furnace water-cooling not only decreased furnace maintenance and boiler slagging but also generated steam.

At first, furnace water-cooling, designed separately from the boiler, was applied to existing boiler designs with the water circulation more or less independent of the boiler circulation. However, boiler water was always circulated in the furnace circuits. Later, the furnace water-cooled surface and the boiler surface were designed together, so that each was an integral part of the other. This principle was applied to an extended series of boiler units of various arrangements and outputs.

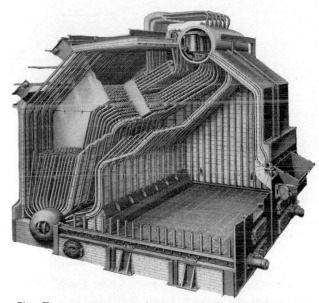

Fig. 7. *Type FF Integral-Furnace boiler (B&W) fitted for spreader-stoker firing with dump grates*

Type F Integral-Furnace Boiler (B&W). One of the earlier designs of the Integral-Furnace boiler was the F-type, which is essentially a two-drum boiler with a distinctive type of gas flow. The furnace gases enter one side of the boiler, flow through the full height, and make three passes horizontally across the boiler surface before leaving at the opposite side (similar to the FH boiler, see Fig. 6). This is a most efficient type of gas flow, since the gases are constrained to flow across all the tubes with no flow along the tubes. This desirable crossflow is obtained by using simple baffles placed between the tube sections. The interior of the steam drum is so arranged that the boiler water circulates down to the lower drum through a section of boiler tubes in the third or last gas pass of the boiler. The water from the lower drum then circulates up through the remainder of the boiler tubes and the tubes in the furnace water walls. The F-type boiler has been superseded by other types with improved features.

Type FH Integral-Furnace Boiler (B&W). This boiler (see Fig. 6, also Fig. 6, Chapter 21) is essentially the same as the F boiler; the main differences are that the boiler tubes are vertical rather than inclined and the drums are directly in line one above the other. Support is simplified, particularly for the larger units, since the boiler can be supported from either the bottom or the top. The outside walls of the FH boiler are completely water cooled with refractory backing supported on the water-cooled tubes.

Type FF Integral-Furnace Boiler (B&W). This boiler (Fig. 7) was developed and standardized for smaller capacities, 10,000 to 50,000 lb of steam per hr, and for pressures up to 600 psi. It is particularly suitable where headroom is limited and is designed for fuel

Fig. 8. Type FM Integral-Furnace boiler (B&W). assembled unit, complete and ready to operate set in place

oil, gas, and stoker firing. The boiler water
tion and gas flow through the boiler are si
those in the F-type boiler. An additional wate
wall in the furnace of the FF boiler prov
"open pass" through which the gases flow af
ing the furnace.

Type FM Integral-Furnace Boiler (B&W). T
shop-assembled boiler unit (see Fig. 8)
shipped complete with support steel and
forced-draft fan, firing equipment, and con
ready for operation when water, fuel, and
connections have been made. Only a stub
required. It is built for outputs from about
36,000 lb steam per hr and for steam pre
250 psi. It can be fired with fuel oil, gas, o
bination of the two. A superheater may be
the gas entrance end if required.

Only a forced-draft fan is required as th
is airtight (welded) and the combustion
under pressure. Size of the unit is varied by
in setting depth and drum length. No chang
essary in width or height, which facilitat
ardization of parts and assembly.

Gas baffles are so arranged that the gas
ture drop ($\triangle t$) and gas pressure drop ($\angle$
gas inlet to outlet are about the same a
rate of steam output, such as maximum
each size of unit. As the unit becomes pro
deeper (from burner to rear) with each in
nominal boiler size, and as the length of
bank increases, the four baffles installed
gressively shortened until, in the largest
gases make but one pass through the bank
to front with little or no baffle diversion.

economizer as a complete unit. The substantial results of such integration in units of moderate steam
output, such as boilers of types F, FH, FF, FM, Two-
Drum and Four-Drum Stirling boilers, have been
outlined above.

In the rapid development of power plant economy,
the single-turbine single-boiler combination is now
favored for the central station and where electric
power is the end product of heat transformation.
There is an incentive to use very large electrical
generators, since the heat rate, unit investment, and
labor costs decrease as the size increases. In the
design of large boiler units for this application, the
important factors are: (a) high steam pressure,
(b) high steam temperature, (c) bleed feedwater
heating, and frequently (d) reheat. High steam
pressure means high saturation temperature and low
temperature difference. High steam temperature
means high initial temperature and, usually, reheating to high temperature for reuse of the steam.
Bleed feedwater heating lowers the mean temperature difference and increases the gas temperature
leaving an economizer. An air heater is then used,
not only to lower the final gas temperature but to
provide hot air for combustion. These factors and,
above all, the economic need for continuity of operation to realize an optimum return on the large investment involved have combined to produce a "boiler
unit" unique in many respects from earlier concepts.
It is therefore apparent that the principle of the
integrated boiler unit is firmly established for very
large boilers as well as for boilers of smaller outputs.

Thus, as steam pressures increased, the steam
temperatures also increased, which required proportionally more superheating surface and less boiler
surface. When pressures exceed 1000 psi, it is usually
more economical to replace whatever boiler surface
is still required with economizer surface. All the
steam is then generated in the furnace, water-cooled
wall enclosures of superheater and economizer, boiler
screens, platens, division walls, and in some cases the
outlet end of a steaming economizer. The B&W
Open-Pass (OP) and Radiant (RB) boilers, illustrated in Figs. 11 and 12, are typical high-pressure
and high-temperature units. Radiant boilers have
been built to generate up to a peak of 2,400,000 lb
of steam per hr which, in this particular example
with steam reheat, required a fuel input at the
burners of 3,135,000,000 Btu per hr. Of this input,
2,840,000,000 Btu were absorbed in the boiler unit
and were delivered (with a boiler efficiency of 90.5
per cent) to the turbine.

Slag-Tap Boiler Unit. The liquid-ash-removal (slag-
tap) boiler unit illustrated in Fig. 11 has an output
of 930,000 lb steam per hr at continuous rating,
with steam pressure 2170 psi, final steam temperature
1050 F, and reheat steam temperature 1000 F. In

this instance of an integrated unit, not only is the
furnace completely water cooled by tube-to-tube
construction but even the boundary walls of the
superheater and economizer are water cooled, although not with touching tubes. This unit is top
supported from a single elevation, permitting downward expansion in all its components. In a unit of
this type, wall tubes usually are 3-in. OD, superheater tubes are 2½-in. and 2¾-in. OD, economizer tubes
are 2¾-in. OD, and reheater tubes are 2½-in. OD.

In the particular unit illustrated, there is very little
so-called boiler surface. The small bank of staggered
boiler convection tubes directly below the superheater is the sole remaining vestige of boiler surface
as formerly defined. Known as an "Open-Pass"
boiler, this type derives its name from the manner
of gas flow, where the gas from the furnace flows
through open "thoroughfares" or "passes" (one such
pass in the unit illustrated) before entering the
convection passes. The lower portions of the furnace
walls on all four sides are full-studded, which is customary practice for B&W slag-tap units. At full load
the gases enter the superheater at about 2250 F
(MHVT, see Chapter 6). At the point of gas entry
the side-spacing of the superheater sections is 12 in.
on centers. At the gas exit end of the superheater
the tube side-spacing is 4 in. on centers. Regulation
of steam temperature is by spray attemperation.

Dry-Ash Boiler Unit. The dry-ash hopper-bottom
boiler unit illustrated in Fig. 12 has an output of
575,000 lb of steam per hr at continuous rating, with
steam pressure 1675 psi (design), final steam temperature 1000 F, and reheat steam temperature 1000
F. This type is known as the "Radiant" boiler and,
like the Open-Pass boiler, is almost devoid of boiler
convection surface. The only remnants of so-called
boiler surface are the single row of tubes before the
pendent superheater and the single staggered row
following it. The entire furnace and pressure-part
enclosures are constructed of 3-in. tubes, touching
in the furnace and slightly separated in the superheater and economizer vestibules. Superheater tubes
are 2½-in. and 2¾-in. OD. Reheater and economizer
tubes are 2½-in. OD.

The entire unit is supported from a single elevation
overhead, and all components expand together. Elements of the horizontal superheater surface drain,
but elements of the pendent superheater surface are
nondraining, and at starting-up the superheater is
boiled to dryness (see Chapter 21). A certain degree
of steam temperature control is possible with burners
at two elevations, as shown in Fig. 12. At low loads,
for instance, the steam temperature can be raised by
firing the top set of burners rather than the bottom set of burners. The over-all (final) temperature control, however, is by spray attemperation.
At full load the gases enter the superheater at about

2100 F (MHVT). At the point of gas entry the side-spacing of the superheater tubes is 12 in. on centers. At the gas exit end of the superheater the side-spacing of the tubes is 3½ in. on centers.

Boiler Supports

Boiler and furnace wall tubes are usually supported by the drums or headers to which they are connected. Some boilers are bottom supported from the lower drums and headers, while others are suspended from the upper drums. The FH boiler is typical of a bottom-supported boiler. The boiler load is taken on saddles placed under the lower drum and under the lower headers of furnace side, front, and rear walls. The Stirling boiler is typical of a top-supported unit, with the upper drums seated on saddles at the ends of the drums. Stirling boilers may also be supported by U-type hangers around the drums carried to steel above. Two-Drum and high-capacity boilers such as the Open-Pass and Radiant are almost always top supported through U-type hangers at the ends of the steam drum and by rod hangers fastened to upper headers and tubes.

In the design of proper supports the following considerations are important:

1. The tubes must be so arranged that they will not be subject to excessive bending-moment stresses in carrying the weight of the tubes, drums, parts, and contained water. When the unit is bottom supported, the tubes must satisfy column requirements.

2. Holding strength of the tube seats must not be exceeded.

3. Provision must be made to take care of expansion of the pressure parts. For a top-supported unit, the hanger rods must be designed to swing at the proper angle, and they must be long enough to take the movement without excessive stresses either in the rods or the pressure parts. Bottom-supported boilers should be anchored only at one point, guided along one line, and allowed to expand freely in all other directions. To reduce the frictional forces and resultant stresses in the pressure parts, roller saddles or mountings are desirable for bottom-supported heavy loads.

Boiler Horsepower and Rating

In the early days the "size" of a boiler was denoted by boiler horsepower. One rated or nominal boiler horsepower was defined as equivalent to 10 sq ft of boiler heating surface. A "developed" boiler horsepower was arbitrarily set as equal to the evaporation of 30 lb of water per hr from an initial temperature of 100 F to steam at 70 psi pressure. When the term "equivalent evaporation from and at 212 F" became popular, the old value of 30 lb at 100 F and 70 psi for a developed boiler horsepower was converted to its equivalent in heat capacity of 34.5 lb of water

per hr from and at 212 F. Still later, when steam flow began to be recognized as a better measure of size (and metering equipment became available), an equivalent heat unit of 33,480 Btu per hr was used for conversion purposes. The relations between rated boiler horsepower, developed boiler horsepower, boiler heating surface (sq ft), per cent rating, and steam flow are given in the following formulas:

$$\text{blr-hp} = \frac{S}{10}$$

$$\text{blr-hp}_D = \text{blr-hp} \times \frac{R_b}{100}$$

$$\text{blr-hp}_D = \frac{w\,(h\text{-}h_w)}{33,480}$$

$$R_b = \frac{w\,(h\text{-}h_w) \times 100}{33,480 \times \text{blr hp}}$$

$$R_b = \frac{w\,(h\text{-}h_w) \times 100}{3348 \times S}$$

$$w = \frac{R_b \times 3348 \times S}{(h\,h_w) \times 100}$$

where: blr-hp = rated boiler horsepower

blr-hp$_D$ = developed boiler horsepower

S = boiler heating surface, sq ft

R$_b$ = boiler rating, per cent

$w\,(h\text{-}h_w)$ = total heat absorbed in steam, Btu/hr

h = enthalpy of steam at boiler outlet or at superheater outlet when unit has superheater, Btu/lb

h$_w$ = enthalpy of water at boiler inlet or at economizer inlet when unit has economizer, Btu/lb

w = steam flow, lb/hr

When the major part or all of the heat-absorbing surface is in the boiler with little or no furnace, superheater, and economizer surface, the terms "boiler horsepower" and "boiler rating" are quite suitable and represent not only some measure of capacity but also some measure of boiler duty. Obviously, a boiler operating at 300% rating is operating at a higher duty than one operating at 200% rating. The term "boiler rating" is still in use today in the small-boiler field, and it indicates some measure of duty where furnace-cooling and superheater surfaces are absent or relatively small compared to the boiler convection surface.

Most boiler units now, as noted above, whether small or large, have a relatively large area of heating surfaces other than boiler convection surface, so that a rating based solely on boiler heating surface has very little or no meaning. The terms "boiler horsepower" and "boiler rating" are, therefore, not properly applied to these boilers.

In all types of boilers and particularly in the medium and larger capacity units, the output is now almost invariably given in lb per hr of steam flow at maximum continuous load. Partial loads are usually designated in percentages of full load, such as 75% of load or three-quarters load. Peak or overloads may be designated in percentages of full load such as 110% load.

The amount of heat-absorbing surface in all parts of the boiler unit is of prime importance in indicating size and capacity. However, many other important factors, as noted below, must be considered in properly evaluating a modern boiler unit.

Boiler Design

The design of boiler heating surface as such must necessarily be governed to a great extent by the design of other heating surfaces and of the unit as a whole. The selection of the type of unit or the design of a new unit for a given service depends upon many factors. Some of the more important factors are:

1. Steam flow, pressure, and temperature.
2. Reheat steam flow, pressure, and temperature, entering and leaving.
3. Feedwater temperature and feedwater conditions.
4. Load characteristics and type of service.
5. Fuel and firing.
6. Draft.
7. Efficiency and economics.

In modern practice the amount of boiler surface ahead of the superheater may vary greatly. In some instances, as in the unit illustrated in Fig. 12, boiler surface is reduced to a single row of tubes, widely spaced to form a slag screen. In other units there is considerable boiler surface arranged in several rows of tubes, the first one or two rows widely spaced to form a slag screen. The boiler surface ahead of the superheater serves to reduce the gas temperature entering the superheater, and, by so doing and by shielding the superheater from the direct radiant heat of the furnace, it protects the superheater from excessive metal temperatures and from fouling and slagging of the surfaces when firing coal or oil fuels with slagging characteristics (see Chapters 2, 3, and 18). The amount of boiler surface, including the slag screen, ahead of the superheater depends upon the desired gas temperature entering the superheater. The screen is usually in two or more rows of tubes.

The gas temperature leaving the furnace or entering the boiler depends mainly upon the furnace size and the extent of furnace-wall cooling surface. Since the cost of furnace-wall cooling surface is relatively higher than that of boiler surface, the furnace size and surface are limited to the requirements for the proper burning of the fuel and for the sufficient lowering of the gas temperature entering the boiler screen to avoid excessive slagging. The gas tem-

perature entering the superheater must be high enough to give the superheat desired with a reasonable amount of superheater surface and the use of economical materials. The superheater surface must also be arranged so that it can be kept clean to absorb heat as intended (see Chapter 12).

Boiler tubes ahead of the superheater may be inclined as in the Long-Drum, Cross-Drum, H-type, and Stirling Four-Drum boilers or vertical as in the FH, Stirling Two-Drum, and Radiant boilers. The tendency to slag adherence is less with vertical or nearly vertical tubes, and many operators prefer this construction where slagging is liable to occur.

Slag screens are arranged in many different tube patterns. It is essential to space the tubes far enough apart, particularly perpendicular to the gas flow. The clear space between tubes should be large enough so that any slag that adheres to the tubes cannot build out and bridge or plug the gas passage. Both staggered and in-line arrangements of tubes, Fig. 13, are used. In the staggered arrangement, not only the spacing perpendicular to the gas flow but also the back-spacing must be made large enough to prevent plugging. In the in-line arrangement the back-spacing is not so important. When the back-spacing is small (tubes nearly touching) compared with the side-spacing in the in-line arrangement, the tube sections

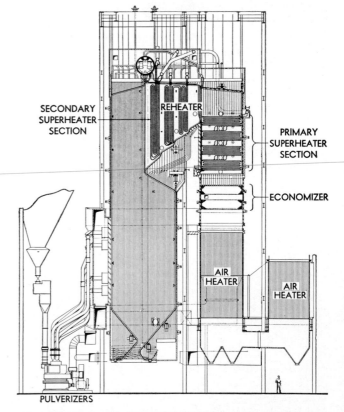

Fig. 12. *Large Radiant boiler (B&W), pulverized-coal fired; dry-ash removal; short air heater section at cold air inlet*

are sometimes called platens. Platens spaced the proper distance apart are effective in dropping the gas temperature through a slagging temperature zone. Clear distance between surfaces should be in the order of 9 to 12 in., or even greater in some instances.

Design of boiler surface after the superheater will depend upon the particular type of unit selected, desired gas temperature drop, and acceptable draft loss through the boiler surface. Typical arrangements of boiler surface for various types of boilers have been illustrated. The object in the design of boiler heating surface—and this is true of other so-called convection heating surfaces of a unit such as superheater, economizer, and air heater—is to establish the combination of tube diameter, tube spacings, length of tubes, number of tubes wide and deep, and gas baffling that will give the desired gas temperature drop with an acceptable draft loss. In other words, the design should provide an optimum combination of heating surface and gas mass flow to give the desired results.

For a given temperature, weight, and specific heat of a gas entering any component of a boiler, sufficient surface must be specified to drop this temperature to a desired value. To lower the gas temperature it is necessary to provide both surface (at lower temperature than the gas) and pressure drop (to cause flow). The amounts of surface and pressure drop required depend upon the gas temperature drop desired. The two requirements are interrelated. If one is reduced the other must be increased. It is, of course, impractical to pursue this procedure beyond obvious limits.

For a given gas mass flow (weight of gas, lb/hr ÷ area of passage, sq ft) or a given gas velocity, a considerably higher gas film conductance, heat absorption, and draft loss result when the gases flow at right angles to the tubes (crossflow) than when they flow parallel to the tubes (longitudinal flow). Gas turns between tube banks generally add draft loss with little or no benefit to heat absorption and should be designed for easy flow.

Economizers—Early Types and Development

In a steam-generating unit, the economizer absorbs heat from the flue gas and adds it as sensible heat to the feedwater before the water enters the boiler. In this way the gases are still further cooled, and a better economy is effected, hence the term "economizer."

The design and use of economizers followed naturally the development of boilers. Among the various designs applied during the nineteenth century, the straight-tube boiler and economizer of the B&W type and the bent-tube boiler and economizer of the Stirling type survived as the most important

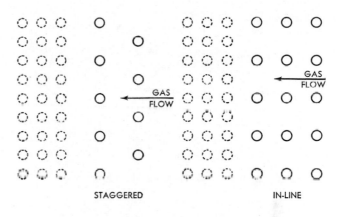

Fig. 13. *Diagrammatic arrangement of slag screens ahead of tube banks*

prototypes for the modern economizer. The earlier designs were based on the requirements for straight-tube boilers operating on natural draft and usually called for large diameter tubes, widely spaced to reduce resistance to gas flow.

Cast iron, commonly used for boilers operating at pressures up to 250 psi, proved to be an economical material for economizers because of its inherent resistance to corrosion, both internal and external.

When steel was first available, it was successfully used in boilers but could not be used in economizers because of the corrosive effect of free oxygen. In the boiler, most of the dissolved oxygen in the feedwater was driven off in the steam drum with the steam, and the corrosive effect on the boiler tubes was therefore reduced. In the economizer, as the temperature of the feedwater rose, the oxygen was gradually driven out of solution to attack the inside of the tubes. Also, at saturation temperature, the temperature of the water in the boiler was above the dewpoint of the gases, while in the economizer, the feedwater, with a temperature often less than 100 F, cooled the surrounding flue gases so much that moisture condensed on the outside of the tubes. This moisture, with some of the sulfur dioxide and sulfur trioxide from the flue gas in solution, caused corrosion. The moisture also formed a bond for the collection of ash on the tubes, which greatly reduced heat transfer and even restricted the gas passages. Cleaning apparatus had to be used to remove this deposit. Early economizers of cast iron were equipped with mechanical scrapers. Some cast-iron economizers of this general type are still in use with low-pressure boilers.

Following these early designs, the economizer was gradually improved in design and performance, keeping step with other developments in the generation of steam. Steel replaced other metals in boilers and engines, so that steam pressures could safely be raised. It became economical carefully to treat the

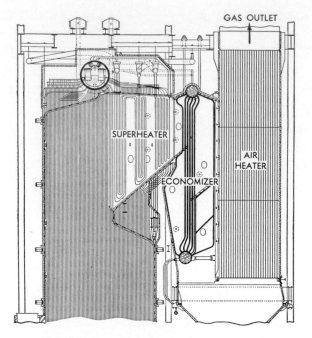

Fig. 14. *Two-drum bent-tube economizer arranged with three gas passes*

feedwater and to remove the oxygen by deaeration. Development of the steam turbine with stage bleeding increased the feedwater temperature to the economizer. The additional pressure drop through the unit, as a result of increased surface, led to the improvement of fans and the development of better soot blowers for surface cleaning.

The steel-tube economizer has now replaced the cast-iron design. Deaeration of feedwater has reduced internal corrosion. High feedwater temperatures have reduced condensation and, consequently, the corrosion and plugging on the outside of the tubes. The higher drafts now available make it possible to use the most desirable tube diameters and tube spacings for economical heat transfer and cleaning by steam or air.

One of the earliest straight-tube steel economizers of B&W design was built to ASME standards in 1915 and, like the boiler, was of the sinuous header type, with three passes for gas flow to improve its efficiency. In 1916 a similar type economizer was built for use with a Stirling boiler.

A successful two-drum bent-tube type of economizer was developed early in 1917. A modern version of this type applied to a Radiant boiler is illustrated in Fig. 14. While an integral-type bent-tube economizer with separate lower drum and with the upper ends of the tubes connected to the rear top drum of a Stirling boiler is occasionally built, the two-drum type is preferred (if drums are to be used) as it is less limited in size, location, and shape. In either case, the tube diameters and spac-

ing can be the same as for the boiler, or they can be modified to improve heat absorption, draft loss, water velocities, and the conditions for external cleaning. Water is fed into the lower drum and flows up through the tubes to the upper drum. Gases flow either along the tubes, preferably entering at the top and flowing down counter to the water flow, or across the tubes in single or multiple passes.

Before 1920, economizers were built with tubes of the same or larger diameter than the boiler tubes. One of the first economizers to use tubes of 2-in. OD was built early in 1920. Compared with larger tube units, the small-tube economizer requires less space, is easier to manufacture, uses less steel for tubes and casing, and is particularly suitable for high pressures.

In the early 1920's, most 2-in.-tube economizers were made with straight horizontal tubes rolled into horizontal square headers. Handhole fittings were used in the headers opposite the ends of the tubes so that every tube could be inspected and mechanically cleaned internally. Water fed into the bottom header flowed up through the tubes from header to header and then from the top header into the boiler. Gas entered the top of the economizer and flowed down across the staggered tubes, leaving at the bottom. This type of economizer was used with the first 650 psi boiler units in 1922, and with the pulverized-coal-fired high-pressure units developed in 1924. (See Figs. 12, 13, and 14, Chapter 1.)

An improved design of the horizontal steel-tube economizer, frequently used when it was necessary to clean the inside of the tubes mechanically, was developed during the 1920's. At one end the tube bends were formed by bending the 2-in. OD tubes through 180 degrees. At the other end special flanged and bolted return-bend fittings were used.

Tube Sizes and Spacing

The use of inhibited acid to clean internal surfaces (see Chapter 21) has materially simplified the design of economizers. The tubes can be continuous from inlet to outlet headers with terminals rolled or welded. The tubes can be made any length and diameter, with 2-in. and 2½-in. OD in most cases. The side-spacing and back-spacing can be arranged for good external cleaning, absorption of heat, and draft loss. Clear lanes of 1 in. and under should be used only for "clean" fuels. Lanes usually not less than 1½ in. and as much as 2 in. are generally used for fuels liable to cause gas-side deposits. For cleaning, back-spacing is less critical and is usually about 3 in. on centers for 2-in. OD tubes and 3½ in. on centers for 2½-in. OD tubes.

All high-pressure and most intermediate- and low-pressure economizers are now designed with horizontal, draining, continuous tubes. In most high-capacity high-pressure units the economizers are located inside the boiler setting (see Fig. 4, Chapter 21).

Steaming Economizer

There is sometimes an advantage in producing part of the steam in an economizer rather than in the more expensive boiler surface. So far as the amount of water that can be evaporated in the steaming type of economizer is concerned, there appears to be no operating limit in size. However, in practice it is customary to limit the evaporation to steam in the economizer to a maximum of about 20% of the feed at full boiler output and, of course, less as the load decreases. Since 1924, steaming economizers have been installed in a considerable number of boiler units. Because of the practical difficulties in treating a high percentage of the feedwater to a condition suitable for steaming economizers, they cannot be used to good advantage in boiler units where a high feed makeup is required.

Economizer Size

Economizer surface can be justified only where it can absorb heat at less cost than other types of surface. The temperature of the feedwater entering the economizer is always less than the saturation temperature in the boiler. Since the economizer surface is at a lower temperature than the boiler surface, the heat remaining in the gases can be absorbed at a greater rate and the gases can be cooled to a lower temperature with economizer surface than with additional boiler surface. Therefore, in a steam-generating unit, there is usually a gas temperature level at which it is economical to stop absorbing heat through surfaces at saturation temperature and to start absorbing heat in an economizer.

Where air preheaters are not used, the gas temperature from the economizer is set by making an economical balance between the cost of economizer surface and the saving in the cost of fuel. Where air preheaters are used, the gas temperature leaving the economizer is determined by the requirement that the temperature of the gas entering the air preheater should be sufficiently high to heat the air for adequate fuel drying or for good combustion performance.

Sufficient surface is installed in the economizer to absorb enough heat economically to give the desired gas exit temperatures. The amount of surface will vary with the temperature of the incoming feedwater. The feedwater should always be deaerated, with the deaerator at or above 212 F to minimize stray air leaks in the system. For high-pressure units, the temperature of the feed to the economizer is determined by the economical bleed points on the

turbine and will rise as the pressure increases, with consequent decrease in size of economizer, since the amount of heat to be absorbed is less.

Location, Arrangement, and Cleaning

Location of the economizer will vary with the over-all design of the boiler unit. Where air heaters are not installed, as in many small boilers of so-called standard type, economizers are located in the gas duct between the boiler gas exit and the fan or stack. It is always preferable that the gas from the boiler should flow down across the economizer tubes and that the water should enter at the bottom and flow up through the tubes. The counterflow design will reduce the required amount of surface and draft loss to a minimum. It will eliminate unstable water flow, give the most uniform gas distribution, and make possible the proper use of a "steaming economizer" wherein some steam is actually generated in a portion of the water-exit end.

In many high pressure units, location of the economizer in an upward flowing gas stream is fixed by the layout. In such cases small economizers can be installed for all-parallel flow. Large economizers require special consideration and should be installed with counterflow for the water inlet section and with parallel flow for the water outlet section (see Fig. 15).

Since the air heater, when installed, is the final heat trap, the economizer is generally located ahead of the air heater in the gas stream. In some cases where very low exit gas temperatures and high air temperatures are desired, it may be necessary to divide the economizer and the air heater and place the cooler section of the economizer between the air heater sections (see Fig. 4, Chapter 28). When difficult deposits from the fuel burned are expected to form on the tubes, the economizer should be located directly over a hopper so that water-soluble constituents of the deposits can be dissolved and the deposits washed off (during out of service periods) and disposed of.

In addition to washing as may be necessary, the external surface of economizers is cleaned with the same type of equipment used to clean boiler surfaces. Economizers are designed with tube spacing and

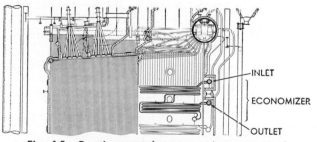

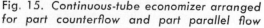

Fig. 15. *Continuous-tube economizer arranged for part counterflow and part parallel flow*

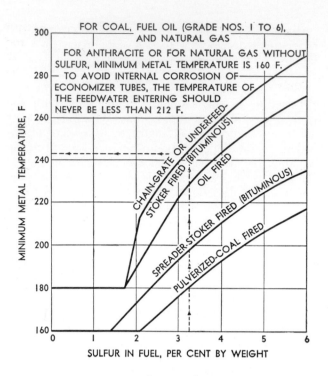

FOR COAL, FUEL OIL (GRADE NOS. 1 TO 6), AND NATURAL GAS

FOR ANTHRACITE OR FOR NATURAL GAS WITHOUT SULFUR, MINIMUM METAL TEMPERATURE IS 160 F. TO AVOID INTERNAL CORROSION OF ECONOMIZER TUBES, THE TEMPERATURE OF THE FEEDWATER ENTERING SHOULD NEVER BE LESS THAN 212 F.

MINIMUM METAL TEMPERATURE, F

CHAIN-GRATE OR UNDERFEED-STOKER FIRED (BITUMINOUS)

OIL FIRED

SPREADER-STOKER FIRED (BITUMINOUS)

PULVERIZED-COAL FIRED

SULFUR IN FUEL, PER CENT BY WEIGHT

Fig. 16. Limiting tube-metal temperatures to avoid external corrosion in economizers or air heaters when burning fuels containing sulfur

depths of banks best suited for external cleaning by either steam or air blowers.

External Corrosion

External corrosion of economizers may occur when the water vapor in the flue gas condenses on the surface of the tubes, and corrosion is accelerated when this happens in the presence of the products of combustion of sulfur. The rate of corrosion increases as the metal temperature is reduced. As the amount of sulfur in the fuel increases, the dewpoint increases and so does the potential rate of corrosion. Pulverized-coal ash seems to act as an inhibitor in retarding the rate of corrosion. Experience indicates that the rate of corrosion can be reduced to safe limits by keeping the temperature of the feedwater to the economizer above certain minimum values. Minimum safe values of tube-metal temperatures for varying percentages of sulfur and for several types of firing are indicated by the curves in Fig. 16. When sulfur is burned under a boiler, as, for instance, in one commercial process in the production of sulfuric acid, the dewpoint is so high that all steel surfaces must be at or above 450 F to assure a reasonable life. Such a boiler would not be fitted with an economizer.

Internal Corrosion

Economizers are also subject to internal corrosion

from dissolved oxygen and low hydroxyl ion concentration (a low pH). Oxygen corrosion can be eliminated by deaeration to zero oxygen (see Chapter 21). Steel in the economizer is attacked faster by pure water, which has equal hydrogen and hydroxyl ion concentrations ($pH = 7$), than by water which has a higher hydroxyl ion concentration. It is therefore necessary to maintain a pH value of between 8 and 9 for the water passing through the economizer. A successful means sometimes used to maintain the desired pH value of the feedwater is to recirculate some boiler water to the inlet end of the economizer.

Air Heaters—Early Types and Development

The air heater in a steam-generating unit reclaims some heat (which would otherwise be lost) from the flue gas or occasionally from some other source and adds that heat to the air required for the combustion of the fuel. Normally, air-cooled furnace walls or floors, which are sometimes used as a source of heat to improve combustion conditions, are not included in the term "air heater."

As in the case of economizers, air heaters originated in Europe before they were used in the United States. Early patent files reveal the invention of air heaters long before the industry had developed to the stage where they could be used economically.

The first air heater to be installed in a commercial boiler unit in the United States was built in 1922. It was made of flat parallel steel plates which formed alternate gas and air passages. It was necessary that the passages be completely separate one from the other, since any air leakage into the gas stream not only reduced the efficiency of the air heater but increased the load on the forced- and induced-draft fans. Plate air heaters are still in use but are not as suitable as tubular or regenerative heaters for the higher gas and air pressures which are now common practice.

The first tubular air heater developed by B&W was placed in service early in 1923. Demand for air heaters developed quickly. A total of 50 air heaters was built by B&W during the two-year period of 1923 and 1924. Several factors influenced this demand. Before 1922, the highest pressures commonly used in power generation ranged from 350 to 400 psi. In 1922, units of 650 psi were developed to generate more kilowatt hours per pound of steam. This in turn increased the demand for more pounds of steam per pound of fuel. The use of air heaters helped to achieve this end.

Before the early 1920's, practically all coal used in the production of steam was burned on stokers or grates. Furnace walls were generally all refractory or, in a few instances, partly water cooled. Hot air supplied to the fire improved stoker performance by raising the temperature level in the combustion zone. While this elevated temperature aided in the combustion of fuel, it also raised the temperature of all stoker parts and furnace surfaces, thus tending to increase the cost of their maintenance. So much, however, was gained in combustion efficiency by reclaiming some of the heat of the flue gas for heating the combustion air that boiler units were soon designed for operation with hot air without excessive maintenance costs. The development of water-cooled furnace walls which could withstand high combustion temperatures contributed greatly to this effective use of air heaters in the early boiler units.

In the early and middle 1920's, there was a tremendous increase in the development and use of pulverized-coal firing in central stations. For this type of firing, hot air was ideal for drying, transporting, and burning the coal in suspension. The demand for air heaters was thus well established before the end of 1924.

Advantages of Preheated Air

Preheated air is always required or justified with certain types of steam-generating units. Practically all pulverized-coal-fired units require hot air for drying the fuel, and the larger stoker-fired units burning bituminous coal operate more efficiently with preheated air up to temperatures suitable for stoker parts. Preheated air, however, is not essential for the smaller stoker-fired units. In deciding on the use of an air heater, as with most other component equipment in all fields, much depends upon the conditions and requirements of the service.

Whether or not an air heater should be installed, and if so, how large the heater should be, will depend upon economic and engineering factors. The major economic factors are: the original cost of the air heater, the operating cost for fuel and fan power, and the maintenance cost. The principal engineering factors are: the available space, the characteristics of the fuel used, and the desired temperatures for the preheated air and the exit gas.

With the common fuels (coal, oil, and gas) and identical furnace conditions, the efficiency of a boiler unit as a whole will increase by about 2.5% for 100 F drop in exit gas temperature from the unit. In terms of an air heater, this corresponds to an increase of approximately 2% for each 100 F rise in air temperature. An air heater providing combustion air at temperatures ranging upward from 300 F will often effect savings in fuel ranging from 5 to 10%, as indicated by the curve in Fig. 17. While temperatures above the maximum in the graph (600 F) have been and are used in boiler practice, it may be noted that the difficulties of arrangement in the boiler unit and in obtaining economical materials suitable for the temperature become increasingly troublesome if this limit is exceeded.

Use of preheated air will speed up combustion at all loads, improve combustion at low loads, and increase efficiency. In a new installation, the use of an air heater will frequently permit a reduction in the size of the boiler. Some saving will likewise be possible in the size and cost of the firing equipment, without impairment of the boiler output.

Classification of Air Heaters

Air heaters may be classified according to the principle of their operation as (a) recuperative and (b) regenerative. Heat is transferred to the air from the flue gases of the boiler or from other sources. Among successful air heaters operating on the recuperative principle, there are tubular and plate types, with the heat provided by 1) the flue gases of the boiler, 2) steam in coils, or 3) separately fired furnaces. Among air heaters operating on the regenerative principle are the rotary regenerative (Ljungstrom) and the diphenyl, with heat provided by the flue gases, and the pebble type, with heat provided by flue gases or a separate furnace.

In a recuperative design, the heat is transferred directly from the hot gases or steam on one side of the surface to air on the other side.

In a regenerative heater, the heat is transferred indirectly from the hot gases to the air through some intermediate heat-storage medium, as in the rotary regenerative, diphenyl, and pebble heaters. Use of the principle of regeneration is not new. Regenerative air heaters were used in other industries before they were used in steam generation. For open-hearth furnaces, it was common practice to control the gas flow from the furnace and the air flow to the furnace by dampers, so that the gas flow would alternately heat one flue and then the other. The air, flowing through the hot flues alternately, would be heated to over 1000 F before entering the

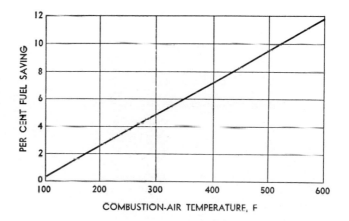

Fig. 17. *Order of improvement in efficiency when heated combustion air is used in boiler units*

combustion chamber. The brickwork in the flues acted as the heat-storage medium.

Tubular Air Heater

The B&W tubular air heater utilizes the heat from the products of combustion after they leave the boiler, economizer, or superheater. It is essentially a nest of straight tubes expanded into tube sheets and enclosed in a suitably reinforced steel casing. This casing functions as the air or gas flue and is provided with air and gas inlet and outlet openings and the necessary hoppers and structural steel supporting members. The vertical type, suspended from above, is illustrated in Fig. 18. The unit can alternatively be supported from below. Horizontal types are also made. The casing is made of flanged steel-plate panels bolted to stiffening bars and supported by a frame of steel bars, angles, and channels. The frame also carries the flanged air-inlet and air-outlet boxes. Dust and cinder-disposal hoppers as required are provided under the tubes to suit flue arrangements.

In the modern tubular air heater the tubes are

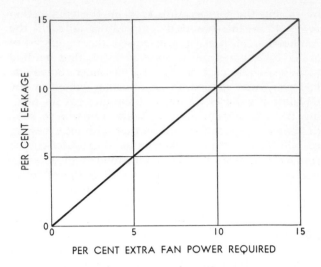

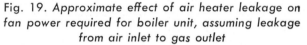

Fig. 19. *Approximate effect of air heater leakage on fan power required for boiler unit, assuming leakage from air inlet to gas outlet*

rolled into tube sheets at both ends. To provide for expansion, one tube sheet should be free to move with respect to the casing, and this must be accomplished without any air leakage. One method is to fit a flexible bellows-type expansion-joint connection as indicated at the bottom tube sheet of the air heater illustrated in Fig. 18. Tests made in actual operation with this type show negligible leakage as reflected in excess air or CO_2 determinations. For over-all tightness of the air heater it is preferable to weld the panel joints of the casing and hoppers. The undesirable effect of leakage on fan power is indicated by the graph in Fig. 19.

Soot blowers are located so that a jet of steam, air, or water in some instances (with the boiler out of service) can be blown through each tube as required (or across the tubes in the infrequently used arrangement where gas crosses the tubes on the outside).

Ample flow paths are provided for the gases, and, where space permits, dust hoppers can be fitted ahead of the heaters. The net result is a material reduction in the amount of dust and fly-ash entering the heaters.

Tube Sizes. In building the first tubular air heaters, tube diameters of 2 in., 2½ in., and even 3 in. and 4 in. were used in various units. Several factors are involved in establishing the size of air heater tubes. With smaller diameter tubes the surface is used more effectively, but tubes of larger diameter are easier to clean. Greater space is required for the large-tube heater. The over-all cost of the heater, including the manufacture, shipment, and erection of the tubes, casing, and supports, and building cost, tends to be a minimum for some particular size of tube. In stationary boiler practice, the 2½-in. and 2-in. tubes

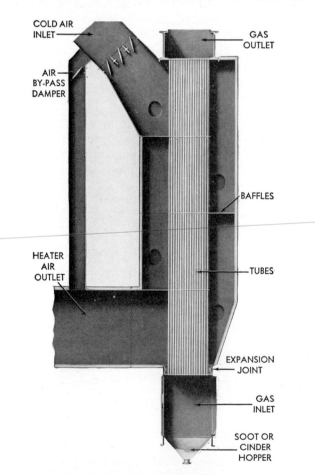

Fig. 18. *Tubular air heater arranged for counter-flow of gas and air, with an air by-pass to control metal temperature at air inlet end*

are now generally used, and in marine practice, where space and weight are limited, the 1½-in. tubes prove to be more economical.

Adaptability for Installation. Adaptability of the air heater to space limitations and to the arrangement of ducts between the heater and the boiler is an important factor in the over-all design of a steam-generating unit. The tubular air heater, as indicated in Fig. 20, can be arranged to suit a wide variety of space conditions and duct layouts. It can be adapted for vertical or horizontal applications and for multipass flow of either gas or air, or both. Where the forced-draft fan is located at a distance from the boiler, the tubular air heater has frequently been used as a flue, thus saving the expense of additional ductwork.

Control of Corrosion. Experience indicates that corrosion is liable to occur in an air heater when its metal temperature falls below certain limits. Sulfur content of the fuel, moisture content of the gases, and type of firing are all important factors to be considered. However, a definite relationship between the minimum metal temperature on the one hand

and the gas and air temperatures, the fuel, and the design of the air heater on the other has been established from operating data and engineering tests. It is possible to obtain an optimum design of tubular air heater for every application, with the added assurance of effective control of corrosion, by applying one or more of the following methods:

1. By-pass a portion, or all, of the cool inlet air to increase the metal temperature. This is especially effective at light loads when the gas temperatures are low and the danger of dewpoint is imminent.

2. Increase the spacing of the first few rows of tubes at the air inlet side of the air heater to decrease the cooling effect (by decreasing mass flow) of the incoming air and thus keep the metal temperature in this zone above the dewpoint.

3. Recirculate a portion of the hot air from the air heater outlet back to the air heater inlet and thus keep the metal temperature at the cold end of the air heater constantly above the dewpoint.

4. Use parallel flow in the air heater, often recommended for stoker-fired units and for chemical recovery units in the paper industry, and thus avoid dewpoint complications (see parallel-flow arrangement in Fig. 20).

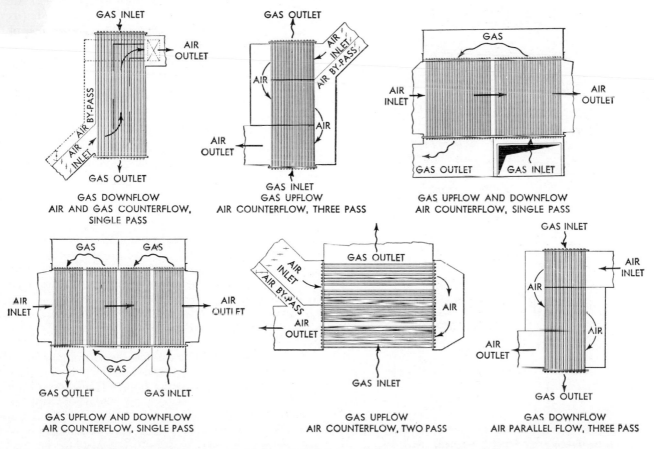

Fig. 20. *Some arrangements of tubular air heaters to suit various directions of gas and air flow*

Primary-Air Heating. Occasionally, for pulverized-coal-fired units it is desirable to have a separate section in the air heater for heating the primary air to the pulverizers, particularly when the temperature leaving the main heater is lower than that required for drying very wet coal, such as a Midwest coal with more than 10 to 12% surface moisture. The primary-air heating section is then designed to give the required air temperature. This arrangement has the additional advantage of permitting use of a smaller forced-draft fan for the secondary air, since a single fan handling clean cold air is used for all the pulverizers of a unit. However, because of complications in the air heater design, a separate primary heater is seldom recommended when the air temperature leaving the main heater is high enough for the pulverizers.

Rotary Regenerative Air Heater

The principle of using steel plates as the best storage medium in a regenerative air heater was first developed and applied in Europe, and the first rotary heater of this type was installed in the United States in 1923. The design has been greatly modified and improved to meet the ever-changing re-

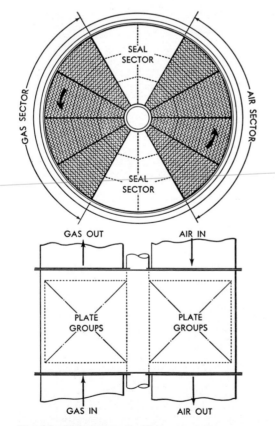

Fig. 21. *Diagrammatic illustration of rotary regenerative air heater (vertical shaft arrangement) with gas and air counterflow*

quirements of the power industry. This type and the tubular (recuperative) type are now the two principal air heater designs used in the generation of steam.

The rotary regenerative air heater is illustrated diagrammatically in Fig. 21. Slightly separated metal plates, supported in a frame attached to a slowly moving rotor shaft, are arranged edge-on to the gas and air flow. As these plates pass progressively through the gas stream they are heated and then, in passing through the air stream, give up heat to the air before again entering the gas stream, thus maintaining the regenerative cycle. The plates are placed in segmental groupings to fill a complete circle around the shaft. Seals are provided to reduce air infiltration into the gas. Gas and air ducts and the casing around the heater confine the gas and air to the desired flow paths.

Soot blowers are used to clean the heating elements of ash and oil residues. During low-load operation, when deposits tend to increase because of low metal temperatures, the heater can be by-passed on the air side or the air recirculated.

The rotary regenerative air heater is made in a number of standard diameters and in various lengths of elements to obtain the desired gas and air temperatures for different gas and air weights. Air heaters of this type are made with vertical (as illustrated) or horizontal shaft rotors. The choice of one over the other depends to some extent upon the gas and air duct arrangement to and from the heater. Some think that the heater with a vertical shaft rotor is easier to clean.

Other Air Heaters (Recuperative)

Plate-Type Air Heater. Several designs of plate-type air heaters have been developed over the years. They all use thin, flat, parallel plates with alternate wide and narrow spacing to match the ratio of gas weight to air weight. Thus the flue gas is made to pass through the wide-spaced passages and the air through the narrower with countercurrent flow. To obtain more heating surface for a given volume, the gas space is made as small as possible within the limits required for cleaning. Commercial designs have differed chiefly in the method of sealing the air spaces from the gas spaces. Many patented constructions were used but only the welded joint survived.

Steam Coil Air Heater. After the development of pulverized fuel there was some demand to apply this type of firing to existing boilers. This application required hot air, and it was not always possible to install a flue gas air heater. In such cases commercially available steam-to-air heat exchangers were successfully adapted to supply the heat to dry and burn the fuel.

To reduce fouling and corrosion, steam coil heaters are used occasionally today to increase the minimum tube-metal temperatures by heating the combustion air before it enters the air heater. Other means, as cited above, are generally more economical for the control of metal temperature.

Separately Fired Air Heater. Hot air is sometimes required for industrial use. Air at atmospheric or higher pressure may be heated to the desired temperature by using a separately fired air heater. The separately fired air heater usually consists of a refractory furnace with a tubular heater arranged for a number of gas and air passes.

To prevent overheating of the tubes, it is essential to control the gas temperatures entering the heater. This may be done by (a) diluting the gas with excess air or by (b) recirculating the gas from the air heater outlet to the furnace, thus reducing the temperature of the furnace gases. The unit will be more efficient if the latter method is used.

Other Air Heaters (Regenerative)

Diphenyl Air Heater. Occasionally use is made of an air heater operating on the regenerative principle where the intermediate heat-conducting mechanism is diphenyl oxide or a similar suitable liquid. The liquid is heated as it passes through a heat exchanger located in the flue gas stream and cooled as it passes through another heat exchanger located in the air stream. By continuous recirculation of the liquid, heat is transferred from the gas to the air.

Pebble Heater. Regenerative air heaters have been designed to heat air and other gases to higher temperatures than is economically possible using the recuperative principle. Arrangement of a pebble heater, designed for heating air from room temperature to 2300 F, is illustrated by Fig. 22. Various suitable materials may be used for the pebble heat-transfer medium. Spherical pebbles, ½ in. in diameter, of mullite composition (72% Al_2O_3, 28% SiO_2), are commonly used as the heat-conducting medium. The pebbles are alternately heated in the upper chamber, A, by hot gases and cooled in the lower chamber, C, by the fluid to be heated. Close control of the pressures of the gas and of the fluid to be heated is

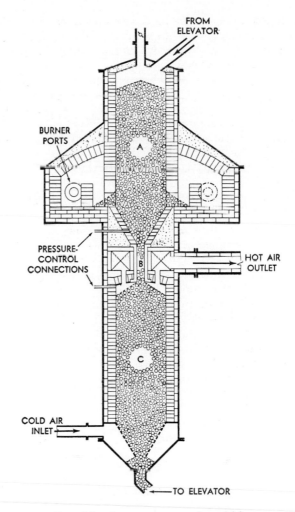

Fig. 22. Arrangement of pebble heater for delivery of air at 2300 F

necessary to prevent mixing of the two at B. The whole unit is surrounded by a gastight cylindrical steel casing which forms a rigid support for the brickwork.

In addition to heating air or steam, the pebble heater has many other applications among which are: heating hydrogen or natural gas for the reduction of metallic oxides, and the production of ethylene from a hydrocarbon feed source.

Temperature, Surface, and Draft Loss Calculations

EVALUATING the performance of a boiler unit for a given set of conditions is fairly complicated, as indicated in the foregoing. One of the principal problems in boiler design is to attain an optimum interrelationship among three main factors: gas temperature drop, surface, and draft loss. Since surface may be disposed in an infinite variety of arrange-

ments, each affecting the value of temperature drop and draft loss, no single useful equation combining the three has been developed. A practical approach, based in large measure on experience, is therefore necessary in establishing economic surface arrangements for specified conditions.

Thus, in the convection surface of a boiler unit,

tubes are disposed in banks for the boiler portion, the superheater, the economizer, and the tubular air heater. A rather narrow range of tube diameters has been established as good practice for these components. From experience, tube spacing (side-spacing and back-spacing) has also been established within a fairly narrow range. All these details of surface and its arrangement reflect experience based on practical performance. The range of variation in detail has been demonstrated as acceptable in draft loss, use of material, space occupied, and tube size and spacing to maintain cleanliness on the gas side when firing fuels liable to deposit dust on heat-absorbing surfaces.

However, even within the finite limits of variety of surface arrangements accepted as good practice, there are still too many possible permutations and combinations to permit the use of surface in an all-comprehensive formula. The problem must therefore be approached in two steps: 1) to establish for a certain gas mass flow, by trial and error computations, the true relationship between surface and the temperature drop or temperature rise desired, and 2) to establish the draft loss (pressure drop) for this gas mass flow over this surface.

For clean surfaces the relationship of gas temperature drop of the hotter fluid (HF), temperature rise of the colder fluid (CF), and surface (S) is given in the general equation:

$$U S \triangle t_m = w c (t_1 - t_2) = w' c' (t'_2 - t'_1) \qquad (1)$$

where:

U = combined conductance, Btu/sq ft, hr, F

$U = \dfrac{U_{HF} \times U_{CF}}{U_{HF} + U_{CF}}$, Btu/sq ft, hr, F

S = total surface, sq ft

$\triangle t_m$ = log mean temp diff, hotter fluid and colder fluid, F

w = wt flow of hotter fluid, lb/hr

t_1 = temp of hotter fluid entering tube bank, F

t_2 = temp of hotter fluid leaving tube bank, F

c = mean sp ht of hotter fluid, Btu/lb, F

w' = wt flow of colder fluid, lb/hr

t'_1 = temp of colder fluid entering tube bank, F

t'_2 = temp of colder fluid leaving tube bank, F

c' = mean sp ht of colder fluid, Btu/lb, F

For boilers, economizers, superheaters, and tubular air heaters, the hotter fluid is gas and the colder fluid is, respectively, saturated steam-water mixture at constant temperature, water at rising temperature, steam at rising temperature, and air at rising temperature. For clean surfaces equation (1) may be expressed as:

For Boiler Surface

$$U S \triangle t_m = w_g c_g \triangle t_g \qquad (2)$$

where:

$U = U_g$ = combined conductance, Btu/sq ft, hr, F

$U_g = U_{rg} + U_{cg}$ = over-all gas-side conductance, Btu/sq ft, hr, F

U_{rg} = radiation conductance (gas side), Btu/sq ft, hr, F

U_{cg} = convection conductance (gas film), Btu/sq ft, hr, F

S = total surface, sq ft

$\triangle t_m$ = log mean temp diff, gas and sat. water, F

$\triangle t_m = \dfrac{t_1 - t_2}{\log_e \left(\dfrac{t_1 - t'_s}{t_2 - t'_s} \right)}$ (Case I, Fig. 23)

t_1 = gas temp entering tube bank, F

t_2 = gas temp leaving tube bank, F

t'_s = sat. temp of boiler water, F

w_g = wt flow of the gas, lb/hr

c_g = mean sp ht of the gas, Btu/lb, F

$\triangle t_g = t_1 - t_2$ = gas temp diff, entering and leaving, F

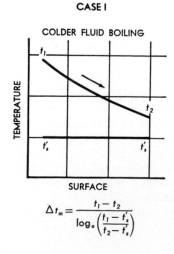

CASE I

COLDER FLUID BOILING

$$\triangle t_m = \frac{t_1 - t_2}{\log_e \left(\dfrac{t_1 - t'_s}{t_2 - t'_s} \right)}$$

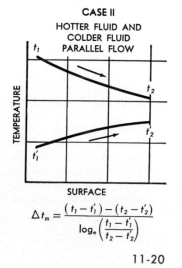

CASE II

HOTTER FLUID AND COLDER FLUID PARALLEL FLOW

$$\triangle t_m = \frac{(t_1 - t'_1) - (t_2 - t'_2)}{\log_e \left(\dfrac{t_1 - t'_1}{t_2 - t'_2} \right)}$$

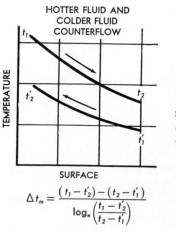

CASE III

HOTTER FLUID AND COLDER FLUID COUNTERFLOW

$$\triangle t_m = \frac{(t_1 - t'_2) - (t_2 - t'_1)}{\log_e \left(\dfrac{t_1 - t'_2}{t_2 - t'_1} \right)}$$

Fig. 23. Log mean temperature difference $\triangle t_m$ of hotter fluid and colder fluid, F

For Economizer Surface

$$U S \, \triangle t_m = w_g \, c_g \, \triangle t_g \tag{2}$$

where:

U, S, w_g, c_g, $\triangle t_g$ are as defined for boiler surface

$\triangle t_m$ = log mean temp diff, gas and water, F

For parallel flow, Case II, Fig. 23

$$\triangle t_m = \frac{(t_1 - t'_1) - (t_2 - t'_2)}{\log_e\!\left(\dfrac{t_1 - t'_1}{t_2 - t'_2}\right)}$$

For counterflow, Case III, Fig. 23

$$\triangle t_m = \frac{(t_1 - t'_2) - (t_2 - t'_1)}{\log_e\!\left(\dfrac{t_1 - t'_2}{t_2 - t'_1}\right)}$$

t_1 and t_2 are as defined for boiler surface

t'_1 = temp of water entering econ, F

t'_2 = temp of water leaving econ, F

Btu Balance for Economizer

$$w_g \, c_g \, \triangle t_g = w_w \, c_w \, \triangle t_w \tag{3}$$

where:

w_g, c_g, $\triangle t_g$ are as in equation (2)

w_w = wt flow of water through econ, lb/hr

c_w = mean sp ht of water in econ, Btu/lb, F

$\triangle t_w = t'_2 - t'_1$, temp rise of water through econ, F

For Superheater Surface

$$U S \, \triangle t_m = w_g \, c_g \, \triangle t_g \tag{2}$$

where:

S, w_g, c_g, $\triangle t_g$ are as defined for boiler surface

$U = \dfrac{U_g \times U_s}{U_g + U_s}$, combined conductance, Btu/sq ft, hr, F

U_g is as defined for boiler surface

U_s = convection conductance (steam film), Btu/sq ft, hr, F

$\triangle t_m$ = log mean temp diff, gas and steam, F

For parallel flow, Case II, Fig. 23

$$\triangle t_m = \frac{(t_1 - t'_1) - (t_2 - t'_2)}{\log_e\!\left(\dfrac{t_1 - t'_1}{t_2 - t'_2}\right)}$$

For counterflow, Case III, Fig. 23

$$\triangle t_m = \frac{(t_1 - t'_2) - (t_2 - t'_1)}{\log_e\!\left(\dfrac{t_1 - t'_2}{t_2 - t'_1}\right)}$$

t_1 and t_2 are as defined for boiler surface

t'_1 = temp of steam entering superheater, F

t'_2 = temp of steam leaving superheater, F

Btu Balance for Superheater

$$w_g \, c_g \, \triangle t_g = w_s \, c_s \, \triangle t_s \tag{4}$$

where:

w_g, c_g, $\triangle t_g$ are as in equation (2)

w_s = wt flow of steam through superheater, lb/hr

c_s = mean sp ht of steam in superheater, Btu/lb, F

$\triangle t_s = t'_2 - t'_1$, temp rise of steam through superheater, F

The surface of a superheater, determined from the above, will be reduced somewhat (as shown in the superheater example below) when account is taken of the heat radiating from the mass of gas *approaching* across a cavity or from a furnace, where the bank can "see" the gas. Because of the relatively low temperature involved in this example, no account is taken of the radiation to the *rear* of the bank by the mass of gas leaving.

For Air Heater Surface

$$U S \, \triangle t_m = w_g \, c_g \, \triangle t_g \tag{2}$$

where:

S, w_g, c_g, $\triangle t_g$ are as defined for boiler surface

$U = \dfrac{U_g \times U_{ca}}{U_g + U_{ca}}$, combined conductance, Btu/sq ft, hr, F

U_g is as defined for boiler surface

U_{ca} = convection conductance (air film), Btu/sq ft, hr, F

$\triangle t_m$ = log mean temp diff, gas and air, F

For parallel flow, Case II, Fig. 23

$$\triangle t_m = \frac{(t_1 - t'_1) - (t_2 - t'_2)}{\log_e\!\left(\dfrac{t_1 - t'_1}{t_2 - t'_2}\right)}$$

For counterflow, Case III, Fig. 23

$$\triangle t_m = \frac{(t_1 - t'_2) - (t_2 - t'_1)}{\log_e\!\left(\dfrac{t_1 - t'_2}{t_2 - t'_1}\right)}$$

t_1 and t_2 are as defined for boiler surface

t'_1 = temp of air entering air heater, F

t'_2 = temp of air leaving air heater, F

Btu Balance for Air Heater

$$w_g \, c_g \, \triangle t_g = w_a \, c_a \, \triangle t_a \tag{5}$$

where:

w_g, c_g, $\triangle t_g$ are as in equation (2)

w_a = wt flow of air through air heater, lb/hr

c_a = mean sp ht of air in air heater, Btu/lb, F

$\triangle t_a = t'_2 - t'_1$, temp rise of air through air heater, F

Mass Flow Set by Good Practice

From a long record of experience it is known that for a given set of conditions, such as fuel (amount to be burned and characteristics) and allowable over-all draft loss, surface (boiler, superheater, economizer, or air heater) is arranged as tubes of a suitable diameter disposed in a bank and spaced (in both directions) within a fairly limited range. Tube length is generally determined by the drum or header locations. In heat transfer and fluid flow problems it is essential to know the limits set by good practice for mass velocity, or "mass flow," ($G = w/A$). With tube diameter, spacing, and length established, the width of the tube bank is based on an acceptable mass flow of the fluids (gas, steam, water, or air) entering, in which the free-flow area is a factor, since:

$$G = \frac{w}{A} = \text{mass flow of fluid flowing, lb/sq ft, hr}$$

where:

$w =$ weight of fluid flowing, lb/hr (w_g for gas)

$A =$ free-flow area, sq ft (A_g for gas)

The "depth" of bank, or the number of rows deep, is frequently limited by the usable circumference of the drums or headers to which the tubes are connected. Other considerations, such as the maximum distance for effective cleaning by soot blowing, will sometimes limit the depth of bank. In any case, since it is necessary to start with a tube arrangement, experience will permit a tentative selection of the height and width of the receiving surface and the tube diameter of this bank for a given mass flow of the entering gases. Having thus selected a specific arrangement of surface, it is possible to calculate the total amount of surface required for the desired temperature drop by the use of the general equation (2).

Temperature Drop, Boiler Surface

As an example of a manipulation of equation (2) for the relation between gas temperature drop and surface, a simple case of boiler surface used to cool combustion gases will do. Equation (2) may be rewritten:

$$S = \frac{w_g c_g \triangle t_g}{U \triangle t_m} \qquad (6)$$

Total surface, S, in tube bank, sq ft – to be determined

Depth of tube bank, number of rows – to be determined

To determine the total surface, S, required to cool the gases to the desired temperature, it is necessary, as noted above, to set certain conditions, known from experience to be fairly applicable to the case selected. For this example the known and assumed conditions are:

Fuel = natural gas, 1000 Btu/cu ft (22,000 Btu/lb)

$w_g =$ 185,000 lb/hr, combustion gas (from burning fuel with 115% total air; moisture in flue gas, 11%)

$\triangle t_g = t_1 - t_2 = 610$ F, desired gas temp drop

$t_1 = 1910$ F, temp of gas entering tube bank

$t_2 = 1300$ F, temp of gas leaving tube bank

$t'_s = 378$ F, sat. temp of boiler water @ 176.4 psi

$\triangle t_m =$ log mean temp diff, gas and sat. water, F (Case I, Fig. 23)

Tubes and arrangement in bank:

2.5-in. OD, in-line (d_o)

Length = 16 ft

Arranged in setting 99 in. wide (including side lanes)

Avg side-spacing, $l_1 = 3.5$ in.

Avg back-spacing, $l_{II} = 4.0$ in.

No. in one row across pass = 28

Surface of one row of tubes = 293 sq ft

Calculations to determine surface, S, from equation (6):

Sum of tube diam = $28 \times 2.5 = 70$ in.

$A_g =$ gas free-flow area through tube bank

$$= \frac{99 - 70}{12} \times 16 = 38.7 \text{ sq ft}$$

$$\frac{w_g}{A_g} = \frac{185,000}{38.7} = 4780 \text{ lb/sq ft, hr}$$

$$\triangle t_m = \frac{1910 - 1300}{\log_e\left(\dfrac{1910 - 378}{1300 - 378}\right)} = 1200 \text{ F}$$

$c_g = 0.318$ Btu/lb, F, from Fig. 24, for 11% moisture

$U = 13.04$ Btu/sq ft, hr, F (established as explained below under *Solution of Values*)

Substituting the above values in equation (6):

$$S = \frac{185,000 \times 0.318 \times 610}{13.04 \times 1200} = 2296 \text{ sq ft}$$

$$\text{No. of rows of tubes in bank} = \frac{2296}{293}$$

$$= 7.84$$

From the calculated value of surface, S, it is evident that, for the assumed conditions of the above example, 8 rows of tubes will be required in the tube bank to give the desired temperature drop.

When the calculated surface differs materially from the initially assumed surface, the values of U_{rg} and U_{cg} must be appropriately adjusted, and the resulting new value of U must be used in a final recalculation of surface.

In the simple illustration of the method used in establishing surface for a desired temperature drop, the conditions assumed in the above example were: crossflow of the gas, in-line tubes, and natural gas as fuel. However, the gas flow may be longitudinal or partly longitudinal and partly crossflow, and the tubes may be arranged in a staggered pattern. A coverage of all possible conditions will not be attempted. The value of the combined conductance, U, can be affected if other fuels are used. The effect on conductance of some ash-carrying fuels is largely a matter of the designer's judgment (see *Absorbing Surface Cleanliness*, below).

Draft Loss

The draft loss for gas in crossflow through a bank of in-line tubes at sea level, and where there is no stack effect, may be determined from the following equation, partly empirical:

$$\Delta p = fN \, \frac{0.95\left\{\dfrac{t_1 + t_2}{2}\right\} + 460}{57,500} \times \left\{\frac{w_g/A_g}{1000}\right\}^2 \quad (7)$$

where:

Δp = draft differential (draft loss), in. water
f = friction factor, from Fig. 40, for established Reynolds number, tube diam, and spacing
N = number of tube rows in the bank
t_1 = gas temp entering bank, F
t_2 = gas temp leaving bank, F
$0.95\left\{\dfrac{t_1 + t_2}{2}\right\}$ = approx avg gas temp, F
w_g/A_g = gas mass flow, lb/sq ft, hr

For each 1000 ft elevation above sea level, the value of Δp should be increased about 4% (see Chapters 5 and 8).

For shallow in-line tube banks of 2, 4, and 6 rows, the value of Δp should be increased by about 12, 3, and 1%, respectively. No increase in Δp is required for tube banks of 10 rows or more (see Chapter 8).

With vertical gas flow, the value of Δp will be increased by stack effect when the outlet is below the inlet and decreased when the outlet is above the inlet (see Chapter 5). However, in the usual boiler tube banks the total effect is small, in the order of 0.005 to 0.010 in. of water per ft of tube bank height.

For the simple example of boiler tube bank and the conditions noted above in establishing surface for temperature drop, the draft loss may be determined by substituting the known values in equation (7):

$$\Delta p = 0.10 \times 8 \times \frac{1525 + 460}{57,500} \times \left\{\frac{4780}{1000}\right\}^2$$

$$= 0.63 \text{ in. of water}$$

Economizer Surface

The surface of a nonsteaming economizer for (a) desired gas temperature drop, Δt_g, or for (b) desired water temperature rise, Δt_w, can also be determined from equation (2) with Δt_m, however, established from the formula in Case II or Case III of Fig. 23, depending upon whether the arrangement is for parallel flow or counterflow.

A general determination of economizer surface, without a specific example, may be derived from equations (2) and (3) listed above and repeated here for convenience:

$$w_g c_g \Delta t_g = U S \Delta t_m \quad (2)$$

$$w_g c_g \Delta t_g = w_w c_w \Delta t_w, \text{ Btu balance} \quad (3)$$

where:

$w_g, c_g, \Delta t_g$ are as in equation (2)

and

w_w = wt flow of water through econ, lb/hr, known

c_w = mean sp ht of water in econ, Btu/lb, F

t'_1 = temp of water entering econ, F, known

t'_2 = temp of water leaving econ, F, not known for condition (a), known for condition (b)

$\Delta t_w = t'_2 - t'_1$, temp rise of water through econ, F

For condition (a), Δt_m may be determined after establishing the value of t'_2 by solving equation (3) for Δt_w, since $t'_2 = \Delta t_w + t'_1$. Knowing the value of all temperatures involved, Δt_m may then be established (see Fig. 23).

For condition (b), Δt_g can be established from equation (3), and so t_2, the leaving gas temperature, is determined. Since the entering gas temperature, t_1, is known, a trial c_g may be established from Fig. 24 by assuming a temperature for the leaving gas. The true values of c_g and Δt_g are determined by successive trials until equation (3) is in balance. Knowing the value of all temperatures involved, Δt_m may then be established (see Fig. 23).

After tube diameter, arrangement of surface, and tube bank dimensions suitable for economizer practice have been tentatively set and knowing Δt_m, the heating surface, S, may be determined from equation (2), for either of the two conditions (a) or (b), by establishing the value of U in the same manner as in the preceding example for boiler surface.

The draft loss across an economizer is calculated from equation (7), as in the example for boiler surface. The feedwater pressure drop through an economizer may be calculated in the same manner (where water is the fluid) as for the steam pressure drop through a superheater (see below).

In the case of a superheater, since the temperature drop through the tube metal is usually small, the average surface temperature, t'_s, is approximated as being the average steam temperature. The gas film temperature then becomes:

$$t_f = t'_s + \triangle t_m/2 = 478 + 642/2 = 799 \text{ F}$$

Using the values established above, U_g can be determined by following the procedure given below for boiler surface under *Solution of Values*. For this superheater example:

$$U_g = U_{rg} + U_{cg} = 0.85 + 13.15$$
$$= 14.0 \text{ Btu/sq ft, hr, F}$$

In equation (8), $\dfrac{U_g \times U_s}{U_g + U_s} = U$

An empiric equation for determining U_s, the steam film conductance (see Fig. 3, Chapter 12) can be expressed as:

$$U_s = \frac{0.0266}{(d_i/12)^{0.2}} \times \left\{ \frac{w_s}{A_s} \right\}^{0.8} \times c_s \times \mu^{0.2} \times \frac{d_i}{d_o}$$

where all values have been established except μ, the absolute viscosity of steam. For this example, $\mu = 0.048$ lb (mass)/ft, hr (from Fig. 11, Chapter 8), evaluated at the average steam temperature, and from the above equation $U_s = 187.2$ Btu/sq ft, hr, F.

The combined conductance, U, then becomes:

$$U = \frac{U_g \times U_s}{U_g + U_s} = \frac{14.0 \times 187.2}{14.0 + 187.2}$$
$$= 13.02 \text{ Btu/sq ft, hr, F}$$

Substituting in equation (8):

$$S = \frac{185,000 \times 0.30 \times 308}{13.02 \times 642} = 2045 \text{ sq ft, neglect-}$$

ing the effect of cavity radiation.

Cavity Radiation

The Btu/hr in the heat balance equation (4) represents the total amount necessary to obtain the desired steam temperature rise. Since part of this heat was already absorbed from the gas mass in the cavity before the superheater, the surface established is too large. This is corrected in the following manner.

The Btu/hr absorbed by the superheater from cavity radiation is the product of the radiation conductance, U_{rg}, the flat projected surface, S_p, of the superheater facing the cavity, and the mean radiating temperature difference, $\triangle t_m$, between the average gas temperature and the superheater surface temperature.

The cavity radiation conductance, U_{rg}, is the product of the basic radiation conductance, U'_r (from Fig. 26) and the factor, K (from Fig. 27). For the specific dimensions of the cavity, which in this instance is 12 ft long, 98 in. wide, and 2 ft deep,

the factor K is 0.9. The flat projected surface, S_p, is $12 \times 98/12 = 98$ sq ft. For this example the average gas temperature in the cavity is taken as 1290 F, and, assuming that the average tube-surface temperature over the face of the superheater bank is the same as the outlet steam temperature, the mean radiating temperature difference is $1290 - 578 = 712$ F.

The superheater absorption from cavity radiation is:

$$\text{Btu/hr} = U_{rg} \times S_p \times \triangle t_m = U'_r \times K \times S_p \times \triangle t_m$$
$$= 5.4 \times 0.9 \times 98 \times 712 = 339,300$$

The total surface of the superheater, as calculated above in equation (8), is reduced by recalculation after subtracting this cavity absorption from the total amount required. The corrected surface, S, then becomes:

$$S = \frac{(185,000 \times 0.30 \times 308) - 339,300}{12.91 \times 642} = 2022 \text{ sq ft}$$

No. of rows of tubes in bank $= 2022/220 = 9.2$

The required number of rows deep may be specified as 9. In this instance a depth factor need not be considered, as the flow will be disturbed leaving a cavity of this depth (see Chapter 7).

It will be noted, for the assumed cavity dimensions and low mean radiating temperature, that the heat input to the superheater bank from cavity radiation is small, less than 2%. If the cavity is large, and particularly if the mean radiating temperature is high (over 1500 F), the proportion of heat input by cavity radiation to any heat-absorbing surface can be appreciable. A rigorous and complete procedure for calculating such heat input under all conditions will not be attempted, since the influence of cavity dimensions and shape and the effect of radiating temperatures are too involved for the scope of this book.

Steam Pressure Drop Through Superheater

The steam pressure drop, $\triangle p$, lb/sq in., through the superheater usually is calculated in three parts, 1) entrance and exit loss, 2) straight-flow loss, and 3) loss at bends:

$$\triangle p = \triangle p_e + \triangle p_f + \triangle p_b, \text{ lb/sq in.} \qquad (9)$$

where:

$$1) \quad \triangle p_e = 1.5 \frac{v}{12} \left\{ \frac{w_s/A_s}{100,000} \right\}^2$$

$$2) \quad \triangle p_f = \frac{fLv}{d_i} \left\{ \frac{w_s/A_s}{100,000} \right\}^2$$

$$3) \quad \triangle p_b = N_b \frac{v}{12} \left\{ \frac{w_s/A_s}{100,000} \right\}^2$$

Inside cross-
sq f
Arranged in
Avg side-spa
Avg back-spa
No. of tubes
Calculations to d
tion (10):

Assume:
Gas mass flow
Air mass flow
then:
$A_g = 185,000/$
$A_a = 150,000/$
No. of tubes =
No. of tubes d
Actual no. of t
Sum of tube c

Length of tube

Actual total c

$$S = \frac{2\pi}{12}$$

Actual gas mass

$= 8040$

Equation (5) is use
find the value of t_2.
specific heat of air thr
Fig. 25. A trial value
by successive trials unt
the true values of c_g an

Substituting the abov

$$\triangle t_g = \frac{150,000 \times}{185,00}$$

so, $t_2 = t_1 - 192 = 605$
then by Case III, Fig.

$$\triangle t_m = \frac{(605-3)}{\log_e(}$$

In the case of an air
temperatures are deterr

Gas film temp $= \frac{t'_1 +}{2}$

$= \frac{80 +}{2}$

Air film temp $= \frac{t'_1 +}{2}$

$= \frac{80 +}{2}$

Since heat transfer by
of the total conductance,

---

where:

$v =$ avg sp vol of steam, cu ft/lb, from steam
tables

$\frac{w_s}{A_s} =$ steam mass flow, lb/sq ft, hr

$f =$ friction factor from Fig. 7, Chapter 8,
for Reynolds number, N_{Re}

$d_i =$ internal diam of tube, in.

$l_i =$ developed length of tube in one circuit,
ft

$N_b =$ total no. of velocity heads lost in bends
$=$ no. of bends per circuit multiplied by
N'_b, from Fig. 11, Chapter 8

$N_{Re} =$ Reynolds number $= \dfrac{d_i \times w_s/A_s}{12 \times \mu}$

$\mu =$ absolute viscosity of steam, lb/ft, hr,
from Fig. 11, Chapter 8

Substituting values for the superheater example
above:

$$\triangle p = 1.5 \times \frac{3.01}{12} \times 5.05 +$$

$$\frac{0.0177 \times 108 \times 3.01}{2.09} \times 5.05 +$$

$$8 \times 0.68 \times \frac{3.01}{12} \times 5.05$$

$$\triangle p = 1.90 + 13.90 + 6.90 = 22.70 \text{ psi}$$

Call steam pressure drop 23 lb/sq in.

Air Heater Surface

In the determination of the amount and disposition
of surface for an air heater, cavity radiation is negligible because of the usually low temperature of
both the gas and the air. With the frequent arrangement, gas passing through the inside of the tubes
(air outside), intertube radiation—while of minor
effect on the value of U, the combined conductance
—should be included on the gas side. Convection
conductance for longitudinal flow of the gas within
the tubes must be considered.

Arrangement of the surface is based on good practice from experience. The mass flow of both gas and
air should be kept within economical limits—usually
from 5000 to 10,000 lb/sq ft, hr for longitudinal flow
and from 3000 to 5000 lb/sq ft, hr for crossflow.
Tube spacing usually may be closer than for a superheater, since only air passes across the outside of
the tubes. As noted above in the general discussion,
metal temperatures below the dewpoint should be
avoided. Usually the most economical arrangement
is with long tubes and multipass on the air side.

In the relationship of air heater surface, S, to air
temperature rise and gas temperature drop, the combined conductance, U, in equation (2) is modified
by the introduction of a value for the air film conductance, as noted above.

From equation (2), total surface for an air heater
may be expressed as:

$$S = \frac{w_g c_g \triangle t_g}{\dfrac{U_g \times U_{ca}}{U_g + U_{ca}} \triangle t_m}, \text{ sq ft} \qquad (10)$$

where:

$\dfrac{U_g \times U_{ca}}{U_g + U_{ca}} = U$, Btu/sq ft, hr, F

U_g is as defined for boiler surface
$U_{ca} =$ convection conductance (air film),
Btu/sq ft, hr, F

All other terms are as in equation (2)

As noted above and repeated here for convenience,
the heat balance equation for an air heater may be
expressed as:

$$w_g c_g \triangle t_g = w_a c_a \triangle t_a \qquad (5)$$

where:

$w_g, c_g, \triangle t_g$ are as in equation (2) or (10)
$w_a =$ wt flow of air through air heater, lb/hr
$c_a =$ mean sp ht of air through air heater,
Btu/lb, F
$\triangle t_a = t'_2 - t'_1$, temp rise of air through air
heater, F
$t'_1 =$ temp of air entering air heater, F
$t'_2 =$ temp of air leaving air heater, F

For a desired air temperature rise, $\triangle t_a$, and reasonable mass flow of gas and air, it is possible, after
finding the value of $\triangle t_g$ from equation (5) and the
value of U, to determine the surface S, from equation (10), with $\triangle t_m$ established from the formula
in Case III, Fig. 23, for counterflow. The surface so
determined must be modified by a correction factor,
1/0.85, to permit the use of the counterflow formula
in finding the value of $\triangle t_m$ for a single-pass crossflow air heater.

As an example of the manipulation of equations
(10) and (5) for the relation of surface, air temperature rise, and gas temperature drop in a single-pass
air heater, the following conditions have been selected:

Fuel = natural gas (as in boiler surface example)
$w_g =$ 185,000 lb/hr, combustion gas (as in
boiler surface example)
$\triangle t_g = t_1 - t_2$, gas temp drop, F
$t_1 =$ 605 F, temp of gas entering air heater
$t_2 =$ temp of gas leaving air heater, F, not
known
$w_a =$ 150,000 lb/hr, air to air heater
$\triangle t_a = t'_2 - t'_1 = 270$ F, desired temp rise of
air through air heater
$t'_1 =$ 80 F, temp of air entering air heater
$t'_2 =$ 350 F, temp of air leaving air heater
$\triangle t_m =$ log mean temp diff, gas and air, F
(Case III, Fig. 23)

Tubing and arrangement in bank:
2-in. OD, in-line (d_o)
1.834-in. ID for wall thickness of 0.083 in. (d_i)

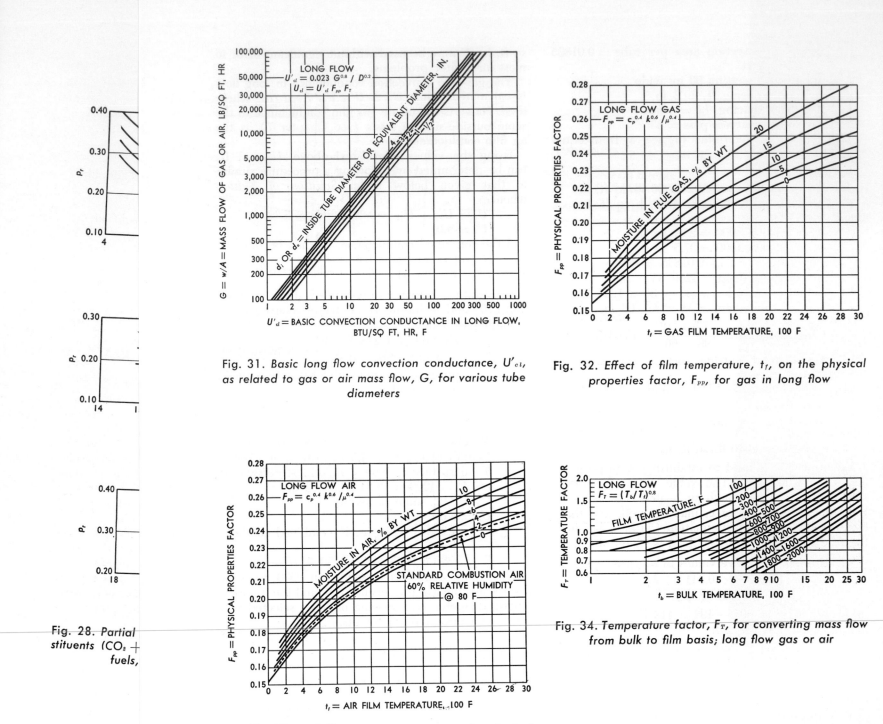

Fig. 31. *Basic long flow convection conductance, U'_{cl}, as related to gas or air mass flow, G, for various tube diameters*

Fig. 32. *Effect of film temperature, t_f, on the physical properties factor, F_{pp}, for gas in long flow*

Fig. 28. Partial
stituents (CO_2 +
fuels,

Fig. 33. *Effect of film temperature, t_f, on the physical properties factor, F_{pp}, for air in long flow*

Fig. 34. *Temperature factor, F_T, for converting mass flow from bulk to film basis; long flow gas or air*

S_b = total surface of tu[bes receiving]
    heat, sq ft

S_p = projected surface [of tubes]
    where gas enters, sq [ft]

$S_b - S_p$ = surface receivi[ng radia-]
    tion, sq ft

Calculations to determine inter[nal con-]
ductance, U_{rg}, for the boiler surfa[ce:]

    $U'_r = 5.70$, from Fig. 26,

    $\triangle t_m = 1200$

    $p_r = 0.25$, from diag ©,

        total air and 22,000 B[tu]

    $L/d_o = 0.13$, from Fig. 29

        $l_1/d_o = 1.4$ and $l_{||}$

    $L = 0.13 \times 2.5 = 0.325$

    $p_r L = 0.25 \times 0.325 = 0.08[1]$

    $K = 0.26$, from Fig. 27, fo[r]

    $S_b = 2344$ sq ft (assuming [ ]

    $S_p = 16 \times 99/12 = 132$ sq [ft]

$$F_a = \frac{S_b - S_p}{S_b} = \frac{2344 - 13[2]}{2344}$$

Substituting in equation (12):

    $U_{rg} = 5.70 \times 0.26 \times 0.944$

    hr, F

Convection conductance, U_{cg},
upon the mass flow of the gas thr[ough]
The relationship between basic c[onduct-]
ance, U'_{cc}, and gas mass flow, $w/[A, and tube]$
diameters, d_o, is given in Fig. 35[. The]
basic convection conductance, $U[$
fied by other factors to obtain th[e value for a]
specific set of conditions. This [is expressed]
by the equation:

    $U_{cg} = U'_{cc} F_{pp} F_a F_d$

where:

U'_{cc} = basic convection co[nductance in cross-]
    flow, Btu/sq ft, hr, [F]

F_{pp} = physical properties [factor,]
    evaluated at gas fil[m temperature]

t_f = gas film temperature[, F]
    (Fig. 30)

F_a = arrangement factor, [ ] evalu-
    ated at established [ ]
    N_{Re}

N_{Re} = Reynolds number, [ ]

F_d = depth factor, see Fi[g.]

Calculations to determine conv[ection conductance,]
U_{cg}, for the boiler surface proble[m:]

    $U'_{cc} = 93$, from Fig. 35

    and $d_o = 2.5$

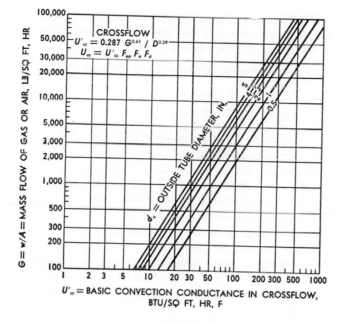

Fig. 35. Basic crossflow convection conductance, U'_{cc}, as related to gas or air mass flow, G, for various tube diameters

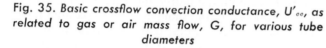

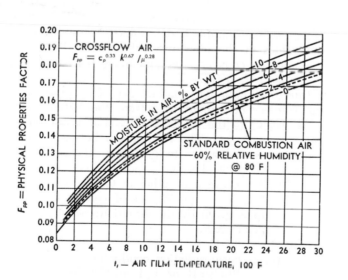

Fig. 37. Effect of film temperature, t_f, on the physical properties factor, F_{pp}, for air in crossflow

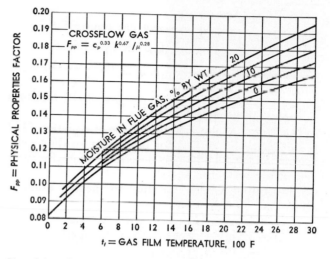

Fig. 36. Effect of film temperature, t_f, on the physical properties factor, F_{pp}, for gas in crossflow

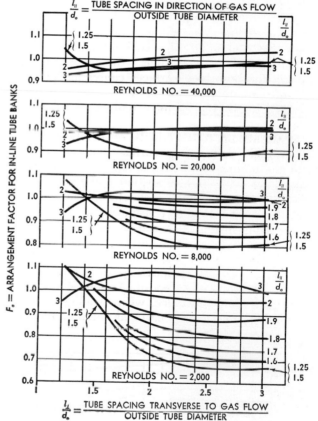

Fig. 38. Arrangement factor, F_a, as affected by Reynolds number for various in-line tube patterns; crossflow gas or air

$$\frac{t_1 + 2t_2}{3} = \text{approx}$$

$w_g/A_g =$ gas mass

$N_{Re} =$ Reynolds nu

$\mu =$ absolute visco
        Fig. 10, Chapt

The draft loss obtained
is subject to corrections f
vation) and stack effect, a
loss in the boiler example

Substituting values fo
above:

$$\triangle p = \frac{0.03}{14.4} \times \frac{14.5}{1.834}$$

$= 1.0$ in. of wa

The air resistance for
bank of in-line air heate
from equation (7) with

air temperature $= \dfrac{1}{0.95}($

Absorbing-Surface Cle

In the examples dealt
the fuel. With this speci
therefore the heat-absorb
fuels that contain an ash
laden industrial gaseous
ash on the absorbing su
sistance, R_f, to the flow
counted for by the use
Fig. 39).

With air or the pro
clean fuels there is no
and the fouling factor,
ash varies with its com
allowance for these facte
ing the proper fouling

Referring to Fig. 39 i
ing factor is plotted a
conductance, which is
vection and radiant com
the resistance of the d
for this fouling resistan
laden flue gases, is $R_f =$

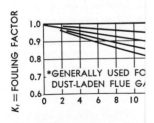

Fig. 39. Fouling facto
cl

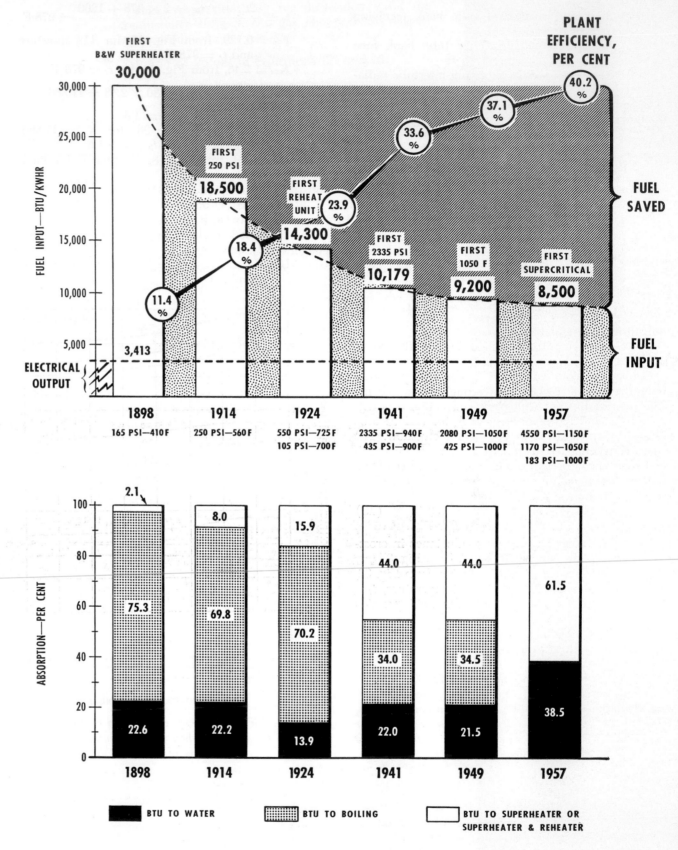

THE HISTORICAL IMPACT OF TEMPERATURE ON STEAM GENERATION

SUPERHEATED STEAM; SUPERHEATERS AND REHEATERS

IN 1705 Denis Papin, in order to reduce condensation, heated a mass of metal in a recess formed in the diaphragm, or piston, of an improved form of Thomas Savery's steam engine. When the metal cooled, it was replaced with another heated mass. Tests of later designs indicated fuel savings of 30 to 50 per cent with engines using superheated steam, and from about 1828 to 1865 much effort was devoted to the development of superheaters. Concurrently, much attention was given also to the development of compound engines which gave improved economy without the lubrication difficulties brought on by even the moderate superheats with the very low steam pressures then in vogue.

Introduction in 1874 of the triple-expansion engine and the further increase in steam pressures to 60 psi resulted in the temporary abandonment of superheat. The use of mineral oil and improved lubricating methods, together with performance tests in 1892 showing savings of as much as 20 per cent with 113 F superheat, provided the impetus for the renewed and far-reaching superheater development which followed.

In 1895 Babcock & Wilcox Ltd., England, began building superheaters, and in 1898 the B&W Company became the first in this country commercially to market superheaters. These were essentially of tubular type and were located within the boiler setting. Combustion gases passing over the outside of the tubes heated the steam flowing inside.

Use of Superheat and Reheat

Commercial development of the steam turbine hastened the general use of superheat, and by 1920 steam temperatures of 650 F, representing superheats of 250 F, were generally accepted. In the early 1920's the regenerative cycle, using steam bled from turbines for feed heating, was developed to improve station economy without going to higher steam temperatures. At the same time superheater develop-

ments permitted raising the steam temperature to 725 F. Further gain in economy by still higher superheat was limited at that time by allowable superheater tube-metal temperatures. This led to the commercial use of reheat, where the steam after passing through the high-pressure stage of the turbine was reheated in a separate reheat superheater and then, at higher temperature and enthalpy, returned to the low-pressure stage.

The first reheat unit for central station use was proposed in 1922 and went into service in September, 1924. The unit, similar to that shown in Fig. 13, Chapter 1, was designed for 650 psi and operated at 550 psi boiler steam pressure with a steam temperature of 725 F. The high-pressure-turbine exhaust

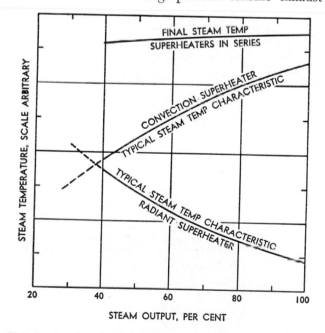

Fig. 1. *A substantially uniform final steam temperature over a range of steam output can be attained by arranging radiant and convection superheater components in series*

CONVECTION SUPERHEATERS

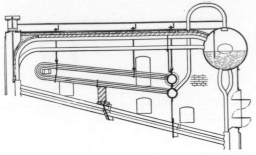

MULTIPLE-LOOP TYPE FOR LOW
SUPERHEAT INSTALLED "OVERDECK"
IN HEADER-TYPE BOILER

MULTIPLE-LOOP TYPE INSTALLED "IN-
TERDECK" IN MARINE HEADER BOILER

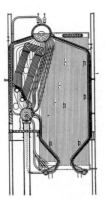

MULTIPLE-LOOP INVERTED TYPE
MULTIPASS ON STEAM SIDE
IN INTEGRAL-FURNACE BOILER
(DRAINABLE)

CONTINUOUS-TUBE PENDENT TYPE
INSTALLED IN STIRLING BOILER
EACH SECTION CONTINUOUS FROM
DRUM TO SH OUTLET HEADER

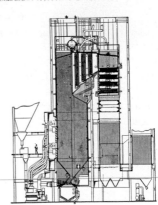

HORIZONTAL MULTIPLE-LOOP TYPE
PRIMARY, SECONDARY, AND REHEATER
INSTALLED IN MARINE BOILER
VERTICAL SECTION THROUGH TUBES

CONTINUOUS-TUBE PENDENT-TYPE
SECONDARY SH AND REHEATER
(NONDRAINABLE)
INITIAL SUPERHEAT IN HORIZONTAL
PRIMARY SECTION
(DRAINABLE)

RADIANT SUPERHEATERS

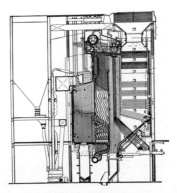

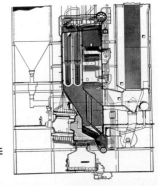

SUPERHEATER AND REHEATER IN FURNACE
LARGE OPEN-PASS BOILER
PRIMARY SUPERHEAT, CONVECTION
SECONDARY SUPERHEAT, RADIANT
REHEAT, RADIANT IN THREE STAGES

SECONDARY-SUPERHEATER SURFACE, RADIANT
AS PLATENS IN LARGE CYCLONE-FIRED BOILER
PRIMARY-SUPERHEATER AND REHEATER SURFACE
INSTALLED IN CONVECTION PASS

Fig. 2. Various types and arrangements of convection and radiant superheaters used in boiler units

steam was reheated at 135 psi to 725 F.

A much higher-pressure reheat unit, designed in 1924 for 1200 psi and 700 F primary steam temperature with reheat at 350 psi and 700 F, went into service in December 1925.

In 1928 live-steam reheaters, in lieu of gas reheaters within the boiler setting, were installed in two stations at Chicago. These, of course, gave only a modest amount of reheat compared with gas units, but it appeared at the time that the economics would justify their use. A year later, live-steam reheaters in series with gas reheaters were installed in the first of three different central stations where initial pressures were 1300 to 1400 psi and primary steam temperatures were 750 F. The real intent of the series combination was to use the live-steam reheaters simply for control purposes. Some of the live-steam reheaters gave a poor account of themselves because of leakage of condensate through porous welds. Other units have remained in successful operation, but this method of controlling reheat was found to be a luxury economically, and the use of live-steam reheaters for new central station plants was generally abandoned in favor of the gas type.

Until the middle 1930's, reheaters represented the best means of improving station economy because the total temperature of the steam was limited to 725 F or 750 F. The practical obtainable saving in heat input from reheating to the original primary steam temperature was of the order of 4½ to 5 per cent. To secure an equal gain by increasing primary steam temperature alone without the use of reheat, it was necessary to increase the primary steam temperature between 150 and 200 F. It was not until the development of alloys and the progress of superheater design to the point where 900 F steam became practical, that the reheater units lost favor to those of the straight high-temperature cycle. Boiler units designed in 1936 and in operation in 1937 at 900 F primary steam temperature relegated reheaters to the background, from which they emerged again in 1941 when the Twin Branch unit, designed for 2650 psi, 940 F primary steam temperature and 435 psi, 900 F reheat, went into operation. By the end of the next decade the development of better metals, which permitted total temperatures up to 1050 F, rendered reheaters more attractive because, during the same period, the price of fuel had risen rapidly and the possibility of any great increase in allowable primary steam temperature seemed quite remote.

Except for the one period in the late 1800's, when lubrication difficulties with reciprocating engines made it unpopular, superheat has demonstrated clearly and forcibly its permanent place in the scheme of power plant economy. Reheat has had a much shorter history, and, while it has only recently been brought out of temporary disfavor, it appears that it too has returned to stay.

Superheater Types

The original and somewhat basic type of superheater and reheater was the convection unit, for gas temperatures where the heat transfer by radiation was very small. With this type the superheat curve for any given unit increases with boiler output because of the decreasing percentage of heat input that is absorbed in the furnace, leaving more heat available for superheater absorption. Since convection heat transfer rates are almost a direct function of output, the total absorption in the superheater per lb of steam increases. (See also *Effect of Operating Variables*, Chapter 13.)

On the other hand, the radiant superheater receives its heat through radiation and practically none from convection. Because the furnace temperature does not increase in direct proportion to boiler output but at a considerably lesser rate, the curve of radiant superheat slopes downward with increase in boiler output.

The two opposite sloping curves have been coordinated by the combination of radiant and convection superheaters to give flat superheat curves over wide ranges in load, as typically indicated in Fig. 1.

A separately fired superheater (see Fig. 1, Chapter 13) has no boiler surface between it and the fire and can be made to function as a combination radiant and convection superheater. In order to avoid excessive superheater tube-metal temperatures, it is necessary with a separately fired unit to recirculate flue gases from the superheater outlet back to the furnace or to operate with high excess air.

Various arrangements of convection and radiant superheaters as components of boiler units are shown throughout this book and by types in Fig. 2.

Advantages of Superheat* and Reheat

The advantages of superheat and reheat are primarily twofold. The first is the strictly thermodynamic gain represented graphically in Fig. 10, Chapter 10, for the Rankine cycle. The second gain, and a greater one, is the improvement in turbine efficiency resulting principally from the reduction in the moisture formed in the last stages. The total gain in station heat rate from primary superheat alone is approximately 3 per cent for each 100 F superheat (see Table 3, Chapter 10). The gain from reheating to the initial temperature of the primary steam in the range above 750 F is between 4½ and 5 per cent as noted above. With mounting costs of fuel, much effort will undoubtedly be applied to the develop-

---

*The term "superheat" is not appropriate in defining the temperature of the working fluid at or above the critical pressure (see Chapter 9). Use of the term in this chapter relates to steam conditions in the more common subcritical pressure ranges.

ment of the equipment which will permit higher primary steam temperatures and higher reheat steam temperatures. Increased costs of materials will make necessary the application of similar effort toward more effective boiler, turbine, and piping design, particularly since there will be an economy loss of approximately 1 per cent for every 10 per cent pressure drop through the reheater system. The pressure drop problem with the single stage of reheating has been solved fairly satisfactorily by limiting the pressure drop in the reheater, piping, and valves to a maximum of 10 per cent. However, multiple reheating will increase economy still further if pressure drop through these subsequent reheat stages can be kept low without a counterbalancing penalty in the cost of piping and reheater. (See Fig. 16, Chapter 1, for an example of double reheat.)

Development of Superheaters

The history of superheaters has, in reality, been a frontier operation. By careful over-all design, progress has been made in overcoming the constant threats of tube overheating, tube leakage, and tube-support failures.

In the early designs, convection superheaters were placed above or behind a deep bank of boiler tubes in order adequately to shield them from the fire or from the highest temperature gases. They were fitted with flooding connections to fill them with water for protection during the starting-up periods. Flooding caused much more trouble than it prevented. Scale formed, tube seats leaked, and tubes warped and twisted from the quenching of hot spots at the steam pockets caused by partial evaporation of the flooding water. Attempts to use scale-free water and to develop adequate circulation within the superheater tubes proved impractical. These difficulties finally established the principles that water has no place in a superheater and that the tubes must be protected against overheating, during periods of starting-up or of no steam flow, by limitation of the firing rate and therefore the gas temperature to which the uncooled tubes can be subjected. The adoption of these principles sometime before 1920 eliminated these early starting-up difficulties.

Steam Mass Flow

As steam temperatures increased, the necessary increase in the superheater surface, for the original location, made it more economical to move the superheater closer to the fire, where the reduction in surface justified the required modifications in design. The first big step was taken in 1922, when the superheater was brought from its overdeck position to the interdeck location, one arrangement shown in Fig.

12, Chapter 1. This new location brought into relief many defects in design which were not apparent with the superheaters located in the original lower gas temperature zone. Steam distribution difficulties brought on the use of ferrules to increase tube entrance loss in order to equalize the flow in each tube. Further advances in capacity and temperature duty revealed instances of general overheating of tube metal where "mass flow" (lb steam per hr, sq ft of flow area) was low. This served to emphasize the prime importance of mass flow in superheater design and in turn brought on the multiple-pass superheater with less steam flow area (higher mass flow) but still dependent upon ferrules or their equivalents for steam distribution. The pending demands and the existing limitations showed the fallacy of adding a ferrule pressure drop to the gainful pressure drop of an increased mass flow which, by itself, was adequate to achieve both uniform distribution to the individual tubes and generally lower tube-metal temperatures.

A reassessment resulted in the fundamental conclusion that the average steam mass flow in the superheater tubes must be great enough to give a pressure drop sufficient to distribute the steam among the tubes and that each tube must have the requisite individual mass flow to keep it cooled within safe metal-temperature limits. There have been times when these principles have been laid aside for expediency, but the experience of many years has demonstrated the value of resisting these temptations. The continuous-tube superheater design, either horizontal or vertical, can, in all but extraordinary cases, be adapted to the mass flow principle without the use of ferrules. The values of steam mass flow for convection superheaters given in Table 1 should serve as a general guide.

TABLE 1
Range of Steam Mass Flow Values
For Convection Superheaters

| Temperature, F | | Steam Mass Flow, |
Steam	Gas	lb/hr, sq ft flow area
less than 750	1200	75,000-150,000
700-800	1600	250,000-350,000
800-900	2400	400,000-500,000
900-1000	2400	500,000-600,000
1000-1100	2400	700,000 and higher

Radiant Superheaters

With the continuous-tube design, it has been possible to place the superheaters closer to the fire, behind one row of boiler tubes as shown in Fig. 25, Chapter 17, or even in the furnace, as radiant superheaters, with no boiler tubes interposed as in Fig. 6, Chapter 28. The recent sharp advances in total steam temperatures of both primary and reheat sections have made it apparent that the large amount of heat absorption required in the superheaters and the reheaters calls for such an extravagant amount of low duty surface that in some cases it is more economical to put some of the surface in the furnace for radiant absorption of superheat.

Experimental installations of radiant superheaters and some commercial installations made under special circumstances have illustrated the additional problems in design which must be met. They have vindicated the accepted practice of not locating the superheater any closer to the fire than the economics of good design make necessary.

With radiant superheaters, it is necessary to adhere faithfully and conscientiously to the principles of mass flow in design and slow firing with dry tubes in starting-up which were developed for the convection superheaters. It is necessary to avoid even the minor infractions which might occasionally be permitted with convection superheaters. In addition it is important in applying these principles to the design and operation of radiant superheaters to guard against the much more severe temperature conditions and temperature stresses which can come about with such uncanny suddenness and severity from disproportionately minor lapses in anticipated functioning of the equipment. The principal reason for this is that in the usual radiant superheater the tubes are heated on only one-half of their circumference by an input much greater per sq ft than is imposed completely around the circumference of convection tubes.

The really new factor in radiant superheater design is the support of the tubes to prevent distortion from the temperature stress which, though higher, may be kept within suitable limits by the more refined application of the convection superheater principles.

Development of Reheaters

The development of reheaters has followed somewhat in the wake of the development of superheaters. The same fundamental considerations governing superheater design apply to reheater design. The pressure drop in reheaters, however, is critical, because if it is not held to a very low value, the gain in heat rate, made possible by the reheat cycle, may be completely wiped out. Nevertheless the same relentless demands of good steam distribution, and proper tube cooling, by adequate steam mass flow are the important functions to serve by improved designs and evaluations in the less robust reheater.

Difficulties from tube seat leakage and handhole cap leakage respond to the same preventive measures taken in the operation of superheaters, namely: keep the headers thoroughly drained of condensate, and prevent other tube to header temperature differences, particularly during starting-up, by protection of the

headers and several inches of the tube near the seats from hot gases.

Relationships in Superheater Design

Effective superheater design calls for the resolution of related, and some potentially discordant, factors. The outstanding considerations are:

1) The steam temperature desired.
2) The superheater surface required to give this steam temperature.
3) The gas temperature zone in which the surface is to be located.
4) The type of steel, alloy, or other material best suited to make up the surface and the supports.
5) The rate of steam flow through the tubes (mass flow), which is limited by the permissible steam pressure drop, but which in turn exerts a dominant control over tube metal temperatures.
6) The arrangement of surface to meet the characteristics of the fuels anticipated, with particular reference to the spacing of the tubes to prevent accumulations of ash and slag, or the provision for removal in their early stages, of such formations.
7) The physical design and type of superheater as a structure.

A change in any one of the first six items will call for a counterbalancing change in all other items.

Even the steam temperature desired, which it would appear must surely be fixed and from which a design can start, is subject to uncertainty. This is so because in advanced power station design the steam temperature desired is the maximum for which the superheater designer and manufacturer can produce an economical structure. Economics in this case requires the resolution of two interrelated factors—first or investment cost and the later cost of upkeep for minimum operating troubles, outages and replacements. A higher first cost is warranted if the upkeep cost is thereby reduced sufficiently to cover in a reasonable time the extra initial cost. The steam temperature desired is, therefore, based on the complete coordinated knowledge available for the optimum evaluation of the combination of the other five items, and by the necessities of the particular project.

After the steam temperature desired is actually set or specified, the next consideration is the amount of surface necessary to give this superheat. The amount of superheater surface required is dependent upon the four remaining items, and since there is no single correlation, the amount of surface must be determined by trial, locating it in a zone of gas temperature which is likely to be satisfactory. In the so-called standard boilers, the zone is fairly well established by the physical arrangements and by the space preempted for superheater surface.

The steam mass flow, the steam pressure drop, and

the superheater tube-metal temperatures are calculated after the amount of surface is established for the trial location and the trial tube spacing. The proper type of material is then selected for the component tubes, headers, and other parts. If these trial results do not show the best arrangement of all the parts, then additional trial arrangements must be made to obtain an optimum combination which will:

1. Require an alloy of lesser cost.
2. Give a more reasonable steam pressure drop without jeopardizing the tube temperatures.
3. Give a higher steam mass flow in order to lower the tube temperatures.
4. Give a different spacing of tubes which will provide more protection against the ash accumulations with uncertain types of fuel.
5. Permit closer spacing of the tubes, thereby making a more economical arrangement for a fuel supply which is known to be favorable.
6. Give an arrangement of tubes which will reduce the draft loss for an installation where draft loss evaluation is crucial.
7. Permit the superheater surface to be placed in a higher gas temperature zone, with a consequent saving in surface which will compensate for deviation from a standard arrangement.

It is possible to achieve a practical design with optimum economic and operational characteristics and with all criteria reasonably satisfied, but a large measure of experience and the application of sound physical principles are required for satisfactory results.

The methods of calculation for superheater performance are given in Chapter 11. It is appropriate, however, to include here Figs. 3 and 4 to show how tube temperatures are governed by steam mass flow and by its related forces of steam viscosity and specific heat. The curves illustrate the advantage, when the superheater is placed in a zone of high heat input, of putting steam with the highest pressure and lowest superheat through the high-duty tubes. The application of these factors is illustrated in the superheater surface problem, Chapter 11.

It is established practice to admit saturated or low-temperature steam to any radiant superheater tube elements. A minor portion of this advantage in the use of low-temperature steam is sometimes sacrificed by the addition of a small amount of superheat before the steam enters the radiant or high-duty section. This is done to make dry and nonadhering the very small amount of foreign matter carried over, even in good quality steam, and thus avoid overheating of the tubes and possible failure by preventing the internal deposit of this foreign matter in the zone where the steam changes from the wet to the superheated condition.

If the steam mass flow is higher than necessary for adequate safety, there is, of course, a needless penalty in steam pressure loss. This must be avoided. Good practice calls for sufficient steam mass flow to limit the steam-film temperature drop between the inside of the tube and the steam flowing within it to not more than 100 F. The corresponding pressure drop through the superheater need not exceed 10 per cent of the boiler operating pressure.

Effect of Gas Mass Flow

Tube-metal temperatures are affected in the reverse order by gas mass flow, that is, they increase with gas mass flow. If the transfer of heat is entirely by convection, the superheater tube-metal temperature will change the same amount by gas mass flow variation as by steam mass flow variation—all at the same gas temperature. Actually in the higher-duty zones of modern superheaters, a substantial portion (about one third) of the heat is transferred by radiation, and, consequently, a given percentage change in gas distribution will have a lesser effect on superheater tube temperatures than the same percentage change in steam mass flow. In the zones of high gas temperature, but away from the direct radiation of the high-temperature cavities, a given percentage change in gas mass flow may have a greater effect upon metal temperatures than the same percentage change in

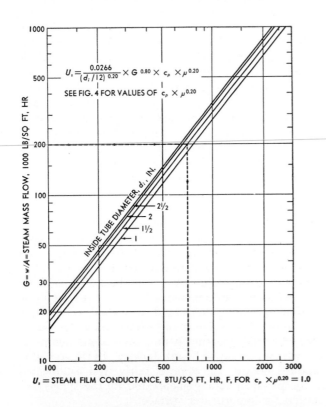

Fig. 3. *The effect of steam mass flow on steam film conductance for several tube sizes (ID)*

steam mass flow. The percentage of heat transferred by convection is high, and a change in gas distribution may result in a higher gas temperature and a higher temperature difference between gas and steam. Superheater tubes sometimes fail at locations beyond the zone of maximum expected heat input because of this.

The gas mass flow is limited primarily by factors other than superheater metal temperatures. A gas mass flow of about 6000 lb per hr, sq ft of free-flow area is generally the economic limit, from the standpoint of draft loss, in the low gas temperature zones. This gas mass flow, with its accompanying close tube spacing, may be maintained to a gas temperature of 1500 F where the limitation of 1) draft loss economics, 2) bridging of ash deposits from fusion, and 3) tube erosion from high velocities with high dust-loading pyramid. Above this 1500 F zone, except for units fired with clean fuel, the slag or dirt problem tends to take precedence and, entirely separate from the other limitations, makes the wider tube spacing necessary. The minimum distances considered adequate call for gas mass flows of less than 3000 lb per hr, sq ft of free-flow area and automatically take care of the other two limitations.

Relationships in Reheater Design

The same general similarity exists between superheater and reheater considerations, but the reheater is limited in ruggedness of design by the permissible steam pressure drop. Steam mass flows in reheater tubes should be sufficient to keep the steam-film temperature drop below 150 F. Ordinarily this may be done with less than 5 per cent pressure drop through the reheater itself. This allows another 5 per cent pressure drop for the reheater piping and valves without exceeding the usual allowable total maximum.

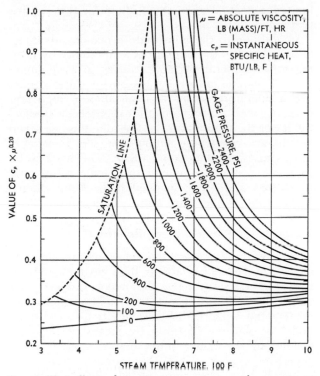

Fig. 4. The effect of steam temperature and pressure on the value of the specific heat-absolute viscosity relationship for steam. For a given steam mass flow, the steam film conductance decreases as this value decreases (see Fig. 3)

Metals for Tubes

Steel is the basic metal for superheater and reheater tubes. Its use should be extended as far as economically feasible and technically sound. Oxidation resistance rather than maximum allowable stress considerations usually limits the use of plain carbon steel. Carefully selected alloys should be used beyond the economic

TABLE 2

Superheater and Reheater Tubes
Maximum Allowable Design Stresses, lb per sq in.

Material	ASME Spec. No. & Type	900	950	1000	1050	1100	1150	1200	1350	1500
Carbon steel	SA210	5,000*	3,000*							
Carbon-Mo	SA209, T1a	12,500	8,500							
Croloy 1¼	SA213, T11	13,100	11,000	7,800	5,500					
Croloy 2¼	SA213, T22		11,000	7,800	5,800	4,200				
Croloy 3M	SA213, T21			7,000	5,500	4,000	2,700			
Croloy 5	SA213, T5				5,200	3,300	2,200			
Croloy 9	SA213, T9				5,500	3,300	2,200	1,500		
Croloy 16-13-3	SA213, TP316†				12,200	10,400	8,500	6,800	2,700	1,000
Croloy 18-8Ti	SA213, TP321				13,100	10,300	7,600	5,000	1,500	750

* Permissible, but not current practice above 1000 psi steam pressure.
† Usually uneconomical for superheaters; SA213, TP321 may be used instead.

limits for steel. The common alloys for this application are included in Table 2.

In addition to the immediate economic advantage of using steel to the limit of its adaptability by keeping tube temperatures and stresses to a minimum, there is another important reason for using steel at low temperature rather than an alloy at high temperature, with the same margin of safety in design—the lower the temperature of the tube the less severe will be any quenching action from soot blowing or other causes of temperature shock. This leads to the principle that the minimum tube temperature with the lowest alloy will, in general, be better than a higher tube temperature with a higher alloy.

Supports for Superheaters, Reheaters

Because superheaters and reheaters are generally located in zones of relatively high gas temperatures, it is preferable to have the major support loads carried by the tubes themselves. In horizontal superheaters, the support load is usually transferred to the boiler or water wall tubes by means of lugs, one welded to the boiler tubes and the other to the superheater tubes. These lugs are, in many cases, made of high chromium nickel alloy. Conditions often make it necessary to have these lugs slide on one another in order to provide relative movement between the boiler tubes and the superheater tubes, as in Fig. 5. Other supports, as the link type and the pin and clevis type, also shown in Fig. 5, provide for relative movement between adjacent components of the superheater itself.

With pendant superheaters, the major load usually is carried from the headers above by the superheater

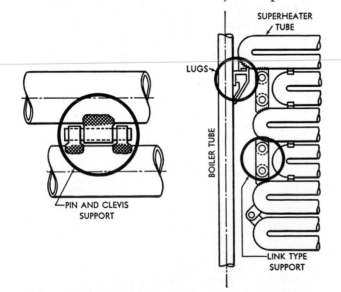

Fig. 5. *Support lugs arranged to permit expansion of horizontal superheater both at main support and within the superheater*

tubes themselves and it is necessary to use lugs only for spacing or for lateral support, all as indicated in Fig. 6.

The same principle applies to the selection of material for supports as for superheater and reheater tubes. It is better to use the minimum metal temperature with the lowest alloy, going to the highest alloys only when proper design requires the use of high temperature.

Experience has shown also that it is good practice to adhere to a second principle, i.e., all parts of the superheater or reheater should be free to move in paths recognized as orderly for all tubes, and any tendency to lateral movement should be eliminated. Any remaining tendency toward lateral movement should be resisted by adequate supports or reinforcements.

Cleaning—Internal

In the early designs of superheaters and reheaters access to tube ends was provided and the tubes were arranged so that they could be turbined for internal cleaning. Current designs of superheaters and reheaters provide for internal cleaning, where such provision does not adversely affect other important features. Access for internal cleaning of the tubes is now subordinated to permit greater freedom in design, so necessary for good performance. The infrequent cleaning required, because of lapses in what is now recognized as good operation, can be done by washing with water or by the use of acid solution which methods do not require physical access to the internal surfaces.

Suggested operating procedures for superheaters and reheaters are given in Chapter 21.

Cleaning—External

In the early designs of superheaters and reheaters little provision was made for external cleaning. The residual space around the superheater was considered sufficient to give the necessary access. In modern units, the maintenance of clean surfaces is so important that a design is not considered successful unless it (1) limits external deposits and (2) provides for the ready removal of minor accumulations.

Tube Spacing

Spacing of the individual tubes is determined by first cost, permissible draft loss, and cost of cleaning to give maximum economy. A spacing (in a direction at right angles to the gas flow) of 1 in. in the clear, as with 2 in. diameter tubes on 3 in. centers, is adequate for most fuels when the gas temperatures are less than 1500F. Above 1500F, 1 in. clear spacing is usually not enough because of the bridging of slag or of fused ash residues. The temperature varies with the fuel.

Increases in tube spacing have often been simply made by omitting every other tube, giving a clear space of 4 in., for instance, with 2 in. tubes on 6 in. centers. This space increment is determined by trial and error, adopting a spacing which does not impose any new unnecessary costs in multiple drilling or in deviation from standard shop practices. Four-in. openings have been adequate in most instances, where furnace designs have been conservative and where the gas temperatures entering the superheaters have been below the initial deformation temperature of the ash particles. It has been ample also with oil fuels where the softening temperature of the cementing materials has been between 1500 and 1600F (see Chapter 18).

There is no truly rational method of adjusting the clear distances between tubes, or the tube spacing, as a sole function of the slag or dirt problem. Sometimes a clear space of 3 in. would be sufficient, but the manufacturing and other related considerations of spacing 2½ in. tubes on 5½ in. centers, might involve so much additional cost that it would be more economical to have the first few rows of tubes on 9 in. centers, or multiples of 4½ in. center to center "standard" spacing in the closer spaced areas.

Until provision for preventing deposits, or for removing those which do form, can be based on fully developed knowledge of this important subject, it is best to use a tube spacing deemed proper from the many other standpoints of design and function and then to adjust this spacing within practical limits to suit the accumulated experience of cleanliness.

Tube Sizes

Plain cylindrical tubes of 2 in. outside diameter have predominated in the history of superheaters and reheaters. Smaller diameters tend toward higher pressure drops and more difficulty in the maintenance of good alignment. Larger diameters unnecessarily bring about higher pressure stresses and undesirable rigidity. Recent designs, however, have called for greater spans between supports for horizontal superheater tubes, and for wider tube spacing or fewer

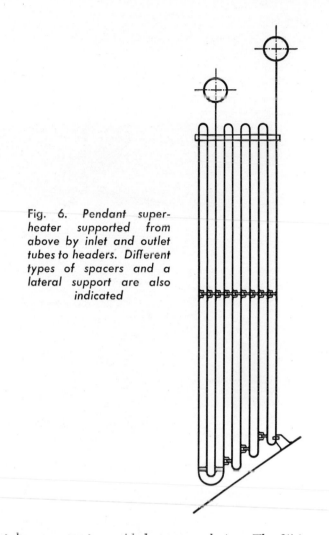

Fig. 6. Pendant superheater supported from above by inlet and outlet tubes to headers. Different types of spacers and a lateral support are also indicated

tubes per row to avoid slag accumulation. The 2½ in. tube has met these new conditions with a minimum sacrifice of the smaller tube advantages. As temperatures increase, the allowable stresses may force the return to the smaller diameter, thinner-walled tube. Extended surface of superheater tubes by the use of fins, rings, studs, or in whatever form not only makes gas side cleaning difficult but the added thickness increases metal temperature and stress where they cannot be tolerated. Plain tubes are used almost exclusively in modern superheater practice.

CONTROL ROOM FOR A LARGE CENTRAL STATION

STEAM TEMPERATURE ADJUSTMENT AND CONTROL

THE use of superheat and reheat with ever higher steam temperatures, in the constant effort to increase efficiency in power generation, makes accurate regulation of steam temperature by adjustment and control vital to successful operation.

Increases in temperature have closely followed advances in metallurgy, and it is therefore of the utmost importance to regulate steam temperature within narrow limits, going as high as possible to increase efficiency and still keep within a safe margin to avoid metal failure. Of equal importance is the control of the fluctuations in temperature from uncertainties of operation.

Saturated steam is used almost universally for processing purposes, and, therefore, the regulation of steam temperature is usually not a problem in this application since the simple operation of controlling the pressure also controls the temperature. However, accurate regulation is required in all cases where superheated steam is used as a catalyst.

While superheat and reheat steam temperatures in power generation are profoundly affected by rating, other important independent variables in operation must be controlled if the temperature is to be regulated within the close limits required. Among these variables are excess air, feedwater temperature, and changes in fuel affecting burning characteristics and ash deposits on the heating surfaces.

Improvement in the heat rate of the modern boiler unit and turbine, as indicated in diagrams of Fig. 10, Chapter 10, results in great part from the high cycle efficiency possible with high steam temperatures. The importance of regulating the steam temperature within narrow limits is evident since a change of 25 F will mean a change of approximately 0.7 per cent in the heat rate.

Other important reasons for accurate regulation of steam temperature are to prevent failures from overheated parts of the superheater, reheater, or turbine, to keep from reducing turbine clearances to the danger point from thermal expansion, and to avoid erosion from excessive moisture in the last stages of the turbine.

Standard performance practice for steam-generating equipment, accepted by the ABAI, permits a tolerance of plus or minus 10 F in a specified steam temperature. Years ago when superheat was seldom more than 100 F, this represented approximately 10 per cent of superheater absorption; however, with present day superheats of 400 F or more, this tolerance corresponds to approximately 2.5 per cent of superheater absorption. Variations in furnace wall heat absorption will produce some change in steam temperature, but since this is only one of many factors affecting superheater absorption, the desirability of reliable means of steam temperature regulation is evident.

Meanings of Terms Used

Brief definitions of the various terms used in discussing steam temperature regulation are given below.

Adjustment: A change in the arrangement of equipment which affects steam temperature but which cannot be used to vary steam temperature during operation. Example—removal of superheater tubes.

Control: Regulation of steam temperature during operation without changing the arrangement of equipment. Example—operation of an attemperator.

Attemperator: An apparatus that will reduce the temperature of a superheated vapor or of a fluid passing through it. Example—A bank of tubes, submerged in the boiler water, through which all or a part of the superheated steam is diverted to give up some of its heat, thereby regulating the final steam temperature.

Radiant Superheater: A superheater which receives heat primarily by radiation, as when it forms part of the furnace enclosure.

Convection Superheater: A superheater which receives

heat primarily by convection. Such a superheater is usually separated from the furnace by one or more rows of boiler tubes.

Effect of Operating Variables

Many operating variables affect steam temperatures. To maintain constant steam temperature, means must be provided to compensate for the effect of such variables, the most important of which are:

1. *Load*. As the load increases, both the gas temperature and the weight of gas increase. In a convection superheater, steam temperature increases with increased load since heat absorption by convection, which is augmented by increased furnace exit temperature and gas flow, increases more rapidly than steam flow, whereas in a radiant superheater, steam temperature decreases as the load increases. In the case of the radiant superheater, this is so because furnace temperature does not increase with increasing load in anywhere near the same proportion as the steam flow through the radiant superheater elements. Sometimes a convection and a radiant superheater of proper proportions are installed in series in a single steam-generating unit to maintain substantially constant steam temperature over a considerable range of load.

2. *Excess Air*. For a change in the amount of excess air entering at the burners there is a corresponding change in the quantity of gas flowing over a convection superheater, and therefore an increase in excess air tends to increase steam temperature.

3. *Feedwater Temperature*. Increase in feedwater temperature causes a reduction in superheat since, for a given steam flow, less fuel is fired and less gas passes over the superheater.

4. *Heating-Surface Cleanliness*. Removal of ash or slag deposits from heat-absorbing surface ahead of the superheater will reduce gas temperature and steam temperature. Removal of deposits from superheater surface will increase superheater absorption and raise steam temperature.

5. *Use of Saturated Steam*. If saturated steam from the boiler is used for auxiliaries, such as pumps and fans, or for soot blowers, an increased firing rate is required to maintain constant main steam output, and steam temperature increases.

6. *Blowdown*. The effect of blowdown is similar to the use of saturated steam but in lesser degree because of the low enthalpy of water as compared with steam.

7. *Burner Operation*. The distribution of heat input among burners at different positions or a change in the adjustment of a burner will usually have an effect on steam temperature.

8. *Fuel*. Variations in steam temperature may result from changing the type of fuel burned or from changes in the characteristics of a given fuel from time to time.

Regulation of Steam Temperature

As noted above under *Meanings of Terms Used*, "Adjustment" and "Control" are the two means by which steam temperature can be regulated. Everything affecting the regulation of steam temperature belongs in either one or the other of these two classifications.

1. Adjustment

(a) Why Adjustment is Necessary

A power-generating unit usually represents a large capital investment, and means should be provided

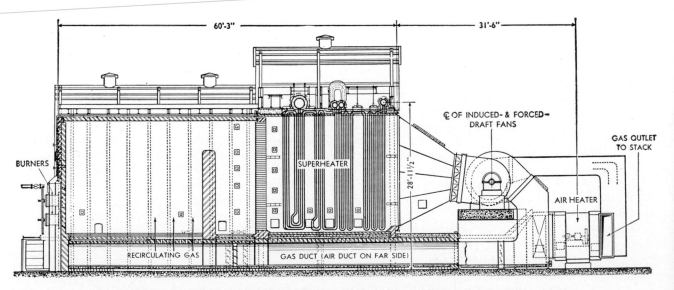

Fig. 1. Separately fired superheater. Steam used in the production of synthetic rubber

13-2

at a reasonable cost for the regulation of steam temperature to meet changed conditions that may be more or less permanent in nature. For instance, if a fuel change that has a considerable effect on steam temperature is anticipated, it is good engineering to provide means to make compensating physical changes in the equipment. This is not necessarily so, however, if the type and range of control provided are adequate to meet the changing requirements without loss in boiler efficiency.

An important application of means for adjustment in regulating steam temperature occurs where the actual operating conditions depart, as they often do, from the conditions on which the design is based. To provide for ultimate adjustment to meet such variations in operation, allowance should be made in the design for the required change at minimum expense.

Quite often a plant is designed with some future change in mind that would affect steam temperature as, for example, a change in fuel or a change from one operating pressure to another. Here again the steam-heating elements (superheater and reheater if used) must be designed having in mind economical means of adjustment when required.

(b) Means of Adjustment

The basic means of adjustment for regulating steam temperature is to modify the steam-heating elements by adding or removing heating surface. A good design should provide for an economical means of doing so.

Adjustment is also possible by a reduction or increase in the saturated-steam surface ahead of the steam-heating elements. Such changes in the convection surface will modify the gas temperature at the inlet to these elements. If saturated surface is to be removed (to increase steam temperature), this type of adjustment is relatively simple and in general will cost less than changes in the surface of the steam-heating elements. However, to add surface in this manner (to decrease steam temperature) is likely to be difficult and expensive or even impractical.

The gas temperature at the superheater inlet can be increased or decreased, without change in the convection surface ahead of the superheater, by changing the effectiveness of the heat-absorbing surface in the furnace by addition or removal of refractory covering on parts of the furnace surface. While the addition of refractory to water-cooled furnace surfaces can have a favorable effect on combustion and carbon loss, refractory should not be added in areas where undesirable ash would deposit.

Probably the most frequent cause of the need for adjustment in regulating steam temperature is the deposit of ash in some form on the surface of saturated and steam-heating elements. This con-

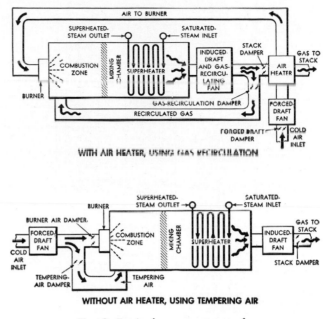

Fig. 2. *Typical arrangements for separately fired superheater*

dition can usually be corrected by simple changes in soot and slag blowers or changes in their operating schedules.

One of the easiest, least expensive, and most effective means of adjustment in regulating steam temperature is to change the gas mass flow over the steam-heating elements by baffle changes if the design of the unit will permit such changes. Several of the so-called standardized boilers, especially in the smaller sizes, have an adjustable baffle suitable for steam temperature regulation. By means of this design, it is possible to vary the steam temperature range as much as 20 per cent. The limit of varia-

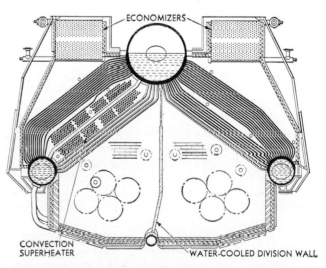

Fig. 3. *Two-furnace marine boiler. Superheat controlled by adjusting furnace firing rates*

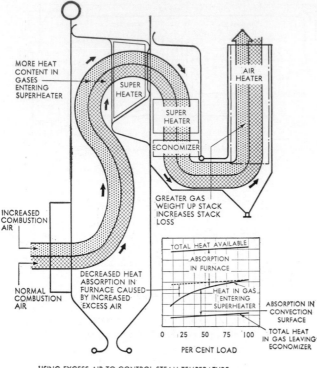

USING EXCESS AIR TO CONTROL STEAM TEMPERATURE

Fig. 4. Steam temperature control by use of increased excess air

tion is the effect on draft loss and efficiency. A 10F change in the temperature of the gas at the exit end of the boiler unit will affect efficiency by about 0.25 per cent.

2. Control

(a) Why Control is Necessary.

Regulating steam temperature within required limits by means of control is necessary, at least in units for high steam temperature, to correct fluctuations due to operating variables noted above.

To hold the optimum heat rate of the turbine, designed to utilize full first stage pressure over a given load range, it is essential to regulate steam temperature over this range by an effective means of control.

The time in which a turbine may be brought to full load is established by the turbine manufacturer in accordance with a safe steam temperature-time curve. Since the temperature of the steam is directly related to the degree of expansion of the turbine elements and consequently the maintenance of safe clearances, it must be regulated within permissible limits by some means of accurate control.

The removal of feedwater heaters for servicing may be cited as an instance of variable operation. To maintain the same load, with the feedwater heaters out, will require an increase in the heat in-

put to the boiler unit with a corresponding increase in superheater absorption. Unless some means of control is available for regulating steam temperature to cover this condition, a drop in load might be required to protect both the steam heating elements and the turbine.

(b) Means of Control.

Among the means of control for regulating steam temperature are:
Separately Fired Superheater
Excess Air
Gas Recirculation
Divided Furnace Differentially Fired
Burner Selection
Movable Burners
Gas By-pass
Attemperation

Separately Fired Superheater. A superheater completely separated from the steam generating unit and with independent means of firing may serve one or several saturated steam boilers. This arrangement is not economical for power generation where a large quantity of high temperature steam is needed, and its use is largely confined to process industries such as chemical manufacture and petroleum refining to meet special requirements. Since

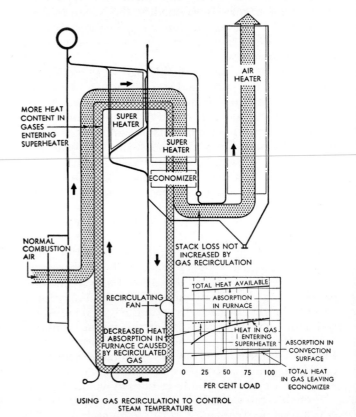

USING GAS RECIRCULATION TO CONTROL STEAM TEMPERATURE

Fig. 5. Steam temperature control by flue gas recirculation

heat absorption can be varied independently of the quantity of steam delivered the separately fired superheater has great flexibility in operation and a wide range of steam temperature regulation at all loads. Either oil or natural gas is customarily used as fuel. An installation designed to superheat 140,000 lb per hr of steam to a temperature of 1400F at a pressure of 50 psi is shown in Fig. 1.

In a separately fired superheater, to keep the use of expensive alloys within reasonable limits, it is necessary to reduce the temperature of the combustion gases entering the tube bank. The upper limit should not exceed 1500F to 1900F. One method of tempering the combustion gases is to operate with high excess air values. This increases the stack loss and lowers efficiency. In most instances where a separately fired superheater is used, efficiency is not an important factor. If a higher efficiency is desired and the cost of additional equipment is justified, the combustion gases may be tempered with recirculated flue gas withdrawn from the setting beyond the superheater. Both methods are indicated in Fig. 2.

Excess Air. Boiler operators have long known that the steam outlet temperature of a convection superheater can be increased at fractional loads by decreasing the furnace heat absorption through an increase in the amount of excess combustion air, resulting in an increase in the heat content of the gases entering the convection superheater. The resulting greater gas weight up the stack increases the stack loss, but where the fractional load operation is normally of short duration the drop in boiler efficiency is usually unimportant. Such an arrangement is diagrammatically illustrated in Fig. 4.

Gas Recirculation. Where the loss in boiler efficiency is important and the cost of additional equipment is justified, recirculated flue gas can be used in conjunction with, or in lieu of, higher excess air values to raise the convection superheat temperature over a desired control range of fractional loads. The recirculated flue gas is preferably introduced into the furnace at a location, and in a manner, so that the entering flue gas will reduce the effectiveness of the furnace heat absorption surface, decrease the residence of the hot gas stream in the furnace, and yet not interfere with the process of combustion. Such an arrangement is diagrammatically illustrated in Fig. 5. As with the use of increased amounts of excess air, the furnace heat absorption is decreased, leaving a higher heat content in the gases entering the convection superheater. The heat absorption graphs for the two cases are almost identical. See Figs. 4 and 5.

Use of recirculated gas as a means of raising steam superheat and reheat temperatures as the boiler load decreases has come into wide use in recent years. With properly proportioned and arranged heat ab-

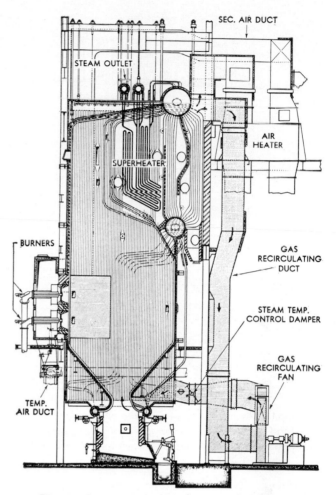

Fig. 6. *One arrangement for gas recirculation*

sorbing surfaces, the steam temperature can be maintained substantially constant over a considerable portion of the boiler load range by introducing the recirculated gas at furnace locations where there is no interference with the combustion process and the heat absorption of the radiant surface is reduced. A boiler unit of this type is illustrated in Fig. 6. The burners are located in a vertical wall and the recirculated gas is introduced at a low velocity through the furnace hopper throat. With this arrangement, the desired steam temperature of 900F can be obtained at 50 per cent of full load by recirculating about 10 per cent of the gas. Without gas recirculation the steam temperature at this load would be about 775F.

Divided Furnace Differentially Fired. In the divided furnace the superheater receives heat from the firing of one section of the furnace only while the other section of the furnace when fired alone generates only saturated steam. Steam temperature is regulated by changing the proportion of fuel input between the two furnaces. This arrangement, similar

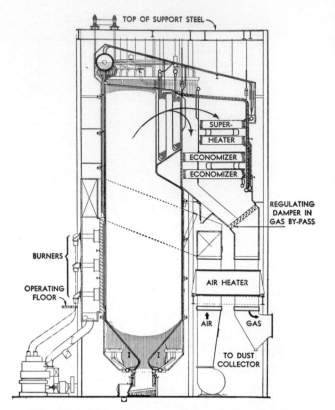

Fig. 7. *In this arrangement the proportion of total gas flowing over part of the super-heater may be varied by regulating dampers*

of the main combustion zone in the furnace. Tiltable corner burners are used for this purpose in boiler units having the furnace outlet to a convection superheater located in the upper portion of the furnace.

Gas By-pass. If the convection banks of a boiler are separated by a gastight baffle into two gas passes only one of which contains superheater surface, the proportion of total gas flow passing over all or part of the superheater may be varied by regulating dampers. An example of this arrangement is shown in Fig. 7. This method has the advantage of low first cost, and high-purity spray water is not required as with a spray attemperator, but there are a number of disadvantages. These are:

1. It is difficult to keep the dampers operable unless they are placed in a cool gas zone.

2. Draft loss through the unit is increased for some designs, particularly if control is desired with alternate fuels.

3. Control is more sluggish than with attemperators.

4. High gas temperature exists at the by-pass dampers if there is no heat-absorbing surface in the gas pass not containing the superheater.

Attemperation. All of the foregoing methods of control in regulating steam temperature are based

in principle to the separately fired superheater, has won wide acceptance in marine practice, where a considerable amount of saturated steam is required, while at sea, for auxiliaries and in maneuvering, and in port, when the main propulsion machinery is idle. The differentially fired divided-furnace method of steam temperature control has also been used in a number of stationary power plants. A typical application of the principle to marine boilers is illustrated in Fig. 3.

Burner Selection. At less than full load, when some burners are idle, it is often possible to regulate steam temperature by operating the burners giving the highest furnace outlet temperature for high steam temperature and by using the other burners for low steam temperature. It is possible to improve this method of control by distributing the burners over a considerable height of the burner wall or by installing a special burner near the top of the furnace.

Movable Burners. Regulation of the steam-super-heating effect of radiant and convection types of superheaters by changing the ratio of radiant to convection heat absorption can also be effected by the use of movable burners operable to shift the position

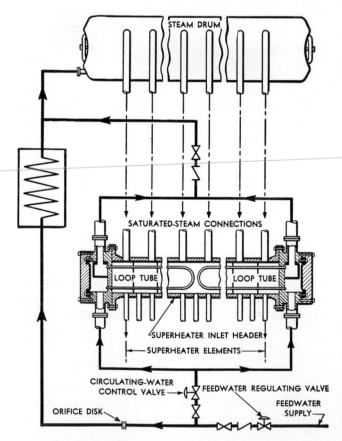

Fig. 8. *Condenser-type surface attemperator*

on varying the amount of heat absorbed by the steam heating elements. In the two general types of attemperators which will be more fully described presently, steam temperature is regulated by removing heat from the steam or diluting high-temperature steam with low-temperature water.

The attemperator may be located in one of three places: between the steam outlet at the drum and the superheater; at some intermediate point between two successive sections of the superheater; or at the superheater outlet.

An attemperator placed between the steam drum and the superheater will condense some of the saturated steam as it passes through and will deliver wet steam of reduced quality and enthalpy to the superheater.

There are important advantages in locating an attemperator between two stages of a superheater. With this arrangement the average steam temperature never exceeds the final steam temperature desired and the steam from the various circuits of the first stage superheater is so thoroughly mixed that it enters the second stage superheater at a uniform temperature. This is, therefore, the most usual location and the only disadvantage is the amount of piping required—from the first stage superheater to the attemperator and from the latter to the second stage superheater.

An attemperator located at the superheater outlet will be somewhat smaller than an interstage attemperator serving the same superheater, since it is handling higher temperature steam, and the piping will be simpler. To keep the cost of alloys required in the construction of the attemperator and the piping within reasonable limits this location

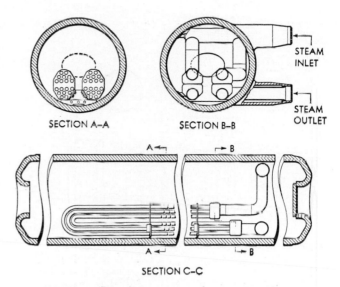

SECTION A–A   SECTION B–B

SECTION C–C

Fig. 10. B&W drum type surface attemperator

should be selected only for moderately high steam temperatures.

Attemperators may be classified as of two types—surface and direct contact. In the surface type the steam is isolated from the cooling medium by the heat exchanger surface. In the direct contact type the steam and the cooling medium (water) are mixed. The surface attemperator includes the condenser type, the shell type, and the drum type. The direct contact attemperator is exemplified by the spray type.

In the condenser type, one form of surface attemperator (also called header type) illustrated in Fig. 8, loop tubes carrying feedwater are installed in the superheater inlet header. Tubes from the boiler steam drum to the superheater inlet header deliver saturated steam which passes over the loop tubes and is partly condensed before entering the superheater tubes. Uniform distribution of the condensed water droplets among the superheater tubes is essential in order to avoid trouble from excessive temperature variation. Also, droplets must not be large enough to quench the hot superheater tubes and cause cracking. This type of attemperator has a limited range of control.

When a shell or drum type attemperator is used interstage, a part of the steam from the primary superheater is diverted to it by an automatic valve. The diverted steam is reduced in temperature by giving up heat to the boiler water and it is then mixed with the rest of the steam from the primary superheater and passes on to the secondary superheater. The final temperature of the steam is regulated by the position of the automatically operated valve which controls the amount of steam diverted through the attemperator.

In the shell type attemperator, illustrated in Fig.

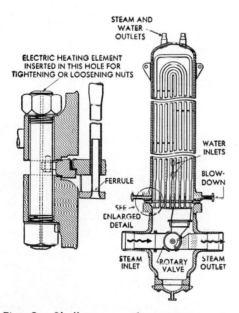

Fig. 9. Shell type surface attemperator

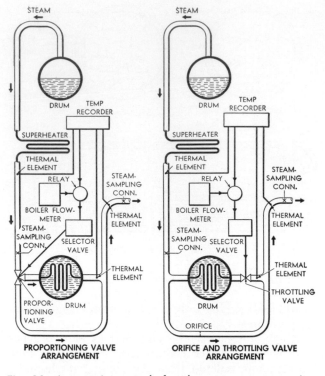

PROPORTIONING VALVE ARRANGEMENT

ORIFICE AND THROTTLING VALVE ARRANGEMENT

Fig. 11. *Automatic controls for drum-type attemperator.
A simplified arrangement is possible with manual controls*

9, a bundle of tubes through which the superheated steam flows is fitted in a cylindrical vessel through which cooling water circulates. A valve in the base of the shell diverts through the tubes the proper proportion of the superheated steam to give the final steam temperature desired. A positive flow of water in the shell at all times is assured by connection to the boiler circulating system. Thermal-sleeve ferrules at the steam inlet ends connect the tubes to an inlet box which protects the tube sheets from severe thermal stresses. Disadvantages of this type of attemperator are the relative inaccessibility of the tubes and tube sheet for inspection and the tendency for sludge to collect on horizontal surfaces.

A more satisfactory design of surface attemperator is the drum type (see Fig. 10), in which tube loops are submerged in one of the boiler drums, and the required portion of superheated steam passes through the tubes. Difficulties with boiler-water deposits are avoided, and an additional high-pressure shell is not required. It may be necessary, however, to increase the size of the boiler drum to accommodate the attemperator tubes, and where this is not advisable the amount of attemperation and therefore the range of steam temperature control are limited by the number and length of tubes for which space is available.

In the drum type, steam temperature is regulated by control of the proportion of total superheated steam flow through the attemperator. In one method of control, a proportioning valve receives all of the superheated steam, diverting some of it to the attemperator while the remainder goes through a by-pass. In another method, suitable for comparatively low temperatures, an orifice is fitted in the by-pass line to give the pressure drop required to divert some of the superheated steam through the attemperator, and a throttling valve is located at the attemperator outlet. By this method a simple valve is used in place of the more elaborate proportioning valve, and since only attemperated steam flows through, construction suitable for high temperature is not required. The two methods are illustrated in Fig. 11. Steam temperature regulation with a submerged-type attemperator can be of the same order as that shown for a spray attemperator, Fig. 13.

Of the direct-contact type, as differentiated from the surface type, the spray attemperator, illustrated in Fig. 12, has proved most satisfactory for regulating steam temperature. Water of high purity is introduced into the superheated-steam line through a spray nozzle at the throat of a venturi section within the line. Because of the spray action at the nozzle and the high velocity of the steam through the venturi throat, the water quickly vaporizes, mixes with, and cools the superheated steam. An important feature of construction is the continuation of the venturi section into a thermal sleeve, downstream from the spray nozzle, to protect the high-temperature piping from shock by incompletely evaporated water droplets striking the hot surface.

The spray attemperator provides a quick-acting

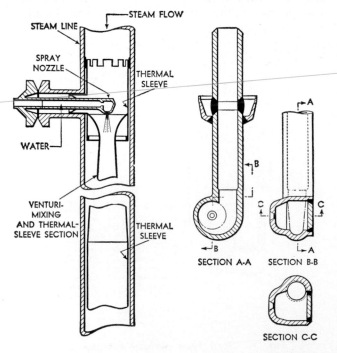

Fig. 12. *Spray attemperator showing thermal sleeve*

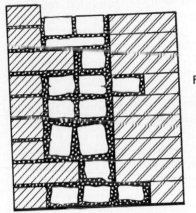

Fig. 3. Dece[...]
work. Uns[...]
deficient i[...]
cour[...]

yet, the core of the wall is improperly [...]
shown in Fig. 3, which is also deficient [...]
courses for so thick a wall. Such a wall is [...]
give trouble because it is not bonded pr[...]
therefore is not stable. The relative positi[...]
and outer courses can be quickly checke[...]
a door or other opening in the wall.

While fire clay alone has been used a[...]
in the outside courses of a solid firebrick [...]
tighter construction is obtained by using [...]
made from ground firebrick (calcined fire [...]
clay and Portland cement. Although th[...]
varies somewhat a typical mix by weight [...]
60 per cent ground firebrick, 30 per cen[...]
and 10 per cent Portland cement. For t[...]
courses, as illustrated in Fig. 4, it is neces[...]
firebrick ⅛ in. to ¼ in. undersize in orde[...]
for a reasonable thickness of mortar joint [...]
be pointed up from the outside when join[...]
due to expansion. In this way, the bric[...]
still be laid up course for course with t[...]
bonding through the full thickness of [...]
When red brick, which is smaller than f[...]
suitable for the outside courses (a thick m[...]
(lime, sand and cement) is also required [...]
course for course with the firebrick.

The temperature gradient through a pr[...]
structed wall is indicated in Fig. 4. If th[...]
of the wall is decreased due to erosio[...]
spalling or any other cause the temperatu[...]
will change as of the order shown. The l[...]
remaining portion of the wall also incre[...]
average temperature increases and failur[...]
fore accelerated.

In any solid brick wall construction, the [...]
effect of temperature and load on the br[...]
principal factor in its failure. The weig[...]
lowermost course of brick in any wall is [...]
for every foot in height. The lowermost [...]
brick in a wall 25 ft. high will, therefo[...]
pressure of approximately 25 psi. The AS[...]
ard hot load test permits 1-½ per cent d[...]

THE "SETTIN[...]
rounds t[...]
a water-[...]
extended by [...]
parts of the [...]
simple brick v[...]
or without ins[...]
covered with [...]
without steel [...]

Brick Setting[...]

From the [...]
commercial u[...]
made of speci[...]
peratures bet[...]
are made fron[...]
are called fi[...]
clay are now [...]
refractories, [...]
refractoriness [...]

In the ear[...]
air, low effic[...]
refractory lin[...]
A reasonably [...]
or even dry, [...]
Air leakage [...]
prolong the [...]
the advent [...]
firing, oil a[...]
higher temp[...]
service requ[...]
more severe [...]

Shortly b[...]
evident that [...]
fractories v[...]
boiler furna[...]
unless refra[...]
the develop[...]
B&W was [...]
research in [...]

and sensitive means of control for regulating steam temperature. An example of steam temperature regulation using both gas recirculation and attemperation is shown in Fig. 13. It is important that the spray water be of highest purity, since solids entrained in the spray water enter the steam and may, if excessive, cause troublesome deposits in superheater tubes, piping, or turbine blades. High-pressure heater drains are a source of extremely pure water but require a separate high-pressure corrosion-resistant pump if used for attemperator supply. Boiler feedwater may be satisfactory provided condenser leakage or makeup does not introduce too much contamination. The total solids concentration in the spray water should not exceed 2.5 ppm.

Reheat Steam Temperature

The need for regulating the temperature of reheated steam and the methods of adjustment and control to do so are, in general, the same as for superheated steam.

When, however, as is usually the case, the reheater and superheater are both part of the same generating unit, the designer does not have the same freedom of action as when only the superheater is used. For instance, the removal of heating surface ahead of the superheater as a means of adjustment to increase superheated-steam temperature will also increase the reheat steam temperature, which may be quite undesirable. Furthermore, to reduce gas temperature below slagging limits for convection tube banks and to give the desired steam temperature, such a large proportion of the total input must be absorbed in the furnace and in the superheater and reheater that the boiler surface is practically eliminated. When this is so, boiler surface ahead of the superheater is not available for adjustment purposes.

Most of the means of control described for regulating steam temperature will also affect the reheat temperature if a reheater is incorporated.

When a spray attemperator is proposed for superheater and reheater steam-temperature control, it is

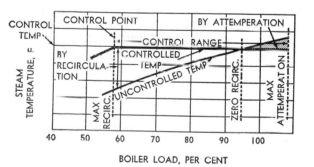

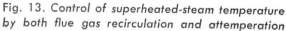

Fig. 13. Control of superheated-steam temperature by both flue gas recirculation and attemperation

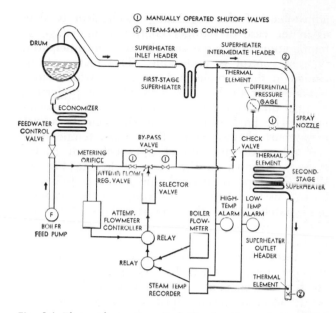

Fig. 14. Three-element control. Single-spray attemperator

necessary to weigh the convenience and good control characteristics of the spray attemperator against reduction in cycle efficiency resulting from diversion of reheater attemperator spray water around the high-pressure turbine.

Instruments and Their Application

Instruments are required to tell the operator how the equipment is performing and to guide him in adjusting the automatic or manual controls to produce the desired results. Among these are instruments for automatic control, indicating, recording, alarm, and for use at test connections.

Instruments for Automatic Control. A single thermal element actuated by the final steam temperature is the simplest and cheapest type of automatic control for adjusting the means provided to give the temperature desired. The temperature-sensitive element may be a thermocouple, resistance thermometer, or bulb-like pyrometer, located in the steam line beyond the superheater outlet. Variation of final steam temperature from the desired standard initiates a correction by adjusting the opening of a gas by-pass damper, moving a proportioning valve to allow a larger or smaller proportion of the total steam flow through a submerged attemperator, or changing the quantity of water supplied to a spray attemperator. A schematic diagram of the elements of such a control system is shown in the view at right in Fig. 11. This type of control is satisfactory for many applications, particularly where steam temperature responds quickly to an adjustment of the regulating mechanism, as in the case of an attemperator at the superheater outlet.

Where the response of steam temperature to the

Bonding of a brick wall shoul[d]
that the weight will be support[ed]
courses of brick at the center and
wall. The bond should also be arr
repairs to the furnace lining with
of brick for this purpose. In the
arrangement, known as the comm[on]
bond, of four header courses a
course on the furnace side is gene
suitable to meet these requiremen
or American bond arrangement f
and 22½ in. walls is illustrated in
rangement for 9 in., and 13½ in. wa
in Fig. 2, with alternate head
courses, is known as English bon
ness is rarely used for furnace wa
only for the cooler areas of the set
through the 9 in. wall since the jo
courses extend through the full t
in the 13-½ in., 18 in. and 22-½ in
are staggered so that there is no o
through the wall even if cracks de
open up due to movement of the

In the 13-½ in., 18 in. and 22-½
nace lining proper is 9 in. thick a
thickness serves as insulation a
purposes. The "step-down" of the
through the wall is shown in Fig.
18 in. and 22-½ in. walls. This st
stability since some of the weig
ferred to the cooler courses shou
posed to the face of the furnace s

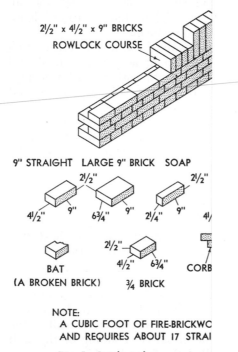

2½" x 4½" x 9" BRICKS
ROWLOCK COURSE

9" STRAIGHT   LARGE 9" BRICK   SOAP

2½"   2½"
4½" 9" 6¾" 9" 2¼" 9"   4/

2½"
4½" 6¾"
BAT   CORB
(A BROKEN BRICK)   ¾ BRICK

NOTE:
A CUBIC FOOT OF FIRE-BRICKWC
AND REQUIRES ABOUT 17 STRAI

Fig. 1. Brickwork terms in c

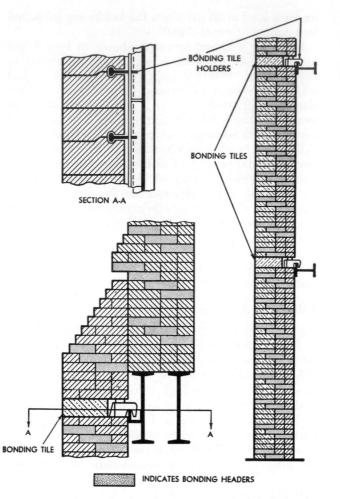

BONDING TILE
HOLDERS

BONDING TILES

SECTION A-A

A   A

BONDING TILE

INDICATES BONDING HEADERS

Fig. 5. Slip wall, showing bonding tile arrangement

firing. The thickness of wall depends upon its height
and the temperature to which it is exposed. It is
usually 13-½ in., 18 in. or 22-½ in. thick.

Solid brick walls form an enclosure around the
boiler and are entirely independent of it. They are
supported at the bottom by a concrete floor or by
steelwork and are restrained by steel buckstays or
beams from outward horizontal movement caused
by furnace pressure or expansion forces. When
heated to operating temperature, each wall will increase in length, height, and thickness due to the
normal reversible thermal expansion characteristics
of firebrick. See typical expansion curves, Fig. 7.

The design of the setting must permit all the
brickwork to expand freely without any interference
with the boiler which also is expanding, frequently
in the opposite direction. If proper provision is not
made for expansion, tremendous forces may develop.
Insufficient expansion clearances on boilers have resulted in tube seat leakage, shearing of boiler support columns, buckling of the walls, and lifting of
the boiler from its supporting steel structure.

Wherever expansion joints are provided, they must
be tightly sealed against air leakage into the boiler
setting in order to attain maximum efficiency. Expansion joints, extending through the wall as shown
in Fig. 8, must be maintained at proper width (usually ½ in.) and must be kept entirely free of mortar.
Good practice is to insert a wooden spacer of correct thickness and width in the joint at the start.
When the wall is completed the spacer is removed
and the outer four inches of the joint (that is, away
from the furnace face) is loosely packed with asbestos rope. In addition, to allow for expansion of the
inner face there is a series of ⅛ in. wide openings,
following the brick joints on the furnace side of the
wall, spaced about 6 feet apart. These joints should
be kept free from mortar by using corrugated card-
board spacers left in place to burn out.

A Stirling boiler, supported at the top from steel
girders and expanding downward is shown in Fig. 9.
The drums lie in saddles which in turn rest on the
support girders. The rear drum saddles are restrained from any front-to-back movement while the
saddles of the middle and front drums are free to
move. Therefore, the boiler moves forward slightly
as it approaches operating temperature. There is
also an increase in width which is taken care of by
endwise movement in the drum saddles. The principal expansion joints required to permit simultaneous
expansion of the boiler and the brickwork in different
directions are also indicated in Fig. 9.

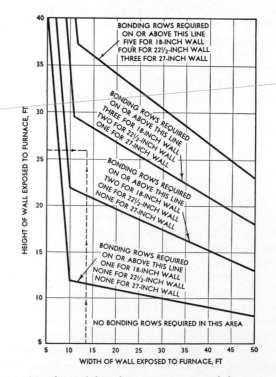

BONDING ROWS REQUIRED
ON OR ABOVE THIS LINE
FIVE FOR 18-INCH WALL
FOUR FOR 22½-INCH WALL
THREE FOR 27-INCH WALL

BONDING ROWS REQUIRED
ON OR ABOVE THIS LINE
THREE FOR 18-INCH WALL
TWO FOR 22½-INCH WALL
ONE FOR 27-INCH WALL

BONDING ROWS REQUIRED
ON OR ABOVE THIS LINE
TWO FOR 18-INCH WALL
ONE FOR 22½-INCH WALL
NONE FOR 27-INCH WALL

BONDING ROWS REQUIRED
ON OR ABOVE THIS LINE
ONE FOR 18-INCH WALL
NONE FOR 22½-INCH WALL
NONE FOR 27-INCH WALL

NO BONDING ROWS REQUIRED IN THIS AREA

HEIGHT OF WALL EXPOSED TO FURNACE, FT

WIDTH OF WALL EXPOSED TO FURNACE, FT

Fig. 6. Number of bonding rows required for varying
thickness, height, and width of furnace firebrick wall

In laying brick around doors, steel or other parts they should not be cut any smaller than absolutely necessary. To get a better fitting job if much cutting is required, a brick saw should be used. In laying brick around drums that extend through a wall an arch construction should be used. If the brick is laid directly on the drum the expansion and contraction as the boiler goes in and out of service will damage the wall and cause air leakage. Clearances around drums, under drum girders and at other points as indicated on the working drawings should be closely held and rechecked when the brickwork is completed.

Sectionally Supported Walls

In large sectionally supported walls the structural load is divided into increments and the expansion is

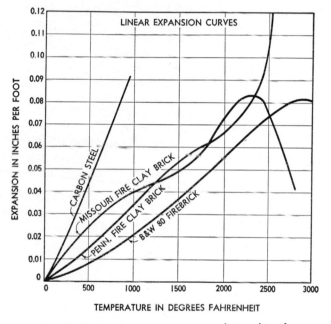

Fig. 7. Expansion-temperature relationship for three types of firebrick, and for carbon steel

sectionalized by suspending the brickwork from castings which are in turn supported by external steelwork. A number of patented constructions of this type are available, among which are: Detrick, Bigelow-Liptak, American Arch and Reintjes. A typical sectionally supported wall is illustrated in Fig. 10. Brickwork expansion is sectionalized in this type of wall. It is sometimes used in oil and gas-fired furnaces.

Sectional walls may be made of tile only, of tile with insulation on the outside or—in the absence of erosive conditions—of insulating firebrick, as shown in Fig. 11. This type of thin wall is generally used in the convection zone of the boiler or in low duty

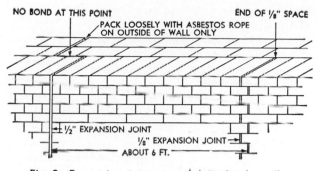

Fig. 8. Expansion joints in solid firebrick walls

furnaces, but may be adapted for use in moderate duty furnaces by facing with high temperature brick or by air-cooling.

Drying-Out

To avoid excessive cracking it is essential that newly laid walls be allowed to expand gradually and uniformly by drying-out all brickwork in a setting slowly from the heat of a slow fire in the furnace. For the brick setting of a large boiler a week to ten days of slow fire is advisable. For smaller boilers and others with water-cooled walls, less drying-out time is required. (See Chapter 21).

Selection of Refractories

(a) Firebrick. For many years firebrick was specified simply by three grades: first quality, second quality and third quality. In the selection of proper firebrick for various requirements these three broad classifications were considered sufficient for all practical purposes. First quality was accepted as suitable for all furnace wall linings; second quality was used for backing-up furnace linings and for lining second and third pass boiler walls; and third quality was used for backing-up furnace and boiler walls.

The chemical composition of the clays used and the manufacturing process determine the refractory qualities of each grade. The better standard firebricks are made from Pennsylvania and Missouri clays. As previously noted, the special high quality B&W firebrick are made from Georgia Kaolin clay, noted for its purity and uniform composition. Careful control of the manufacturing process, including the firing temperature, is a very important factor in the quality of the firebrick produced.

To meet the increasingly severe service of firebrick in modern furnaces, manufacturers of refractories have improved their product and the simple classifications noted above are no longer sufficient. To cover the various qualities now expected the ASTM lists seven grades of firebrick for service as follows: one for "super duty", four for "high duty", one for "intermediate duty", and one for "low duty." The corresponding designation of firebrick quality suitable for these services are: "super duty quality", "first quality", and "third quality." Special firebrick, known as B&W 80 and B&W Junior, developed by B&W for severe service, do not fit into any particular standard specification. (See Table).

The refractoriness of the various grades of firebrick is indicated by "pyrometric cone equivalent" (PCE) and limits are noted for deformation under hot load, permanent linear shrinkage and loss due to spalling. It is, therefore, now possible to specify the particular type of firebrick possessing the qualities desired to meet the requirements of any reasonable duty. A typical laboratory analysis of high and super duty fire clay brick is given in Table in which all characteristics noted have been determined in accordance with ASTM requirements.

It will be noted from the analysis (Table) that the total of fluxes (the designated oxides and alkalies) in the material for the B&W 80 firebrick is very low and consequently the melting-point is higher and the deformation-point is much higher and sharper. Compared with the two other fire clay brick the alumina-silica ratio for B&W 80 firebrick is from about 6 to 20 per cent higher, while for B&W Junior firebrick it is from about 4 per cent lower to 10 per cent higher. However, this is not a true indication of the relative value of B&W 80 and and B&W Junior firebrick, since, for the proportion of alumina and silica in the material, a maximum amount of mullite (a particularly stable form of alumina-silica)

is developed by the special process and by the very high temperature used in the manufacture of these firebrick.

Service records show that B&W 80 and B&W Junior firebrick have an extremely high melting point and that they are unusually resistant to spalling. Neither B&W 80 nor B&W Junior firebrick will change appreciably in dimensions after repeated reheating at high temperature, while many super duty fire clay brick will undergo progressive shrinkage or expansion when reheated a number of times at high temperature. One of the outstanding qualities of B&W 80 firebrick is its capacity for carrying loads at high temperatures which makes its use possible under service temperature conditions near its melting point. It has been installed with safety in furnaces operated at 2950F.

A comparison of the expansion for three types of firebrick is given in Fig. 7. It is evident that the expansion of B&W firebrick is less than the others, and that the point at which permanent volume change begins is 2900F for the B&W 80 compared with 2300F for first quality firebrick.

For high furnace walls where the dead weight load is heavy on the lowermost courses a firebrick with low deformation under load should be selected. The more porous or less dense varieties with low spalling loss are better suited to applications where there is likely to be thermal shock from widely varying furnace temperatures since, under these con-

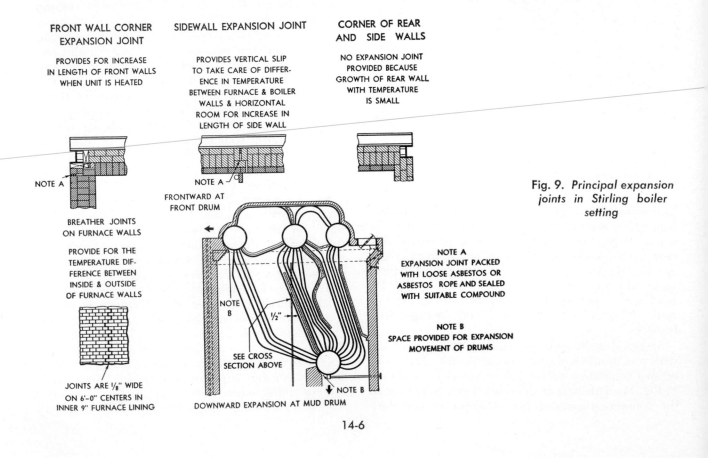

Fig. 9. Principal expansion joints in Stirling boiler setting

ASTM Procedural Test Analysis and Properties of Typical
High Duty, Super Duty Fire Clay Brick, and also B&W Brick

	High Duty	Super Duty	B&W Jr.	B&W 80
PCE (Cone #) ASTM C24-46	32-33	33-34	33	34
Chemical Analysis (%) ASTM C18-45				
Silica	57.1	52.47	53.5	51.9
Alumina	38.1	42.70	41.2	45.4
Ferric oxide	1.5	1.56	1.9	0.6
Titanium oxide	1.72	1.97	2.4	1.7
Calcium oxide	0.53	0.48	0.05	0.1
Magnesium oxide	0.63	—	0.20	0.22
Alkalies	0.71	0.62	0.41	—
Ignition loss	—		0.08	—
Load Test (% deformation) ASTM C16-41				
High duty (Schedule #2)	4.9	—	—	—
Super duty (Schedule #3)	—	5.0-7.0	1.45	0.8
Spalling Test (% loss)				
High duty (ASTM C107-47)	6.0	—	—	—
Super duty (ASTM C122-47)	—	0.0-2.5	*	*
Reheat Shrinkage (%) (ASTM C113-46)				
High duty (Schedule B)	0.85	—	—	—
Super duty (Schedule C)	—	0.0-+1.5	1.6	0.0
Porosity (%) (ASTM C20-46)	18.4	13-15	18.0	16.1
Cold crushing strength (lb) (ASTM C133-39)	1500	1900	4200	4500
Wt. of 2½" x 4½" x 9" brick (lb) (ASTM C134-41)	7.6	8.1-8.4	7.9	7.9

*Actual service records show that B&W 80 and B&W Junior firebrick are unusually resistant to spalling.

ditions, a very dense brick tends to spall. However, where there is likely to be running slag a porous brick will absorb molten slag which will completely alter the brick's characteristics and may make it quite susceptible to spalling because of slag penetration. For service under these conditions a brick should be selected which, on test, shows low water absorption.

Some bricks are particularly well suited to withstand thermal shock. Lower expansion as indicated in Fig. 7 for B&W 80 firebrick is an important favorable factor for this service. Where gas or oil is the fuel, with high furnace temperatures, a firebrick able to withstand extreme temperatures, as indicated by test, should be selected. When gas only is the fuel, insulating firebrick can be used to good advantage.

Firebrick made from materials other than fire clay are used for special service. A firebrick made from silicon carbide is used as a furnace lining adjacent to the fuel bed on certain stoker fired furnaces in an all refractory setting. In addition to high re-

fractoriness and high load carrying properties this material is also a good conductor of heat. The furnace face of such a lining is somewhat cooler than it would be if made of fire clay brick and consequently slag does not adhere as easily.

Firebrick of chromic oxide or chromite and magnesium oxide or magnesite are used for special purposes in brick settings. Chrome brick has the property of extreme refractoriness and is chemically comparatively neutral to the ash from most coals. It has poor load bearing characteristics and its coefficient of expansion is higher than that of the better fire clay bricks. Firebrick made from magnesium oxide or magnesite has a high coefficient of expansion and is, therefore, particularly subject to spalling under conditions of varying furnace temperatures. The application of magnesite brick in boiler furnaces is very limited. However, it does find some use in metallurgical furnaces where the slag tends to be basic in nature and furnace temperatures can be held comparatively constant, ASTM grades A to G.

Special firebrick of the alumina-silica class, de-

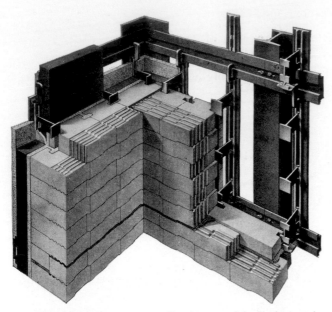

Fig. 10. *Tile wall—sectionally supported from the steel*

pending largely on mullite content, are also used for extremely severe service conditions. Mullite, the final conversion form of any alumina-silica refractory is very stable when subjected to high temperatures, and fluctuating temperatures. A true mullite brick has a ratio of 72 per cent Al_2O_3 and 28 per cent SiO_2. B&W Allmul firebrick, which is an all-mullite brick containing about 75 per cent alumina, was recently developed for extremely severe service conditions in furnace structures. This brick, because of its strong massive mullite crystals can be used for temperatures up to 3200F, has unusual hot-load strength at 3000F and shows no spalling loss when tested under ASTM standards.

There are other materials of which firebrick may be made but they are rarely or never used in firebrick for boiler settings. Brick made of silica has had some limited use but its porosity and tendency to crack due to expansion characteristics makes it generally unsuitable for anything but special applications. In the paper industry silica brick has been used in the bottoms of chemical recovery furnaces of steam producing boilers.

(b) Insulating Firebrick. Insulating firebrick of light weight and porous structure is available in standard firebrick size (9 in. x 4-½ in. x 2-½ in.). It has low heat-conductivity and can withstand direct exposure to furnace gases where slag or abrasion is not present. Since its introduction by B&W in 1931 it has replaced, to a large extent, the combination of dense firebrick and unfired insulating materials formerly used in the construction of industrial furnaces and kilns. It also has been widely used in insulating water cooled boiler walls and to a lesser extent in the outer courses of all-brick settings.

With its low heat-storage capacity the time required to heat up a furnace is reduced as much as 80 per cent. Consequently fuel is saved during the heating-up period and production is increased due to the lower proportion of heat absorbed by the furnace lining in reaching a steady-state condition. For industrial furnaces less steel work is required for supporting the thin light walls and arches, and the foundations can be reduced in weight. Also lighter buckstays may be used for taking the thrust from sprung arches.

When mechanical abrasion and active slag are present insulating firebrick is used as insulation in backing the heavy firebrick of the inner lining. In this type of construction insulating firebrick combines the highest insulating value available with stability which is essential for satisfactory service.

In the B&W insulating firebrick stability has been developed to the highest degree by processing the brick at temperatures higher than those for which its use is recommended, and consequently, within its temperature use limits, it does not lose insulating value with use due to shrinkage and decrease in porosity. Within its service temperature range this insulating firebrick has high resistance against spalling and it will not crumble nor shrink away from the furnace lining to form lanes for the admission of air or the escape of gases. It is made in six grades suitable for temperature limits of 1600F, 2000F, 2300F, 2600F, 2800F, and 2900F. The corresponding average weight in lb. per brick is 1.10, 1.48, 1.52, 2.44, 2.49, and 2.96.

(c) Refractory Mortar. Refractory mortar serves the following functions: (a) as a bond for refractory brick; (b) as a seal to prevent escape of gases and penetration of slag through the joints; (c) as a seal to prevent the penetration of air into the furnace; and (d) occasionally as a wash coating over the face of the brickwork. It comes in two broad classifications: (a) heat-setting mortar and (b) air-setting mortar. In each of these two categories mortar may be classed according to maximum use limits, and again, within these limits, whether supplied in dry or wet form.

Heat-setting mortar has a low initial strength. By vitrification high strength is developed in that part of the mortar nearest the hot face of the furnace when fired to the proper temperatures. Except where vitrification occurs the joint is comparatively "soft" through most of the structure. The strength of air-setting mortar is developed by the action of chemical binders. A strong, welded joint is formed giving the refractory structure a monolithic character.

While no definite rule is followed in the selection of either type of mortar, other things being equal, if the brick is to be salvaged for easier and less cost-

temperatures are too high for satisfactory resistance with brickwork.

3. The general use of pulverized coal precludes the use of an all-brick setting because of the greatly increased "traffic" of ash particles over the furnace wall surfaces, and slagging that may take place at the existing high temperatures.

4. The all-brick setting is not suitable because of the greater economy obtained by including the envelope of the furnace in the boiler heating surface, using boiler water for circulation in the cooling elements which are almost always tubes in one arrangement or another.

5. Relative movement between boiler and furnace due to expansion, a serious problem in an all-brick setting, is automatically reduced or completely eliminated when water-cooling is used.

Types of Water Walls

Water-cooled settings of water-tube boilers as distinct from fire-tube boilers are all fundamentally an arrangement of tubes which form the envelope of the furnace and which are connected to the boiler circulation so that the water inside these furnace wall tubes is the same as that inside the boiler itself. The most commonly used arrangements of water-cooled settings are described below:

(a) Tube and Brick Walls. The arrangement of a tube and brick wall is shown in detail in Fig. 12. The tubes are spaced at intervals and are usually backed with 2½ in. refractory tile. The brickwork is sufficiently cooled by the water circulating in the tubes to permit the use of this type of wall as a part of the setting envelope even in high duty furnaces fired by gas, stoker, pulverized coal or oil if its location is limited to the cooler convection zones of the boiler adjacent to boiler tube banks, convection superheater banks, and economizers. This type of wall may also be used in the main furnace of most gas and oil fired boilers but its use with stokers and particularly pulverized coal should be limited to units where the coals are of a relatively high ash fusion temperature, and to dry ash or hopper bottom furnaces only when pulverized coal is fired. This wall should not be used in the main furnace of slag tap boiler units.

To resist spalling due to temperature differential shocks and to resist flyash erosion the refractory tile behind the tubes (see Fig. 12) should be of first quality material. To prevent air leakage into the setting and to give structural strength the brick or tile are normally laid in air-set mortar. To give a reasonable external surface temperature for comfort in the boiler room, block insulation or insulating firebrick is applied directly behind the refractory brick in back of the tubes and is held in place by expanded metal lath. This is then followed by plastic insula-

14-11

tion in seve...
chicken wire...

In zones o...
against air ...
brick in bacl...
backed by c...
lath. For thi...
crete, is wide...
tion for app...

Fig.
with

ly repairs, heat-setting mortar should be used. Also in thick wall furnaces with large unbroken areas, heat-setting mortar will provide soft, cushioned joints allowing each brick to expand and contract. Where monolithic construction is required, and in relatively thin furnace walls, removable wall or roof sections, bonding brick in door liners or joints, and in low and wide arches, air-setting mortar should be used.

Improvement in mortar in which to lay firebrick has kept pace with the general improvement in refractories to meet the requirements of higher furnace temperatures and more severe service. The material from which mortar is made should be as good or better than the firebrick in the wall. Six types of mortar of high quality, suitable for all the various requirements of firebrick construction are manufactured by B&W. The maximum service temperatures range from 2000F to 3000F.

(d) Refractory Castable. Refractory castable is simply concrete that will withstand high temperatures. Materials, unlike gravel or crushed rock, that are stable at high temperatures and that can be repeatedly heated and cooled without distintegration form the base of refractory castable. These materials, known as refractory calcines or grogs, are blended with suitable hydraulic binders to give the castable cold-setting properties. The initial strength of refractory castable is thus developed, as in ordinary concrete, through the chemical action between the water and the binder. When refractory castable is subjected to temperatures above the vitrification point a strong ceramic bond is formed.

There are seven different types of refractory castable manufactured by B&W, ranging in temperature use limits from 2000F to 3100F, and in melting points from 2390F to 3200F. These types vary in average weight per cu ft as follows: from 93 lb to 194 lb as molded; from 58 lb to 178 lb as dried; and from 53 lb to 174 lb after firing. The heavier weights have characteristics corresponding to those of dense firebrick while the lighter weights have insulating properties similar to those of insulating firebrick.

The primary purpose of refractory castable is to reduce the cost of furnace construction and maintenance. It is as easy to use as structural concrete and can be poured or plastered (not pounded,) into place or sprayed on. It may be used in place of expensive kiln-dried shapes to save cost in new construction and to avoid delays in repairs. By its use it is often possible to arrive at a simpler and more economical furnace design.

Refractory castable has been used to advantage under all kinds of service conditions in the following important applications: for special shapes such as burner tile, peephole blocks, T-tile, and ship-lap tile (cast in place or in mass production); for lining fur-

nace floors or for complete furnaces, especially where extensive use of special shapes are required; for protecting furnace car tops; for forming boiler baffles; for covering studs in water-cooled furnace walls; for lining stacks, dampers, flues and ducts; for protecting furnace steelwork, or ordinary concrete foundations; for backing up dense firebrick; for forming pier walls in stoker-fired boilers; for capping refractory walls; and for patching spalled or eroded brickwork.

(e) Refractory Plastic. Refractory plastic is a blend of refractory calcines or ores and carefully selected clays, mixed to a proper consistency with water. Other materials are sometimes added to give initial cold-setting strength. When refractory plastic is fired at temperatures above the vitrification point, a ceramic bond is formed.

Generally, refractory plastic is used for the same reasons as refractory castable—to speed furnace construction and maintenance, and to eliminate the need for a large inventory of special shapes. But since it

ANY SECTION CAN BE REPLACED WITHOUT DISTURBING ANY OTHER SECTION

Fig. 11. *Insulating firebrick makes an excellent light weight sectionally supported wall for low duty service*

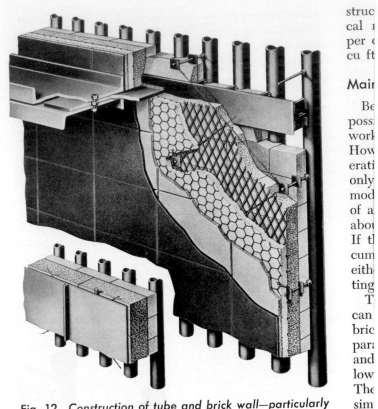

Fig. 12. *Construction of tube and brick wall—particularly suitable for oil and gas fired boilers.*

must be pounded into place its application often requires more labor than in using castable. Nevertheless, before deciding whether to use plastic or castable, a careful investigation of the specific application should be made. Two refractory plastics are marketed by B&W, one known as Plastic Moldable, and the other as Plastic Chrome Ore.

The Plastic Moldable has a temperature use limit of 3000F and a melting point of 3245F. The average weight per cu ft is 140 lb as molded, and 126 lb as fired. It is suitable for service in the great majority of industrial furnaces. In addition to its use for complete furnace linings it also has been applied with excellent results for: burner openings; small door openings; bull rings in Scotch boilers; capping walls; lining high temperature inspection and access doors; forming special shapes in place; and patching deeply spalled and eroded brickwork.

The Plastic Chrome Ore has a melting point of 3300F, is chemically neutral, and is highly resistant to abrasion and the effects of molten metal, acid or basic slags under both oxidizing and reducing conditions. This combination of excellent characteristics has led to its widespread use in such application as: floors and hearths of all types of heating and forging furnaces where mill scale is present; cyanide furnace bottoms; molten-slag-tap boiler furnace floors; water-cooled furnace walls of stud-tube con-

with cold clear water, taking care to avoid an excess of water, using about 5 gallons to a bag which will give a density of 57 lb per cu ft.

The K-20 concrete is applied preferably by gunniting although hand application is acceptable. If applied by hand the refractory should be thrown through the metal lath with the greatest possible force. In either case it is applied to cover the metal lath and to the specified thickness. If block insulation is to be fitted directly to the K-20 refractory it is troweled to a smooth surface but if plastic insulation is to be applied, the surface is left unslicked to obtain better adhesion.

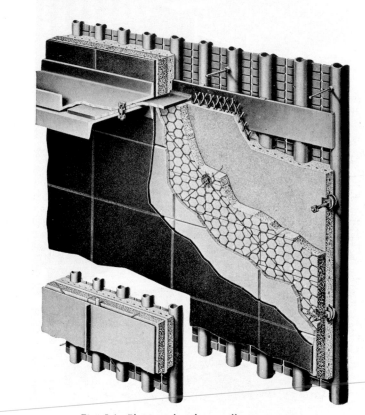

Fig. 14. *Flat stud tube wall construction*

(b) *Closely Spaced Tube Walls.* The closely spaced tube wall, illustrated in A and B, Fig. 13, where the water wall tubes touch one another, may be used, for any type of firing, to form a continuous steel envelope enclosing the furnace of a steam generating unit. When its area is properly proportioned an enclosure of this type will eliminate trouble from excessive accumulation of slag. It is usually sealed against air leakage with refractory concrete, backed with block and plastic insulation.

The castable refractory backing as shown in Fig. 13, is reinforced with expanded metal lath, close to its outer surface, which makes the castable act as a reinforced concrete mat outside the tubes. The

metal lath is installed on the wall first and the castable applied through it so that the lath will act as a support. The block insulation, in turn, is covered by plastic insulation (A in Fig. 13), and a finish coat, of a sealing compound, is trowled on smooth (not required with steel casing, B in Fig. 13).

(c) *Flat Stud Tube Walls.* The flat stud tube wall, illustrated in Fig. 14 is intended for use under conditions similar to those that apply to the use of the closely spaced tube wall. It is somewhat more economical in the use of steel as it is made of tubes spaced at intervals. Each tube has a series of flat rectangular steel plates welded along its entire length on both sides. The plates or studs on two adjacent tubes close the space between them and present a practically continuous metal surface to the furnace. This type of wall is backed by a comparable arrangement of castable refractory, insulation, and casing or plastic insulation finish described for the closely spaced tube wall.

(d) *Partial or Full Stud Tube Walls.* Where a higher furnace temperature is desired than it is possible to maintain with the closely spaced tube or flat stud tube wall because of their high absorption of furnace heat, the partial or full stud tube wall, illustrated in Fig. 15, is used. This type of wall is made of water wall tubes spaced at intervals. The space between tubes is (a) partially closed with two rows of round studs welded to each side of each tube (see Fig. 15), and (b) for the full stud wall the furnace side of each tube as well is covered with studs. Sometimes close spaced tubes are also full studded on the furnace side.

The studs are packed with a chrome base plastic pounded in place or a chrome base castable gunnited or trowelled in place to form a continuous wall. When plastic chrome ore refractory is used it is put on in the closest possible contact with the tubes and studs and is itself thoroughly bonded as it is applied lump by lump. In service the chrome refractory is, in effect, water cooled because of the extended surface heat transfer effect of the studs.

The stud tube wall is sealed against air leakage and insulated in a manner similar to that used for closely spaced and flat stud walls. A wall of this type will be gastight and will offer great resistance to high temperature and slag erosion.

One particular application of the full stud tube wall is in the lower portion of a slag tap furnace where it is necessary to keep the coal ash above its fluid temperature in order to remove it as a liquid. This construction is very resistant to the fluid slag found in this type of furnace. In the upper part of the furnace a partial stud, flat stud or close spaced tube wall construction may be used.

(e) *Slag Tap Furnace Floors.* The floor of a furnace designed for liquid removal of coal ash must hold a pool of liquid slag which sometimes contains a high percentage of iron. This difficult refractory problem is best solved by making the floor of cast iron Bailey blocks clamped tightly to tubes which are part of the boiler steam generating surface, as are the water wall tubes. The blocks are initially covered with several inches of tightly packed plastic chrome ore.

In early water-cooled furnaces the Bailey block was also used extensively for walls. Use of the Bailey block for water walls has been practically abandoned in the United States principally because the construction is more expensive than for other types of wall which are equally or more satisfactory.

Typical Applications of Water Walls

Various wall constructions and refractory applications are illustrated in Fig. 16 showing a B&W type FH integral furnace boiler for firing pulverized coal, oil, or gas either singly or in combination. The furnace cooling surface is proportioned to keep the temperature of the gases leaving the furnace below the ash initial deformation temperature (oxidizing basis) when pulverized coal is fired. This keeps most of the coal ash in the furnace in a dry state and permits it to slide down the sloping hopper to the ash pit (not shown) which may be flooded with water or may be dry and fitted with a water sluice or vacuum system for ash removal. (See Chapter 18 on fuel ash).

The B&W radiant boiler unit shown in Fig. 17 is designed primarily for pulverized coal firing but is capable of full steam output while using oil fuel. To avoid troublesome ash deposits on the tubes of the boiler banks when burning coal, the total furnace cooling surface of this boiler is sufficient to keep the temperature of the gases leaving the furnace below the initial deformation temperature of the coal ash. However, the location of burners and the use of fully studded tubes in the burner area makes it possible to keep the temperature at the furnace floor high enough to melt the coal ash which collects there. The liquid slag which is thus formed drains continuously into a flooded slag tank. The tank is lined with refractory which must be impervious to water (to protect the tank steel) and highly resistant to spalling. Several commercial castable refractories are suitable for this purpose.

Expansion

Minor expansion problems potentially still exist in the various types of water-cooled settings. In these types, while the pressure parts (boiler and furnace) expand together and equally in all their parts, brick or refractory is still present to some degree in many types as a final closure or seal. Local expansion differences between the steel and the re-

fractory are nullified as follows without resort to expansion joints.

1. In the tube and brick wall illustrated in Fig. 12 the wall tubes are spaced so that the operating temperature of the refractory is about twice the temperature of the boiler pressure parts. Since the coefficient of expansion of firebrick is about one half that of steel this arrangement permits a continuous refractory envelope around the boiler setting without expansion joints. This type of boiler setting will remain airtight and will require little or no maintenance.

2. For the closely spaced tube wall, illustrated in Fig. 13, there is a small theoretical difference, at

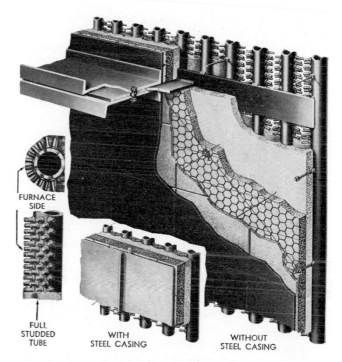

Fig. 15. *Partial and full stud tube wall construction*

operating pressure, between the width and height of the tube wall and the corresponding dimensions of the refractory backing due to the drying shrinkage of the castable (about 0.3 per cent at 600F) plus a slight difference between the expansion of the boiler steel and the castable, the coefficient of expansion of the latter being about ⅔ that of steel. This slight difference in expansion will cause a series of well distributed (by the reinforcing metal lath) hair-line cracks to appear in the refractory backing. This type of enclosure requires very little maintenance and is tight against air leakage.

What is said above for the closely spaced tube wall applies in general to the flat stud tube wall and partial or full stud tube wall, illustrated in Fig. 14 and Fig. 15.

Support and Alignment

By proper support of the integrated unit the relative expansion movements between boiler and furnace are automatically reduced or completely eliminated. It will be noted from the designs illustrated in Figs. 16 and 17 that all parts of each unit are tied together through the pressure parts and that expansion takes place uniformly from the points of support. The points of support indicated in Fig. 17 are at the drum and the side walls, all of which in turn are suspended from the steelwork structure at a common elevation. The principal expansion of this unit is, therefore, downward and lateral, and no joints or slip seals are required to make the unit tight against air infiltration or dust leakage. A different method of support is indicated in Fig. 16. Here the support is from the bottom at both the lower drum and the long side wall. The boiler is free to expand upward and laterally. There is no relative expansion between different parts of the setting, since all pressure parts of the setting are at the same temperature of saturated steam corresponding to the pressure.

To hold the tubes in alignment and as reinforcement against the effect of draft in the furnace and in the boiler passes, the tubes are stayed and fastened together on suitable vertical centers, about 8 ft apart as shown in Fig. 17. It is customary to weld these stay members or tie bars solidly to the tubes, and therefore they lie wholly within the wall insula-

tion, as shown in Figs. 14 and 15. This location keeps the tie bars at tube temperature, so that there is no differential expansion between the tie bars and the tubes. To consolidate the furnace walls further, the tie bars are joined by welding to form continuous bands around the furnace envelope. Buckstays, of the required section modulus to resist vibration and any difference in pressure within and without the setting, are attached to the tie bars by bolting to bracket plates welded to the tie bars. As indicated in Figs. 14 and 15, this method of attachment to the tie bars will permit the buckstays to move up and down with the wall. The section modulus of the buckstay should be sufficient to limit deflection at center of span to a maximum of $\frac{1}{16}$ in. per 1 in. of water difference of pressure within and without the setting.

Another assembly of tie bar and buckstay, illustrated in Fig. 18, shows the tie bar as a continuous band (referred to above) carried around a corner. The tie bar acts as a restraining member, taking the reaction of any horizontal load on the buckstay. This reaction is transferred from the buckstay to the tie bar through the links. The latter also allow for the difference in lateral expansion of the buckstay, which is outside of the installation, and the wall and tie bar, which are inside and at saturation temperature.

Insulation of Modern Water-Cooled Walls

In the days when all boilers had solid brick settings without furnace water cooling, the outside

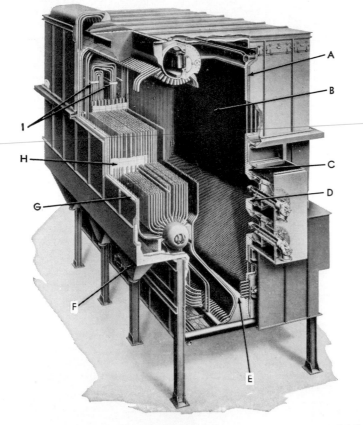

A—TUBE-AND-BRICK WALL

B—CLOSE-SPACED TUBES

C—13½-INCH BRICK WALL IN BURNER AREA

D—HIGH-FIRED KAOLIN BURNER TILE

E—FURNACE HOPPER

F—BOILER HOPPER LINED WITH FIREBRICK AND INSULATING BLOCK

G—TUBE-AND-BRICK WALL

H—TILE BAFFLE LAID IN AIR-SETTING MORTAR

I—SUPERHEATER TUBE SPACERS OF CASTABLE REFRACTORY REINFORCED WITH ALLOY-STEEL RODS

Fig. 16. *Various refractories and wall constructions used in a boiler setting (Integral-Furnace boiler shown)*

temperature of the furnace walls was often as high as 350 F. This made a fireman's life an uncomfortable one. On most of these boilers, if insulation had been placed outside the walls to improve working conditions and to reduce heat loss, the temperature of the brick would have risen enough adversely to affect its performance and life. Therefore, the only practical ways of approaching comfortable conditions were by good boiler-room ventilation and, in some instances, by the use of air-cooled furnace walls.

Water-cooled walls can be covered with any desired thickness of insulation without materially changing the inside temperature. It is now general practice to make the insulation thick enough to assure comfortable working conditions and at the same time maintain a reasonable balance between the cost of the fuel saved by insulating the boiler and the cost of the insulation. The heat economy and comfort requirements, of course, can be satisfied with practically any arrangement and type of insulation if it is of correct thickness and if the material will stand the temperature to which it is exposed. However, insulation can also be used as an effective seal against air infiltration into the boiler. Therefore, the possibility of using the insulation in this manner must also be considered in the economics of the design.

Insulation. Materials used in the insulation of water-cooled walls must have a reasonably low conductivity, which will not increase appreciably in service; sufficient mechanical strength to withstand shipping, application, and handling; resistance to moisture; low shrinkage when heated; good resistance to disintegration or settling by vibration even after prolonged service at operating temperature; and the ability to retain structural strength at operating temperature. For some special applications such as on boiler settings under pressure instead of draft, the insulating material should be capable of retaining its strength and thermal properties after repeated exposure to dilute solutions of sulfuric or sulfurous acid.

The basic materials most frequently used in heat insulation and some of the commercial forms of insulation made from these materials and their use are listed below:

Insulating Materials

1. *Diatomaceous-Earth-Base Blocks.* A silica composed of the skeletons of simple organisms, uncalcined or calcined, with asbestos fibre and clay, molded under heat and pressure. Temperature limits, 1600 to 2000 F. Comes in 6-in. by 36-in. rigid blocks 1 in. to 4 in. thick, or molded pipe covering from 1 in. to 3 in. thick for pipes up to 30 in. in diameter. Used principally for boiler walls, flues, ducts, fans, and steam lines.

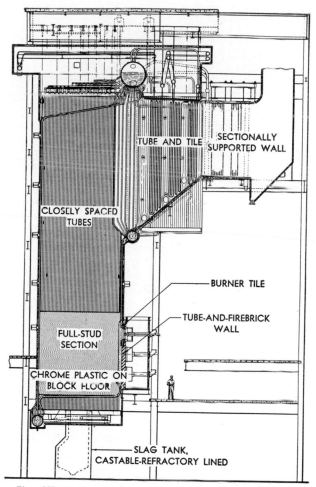

Fig. 17. *Various refractories and wall constructions used in a slag-tap-furnace boiler*

2. *Mineral Wool.* Molten slag, glass, or rock, blown into fibres by steam or air jet.

(a) Mineral-Wool-Base Block: Mineral-wool fibres and clay, molded under heat and pressure. Temperature limit (controversial) up to 1800 F claimed by some manufacturers. Usual size, form, and principal uses are the same as for 1.

(b) Mineral-Wool Blanket: Mineral-wool fibres compressed into blanket form held in shape by retaining between chicken wire or expanded metal lath. Temperature limit, 1000 F. Comes in 24-in. by 48- or 96-in. flexible blanket up to 6 in. thick. Used mainly on cased boiler walls and tanks. Sometimes it is also used on flues, ducts, and uncased boiler walls, but it is difficult to cover with a good finish coat.

3. **85% Magnesia Block.** Magnesium carbonate ($MgCO_3$), asbestos fibres, and clay, molded under heat and pressure. Temperature limit, 600 F. Usual size, form, and principal uses are similar to 1.

4. *Insulating Firebrick.* A fired clay brick with porous structure. Temperature limits, 1600 to 2800 F, but the lower the temperature limit the better the insulating value. Comes in standard firebrick

Fig. 18. *Tie bar and buckstay arrangement of furnace*

size (9 in. x 4½ in. x 2½ in.). Used principally on boiler walls and industrial furnaces and can be exposed directly to furnace gases where slag or abrasion is not present.

5. *Kaolin Wool.* A pure white wool blown from melted kaolin clay. Because of the high (3200 F) melting point of the clay, the final product retains its resiliency up to 2100 F. It can be used commercially in blanket or block form as described for mineral wool.

6. *High-Temperature Plastic.* Insulating cement made of mineral-wool fibres processed into nodules and then dry-mixed with clay. To apply, mix with enough water to give good troweling consistency. In final dried condition it is a tough fibrous monolithic insulation. Drying shrinkage is as much as 20 per cent, and there is a tendency to crack upon drying. Temperature limit (controversial) up to 1800 F claimed by some manufacturers. Used principally on boiler walls, irregular shaped valves and fittings, and heated tanks. Thickness should be limited to from 1 to 2 inches.

7. *Asbestos Cement.* Asbestos fibres dry-mixed with clay. To apply, mix with enough water to give good troweling consistency. In final dried condition it is fairly hard but not as tough as the mineral-wool-base cement, 6, and is easily damaged. The drying shrinkage and tendency to shrink upon drying are comparable to that of high-temperature plastic. Temperature limit 1000 F. Used principally as a finish coat for insulation on flues and ducts and also sometimes on uncased boiler walls.

The conductivity of a wide range of commercial refractories and insulants, at the temperatures for which they are suitable, may be determined from the conductivity curves, Fig. 19. Also, for convenience in following the example calculations of the total heat flow through an insulated wall, as given below, the curves of values for surface conductance used in the *Manual of ASTM Standards on Refractory Materials* (1948) appear in Fig. 20.

To maintain reasonably good working conditions around a boiler, the insulation must be thick enough so that the heat loss through the walls can be removed by the air circulating in the room without an appreciable increase in its temperature. In addition, the outside surface of the wall must be kept reasonably cool.

Heat Loss. Experience indicates that a heat loss through the boiler setting of from 120 to 170 Btu per sq ft, hr can be readily absorbed by the air circulating through the average boiler room. The exact amount depends upon the rate of air change in the room and the percentage of the room's volume filled by the boiler.

Obviously, the insulation of a boiler to reduce the heat loss to a value which can easily be absorbed by the total volume of room air does not in itself assure comfortable working conditions. Good air circulation around all parts of the boiler is necessary to prevent the accumulation of heat in the areas occupied by the operating personnel. This can be achieved by the use of operating platforms made of grating instead of solid floors, by leaving ample aisle space between adjacent boilers, and by locating the forced-draft fans so that they help the natural circulation of air around the boiler.

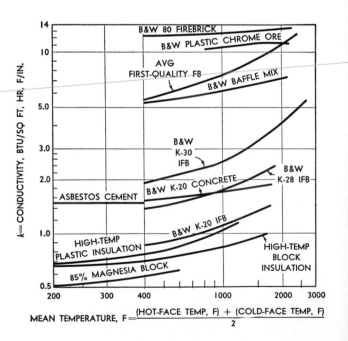

Fig. 19. *Conductivity of various refractories and materials*

Happily, good ventilation does not significantly increase the heat loss from the wall surface of the boiler. Heat loss through the insulation is not much affected by changes in outside surface conditions. The reason for this is evident from the heat transfer relations for a tube-and-brick wall insulated with high-temperature block, illustrated in Figs. 21 and 22.

The total heat flow through a wall is established in the same manner as the current flow in a series electrical circuit. The resistances through the various insulating components of the wall and of the surface film are added together to give the total resistance to heat flow. This over-all resistance is the reciprocal of the combined conductance or unit thermal current per unit of thermal potential, just as in a series electrical circuit the resistance is the reciprocal of the conductance or unit electrical current per unit of electrical potential. (See Chapter 7 on *Heat Transfer*.) For a tube-and-brick wall with conditions as indicated in Fig. 21:

t_1 = Temp of furnace side of firebrick = 1300 F

t_2 = Temp at inner surface of insulation = 1258 F

t_3 = Temp at outside surface of insulation = 140 F

t_4 = Temp of boiler room = 80 F

Q = Heat flow, Btu/sq ft, hr = $\dfrac{t_1 - t_4}{R}$

k = Conductivity, Btu × in. thickness ÷ sq ft × hr × F

U_s = Surface conductance, Btu/sq ft, hr, F

R = Total resistance = $R_1 + R_2 + R_3$

$R_1 = \dfrac{2.5}{k \text{ for firebrick @ } \dfrac{t_1 + t_2}{2}}$

$R_2 = \dfrac{6}{k \text{ for high-temp block @ } \dfrac{t_2 + t_3}{2}}$

$R_3 = \dfrac{1}{U_s @ t_3 - t_4}$

From curve for avg first-quality firebrick @ 1279 F, Fig. 19

$R_1 = \dfrac{2.5}{8.5} = 0.29$

From curve for high-temp block insulation @ 699 F, Fig. 19

$R_2 = \dfrac{6}{0.77} = 7.80$

From curve for 50 fpm air velocity @ $\triangle t = 60$ F, Fig. 20

$R_3 = \dfrac{1}{2.40} = 0.42$

$R = 0.29 + 7.80 + 0.42 = 8.51$

$Q = \dfrac{t_1 - t_4}{R} = \dfrac{1300 - 80}{8.51} = 143$ Btu/sq ft, hr

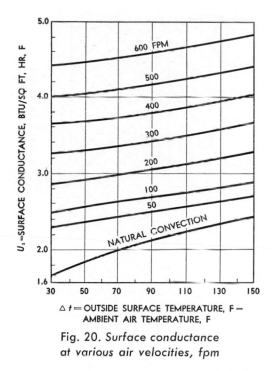

Fig. 20. *Surface conductance at various air velocities, fpm*

The surface film resistance in the above example, for the conditions illustrated in Fig. 21 and an air velocity over the wall surface of 50 fpm, is 0.42 or 4.9 per cent of the total resistance. A change in so small a factor obviously will not affect greatly the over-all heat loss. For instance, an increase in the air velocity from 50 to 600 fpm will reduce the surface resistance from 0.42 to 0.22 and this will increase the total heat loss through the wall only from 143 to 147 Btu per sq ft, hr, as indicated in Fig. 22. Since this entire heat loss is less than 1 per cent of the fuel input to the boiler, the change in boiler performance chargeable to a change in air velocity as in the above instance is negligible.

Casing Temperature. The casing temperatures corresponding to the heat loss limits of 120 and 170 Btu per sq ft, hr are 130 F and 150 F, respectively, with 80 F surroundings and a surface air velocity of 50 fpm. Under design conditions, these temperatures certainly are within the comfort zone.

However, unlike heat loss, casing temperature is affected considerably by surface conditions, as demonstrated by the increase in casing temperature over the calculated values when two walls of the same temperature are close together, as indicated in Fig. 23. In this condition all radiant heat transfer from the wall is eliminated, and heat transfer through the surface film is by convection only. The surface conductance by convection only, under the design conditions, is 1.18, determined by the formula $U_c = 1 + 0.22 V$, where V is equal to the surface air velocity in fps. The surface resistance, which is the

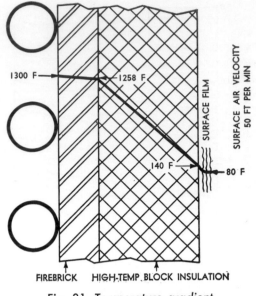

Fig. 21. *Temperature gradient through tube-and-brick wall*

reciprocal of the conductance, therefore becomes 0.85 instead of 0.42, the surface resistance when both convection and radiation apply, as determined above in the example computation for total heat transfer. This change alone, as will be noted from Fig. 22, would raise the casing temperature from 140 F to 196 F even if a steady supply of air at 80 F were blown through the cavity between walls. In practice, however, the natural circulation of air through the cavity would probably be inadequate, and the temperature of the air passing through the

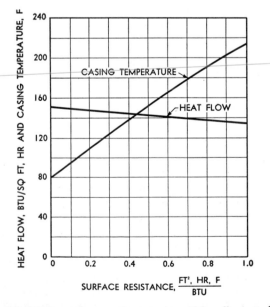

Fig. 22. *While surface resistance has little effect on heat flow, its effect on casing temperature is considerable*

cavity would increase considerably. This would result in a further rise in casing temperature.

Under these conditions, an increased thickness of insulation would be of little help in reducing the casing temperature. Therefore, wherever operators must work regularly, such cavities must be avoided by careful boiler and building design. Aside from avoiding cavities, the precautions to be taken, as already noted, to maintain good air circulation in the boiler room will assure low casing temperature for a well-insulated boiler.

Economics of Insulation

The economics of insulating a 1000 F boiler flue, using high-temperature block and 85% magnesia insulation, are indicated by the curves shown in Fig. 24.

The basic assumptions are:

Room temperature	= 80 F
Surface air velocity	= 50 fpm
Dollar value of heat	= $0.42 per 1,000,000 Btu
Annual operation	= 6000 hr
Cost of insulation	= applied cost per sq ft
Annual fixed charges on insulation investment	= 20%

In plotting the curves in Fig. 24, the thickness of the high-temperature block is taken at 2½ in. (the approximate thickness required for the protection of the 85% magnesia), and the thickness of the 85% magnesia is to be determined. The economic thickness is the one giving the lowest total of insulation fixed charges plus cost of heat loss.

It will be noted from Fig. 24 that, in this case, the most economical thickness of 85% magnesia insulation over the high-temperature block is 2 inches. Since the total resulting thickness is adequate for the comfort of personnel, this is the optimum thickness of insulation for maximum economy. However, if greater total thickness is required for personnel comfort, the thickness of the insulation should be increased as may be necessary beyond the economic limit. The maintenance of comfortable working conditions is more important than the theoretical economics. Therefore in practice some types of surfaces are insulated with more than the economic thickness.

Prevention of Leakage

Tube-and-Brick Wall. In designing a tube-and-brick wall, the inner refractory lining is made as airtight as possible. Without any supplementary seal, where the draft within the setting is fairly low, this makes a commercially tight wall. However, in high draft zones the brickwork is not sufficiently airtight. Therefore the entire wall may be covered with a casing which is sealed against air leakage by using welded or gasketed panel junctions. With a casing of this type, some slip seals are required to take care of relative expansion caused by a temperature differential of about 400F between wall tubes and casing. The refractory serves to limit the amount of leakage which occurs through the slip seals and often at casing terminals. The insulating block can be used to supplement the leakage resistance of the refractory by being tightly laid up.

The performance of recent designs indicates that an airtight casing is not required if, by careful arrangement and installation, the insulation setup is made to act as an air seal. Tests show that the air leakage for settings built in this way is consistently as low as for those with welded casing. Thus airtight insulation may be arranged so that no casing at all is necessary.

A tube and brick wall with the insulation designed so that no casing is required is illustrated in Fig. 12. The small insert shows the construction used with a welded casing.

In the uncased construction, a single thickness of block insulation is placed outside the firebrick. High temperature block (diatomaceous earth base) is most frequently used since it has high temperature resistance and is rugged structurally. Expanded metal lath (1½ in. x 13 BWG) is placed over the block insulation. The lath acts as an "explosion mat" to back up the firebrick in case of an explosion within the setting. The expanded metal lath is then covered with a coat of plastic insulation 1 in. or more thick in order to bury the metal lath deeply enough to overcome its tendency to bulge after repeated shutdowns and startups. Chicken wire is stretched over the plastic insulation to serve as a reinforcement for the finish coat. The finish coat is applied in two layers. The first is ½ in. of plastic insulation (mineral wool base) which serves as a foundation for the final layer. The outside layer is ¼ in. of asphaltic compound and acts as the major air sealing barrier.

Since an uncased surface like this is easily damaged, many operators prefer to have an exterior casing. An airtight welded casing is preferable, but it may be another arrangement which does not primarily serve as an air seal. In the latter case, airtight insulation is applied similar to the uncased construction.

Closely Spaced Tube Walls. A closely spaced tube wall as shown in Fig. 13 is made airtight by the backing of reinforced insulating (also refractory) concrete and does not require supplementary sealing by the insulation to permit the use of a nontight casing. However, when this type of wall is built without a casing of either kind, the arrangement of the finish coat is identical to that described for the tube and brick wall.

Stud Tube Walls. The arrangement of insulation for the flat stud tube, partial stud tube and full stud

tube walls, as shown in Fig. 14 and Fig. 15, is similar to the closely spaced tube wall since these walls are also sealed by castable or plastic refractory and the surface to be insulated is substantially at saturation temperature.

Application of Insulation

To obtain the first-class performance required from boiler insulation careful application is essential. This is particularly true for units with a nontight casing or without any casing where a major part of the job of sealing the setting against air leakage depends on the insulation. The details of the application

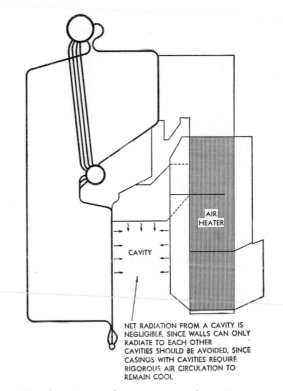

NET RADIATION FROM A CAVITY IS NEGLIGIBLE, SINCE WALLS CAN ONLY RADIATE TO EACH OTHER CAVITIES SHOULD BE AVOIDED, SINCE CASINGS WITH CAVITIES REQUIRE RIGOROUS AIR CIRCULATION TO REMAIN COOL

Fig. 23. *Cavities tend to raise outside wall temperature*

methods noted below have been developed by trial and error over a period of many years.

Insulating Block. Insulating block should be held tightly in place with 14 BWG annealed galvanized lacing wire, criss-crossed between insulation retainers. These retainers are usually located at about 18 in. centers on vertical walls and at about 12 in. centers on overhead surfaces. The blocks should be closely butted together with the joints of the inner and outer blocks staggered when more than one layer is used. Each layer should be pointed up wherever necessary with insulating cement of the same material as the block.

By application in this manner the insulation will provide all possible tightness against air infiltration and the blocks will not sag away from the surface. Also by holding the blocks tightly against the inside surface, an unsightly external appearance is avoided, and the possibility of leaving a channel between refractory and insulation, through which flue gas can by-pass from a low-draft to a high-draft zone, is eliminated.

High-Temperature Plastic Insulation. When plastic insulation dries, the shrinkage may be as high as 20 per cent. Therefore whenever possible, this material should be built up in multiple layers. The surface of each layer should be scored (to help adhesion of the next) before the layer is fully set,

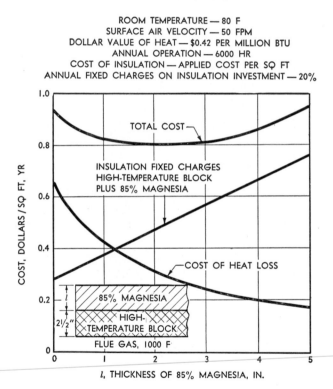

ASSUMED CONDITIONS

ROOM TEMPERATURE — 80 F
SURFACE AIR VELOCITY — 50 FPM
DOLLAR VALUE OF HEAT — $0.42 PER MILLION BTU
ANNUAL OPERATION — 6000 HR
COST OF INSULATION — APPLIED COST PER SQ FT
ANNUAL FIXED CHARGES ON INSULATION INVESTMENT — 20%

Fig. 24. *Selection of economical thickness of insulation*

and then it should be allowed to dry and the shrinkage cracks should be filled in before application of succeeding layers. To prevent sagging away from the surface to which it is applied, plastic insulation exceeding 1½ in. in total thickness should be reinforced with wire mesh or expanded metal lath located at each 1½-in. increment in thickness.

It is preferable that the surface to which plastic insulation is to be applied should be hot. This will give better adhesion to the initial surface and also between successive layers of the plastic. Drying will be rapid and uniform throughout the body of the plastic, and the otherwise pronounced tendency to curl away from the initial surface, as a result of the

quicker shrinkage of the outer surface of the plastic when drying is from the outside alone, will be practically eliminated.

Expanded Metal Lath. When expanded metal lath is used to reinforce insulation, it should be held down very firmly by threaded washers or by washers and nuts applied to threaded insulation retainers. In the past, expanded metal lath was often held in place merely by wiring to the insulation retainers. When this method was used, there was a tendency to buckle in service because of expansion and contraction when heating and cooling the boiler unit.

Wire Mesh Reinforcement. Hexagonal galvanized wire mesh (chicken wire), 2 in. by 20 BWG, is used to reinforce the finish coat over the insulation, where it serves as the air-seal barrier, the outside finish of an uncased boiler, or the air seal of a boiler with a nontight casing. Light gage wire is used because the tendency to crack the finish coat at the joints of the wire is considerably less than with heavier gage material.

The wire mesh should be stretched tightly over the surface of the insulation underneath, and it should be held in place by wiring firmly to the lacing wires and insulation retainers. To prevent slipping, the tie wires should be anchored behind nuts on the retainers. If the wire mesh is not held firmly in place at frequent intervals, the finish coat will sag away from the surface underneath. This will cause unsightly bulges, and, because of the constant flexing or "breathing" caused by draft fluctuations within the boiler, such bulges will eventually disintegrate.

After it is secured, the wire mesh should be kinked out at about 2-ft intervals to hold it slightly away from the insulation surface underneath. This will permit the finish coat to be troweled in behind the wire, so that the wire will function properly as reinforcement and anchorage. In many cases the finish coat has peeled off because it was not thus properly reinforced and anchored.

Adjacent strips of wire mesh should be overlapped and laced together to prevent the edges from curling outward. This will avoid deterioration of the finish coat at these junctions.

Finish Coat. The finish coat is applied in two layers. The first layer is ½ in. of plastic insulation (mineral-wool base), which serves as a foundation for the final air-sealing layer. Because it is tougher and better resists cracking, although it is by no means elastic, this material is preferred to other types of finishing cements. While it has been general practice for a number of years to add Portland cement to this plastic insulation used in the first layer of the finish coat, experience indicates that this is not advisable because the cement makes the material more vulnerable to cracking from expansion differences and vibration.

The boiler should be cold when the first layer of the finish coat, the ½ in. of plastic insulation, is applied, and the plastic should be well keyed in behind the reinforcing wire mesh, as noted above. Since the inner boiler structure expands more than does this cooler outer surface, to compensate in some degree for this difference in expansion the layer of plastic is grooved, entirely through to the chicken wire, into panels approximately 3 ft by 4 ft. Random cracking of the surface is prevented or greatly minimized by concentrating in these grooves the effects of the drying shrinkage of the plastic and the expansion of the boiler. After the plastic has dried, any shrinkage cracks which may have developed in spite of the grooving should be filled in.

The final layer of the finish coat is a compound of asphalt and asbestos fibres, ¼ in. thick. It is applied after the first layer of plastic insulation has completely dried and is troweled over the entire surface, filling all the grooves. The shrinkage is high, so the compound recedes into the grooves of the first layer, and, after drying, a paneled effect is plainly visible. This asphaltic compound is the major air-sealing barrier of the wall. The asphalt gives the compound a reasonable flexibility, which helps in bridging over and in sealing any cracks which may form in the plastic insulation despite the steps taken to avoid them. The grooves and the pores of the plastic insulation are also sealed against air leakage.

This final layer of the finish coat is not perfectly smooth because shrinkage makes it conform to the grainy surface of the plastic insulation underneath. However, if the method of application is good, it will not show trowel marks. If it is primed with an asphalt-base aluminum paint, the surface can be painted any color.

Boiler Casing

Ordinary boiler casings are of two basic types—"airtight" and "nontight" construction—and are usually made of steel, although, the use of aluminum, when available, is increasing because of its light weight and pleasing appearance. Casings may be supported from the wall structure by (a) attachment to floating buckstays and (b) direct attachment to the tubes by fastening to the same retainers which hold the insulation and refractory, or they may be completely independent of the boiler wall by being entirely supported from external steel work.

Provision must be made for relative expansion since the temperature of the casing is, of course, lower than the temperature of the tube envelope inside.

The "airtight" casing must be tight enough to keep the air infiltration to the unit below a tolerable limit, which should not exceed 10 per cent of theoretical air from burners to boiler outlet. It also protects the insulation. In general, flanged casings, with the flanges either welded or bolted together, can be made airtight at the panel junctions. These casings must be reasonably airtight throughout, and, in addition to the panel junctions, every effort should be made to seal all areas of possible air leakage, such as the terminals, door openings, and soot blower openings.

A "nontight" casing serves only as insulation armor and to improve the appearance of the boiler. When this type of casing is used, the effectiveness of the air sealing of the wall will depend entirely upon the arrangement and application of the refractory and insulation. For such a nontight casing, costs are also reduced by eliminating air sealing at the terminals, door openings, and elsewhere.

Pressure Casings. The design of boilers to operate with the setting under pressure instead of draft is a comparatively recent development. In this type of unit the setting must be completely tight against outward leakage under a pressure of 10 in. or more of water, not only to prevent the discharge of noxious gases into the boiler room but also to maintain efficient operation. The casing, therefore, must be entirely welded.

Slip seals do not give the degree of tightness required for this service and, consequently, cannot be used to compensate for any expansion differences between the wall tubes and casing or between the casing and doors, soot blowers, or other attachments that penetrate the casing. To overcome this difficulty, recent boiler units of this type have been built with a rugged, completely welded casing of 10 BWG steel in contact with the wall tubes of the setting. The exterior of the casing is then insulated, and the insulation is covered with a plastic or other type of finish. By placing the heavy-gage all-welded casing against the tube surfaces and insulating it on the outside, it is held very nearly at saturation temperature. Therefore, expansion differences between the tube envelope and the casing are virtually eliminated.

Power plant with adjacent coal storage

COAL—PREPARATION AND STORAGE

THE purpose of coal preparation is to improve the quality of the coal or to make it suitable for a specific purpose by (a) cleaning to remove inorganic impurities, (b) special treatment (such as dedusting), or (c) sizing—either crushing or screening or both.

Economic Factors

The properties and quantities of impurities in coal are of major importance in the design and operation of steam-generating equipment. Although boilers are often designed and equipped satisfactorily to use a wide range of coals, no boiler installation will perform equally well with all types of coal. In all cases there is some limitation of the properties of the coal which can be used to advantage. These limitations are particularly stringent for many of the older installations.

To suit the limitations of various types of coal-burning equipment in service, specifications covering several important properties of coal are necessary. For certain types of stokers, for instance, to prevent excessive clinkering, a minimum ash-softening temperature, maximum ash content, and maximum sulfur content of the coal are specified. For pulverized-coal firing, it may be necessary to specify a maximum ash-fluid temperature for a unit designed for removal of ash as a liquid slag and a minimum ash-softening temperature for a dry-ash installation. Within these and other equipment limitations there is usually a wide range of coals which can be satisfactorily burned in a specific steam boiler, and the choice depends primarily on economics—which coal will produce steam at the lowest over-all cost including cost at the mine, shipment, handling, ash disposal, maintenance, and efficiency. To burn a wide range of coals often requires a larger initial investment than would otherwise be necessary. However, fuel cost is usually the predominating factor because it represents so large a part of the over-all operating cost. The fuel bill for a year, for instance, may equal the initial cost of the entire steam-generating unit.

Cleaning to Remove Inorganic Impurities

Because of a general lowering of quality of raw coal in recent years, the need for coal cleaning has increased greatly. Among the factors contributing to the lowering of coal quality are:

1. Depletion of some of the high-quality coal seams.
2. The greater use of mechanical underground mining methods including mechanical cutting and loading.
3. Increased production by strip mining.

Use of mechanical methods in mining coal has increased greatly during the last 25 years. In 1950 the total (strip and underground) production of lignite and bituminous coal in the United States was about 512,000,000 tons, of which 68 per cent was mechanically loaded underground as compared with only about 2 per cent of the 520,000,000-ton production in 1925. Mechanical cutting of coal underground increased at a fairly uniform rate from about 35 per cent of the total bituminous and lignite production in 1906 to about 60 per cent of the total production in 1949. The latter represented about 91 per cent of the total underground production. In 1906 the percentage of strip-mined coal was negligible; in 1950 it represented 24 per cent of the total bituminous coal production.

Mechanical cleaning at mine increased from about 4 per cent of the total bituminous and lignite production in 1925 to about 35 per cent of the total production in 1949. In the same period cleaning at consumers' plants increased from 0.6 to 2.0 per cent of the total bituminous and lignite production.

It is estimated that in 1921 about 25 per cent of the total anthracite production was cleaned, exclusive of recovered coal cleaned at washeries. By 1940 practically all the anthracite produced was

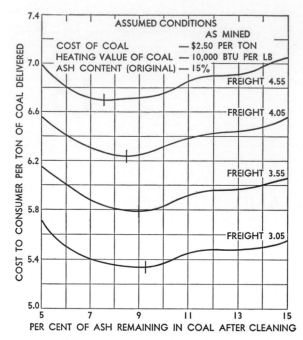

Fig. 1. *Optimum reduction in ash content of coal for minimum delivered cost. An increase in cleaning cost is justified as shipping distance increases*

zones of steam generating equipment.

The principal benefit of cleaning is the reduction in ash content. With ash content reduced, shipping costs and the requirements for storage and handling decrease because of the smaller quantity of coal necessary per unit of heating value. Also, an increase in boiler efficiency may sometimes be realized because of less fouling of heat absorbing surfaces.

Cost of cleaning must be balanced against the benefits obtained. Items included in the cleaning costs are: cleaning plant operating costs, capital charges, the value of the coal in the discarded refuse and the cost of disposing of the refuse. In 1946 over 21 million tons of refuse was discarded by bituminous-coal-mine-cleaning-plants. This amounted to 15.5 per cent of the coal supplied to the cleaning plants. Generally the quantity of coal lost in the refuse increases as the reduction in ash content is increased, hence cleaning costs are directly related to the ash reduction obtained. A careful evaluation of the benefits from cleaning is required to determine if this loss plus the other cleaning costs are justified.

By balancing shipping costs against cleaning costs, an optimum reduction in ash content can be established which will give a minimum delivered cost of coal, neglecting differences in handling costs and performance at the steam plant. Because of freight costs, it is generally found that an increase in the cost of cleaning is justified as the distance the coal is shipped increases. This is illustrated graphically in Fig. 1 for coal from strip mine operation.

Nature of Impurities in Coal

As found in seams, coal is a heterogeneous mixture of organic and inorganic materials. Not only are there large differences in the properties of coal from different seams but also in coal removed from different elevations and different locations in a single seam.

Impurities in coal can be divided into two general classifications—inherent and removable. The in-

treated in coal washing or cleaning plants called "breakers." Approximately 80 per cent of all anthracite produced is used for domestic or other space heating and less than 20 per cent is used in the generation of power.

The effect of cleaning on the properties of coal cannot be generalized because of differences in coal characteristics. For example, the ash fusion temperature of one coal may be lowered by cleaning and that of another raised. Some reduction in sulfur content is usually obtainable and this is invariably a benefit as experience indicates that the higher the sulfur content of coal, the greater the likelihood of spontaneous combustion in storage; corrosion of conveyors, bunkers, etc.; and corrosion of heat absorbing surfaces in the lower temperature

TABLE 1

Chemical Distribution of Sulfur in Various Coals

Location of Mine	Coal Bed	Total Sulfur %	Pyritic Sulfur %	Organic Sulfur %
Washington County, Pa.	Pittsburgh	1.13	0.35	0.78
Franklin County, Ill.	No. 6	2.52	1.50	1.02
Pike County, Ky.	Freeburn	0.46	0.13	0.33
McDowell County, W. Va.	Pocahontas #3	0.55	0.08	0.46
Walker County, Ala.	Pratt	1.62	0.81	0.81
Meigs County, O.	8A	2.51	1.61	0.86
Clearfield County, Pa.	Upper Freeport	3.56	2.82	0.74
Boone County, W. Va.	Eagle	2.48	1.47	1.01
Clay County, Ind.	No. 3	3.92	2.13	1.79

herent impurities are inseparably combined with the coal. The removable impurities are segregated and can be eliminated, by available cleaning methods, to the extent economically justified.

Ash consists of slate, shale, carbonaceous shale, clay, sandstone, limestone, and the mineral residue of the plant life from which the coal originated.

Sulfur exists in organic compounds, in the sulfate radical (SO_4), and in pyrites ($Fe\ S_2$). The organic sulfur is an inherent impurity and cannot be removed by cleaning. Sulfate sulfur in coal as mined is usually not over 0.1 per cent and consequently is not of great importance. Generally the largest source of sulfur is from pyrites present in coal as mined and used. Pyrites may appear in the coal bed as strata, veins, and balls or lenses, all of varying and sometimes of considerable dimensions. It is also found as very thin seams or balls so small that they are not visible to the eye. Table 1 shows the chemical distribution of sulfur in several different coals.

Moisture, which is inherent in coal, will vary for different grades from 2 to 4 per cent in low-volatile bituminous coal up to above 35 per cent in lignitic coal. In mining and subsequent sizing, moisture also collects on the exposed surfaces of the coal. Surface moisture can collect on the coal from wetting while cutting, during washing, transit, and outdoor storage. See Chapter 17, for reference to the use of the terms "surface" and "inherent" in defining moisture in coal.

Cleaning Methods—General

The principal methods used in the United States for cleaning bituminous and anthracite coals are: (a) cleaning at mine face; (b) picking out impurities by hand or mechanical means; (c) froth flotation; (d) gravity concentration.

Fig. 2. Shaking table used in hand picking coal

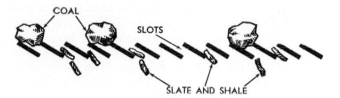

Fig. 3. Rejection of flat refuse by slot shaker

Cleaning at Mine Face

When manual cutting and loading of coal are used, it is possible to minimize the quantity of impurities. In cutting, the miner can more easily distinguish between coal and rock, and in loading he can often discard visible impurities. With mechanical cutting and loading of coal, the miner has much less control over the product loaded; however, it is often possible to follow mining practices which will reduce the quantity of impurities.

Efforts to reduce the impurities loaded in the mine usually result in increased mining costs, hence economics play an important part in determining the amount of cleaning done. In general, cleaning at the mine face is greatly reduced when mechanical mining methods are employed. The wide use of recently developed types of combination, continuous cutting and loading equipment can be expected to result in further reduction in cleaning at mine face.

Picking by Hand or Mechanical Means

Hand picking is the earliest method used in cleaning coal at the mine. A shaking type table used for hand picking is shown in Fig. 2. The run-of-mine coal is screened and only the oversized material, usually 4 in. or more, goes to the picking table. Refuse from hand picking tables may run from 50 to 60 per cent coal and it is common practice to crush the refuse and clean it by mechanical means.

Many mechanical picking devices employ differences in physical dimensions of coal and impurities as a means of separation. Bituminous coal fractures into rough cubes, whereas slate and shale normally fracture as thin slabs. A slot type of flat picker which can be installed on shaker screens, shaking conveyors and chutes is shown diagrammatically in Fig. 3.

Froth Flotation

While froth flotation cleaning is of long standing for ore separation and has been widely used in Europe over a long period for cleaning coal, its application for this purpose in the United States is of recent origin. Its use has greatly increased within the last few years. This method can be used in cleaning smaller sizes, 1/10 in. by 0 and particularly smaller than 48 mesh, a consist for which a market has been developed only lately.

The incoming coal feed is agitated in a controlled

amount of water, air and reagents that cause a surface froth to form, the bubbles of which selectively attach themselves to coal particles and keep them buoyant while the heavier particles of slate and shale remain dispersed in the water. The components thus segregated can be suitably diverted to salvage and waste, respectively.

Gravity Concentration

Removal of segregated impurities in coal by gravity concentration is the most widely used method of mechanical cleaning. This method is based on the difference in the specific gravities of coal and the impurities found with the coal. Commercially the processes used in gravity concentration can be divided into two main classifications—wet and pneumatic. In the first, water is the separating medium applying the principle of segregation of heavier from lighter particles when settling in a fluid. In the second, generally confined to coal sizes ¾ in. or less, air is used as the separating medium. The specific gravities of bituminous coal and several common impurities are given in Table 2.

TABLE 2

Specific Gravity of Coal and Impurities

Material	Specific Gravity
Bituminous coal	1.12 - 1.35
Bone coal	1.35 - 1.7
Carbonaceous shale	1.6 - 2.2
Shale	2.0 - 2.6
Clay	1.8 - 2.2
Pyrite	4.8 - 5.2

In gravity concentration it is possible to separate the coal into two or more gravity fractions modified somewhat by size classification effect. Assuming separation is made at a specific gravity of 1.5, particles with a specific gravity less than 1.5 will be recovered as clean coal and particles with a specific gravity higher than 1.5 will go to refuse. The quantity of impurities found in the clean coal and the quantity of coal found in the refuse depends on the quantity of impurities in the coal, the specific gravity of separation used and the efficiency of the separation.

In contrast to the values noted in Table 2 the bulk density of crushed coal is much less and is fairly constant even for different size consists. For instance a sizing of run-of-mine bituminous coals of 60 per cent lump (over 3″), 25 per cent nut (¾″ to 3″) and 15 per cent slack (under ¾″) will weigh between 45 and 55 lb per cu foot. Bituminous coal of "bug dust" (⅛″ x 0″) sizing weighs about 52 lb per cu foot. Anthracite in egg sizing will run 52 to 58 lb per cu ft, and No. 1 buckwheat will have a bulk density of about 50 lb per cu ft.

Washability Characteristics of Coal

In design and operation of coal washing plants, careful studies are made to determine the properties of the various specific gravity fractions and how these properties vary with coal sizing.

In most cleaning processes the low gravity fractions (below 1.40 sp gr) which represent the relatively low ash coal, and the high gravity impurities (above 1.80 sp gr) are easily separated. The middlings material (1.4 to 1.8 sp gr) is most difficult to separate.

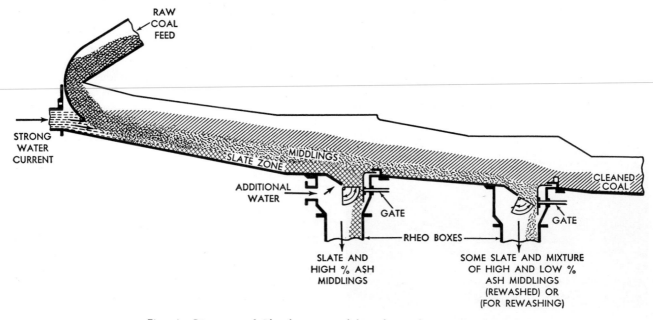

Fig. 4. Diagram of Rheolaveur coal launder with two Rheoboxes

Where the segregated impurities in the coal are soft compared to the coal, more impurities will be found in the fine coal sizes. Where the segregated impurities are hard compared to the coal, more of the impurities will be found in the larger size coal.

There is a general correlation between specific gravity and ash content; although, the relation differs for various coals. Ash contents corresponding to various specific gravities for bituminous coals are shown in Table 3.

TABLE 3

Ash Contents of Various Gravity Fractions In Bituminous Coal

Specific Gravity	Ash Content Per Cent
1.3 - 1.4	1 - 5
1.4 - 1.5	5 - 10
1.5 - 1.6	10 - 35
1.6 - 1.8	35 - 60
1.8 - 1.9	60 - 75
1.9 - & above	75 - 90

In actual washery operation it is not possible to realize the results obtained under laboratory conditions of the float-and-sink tests. But data obtained by such tests can be used to rate and control cleaning equipment and to evaluate the quantitative and qualitative efficiencies of the operation.

Cleaning by Gravity Concentration

Wet Processes

In common practice several well known types of equipment are used in cleaning coal by the wet process. In recent years four of these known as (a) launders, (b) jigs, (c) classifiers and (d) the dense media method have been used in cleaning about 90 per cent of all the bituminous coal washed in the United States.

The "Rheolaveur" process is representative of the launder type. It consists of two parts, a short steeply inclined section at the coal and water inlet end and a longer more gradually sloped section beyond. A diagrammatic arrangement of a primary Rheo launder is shown in Fig. 4. In passing through the steeply sloped section, relatively high velocities are attained and the particles quickly stratify. In the gradually sloped section the velocity decreases and the heavy particles settle to the bottom of the trough where they are removed through two or more Rheo boxes. An important factor in separation is the relatively high coefficient of friction of the impurities as compared to the coal causing the impurities to slide along the trough bottom at a slow speed, the velocity being progressively higher from the bottom to the top of the flowing stream. The difference in velocity between the bottom and top of the stream keeps the impurities below the settling velocity and the coal above the settling velocity, hence the coal is carried through the launder with the water stream. The Rheolaveur launder has a wide range of application for all types of coal.

In jigs, pulsating currents of water pass through a bed of coal resting on a screen plate. At the start of the upward flow of water through the coal bed, the coal is at rest. The upward flow called the "pulsion stroke," opens up the bed and brings it into a mobile state. The bed is closed and brought to rest during the downward flow of water, called the "suction stroke." Optimum conditions for classification occur at periods during the pulsion and suction strokes when the mixture is of high density with freedom of movement between particles. Thus are the two fractions separated and finally diverted in two separate streams.

Some types of jigs require rather careful sizing of the feed coal for best results, while with others, such as the Baum jig, which take a wide range of sizing, fair results are possible even for the smaller sizes. The water pulsations in the Baum jig are produced by air pressure. The following specific application is typical of the performance of this equipment. In cleaning Roslyn bed coal (from eastern Washington State) on a Baum jig the ash was reduced from 15.4 per cent in the raw coal to 10.5 per cent in the washed coal. In this case 95 per cent of the weight of the raw coal washed ranged in screen size from 20 mesh to 1½ in. and over, and 73 per cent of this weight ranged in size from ⅜ in. to 1½ in. and over. Weight of the refuse from the operation was about 18.7 per cent of the raw coal.

In the many forms of classifiers the principle of free and hindered settling in water is applied to obtain classification. The feed coal is immersed in a flowing current of water (usually upward) having a velocity greater than the settling velocity of the low gravity fractions (coal) and less than the settling velocity of the high gravity fractions (refuse) which serves to separate the coal from the refuse. Classifiers are suitable for a wide variety of coals but efficient operation usually requires careful sizing of the feed coal.

The dense media method utilizes the principle of the laboratory float-and-sink tests on a commercial basis. Coal is immersed into a medium with an intermediate specific gravity between coal and refuse. Hence the impurities sink and the coal floats. A well known type is the Chance-Cone shown in Fig. 5. The separating medium is a suspension of fine sand in water. An upward current of water and stirring is provided to maintain the sand in proper suspension to give the specific gravity required for the separation. This method is widely accepted for cleaning anthracite and its use in the bituminous field is increasing.

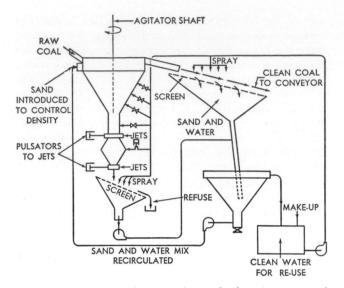

Fig. 5. *Chance-Cone dense media method of cleaning coal*

Dry Processes

Within recent years pneumatic or dry processes have been used for about 12 per cent of all the bituminous coal cleaned in the United States and are generally applied to coal sizes ¾ in. or less. The raw coal is often screened ahead of the cleaning plant so that the oversize may be cleaned by a wet process and the undersize by pneumatic means. For successful results by pneumatic means the feed coal should have a uniformly low moisture content.

The principal types of pneumatic cleaning processes are jigs and tables. Both methods are similar in principle to the corresponding wet processes except that air is used as the separating medium.

In the pneumatic process, using tables, air is admitted through holes in the table and is blown up through the bed of coal. The motion of the table plus the air flow segregates the coal and impurities bringing low gravity fractions to the top of the bed where they can move down across the table in a direction perpendicular to the riffles. The heavy impurities settle in the riffles and move along the riffle troughs discharging at the end opposite the feed. The middlings move diagonally across the bed. This permits separation of two or three products at desired specific gravities by the selection of proper points of withdrawal on the table discharge.

Air used in pneumatic cleaning methods can be passed through cyclone separators and bag filters for recovery of the fines from the coal. The recovered fines can be remixed in the clean coal providing their ash content is not excessive.

Special Treatment

De-Dusting

De-dusting is a type of air separation, the classification being according to size. Air is passed through the coal and entrains a large percentage of the fines. The fine coal is recovered from the air with cyclone separators and bag filters.

This process is often employed to remove fines ahead of wet cleaning. The fines, if low enough in ash, may be added to the cleaned coal or disposed of separately. Both wet and pneumatic cleaning processes provide at least partial de-dusting. However, degradation of coal in screening, handling, and shipment after cleaning may increase the percentage of dust so that additional treatment is required.

Increased surface moisture reduces dustiness and additions of water are sometimes used to prevent dust. To reduce the quantity of water required special wetting agents may be used.

Oil Spraying

Spraying with oil to reduce dustiness of coal during handling, transportation and storage has increased greatly in recent years. This treatment, usually applied at the mine, is currently in use for over 50 million tons of bituminous coal yearly in nearly 900 preparation plants. The oil film causes some dust particles to adhere to the larger pieces of coal, and others to agglomerate into larger lumps not easily airborne. A wide range of oils and viscosities can be used but the oil must be free of objectionable odor. Either dry or wet coal may be treated, but for a given dustiness index and for a given coal sizing somewhat more oil is required for wet coal. In general, the amount of oil used ranges from 1 to 8 quarts per ton of coal; fine consists and coals of porous structure, requiring the larger amounts.

In spraying, the oil mist is directed at a moving stream of coal with the intent to cover each piece. Equipment for oil storage, handling, heating if necessary, and spraying varies and depends largely on local conditions. Since mixing and elapsed time tend to make the treatment more effective it usually is applied as far ahead of final loading as possible.

In addition to a reduction in dust, oil sprayed coal tends to shed moisture and there is less chance of freezing. Treated coal is said to deteriorate less in storage since the partly sealed pores retard oxidization.

Prevention of Freezing

To prevent freezing, calcium chloride and rock salt are often added to coal. By retaining water in solution on the coal surface they also help to prevent dust.

Because of variations in the hygroscopic property of coals and differences in humidity, actual tests are required to determine within close limits the quantities of rock salt or calcium chloride required to prevent freezing. Table 4 gives approximate quan-

gas or oil burners must be arranged so that the flame does not impinge on furnace walls or grate surfaces. A layer of ash 4 or 5 in. thick on the chain will serve as sufficient protection for a short period of operation. For permanent operation with the auxiliary fuels, it is recommended that the grate be protected with two courses of firebrick of a total thickness of 5 inches, so laid that all joints are staggered. If there is frequent change-over during extended periods, between the regular coal and the auxiliary fuels, care should be taken to prevent clogging of the auxiliary gas or oil burners with ash when burning coal. Sometimes this is done by admitting a little cooling air through the idle auxiliary burners.

Stack Discharge—Carbon Loss

In a chain-grate or traveling-grate stoker firing bituminous coal, the fuel bed suffers less disturbance than in any other type of stoker. While this may be a disadvantage in excluding caking coals as suitable fuel, it is an actual asset in reducing cinder carry-over. In many instances of a chain-grate stoker firing bituminous coal, dust loads in the flue gas leaving the boiler are below the requirements of dust ordinances (ASME tentative standard, 0.85 lb per 1000 lb of flue gas), and a dust collector would not be required. The carry-over in proper operation with good coal in common sizings is indicated in Table 2. At the same time, the combined combustible loss up the stack and to the ashpit can be very low.

For small anthracite, however, particularly sizes Nos. 4 and 5, the carry-over is relatively high. Small burning particles tend to be dislodged from the fuel bed by a strong blast through the grate. Some of these particles fall back on the surface of unburned coal and thereby aid ignition, but some tend to remain in suspension and are carried along with the flue gases. When firing small-size anthracite, dust collectors are often installed to collect this carry-over of unburned particles. These unburned particles are returned by suitable means, usually air injection, to the furnace for reburning (see Fig. 7).

Response to Load Changes

With favorable coal sizing, a properly designed chain-grate stoker will operate smokelessly over its entire range of load (from 10 per cent to full). This very desirable performance results from the effec-

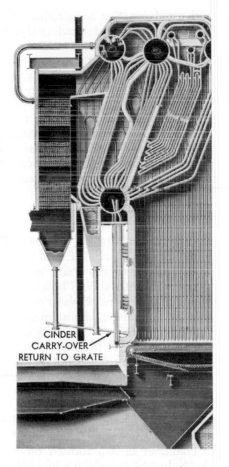

Fig. 7. Spreader-stoker application of returning unburned cinder carry

tiveness of the overfire-air jets and from the arches. Generally speaking just a little care in maintaining suitable condition for fluctuating-load response to load swings over a wide smoke is possible with the chain-type of stoker. When there is a for an increase in fuel, ignition ca is not taken to see that the coal than it can be ignited. For a drop cipal difficulty is the danger of over unless proper care is taken to cont of the stoker.

For operation with rapidly swing bed is carried somewhat longer t

TABLE 2
Dust Loadings with Chain-Grate Stoker

Coal Sizing	1″, 60% through ¼″ screen		1½″, 20% through ¼″ screen	
Burning rate, Btu/sq ft, hr	400,000	500,000	400,000	500,000
Dust loading, lb/1000 lb gas at 50% excess air	0.63	0.75	0.26	0.39

part of the it will be m purpose of capacity of efficiently continual su Cyclone fur consideratio factors, as

Capacity. bunkers sh at top load or equipme or where th desirable to

Material. inforced co clad plate, crete, and s lined carbo should be sion. Bunke cipal carbo reducing h coal stream ging occur. Th descri

---

tities of rock salt or calcium chloride required to freeze-proof coal at various temperatures.

TABLE 4
Calcium Chloride or Rock Salt
To Freeze-Proof Bituminous Coal
(Lb per Ton of Coal Treated)

Temp F	Surface Moisture		
	3%	6%	9%
20	3.4	6.8	10.2
10	5.0	10.6	15.0
0	6.6	13.2	19.8
-10	8.2	16.4	24.6
-20	9.2	18.4	27.6

Calcium chloride and also rock salt can be added as crystals or in solution, but in either case must be thoroughly mixed with the coal.

Sizing by Crushing and Screening

In America the earliest practice in the sizing of bituminous coal was to hand load the lump coal and to leave the small coal in the mine. Until around 1880, when mechanical stokers were introduced, practically all boilers were hand-fired with lump coal, and in early surface preparation plants at the mines it was the custom merely to screen out the lump coal and to discard the slack. With the adoption of the mechanical stoker the demand for smaller coal sizes increased, and to meet this demand equipment was installed at the mines to prepare the smaller sizes. The demand for smaller coal sizes again increased with the later development of pulverized coal firing, so that as early as 1946 approximately 33 per cent of all the bituminous coal shipped was under 2 in. maximum size. Because of the growing demand for coal of smaller sizing the price differential between run-of-mine and slack has been completely eliminated for many coals.

Sizing operations at steam plants are usually confined to crushing and pulverizing. Except in removing large impurities by the use of simple grids, screening at the plant is not generally required. For stoker-fired installations it is customary to specify coal of the proper size to suit the stoker, so that no sizing is necessary at the plant. For pulverized firing, after crushing if necessary, the coal is ground, to the very fine sizing required, in pulverizers generally integrated as a part of the firing equipment. Crushers are used for the coarser sizing required for Cyclone furnaces. When intended for pulverized firing it is common practice for steam plants to specify a maximum coal sizing with no limitation on the percentage of fines, so that the coal delivered will be suitable for crushing and pulverizing in the available equipment.

To save cost by taking advantage of market conditions, some pulverized coal or stoker-fired boiler plants have installed crushers to size the coal for pul-

---

verizing or, if necessary, for stoker use. If the most economical coal available is a slack which does not require sizing, the crusher may be by-passed. If a larger size such as run-of-mine coal is most economical, the crusher is used. In plants where both pulverized coal firing and stoker firing are used all the coal supplied may be sized to suit the stokers; crushing the portion going to the pulverizers if necessary. In this way the arrangement of storage and handling facilities is simplified.

Because of the wide diversity in use and characteristics of bituminous and lignite coals, no uniformly accepted sizings have been established. The screen sizes generally used in specifications conform to the ASTM standard D-431-44 "Designating the Size of Coal From Its Screen Analysis." Standard sizings of anthracite are definitely established as given in ASTM standard D-310-34.

Sizing Requirements

Generally acceptable coal sizings for various types of fuel burning equipment are given in the chapters covering the equipment. The degradation in coal sizing due to handling and slacking is an important consideration in establishing sizing specifications for steam plants where the maximum permissible quantity of fines in the coal is set by firing equipment limitations.

Crushers and Breakers

Numerous types of crushing and screening equipment are used commercially. Representative types are described below:

Bradford Breaker. The Bradford breaker (see Fig. 6) breaks the coal to predetermined size and rejects large refuse and tramp iron. It consists of a large cylinder rotating at approximately 20 rpm. The cylinder consists of steel-screen plates, the size of the screen openings determining the size of the crushed coal. The breaking action is accomplished by dropping the coal. The coal fed at one end of the cylinder is picked up by lifting shelves and carried up until the angle of the shelf permits the coal to drop. Because the gravity force used in shattering the coal is low, the production of fines is small. The Bradford breaker may be used at mine or plant.

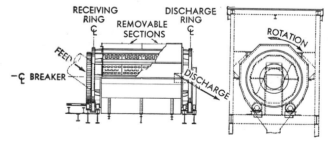

Fig. 6. Bradford breaker, for use at mine and plant

oxidation that takes place, at an exceedingly slow rate, seems to decrease the caking tendency. Weathering may not always be possible since it is usually the practice in storing coal to keep air from reaching the interior of the storage pile.

Size Limitation. Sizes of fuel best suited for the chain grate stoker are as follows: Bituminous coal should pass through 1 in. ring with not more than 60 per cent passing through 1/4 in. screen. The size for anthracite varies from No. 2, which is all through 5/16 in. and over 3/16 in., to No. 5, which is all through 3/64 inch. Coke breeze should pass through 3/8 in., with not more than 20 per cent passing through 3/32 inches. Lignite should be the same size as bituminous coal.

Rates of Burning

Chain grate stokers are now usually offered for a maximum continuous burning rate of from 425,000 to 500,000 Btu per sq ft per hr, with bituminous coal. For anthracite the corresponding rate is from 325,000 to 400,000 Btu per sq ft per hour.

For bituminous coals the lower burning rate noted above would apply to high moisture (20 per cent), high ash (20 per cent) coals as from some

Fig. 6. *Chain grate stoker for anthracite and coke breeze. Note long rear arch in furnace*

districts in Illinois, while
apply to more favorable
ash and 10 per cent
High caking coals, (free s
5, see ASTM-D-720 speci
for the traveling grate stok
burned (even up to an i
the chain grate stoker. W
centage of fines (greater
200 mesh) is chiefly resp
rate.

In all cases, coals of low
8 per cent, dry basis) do n
to protect the grates from
erally unsuitable for chain
stokers.

Air Temperature

The use of preheated air
stokers is not an unmixe
grate stoker is no exceptio
minous coals that burn
combustion air is deliver
show definite caking tend
plied for combustion exce
250F. However, it is pos
air temperature of 350F w
and, with anthracite and
temperature may go as hi
from the use of preheate
ignition with greater flexi
crease in overall boiler u

If the preheated air t
grates may overheat and
high velocity of hot air th
required with fine coal siz
carryover. Nevertheless,
with the chain grate stok
refinements of operation
there is a definite net gai

Ash Discharge and Dispos

Ashes are carried to the
dumped into the ash pit as
rear idler drum. From the
out by hand for final disp
equipment such as a wa
chain or hydraulic suction
be dumped directly into a
quenched. Coal ash from
readily saleable to the bu
special concrete and in t
blocks.

Change Over to Oil and (

Chain grate stoker furna
converted for auxiliary fir

portion of the fuel bed may be cleaned without affecting other portions. Coal feed to a section is stopped during the cleaning operation.

For medium and larger installations, over 75,000 lb of steam per hr and up to a maximum (300,000-350,000), the traveling grate, as shown in Fig. 4, provides a very satisfactory arrangement. In the type illustrated the direction of grate travel is from rear to front, with continuous ash discharge to a front ash pit. It is possible to have an arrangement with the direction of motion from front to rear.

One spreader stoker differs from others in that the grate is not level laterally. In this type, moreover, the individual grate sections are given an undulating motion, and the ash is discharged at the sides. This arrangement is illustrated in Fig. 11.

Furnace Design

Furnace walls, water-cooled to some degree, are used with most spreader stoker installations, as is the case with chain grate stokers. In general the extent of water cooling increases with the size of the installation and as the ash fusion temperature of the coal ash decreases. Water-cooled tubes in both side walls and rear wall and in the front wall are shown in Fig. 7. Also, as with the chain grate stoker, overfire air or steam jets are the most effective means of obtaining turbulence for completing the combustion of gases that may exist in stratified layers. In some cases the jet air is introduced at or in the vicinity of the rotor or it may be admitted through the arch as illustrated in Fig. 9. In general, the front, side and rear walls of a spreader stoker furnace, whether water-cooled or refractory, are vertical.

Drive Arrangement

Multiple rotors are conventionally driven from a line shaft extending across the stoker front. Means are provided for speed control. Sometimes the rotor drive is sectionalized so that one portion may be idle while the other is operating. The feeders may be similarly driven from a line shaft or may be independently driven by motor or turbine and a hydraulic drive may be used. The drive for the traveling grate is a separate unit with a variable speed transmission.

Air Distribution

Control of the quantity and distribution of combustion air is important, as it is with all methods of fuel burning. For the stationary or dump grate spreader stoker combustion air is compartmented from side to side, usually with one compartment for each spreader unit. On the other hand, the spreader stoker with traveling grate usually has one big plenum chamber (windbox) under the grate, al-

though very long stokers may be compartmented from front to rear.

Fuels and Fuel Bed

The spreader stoker, as already noted, is well adapted for coals with a wide range of burning characteristics, including those with caking tendencies. High moisture, free burning, bituminous and lignite coals are successfully burned as is also coke breeze and some varieties of wood fuel. In general, anthracite is not satisfactory for use with the spreader stoker.

Coal size segregation may be tolerated to a certain extent, since it is possible partly to compensate for the tendency toward a uniform fuel bed by varying the feed to individual spreader rotors. Coal of uniform size is not particularly well suited for the spreader stoker. This is especially true when the coal is all fines or all coarse. With too high a proportion of fines in the coal, too much of it will burn in suspension, with consequent increase in carryover, and if the coal is too coarse too much of it will burn on the grates. An optimum size consist is a mixture, fairly proportioned, from ¾ in. maximum to zero.

The fuel bed on a spreader stoker is relatively thin (less than 3½ in.) although burning rates may be attained of from 450,000 Btu on dumping grates, to 900,000 Btu per sq ft, hr on traveling grates. There is a tendency for spreader stokers to carry a smoky fire at low loads. This usually occurs at the lower end of a load range greater than about 4 to 1. As with chain grate stokers, overfire air or steam jets have been useful in obtaining sufficient turbulence to keep combustion at low loads and as already noted they are essential for an approach to complete combustion at the high loads.

Refuse Handling and Disposal

In a stationary grate installation ash is removed manually from the furnace, and, in the case of dumping grates, it is dumped into a shallow pit. From the traveling grate spreader stoker, ash is discharged continuously into a suitable ashpit, usually at the front. Final disposal from the ashpit may be by steam or water jet, ash conveyors, or by sluice or other arrangements. Spreader stoker ash is in considerable demand for use as aggregate in cinder block manufacture and for fill.

Control

The thin active fuel bed of a spreader stoker requires close regulation of fuel and air supply. Various types of automatic combustion controls are suitable and the air-flow, steam-flow type serves to proportion air and fuel more accurately than the simple positioning type. Coal feed and air flow are reduced when there is a drop in load. Since the fuel bed is thin there is little tendency to over-run steam pressure. For a load pickup, coal feed and air flow are increased and the response is immediate. In this respect the action of the spreader stoker is somewhat like pulverized coal, since a considerable portion of the fuel is burned in suspension. Distribution of coal on the fuel bed is usually controlled manually by regulation of the individual feeders and spreader rotors.

Cleaning Heating Surfaces

Usually, not much cleaning of furnace and boiler surfaces is necessary with this type of stoker. Occasionally, clinker on the side walls near the bottom may require removal if there is interference with fuel bed movement. Generally, the boiler heating surface remains fairly clean due to the natural cleaning action of the dust particles with which the gas is highly laden. Economizers and air heaters also tend to remain clean by this natural scrubbing from ash particles. However, with very high sulfur fuels and low gas end temperatures dewpoint conditions may be produced that are conducive to corrosive acid fouling. Such conditions should be anticipated in the design of the boiler unit. To keep metal temperatures up means should be provided for by-passing the air heater or recirculating air, as is sometimes done, to obtain the same result. With such difficult fuels, provision should also be made for periodic washing of the economizer or air heater and disposal of the corrosive wash water.

Aids to Operation and Low Maintenance

Observance of the practical suggestions listed below for the operation of a spreader stoker unit of stationary, dumping or traveling grate type, will improve performance and reduce maintenance cost:

1. The fire should be cleaned as rapidly as possible so that the whole grate will be back in service in the shortest time possible.

2. Do not operate stoker with one section of the grate clean and another dirty. The clean section will take most of the air and the other section will be smoky due to lack of air.

3. Do not allow ash to build up on the grate to a depth that makes blow holes or dead islands.

4. Keep grates in good condition.

5. Do not permit coal hopper to run empty.

6. Do not permit ashes to remain long in the ashpit.

7. Wet down the ash and remove.

8. Maintain good fuel distribution on the active grate area by adjustment of spreader controls.

Operating Procedure

Starting Fire. Preparatory to lighting-off, the spreader mechanism should be operated to spread the coal evenly over the grate to a depth of approximately 1 inch. Then the kindling which has been placed over a large portion of coal surface, should be ignited and the stoker spreaders should be started at slow speed. As fuel ignites the fan speeds or dampers should be adjusted to supply sufficient air for combustion. The furnace draft should be maintained at approximately 0.1 in. of water.

The coal and air supply to the stoker should be regulated to permit placing the boiler unit on the line in accordance with established procedure as specified by the boiler manufacturer. After this is done the steam demand will be the guiding factor in the operation of the stoker. In the case of the traveling grate spreader stoker, the stoker drive may be started at this time or slightly before the boiler goes on the line. In normal operation the thickness of ash carried by the grate at the point of dumping is the governing feature in adjusting the speed of grate travel. Normally, with common bituminous coals, ash thickness should be about 3 in. to 5 inches.

The cinder return fan and return lines should be put in operation whenever coal is fed.

The best fuel bed for spreader stoker operation is when the combustion rate over the entire active grate area is uniform and a minimum of excess air is used. Minimum excess air is commonly in the range from 25 per cent to 40 per cent. This value is somewhat higher than the normal practice for the chain grate stoker.

Banking Periods. When banking the boiler the coal feed and air supply to the stoker are reduced in accordance with the diminishing steam load until the boiler is at or near zero output. A layer of ash should be left on the grates for protection. To keep the fire on bank, it is best to add coal by directing it to the front or center of the fuel bed area to more or less concentrate it in a pile. To get a good fuel bed on bank some operators add coal through the access or rake-out doors with a shovel. Under banked condition, by regulating the furnace draft and position of the damper, sufficient air should be admitted to carry off the gases. The banked fire should be maintained by adding fresh coal from time to time as required.

To start up from bank the boiler damper and air supply should be adjusted as in starting the boiler, the banked fuel should be spread over the grate, and then proceed as in starting up.

Emergency Shutdown. For an emergency shutdown the coal feed and air supply to the fuel bed are shut off. This will reduce the burning rate to practically zero almost immediately, due to the small quantity of active fuel burning on the grate at any one time.

Underfeed Stoker

In the underfeed stoker coal is force-fed to the underside of the fuel bed, intermittently in small increments by a ram or continuously by a screw. The coal moves along in a longitudinal channel known as a retort, and as the volume increases it fills this space and spills over on each side to make and to feed the fuel bed. Air is supplied through tuyeres in the grate sections adjoining the retort on each side. As the coal rises from the retort it picks up oxygen from the incoming air and heat from the burning fuel above. Gases driven off by distillation burn on their way up through the incandescent fuel bed. As the feed moves up into the active burning area it is ignited by conduction from adjacent glowing particles of coal. Due to the pressure exerted by the incoming raw fuel and the agitation of the grates, the burning coal progresses slowly toward the ash discharge grates. Combustion is completed on the side grates or the extension grate and the ash is discharged at the dump grates. According to the design arrangement desired the ash may be discharged to the pit periodically or continuously.

Two Types of Underfeed Stoker

The underfeed stoker is classified in two types: (a) horizontal feed and (b) gravity feed. In the horizontal feed type, as the name implies the line of travel of the coal in the retort within the furnace is parallel to the station floor, while in the gravity type it is inclined at an angle of 20° to 25°. The latter type consequently requires a basement or tunnel under the floor for ash disposal while for the horizontal feed type only a shallow depression or pit is necessary.

Horizontal Feed

Only the multiple retort gravity type is suitable for the higher capacities within the range possible with an underfeed stoker. But the horizontal feed type, using a single, double or triple retort, was de-signed for reasonably high capacities under conditions where it is not feasible to provide either a basement or tunnel for ash disposal. A single retort stoker of this type is illustrated in Fig. 12. Double and triple retort stokers of this general type are quite similar in principle.

Two methods of feeding the coal from the hopper into the retort are used for horizontal feed single, double, and triple retort stokers: (a) by worm or screw and (b) by ram or plunger. For protection from the heat the mechanism for this purpose is located outside the fire zone. To receive the coal, to aid in its distribution on the fuel bed from front to rear, and to produce agitation for maintaining a level and porous fuel bed through which combustion air may pass, an adjustable reciprocating feed ram is usually provided in the bottom of the retort.

Grates. For the horizontal feed type of stoker a shearing type of grate, with alternating moving and stationary grate bars, is commonly used. The moving grate bars have a short rocking lateral motion. This motion in combination with the action of the reciprocating ram in the retort distributes the fuel evenly over the grate area and gradually moves the burned-out refuse to the side-dumping grates.

Another type of grate often used consists of links extending laterally from either side of the retort to the dump grate. They may number from 2 to 5 (see Fig. 13) depending upon the overall width of the stoker. The lateral sets of links are arranged in groups longitudinally with the retort, each group comprising a unit section assembled upon loose fitting rods. An oscillating shaft on each side, actuated by gears from the main driving mechanism, imparts a wave-like motion to the grates.

Air Distribution. Air for combustion is supplied, in quantities and at pressures suitable for the fuel bed conditions, from a plenum chamber (commonly known as the windbox) equipped with dampers for control to the various zones. Under certain conditions of operation some manufacturers use overfire air to complete combustion of the hydrocarbons and

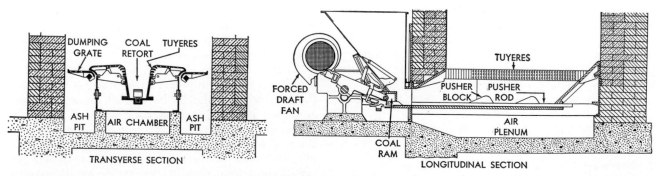

Fig. 12. *Underfeed single retort stoker*

16-14

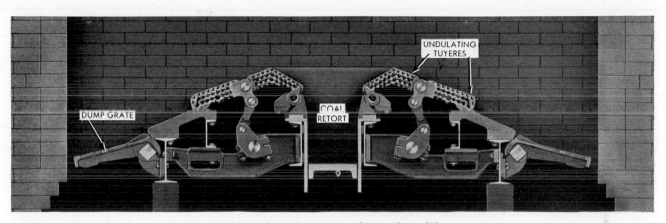

Fig. 13. *Underfeed single retort stoker with undulating grates*

thus prevent smoke. Combustion air may be pre-heated if desired.

Combustion may be said to take place in three well defined zones:

(a) A portion of the combustion air first comes in contact with the raw coal in the zone of the retort. Some drying and some degree of oxidation takes place in this zone. Volatile gases are driven off and the raw coal receives heat from the burning fuel above it.

(b) In the zone over the moving grates on either side of the retort, as the coal approaches the incandescent surface of the fuel bed, the combustible gases are thoroughly mixed with the proper quantity of air. On coking and burning the fuel is moved to either side by the lateral motion of the grates. By this movement the fuel bed is agitated constantly and thus kept in an active broken-up condition. Combustion of the fuel is nearing completion as the bed approaches the side grates and ash dump plates on either side of the stoker.

(c) The remaining combustible is burned out in the zone over the side grates and ash dump plates before the refuse is discharged to the ash pit.

Gravity Feed

The gravity feed type of underfeed stoker is usually longer than the horizontal feed type and is always fitted with multiple retorts. The multiple retort gravity feed stoker was a natural development of the principles successfully applied in the single retort. A typical installation of this type is illustrated in Fig. 14. The multiple retort stoker, as illustrated in Fig. 15 and Fig. 16, consists of a series of inclined single retorts placed side by side with tuyeres between and sloped from front to rear for constant discharge of ash. Each retort is equipped with a round or square primary ram which feeds the coal into the ram box at the head of the retort. From this point the fuel bed is moved slowly to the rear

and at the same time is forced upward over the bank of tuyeres by secondary pushers or by the moving bottom of the retort. Most of the air for combustion is admitted through the boxes supporting the tuyeres which are located between the retorts. An overfeed or cleanup section is provided at the rear end of the bank of tuyeres for completing combustion before the refuse is discharged to the pit for disposal.

Grates. It is evident from Fig. 15 that the grouping of retorts and tuyeres occupies about 2/3 of the

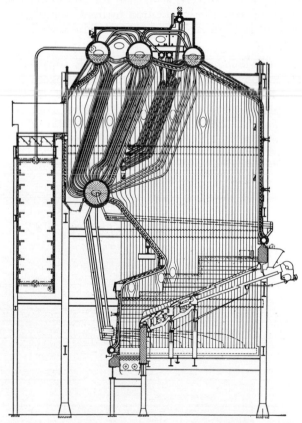

Fig. 14. *Multiple retort stoker in large Stirling boiler*

combustion surface. The more active burning lanes of the fuel bed are over the tuyere rows or air admission ports, while the relatively inactive fuel lanes are over the retorts. As the fuel bed completes its movement over the retorts and tuyere banks and reaches the extension-grate section, the burning lanes gradually widen. The constant agitation of the grate section keeps the fuel bed broken up and porous, permitting the gradual completion of the combustion of carbon. The ash then moves to the ash-discharge plates, where it is ejected in a continuous discharge for removal.

The extension grates permit the effective burning of coke in the refuse before it reaches the dumping grates. They are usually equipped with a reciprocating-action drive, either separately or in series with the pushers. The grates may be flat or placed in a stepped arrangement. The agitation of these grates keeps the fuel bed active, breaks up any large clinker formation, and moves the refuse to the dump grates.

The dump grates, or ash-discharge plates, located directly aft of the extension grates, rid the stoker of refuse after combustion of the fuel is completed. They may be arranged to lower at intervals to dump the accumulated ash and clinker into the pit, or they may be given a reciprocating motion by connection to the stoker mechanism for continuous discharge of ash. Air is admitted to most dump grates for the last possible stage of combustion before dumping.

Air Distribution. Air for combustion is supplied, as noted above for the horizontal-feed stoker, from a plenum chamber (windbox), and the quantity and pressure for the various sections are controlled by dampers. Most of the air is admitted through the tuyere blocks. A more elaborate system of controls is usually provided for these longer stokers of the gravity-feed type. The pressure for the various sections is indicated by gages so that a closer control can be maintained for greater efficiency. With closer control of combustion air it is also possible to obtain higher burning rates without serious increase in maintenance cost.

Features Applicable to Both Types

Fuel-Bed Contour. In either type of underfeed stoker using multiple retorts, as the coal leaves the ram boxes and enters the furnace, a cross section of the flow of the fuel bed takes on a sine-wave contour. The crest of each wave will be directly over the retorts which are the channels of feed, while the trough will be over the tuyere sections. Most of the air for combustion is admitted through the tuyeres. By lateral flow from the adjacent retorts the coal is distributed over the tuyeres, and these zones become the active burner lanes, with much slower burning over the retorts, as previously noted. In the gravity-feed type, as the fuel bed approaches the lower end of the grate, particularly the overfeed or clean-up section, the contour tends to level out.

Stoker Drives. The type of mechanical drive for the underfeed stoker will depend upon plant load conditions and the flexibility desired. Motors are commonly used where the application is for low-pressure boilers or when mechanical power is not produced at the plant. Where sufficient steam pressure is available, a steam turbine or reciprocating steam-engine drive may be used to advantage, particularly when the steam required is a factor in heat balance conditions. The speed range and flexibility of stoker drives may be increased by variable-speed transmission. To protect stoker parts from damage, the driving mechanism is equipped with a shearing-pin device.

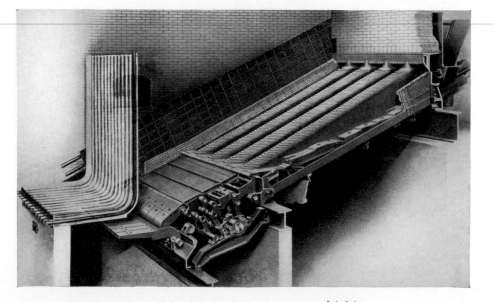

Fig. 15. Multiple-retort stoker showing details of components

16-16

Sor
mizer
The
econc
coal
comp
phosp
a bor
is in
seque

Alt
there
boile
exces
of ga
surfa
gases
of sn
the fl
and

Cle
effici
walls
funct
produ
tema
proce
tubes
forma
regul
water

Th
clean
upon
optin
by u
guide
draft
posit
tion,
ash a
it m
econ

Cir
the u
rate,
fired.
sq ft
burn
gases
a mu
high
per

Ge

Fo
stoke

Two types of hydraulic drive systems are used. In one a constant speed motor or turbine drives a variable displacement oil pump, fitted with proportioning valves, which supplies oil pressure for all drives and controls required for operating the stoker. In the other type the oil pressure from the pump acts directly on the hydraulic cylinder driving the rams and the mechanism for agitating the grates.

Rams and Ram Boxes. Most rams are cylindrical, some are rectangular. They may be horizontal or inclined at the angle of the grate. Usually the ram boxes have renewable wear plates. In the case of the rectangular boxes the wear plates may be adjustable. By the use of separate adjustments for each ram and distributor or retort pusher, the quantity of coal fed to the stoker as well as its distribution from front to rear within the furnace can be closely regulated. These adjustments are made while the stoker is in operation. Therefore, regardless of the variation in the kind and condition of the raw feed, the fuel bed can be maintained at the proper thickness and distribution for efficient operation.

Tuyeres. Tuyeres are mounted between the retorts and, as assembled in banks (shown in Fig. 15), provide a system of graduated openings for admission of the proper quantity of air for combustion. Long webs provide effective air cooling, which, with minimum exposure to heat, assures long life. Side tuyeres are usually provided to prevent clinker adhesion to the side wall brickwork. Side tuyeres permit the use of water-cooled or air-cooled walls when desired.

Ash Discharge. In the horizontal feed, single, double or triple retort stoker the ash discharge is usually at the sides. The ash may accumulate on the dump plates at the sides, to be disposed of periodically, or for units equipped with moving dump grate sections it may be discharged continuously into a pit.

In the gravity feed multiple retort stoker, as previously noted, ash is disposed of at the rear. Dump grates that open intermittently are usually operated by a steam or air cylinder. The period of intermittent dumping will depend upon the percentage of ash in the coal and the combustion rates per retort. Water sprays are normally installed in the ash pit to cool the refuse immediately after dumping. Ash hoppers of ample capacity should be provided for this type of stoker. Higher efficiency is possible with continuous discharge of ash, because of the reduction in carbon loss and lower excess air requirements. With this method it is also possible to obtain higher capacities with a more flexible load range. In this type of installation, particularly where the ash is to be removed by sluicing, clinker grinders are usually fitted. The grinders may be single or double rolls, driven by a separate motor, a drive chain from the stoker shaft or a hydraulic cylinder,

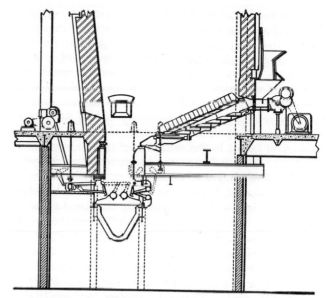

Fig. 16. *Multiple retort stoker showing drive and clinker grinder ash discharge*

depending upon plant preference or conditions. Grinders usually have replaceable teeth.

Use of Water Cooling. In the early days of stoker application furnaces were of all-refractory construction. As furnaces became larger and burning rates increased, it became necessary to improve furnace wall and grate construction to meet the new requirements. This was done by the use of water cooling. Water-cooled tubes absorb radiant heat and protect the refractory. The retorts and tuyeres have sometimes been water-cooled to lower the fuel bed temperature and to chill the ash. This helps to prevent closing the air ports by slag and thereby to lengthen the life of the parts.

Suitable Coal Characteristics. A wide range of coal can be used with either type of underfeed stoker. The horizontal feed type is better suited for free burning bituminous and will also burn anthracite with satisfactory results. On the other hand, in the gravity feed stoker, caking coals having a relatively high ash fusion temperature will give good results, while free burning coals have a tendency to drift and avalanche.

The size of the coal has a considerable effect on the relative capacity and efficiency of a boiler-stoker combination. For optimum size, experience indicates that the largest percentage of the fuel should be 3/4 in., with maximum size 1 1/2 in., and not more than 50 per cent to pass through a 5/16 in. round sieve. A non-stratified distribution of the raw coal across the hopper is important, particularly for a stoker with multiple retorts. By reducing the percentage of fines, to help keep the fuel bed more porous, a wider choice is possible of coals with a high coking index.

this is due principally to the type of fuel bed which is ordinarily heavier than for any other method of stoker burning. The combustion air pressure required is, therefore, appreciably higher than for the chain grate stoker. For high loads, a windbox pressure of 5 to 6 in. of water is normal.

For the correct operation of a large underfeed stoker, in addition to observation of the fire, it is essential to give close attention to the readings of draft gages and panel board instruments, and to act promptly in making the adjustments required as indicated by these readings. Depending upon the burning characteristics of the coal used, depth of the fuel bed above the top of the tuyeres may vary between 12 in. to 30 inches.

Starting Fire. To start the fire with a horizontal feed type stoker, it should be run at minimum motion to feed in sufficient coal to cover the moving grate surface to a depth of 3 inches. The coal should be spread manually to a uniform thickness. Kindling or oiled waste should be placed over the coal on each side of the retort. Just before igniting the kindling, the boiler damper and windbox door should be opened. When the coal is well ignited the stoker should be operated at a sufficient speed to replace the coal being burned. When load is to be placed on the boiler, the windbox should be closed and forced draft should be supplied.

When initially feeding raw coal into the stoker, an even distribution of fuel should be maintained by observing the contour of the fuel bed, and then, as the stoker picks up load, the supply of fuel and combustion air should be adjusted for the correct thickness of fuel bed. The correct thickness will depend somewhat on the width of the stoker and the type of coal used; and the depth of the fuel bed over the tuyeres may vary within the limits noted above. Usually low volatile coals can best be burned with a heavy fuel bed. Coarser size coal will require a heavier fuel bed.

The gravity feed type of stoker will require about 8 in. to 9 in. of fuel distributed over the tuyeres of the underfeed section. A fire should be started by lighting oiled waste or kindling placed on the top close to the front wall. When ignition is well established, light air pressure can be applied to hasten burning. After sufficient ash has accumulated to protect the tuyeres and the moving and dump grate section, the stoker can be put in general operation. The stoker should not be forced until the fuel bed is in a good coked condition and evenly distributed.

Normal Operation. The best fuel bed is the one which carries the load with just enough thickness to burn freely throughout the length of the stoker when operating with the desired quantity of excess air. Distribution and agitation of the fuel bed is controlled by adjustments to the stoker mechanism.

Speed will control the fire for proper thickness and length.

Banking. Ash should not be dumped just before banking, since it is best in this condition to leave as much ash as possible on the stoker. In anticipating banking the fire should be burned down thinner than for normal operation, and, if practical, the coal hopper should be emptied. After the stoker is stopped and the forced draft is cut off, the boiler damper should be closed gradually as the furnace cools. If it is necessary to bank with coal in the hopper, the stoker should be run a few minutes every hour until the hopper is empty or the boiler is again under load.

Emergency Shutdown. The object of an emergency shutdown is, of course, to stop the heat release of combustion as quickly as possible.

The best procedure to follow in an emergency shutdown due to the sudden loss of load would be as follows: The stoker should be stopped. The forced draft fan should be shut off and the damper should be closed tight. All doors in the boiler above the grate line should be opened. Under these conditions burning of the fuel bed will be retarded, and, with the admission of air above the grate, the furnace will be permitted to cool gradually. Water should not be used on the fire as the rapid expansion of gases and steam or the generation of hydrogen may cause an explosion.

In the case of a water-wall tube or a boiler tube failure where the steam and water is discharged into the furnace proper, the steam and water so discharged usually serve to extinguish the fire. Under such circumstances the problem is to keep the gases and steam confined within the setting to protect the personnel. Furnace doors should have lock latches for this reason.

For an emergency shutdown due to low water within the boiler, the operating procedure so far as the stoker is concerned should be as in the case of sudden loss of load. Detailed procedure for the protection of the boiler is covered in Chapter 21.

Change Over to Oil or Gas, All Type Stokers. Oil or gas burners can be applied to underfeed stoker-fired furnaces. Certain precautions must be observed, however, when arranging to burn oil or gas alternately with coal. If the burning of the alternate fuel is on a temporary basis a good layer of stoker ash will serve to protect the grates. If the change over is to be for a period of several days, the grates should be protected in a more permanent way by using firebrick. For an extended period it may be expedient to remove the stoker and to build a false refractory floor over the steel work. On the other hand, if the gas or oil burners are to be idle for some time it probably will be desirable to brick-in the burner openings to prevent plugging of the parts by slag.

PULVERIZED-COAL EQUIPMENT

O F the three commercial fuels, coal, petroleum, and natural gas, found in abundance and widely distributed in the United States, coal is predominant and indispensable for domestic and industrial use. Because of its distribution, availability, and stable price, coal is the basic fuel for the generation of steam in the production of light and power. The production of bituminous coal in the United States in 1947 was 619,000,000 tons, compared with an average of 491,000,000 tons per year for the period 1920-1924.

The preparation and burning of coal in pulverized form are covered in the present chapter. Hand firing has been almost entirely replaced by mechanical means. For stoker firing see Chapter 16. The burning of coal in a Cyclone Furnace and the application of this method to steam-generating units are covered in Chapter 28.

Development of Pulverized-Coal Firing

While pulverized-coal firing has been used for over 100 years, its successful application goes back some 50 years when it was first used in firing cement kilns. At the present time practically 90 per cent of the fuel used in the cement industry is coal in pulverized form. About 1910, before the fuel oil and natural gas era, pulverized coal was recognized as a valuable fuel in the iron and steel industry, and it was adopted in the nonferrous-metal industry soon thereafter.

Because of the economic advantages of pulverized coal over hand and stoker firing as a result of higher thermal efficiency, reduction in labor cost, and flexibility in operation, there has been a progressive increase in its use for power generation in public utility and industrial plants and for process-steam generation. Pulverized coal is now the outstanding fuel in electric-utility and industrial-power generation. It has made possible, in no small degree, the development of large steam-generating units and the improvement of the steam cycle. With modern equip-

ment it is possible to burn efficiently, dependably, successfully, and safely almost any kind of coal mined in the United States. Pulverized coal can be burned and controlled as effectively as gas.

Properties of Pulverized Coal

The weight of crushed coal and freshly dried pulverized coal varies as noted in Table 1.

TABLE 1

Weight of Crushed Coal and Pulverized Coal

Kind of Coal	Weight, lb/cu ft
¾-in. crushed average bituminous	45 to 55
½-in. crushed anthracite	45
Pulverized dry bituminous	35 to 45

Freshly prepared pulverized coal when mixed with air has the inherent physical characteristics of a fluid, in that it can be transported through pipes in the same manner as liquid or gaseous fuels. It can be burned in suspension with a long or short flame and with a small amount of excess air matched only in burning gas and in the Cyclone Furnace.

Although it is possible to pulverize and burn successfully and with safety almost any kind of coal mined in the United States, high- and medium-volatile bituminous coals are predominantly used for pulverizing. With high-volatile coal, which burns much more readily, it is possible to operate at wider range than with low-volatile coal, such as anthracite. High-volatile coal need not be pulverized to as high a degree of fineness as low-volatile coal to insure stable ignition.

The character rather than the amount of the ash is important in burning pulverized coal. Ash-fusion characteristics are important in the design of the combustion chamber, surface arrangements, and the burning equipment for steam generation. On the other hand, the composition of the ash becomes an important factor in process and metallurgical applications, as some of the elements chemically or physically may affect the product being heated.

The sulfur in the coal, together with the ash, usually is an index of the abrasiveness of the coal which will affect the rate of wear on the grinding elements. However, coals high in sulfur and ash are not necessarily hard coals to pulverize. Sulfur in the coal usually occurs in the form of iron sulfides known as pyrites. Unless the coal is washed at the mine, all the pyrites will go through the pulverizing equipment, causing excessive wear of the equipment and usually with undesirable effect in the furnace. Pulverized high sulfur coal is not suitable for metallurgical or process work and is usually limited to the generation of steam and heating processes where the gas and ash do not come in contact with the products being processed.

One of the important characteristics of coal is the grindability index which indicates the relative hardness of one coal with respect to a standard material of "unit" grindability. Usually the capacity of the pulverizer is proportional to the grindability index and this is taken into account in the selection of pulverizing equipment. A complete explanation of the grindability index appears later in this chapter.

Controllable Factors

Inherent properties of pulverized coal such as grindability, volatile and ash content, and the like vary with the type of coal and locality from which it is mined, and these are uncontrollable as received at point of use. The controllable factors in the production and efficient combustion of pulverized coal are: (a) preparation as to size; (b) fineness; (c) moisture content; (d) density of coal-air mixture; (e) conveyance in suspension. These are the basic factors which must be considered in selecting and designing equipment for efficient and economical burning of pulverized coal. All of these factors will affect the operation and the results obtained with the equipment.

Preparation. The main item of cost in the preparation of pulverized coal is power. Therefore, the burden on the pulverizer should be reduced by preliminary preparation of the coal outside the mill, where it can be done at a much lower cost. The raw coal should be crushed to sizes which will pass through a ¾ in. and 1¼ in. ring, respectively, for small to medium and medium to large size pulverizers. To insure an uninterrupted and uniform supply, the crushed coal is conveyed to the pulverizer over an electric magnetic separator to remove tramp iron.

Fineness. Coal fineness may be considered as the most important factor in the successful application of pulverized coal, both for steam generation and industrial furnaces. The degree of fineness required will vary for different coals and applications, but for practical purposes the specifications noted in Table 2 may be used.

"Ignition-wise," bituminous coal may be classified in two groups: (1) high volatile (volatile over about 30 per cent), free burning coals, and (2) medium volatile (volatile between about 20 and 30 per cent), coking coals. The particles of free burning coal, when exposed to heat in an oxygen containing atmosphere, burn without growing in size and, therefore, the carbon tends to be consumed within the burning zone. The particles of coking coal, on the other hand, tend to grow in size, liberating the volatile matter, and, because of the reduction in specific weight, tend to float out of the burning zone before the carbon is consumed. This is the reason for the difference in fineness requirements for high and medium volatile bituminous coals.

The lack of volatile for the generation of heat for ignition of the carbon particles is the reason for the

TABLE 2

Required Pulverized Fuel Fineness at Maximum Rating
Per Cent Through #200 Sieve*

	Fuel Classification					
	FC 97.9%	FC 85.9%	FC 76.9%	FC Below 69%		
Type of Furnace	to 86% Pet. coke	to 77%	to 69%	Btu above 12,900	Btu from 12,900 to 11,000	Btu below 11,000
Marine boiler	—	85	80	80	75	—
Stationary water-cooled boiler						
Max. input below 15MkB	85	80	75	75	70	65
Max. input above 15MkB	80	75	70	70	65	60
Metallurgical	—	85	80	80	80	—
Cement kiln	85	80	80	80	80	—

* The 200 mesh screen (sieve) has 200 openings per linear in. or 40,000 openings per sq. inch. From U. S. and ASTM sieve series the nominal aperture for 200 mesh is 0.0029 in. or 0.074 mm. The ASTM designation for 200 mesh is 74 microns.

high degree of fineness required for anthracite and petroleum coke. Heat radiated from the surrounding surface, and high uniform fineness are important factors in the successful burning of pulverized anthracite and petroleum coke.

Production of the fine coal is a costly operation, both in power and maintenance. Therefore, careful consideration should be given to the selection of equipment for each application. The relation between fineness on the one hand and power and also maintenance on the other, for any given type of coal, is illustrated in Fig. 1. This relation is based on bituminous coal and a grindability index of 50.

Moisture. While it is an over simplification to refer to "surface" and "inherent" as the moisture forms in coal these terms are used in this discussion as a matter of convenience. The term "surface" moisture has been generally replaced by the term "air dried" moisture as determined by ASTM procedures. Total moisture is also determined by ASTM procedures. The value of the "inherent" moisture component might therefore be taken as the difference between the established values for total moisture and the air dried moisture component. Reference to moisture in coal also appears in *Industrial Standards and Engineering Information* (1947) issued by ABAI.

The inherent moisture will vary with the type of coal and locality of mine. Performance of the pulverizing equipment and combustion are adversely affected by surface moisture, and it should, therefore, be removed from the coal before or while in the process of pulverization. Surface moisture in the coal, as fed into the pulverizer, under a temperature below the dewpoint, tends to cause the fine particles to conglomerate. This reduces the pulverizer capacity because of inability to effect efficient separation in the grinding zone. Furthermore, this same action, causing the finely divided particles to adhere in small masses, has the same effect on combustion as coarse coal. Drying is therefore, an important factor in efficient and economical preparation and burning of pulverized coal. Drying may be done externally in a separate dryer; or in the pulverizer, by supplying pre-heated air to the grinding zone. Drying in the pulverizer is the accepted and almost exclusive practice for all methods of burning pulverized coal.

The extent of drying within a given pulverizer depends on its design and the method employed in introducing pre-heated air into the grinding zone. Raw coals with very high surface moisture can be very efficiently dried when fed into the grinding zone of pulverizers designed for high circulating load. On the other hand, where the design does not permit rapid mixing of raw coal with the partially dried coal within the grinding zone the pulverizer

is not suitable for handling high moisture coal, and the grinding efficiency will drop as the surface moisture increases.

The two controllable factors in drying are temperature and weight of air, since the total heat is the product of the temperature, specific heat and the weight of air injected with the coal. However, for a given pulverizer performance the volume of air is usually a fixed quantity, which leaves the temperature of the air injected with the coal as the only variable factor. In all cases for satisfactory drying the pulverizer outlet temperature should be maintained at not less than 25F above the dewpoint of the air leaving. This temperature usually ranges between 130 and 160F, while the temperature of the air injected with the coal may run as high as 500 to 600F, depending on the surface moisture and the type of pulverizer.

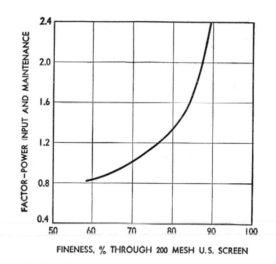

Fig. 1. *How power and also maintenance vary with fineness of coal pulverization*

The relation between fuel per lb of air and temperature of air entering pulverizer for various surface moistures for a particular type of pulverizer is shown in Fig. 2. As noted, the relation is a straight line function of weight of air and temperature for any given per cent of surface moisture in the coal.

Density of Coal-Air Mixture. The air-coal ratio may be defined as the weight of air per unit weight of coal injected with the coal into the pulverizer, and in practice, is known as the primary air-coal ratio because, through usage this same air, which also conveys the coal beyond the pulverizer (to the burners in a direct fired system, for instance), has become known as primary air. The ratio may be expressed in lb of air per lb of coal or cu ft of air at stated temperature per lb of coal.

The primary air ratio is a variable quantity within the pulverizer operating range, and, to some degree, it will vary with the type of coal, and the design of the pulverizer. In general, the primary air ratio increases with a decrease in grindability and decreases with a decrease in volatile matter. Most pulverizers are designed to operate at rated load with approximately 15 to 25 per cent of the total air used for combustion. This ratio increases with a decrease in pulverizer output, the limiting factor being ability to maintain ignition. The increase or decrease in primary air ratio will, in a given pulverizer, vary the effect on the classification of the coal particles and conveyance of coal to the burner.

Conveyance in Suspension. Regardless of the fineness of the coal particles, they are still solids, and, to keep them in suspension, conveying or carrying air velocities of definite values are required through the conveying lines. The required velocities expressed in feet per minute vary with the average particle size but in common practice, the velocities noted in Table 3 may be considered typical. Velocity in excess of that necessary to maintain the coal particles in suspension serves no useful purpose and increases operating cost. Heated air is beneficial in moving pulverized coal through the conveying lines, as it tends to minimize segregation and stratification. The velocities given in Table 3 are based on a conveying air temperature of 150F.

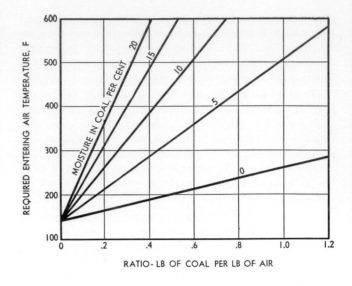

ASSUMED CONDITIONS

1. FUEL AND MOISTURE ENTERING PULVERIZER AT 32F (NOT FROZEN)
2. OUTLET TEMPERATURE, 130F
3. RADIATION LOSSES OFFSET BY CONVERSION OF ELECTRICAL ENERGY TO HEAT IN GRINDING

Fig. 2. *Air temperatures and coal-air ratios to evaporate surface moisture of coal within pulverizer*

TABLE 3

Average Velocity of Primary Air and Coal Mixture Through Conveying Pipes
Air-Coal Ratio 2 lb Air per lb Coal

Pulverized coal fineness, % through 200 mesh screen	70	80	85
Normal velocity ft per min	5000	4500	4000
Minimum velocity ft per min	3000	2500	2000

Major Pulverized Coal Systems

In general, there are three systems currently in use in processing, distributing and burning pulverized coal in the generation of steam, manufacture of cement and metallurgical heating processes. These are: (a) bin system; (b) direct-firing system; (c) direct-firing circulating system.

In all three systems, the coal is pre-dried or dried while being pulverized, and it is pulverized to a fineness suitable for the particular application. Each system has been developed to meet the requirements in various fields. The development and improvement in coal pulverizing and burning equipment have had a marked influence on the trend in the use of the three systems.

Bin System

The bin system was the forerunner of the large scale use of pulverized coal in the cement industry, metallurgical process heating and manufacture of iron, and for steam generation. In this system, the coal is processed at a location apart from the furnace. The distance of the processing plant from the point of application is limited only by available means for transporting the coal.

Elements of the bin system are dryers, pulverizers and transport. The coal is dried, pulverized, and classified continuously in the pulverizer. The finished product is pneumatically conveyed to cyclone collectors, where approximately 98 per cent of the coal is separated and discharged by gravity into storage bins or hoppers. The remaining 2 per cent is not always, but should be recovered in suitable equipment, such as cloth filters or high efficiency cyclones, and the clear gas vented to the atmosphere. When partial venting is used, the recirculated gas or air carries with it a proportional amount of fuel, generally with a reduction in pulverizer efficiency in the same proportion. From storage the pulverized coal is conveyed by pneumatic transport through pipe lines to bins at the location where it is used, sometimes as far as 2000 to 5000 ft from the point of preparation, although usually only 100 to 500 feet. At the beginning of the century, the coal was pre-dried in rotary or other type dryers of various designs. Pre-dried coal was pulverized in an air swept or screen type gravity discharge pulverizer, and the finished product was transported to bins at the point of use.

The disadvantages of pre-drying coal, including

some attendant dust nuisance and incidence of fires, and the increased demand for coal pulverizing equipment in the generation of steam and in the metallurgical field, led to the development of a bin system (see above) where the coal is dried, pulverized, and classified in the pulverizer. This required the use of pre-heated air through the pulverizer and partial or total venting, depending on the moisture in the coal and the air temperature. Bin systems of this type are illustrated in Fig. 3, and a typical transport system is shown in Fig. 4.

Bin system vents are usually connected to dust cleansing devices, such as cloth filters, or steam-water washers, although some vents discharge to the atmosphere or stack. The dust from the cloth filters is recovered. The dust precipitated in the dust washers is lost with the water in the form of sludge, the disposal of which is often a major problem. In this case, the operating cost increases with the value of the coal washed away and the cost of water and steam.

For the coal-air transport system a spiral conveyor is provided to continuously feed pulverized coal into a pipe line at the entrance of which the coal is aerated or fluidized, so that it will flow through the pipe somewhat like a heavy fluid. A spiral conveyor pump is shown in Fig. 5. The transport line may run in any direction, underground, overhead, within the building or outdoors, with numerous bends, risers, and branch lines. Through a system of two-way valves the coal can be distributed to any number of bins. The system may be arranged for any combination of control, manual, remote and completely automatic. Air transport systems are built in sizes from 1 to 100 tons of pulverized coal per hour. For successful operation the moisture in the pulverized coal must not be over 3 per cent, and the fineness should not be less than 90 per cent through 50 mesh screen. An application of a pump for conveying fly ash is illustrated in Fig. 6.

Features of the Bin System

Pulverized coal was used extensively before pulverizing equipment had reached the stage of development where it could be relied on for continuous, uninterrupted operation, flexibility, and consistent performance. In that period the bin system served as a means of insuring a continuous supply of pulverized coal in a plant where no other fuel was available as a standby.

Where the coal has to be pre-dried in this system before it is pulverized, it is possible to handle very high moisture coal, which cannot be done with other means of pulverized coal preparation. It also has some advantage in pulverized anthracite firing since this fuel can be stored in bins with comparative safety from fires, and with its low volatile content

it is easier to maintain stability of ignition over a wide load range.

However, there are serious inherent disadvantages in the use of the bin system. Except with anthracite, storage of pulverized coal for any length of time involves fire hazard due to spontaneous combustion. Under certain conditions there may even be serious explosions of coal gas emanating from the fuel in

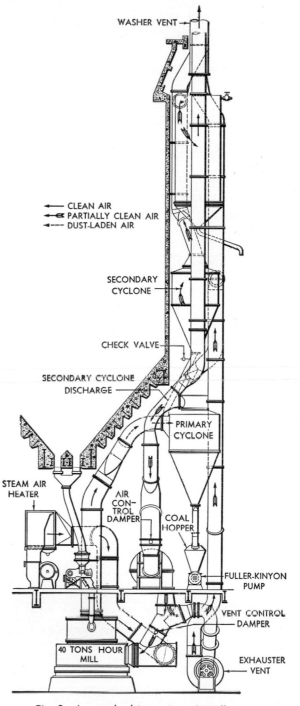

WASHER VENT

← CLEAN AIR
← PARTIALLY CLEAN AIR
←--- DUST-LADEN AIR

SECONDARY CYCLONE

CHECK VALVE

SECONDARY CYCLONE DISCHARGE

PRIMARY CYCLONE

STEAM AIR HEATER

AIR CONTROL DAMPER

COAL HOPPER

FULLER-KINYON PUMP

VENT CONTROL DAMPER

40 TONS HOUR MILL

EXHAUSTER VENT

Fig. 3. *An early bin system installation (1930). Coal dried within pulverizer*

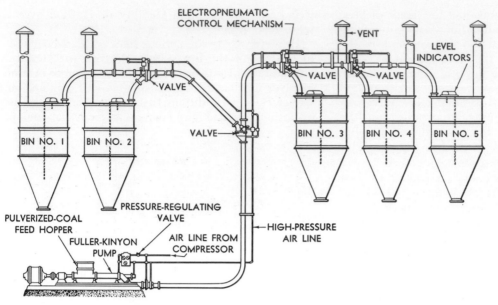

Fig. 4. Pneumatic transport system for conveying pulverized coal. Capacity, 1 to 100 tons per hour

the bin. Freshly pulverized coal is hygroscopic in character, and, after a time, it will pack and hang in the corners of the storage bin. This is to a minor extent true even with anthracite. In processing coal for storage, from one third to all of the air circulating through the pulverizer must be vented. Unless suitable dust-cleansing devices are provided, the vents will create a nuisance, and coal will be lost. Close temperature control and supervision are necessary to prevent fires in separately fired dryers. Both the initial investment and operating costs are higher.

In general, the bin system for new installations in the metallurgical industry or for steam generation has been superseded by the direct-firing system because of the greater advantages of the latter in simplicity, low cost of operation, and lower initial investment.

Direct-Firing System

Increasing demand in the electric utility field for generating units of greater capacity and higher pressure and temperature led, in the period 1920 to 1925, to the development on a larger scale than before of pulverizing equipment to permit direct and continuous firing of coal processed as received without predrying and storage as in the bin system. A direct-firing installation is simple and efficient, and, since the raw coal is dried and pulverized simultaneously in the mill as used, the cost of operation and the initial investment are lower. The costly and, to some degree, hazardous operations of storing the pulverized coal and the complication of feeding and remixing required with the bin system are eliminated. Typical direct-firing installations are illustrated in Figs. 7, 8, and 9.

Fig. 5. Fuller-Kinyon pump used in transporting pulverized coal

Components of the direct-firing system, in general, are:

a) A steam or gas air heater to supply hot air through the pulverizer for drying the coal as pulverized.

b) A pulverizer fan, known as the primary air fan, arranged either as an exhauster or as a blower.

c) A pulverizer arranged to operate under suction or pressure.

d) Automatically controlled raw coal feeder.

e) Coal and air conveying lines to the burners.

The two methods of direct-firing in common use are differentiated as suction and pressure by the manner in which the primary air is moved through the pulverizer. In the suction method, the air and entrained coal are drawn through the pulverizer by an exhauster, located on the outlet side of the pulverizer. In this case the fan handles a mixture of coal and air, and distribution of the mixture to more than one burner is controlled by a distributor located beyond the fan discharge. In the pressure method, the fan, located on the inlet side of the pulverizer, either forces cold air through a steam air heater or handles pre-heated air from a gas air heater. In this case the fan handles air only. Distribution of the coal and air mixture takes place within the pulverizer housing, which is more positive than distribution by the suction method with its external classifier following the the fan. The principal differences between suction and pressure methods are summarized in Table 4.

Fig. 6. Fuller-Kinyon pump conveys fly-ash to storage (25 tons/hr). Rotary single-stage compressor at left

Features of the Direct-Firing System

In the direct-firing system the coal is dried in the pulverizer while it is being pulverized, and the finished product moves to the burners in a continuous, uninterrupted operation. The direct-firing system is widely used for steam generation, cement manufacture, and in melting iron and non-ferrous metals. The advantages of this system are:

a) Reliability in operation.

b) Flexibility in control.

c) Safety from fire hazard.

d) Low operating cost.

e) Compactness of the installation and low first cost.

Disadvantages of the direct-firing system are few

TABLE 4
Direct-Firing Suction and Pressure Systems

Method	Suction	Pressure
Type of fan	Exhauster	Blower
Location of fan	Pulverizer outlet	Pulverizer inlet
Fan construction	Explosion proof	Standard
Fan is handling	Pulverized coal and air	Air only
Relative fan eff	Low	High
Fan wear	High	Low to none
Pulverized coal distribution	Tends to be difficult	Good

Coal feed and air to the pulverizer are controlled in two ways: 1) The coal feed is adjusted so that it is proportional to the load demand, and the primary air supply is regulated to the rate of feed. 2) The primary air through the pulverizer is controlled so that it is proportional to the load demand, and the coal feed is automatically regulated to the rate of air flow. In either case, a definite air to coal ratio is maintained for any given load.

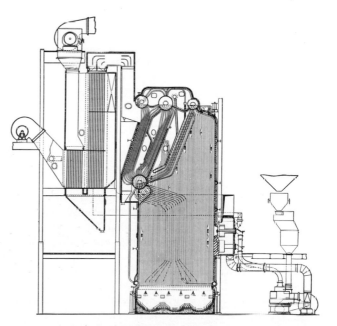

Fig. 7. Stirling boiler direct-fired with pulverized coal

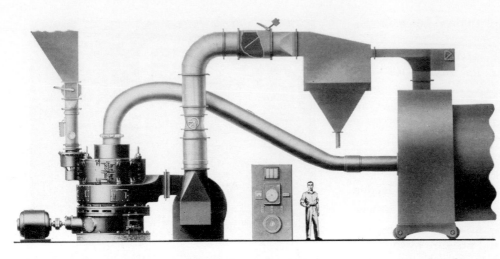

Fig. 8. Rotary cement kiln
direct-fired with
pulverized coal

and minor. The operating range of the pulverizer is usually not more than 3 or 4 to 1, because the air velocities in lines and other parts of the system should not go below the minimum values required to insure keeping the coal in suspension (see Fig. 23). With more than a single burner per pulverizer and with multiple pulverizers and multiple burners per boiler unit, this limitation rarely exists in practice. If the inlet air to the pulverizer is hot enough, coals with total moisture up to 20 per cent (surface moisture 15 per cent) can be dried in the pulverizer. For these extremely high-moisture coals an inlet air temperature of 600 F is practical. Outside drying of coal going to a pulverizer has become practically an obsolete procedure in this country.

Direct-Firing Circulating System

With a direct-firing circulating system (a modification of the direct-firing system) it is possible independently to control the coal supply, at various capacities, to each of a number of small and large furnaces located in separate areas throughout a plant. A typical installation is illustrated in Fig. 10.

There is a close similarity between this system and firing with gaseous fuel, in that the fuel supply is controlled by valves at the point of consumption regardless of the location of the coal pulverizer. Throughout the operating range of the unit, the density of the coal-air mixture is automatically maintained by the feeder controller. A uniform mixture of the coal-and-air fluid is maintained throughout the distributing system by using air velocity sufficiently high under all load conditions and by recirculating a portion of the fluid through the conveying lines.

The direct-firing circulating system was developed primarily to serve process-heating industrial furnaces, located over a large area and inaccessible to a main raw-coal supply. A multiplicity of small-capacity burners individually controlled is generally used for process furnaces, and the circulating

system provides the required control flexibility. The distributing line may be carried overhead or underground to clear obstacles on its way to various furnaces. Each burner take-off, large or small, can be independently controlled for more or less fuel, or shut off entirely. This system has been effectively applied in the malleable iron, chemical, and cement industries as a substitute for gas and oil firing.

Advantages. The principal advantages of the direct-firing circulating system are:

1. Distribution and control of pulverized coal, in much the same manner as gaseous fuel, to widely scattered furnaces for process heating.

2. Freedom from fire hazard, since dryers for predrying the coal and storage of pulverized coal are not required.

3. Convenient location of the coal-pulverizing equipment irrespective of the location of the furnaces to be served.

Disadvantages. The disadvantages of the direct-firing circulating system are:

a) The high total-power consumption per ton of fuel output, which varies inversely with the size of the system and directly as the length of the distributing line. A comparison of the power input required per ton of fuel output for a direct-firing circulating system (for various

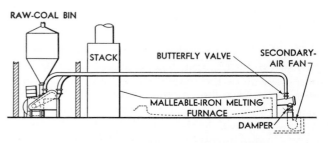

Fig. 9. Malleable-iron melting furnace
direct-fired with pulverized coal

distributing distances) and for a typical direct-firing system, for the same fuel consumption, is shown in Table 5.

b) The pulverizer fan handles all the coal and air, and consequently the wear is greater and the maintenance is higher per unit output than for the direct-firing system.

c) Based on output alone, and varying with the length of the distributing line, the initial cost is relatively high compared with a direct-firing system.

Table 5
Power Consumption Compared for
Direct-Firing and Direct-Firing Circulating

Conditions

Type of coal	Bituminous
Heating value	13,500 Btu/lb
Grindability index	60
Fineness of coal	85% through 200 mesh

System	Direct-Firing	Direct-Firing Circulating		
Average fuel consumption lb/hr	4000	4000		
Number of furnaces served	1	4		
Max length of distributing line, ft	100	200	300	400
Average power consumption of fan and pulverizer at full load, kwhr/ton	18.3	26.5	28.2	30.3

The direct-firing circulating system is not an alternative for the direct-firing system. It was developed to provide wide distribution and individual control, not practical with a direct-firing system, in burning pulverized coal where that fuel is more economical than other fuels.

Types of Pulverizers

Reducing materials to a fine state, for countless human needs, is one of the oldest arts of civilization. Coal pulverizing equipment may be said to be based, in general, on rock and mineral ore grinding machinery. The principles involved in all pulverizing machinery are grinding by attrition (as in the mortar and pestle), and impact, or a combination of the two, as in rolling action.

In modern equipment, classification of fineness with simultaneous drying within the grinding zone is a comparatively recent and one of the outstanding developments in the preparation of pulverized coal for steam generation and process heating. While there are numerous modifications, the principal types of pulverizers commonly used may be classified as follows under high, slow and medium speed:

High speed
a) Impact pulverizer
Slow speed
b) Tube mill pulverizer
Medium speed
c) Roll and race pulverizer
   1) Standard roll and race
   2) Bowl mill
d) Ball and race pulverizer

a) High Speed Impact Pulverizer

The high speed impact pulverizer was one of the earlier types used extensively in firing rotary cement kilns and in the generation of steam during the pioneering period in the application of pulverized coal. The grinding elements are a series of hinged ham-

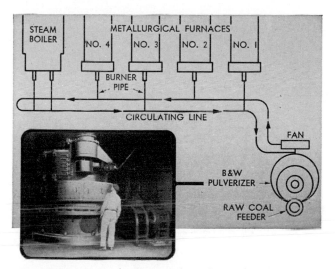

Fig. 10. *Direct-fired pulverized coal circulating system applied to boiler and metallurgical furnaces*

mers revolving in a chamber lined with hard metal plates, with serrated surfaces in some instances. This type of pulverizer has been superseded by a high speed, combination impact and attrition machine. In this machine the grinding elements consist of hammer like beaters revolving in a chamber lined with hard metal plates to which one or two rows of beaters are attached. The exhauster rotor is mounted on the main pulverizer shaft. In the inlet chamber, where preliminary crushing takes place, means are provided for collecting tramp iron and other foreign material.

The grinding efficiency of the high speed impact pulverizer is affected by the progressive wear of the grinding elements. Unless an independent classifier is provided, the fineness of the finished product of the pulverizer will decrease as the clearance between the revolving and stationary grinding surfaces increases. Use of hard alloy-steel beaters and liners will minimize the effect on fineness by reducing wear and will extend the running period between replacements.

These machines are self-contained. Coal fed to the machine is pulverized and dried and is then delivered to the burners. A feeder, usually an integral part of the machine, feeds raw coal into the crushing chamber and through the grinding zone, and then, induced by the fan, the mixture of coal and air is discharged to the burner. Preheated air is used to dry the coal during the process of reduction. Since the fineness of the finished product is affected by the air velocity through the grinding zone, the total heat available for drying is limited

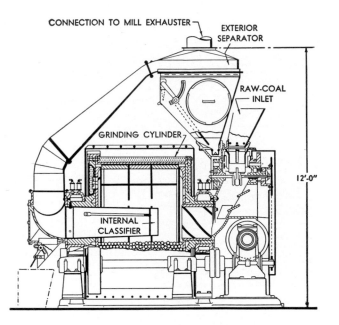

Fig. 11. *Slow-speed cylindrical air-swept pulverizer or "tube mill"*

to the low primary-air ratio and temperature, which, in turn, limit the amount of drying. The absence of load circulation in this type of pulverizer imposes a further limitation on the amount of moisture tolerated in the coal for satisfactory performance.

b) Slow-Speed Pulverizer or Tube Mill

One of the oldest practical pulverizers is the tube mill, in which a charge of mixed-size forged-steel balls in a horizontally supported grinding cylinder is activated by gravity as the cylinder is rotated at the relatively slow speed of 26 to 32 rpm. With some modifications, it is still being used almost exclusively in mineral ore and cement clinker grinding processes, and it is also widely used in grinding

raw material in the manufacture of cement. Its continued use in these industries, notwithstanding its low mechanical efficiency compared with some other types operating on entirely different principles of grinding, is chiefly because of its simple and sturdy construction.

Because of its dependability, the tube mill was considered a suitable unit for direct-firing of pulverized coal when this system first became popular. However, as the use of pulverized coal in the metallurgical industry and for power generation increased, the tube mill was gradually replaced by more efficient modern machines for grinding coal.

Much has been done to improve and adapt the tube mill for grinding coal, and it is successfully applied for this purpose where power is not a governing factor in the operating cost of the system and where there is ample room for installation. Tube mills of modern design for pulverizing coal for firing industrial furnaces and for steam generation are illustrated in Figs. 11 and 12.

A grinding cylinder, a ball charge, internal and external classifiers, and a raw-coal feeder, all assembled as a unit, are the principal components of the machine shown in Fig. 11. The machine shown in Fig. 12 has a grinding cylinder with conical ends, a ball charge, external classifier, and means for circulating air over the charge to convey the finished product to the classifier. The coal rejected in the classifier returns to the grinding zone by gravity. This machine is used for direct-firing systems by placing the pulverizer fan to draw from the classifier outlet and discharge to the burner lines. The conical-end feature of the mill causes size segregation in both ball charge and material within the grinding zone. This natural phenomenon is highly beneficial in wet-process grinding, where the fine material is floated out from the mill in the form of slurry.

The outstanding features of the tube mill are dependability and low maintenance because of the simple arrangement of liners and ball charge in the grinding zone. No provision is required for removing tramp iron from the raw coal. To obtain the optimum effect of the grinding elements, the speed is limited to produce the maximum impact of the outer layer of the balls on the toe of the charge where the coarse coal usually segregates. The coal is finely ground by attrition between the balls as they ascend and slide down in the charge.

The tube mill is a slow-speed pulverizer, and for any given capacity it is relatively larger in size and heavier in construction than high- or medium-speed pulverizers using different principles of grinding. The tube mill requires higher power per unit output than other types. Because of the absence of load circulation within the mill, the excessive amount of fine product within the ball charge, and the circulation of preheated air over the top of the charge it is not as efficient in drying the coal as the medium speed pulverizers with high air circulation through the grinding zone. This is particularly true with very wet coal.

c) Medium Speed Roll and Race Pulverizer

In the medium speed pulverizer there are two groups, classified as roll and race, and ball and race. The same principle of pulverizing by a combination of crushing under pressure, and attrition between grinding surfaces and material is used in each group, but the method is different. In both groups, air is the predominant means for circulating the material through the grinding zone and conveying the finished product to the burners or cyclone collectors. The first group is operated under suction, while the second group may be operated under either suction or pressure.

The roll and race class of pulverizer is sub-divided into two types known as 1) standard roll and race, and 2) bowl mill.

1. Standard Roll and Race. In the standard roll and race pulverizer the grinding elements of four or more rolls, suspended from driving arms, revolve in a horizontal race. The pressure exerted by the rolls against the race is proportional to the centrifugal force due to the speed of the driving shaft. Roll and race pulverizers of this type have been used extensively in processing coal for the bin system, and also for grinding various materials in the ceramic and chemical industries. Air is the principal means for load circulation, conveying the fine coal to the classifier, and collecting the finished product. By the introduction of preheated air it is possible, within certain limits, to pulverize coal without pre-drying. However, this type of pulverizer is not usually considered suitable for direct-firing conditions as it has to be taken out of service to lubricate the internal roll journals.

A classifier above the grinding elements is an integral part of the pulverizer. It is a high sided chamber with an internal cone classifier provided with adjustable vanes, and a reject discharge trap at the bottom.

The feeder is usually driven direct from the main drive. The air to coal ratio is adjusted as required by an automatic control, actuated by the pressure differential across the pulverizer.

2. Bowl Mill. A rotating bowl equipped with a replaceable grinding ring, two or more tapered rolls in stationary journals, an automatically controlled feeder, a classifier, and main drive are the principal components of the bowl mill. As noted above, the bowl mill is another type of the roll and race class of pulverizer. The principal difference from the standard roll and race pulverizer is the method of applying grinding force on the material and load

circulation within the grinding zone. In the standard roll and race pulverizer the grinding action depends entirely on the centrifugal force exerted to press the rolls against the race, while in the bowl mill the rolls are held in the desired position relative to the grinding ring by mechanical springs, and the centrifugal force acts only to feed the coal between the race and the rolls. The bowl mill is suitable for the direct-firing system since the roller journals can be lubricated and the rolls can be adjusted without shutting down. The fineness of the coal is externally controlled by adjusting the entrance vanes in a classifier of the same general design as used with the standard roll and race type

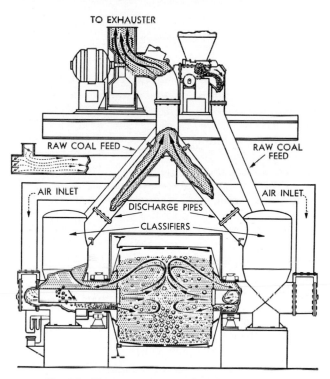

Fig. 12. *Slow-speed conical-end pulverizer with segregated ball-size indicated*

pulverizers, as well as by controlling the pressure of the rolls on the material by adjusting the compression springs.

The bowl mill has been designed to operate only under suction, and the pulverizer fan is placed on the outlet side of the classifier. Heavy scroll liners and rotor blades are usually provided to withstand the abrasive action of the material on the fan. These mills are used extensively in direct-firing systems, for steam generation and in the manufacture of cement.

d) Ball and Race Pulverizer

While the principle of pulverizing by rolling action, impact and attrition is the same, and both

Fig. 13. B&W Type B, single row, ball pulverizer

are of medium speed, the ball and race class of pulverizer is distinguished from the roll and race class by the nature of the grinding elements. In the ball and race pulverizer these elements are balls and one or more races. High load circulation through the grinding zone, very desirable for effective drying and classification of the finished product, is a feature of the ball and race pulverizer. In one group of the ball and race class pulverizer, known as a "pusher mill," and now obsolete, use is made of centrifugal force to apply the pressure for grinding, while in the other group, known simply as the "ball and race pulverizer," positively controlled spring pressure supplies the force. The pusher mill has been superseded by the tube mill for cement grinding and by the roll, and ball and race pulverizer for grinding rock products, fertilizer and coal for various processes.

The ball and race pulverizer, a natural development of the pusher mill, works on the ball-bearing principle. This B&W group is sub-divided into two general types, classified as Type B and Type E. Type B is further divided into what is known as the 100 series, meaning one row of balls, and the 200 series, meaning two rows of balls. A single row of balls is used in all Type E pulverizers. (See Figs. 13, 14 and 15.)

Type B 100 Series Pulverizer. In the Type B 100 series pulverizer (see Fig. 13) there are two races, one revolving and one stationary, with one set of balls interposed rotating in a horizontal plane. The revolving race (the top grinding ring), driven by a vertical shaft through a yoke and spring assembly, provides traction and rotating motion to the balls. Raw coal is fed to the outer ball periphery, and the pulverized coal, coarse and fine, is conveyed by air through the radial ports in the driving yoke. Classification is effected in the housing above the grinding zone and the fineness is controlled entirely by vary-

ing the air flow through the pulverizer. Because of the high circulating load and high air-to-coal ratio possible through this type of pulverizer, high moisture coal can be pulverized satisfactorily.

Type B 200 Series Pulverizer. In the Type B 200 series pulverizer (see Fig. 14) an intermediate revolving grinding ring is interposed with two sets of balls between the races of two stationary rings (an upper and a lower). The intermediate ring provides traction and rotating motion to the two sets of balls. The bottom ring, fixed in position, carries the entire thrust load. Through the top ring (with race on under side), supported from the housing but free to move up and down within limits, force is applied to the grinding elements assembly by four or more mechanical springs. Spring adjustment, without shutting down the pulverizer, is made from the outside of the housing by screw-down bolts.

Raw coal is fed inside the grinding rings to the table attached to the intermediate revolving grinding ring. As it passes through the top row of balls, the coal is partially pulverized and the fine particles are entrained and conveyed by air to the classifying section. The coarse particles fall behind the lower row of balls and flow by gravity through the bottom grinding zone. Preheated air from the windbox, flowing through the throat orifice between the bottom grinding ring and the driving yoke, entrains all the coal, coarse and fine, as it passes through the lower row of balls. This mixture of air and coal flows into the pulverizer housing through the radial ports in the rotating yoke and then into the classifier for final classification.

The classifier is a concentric cone provided with adjustable inlet vanes and a reject trap at the bottom. Within a limited range, the fineness of the finished product is determined by the position of the outlet sleeve and inlet vanes. Low air velocity through the mill housing is one of the controlling factors for a high degree of fineness.

The revolving grinding ring is propelled by the main shaft driven by a spiral gear and pinion assembly located in a housing supported from the main base plate of the foundation. Both main and pinion shafts are mounted in roller bearings, and the thrust due to the weight of the drive and yoke is carried by a step roller bearing integral with the gear housing. The entire gear assembly and bearings are forced lubricated. The oil pump, driven from the pinion shaft, is connected to the main oil reservoir in the gear housing with an intermediate oil strainer. No lubrication necessitating shutdown, is required in the grinding zone.

Type EL Pulverizer. The Type EL pulverizer, illustrated in Fig. 15, has one revolving and one stationary race interposed with one set of balls propelled in a horizontal plane. Through the stationary top ring (with race on under side), supported from the housing but free to move up and down within limits, grinding force is applied to the lower revolving ring (with race on upper side) by mechanical springs, externally adjusted for more or less pressure. The raw coal, fed inside the grinding rings to a table to which the revolving race is attached, is swept into the path of the balls by centrifugal force due to rotation. The table, with attached grinding ring, is driven by a vertical shaft extending from the gear housing through the air seal above the upper radial bearing.

The stationary ring, known as the top grinding ring, is held in position by the dual-purpose mechanical springs. The bottom ends of the springs are secured to lugs on the grinding ring and the upper ends are secured to the adjusting screw-down bolts. The springs are designed to provide the necessary pressure on the balls, and to resist the turning moment of the ring.

Finely pulverized coal is first separated from coarser particles by the swirling action of the air and coal imparted by the rotating action of the grinding ring and balls, and then in a classifier attached to the pulverizer top. Oversize material is returned by gravity through a vane to the grinding zone where it mixes with the raw coal.

The classifier is a stationary cyclone with inlet ports made up of flat blades arranged with the openings counter to the direction of rotation so that coarse particles are removed from the air stream by inertia. This arrangement utilizes the swirling action of the coal laden air outside the classifier. The fineness of the finished product is controlled by the length of the adjustable blades forming the inlet.

Foreign material, such as tramp iron and pyrites, that may enter the pulverizer is collected by what is commonly known as a "pyrites trap," whence it is removed periodically.

The raw coal feeder of the rotating table type is usually an integral part of the pulverizer, although it is driven and controlled independently by a two speed motor. The rate of feed is controlled either by the speed of the feeder or by adjusting the orifice above the table and fixed plow blade.

The main drive, housed in the base of the pulverizer, is completely separated from and sealed against the grinding zone. A spiral bevel gear is driven by a pinion shaft mounted in roller bearings. The main shaft, on which the spiral beveled gear is mounted, is supported on a thrust bearing and is guided in two vertical roller bearings, one at the base of the shaft and the other in the gear housing cover plate. The entire thrust load, due to the grinding pressure and the weight of the grinding elements, is supported on the thrust roller bearing at the bottom of the shaft. Forced lubrication is provided for the entire gear assembly and bearings by an oil pump submerged in the oil reservoir and driven direct from the pinion shaft. Except for the feeder gear reduction unit, no other external or internal lubrication is necessary. Since the applied force on the grinding elements is adjusted externally, it is possible to operate the pulverizer continuously for long periods of time, shutting down only for inspection.

The Type EL pulverizer is made in sizes from EL 17 (17 in. across the race) to EL 70 (70 in. across the race) with capacities from 1½ tons to 17 tons per hour, respectively, based on a coal of 50 grindability (Hardgrove).

Air Flow Through Pulverizer. One of the principal features of the ball and race type pulverizer is that it can be and almost always is operated under pressure, i.e., the cold or preheated air through the pulverizer is supplied under pressure by the primary air fan. This is an important feature, because wear on the fan rotor and housing is eliminated, and since only clean air is handled, it permits a wide selection of fan for high mechanical efficiency. A further advantage is better coal and air distribution to a plurality of burners in a direct-firing system, since each burner take-off is connected to a common outlet chamber wherein there is a uniform mixture of coal and air.

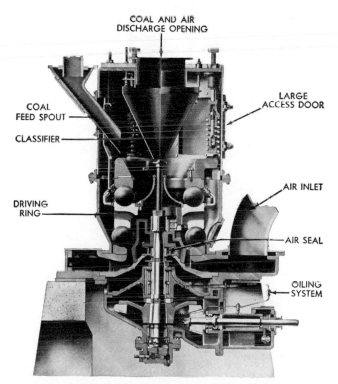

Fig. 14. B&W Type B, double row, ball pulverizer

Pulverizer Feeder Controller. All ball-and-race pulverizers operating as air mills have a common characteristic in that the material-to-air ratio should be maintained at some definite relation. The ratio depends upon the type of pulverizer, installation, and material characteristics. For efficient and consistent results, once the ratio is established for any given set of conditions it should be maintained.

For any given set of conditions there is a definite relation between the pressure drop across the pulverizer and the pressure differential of a pitot tube or orifice in the air supply to the pulverizer. This relation is the principle on which the feeder controller system, illustrated in Fig. 16, is based. Only the air flow through the pulverizer needs to be varied (manually or by combustion control) to meet load requirements. The feeder controller then automatically adjusts the coal feed to the air flow. Hence by the use of this controller, the correct material-to-air relation can be maintained automatically over the entire operating range of the pulverizer while at the same time maintaining (a) the proper velocity through the conveying lines at the lowest practical load and (b) satisfactory fineness at maximum output.

Summary of Pulverizer Characteristics

There are many variations in the design of machines currently used in different industries. In

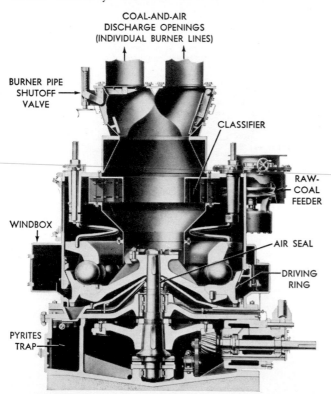

Fig. 15. B&W Type EL pulverizer. Size range, 1 ½ to 17 tons of coal per hr based on 50 grindability (Hardgrove)

their application to the process of grinding various materials, consideration should be given to the effect of the characteristics peculiar to each design on dependability in performance, economy in operation, and initial investment. The optimum selection would naturally be the design that will produce the desired results at least cost per unit output. Operating characteristics and the principles of design of the B&W ball-and-race pulverizer are summarized in Table 6.

TABLE 6

Characteristics of B&W Ball-and-Race Pulverizer
Coal at 50 Grindability (Hardgrove) and
70% Through 200 Mesh

Type	Ball-and-race
Size range	EL 17 - EL 70
Output, maximum	1½ - 17 tons/hr
Speed	Medium
Rev per min, main shaft	220-82
Operating under	Pressure or suction
Location of fan	Pulverizer inlet or outlet
Load circulation	High
Classification	Internal
Classification control	Mechanical adjustment
Drying, range of moisture	Up to 20% total, surface 15%
Effect of moisture on output	None, up to 15% surface, if air is hot enough
Effect of wear on fineness	None
Method of control	Control primary air, which controls coal feed
Response to load change	Fast
Power input per unit output, including fan	Low, 14 kwhr/ton
Maintenance, material only	Low, 0.5¢ to 2.0¢ per ton
Noise level	Medium

Safety Features—All Types

As a measure of safety in case of internal fires, the design of pulverizing equipment used in processing coal for firing furnaces and other purposes should conform to the specific requirements of the *Fire Underwriters' Code,* as follows:

"All equipment containing dust-laden air shall be designed to withstand an internal pressure of 50 lb per sq inch. If made of steel or other ductile material, the allowable stress shall not exceed:

a) ¼ the ultimate strength of the material for cones, cylinders, tie rods, bolts, studs, or other sections in tension.

b) ½ the ultimate strength of the material for flat areas and sections subject to bending."

Any design not complying with the Code's requirements is generally considered inadequate for safe operation, and potentially dangerous to life and property.

In grinding material other than coal, i.e., all non-volatile material, temperature in the grinding zone is of consequence only in its effect on the equipment. However, under certain conditions, in grinding coal, sulfur, and plastics of a volatile nature, the temperature of the grinding zone atmosphere is of paramount importance in safe operation. Safe operating pulverizer outlet temperatures for coal are well established, as noted in Table 7.

TABLE 7

Maximum Safe Operating Pulverizer Outlet Temperature for Pulverizing Coal

System	Direct Firing F	Storage F
High volatile bituminous	150	130
Low volatile bituminous	175	130
Lignite	120	120
Anthracite	200	200

In cases of fires in coal pulverizing systems, two general practices are usually followed:

a) The pulverizer is isolated from the rest of the system, and carbon dioxide (CO_2) gas is injected into the pulverizer.

b) The atmosphere within the pulverizer is displaced with saturated steam.

In either case, to avoid excess pressure in the pulverizer, means are usually provided for controlled release of the displaced atmosphere through the conveying lines.

General Range of Sizes

Various coals have their own peculiar characteristics which greatly affect the performance of a pulverizer. The range of sizes of pulverizers is, therefore, based on the average characteristics of the three general classes of commercial coals used in the generation of steam, as noted in Table 8.

In general, the output of any pulverizer is af-

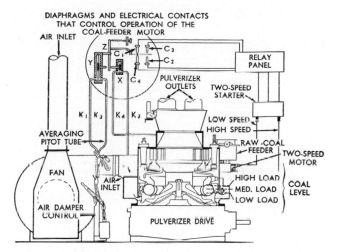

Fig. 16. *B&W automatic feeder controller applied to Type EL pulverizer for regulating amount of coal*

fected by various factors. The principal factors are:

a) Grindability, i.e., the ease with which a coal can be reduced by applied mechanical energy.

b) Surface moisture in the coal, not evaporated within the pulverizer.

c) Fineness of the coal, i.e., the amount of new surface produced.

Grindability Index (Hardgrove)

The grindability of a coal is expressed as an index showing the relative hardness (or ease of pulverizing) of that coal compared with a standard coal chosen as 100 (unity) grindability. Compared with standard coal, having a grindability index of 100, a coal is harder or easier to grind if its grindability index is less or greater, respectively, than 100. Usually, the capacity of a pulverizer is assumed to be proportional to the grindability index of the coal.

A tentative method of testing to determine the grindability index of coal is described in ASTM

TABLE 8

General Range of Pulverizer Sizes - B&W Ball and Race

Types B and E Series

	Grindability index		Fineness, per cent through 200 mesh
Bituminous	50		70
Lignite	50		60
Anthracite	50		85
Size of pulverizer	B226 - B282	EL17 - EL70	B109 - B156
Bituminous lb/hr	15,000 - 60,000	3000 - 34,000	500 - 15,000
Lignite lb/hr	16,500 - 66,000	3700 - 41,000	550 - 16,500
Anthracite lb/hr	6,100 - 24,000	1900 - 20,000	200 - 6,100

proceedings D409-37T, issued in 1935 and revised in 1937. The method is based on the premise that: "The work done in pulverizing is proportional to the new surface produced". A definite amount of grinding energy is applied to a prepared sample in a minature pulverizer, and the new surface is determined by sieving.

The laboratory sample of the coal to be tested, after air drying until the loss in weight is not more than 0.1 per cent per hour, is placed on a 1190 micron (#16) sieve nested with a 590 micron (#30) sieve and bottom pan. The sieves are shaken by a mechanical sieving machine for approximately 2 minutes, or an equivalent amount of hand sieving. The material remaining on the #16 sieve is crushed and sieved as described above, and the operation is repeated several times until the entire sample has passed through the 1190 micron (#16) sieve. The material remaining on the 590 micron (#30) sieve, after thorough shaking, is the testing sample composed of particle sizes ranging from 1190 microns to 590 microns.

The machine for the grindability test (see Fig. 17) has eight 1 in. diam balls interposed between a stationary and a revolving race. A definite pressure of 64 lb ± ½ lb is imposed on the balls as shown in Fig. 17. The action of the rolling balls causes an increase in the surface of the sample being tested. A predetermining counter is set to stop the motor automatically as soon as the vertical shaft has made exactly 60 revolutions.

Fifty grams of the sample to be tested (prepared as described above) is distributed evenly over the balls of the machine. The predetermining counter is set at zero and the switch is closed. When the machine automatically stops, after completing 60 revolutions, the sample is transferred to the 74 micron (#200) sieve, and is shaken by a mechanical sieving machine for 20 minutes. The material passing through the 74 micron (#200) sieve is discarded, and the material retained on the sieve is weighed to within 0.1 g and the weight is recorded. The grindability index is then calculated by the following equation: The grindability index (Hardgrove) = 13 + 6.93W. Where W, the weight of material passing the 74 micron (#200) sieve, is determined by subtracting the weight of the material retained on the 74 micron (#200) sieve from the weight (50g) of the original sample.

Fineness

Fineness is a factor which, while it might be looked upon as controllable, is a fixed end result of any pulverizer operation. The output of the pulverizer varies inversely with the fineness, in accordance with Fig. 18. This graphic illustration applies to the ball and race class of pulverizer, and is not strictly applicable to other types since the operating characteristics, both in grinding and classification, are different in each case. The trend, however, is the same for all types, but in varying degree. Fineness requirements for various applications and commercial solid fuels are noted in Table 2.

Moisture

Coal in the pulverizer is dried by preheated air at inlet temperatures depending on the amount of moisture in the coal, but controlled within safety limits established by practice. The following coal-air temperatures in F leaving the grinding zone (and pulverizer exit) are generally accepted as safe:

a) High volatile bituminous coal 150
b) Lignite class coals 120
c) Low volatile bituminous coal 150 — 175
d) Anthracite coal 200
e) Petroleum coke 200 — 250

For heating the coal in the pulverizer and evaporating the moisture, the effective heat applied is the product of the temperature differential, the air quantity, and the specific heat. In practice, to determine the heat required for drying the coal, no account is taken of the heat energy imparted by the electric power applied to the motors driving the pulverizer and the pulverizer fan since it is assumed to be equal to the radiation and other heat losses. Load circulation within the grinding zone is one of the contributing factors in the process of pulverizing high moisture coals. For the ball and race pulverizer, the relation between air-coal ratio and air temperature requirements for various moisture content is shown in Fig. 2.

Preheated air for the pulverizer is generally sup-

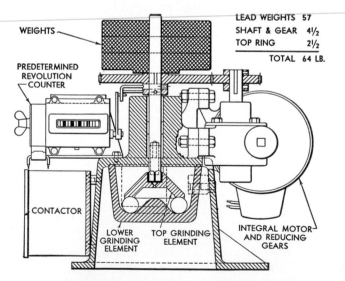

WEIGHTS

LEAD WEIGHTS 57
SHAFT & GEAR 4½
TOP RING 2½
TOTAL 64 LB.

PREDETERMINED REVOLUTION COUNTER

CONTACTOR

LOWER GRINDING ELEMENT
TOP GRINDING ELEMENT
INTEGRAL MOTOR AND REDUCING GEARS

Fig. 17. Machine for determining grindability (Hardgrove)

plied from either a gas or a steam air heater, which is a component of the unit served by the pulverizer. Where preheated air is not available in this manner, high temperature flue gas, tempered with air, is another source of heat supply to the pulverizer. The temperature of the air to the pulverizer is controlled either manually or automatically. When the supply comes from a gas air heater, the temperature is adjusted by controlling the tempering air inlet, just ahead of the pulverizer, to maintain a predetermined coal and air outlet temperature. With a steam air heater, the air temperature is limited by the saturated steam temperature available for any given installation and is regulated by controlling the rate of steam flow through the heater.

Classification

Classification of the ground product is the segregation of particles not over a set limit in size from those over that size, and the rejection of the oversize particles. The product may be classified by any of the following methods:

a) Centrifugal action by subjecting the particles to a circular motion in a chamber, usually outside the grinding zone.

b) Mechanical means within the grinding zone.

c) A combination of centrifugal and mechanical action.

The centrifugal type of classifier is usually a cyclonic chamber, with adjustable directional vanes, and adjustable outlet, and an air sealed reject discharge.

In the mechanical type of classifier, illustrated in Fig. 15, a stator with angular inlet blades, is arranged to reject the over-size particles from the incoming air and coal stream and to channel them back into the grinding zone. The direction of the incoming mixture of air and coal flow (from the periphery to the center) is opposite to the direction of the currents imposed by the centrifugal force due to the rotation of the pulverizer parts. There is a separating chamber above the grinding zone. The fineness is controlled by adjusting the inlet blades as well as regulating the amount of air through the grinding zone.

Benefits of Fine Grinding

The primary purpose of grinding solid fuels is to accelerate combustion of carbon. High new surface production is, in general, a measure of the efficiency of a grinding process. In practice, for solid fuels, fineness is accepted as a measure of new surface and it is expressed in per cent of the product passing through various sizes of sieves, graded from #16 to #325 in the United States standard.

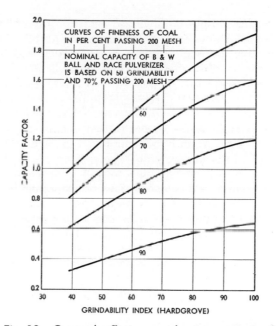

Fig. 18. General effect on pulverizer output of (a) grindability of coal, and (b) fineness required

In dealing with solid fuels, the coal must be fine to insure complete consumption of the carbon for maximum combustion efficiency, and to avoid the deposit of coarse ash and carbon on the heat absorbing surfaces.

Fine grinding is necessary in heating processes other than steam generation where close temperature control and the avoidance of carbon contamination are of paramount importance. The nature of the solid fuel usually determines the fineness of the product for any given application. In general, the fineness requirements are lower for the higher volatile coal in the range above 22 per cent, than for fuels ranging below 22 per cent in volatile. Usually the highest fineness is required for anthracite and petroleum coke, neither of which are considered as free burning fuels. General specifications of fineness requirements for various standard processes are noted in Table 2.

Sampling Pulverized Coal

A true sample of the pulverized coal used in bin system firing may generally be obtained from the common hopper in which all the pulverized coal is collected. The procedure for obtaining a true sample of pulverized coal from a direct-fired system is much more involved and the accuracy of a representative sample is considerably more uncertain. There is no universally adopted procedure but the following, taken from the "Test Code for Coal Pulverizers", ASME 1944, and the ASTM standard D197-30, may be considered as recommended practice:

Two general arrangements of the equipment required for sampling pulverized coal in a direct-fired system are shown in Fig. 19, the principal difference being that in one (shown at the right) the bag collector is replaced by a cyclone collector.

In collecting the sample, the tip of the sampling pipe is inserted in the extension nipple in the burner pipe until it touches the closed valve. The cloth sleeve is attached as shown to seal against the coal and air flow around the sampling pipe when it is inserted in the burner pipe. The aspirator is started, keeping the discharge end, to which the bag collector is attached, closed. The quick-acting valve is then opened, the sampling pipe is inserted through the open valve into the burner pipe, and finally the discharge of the aspirator to the bag collector is opened. As the sampling pipe is inserted, the air from the aspirator forces the accumulated coal in the nipple (ahead of the valve) back into the burner pipe, so that it will not be drawn into the collecting bag.

In taking the samples the section is carefully traversed on two diameters, 90 degrees apart. The usual practice is to divide the burner pipe section into concentric bands of equal area, and to center the sampling stations in each band on each side of the center of the pipe. The preferable location for sampling is in vertical pipes, and as far as possible from preceding bends. In withdrawing, the aspirator discharge is closed until the sampling pipe is pulled out beyond the valve and the valve closed, so that coal from the nipple will not be drawn into the sample. The same amount of time is used in collecting all sample increments.

Water in the compressed air, which may be absorbed by the cloth, will reduce the effectiveness of the bag collector as a filter. Furthermore, the moisture absorbed by the coal affects the accuracy of the fineness determination, and also makes screening through fine mesh difficult. Where the compressed air supply is not free of moisture, a motor driven vacuum cleaner exhauster should be substituted for the aspirator, or it may be advisable to use a cyclone collector. Two types of sampling pipe tips are illustrated and dimensioned in Fig. 20. Type B is considered preferable.

To obtain samples of coal approximately proportional in weight to the coal pulverized and delivered through one or more burner pipes, the velocity through the sampling pipe must be of the same order as the velocity through the burner pipes. The weight in a given time will vary according to the velocity through the sampling pipe. The approximately correct velocity can be determined by comparing the weight of the sample obtained in a given time with the weight of coal being pulverized, multiplied by the ratio of the sampling tip area to the burner pipe area. If the weight of the sample obtained is less or more than the amount so determined the proportional recovery will be correspondingly less or more than 100 per cent. The aspirator should be adjusted to give proportional recovery within the limits of 90 to 110 per cent. Samples not within the limits of 90 to 110 per cent recovery should be discarded. When the sampling stations are in the burner pipes, and there are two or more burner pipes, the weight of samples from all the burner pipes should be added together to check the percentage recovery. The opening into the collector bag should be the same for each burner pipe.

The average fineness of the pulverizer output may be obtained by screening each sample separately,

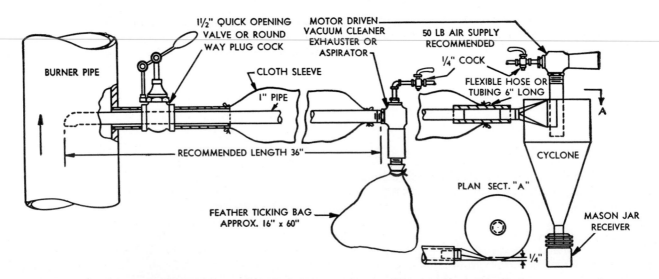

Fig. 19. Recommended arrangement for sampling pulverized coal in a direct-fired system using aspirator and bag or cyclone collector

and using the weighted average. The usual practice, however, is to thoroughly mix the samples and make one screen determination of the mixture. The fineness is calculated from the weights of the residues on the sieves, and is usually expressed as percentages *through* a given sieve number.

Cost of Pulverizing Coals

Aside from capital investment and fixed charges, the cost of preparing and delivering pulverized coal to burners for the generation of steam and heating processes is the sum of the costs of operating labor, power, and maintenance. These operating costs, per unit output, are affected by (a) size of the installation, (b) characteristics of the coal, and (c) fineness and distribution of the finished product. For a given set of requirements, it will generally cost more to operate a bin system than a direct-fired system, as noted in Table 9.

TABLE 9

Preparation of Pulverized Coal Operating Cost

(Based on)

Coal from	Pittsburgh seam
Heating value	14,050 Btu per lb
Moisture	10%
Sulfur	1.5%
Grindability (Hardgrove)	50
Power cost	1.0¢/kwhr
Labor rate	1.65¢/hr
Fineness	70% through 200 mesh
Rate of pulverizing	12 tons/hr

	Direct Firing (Cents per ton)	Bin System (Cents per ton)
Power	15.75	22.61
Steam for drying	9.65	9.65
Maintenance, including labor	2.00	4.50
Operating labor	13.75	20.60
Total	41.15	57.36

The life of the grinding elements of ball and race type pulverizers varies from 6000 to 14,000 hours of operation. The rate of wear is affected by the sulfur and ash content rather than the grindability of the coal. Futhermore, operating time seems to be a better index of the life of the grinding elements than the rate of output. However, the operating cost per unit output is a function of the total coal pulverized in the given life of the grinding elements. The maintenance cost is usually expressed in cost per ton of coal pulverized. The power consumption per ton of coal delivered to the burners is the sum of the power required to drive (a) the auxiliaries delivering coal to the pulverizer, (b) the pulverizer, and (c) the fan delivering air to the pulverizer and coal to the burners. The power requirements of the auxiliaries depend on the type of raw coal handling equipment, and this factor usually is not evaluated in determining the power consumption of a pulverizer installation. The power consumption of the pulverizer fan varies with the type of installation, but, generally, for direct-firing systems, it is considered a part of the total power required, and is so evaluated in common practice. Where pulverized coal is delivered to a group of furnaces located at some distance from the pulverizer, the power consumption of the fan is considerably higher than for a standard direct-firing system. The fan power varies directly as the system resistance.

Maintenance of Equipment

To insure efficient operation and uniform quality of the finished product in any pulverizing system,

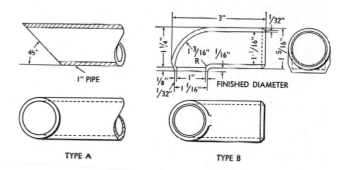

Fig. 20. *Types of tips for sampling pulverized coal*

the grinding elements must be maintained in good condition at all times. The grinding force, if mechanically applied, must also be maintained at a predetermined value, consistent with the type of fuel pulverized. Power is wasted if the applied grinding pressure is higher than necessary to produce the fineness required. On the other hand, if the grinding force applied is inadequate efficiency will suffer because the coal is too coarse for complete combustion. Periodic inspection and adjustments are, therefore, established requirements. In the ball and race pulverizer, the grinding elements are replaced through the access doors, without disturbing the housing.

Exhausters and Blowers

In both the direct-firing and bin systems, air is required for classifying and conveying the finished product to the burners or collecting bins for distribution. This is commonly known as primary air. In the bin system, the conveying air is usually discharged through a dust cleansing system to the atmosphere.

Primary air to the pulverizer is usually supplied by either (a) a standard commercial blower handling clean air and discharging directly into the pulverizer, or (b) an exhauster, handling pulverized-coal-laden air. Where the blower is handling clean air, the system is identified as under pressure, and the fan is not subjected to abrasion by the pulverized coal. In this case a high efficiency fan can be used, since the conditions permit an efficient rotor design and high tip speed. When the fan or exhauster is handling pulverized-coal-laden air, the system is identified as under suction. To comply with the Fire Underwriter's Code (see above) the exhauster housing is heavy (to withstand a pressure of 50 psi). Futhermore, since the exhauster is subject to excessive wear, the design is limited to a paddle wheel type of heavy construction and hard metal or other surface coatings. All of these features of construction are detrimental to the mechanical efficiency of the fan.

The speed of the pulverizer fan depends on the pressure requirements of the system, and will vary from 1200 to 1800 rpm, the latter in most installations. The fans are usually independently driven, but in small sizes one motor may be used to drive both the pulverizer and the fan.

Power consumption of the pulverizer fan is an important item in the operating cost of a pulverized coal installation, and the selection of a fan for this purpose should receive careful consideration. This is evident from Fig. 21, showing average relative power consumption, under given conditions, for a standard commercial blower handling clean air, and the fan used as an exhauster handling dust-laden air.

Pulverized Coal Conveying Pipes

All piping, conduits and vessels containing pulverized-coal-laden air are designed to withstand the specified pressure (50 psi) required by the Fire Underwriter's Code, and extra thickness or hard metal liners must be provided as necessary in the system to allow for excessive wear due to erosion caused by the impingement of coal-laden-air. All lines for conveying coal are of standard weight steel piping, with an average wall thickness of ⅜ inch. Removable liners are usually fitted in the areas of the conveying system subject to excessive wear. To reduce pressure drop and erosion the radii of bends are made as large as possible, consistent with good design.

If the coal is of uniform fineness and the system is properly designed for bends and velocities through the pipes, the maintenance of the conveying lines is very low. Records indicate that conveying lines of direct-fired installations have operated from 10 to 15 years without any maintenance. The coating of the internal surface of the conveying lines with a graphite-like substance from the coal protects the pipes from corrosion and erosion. This protection is especially effective in straight runs of pipe and where impingement is not severe.

Burners—General

To best utilize the heat released in burning a substance, the fuel burner is surrounded by a combustion chamber or furnace to provide (a) space to burn the fuel and (b) to form a flue or duct for conveying the hot gases to the remainder of the heat absorbing surfaces or process. Some fuels burn readily in suspension, others are burned on a grate, and some may be burned either way. This discussion is concerned particularly with coal fuels burned in suspension under steam producing equipment. (See Chapter 28, on the Cyclone furnace, and Chapter 16, on stokers, for comparing other methods of burning coal).

To burn a fuel in suspension it must be reduced to exceedingly fine particles so that a large amount of surface is intimately and promptly exposed to contact with the combustion air. The fineness for a burner firing a steam boiler should be such that at least 98 per cent of the fuel will pass through a 50 mesh sieve and at least 65 per cent through a 200 mesh sieve. In general, the finer the fuel the better. A good average practice for all but the lowest volatile coals is 75 per cent through 200 mesh. Fine pulverization is required:

1. For maximum combustion efficiency.

2. For coals that are difficult to ignite and burn.

3. Where the walls of the combustion chamber are extensively water-cooled and the ash from the coal is removed from the furnace in a dry state.

As fuel prices and the efficiency of coal preparation increase, higher fineness of pulverization may be justified because of the gain in combustion efficiency. Similarly, the water-cooled furnace has been almost universally adopted because of higher boiler availability and less maintenance. Also, to reduce over-all boiler installation costs and to permit the use of coals having widely differing characteristics, there has been a strong trend in recent years to the dry ash removal type of furnace. In modern installations, therefore, the trend is to use finer pulverization.

The quantity of air required to burn any fuel depends on its constituents. To burn a fuel, a definite quantity of oxygen and consequently air is required for each pound of carbon, hydrogen, sulfur, and combinations of these elements in the fuel. As each combustible substance when burned with the theoretical amount of air liberates a definite quantity of heat, the heating value of the fuel can be used, instead of its analysis, as a ready measure of the quantity of air required for its combustion. If the heating value is used as a measure it will be found that the variation in weight of theoretical air required to release 10,000 Btu in burning all the usual fuels is remarkably small, varying from 7.19 lb for a typical natural gas to 7.7 lb for a low volatile anthracite. For coals only, the range in value is even narrower as may be noted in Fig. 22.

Since air under control cannot be obtained without cost, and its use in excessive amounts decreases efficiency, air, as well as coal should be conserved. It is now general practice to measure, (with a boiler meter or other means) both the air and the coal injected to a combustion chamber, and it is recognized that, even in the best apparatus used to combine air and coal for combustion, some air in excess of theoretical is required. For instance, referring to Fig. 22, the weight of air required with a 20 per cent volatile coal would be 7.605 x 1.15 or 8.75 lb per 10,000 Btu released. In this example, for the particular conditions taken, it is assumed that 15 per cent excess air or 115 per cent total air is necessary. As a further illustration: The amount of air to be supplied to a boiler burning 51.5 tons per hr of a typical Illinois coal, 47.7 per cent volatile, (moisture and ash free), 9930 Btu as fired, with 19 per cent excess air, would be (see Fig. 22)

$$\frac{51.5 \times 2000 \times 9930 \times 7.55 \times 1.19}{10,000}$$

or about 918,930 lb per hour. The excess air

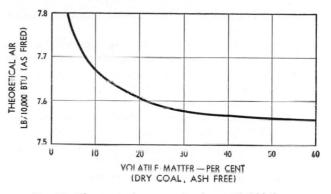
Fig. 22. *Theoretical air required per 10,000 Btu varies little for a wide range of fuel characteristics*

quantities required in common practice for different fuels are noted in Chapter 4, on combustion.

The pulverized coal generally is dispersed in an air stream, in the pulverizer for the direct firing system and immediately following the pulverized coal feeder for bin system firing, and the complete mixture of fuel and air is conveyed through suitable pipes to the burner. This conveying air, known as primary air, represents only a small portion of the air required to burn the fuel. For direct firing the quantity of primary air generally depends on the pulverizer characteristics and currently ranges from 15 to 20 per cent of the total air required for combustion. For bin system firing the primary air is about 15 per cent of the total. The balance of the air required to burn the fuel is known as secondary air. The burner is the device by which the primary air-fuel and secondary air are mixed just prior to or immediately after their introduction into the furnace.

Standards of Burner Performance

Operators of pulverized coal equipment should expect burner performance to meet the following conditions:

1. For most modern applications, ignition of the pulverized coal should be stable, without the use of an auxiliary fuel, over a load range of about 3 to 1. Since the majority of steam boilers is equipped with a multiplicity of burners, considerable range of capacity in excess of 3 to 1 may be obtained by varying the number of burners in use.

2. Unburned combustible loss should be less than 2 per cent. With most modern installations having well designed equipment it is possible to keep the unburned combustible loss under 1 per cent with excess air in the range of 15 to 22 per cent.

3. Only minor repairs should be required at annual overhauls. Burner parts, subject to abrasion, that may require replacement at more frequent intervals should be easily renewable at reasonable cost. Parts, subject to high temperature, that can-

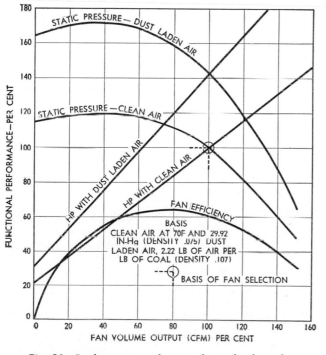
Fig. 21. *Performance of typical steel plate fan*

not be protected by other means, should be made of alloy steels.

4. The burner should not require adjustments to maintain flame shape and freedom from deposits that will interfere with the continued efficient and reliable performance of the boiler unit in the normal range of operating load.

5. The burners should be efficient in burning all of the coals anticipated as fuel and also such other fuels as may be economically justified or required by loss of the usual supply. However, the designer should be apprised of these facts when the burner equipment is ordered.

Measurement and control of air (including excess air) and coal for any combustion process for heat generation should be considered a minimum requirement. However, in many instances the correct proportion of air and coal does not alone insure complete combustion, principally because of failure to obtain an intimate mix. This may be illustrated by considering an early form of pulverized-coal burner —a round or flattened pipe located in a furnace wall or arch. Although the sum-total of air and coal may have been in the proper proportion, some portions of the air were always too remote from some portions of the coal to unite, and the result was both unburned coal and unburned air. In this primitive arrangement, even to come close to complete burning of the coal it was customary to use values of excess air as high as 50 per cent or more. Ignition of the fuel was sensitive and might be lost without warning. The unit usually had to operate at or near a base-load condition. The loss in efficiency from unburned combustible was in the order of 4 per cent, and maintenance was extremely high. This was waste, and in addition there was the cost of moving the air and the subsequent loss of usable heat carried off through the stack.

Mechanism of Burning Fuel

Fundamentally, the mechanism of burning a particle of coal in its quota of air is the union of oxygen with the substance of the outer surface layer of the particle to form CO_2, leaving residual ash and residual nitrogen. The inert CO_2 (plus the inert nitrogen) must be displaced and the residual ash must be permeable, if more oxygen is to penetrate to unite with a new outer surface layer of carbon in the original particle. Thus, to continue the process of burning until all the carbon has united with oxygen, prompt and continuous removal of the outer envelope of inert gases is necessary. This requires a scrubbing action. An example of this action is the moving stream of air over a stationary piece of coal on a stoker, scrubbing off products of combustion and bringing new air (oxygen) to the new surface. Another striking example of scrubbing action is in the Cyclone Furnace (see Chapter 28), where the coal particle adheres to the molten slag surface and is burned and scrubbed to the vanishing point.

With pulverized coal this necessary scrubbing action is not so evident as in the case of the Cyclone Furnace. In the coal-and-air stream there is little relative velocity between the coal particle and the carrying air, since the velocity of the air is regulated to keep the fine pulverized-coal particles in suspension and moving with the air. However, combustion air (secondary air) for various types of burners is introduced to the coal particles carried by the primary air at a slightly different direction of travel and at a different velocity (usually higher). Thus the inert envelope repeatedly forming around each coal particle is displaced by continuous scrubbing, and oxygen is admitted to successive surface layers of the particle until only the ash remains.

Experience has shown that the angle of con-

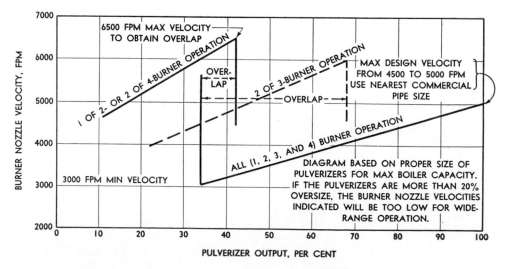

Fig. 23. Burner nozzle velocities for different number of burners per pulverizer

fluence of the primary-air-and-coal stream with the secondary air stream is quite sensitive. Even two burners can interact with each other to produce disappointing results. If the secondary air is introduced into the furnace in the same direction as the coal particles the whole mass tends to assume the same velocity with a reduction in scrubbing effect so necessary to prompt burning. In the circular burner, if the impeller causes the primary-air-and-coal stream to rotate in a direction counter to the secondary air admitted through the registers, there is a tendency to slow up velocities of both streams, and each stream tends to stagnate. For this type of burner the direction of rotation of the coal stream and the secondary air stream should be the same. A similar stagnation can be observed if burners are directly opposed to each other at close range. Here the opposed velocities offset each other with a resultant velocity of low value.

Stability and Ignition—Velocities

Perfect dispersion of the fuel in the air, while desirable for completeness of combustion, does not insure stability of ignition. To obtain ignition stability it is necessary that a small part of the fuel stream should not be so thoroughly dispersed in the air and that it should move at a lower velocity than the main stream. To attain this needed low velocity rich stream is not difficult since there is a certain amount of drag in the different parts of the burner. On the other hand, once coal dust actually settles out, because of too low a velocity in transportation, it is not easily put in suspension again. Rather it tends to "drift" along to the burner. Such drifting utterly frustrates any attempt to subdivide the mixture and can be hazardous if slugs of pulverized coal are suddenly and erratically allowed to dribble into a hot furnace.

Current practice is to use primary air velocities upward of 3000 fpm for horizontally arranged burners, and upward of 2000 fpm for vertically arranged burners. Experience has established that these velocity limitations are necessary to avoid settling of the fuel particles and consequent formation of coke within the burner parts. Maximum velocities range from 4500 to 5500 fpm for all burners in service (see Table 3). The upper limit for velocity depends on a number of factors, the most important of which are: pressure drop—reflected in the additional power requirements for the primary air fan, stability of ignition, and wear of the burner parts. The velocities usually found in burner nozzles for operation at different loads are indicated in Fig. 23. The diagram given is for one, two, three, or four-burner per pulverizer arrangement. For large multiple-pulverizer-fired boilers an entire pulverizer with all its burners is often put in or taken

Fig. 24. B&W circular type pulverized coal burners

out of service as required by the load, instead of shutting down or lighting off individual burners.

Most pulverized coal burners of all types are equipped with an impeller or equivalent device which performs the following functions:

1. When the coal-air stream, at the velocity required to keep the fuel in suspension within the burner proper, strikes the impeller the velocity of a portion of the fuel particles (the finer components) is reduced so that ignition can take place.

2. The impeller (or equivalent) deflects the fuel particles into the stream of secondary air and thus a more intimate mixing of air and coal is obtained.

The velocity of the secondary air stream varies for different burner types, the temperature of air involved, and the construction and arrangement of furnace envelopes. In the following description of several different types of burners the secondary air velocity required for each will be discussed.

Modern Burner Types

Circular Type. The most frequently used burner is the circular type illustrated in Fig. 24. This burner has several desirable characteristics. It does not require much attention to obtain reliable and efficient performance. It can be equipped to burn efficiently either gas or oil as alternate fuels. The only part sub-

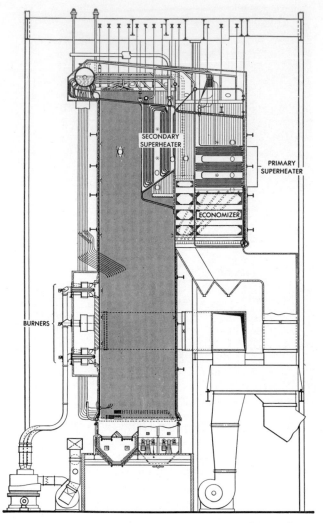

Fig. 25. *B&W circular register type pulverized coal burners installed in large boiler*

furnace with the burner wall formed entirely of furnace cooling tubes, bent around the burner as required, with all refractory eliminated.

For burners of this type installed in the dry ash removal furnace, the velocity of secondary air, as measured in the annular space surrounding the end of the coal nozzle, ranges from about 4000 fpm where unheated secondary air is used, to about 6000 fpm where 600F air is used. For burners of this type installed in the slag tap furnace, the velocity of the secondary air, measured at the same location, is 7500 fpm for 600F air. The velocities noted are all at maximum burner capacity.

Multiple Intertube, Multi-tip Type. Another much used burner is the multiple intertube, multi-tip type, shown in Fig. 26. The seemingly complex arrangement of burner tips is necessary to disperse the fuel thoroughly over the secondary air stream. In the type shown the fuel stream is divided into 12 smaller streams, each introduced to approximately 1/12 of the secondary air at each stream of coal. There are two general forms of this burner type. In one form, Fig. 26 (a), the fuel on leaving the burner tips strikes a tube protector and is deflected laterally into the secondary air stream flowing between the tubes forming the burner ports. In the other form, Fig. 26 (b), the direction of the fuel ports is into the spaces between the water-cooled tubes of the furnace roof, and the secondary air, admitted through inclined ports, meets the fuel stream about a foot below the furnace roof tubes. The first form of this burner type mentioned is used for coals that are not severely abrasive such as those available in the eastern part of the United States, whereas the latter is used for more abrasive coals prevalent in the central part of the country.

In the burner shown in Fig. 26 (a) the tube protector functions as the impeller (described above for the circular burner) and not only deflects the fuel into the secondary air stream but protects the tube directly under it from the abrasive pulverized coal. The tube protectors also serve as a "drag" on a small part of the fuel stream to provide the stabilizing, lower velocity, "rich torches" that are necessary. In general the tube protectors have smooth surfaces, but where a coal difficult to ignite is to be burned the surfaces can be ribbed to increase the number of slower moving rich streams in the burner.

For good combustion, the burner shown in Fig. 26 (b) depends upon high velocity secondary air to mix with the fuel stream. The low velocity, rich stream stabilizing torches are less pronounced than in other burners since there is no abrupt deflection of the fuel stream by any metal parts. However, since this burner is used primarily with Midwest coals which ignite easily, it is neither necessary nor desirable to have too many of these richer streams.

ject to more serious wear is the impeller which can be replaced by simply removing the affected burner from service. Access to the impeller is through the cover on the burner elbow. In normal service an impeller should last more than a year, unless it is severely burned because of an accident. The individual burners of this type shown in Fig. 25 have a maximum capacity of 125 million Btu per hour.

In the circular type burner, the effect of the tangentially disposed vanes built into the air register itself is to mix the fuel and air and to produce the necessary scrubbing action on the fuel particles. Thus, while the fuel is introduced to the burner in a fairly dense mixture at the center, the direction and velocity of the secondary air as dispersed by the impeller are such that it completely penetrates the stream. The resulting flame is among the shortest produced by any burner. This burner is generally used in the so called dry ash removal type furnace. However, it is used occasionally in the slag tap type

Since the fuel is not abruptly deflected by any wearing surface in its passage into the furnace, maintenance of this burner even with a highly abrasive coal is nominal.

Both forms of this type of burner were developed initially for the slag-tap furnace to fire downward on the slag pool to facilitate melting and tapping. Use of these burners in this service, particularly in large boilers, continues. Secondary-air temperatures are usually 450 F or even higher. The burners are shielded from direct furnace radiation by rather closely spaced water-cooled tubes forming the roof of the furnace. This protection from direct radiation permits a construction using a minimum of heat-resisting material and insures long life of the burner parts under the severe conditions of a hot slag-tap furnace with high secondary-air temperatures.

In more recent years this type of burner has been successfully applied to the dry-ash-removal furnace field, where, with its very desirable highly efficient combustion, there are now many satisfactory installations.

This burner type is available with either, or both, oil- or gas-burning equipment, for firing with these alternate fuels if necessary. The range in size for both the combination fuel burner and the all-coal burner is from 50 million to 150 million Btu per hour.

Cross-Tube Burner. Still another type is the cross-tube burner (Fig. 27), in which the primary air-fuel mixture is brought into the furnace in a thin wide layer. The furnace end of the fuel port is shielded from radiation by the water-cooled tubes in front of the port. These tubes are rather close together and thus prevent furnace radiation reaching the burner parts. The fuel is prevented from impinging on the pressure parts by suitable protectors. Just as

the fuel enters the furnace, it is directed upward and downward by a deflector block, serving the same purpose as the impeller described above. The secondary air is admitted to the burner above and below the fuel port through adjustable dampers for regulating the quantity of air as well as its direction. At its full capacity, the velocity of secondary air for this burner is in the order of 10,000 to 12,000 fpm. While not restricted to large boiler applications, the cross-tube burner is widely used in the large boiler field, where air temperatures of 450 F and above are common. The range of sizes is from about 50 million to 150 million Btu per hour. Designed initially for slag-tap units, this burner is used successfully for dry-ash-removal furnaces as well. It is particularly useful for slag-tap units, where the ash-fluid temperature is relatively high. In such instances the proximity of the burners to the slag level and the ability to regulate the flame elevation (by adjusting the secondary-air dampers) permit tapping slag when it would not be possible to do so with other burner types. As with other burners, the cross-tube burner can be equipped to burn either oil or gas or both if desired.

Distribution of Coal and Air

In the foregoing, the ability to effect complete combustion of the fuel with a minimum of excess air has been emphasized. To consume each particle of fuel efficiently, it must have intimately associated with it the required amount of air and no more. It follows, therefore, that the fuel as it enters the furnace must be uniformly distributed into a well-distributed secondary-air stream. Where pulverized-coal burners are concerned, the distribution of the fuel stream is rather difficult since, contrary to popular belief, the primary air-coal mixture is not

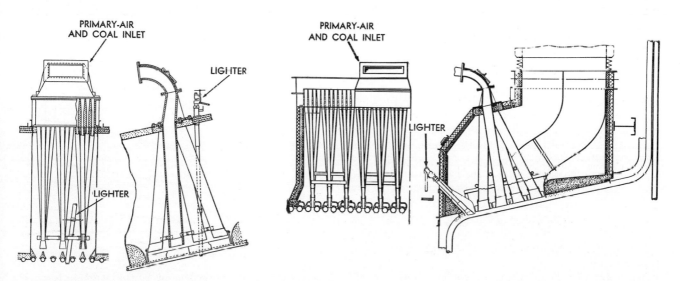

Fig. 26. *B&W multiple-intertube pulverized-coal burners, multitip type. Form (a) left, form (b) right*

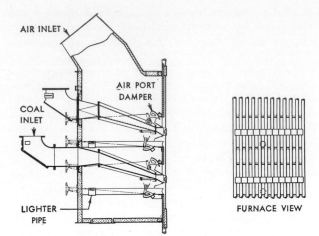

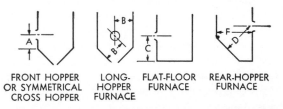

Fig. 27. B&W cross-tube pulverized coal burners

inexperienced it appears that a non-uniform flame characteristic is caused by mal-distribution of the primary stream whereas, in fact, the secondary air stream may be at fault. As one looks into a fire through a colored glass there should be a uniform and symmetrical pattern, predominantly bright with short dark streaks present. Where there is faulty distribution a fire will show particularly bright in one sector and there will be quite an area of dark in another sector. This may be accompanied by pulsation as well. The dark spot in the fire can be the result of either excessive coal in this sector of the

homogeneous, being deflected one way or another by bends in the coal pipe between the source and the burners with the result that often a non-uniform mixture arrives at the burners. Similarly, the secondary air as it reaches the burner windbox may be concentrated in one part of the duct.

In the circular pulverized coal burner some form of distributor usually is installed in the coal nozzle or in the coal piping approaching the nozzle. This distributor is adjusted in the early days of operation of a new installation as required for optimum performance.

In the cross-tube type of coal burner the shape of the coal nozzle is designed to give uniform distribution at the furnace if the fuel approaching the nozzle is reasonably well distributed. In most instances the distribution is satisfactory but where there are several severe bends in the coal pipe (to avoid some external obstruction), it is sometimes necessary to supplement the inherent distributing effect of the coal nozzle itself, with a correcting distributor in the coal pipe. In a new installation, this adjustment is usually made in the early days of operation.

It is in the multiple intertube, multi-tip type burner that the farthest advance has been made in correcting for mal-distribution within the burner itself. The arrangement and design of the piping for about 15 ft preceding the burner are rigidly controlled. By a series of elbows and changes in piping section, uniform distribution is obtained as the fuel enters the burner tips. To further improve the distribution, the tips are so arranged that the entering fuel stream from the piping is well dispersed over the burner area. The inherently better distribution with this arrangement is obtained at the price of some increase in the pressure drop of the primary air-fuel part of the circuit over that of the circular type burner.

In years past, secondary air distribution did not receive its share of criticism and even today to the

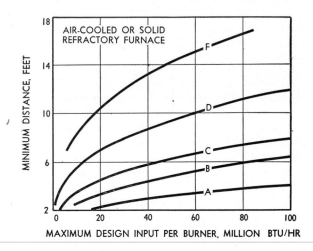

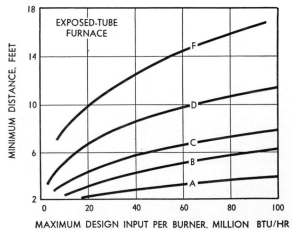

Fig. 28. Typical burner clearances to confining furnace walls for circular type pulverized coal burners

FUEL ASH RELATED TO

FROM the beginning of the production o
much attention has been devoted to th
lems created by the residues of con
broadly known as "ash"; and the compl
these problems has increased with the s
rating of modern units. On burning, all bu
fuels have certain residues and in some i
the quantity is considerable. At best, som
must be provided to dispose of the ash; a
ash in its various forms may seriously con
operation or even cause shutdown. Experi
dicates that it should always be of major
to the designer and the operator. Commerc
containing ash, and others with little or no
listed in Table 1.

TABLE 1

Fuels Containing Ash	Fuels Conta Little or no
All coals	Natural gas
Fuel oil—"Bunker C"	Manufactured ga
Refinery sludge	Coke oven gas –
Tank residues	Refinery gas
Refinery coke	Kerosene
Most tars	Distillates – (mos
Wood and wood products	
Waste heat gases – (most)	
Blast furnace gas	
Cement kiln gases	

Due to the prominence of coal as a fuel, a
all coals contain ash, the following discussio
concerned with the refuse from coal, but
due from petroleum fuels is also considered.
on becoming hot enough, a quantity of ash t
a sticky or molten state it is referred to, by
usage, as slag. Sometimes slag that has s
is also called slag, or it may be called clin
The ash content of coal varies over

flame, or it could be, just as well, the result of a
deficiency in secondary air. Even though the duct
arrangement to the burner windbox may appear
ideal, improper distribution of air at the burners is
still possible because of excessive velocities entering
and within the burner windbox or undesirable deflection of the air because of obstructions in the air
path.

Air flowing in a duct has a strong tendency to
continue in its direction and will not uniformly follow a new direction because of some change in duct
contour or other influence. If the duct makes a turn,
the air will crowd to the outside of the bend. In so
doing it will produce a low-pressure area at the inside of the bend. Therefore the inside corners of
all bends should have a generous radius, and the
bends should be fitted with turning vanes to distribute the air uniformly around the turn. In this
way, not only is the distribution of the air going into
a burner windbox improved, but there is also a reduction in air resistance in the duct. In general, the
velocity of the secondary air entering the burner
windbox should not exceed 2500 fpm, and it should
be uniformly distributed over the entrance. Under
these conditions secondary-air distribution is usually
good. Generously proportioned ducts and windboxes always aid in obtaining good distribution.

Wall Impingement and Tube Wastage

It is not good practice to have pulverized-coal-
burner flames blast against furnace walls—either refractory or water-cooled. Intensely hot ash particles
(always molten when newly formed) have the property of dissolving most refractories, hence heavy
"traffic" of ash over a refractory wall may seriously
damage the brickwork. An active flame impinging
on, or in close proximity to, furnace wall tubes may
also cause damage, but of a somewhat different
kind. Even if the boiler water within the tubes is
good and truly nonscale forming, certain conditions
—such as high heat release per sq ft, coals high in
sulfur and alkali content, and localized areas deficient in oxygen—may induce a slow attack on the external surface of the furnace tubes, which is known
as "tube wastage." This phenomenon seems to occur
only in a reducing atmosphere. Aside from this possibility of damage, an actively burning stream of
coal and air in close contact with the comparatively
cold surface of furnace tubes tends to delay, by a
chilling action, the prompt chemical union so much
desired. Experience is the best guide in this matter.
Conservative clearances between various circular
burner arrangements and various type furnace surfaces at different rates of heat input are given in
Fig. 28.

From time to time instances occur where the
flame tends to whip against a particular surface or

is directed in the wrong way. Assuming that clearances for the fire are adequate as based on past
experience, the chances are that the deflection of
the fire is caused by the secondary-air stream.
Countless hours have been spent in the field trying
to correct flame shape by deflecting the primary air-
fuel stream, whereas a little work on the secondary-
air stream would have quickly resolved the difficulty.
The importance of the manner in which the sec-

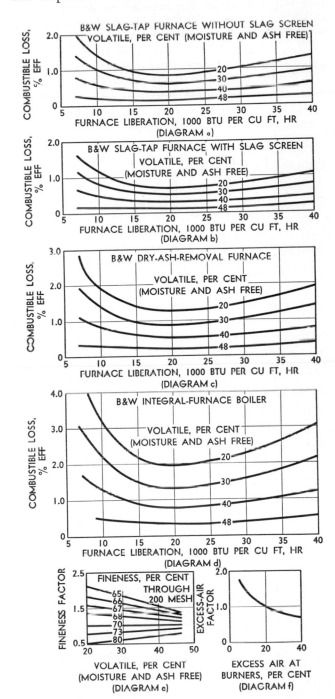

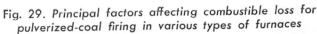

Fig. 29. *Principal factors affecting combustible loss for
pulverized-coal firing in various types of furnaces*

17-27

ondary-a
operation
the total
through

Air Tem

The te
should b
ignition.
fuel, whe
should be
over 175
(United
range fro
only by t
burner in
mentione
erated w
750 F.

Unburne

To con
either lef
pulverize
proached
using in t
loss of 0.
favorable
combustil
ous condi
furnaces
base carb
a, b, c, an
respective
and per
ample, th
may be e

Furnace li
Volatile (n
Fineness (
Excess air
From diag
C

An even
as follows:

Furnace li
Volatile (n
Fineness (
Excess air
From diag
C

coal, high purity metal can be obtai
nace atmosphere and temperature
trolled. The flame is always unde
oxidizing or reducing atmosphere
at will. In this industry, where the
between coal and natural gas or
coal, the other advantages of pu
the high rate of smelting and refini
readily to oxidize the sulfur.

Copper reverberatory furnaces f
and refining are fitted with waste
the generation of steam. These boi
stantial portion of power for au
and also provide the means for
leaving the furnace.

Approximately 65 to 70 per cent
able-iron tonnage produced in this
from white cast iron that is melted
furnace of the reverberatory type
ized coal, in a direct-firing system
draft burners.

For fuel-bed and stoker operation, the ash-soften-ing temperature on the reducing basis is most suit-able as a design criterion, since the atmosphere in the fuel bed is reducing and the iron in any clinker formed is predominantly in the ferrous state. Fuel-bed operating temperatures approaching the ash-fluid temperature should definitely be avoided to preclude serious clinker trouble. The ash initial-deformation temperature, reducing basis, is con-sidered the best guide in setting the temperature of gases entering the tube bank, since fuel or coke par-ticles blown out of the fuel bed are usually observed to be still burning (leaving the ash mostly in the reduced state) as they approach the bank.

The pulverized-coal-burning slag-tap unit illus-trated in Fig. 3 may serve as an example of intelli-gent application of ash-fusion-temperature values. This unit burns Pennsylvania coals with ash-fusion temperatures of the order noted. Both reducing and oxidizing values are given in Fig. 3. Slag is easily tapped from full load down to about 1/3 load, which is a creditable range. Noting the ash-fluid tempera-ture on a reducing basis, this result is not unexpected since much of the iron in the ash in the primary furnace is in a ferrous form and hence the ash-fluid temperature is lower. On the other hand, the ash that leaves the furnace with the gases contains a higher proportion of completely oxidized iron, or iron oxide in the ferric form, and the design value of 2260 F for the furnace exit gas temperature is entirely appropriate and well below the "sticky" stage of the ash, since the initial-deformation temperature on an oxidizing basis as given in Fig. 3 is 2440 F.

From the foregoing, it will be apparent that it is important to recognize which ash-fusion-temperature value to use as the significant index of performance and whether the reducing basis or the oxidizing basis is the more suitable for the particular region in the unit under consideration.

Design for Slag-Tap Operation

In a boiler furnace designed to dispose of furnace ash in the form of molten slag, it is imperative that the pool of this hot molten material be safely con-fined and that it be released in orderly fashion from a slag spout, either intermittently or continuously. Brickwork, or any refractory alone, is not suitable for permanent lining of slag bottoms, since molten slag at high temperature will actively attack brick-work by taking it into solution. Generally, to hold molten ash safely, a boiler furnace should be water cooled in one or another form. All four walls and the bottom must be water cooled. All walls and the bottom expand and contract together, so that there is no relative movement between the floor struc-ture and the walls. Cast-iron blocks are clamped

to the floor tubes with the joints sealed, and the sur-face presents an impervious barrier against slag leakage. These principles are illustrated in Fig. 17, Chapter 14.

Ash Produced by Stokers

In the fuel bed of a stoker, whether of the under-feed, chain-grate, or spreader overfeed type, ash particles tend to become fused together. In a prop-erly operated stoker burning a suitable coal, the passage of air and the agitation of the fuel bed serve to keep ash accumulations more or less porous, and the ash is discharged to an ashpit in fairly large pieces varying from popcorn size upward.

Not all the ash is retained in a fuel bed. With the types of stokers mentioned, and particularly the spreader stoker, some of the fuel is burned in suspen-sion. A considerable quantity of ash particles, con-taining some unburned and still burning fuel, is consequently "carried over" with the gases. With the spreader stoker, this material is almost always collected in hoppers provided for the purpose and is reinjected into the furnace, by simple means, for further burning of any combustible that it contains (see Chapter 16). Reinjection is sometimes used with other types of stokers.

Stoker-Ash Erosion

When burning particles of fuel impinge on a tube bank, there is a tendency to build up an accumulation since the ash constituent is still hot enough to be sticky. Such accumulations must be removed during operation by some form of soot blower. Burnt-out particles or those that have been extinguished by further passage through a tube bank sometimes help to keep heat-absorbing surfaces clean by a scrubbing action. However, gas velocities must be low enough to prevent erosion. Experience is the best guide in setting the limiting gas velocities for different fuels, types of stokers, and boiler gas-pass arrangements. The usual limiting values for gas velocities are given in Table 3. Limiting gas velocities are also given in this table for fuels, other than coal, sometimes used for grate and stoker firing.

Ash From Pulverized-Coal Burning

No matter how finely coal may be pulverized for burning, the fuel fed to the furnace still has all its original ash. However, the final ash product ejected from a pulverized-coal-fired unit is different in its gross appearance from the refuse of a stoker-fired unit. This is because, with pulverized coal, nearly all of the ash particles are formed in suspension and tend to remain in suspension in a dry-ash furnace, with the individual particles well dispersed and very much smaller than with stoker firing. In the slag-tap furnace, a portion of the ash particles coalesces on walls or other suitably designed surfaces and drains to the furnace bottom.

Where pulverized coal is burned in a dry-ash furnace (one example illustrated in Fig. 16, Chapter 14), it is not unusual for the ash escaping toward the stack to be in the order of 80% of the ash originally in the coal. On the other hand, with pulverized coal burned in a slag-tap furnace of the general type illustrated in Fig. 17, Chapter 14, as much as 50% of the ash may be retained, part in the furnace as fluid slag and part in the gas-pass hoppers in the form of dry dust. The other 50% of total ash in the coal escapes toward the stack, also in the form of dust. Dust collectors, frequently placed ahead of the stack, serve to prevent the final ejection of large quantities of this ash to the atmosphere.

Significant as are these comparative figures favoring the slag-tap arrangement as contributing less to atmospheric pollution by dust, still more impressive is the performance of the Cyclone Furnace. This special slag-tap furnace, described in Chapter 28, permits less than 10% of the total ash in the coal to escape from the boiler unit, and the stack discharge is correspondingly clean. If dust-collecting equipment is installed for a Cyclone Furnace boiler unit, the ash finally escaping from the stack to the atmosphere may be diminished to 1 or 2%.

Operational Problems

The effect of ash and slag on boiler operation can be very evident in pulverized-coal firing. The tonnage of the fuel burned, and consequently the refuse formed, can be increased, since it is easy to force the firing rate. To meet performance requirements, the heat-absorbing surfaces must be thoughtfully designed and arranged properly to cool the gases and ash particles. It is possible, with pulverized-coal and Cyclone Furnace firing (see Chapter 28), to burn coals of the so-called inferior grades, which in this sense are those with higher ash percentages, lower Btu values, and usually lower ash-fusion temperatures.

These conditions must be recognized in designing a pulverized-coal-fired unit, and, obviously, much experience and skill are required to produce a unit that will give performance with the poorest grade of fuel comparable to that with the best fuel.

Use of Dry-Ash or Slag-Tap Units

Considered answers to the following pertinent questions relating to fuel are essential in initiating the design of a successful pulverized-coal-fired unit:

1. Has the particular coal selected been burned extensively in pulverized form, so that its characteristics are well known?

2. Will the source of coal and the characteristics of the coal remain substantially constant during most of the life of the equipment? What is likely to be the "worst" fuel supplied?

3. What auxiliary fuel may be made available for periods of temporary suspension of coal delivery?

4. What type of equipment is best suited to the experience of the operating personnel?

5. In the public interest, for better public relations or to comply with civil regulations, what is required to prevent atmospheric pollution from dust?

6. What method of final refuse disposal is available to the owner?

On the basis of this information it will be possible to

TABLE 3

Maximum Allowable Gas Velocity, Feet per Second

Through Net Free Area, to Prevent Ash Erosion

Type of Firing	Gas-Pass and Baffle Arrangements	
	Multipass With Baffles	Single Pass No Baffles
Spreader stoker	60	75
Anthracite chain-grate stoker	60	75
Coke breeze chain-grate stoker	60	75
Bituminous chain-grate stoker	100	100
Underfeed stoker	75	100
Wood or other waste fuels°	50	60
Bagasse	60	75

° Containing sand.

assign proper equipment for the specific method of utilizing the coal. For instance, pulverized coal should not be burned in a slag-tap furnace if the ash fusion temperature and viscosity are higher than experience indicates they should be for successful tapping. Slag-tap furnaces are rarely suitable for ash fluid temperatures (reducing basis as per ASTM procedure) in excess of 2600F, or for an ash viscosity greater than 250 poises* at 2600F. If the ash fluid temperature or ash viscosity of the coal selected is too high or marginal, equipment permitting the ash to be removed in dry form is indicated.

Pulverized Coal Ash Erosion

Ash erosion must not be ignored even though pulverized coal ash particles are exceedingly fine. Where the travel of ash particles is confined to a given path, erosion is potentially present at almost every turn. The induced draft fan is a well known example and reduction in erosion is an important factor in selecting the type of fan and its performance characteristics. The wear of blading in high speed fans is much faster at 1800 rpm than at the lesser and more generally used speeds of 1500 or 900 rpm or even less for variable speed fans. Dense traffic of ash through the boiler setting may cause erosion of highly critical pressure parts. This action is likely to be found where ash tends to concentrate in streams, at turns formed by baffles within the boiler banks. In the latter case the remedy is to limit gas velocities and to eliminate baffles so far as possible. Elimination of baffles has been the tendency in the development of pulverized-fuel-burning boiler units, as illustrated in Fig. 4, where the gas flow continues horizontally through the boiler, without turns. Maximum allowable gas velocities with pulverized coal, blast furnace gas and Cyclone furnace firing are given in Table 4.

TABLE 4

Maximum Allowable Gas Velocity, Ft per Sec
Through Net Free Area to Prevent Flue Dust Erosion

Type of Firing	Gas Pass Arrangements	
	Multi-Pass	Single-Pass
Pulverized Coal	75	100
Cyclone Furnace	No known erosion limit	No known erosion limit
Blast Furnace Gas	75	100
Cement Dust	—	45

* Absolute viscosity, $\mu = 250$ poises, $\dfrac{g\,(\text{mass})}{cm,\ sec}$

$= 60{,}500,\ \dfrac{lb\,(\text{mass})}{ft,\ hr}$.

See Table 5, Chapter 8

If the unit is of the slag-tap variety, the molten refuse or slag, tapped from the furnace, must be cooled to be conveniently handled. This is done with water and the quenched product usually is broken up into small sharp-edged particles like coarse sand which, regardless of the mode of transport, tend to wear the material of the conduit. When water is used for transport, pump and pipe lining, and turns in pipes or in sluices are particularly subject to localized wear and are usually protected by replaceable sections of lining of special alloy steel or chilled cast iron.

Design and Operation of Slag-Tap Furnaces

The term slag-tap or slag-tap furnace, used in the preceding text, refers to the manner in which the

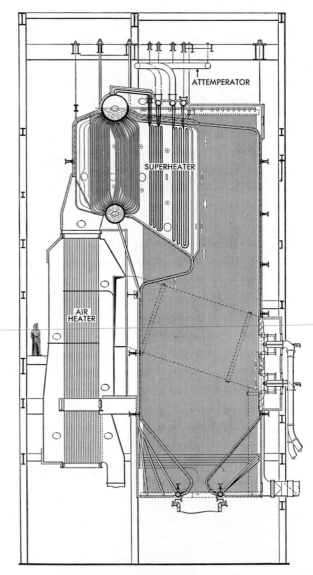

ATTEMPERATOR

SUPERHEATER

AIR HEATER

Fig. 4. Boiler designed for horizontal gas flow without baffles

refuse from the burning of pulverized fuel is disposed of or rejected from the boiler unit. The following is related to this operation as applied to power boilers since a similar operation in the metallurgical field is quite different in both intent and procedure.

The method of disposal of pulverized coal ash by tapping from a boiler furnace was evolved in 1926, more by accident than by design, in a boiler furnace originally expected to operate under dry-ash disposal conditions. When operation was established, the low fusion ash melted to the fluid state and collected in a pool at the bottom of the furnace whence it was drained at intervals by means of an improvised arrangement.

Many features of this furnace, the forerunner of later slag-tap furnaces, were totally inadequate for the formation, retention, and disposal of fluid ash. The furnace bottom was of ordinary brick which quickly became saturated with molten slag and ceased to be an impervious bottom. It was also apparent that the proper handling of a stream of molten slag was no light undertaking. Nevertheless, this crude beginning opened the way to the development of a method that promised easier handling and disposal of refuse in furnace operations. Almost immediately deliberate designs were evolved and some of the outstanding features of this development are outlined in the following specifications for a furnace and equipment designed to handle fuel ash in fluid form:

1) To be tapped easily from a furnace as a thin liquid, the temperature of molten coal ash must be somewhat above its ash fluid temperature. It follows that the furnace temperature must be still higher; therefore, a slag-tap furnace should be built to withstand the maximum temperatures in the active zone of combustion, usually in excess of 3000F.

2) Since fluid slag is heavy as well as extremely hot, it must be securely contained in those regions in the furnace where it tends to collect.

3) The interior surface of the furnace must be chemically inactive to the constituents of the hot slag. In a practical sense no refractory alone has been satisfactory in fully meeting this requirement in steam boiler furnaces.

4) Since tapped slag must be disposed of, means must be provided to drain slag from the furnace as fast as it is formed, or in any case at frequent intervals.

5) Once the molten slag has left the furnace it must be cooled to a condition and temperature suitable for ultimate disposal to waste.

To withstand the high temperatures noted above a completely water-cooled envelope, including all sides and the floor is required for the furnace. This is accomplished by various arrangements of water-

Fig. 5. Typical flow during intermittant removal of molten slag

cooled tubes. This construction represents a gradual evolution over many years. Many, more or less unsuccessful, attempts have been made at different times to employ various other arrangements including solid refractories in brick and molded form, air-cooled refractories, and water-cooled tubes on various centers and embedded in a variety of refractories.

A common arrangement for withdrawing molten slag from the furnace is illustrated in Fig. 3. An early type of slag removal is illustrated in Fig. 5. These two illustrations indicate the two methods of slag removal, and they are conventionally termed continuous tap and intermittent tap respectively. In both cases, the molten slag is disintegrated in water to the consistency of sand. In both cases also, the final sand-like product is conveyed by water either to storage sites or to ash cars.

It is impractical to operate a slag-tap furnace when the ash fluid temperature is equal to, or nearly equal to the furnace temperature at maximum steam output. There must be some margin of excess furnace temperature over the fluid temperature of the ash to keep the slag fluid enough for disposal by tapping.

The effect of a high fluid temperature of ash in making tapping difficult can be simulated by operating conditions under a low load factor. Under these conditions, a coal with a medium ash fluid temperature may not be suitable fuel for slag-tapping since the furnace temperature may not be high enough to give the proper differential in temperature to attain the degree of fluidity necessary for tapping.

Where there is a variable load with periods of high and also low furnace temperatures, it is sometimes possible to use intermittent tapping successfully. In intermittent tapping as differentiated from continuous tapping, the slag is permitted to accumulate in a furnace bottom for a nominal period; in practice this may be from 8 to 12 hours. From the daily load curves it is possible to anticipate when the steaming load will be high enough to reduce the ash to the proper degree of fluidity, for a long enough time, to insure removal of the slag through the tap hole. In other words, in intermittent tapping the operator synchronizes the time of tapping with a well established high load period in a particular schedule of operation.

In the selection of power plant equipment in recent years the trend has been toward single-boiler, single-turbine operation. For best returns on the investment such high duty and expensive equipment must be operated continuously at its maximum output. Continuous-tap furnaces are usually installed under this condition. With this method the molten slag is drained from the furnace at all times, and no considerable quantity of slag is allowed to accumulate in pools.

Coating of a portion of the furnace near the bottom with sticky ash, a result from the very nature of its operation, is one of the most important attributes of the slag-tap furnace. The sticky surface of molten ash deliberately maintained in selected high temperature zones of the furnace serves to entrain other particles in transit. The ash so collected drains continuously downward toward the bottom of the furnace and is removed in due course through the tap hole. The consequent reduction in the quantity of dust and ash leaving the boiler unit has a definite practical value, since it decreases the amount of dust to be intercepted by the dust collector and, therefore, decreases the size and cost of the dust collecting equipment. With the Cyclone furnace-fired boiler unit it is possible to go even farther in the direction of reducing ash discharge to the atmosphere (see above and Chapter 28).

It may be possible to reduce building costs in housing units with slag-tap furnaces. Since slag-tap furnaces are usually built without hoppers, a reduction in building height is possible. In planning new buildings, this may be a considerable factor in saving cost, and even in outdoor installations the height of the supporting steel structure can be less. For the same reason, installation of slag-tap units in older plants may be possible where it would be difficult, because of the greater height required, to install a unit equipped with ash hoppers.

Attempts have been made to utilize slag from slag-tap furnaces but without much success. It has been proposed that it be used as fill for low waste land, as an aggregate for cinder or concrete blocks, and as a source of metals which it contains in oxide form. Perhaps the chief obstacle to utilizing slag as a by-product of some value is that all operations at a power plant are subordinated to its prime function of producing electrical energy. It has not been found generally practical to coordinate the use of the equipment and procedures necessary for the utilization of a minor by-product with the major function of a power plant.

Dry-Ash and Slag-Tap Furnace Installations

For the 17-year period, from the beginning of 1936 to the end of 1952, slag-tap and dry-ash boiler units in sizes of 300,000 lb steam per hour and above, sold by B&W, totaled 313 units with an aggregate capacity of 205,011,000 lb of steam per hour. Of these totals, 110 units of 63,607,000 lb of steam per hour or 35 per cent are of the slag-tap type, and 203 units, of 141,400,000 lb of steam per hour are of the dry-ash type. In the size range considered, the steam output of B&W dry-ash and slag-tap units by years is shown graphically in Fig. 6. It will be noted that in the earlier years of the period the greater part of the steam output was produced with slag-tap units. However, in the latter years of the period, the proportion of dry-ash units steadily increased, and in 1948 virtually an equal amount of steam was produced by each type. In the years 1948 to 1952 (both inclusive) more steam was produced by dry-ash units than by the slag-tap type.

By the very nature of its operation, the Cyclone furnace is a slag-tap design. Since units of this design where first installed in 1946 its effect on the proportions indicated in Fig. 6 applies only to the last seven years. The inherent advantages of a Cyclone furnace in reducing the dissemination of dust to the atmosphere may be expected to exert a considerable influence on the course of similar statistics for the years following 1952.

The statistics plotted in Fig. 6 do, however, indicate, for the sizes included in the study, a steep increase in the application of the dry-ash method of burning pulverized coal during the latter as compared with the earlier years of the period under consideration. Not the least of the reasons for this increase is that boiler manufacturers, by improvements in burners and furnace proportions and the arrangement of heating surfaces to preclude furnace and tube bank fouling, have largely overcome the early difficulty in a dry-ash boiler unit of keeping all portions of the unit free of slag or troublesome ash. In addition to the improvement in design of dry-ash boiler units, some users have also been influenced in their choice of this type by finding it profitable to buy their coal supply in a broad market. A properly designed dry-ash unit is well adapted for burning a wide variety of coals with a considerable range in ash fusion temperatures.

Fuel Oil Ash

In recent years, there has been a marked increase in the deposition of slag and ash on the heating surfaces of oil-fired boilers in both stationary and marine service. This condition has affected boiler operation in the following ways:

1) Fluxing of refractory furnace walls.

2) Slagging of high-temperature superheater surfaces with deposits not successfully removed by air or steam soot blowers.

3) Attack on steels including high-chromium-content alloys, such as superheater spacers and hangers, when the metal temperatures are above 1200F.

4) Coating of boiler, economizer and air heater surfaces.

5) Corrosion of the cold sections of air heaters.

Of these difficulties, the most serious has been the slagging of superheater surfaces resulting in lower availability, increased draft loss, and decreased steam temperature. In some plants outages for cleaning have been required as often as once a month.

The gradually increasing use, since the early 1930's, of boiler units designed for higher steam temperature and the attendant increase in superheater metal temperature, together with a progressive deterioration, over the same period, of the available fuel oils are the major factors responsible for the troublesome conditions noted above. In 1949 the Babcock & Wilcox Co. undertook an intensive investigation of the problem to establish basic facts as a prerequisite to developing suitable relief methods for oil fuel users in the field of steam generation.

There are two principal reasons for the deterioration in the quality of heavy fuel oils used for steam generation. First, the quality of the crude oil from certain new oil fields, particularly the foreign fields, is lower than that from the older domestic fields which supplied most of the demands in the past. A change in the nature of the ash and an increase in the sulfur content are indices of the lower quality. Second, changes in refinery practice, including the extraction of larger quantities of top-quality products from the crude, have increased the concentration of undesirable ash in the heavy residual oil. Thus, there is an increase in ash content as well as a change in ash quality.

Earlier records show oil ash content ranging from 0.01 to 0.10 per cent. Today, ash content may be

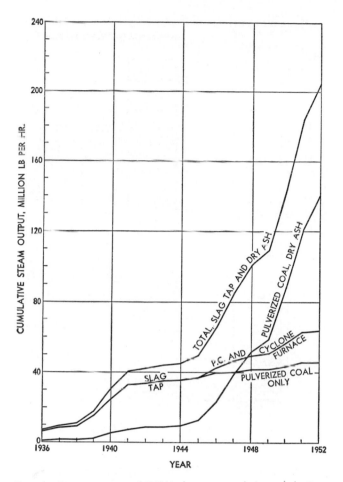

Fig. 6. *Steam output of B&W slag-tap and dry-ash boiler units of 300,000 lb steam per hr and above, over a 17-year period*

as high as 0.2 per cent, and 0.10 to 0.15 per cent ash is common. Despite this relatively large increase, the ash content of present-day heavy fuel oils is still quite low—in the order of 1/100 of the amount commonly found in coal. Without the accompanying change in oil ash composition, this increase would not be significant.

There is a great difference in the composition of the ash of present-day troublesome fuel oils compared with the earlier trouble-free fuel oils. Ash from the trouble-free fuel oils contains chiefly iron oxide, silica, lime and magnesia compounds with small amounts of other materials. The ash from troublesome fuel oils contains large quantities of alkali sulfates and, in many instances, considerable vanadium. Vanadium is more prevalent today and in much larger quantities than in the past. The source of the vanadium is the crude oil itself. Heavy fuel oils from Venezuelan crudes are particularly high in vanadium. Several other fields also yield crudes high in vanadium.

The transition from the trouble-free oils through

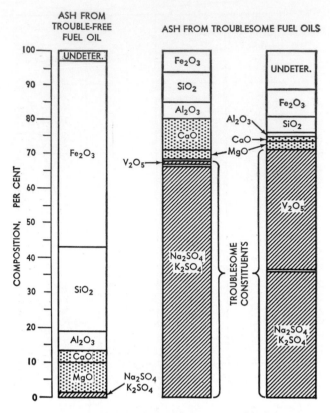

Fig. 7. *Composition of some trouble-free and troublesome ash from fuel oils*

though the increase in fuel oil sulfur content has not been as clearly related to the increase in slagging difficulties as has the change in ash quality, it is believed that the higher sulfur content contributes to slagging troubles. High sulfur content, however, has been definitely related to increased troubles with air heater fouling and corrosion.

Oil Slag Formations and Deposits

It has been found that alkali sulfates and vanadium pentoxide are the principal constituents of troublesome superheater oil slags. Both of these compounds, which have low fusing temperatures, are usually present in far greater proportion in the slag than in the oil ash. Also, the highest concentrations of alkali sulfate and vanadium pentoxide are found in the inner layers of the deposit next to the tube surfaces, with progressively lower concentrations toward the outer layers. As might be expected from this, the sintering temperatures of the deposit increase toward the outer layers.

It is generally agreed that oil slag forms on super-

those containing alkali sulfates as the principal trouble agent to those containing both alkali sulfates and vanadium pentoxide is illustrated in Table 5 and graphically in Fig. 7. The data presented is an average of analyses of ash from heavy fuel oils.

TABLE 5

Averaged Analyses of Ash from Heavy Fuel Oil

| | | Analysis, per cent | | |
		Trouble-free Fuel Oils	Troublesome Fuel Oils	
Ferric Oxide	Fe_2O_3	54	8	6
Silica	SiO_2	24	9	5
Alumina	Al_2O_3	6	4	1
Lime	CaO	3	10	1
Magnesia	MgO	9	3	2
Vanadium Pentoxide	V_2O_5	—	1	35
Alkali Sulfates		1	67	37

In the past, the sulfur content of the heavy fuel oils burned in the United States, with some exceptions, was in the order of 1 per cent or less. Today, the sulfur content can be as high as from 3 to 3.5 per cent, and 2 per cent sulfur is common. Al-

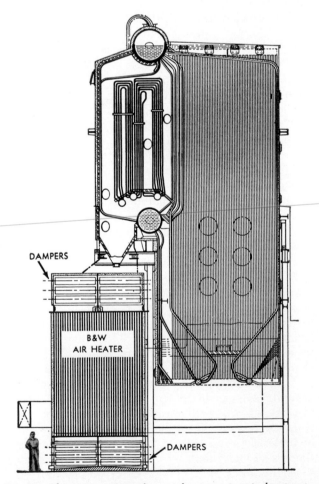

Fig. 8. *Showing sectionalizing dampers in air heater to permit in-service water washing half of heater at a time*

heater tubes as a bonded deposit. The bonding is due to low fusing temperature constituents which sinter or become sticky at these temperatures.

In new superheaters or where they have been cleaned to bare metal by washing, there usually is a "period of immunity" which may last for several weeks or months. During this period, there is no trouble from slagging. However, once the deposit begins to accumulate, the rate of slag deposition increases rapidly. Generally, with mechanical or manual cleaning a part of the old deposit, including the inner layer on the tubes, remains to serve as a base for the rapid accumulation of new deposit. Consequently, superheaters cleaned in this manner, in service or out, do not stay clean very long. The alternative is to clean down to bare metal by water washing. This is particularly true of superheater banks with close tube spacing and high metal temperatures.

Various constituents of oil slag deposits have different melting points, which, in some instances, are affected by the nature of the surrounding atmosphere during heating. A few examples are given below:

Constituent	Melting Point in Air, F
V_2O_5	1274
Na_2SO_4	1625
$MgSO_4$	2165
$CaSO_4$	2640
Fe_2O_3	2850

Under reducing conditions, V_2O_5 becomes V_2O_3 which melts at 3600F, compared to a melting point of 1274F for V_2O_5. This is the reason oil ash and slag high in vanadium will often have higher fusing temperatures in a reducing atmosphere than in an oxidizing atmosphere.

Removal of Deposit by Water Washing

As noted above air or steam soot blowers are often relatively ineffective in oil ash removal and operators generally resort to out-of-service cleaning by water washing. Fortunately oil ash deposits soften or are partially dissolved upon the application of water. Suitable means for disposal of wash water is necessary at all regions of the unit where this method of periodic cleaning is used. To avoid weak acid corrosion of metal parts a quick return of the unit to service for drying out is necessary.

In-service water washing has been used to some extent on oil fired units using the hot, high-pH boiler water in carefully regulated amounts either through hand lances or specially equipped soot blowers. Under proper control the method is generally safe for use on carbon steel surfaces such as

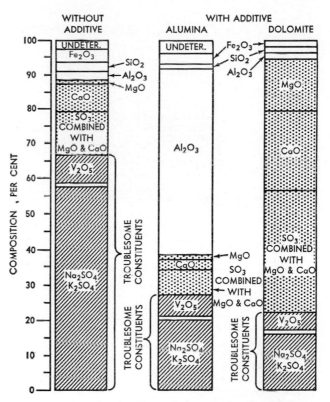

Fig. 9. Beneficial effect of two fuel oil additives in reducing troublesome constituents in ash

boiler, economizer and air heater tubes. The practice of in-service water washing carbon steel superheaters is somewhat questionable because of the higher metal temperature and the consequent possible damage from quenching the hot metal of the tube. High alloy steel superheater tubes should never be water washed in service since these alloys are generally quite susceptible to quench damage (quench cracking).

An air heater arrangement, with ducts and dampers designed so that, with the boiler remaining in service at reduced rating, one-half of the heater can be isolated at a time and water washed, is illustrated in Fig. 8. Service water at room temperature is satisfactory for this operation which can be performed in a few minutes with an ordinary hose and nozzle manually directed through the cleaning and access doors. Large quantities of water should be used to keep in dilute and relatively harmless solution any acid that is formed. The drains for suitable final disposal of wash water are at the bottom of the air heater.

Fuel Oil Additives

The practice of water washing out-of-service and to a limited extent, in-service, has been of considerable help in overcoming some of the trouble

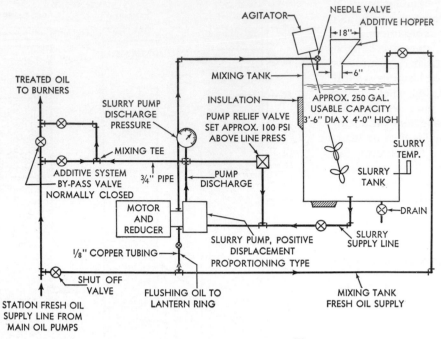

AGITATOR — NEEDLE VALVE — ADDITIVE HOPPER

TREATED OIL TO BURNERS

SLURRY PUMP DISCHARGE PRESSURE

MIXING TANK

INSULATION

PUMP RELIEF VALVE SET APPROX. 100 PSI ABOVE LINE PRESS

APPROX. 250 GAL. USABLE CAPACITY 3'-6" DIA X 4'-0" HIGH

MIXING TEE

ADDITIVE SYSTEM BY-PASS VALVE NORMALLY CLOSED

3/4" PIPE

PUMP DISCHARGE

SLURRY TEMP.

SLURRY TANK

MOTOR AND REDUCER

SLURRY PUMP, POSITIVE DISPLACEMENT PROPORTIONING TYPE

1/8" COPPER TUBING

DRAIN

SLURRY SUPPLY LINE

SHUT OFF VALVE

FLUSHING OIL TO LANTERN RING

MIXING TANK FRESH OIL SUPPLY

STATION FRESH OIL SUPPLY LINE FROM MAIN OIL PUMPS

Fig. 10. *Fuel oil additive system (diagrammatic) for a 275,000 lb steam per hr boiler unit*

Table 6

Fuel Oil Additives—Effect on Oil Slag

Analyses of Typical Superheater Deposits Before and After Use of Additives

		Without Additive	With Alumina Additive	With Dolomite Additive
Silica	SiO_2	2.8	1.1	2.0
Alumina	Al_2O_3	2.1	53.7	1.7
Titania	TiO_2	0.1	0.1	—
Ferric Oxide	Fe_2O_3	1.8	3.2	1.6
Ferrous Oxide	FeO	1.4	0.3	—
Phosphorous Pentoxide	P_2O_5	0.037	0.06	0.1
Manganese Oxide	MnO	—	—	—
Lime	CaO	7.8	2.4	22.6
Magnesia	MgO	1.8	1.0	15.2
Sulfur Trioxide	SO_3*	43.8	18.6	44.8
Vanadium Pentoxide	V_2O_5	8.6	6.6	4.9
Nickel Oxide	NiO	2.9	1.3	2.0
Potassium Oxide	K_2O	8.6	1.2	—
Sodium Oxide	Na_2O	18.6	8.4	7.6
Ignition Loss		0.2	0.4	—
Undetermined		—	1.7	—
Total		100.5	100.0	102.5

		Physical Appearance	Semi-fused, rock-like		Friable		Powdery	
		Atmosphere	Reducing	Oxidizing	Reducing	Oxidizing	Reducing	Oxidizing
Fusing Temp, F	Shrinkage began		1750	2050	——	——	2280	2640
	Initial deformation		2260	2640	2900+	2900+	2790	2800
	Softening		2380	2660	2900+	2900+	——	——
	Fluid		2460	2900+	2900+	2900+	——	——

* Combined with magnesia (MgO) and lime (CaO)

in using present oil fuels. However, continuing study of the problem along quite a different line indicated another approach which is effective where the fuel oil ash is most troublesome. In brief, the method involves the addition, in small amounts, of materials to the fuel oil which change the character of the ash sufficiently to permit removal by steam or air soot blowers or air lance.

In general, the most effective additives are alumina and dolomite. Analyses of typical superheater deposits from a troublesome fuel oil before and after treating the fuel oil with the above additives are given in Table 6 and are shown in the bar graph, Fig. 9. The marked increase in ash fusion temperature after treating the fuel oil with additives is evident, as is the effect on the physical structure of the deposit. A friable or powdery deposit is easily removed.

In general, the amount of the additive, either alumina or dolomite, should be about equal to the ash content of the fuel oil. In some instances, slightly different proportions may be required for optimum results. The use of one or the other of the additives will depend somewhat on the location of the plant in relation to the supply. In most localities dolomite will be the more easily available and will cost less. There is less burner atomizer wear in using dolomite. The additive should be pulverized to a fineness of 100 per cent through a 325 mesh screen and may be introduced to the system as indicated in the arrangement shown diagrammatically in Fig. 10 for a 275,000 lb steam per hr boiler.

CARBON MONOXIDE, FORMERLY A WASTE GAS, IS THE BOILER FUEL
FOR THIS MODERN CATALYTIC CRACKING PLANT

UTILIZATION OF MISCELLANEOUS FUELS AND WASTE HEAT

The progressive increase in the cost of fuel and the technical progress in the utilization of waste energy have led to specialized designs and applications of boilers. Many industries have their specific problems with waste-product recovery. For example, the oil industry has a tremendous amount of energy in the gas discharged from the catalytic regenerators; steel mills have their blast-furnace gas; the sugar industry has its cane refuse; the wood-and-pulp industry has sawdust, hogged fuel, bark, and process liquors (see Chapter 20) as wastes. All these waste products or residuals can be burned as fuels for the generation of steam. In addition, there are industries or processes that have large quantities of high-temperature gases from which the sensible heat may be abstracted for steam generation. Such gases are produced in copper reverberatory furnaces; an-

nealing, forge, and billet-heating furnaces; open-hearth furnaces; and fired kilns of many types.

Gaseous By-Product Fuels

Carbon Monoxide

In the petroleum industry, the efficient operation of a fluid catalytic cracking unit produces gases rich in carbon monoxide. To reclaim the thermal energy represented by these gases, the fluid catalytic cracking unit shown in Fig. 1 was designed to include a pressure fired "CO" boiler as an integral part. The arrangement is such that it can be operated independently or taken out of service without affecting the operation of the cracking unit.

The fluid catalytic cracking unit consists essentially of a reactor and a regenerator. In this process the

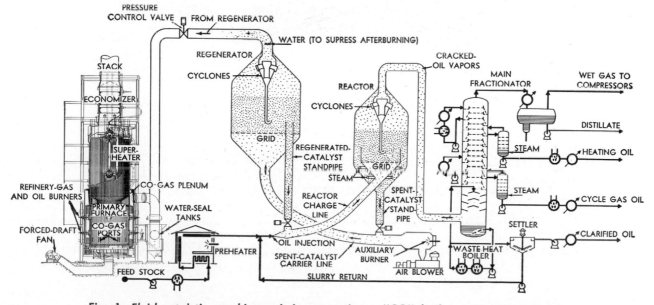

Fig. 1. *Fluid catalytic cracking unit incorporating a "CO" boiler as an integral part*

finely divided catalyst, suspended in the vapors, flows continuously in a cycle from the reactor to the regenerator and back to the reactor. Gas-oil feed stock is injected into the hot regenerated-catalyst line just before it enters the reactor. The catalyst circulation rate is controlled to maintain the required reaction temperature of about 950 F. Hydrocarbon vapors leave the reactor through cyclone separators, which return the entrained catalyst to the reactor bed, and the cracked petroleum products are separated in the fractionator.

In the reactor the catalyst accumulates a carbonaceous deposit. The spent, or carbon-coated, catalyst is transported to the regenerator by injecting compressed air into the catalyst stream. Additional air is supplied directly to the regenerator to burn the carbon from the catalyst. The heat of combustion is absorbed by the regenerated catalyst, which, in turn, heats the oil feed stock to effect vaporization. The oil vapors and catalyst are then discharged into the reactor to begin the cracking and refining process.

The products of combustion from the burning of the carbon coating have a CO_2/CO ratio of nearly 2/1, with CO percentage ranging from 5 to 8. The gases are discharged from the regenerator through cyclone separators to remove as much of the entrained catalyst as possible, prior to entering the CO boiler for heat recovery.

The CO boiler (Fig. 2) was developed to recover the heat discharged from the catalytic regenerator —practically all the heat of the combustibles and approximately 50% of the sensible heat.

The gases leave the regenerator at approximately 1000 F, which, with a temperature drop of 500 F, provides 145 Btu/lb as sensible heat for steam generation. The combustible content of the gas stream is the result of the incomplete burning of the carbon at low temperature with, in most instances, a deficiency of air. The unburned combustibles consist primarily of carbon monoxide with some traces of entrained hydrocarbons. In catalytic cracking units it is desirable to burn the carbon to produce a maximum of CO instead of CO_2, since a cubic foot of air combines with twice the amount of carbon when CO is made. Thus, blower power is saved by burning the maximum amount of carbon with a minimum amount of air, and the catalyst temperature is held down to 1000 F by releasing a minimum amount of heat. These reactions are:

$$2C + O_2 = 2CO + 3,958 \text{ Btu/lb of carbon}$$

compared with

$$C + O_2 = CO_2 + 14,093 \text{ Btu/lb of carbon}$$

Supplementary fuel is always required in the operation of a CO boiler. It is necessary not only to raise the temperature of the CO gases to the ignition point but also to assure complete burning of the combustibles in the CO-gas stream. The following design criteria have been established:

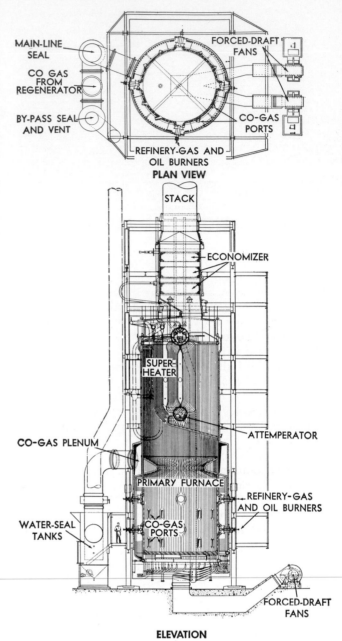

Fig. 2. The "CO" boiler, a pressure-fired top-supported unit

1. The basic firing rate shall produce a temperature of 1800 F in the primary furnace, to provide safe and stable combustion of the fuels.
2. The combustion air supplied by the forced-draft fan shall be sufficient to furnish the oxygen for combustion of the supplementary fuel, the oxygen for combustion of the CO gases, and the excess air required to provide 2% excess oxygen leaving the unit.
3. The firing equipment shall be sized to permit supplementary firing for raising the temperature of

the CO gases to 1450 F to start the burning of the combustibles in the CO gases.

The furnaces, both primary and secondary, and the boiler tube bank are designed as a single integrated boiler unit supported at the top, with provision for downward expansion. The supplementary-fuel burners (Fig. 3) and the CO-gas nozzles are positioned tangentially to the cylindrical furnace to effect thorough mixing and promote rapid and complete combustion. The fuel burners are arranged in a staggered pattern with respect to the CO-gas nozzles. The wall tubes are covered with refractory to aid in burning the CO gas with minimum supplementary fuel. The wall tubes also cool the refractory, thus protecting it when only supplementary fuel is fired.

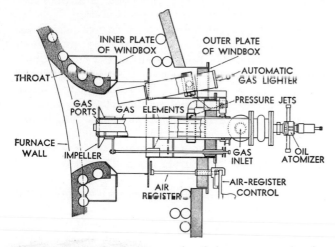

Fig. 3. Center-fired gas and oil burners supply the supplementary fuel to "CO" boilers

The CO-gas and combustion-air windboxes, or distribution chambers, are designed as an integral part of the furnace. Thus, a simple water-cooled arrangement for the high-temperature CO gases is provided to eliminate difficult and expensive differential-expansion and seal problems, especially important with toxic gases.

Normally the CO-boiler unit is designed for full-load operation when firing only supplementary fuel, so as to provide steam for starting the cracking unit. Operators have found that the CO boiler is different from the conventional waste-heat boiler in that steam is always available during not only normal operation but also start-up and shutdown. It is possible that a cracking unit may require more steam at start-up than under normal full-load operating conditions. It is not necessary to "boot strap" the cracking unit on the line when the CO boiler is used, nor is it necessary to "borrow" steam from other processes.

During this short period of operation with supplementary fuel, the combustion-air requirement is considerably higher than when utilizing CO gases. Con-

sequently two fans are installed, each designed to supply one half of the maximum requirement. Both fans are used while operating the boiler at full capacity with supplementary firing only. Each fan is capable of supplying the combustion air for full-load operation with CO-gas firing and the necessary supplementary fuel; thus, only one fan is required for CO-boiler operation, and the second fan is a spare. Each fan is equipped with a pressure-interlock system that prevents the discharge of gas through the fan inlet in the event of fan failure. The system automatically closes the fan-discharge damper for a preset minimum pressure and admits purging steam to the duct.

The possible variations in the combustible and oxygen content of the CO gases, in the sensible heat of the CO gases, and in the amount of supplementary firing make it impractical to set up a fuel-air relationship as is done for conventionally fired units. Because of this variable relationship when firing multiple fuels simultaneously, it is necessary to determine directly the amount of excess oxygen leaving the unit. This may be determined intermittently by an Orsat, continuously by an oxygen recorder, or by a combination oxygen-combustible recorder.

Water-seal tanks (Fig. 4) are installed to provide for the independent operation of the CO boiler without interfering with the operation of the regenerator, so that the CO gases from the regenerator may be passed through the boiler or sent directly to the stack.

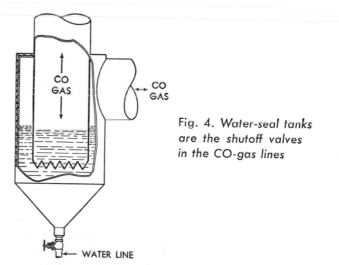

Fig. 4. Water-seal tanks are the shutoff valves in the CO-gas lines

Actually these water-seal tanks act as shutoff valves in the large gas lines. The flow of gas through any one of the seal tanks may be stopped by filling it with water to the level where the differential water pressure equals the CO-gas pressure, thus forcing the CO gas to flow through the other seal tanks. The CO-gas pressure at the seal is determined by the resistance to gas flow of the equipment downstream from the seal. To aid in establishing the water seal, a mechanical damper is installed ahead of the seal tank to throttle the gases while making the water seal. This mechanical damper is not a positive shut-off damper. Water-seal tanks are preferred to mechanical shutoff dampers because of the high gas temperature, the size of the CO ducts, and the necessity for a leakproof arrangement.

The operation of the CO boiler is coordinated with that of the catalytic cracker. Normally, the boiler will be required to supply steam for the operation of the catalytic cracking unit and will be started earlier, using supplementary fuel. However, the CO boiler should always be started using only the supplementary-fuel burners and by-passing the gases from the regenerator to the atmosphere. CO gases should not be introduced into the boiler until it is in operation, since they usually are at or below 1000 F and consequently tend to cool the furnace. They augment the swirling action in the furnace and should therefore be brought in gradually to provide a smooth changeover. They ignite quite readily and burn with a nonluminous flame. As they are introduced to the boiler, steaming increases materially, making it necessary to cut back on the supplementary fuel and requiring a major downward adjustment of the combustion air. This readjustment in the air requirement is determined from the oxygen-recorder readings.

Since there are only slight variations in the operation of a catalytic cracking unit, the CO boiler is normally base loaded. The CO boiler handles all the gases from the regenerator regardless of the CO_2/CO ratio. A change in this ratio merely affects the quantity of supplementary fuel necessary to maintain the required furnace temperature of 1800 F. This temperature provides a reasonable operating margin for possible variation in the operation of the regenerator or the boiler. Stable operation can be maintained at furnace temperature as low as 1500 F, but the margin above the ignition temperature of the CO gas is considerably reduced.

The economics of the CO boiler depend upon the amount of available heat—both sensible heat and heat from combustibles—in the regenerator exhaust compared with an equivalent amount of heat from an alternate fuel. The amount of heat from the CO gases available for steam generation may be calculated by taking the sensible heat above an assumed boiler stack temperature plus all the heat from the combustibles. The additional steam generated in the CO boiler by the supplementary fuel is comparable with the steam generated in a conventional power boiler using the same fuel. Normally, the supplementary-fuel requirement will account for ¼ to ⅓ of the output, when the temperature of the entering CO gas is maintained at 1000 F.

The application described above has been confined to the oil-refining industry. There are areas in other industries where these principles could be used to advantage. An economic study will show the feasibility of burning waste gases as fuel for the generation of steam.

Blast-Furnace Gas

A gas containing about 25% by volume of CO is generated in the blast furnaces of steel mills. This valuable by-product fuel is called blast-furnace gas and is used principally for the generation of steam.

Although this gas can be burned in the condition in which it is discharged from the blast furnace, its high dust loading (5 to 7 grains/cu ft) would cause plugging of burner ports and excessive fouling of heat-absorbing surfaces. It is desirable, therefore, to reduce the amount of entrained dust through washing, followed by electrostatic precipitation.

The gas most difficult to burn is that which has been washed only. Since washing does not remove all the solids, those that remain mix with the water entrained in the gas. The mud thus formed adheres firmly to hot surfaces and is very difficult to remove. A gas with solids content reduced to 0.15 grain/cu ft would carry 14 lb of solids per hour to a burner of 650,000 cu ft/hr capacity (60 million Btu/hr). If only 1% of this amount (a very conservative estimate) collects in the burner itself, 3⅜ lb of solids will accumulate in 24 hours.

A modern combination blast-furnace-gas, coke-oven-gas, and pulverized-coal burner that is admirably suited for such a gas is shown in Fig. 5. Note the large-area scroll entrance to the nozzle, where much of the foreign matter in the gas deposits. The scroll is cool, therefore the "mud" does not bake and can be removed readily through the quick-opening clean-out doors shown. The nozzle itself has a large area, and deposits that accumulate between normal boiler outages do not materially affect the burner capacity. No plugging or bridging is possible.

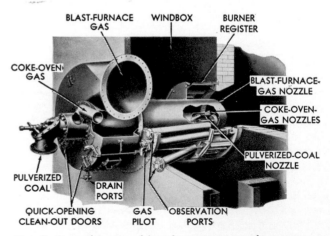

Fig. 5. A combination blast-furnace-gas, coke-oven-gas, and pulverized-coal burner

Several times a day the charge of iron, coke, and chemicals in a blast furnace will arch over. The collapsing of this arch is known as a furnace "slip." When a slip occurs, there is a resulting surge in gas pressure throughout the system, and, although momentary, it can extinguish the flames from the burners. Consequently, provision for immediate re-ignition is made in the design of blast-furnace-gas-fired boilers, in order to prevent serious explosions of furnace gas. Older units with refractory furnaces had the burners mounted in extension furnaces (Dutch ovens), in which small hand-fired grates were installed. The combination of hot fuel bed and incandescent brickwork served to reignite the burner after a blast-furnace slip. Modern boiler units use little or no refractory in order to minimize maintenance, and, to re-establish ignition after a slip, continuous-burning pilots are used. These pilots burn coke-oven gas, natural gas, or fuel oil.

Liquid By-Product Fuels

Pitch and Tar

The liquid and semiliquid residues from the distillation of petroleum and coal are known as pitch and tar. Most of these residues are suitable for use as boiler fuels. Some handle as easily and burn as readily as does kerosene, whereas others give considerable trouble. To determine whether a particular pitch or tar might be a suitable fuel for a given installation, the following items are important.

Moisture. If the fuel contains moisture, it must be well emulsified to avoid reaching the burner in slugs. If there is a brief break in the continuous flow of fuel to the burners, the fires will be extinguished. Upon re-establishing the fuel flow, a furnace explosion might occur if there is any delay in reigniting the burners. Consequently, a slug of water in the fuel supply can be disastrous if it extinguishes the flame briefly. Tars and pitches containing as much as 35% moisture may be burned in properly designed units.

Flash and Fire Points. Many liquid fuels are blends of two or more different liquids. One of these might have low flash and fire points, whereas the other might have high flash and fire points. Such a fuel usually burns with a bright flame at the burner, where the low-flash-point constituents are burning off; but beyond, where the components with the higher flash and fire points are burning, the flame is a dark yellow. Actually, if there is too little turbulence at the burner or if the burning products are quenched by passing too quickly from the active combustion zone, combustion is incomplete, and high unburned-combustible loss results. Consequently, while the flash temperature is useful for determining the possible hazard involved in storing the fuel, the fire point determines its suitability for firing in a boiler. Fuels with fire points as high as 600 F can be burned in properly designed equipment.

Viscosity. Practically all tars and pitches are burned in the same manner as fuel oil. They are reduced to a foglike dispersion in an atomizer located in a burner and then vaporized and burned. To produce the fine particles, the viscosity of the fuel must be correct—not over 180 Seconds Saybolt Universal (SSU) for most atomizers, although if favored by the burner-furnace arrangement, viscosities as high as 1000 SSU may be used.

Suspended Matter. Many of these fuels contain suspended matter. If they are delivered to the burners in this condition, there will be:
1. Abnormal fouling of the atomizers, requiring excessive cleaning.
2. Excessive rate of wear of burner parts.
3. Deposition of unburned carbon throughout the unit or objectionable stack emission.

Such fuels should therefore be passed through strainers before they are fed to the burners.

Compatibility. When some of these fuels come into contact with ordinary fuel oil, they combine to form liverlike substances. If this happens in tanks or piping, trouble results. The mixture cannot be pumped from the tanks, and pluggage in the piping often requires complete dismantling for cleaning. Burner operation, too, is erratic and spasmodic. Therefore, before mixing large quantities of tar or pitch with fuel oil, sufficient laboratory tests should be made at both storage and pumping temperatures to determine the compatibility of the fuels.

Solid By-Product Fuels

Bagasse

Bagasse is the refuse from the milling of sugar cane. Physically it consists of matted cellulose fibers and fine particles, the percentage of each varying with the process. In the older plants the raw cane was ground by passing it in series through sets of grooved rolls, each set comprising a mill having finer grooves than the preceding one. Modern practice incorporates a shredder that cuts the cane with revolving knives prior to the tandem milling previously described. The end product has a higher percentage of fines and short fibers.

A typical analysis of bagasse is given on page 3-A3 of the Appendix. Bagasse generally contains about 50% moisture and has a heat content of 3600 to 4200 Btu/lb as fired. It is used chiefly as a fuel to generate steam and power for the plant. Other by-product uses are for cellulose, for paper and paperboard manufacture, and for furfural production.

As a fuel for the production of steam, bagasse has been burned in several types of furnaces, the oldest being a Dutch oven with flat grates. Since it was difficult to distribute the bagasse evenly on the grates, the latter were subject to high maintenance costs from burning. A new type of furnace was therefore developed to burn the bagasse in a pile on a refractory hearth. Air was admitted to the pile around its circumference through tuyères. The most popular of these extension furnaces was the Cooke, but it also suffered from high maintenance costs because of excessive radiation and cleaning difficulties. To overcome these problems the Ward furnace was designed, as illustrated in Fig. 6.

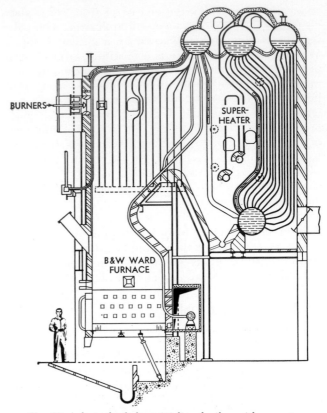

Fig. 7. A low-draft-loss Stirling boiler with a water-cooled Ward furnace

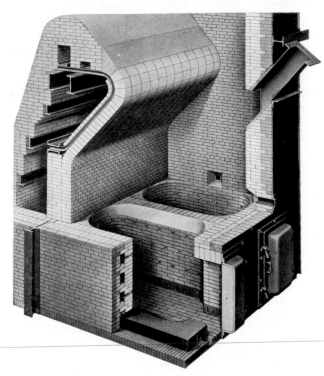

Fig. 6. A Ward furnace for burning bagasse

The Ward furnace has been very successfully used under sugar-mill boilers. It is easy to operate and maintain. Bagasse is gravity fed through chutes to the individual cells, where it burns from the surface of the pile with approximately 85% of the air which is injected into the sides of the pile adjacent to the hearth. This causes local incomplete combustion, but there is sufficient heat released partially to dry the raw fuel entering. Additional drying is accomplished by radiant heat reflected from the hot refractory to the cells. Combustion is completed in the secondary furnace above the arch. Ward furnaces are now equipped with dumping hearths, which permit the ashes to be removed while the unit is in operation.

Mechanical harvesting of sugar cane increases the amount of dirt in the bagasse to as much as 5 to 10%. To overcome the resultant slagging tendency of the ash, water-cooling is incorporated in the furnaces. Fig. 7 shows a modern unit with water-cooled furnace.

In the older mills, the drives for the milling equipment were large reciprocating steam engines, which used steam at a maximum of 150 psi and with a few degrees of superheat, exhausting at 15 psi to the boilinghouse steam supply. In more modern mills the drives are either turbines or electric motors with reducing gears. Both the turbines and the turbo-generators use steam at pressures of 400 to 600 psi and with temperatures up to 750 F.

Raw-sugar mills produce sufficient bagasse to meet all their steam requirements and in some cases an excess. Sugar mills that also refine usually generate from 80 to 90% of their steam requirements with bagasse, the remainder with supplementary fuel oil. Because of the high moisture content of the gas, the weight of the gaseous combustion products is about twice that from oil and one and one half times that from coal. This high gas weight causes excessive draft loss and requires either extremely high stacks or fans to obtain the required steam capacity from the boilers. To alleviate these conditions a low-draft-loss Stirling boiler, as shown in Fig. 7, was designed. The vertical tube bank facilitates cleaning, and the special baffle arrangement usually permits natural-draft operation to the required peak capacity at thermal efficiencies in the order of 57%. In sugar mills with refineries, a higher efficiency is necessary to reduce the amount of supplementary oil required. A thermal efficiency of 65% may be obtained by the addition of an air heater and an induced-draft fan, as shown in Fig. 8.

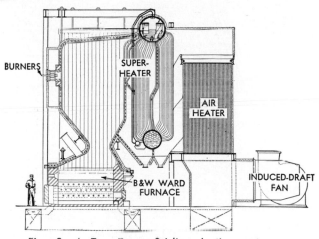

Fig. 8. A Two-Drum Stirling boiler with air heater and water-cooled Ward furnace

In recent years bagasse has been burned on stokers of the spreader type. This method of burning, however, requires bagasse with a high percentage of fines, a moisture content not over 50%, and a more experienced operating personnel. Because of such limitations, the Ward furnace is considered the most reliable, flexible, and simple method of burning bagasse.

Wood Refuse

The burning of wood as a fuel for steam generation is generally confined to those industries or operations where wood refuse is available. Average sawmill practice shows that, in the cutting of lumber, nearly half the total weight of a log appears as refuse—sawdust, chips, slab, and bark. The pulp-and-paper, furniture, and plywood industries are typical operations where such refuse appears in appreciable quantities.

All woods have substantially the same chemical analysis but may vary considerably in density and moisture content. Typical analyses of several kinds of wood are given on page 3-A3 of the Appendix.

Wood refuse available as a fuel may consist of large pieces, such as slabs, logs, and bark strips, and small pieces, such as sawdust and shavings. Furnaces for burning wood refuse are usually designed to handle chip size, in which case it becomes necessary to pass the large pieces through a hogger or chipper. Reducing the wood to chip size permits uniform continuous feeding, a more rapid burning of the small particles, and a more complete coverage of the grate.

Wood refuse from some processes contains 75% or more moisture. In order to obtain useful heat from the combustion of this type of fuel, it is necessary to reduce the moisture content to 60 or 65%. Mechanical presses are generally used for this purpose.

Wood-burning furnaces are not usually troubled with severe slagging conditions unless the wood is burned in combination with other fuels or unless the refuse comes from salt-water-borne logs. Ashes from two fuels often combine to form an ash of lower melting temperature than that of either ash taken separately. In some parts of the country, provision must be made for the removal of large amounts of sand and dirt which are dragged in with the logs. Such foreign material entrained in the combustion gases would cause the erosion of such surfaces as tubes, baffles, flues, and fans.

Grates for furnaces may be divided into air-cooled and water-cooled classes, or they may be a combination of the two. They should have about 30% free air space. For ash removal, grates may be of the rake-out, dumping, or moving type.

To design an efficient wood-burning furnace, the following steps in the combustion process must be considered: 1) drying, which proceeds rapidly on the surface but requires time to reach interior parts of large pieces, 2) distillation and burning of volatile matter, and 3) burning of fixed carbon. The temperature in the furnace must remain above the kindling point (between 750 and 1000 F), or the fire will go out. Furnace temperature depends upon the calorific value and the moisture content of the fuel, the weight of air flowing through the fuel bed, and the heat loss from flame and fuel bed by radiation. Furnaces designed for the burning of wood refuse fall into three types: pile, thin-bed, and cyclonic.

Pile Burning. The Dutch oven, or extension type of furnace with a flat grate, is the oldest design of furnace for burning wood refuse in a pile. Fig. 9 shows a modern version having water-cooled side walls, roof, and partial front wall. The hogged fuel is fed continually through a low roof and is permitted to pile up in a cone, the apex of which is directly under the feed hole in the roof. Most of the air for combustion enters through the grate around the edge of the pile and sweeps over the fuel, so that most of the burning takes place on the surface of the pile. Some of the air is injected through the side walls toward the pile in order to obtain turbulence for completion of combustion.

The fuel supply cannot be closely regulated with this method of firing, and frequent manual adjustment is required for good operating results. Excess air at the boiler outlet is between 30 and 40%. Combustion rates of 125 lb per hr per sq ft of grate have been attained, burning wood having 45% moisture

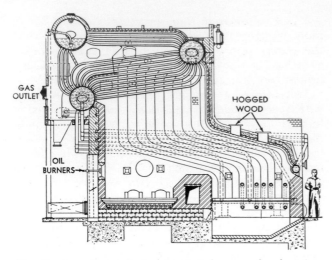

Fig. 9. A water-cooled extension furnace for burning hogged wood under a Type H Stirling boiler

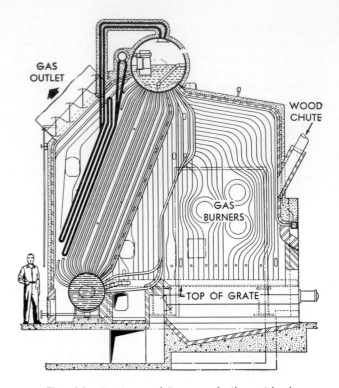

Fig. 10. An Integral-Furnace boiler with the furnace serving as a Dutch oven

(as fired), using cold air. With hot air (300 to 350 F), the burning rate can be increased 25%. Above 45% moisture the combustion rate decreases rapidly. Ash is removed by rake-out or by dumping grates.

A small two-drum boiler unit designed to utilize the furnace as a Dutch oven is shown in Fig. 10. The wood drops by gravity into the furnace through circular chutes located in the upper front wall and falls into piles on top of dumping-type air-cooled grates.

A large two-drum single-pass boiler unit, in which the furnace acts as a Dutch oven, is illustrated by

Fig. 11. In addition, provision has been made to burn oil in combination or alone. The furnace consists of two cells having water-cooled pinhole grates. Each cell is fed by its own air-swept chute through the

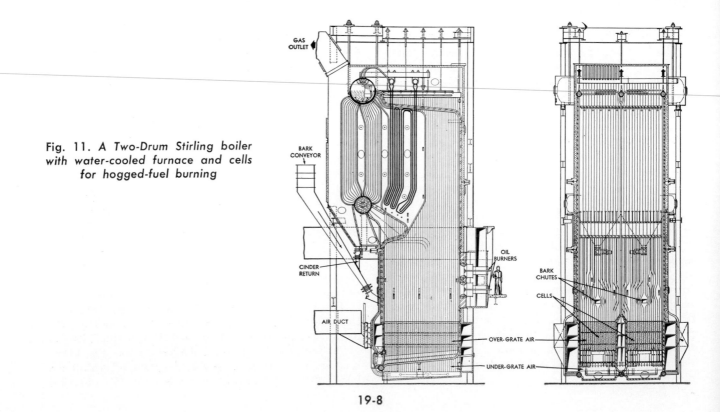

Fig. 11. A Two-Drum Stirling boiler with water-cooled furnace and cells for hogged-fuel burning

bridge wall. Most of the 600 F air for combustion is introduced through tuyères at three elevations around the four sides of each cell. Some undergrate air is required to aid ignition, particularly when fuel is first fed to the cell or when burning-down preparatory to removing ash. This unit is capable of burning hogged fuel having 00 to 65% moisture at a rate of 285 lb per hr per sq ft of grate with 30% excess air at the boiler outlet. Ash is raked out every third day.

where combustion is completed. Most of the air for combustion goes through the grate, a small portion being injected at high pressure (30 in. of water) through tuyères in the front and rear walls to promote turbulence. This type of unit is designed to burn refuse containing 45 to 60% moisture at rates up to 1,000,000 Btu/hr, sq ft, when supplied with 35 to 70% excess air at 400 F. Ash is continuously discharged from the moving grate.

Another variation of a two-drum single-pass boiler design for wood burning in combination with oil, gas, or pulverized coal is shown by Fig. 13. The air-swept wood chutes are located across the front wall. With this arrangement most of the wood burns in suspension. Oil burners are located in the bridge wall as shown.

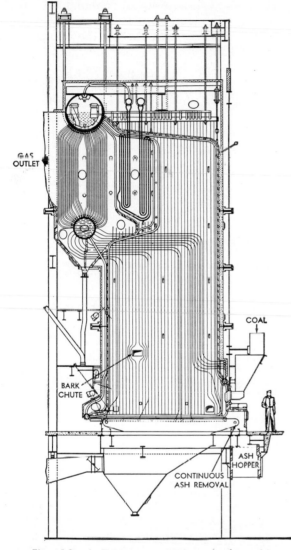

Fig. 12. A Two-Drum Stirling boiler with spreader stoker for coal and/or wood firing

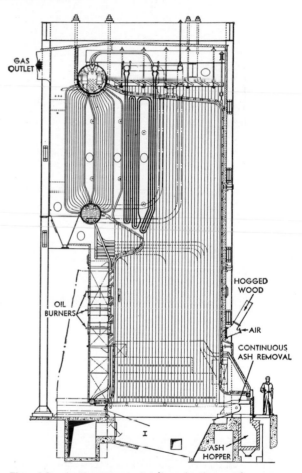

Fig. 13. A Two-Drum Stirling boiler with water-cooled furnace designed to burn wood with either oil, gas, or pulverized coal

Thin-Bed Burning. Fig. 12 illustrates a two-drum single-pass boiler equipped with a conventional spreader stoker for coal firing and single chutes through each side wall for wood firing. With this arrangement wood and coal can be burned separately or in combination. Introduction of the wood refuse well above the grate permits the smaller particles to dry out and burn in suspension, while the remainder of the fuel continues in flight to the grate,

Still another variation for a combination of wood and coal firing is that wherein the wood chute is located in the front wall directly above the coal flippers. The wood feed, consisting of unhogged refuse, passes through a rotating distributor that directs the flow sequentially through the chutes distributed across the furnace width. This permits the individual piles of wood partially to dry out before receiving the next feed fraction.

Cyclonic Burning. A furnace-boiler combination designed primarily for coal firing in a Cyclone Furnace is shown by Fig. 14. Provision has been made to burn some bark within the Cyclone Furnace in conjunction with coal. In order to accomplish this, however, it has been necessary to use double-screened hogged fuel for ease of handling and adequate control.

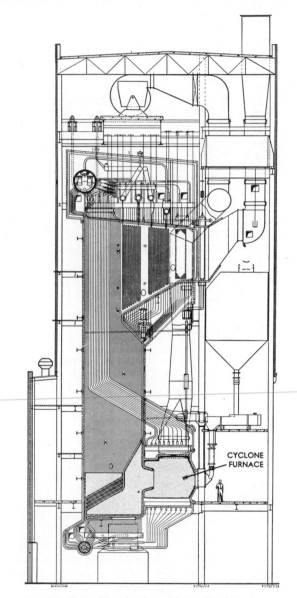

Fig. 14. *A Radiant boiler with Cyclone Furnaces adapted to burn hogged fuel with coal*

Coal Char

Coal char is a residue from the low-temperature (900-1000 F) carbonization of coal or lignite. The removal of gas and tar leaves a "char" which may

be used as a fuel. Not until recently has there been any active interest in char as a boiler fuel.

Char varies in analysis, depending upon the source of the coal from which it is produced. In the carbonization process about half of the volatile matter is removed. This results in increased percentages of fixed carbon, ash, and sulfur, with a corresponding reduction in heating value of the char itself. The ash-softening temperature is quite close to that of the ash from the original coal, since the process does not change the nature of the ash. Grindability ranges from 41 to 150 (Hardgrove). A comparison of a typical char analysis with that of the original coal is shown in Table 1.

TABLE 1

Analyses of Coal and Coal Char

Fuel	Original Coal	Coal Char
Analyses (Dry Basis), % by wt		
Proximate		
Volatile matter	41.4	15.1
Fixed carbon	48.7	69.0
Ash	9.9	15.9
Sulfur	4.2	4.6
Heating value		
Btu/lb, dry	13,340	11,910
Btu/lb, moisture-and-ash free	14,810	14,160
Ash-fusion temperatures, F		
Reducing atmosphere		
Initial deformation	1960	1930
Softening	2100	2020
Fluid	2410	2500
Oxidizing atmosphere		
Initial deformation	2440	2360
Softening	2520	2490
Fluid	2670	2680

The char resulting from most of the present processes is of a sizing represented by the data of Table 2.

TABLE 2

Char Sizing (As-Received Basis)

Screen Size, No.	% Through
8	100
16	97.9
30	87.1
50	68.3
100	40.2
140	28.1
200	21.4

Apparently the volatile matter of *low* ignition temperature is driven off in the carbonization process, since char is more difficult to ignite than coal having the same percentage of volatile matter. Because of its sizing and high ignition temperature, most char is not well suited for burning on stokers. However, char which has been properly sized may be burned in a furnace resembling that used for anthracite. The two most successful methods for burning char are in suspension after pulverizing and in Cyclone Furnaces.

If char is pulverized to a fineness of at least 80% through 200 mesh, it can be burned in a dry-ash-removal furnace. The air for combustion must be preheated to 600 F. If downshot burners are used with the major part of the combustion air introduced through the front wall of the furnace, as is done for anthracite firing, no auxiliary fuel is required to maintain ignition. However, if burners are used where all the combustion air is introduced into the furnace through the burners, as in modern bituminous-coal-fired furnaces, auxiliary fuel in the form of oil, gas, or bituminous coal is required to stabilize ignition.

It is not necessary to have exceptionally fine raw fuel for Cyclone Furnace firing. Therefore many chars can be burned in these furnaces without pulverization or other conditioning. If the ash-softening temperature is above 2200 F (reducing), it may be necessary to include a flux to reduce the slag viscosity, or to fire oil, gas, or coal along with the char. Dust collectors are essential with both of these firing methods to eliminate objectionable stack discharge.

Waste Heat

Utilization of the heat in the exhaust gases from industrial process furnaces becomes more important as fuel costs increase. Boiler equipment, properly designed to absorb the heat in what was formerly waste gas, often will generate all the steam required to power the process. Also, where the waste gases carry some of the process material in suspension, suitable hoppers associated with the boiler equipment will collect a portion of the material, and the cooled gases leaving the boiler may be passed through precipitators for a major recovery of the remainder. Many types of boilers are necessary to meet the wide range of requirements in this field. Their design depends upon the chemical nature of the gases, their temperature, pressure, quantity, and cleanliness.

Heat Transfer From Waste Gases

The rate of heat transfer from the gas to the boiler water depends upon the temperature and specific heat of the gases, their velocity and direction of flow over the absorbing surfaces, and the surface cleanliness. To obtain the proper velocity of the gases over the surfaces, sufficient draft must be provided, either by a stack or a fan, to overcome the losses caused by the flow of gases through the unit, with adequate allowance for normal fouling of the heating surfaces. Temperatures of process gases are relatively low, as shown in Table 3; consequently the radiation component in heat transfer also is low. The tendency, therefore, is to design waste-heat boilers for much higher gas velocities than those for fuel-fired units, in order to compensate for these factors. However, high velocities with dust-laden gases should be avoided to prevent abrasion of tubes from sandblasting action. This is particularly critical where changes in direction of gas flow occur.

TABLE 3

Temperature of Waste-Heat Gases

Source of Gas	Temp, F
Ammonia oxidation process	1350-1475
Annealing furnace	1100-2000
Cement kiln (dry process)	1150-1350
Cement kiln (wet process)	800-1100
Copper reverberatory furnace	2000-2500
Diesel engine exhaust	1000-1200
Forge and billet-heating furnaces	1700-2200
Garbage incinerator	1550-2000
Open-hearth steel furnace	1000-1300
Petroleum refinery	1000-1100
Sulfur ore processing	1600-1900
Zinc-fuming furnace	1800-2000

Diagrams A and B, Fig. 15, give an approximate measure of the convection heating surface required for usual conditions in waste-heat boiler practice. A water-cooled "vestibule" or furnace is a feature of many modern waste-heat boiler units, as shown by Figs. 19 and 20. The vestibule provides cooling of the gases to the temperature necessary for prevention of slagging before they enter the convection surface. The approximate amount of surface required for this purpose is given in Diagram C of Fig. 15.

Types of Waste-Heat Boilers

The design of boiler for a particular requirement depends upon many factors, most of which vary not only from process to process but also within an industry. The cost of equipment, auxiliary power, and maintenance must be compared with the dollar value of the savings expected. The design of the boiler itself is subject, to a degree, to the cost of power at the plant. A small unit with close-spaced tubes will cost less but will require more fan power, because of high draft loss, than a larger, more expensive unit with lower draft loss. However, if power costs are low, the small inexpensive unit may be justified. Other factors to be considered are the available space, the location required for the proper flue connections, the corrosive nature of the gases, the effect of dust loading on erosion, and the process operation (pressure or suction).

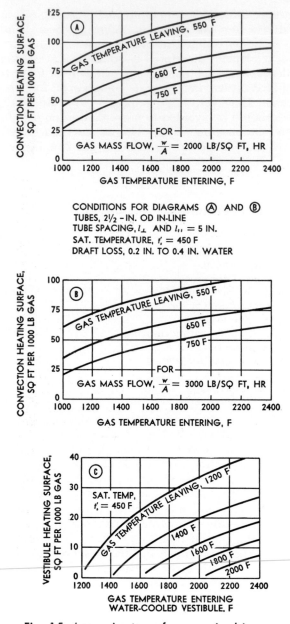

Fig. 15. *Approximate surface required in convection tube bank and vestibule for various entering and leaving waste-gas temperatures*

If the gases carry dust, attention must be given to tube spacing and provisions for the removal of dust dislodged from the heating surfaces. The tubes must be spaced reasonably close for good heat transfer and must still be far enough apart to prevent bridging of deposits. Quite often the boiler is arranged for wide tube spacing where the gases are hottest, with spacing reduced where the gases are cooler.

Sometimes the deposits that are carried into the boiler from the process can be removed by mechanical cleaners, whereas the nature of the deposits from other processes may call for periodic manual lancing

to keep the boiler passes open. In either case, suitable hoppers should be provided to collect the removed deposits.

Gases from oil- or gas-fired process furnaces are relatively clean and, therefore, can be used in units with close tube spacing (one inch in the clear) without fear of bridging and plugging.

Relatively Clean Waste Gases

In the reclamation of heat from relatively clean gases leaving some industrial furnaces (such as billet-heating and open-hearth furnaces), where the dust loading does not exceed 0.5 grain per cu ft, the very compact design of gas-tube waste-heat boiler, illustrated in Fig. 16, is widely used. Since the boiler and flues are inherently tight, this unit is well suited for the use of gases under pressure or gases that should not be permitted to escape from the system except through the stack. The boiler has no refractory lining, and round flues may be used—an advantage with gases in pulsating flow, such as the exhaust from a Diesel engine when used as a waste gas to generate steam for heating or process. This boiler occupies but little space and, depending upon its shell diameter, may be used for steam pressures of 450 psi and entering gas temperatures as high as 1800 F.

In the circulating system of this boiler, water enters the steam-and-water drum and passes down through vertical circulating tubes to a header below the shell, then through the shell, and returns to the drum as a mixture of steam and water through the circulating tubes.

Feedwater enters the upper steam-and-water drum through a perforated pipe with the holes at the top. There it mixes with the boiler water, and dissolved gases, including traces of oxygen that may not have been eliminated by the treating system, are driven off with the steam before they come in contact with the heating surface.

This design of gas-tube boiler eliminates the leakage problems usually associated with boilers of this type for the following reasons:

1. Incoming feedwater mixes with the water in the steam-and-water drum and in the circulators to the main shell, raising its temperature close to saturation before it reaches the shell. Thus there is no temperature shock on the tube sheets or the shell.

2. The tubes themselves are the "staybolts," and, as they are all at saturation temperature, there are no expansion strains.

3. Circulation in the shell is positive, with separate downcomers and risers so located as to assure circulation throughout the shell.

The shell is completely filled with water at saturation temperature, and since all tubes are submerged, they are at substantially the same temperature. Unequal expansion of metal parts is thus avoided, and this cause of troublesome leakage is removed. This is in contrast to designs having some tubes in the shell above the water level and some below. The difference in temperature between the submerged and the dry tubes will lead to leakage at the tube seats and at the joints between the tube sheets and the shell.

Gas flows through the tubes in a straight path. The tubes are kept clear of ordinary deposits by a rotating-arm soot blower, with nozzles directed toward the tube ends and tube sheet. For heavier incrustations, hand lances can be used through lance doors located in the vertical wall of the connecting flue.

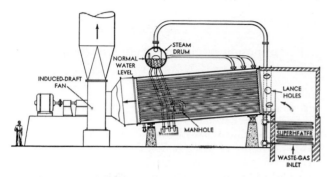

Fig. 16. *Gas-tube type of waste-heat boiler suitable for relatively clean waste gases*

To absorb some heat before the gases come in contact with the tube sheet, a superheater or economizer section, as shown in the illustration, may be installed in the flue to the boiler. Typical data and performance of the unit shown in Fig. 16, applied to an open-hearth furnace, are given in Table 4.

TABLE 4

Performance of Gas-Tube Unit (Fig. 16)

Waste Gas from Open-Hearth Furnace

Boiler heating surface, sq ft	7,900
Superheater surface, sq ft	478
Steam flow, lb/hr	22,000
Flue gas entering superheater, lb/hr	125,000
Gas temperature entering superheater, F	1,300
Gas temperature leaving boiler, F	545
Steam pressure at superheater outlet, psi	300
Steam temperature at superheater outlet, F	665
Feedwater temperature entering boiler, F	220
Draft loss, boiler and superheater, in. water	3.2

Use of Dust-Laden Waste Gases

Where a considerable amount of dust (exceeding 1 to 2 grains/cu ft) is carried in the waste gases, the principal problems in the utilization of waste heat in some industrial heating processes are the reduc-

tion of product losses and the maintenance of clean absorbing surfaces. In some instances this dust is a fine powder, which clings tenaciously to the tubes. In the absence of effective soot blowers for such service, hand-lance doors must be provided for access to every space between the tubes.

Three-Drum Waste-Heat Boiler

A simple three-drum waste-heat boiler, designed to operate with dust-laden gases, is illustrated in Fig. 17. This type of waste-heat boiler is particularly well suited for use with waste gases of high solids content (up to 10 grains/cu ft) from cement kilns. Maximum precipitation of solids is assured by the horizontal flow of the gases through the vertical tube banks and by the effective arrangement of baffles. With this tube arrangement, hand lancing is possible from both sides. Every space in the full width of the boiler can be lanced. Hand lancing can also be done through the roof and above the lower drums, making all absorbing surfaces accessible with a short hand lance.

With gases of high solids content it is frequently possible to reduce the amount of hand lancing by the use of long retractable soot blowers (see Chapter 20). These are located at one, or sometimes two, elevations along the depth of tube banks at gaps provided by the omission of a single row of tubes. Fixed-position rotary soot blowers are not very effective in the staggered tube arrangement of this unit.

To maintain optimum conditions of heat transfer without changing the direction of gas flow, the tubes in the rear sections of the boiler are closely spaced. Steel baffles and baffled sectional hoppers prevent the gases from by-passing the tubes by flowing below the tube bank. Since the baffles in both boiler and hoppers are made of smooth steel plates and are positioned vertically, no appreciable dust build-up is possible.

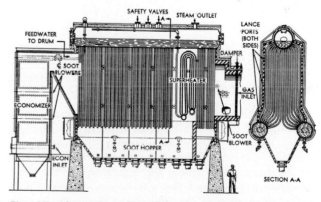

Fig. 17. *Three-drum bent-tube waste-heat boiler fitted with lance ports and soot blowers*

Circulation in this boiler is very simple, with the boiler tubes in the hot-gas end acting as risers and the tubes in the cooler-gas zones acting as downcomers or supply tubes. The boiler has a relatively long drum, in which steam separation takes place without the use of baffles. The steam is collected in a dry pipe located in the quiet cooler-gas end of the drum. Feedwater is thoroughly mixed with the boiler water rising into the steam-and-water drum at the hot-gas end.

Expansion and contraction of the drums and tubes have no effect on the steel casing, firebrick, or insulation; hence, the most common source of brickwork trouble is eliminated, and air infiltration is reduced to a minimum. All pressure parts rest upon supports below the lower drums.

The location of the superheater can be varied to secure the degree of superheat required. Further to increase heat absorption, an economizer can be installed in the flue leaving the boiler. The economizer is arranged for downward flow of gases to aid in the collection of solids.

Solids collected in the hoppers under the boiler and economizer can be readily removed while the boiler is in service. In a single boiler behind a cement kiln, from 20 to 40 tons of cement dust may be recovered each day from these hoppers.

Typical data and performance of the waste-heat boiler shown in Fig. 17 are given in Table 5.

TABLE 5

Performance of Three-Drum Unit (Fig. 17)

Waste Gas from Cement Kiln

Boiler heating surface, sq ft	12,000
Superheater surface, sq ft	523
Steam flow, lb/hr	43,000
Flue gas entering boiler, lb/hr	150,000
Gas temperature entering boiler, F	1,500
Gas temperature leaving boiler, F	438
Gas temperature leaving economizer, F	320
Steam pressure at superheater outlet, psi	200
Steam temperature at superheater outlet, F	480
Feedwater temperature entering economizer, F	212
Draft loss, boiler, superheater, and economizer, in. water	9.6

Waste-Heat Boiler for Ore Roaster

Another three-drum bent-tube boiler, arranged to reclaim heat in the waste gases from ore roasters, is shown in Fig. 18. Hoppers under the boiler gas passes are arranged to collect ore dust that is thrown out of suspension when the gases make the low-velocity turns around the gas baffles. Typical data and performance of the unit illustrated are given in Table 6.

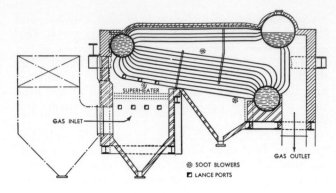

Fig. 18. *Three-drum waste-heat boiler arranged to use waste gases from ore roasters*

TABLE 6

Performance of Three-Drum Unit (Fig. 18)

Waste Gas from Ore Roasters

Boiler heating surface, sq ft	2,617
Superheater surface, sq ft	137
Steam flow, lb/hr	9,200
Flue gas entering boiler, lb/hr	52,000
Gas temperature entering boiler, F	1,435
Gas temperature leaving boiler, F	690
Steam pressure at superheater outlet, psi	450
Steam temperature at superheater outlet, F	720
Feedwater temperature entering boiler, F	340
Draft loss, boiler and superheater, in. water	2.0

High Solids—Relatively Low Temperature

Waste-heat boilers are also widely applied to some types of refining furnaces and to cement and dolomite kilns. The temperature of these gases rarely exceeds 1400 F, and the solids content is high—4 grains and over per cu ft. In many applications the boilers are quite large, so that they can serve as fuel-fired units when the process furnace is idle. The usual requirements for such units are maximum heating surface for a given floor area, vertically arranged heating surface to shed deposits readily, and a chamber ahead of the tube banks. For these applications this chamber serves as the combustion space for burning the direct-fired fuel. Two waste-heat boiler designs that admirably meet these requirements are illustrated in Figs. 19 and 20.

Smelter-Furnace Waste Gases

For smelter-furnace gases carrying solids in a semi-molten or sticky form, the designs of waste-heat boilers illustrated in Figs. 19 and 20 are particularly suitable because of the cooling of the gas by radiation in the large water-cooled areas of the furnace ahead of the convection surfaces. The absence of baffles in the convection banks is a further advantage when carry-over dust is abrasive.

Zinc-Fuming-Furnace Gases

The reclamation of zinc from slag waste as a by-product of lead-smelting furnaces requires a fuming furnace, in which pulverized coal and air are injected into the molten slag. The zinc and lead are boiled out from the slag as a metal vapor and then reoxidized above the slag bed in an atmosphere free of slag and other impurities.

The products leaving the fuming furnace at a temperature of about 2200 F must be passed through a combustion chamber, where the zinc vapor is completely oxidized and then cooled to permit recovery of the zinc oxide. If this cooling takes place in a waste-heat boiler, a considerable portion of the heat in the gases can be recovered in steam for generating power. A waste-heat boiler unit for this service should be designed to reduce the temperature of the gases and entrained solids before the gases enter boiler and superheater convection surfaces, so that the solids can be readily removed as dust from these heat-absorbing surfaces.

Water-Cooled Furnace. A water-cooled furnace waste-heat boiler unit of this type, designed to operate with gases from a fuming furnace, is illustrated in Fig. 19. Heat absorption by the water-cooled furnace walls and the baffle wall in the furnace reduces the temperature of the gases entering the superheater from approximately 2200 to 1400 F. Good separation of dust from the gases is obtained in the furnace by the 180-degree turn ahead of the

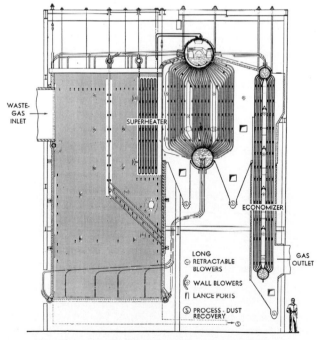

Fig. 19. *Waste-heat boiler unit suitable for high-temperature waste gases carrying sticky or semimolten particles*

superheater. The dust, thrown out of suspension, drops into the water-cooled hopper bottom of the furnace and then into a dust-collecting hopper, from which it is removed by a screw conveyor. Some dust accumulates on the walls of the furnace, from which it can be removed periodically by rotating blowers, using air or steam (see Chapter 20). These are distributed over the furnace wall areas, as shown in Fig. 19.

Boiler Heating Surfaces. Boiler heating surface, arranged between two drums, provides a single gas path over the surface with no baffles required. To reduce the gas temperature to desired limits, an economizer is included. The permissible final gas temperature will depend upon the sulfur content of the gases. The gas temperature should be maintained above the dewpoint to avoid corrosion of the flues and the dust-separating equipment between the boiler and the stack. Hoppers are arranged under the boiler, the economizer, and the long flue to the stack to collect the valuable zinc dust.

Automatic soot blowers of the long retractable type are fitted to remove the dust that accumulates on the tube banks of the boiler, superheater, and economizer. This type of soot blower has generally replaced other types for this service. By concentrating the operation through two or three nozzles, the soot blowing is more effective. Since the blower remains outside the setting except when in actual use, maintenance is less, and there is no additional surface to which dust can cling. Lance ports of the type illustrated in Chapter 20 are distributed over the wall areas for hand lancing when necessary.

Reverberatory-Furnace Gases

Copper ore concentrates are melted in reverberatory furnaces fired by pulverized coal, oil, or gas. The impurities float to the top of the melt and are skimmed off as slag. The copper, tapped in molten form, is transported to other furnaces for further refinement. The products of combustion leave the reverberatory furnace at about 2300 F, heavily contaminated with slag particles and solids, a portion of which may be in a pasty or semifused state. As large quantities of steam are required for the power used in the process, waste-heat boilers are installed to recover the heat in the products of combustion from the reverberatory furnaces.

In the operation of a copper reverberatory furnace, the draft at the outlet of the furnace must be maintained at about 0.06 in. of water, which is practically a balanced draft. The smelter operation is adversely affected by higher drafts. To avoid uncomfortable conditions in the boiler room, the stack effect within the setting must be reduced to a minimum. This is accomplished by so positioning the waste-heat boiler that the boiler passes and boiler gas outlet are about

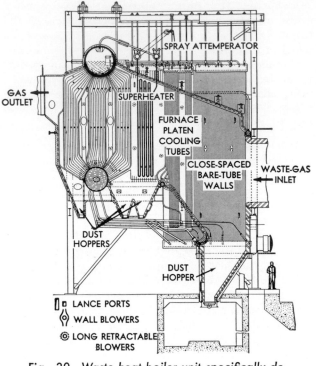

GAS OUTLET

SPRAY ATTEMPERATOR

SUPERHEATER

FURNACE PLATEN COOLING TUBES

CLOSE-SPACED BARE-TUBE WALLS

WASTE-GAS INLET

DUST HOPPERS

DUST HOPPER

▯▯ LANCE PORTS
◍ WALL BLOWERS
◎ LONG RETRACTABLE BLOWERS

Fig. 20. *Waste-heat boiler unit specifically designed for the use of waste gases from copper reverberatory furnaces*

level with, or even above, the outlet of the reverberatory furnace (see Fig. 20). With such an arrangement there is no plus pressure to force sulfur-laden gases out through doors, around soot blowers, or through setting cracks in the walls.

Water-Cooled Furnace. A waste-heat boiler unit with water-cooled furnace, designed for use with a copper reverberatory furnace, is illustrated in Fig. 20. The gases leaving the reverberatory furnace are highly contaminated with sticky slag particles, which will adhere tenaciously to boiler and superheater tubes. To cool these slag particles, a large water-cooled furnace area and spaced platens of heat-absorbing tubes are provided in the furnace.

Slag cannot bridge from one platen to the next, when these are spaced at 18-in. centers. Long retractable soot blowers are fitted at two elevations in the gap between the two banks of platens. Slag is removed periodically from the heat-absorbing surfaces by jets of steam or air from opposed nozzles near the ends of these soot blowers. Similar blowers are fitted, as indicated, for cleaning the tube banks of the superheater and the boiler. Wall blowers are provided for cleaning the furnace walls.

The heat absorption of the water-cooled furnace walls and the water-cooled platens reduces the temperature of the gases from 2300 F to approximately 1600 F before they enter the superheater. The

"sticky" slag particles suspended in the gases are thus cooled to a dry ash that will not bridge the gap between the superheater tubes spaced on 6-in. centers. Boiler convection surface following the superheater has a tube spacing of 4 in. on centers. The deposits that adhere to superheater and boiler convection tubes can be removed periodically by the soot blowers, arranged as shown. Experience indicates that no additional hand lancing is required.

Dust and Slag Particles Reclaimed

The floor of the furnace is arranged as a hopper bottom to facilitate the collection of dust and slag particles. The boiler and the long flue to the stack are also equipped with hoppers, all for the purpose of collecting the copper-bearing particles of dust and ash, which are returned to the reverberatory furnace for reclamation of the copper.

Typical data and performance of this type of unit (Fig. 20) are given in Table 7.

TABLE 7

Performance of Two-Drum Unit (Fig. 20)

Waste Gas from Copper Reverberatory Furnace

Boiler heating surface, sq ft	12,085
Superheater surface, sq ft	2,170
Steam flow, lb/hr	71,000
Flue gas entering boiler, lb/hr	166,000
Gas temperature leaving reverberatory furnace, F	2,269
Gas temperature entering superheater, F	1,687
Gas temperature leaving boiler, F	770
Steam pressure at superheater outlet, psi	475
Steam temperature at superheater outlet, F	775
Feedwater temperature entering boiler, F	350
Draft (static) at furnace bottom, in. water	0.1
Draft loss, boiler and superheater, in. water	0.2

It will be noted that the boiler surface is arranged for a single pass of gases. The draft loss of 0.2 in. water is exceptionally low and reflects the low gas velocity over the heating surface, which is desirable to avoid tube erosion. The high sulfur content of these gases makes the addition of an economizer to these boilers inadvisable, since lowering the gas temperature would cause corrosion in the long flues and dust separators between the boilers and the stack.

Waste-Heat Boilers for Special Conditions

Other types of waste-heat boilers to recover the heat from waste gases or fluids from industrial heating processes have been designed for special conditions of space, temperature, pressure, and draft. With all of the limitations known, waste-heat-recovery boilers can be designed to accommodate almost any set of conditions.

CHEMICAL AND HEAT RECOVERY IN THE PAPER INDUSTRY

THE pulp and paper industry is of far more than passing interest to the engineer involved in the generation of steam and power. Every type of pulp or paper produced requires large quantities of steam for evaporation of the water in which individual cellulose fibers are dispersed before being formed into a sheet of paper or pulp. In chemical pulping, huge quantities of steam are used in the cooking of wood chips, to separate the individual cellulose fibers from the material which binds them. Thus, steam and its companion, electric power, are two of the basic "raw materials" in the manufacture of pulp and paper. In 1955 this industry in the United States alone used more than 30 billion kwhr of electricity, more than twice the electrical needs of New York City. Between 1945 and 1956 B&W installed steam-generating capacity in excess of 30,000,000 pounds per hour in pulp and paper mills.

The pulp, paper, and paperboard industry is the fifth largest in the U. S. in value of its assets, following the automobile, steel, petroleum-refining, and chemical-processing industries. In the generation of steam and power, the pulp and paper industry has a prominent place among the major industries in the U. S. For the year 1955 pulp and paper was rated: first in power used per ton of products, second in total power generated, and third in total electric power consumption.

The past and predicted production of this industry and the annual per capita consumption of paper and paperboard products in the U. S. are illustrated by Fig. 1.

The following tabulation, compiled by the United States Pulp Producers Association, shows the per capita use in pounds of paper products in various countries of the world for the year 1955:

United States	418
Canada	280
Sweden	194
Australia	167
United Kingdom	163
Switzerland	140
Norway	139
Denmark	136
Netherlands	131
Finland	124
Germany (West)	109
New Zealand	104
Belgium	100
Avg for Whole World	47.4

A large share of the steam and power consumed by this industry is generated by the combustion of waste fuels. The collection, combustion, and recovery of chemicals and heat from these waste fuels present many interesting and unique problems for the engineer.

Historical

Discovery of the art of paper making is attributed to the Chinese in the year 105 A.D. The Chinese produced paper from waste rags and from raw fiber, such as bark of the mulberry tree and bamboo. It was not until modern times that significant changes occurred in the art of paper making. An early indication of the trend leading to manufacture of paper

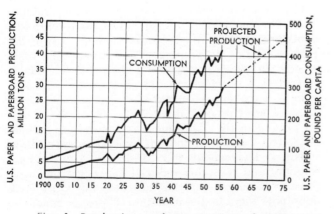

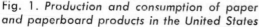

Fig. 1. Production and consumption of paper and paperboard products in the United States

from wood pulp is a letter written in 1719 to the French Royal Academy by René de Reaumur: "The rags from which paper is made are becoming rare. While consumption of paper increases every day, production of linen remains the same. The wasp seems to teach us that paper can be made from fiber without the use of rags and linen and to invite us to see whether we cannot make fine and good paper from the use of certain woods."

Even though numerous experimenters worked on the problem, it was not until the middle of the nineteenth century that wood was used as a raw material in making paper by the major basic pulping processes. These processes are: groundwood, alkaline pulping, and acid pulping. The first groundwood mill and the first chemical wood-pulp mills for both the alkaline and the acid processes were started in the period from 1852 to 1874.

In the past 100 years phenomenal progress has been made. The range of wood species used as raw material has required many technical modifications to the several processes. Refinements have been made in the techniques of forestry, logging, barking and chipping the logs, digesting and washing the pulp, supplementary purification of the pulp for chemical use, bleaching, and loading. As an example of progress in the production of paper, early Fourdrinier machines for making a continuous sheet of paper on an endless screen, invented by Robert in 1798, were 48 in. wide and produced the sheet at a speed of about 50 fpm. This machine today is built up to 300 in. wide and runs at a speed of 1500 to 2400 fpm, depending upon the type of paper or paperboard produced.

The virtual existence of modern man is dependent upon pulp and paper products. These products are necessary in business and in the home for magazines, books, newspapers, records, contracts, checks, money, stocks, reports, correspondence, advertising, packaging, insulation, and construction materials. In the production of such products as rayon, explosives, lacquers, and photographic film, wood pulp in a refined form is the basic raw material.

In 1955 the industry in the U. S. produced 20,800,-000 tons of wood pulp, and 30,140,000 tons of paper and paperboard (including reclaimed waste paper and pulp imports). An additional 5½ million tons of paper and board were imported, most of which was newsprint from Canada. For this production, the steam requirements varied within wide limits, from a minimum of 5,000 lb per ton to a maximum of perhaps 20,000 lb per ton, depending upon the grade and degree of bleaching and converting done at the mill.

Boilers to supply the heavy steam demands of this industry, when fired by the usual primary fuels (coal, oil, gas, wood refuse, or bark), are of conventional design, as covered in other chapters. Some departure from the conventional, involving special design of the furnace, is required to burn successfully sand-impregnated and salt-water-borne bark and hogged wood. A large proportion of the steam requirements for the pulp mills, however, is produced in highly specialized chemical and heat recovery units.

Electric power requirements in the making of pulp and paper have risen faster than process steam requirements. This factor coupled with steadily rising fuel costs has led to higher pressures and temperatures and higher efficiencies in boilers for pulp and paper mills. The increased value of steam has led to a demand for more reliable and efficient heat and chemical recovery units. Where steam from such units was formerly looked upon as a desirable bonus over straight chemical recovery, today such steam is a vital part of the mill operation, primarily because of the electric power that can be extracted from it before its use in process. Consequently recovery boilers are being built today for reliable operation at steam conditions up to 1525 psi and 900 F at the superheater outlet.

Alkaline Process

The alkaline pulping process using caustic soda was discovered by Burgess and Watt in England in 1851, but it did not gain commercial acceptance there. In this soda pulping process, the nonfibrous constituents of the wood are dissolved by digestion in a liquor that is essentially sodium hydroxide (NaOH), at a pressure of approximately 125 psi and a temperature of 350 F.

In 1854, on setting up a soda pulping mill in the United States, Burgess devised a method to recover some of the expensive soda chemical which reduced production costs to a reasonable level. While a limited recovery was achieved through partial incineration of some of the waste liquor, the process was not efficient. In 1871, in an attempt to utilize a cheaper chemical, Dahl, in Poland, introduced the use of salt cake (sodium sulfate, Na_2SO_4) as a make-up chemical. In the incineration process, the sodium sulfate was chemically reduced to sodium sulfide, Na_2S. The recovered cooking liquor, therefore, was a mixture of sodium sulfide and sodium hydroxide. This was the inception of the present-day kraft process, in which a mixture of these two chemicals is used as a cooking and digesting liquor with salt cake as a makeup chemical.

In the kraft process about 20 to 30% of the chemical present in the digesting liquor is sodium sulfide, Na_2S. The solution of sodium hydroxide and sodium sulfide is less caustic than a straight caustic soda solution, and it is this reduced causticity that presumably accounts for the fact that the kraft cook does not degrade the cellulose fibers as much as does the soda cook. The kraft process, therefore, yields a stronger fiber.

Development of Chemical Recovery Process

Rotary Kiln Smelter

Recovery of chemicals in the early use of the soda process consisted of drying and roasting the waste liquor in a rotary kiln until a char was obtained. This char contained the nonvolatile portion of the constituents dissolved from the wood in addition to the inorganic chemicals of the original cooking liquor. These inorganic chemical substances were then water-leached from the char to obtain a solution of sodium salts, which was processed to regenerate the soda (sodium hydroxide) solution for reuse as cooking liquor. The early practice in the kraft process differed in that the char, or so-called black ash discharged from the rotary kiln, was used as the fuel of the smelter firing the rotary kiln. A reducing condition was maintained in the fuel or char bed of the smelter, and, as the organic constituents burned away, the chemicals of the cooking liquor remained as an ash. This ash, thus chemically reduced, was smelted and tapped from the smelter in a molten state.

Later, a waste-heat boiler was added to the smelter furnace-rotary kiln combination, permitting recovery of a part of the heat from the gases discharged from the kiln. These economies in the kraft process led to similar treatment of the soda black ash, since it also could be burned readily, tapping the remaining chemical ash as a smelt and utilizing waste-heat boilers after these units.

An additional improvement was the development and use of multiple-effect evaporators to deliver the waste liquor at high solids content to the rotary kiln, thus reducing the heat loss in evaporating the liquor. Another improvement along this same line was the addition of the disc or cascade evaporator behind the waste-heat boiler. Through direct contact with the waste gases from the boiler, the liquor was further concentrated before introduction to the rotary kiln.

Introduction of the Murray Waern unit, about 1930, was the final step in the development of the rotary kiln smelter. The components of this unit were: a water-cooled smelter (to overcome the maintenance difficulties of the refractory smelter previously used), a rotary drier, a waste-heat boiler to which the water-cooling tubes of the smelter were connected, a steam superheater if desired, and a disc or cascade evaporator.

Stationary Refractory Furnace

Elimination of the rotary drier in the Ross-Wagner unit, introduced about 1930, was the first step leading to the development of the modern recovery unit with its stationary furnace.

The principal component of the Ross-Wagner unit was a vertical, cylindrical, stationary, refractory furnace. The liquor, at about 55% solids content and atomized with compressed air, was introduced through the roof of the furnace and directed downward toward the furnace floor or hearth. The atomized liquor droplets falling through the furnace were dehydrated by the heat and deposited as char or black ash on the hearth, where the ash was burned under reducing conditions. The primary combustion air was admitted by water-cooled blowpipes protruding through the furnace walls into the mass of black ash on the furnace hearth. As the gases rose from the char bed, combustion was completed with jets of secondary air admitted at an intermediate height. The chemical ash in molten form was tapped from the furnace floor into a tank, where it was dissolved in a weak caustic solution.

The gaseous products of combustion passed to the associated waste-heat boiler through a refractory flue connected at one side to the top of the circular furnace. The waste-heat boiler normally was followed by a scrubber tower, in which a portion of the sodium fume content in the waste gas was recovered by scrubbing with weak-liquor sprays. At the same time some of the water content of the weak liquor was evaporated, thus reducing the work to be done by the multiple-effect evaporator.

The Ross-Wagner unit was significant since it demonstrated the principle that all of the steps of the recovery incineration process could be accomplished in a single stationary furnace. But it was subject to the problems of refractory furnace maintenance and the burning of liquor solids which were on the border line for stable operation. As a result of the relatively weak liquor concentration, loss of ignition and "blackouts" in the furnace operation were frequent. However, it was a big step forward from the rotary unit in eliminating air infiltration (with its attendant heat loss) and the maintenance of the refractory lining and seals of the rotating kiln.

Water-Cooled Stationary Furnace

In the Babcock & Wilcox-Tomlinson unit, introduced in 1936, the advantages of the Ross-Wagner unit were retained, but there were several important changes designed to eliminate the difficulties noted. Refractory maintenance was eliminated by the use of a water-cooled stationary furnace and a water-cooled flue connection from the furnace to the waste-heat boiler. To overcome the unstable furnace condition, the liquor was sprayed onto the walls of the furnace, where it was essentially dehydrated and remained until its thickness and weight were sufficient to cause it to break off and fall to the char bed below. The spray nozzle, directed at the furnace walls, was oscillated, continuously depositing on a given area of the walls a relatively thin layer of liquor, which dried before the spray was redirected to the same area to deposit additional liquor. Furthermore, and of considerable importance, the angle of oscillation of the spray was adjustable, so that the operator could use more or less wall area for drying the liquor, depending upon its water content.

By thus providing a separate adjustable means of evaporation within the furnace itself, it was possible to use the cooler water-cooled furnace, eliminating the high maintenance of refractory, and to establish stable furnace conditions with the relatively weak liquor available from the evaporators of that day. The introduction of this type of unit led to rapid developments in the efficiency of heat recovery from the furnace. Use of economizers and gas air heaters followed quickly.

Since the soda and kraft processes are quite similar, the discussion of alkaline pulping and application of a recovery unit will be confined to the kraft process, with subsequent comments (see *Soda Process Recovery Unit*, below) on differences in detail for the soda process.

Kraft Process Recovery Unit

The process flow diagram (Fig. 2) will serve to show the relationship and importance of the recovery unit in the chemical and heat balances of a typical kraft pulp mill. Following the flow diagram: the logs entering the mill are first debarked, reduced to chips and then charged into a digester, where they are cooked under pressure with steam in an aqueous digestion solution of sodium hydroxide and sodium sulfide known as "white liquor" or "cooking liquor." In the cooking operation the lignin binder, which holds together the cellulose fibers of the wood, is dissolved.

After cooking, the cellulose fibers, now called "pulp" or "brown stock," are separated from the spent cooking liquor in the pulp washers. The pulp then goes through several refining processes and finally to the paper machine.

The spent cooking liquor containing the lignin dissolved from the wood is called "black liquor." As the dilute black liquor (about 15% dissolved solids) comes from the washers, it is first concentrated in multiple-effect evaporators by the use of steam. It then goes to the exit-gas end of the recovery unit, where it is further concentrated in a direct-contact evaporator using the sensible heat of the flue gas.

The concentrated black liquor then goes to the mixing tank where salt cake (sodium sulfate) is mixed with the liquor to make up the chemical losses in the cycle. Salt cake recovered from the boiler hoppers and from the dust or fume collector (not shown) following the direct-contact evaporator is also returned to the liquor cycle at this stage, either by conveying the salt cake to the mixing tank or by pumping the black liquor to the collection hoppers. The concentrated black liquor, with its salt cake burden, is heated to lower its viscosity and is then pumped to the recovery-furnace spray nozzle

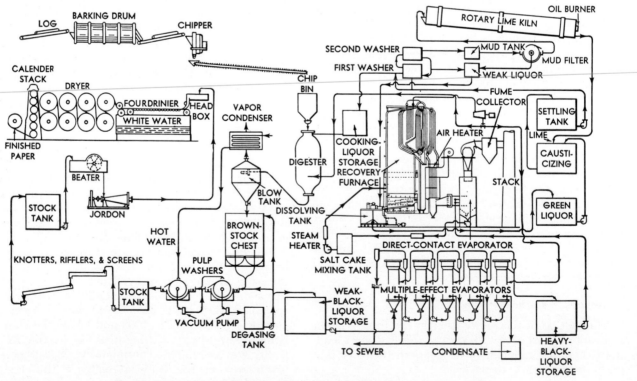

Fig. 2. Process flow diagram of a typical kraft pulp and paper mill

In the recovery unit, the concentrated black liquor is sprayed upon the furnace walls for dehydration prior to final combustion of the dried char on the furnace hearth.

Chemical and Heat Recovery

In the recovery furnace, heat is obtained from the combustion of the organic liquor constituents (dissolved from the wood), and, equally important, the inorganic constituents (sodium salts) in the liquor are recovered as molten ash or smelt. Another essential function of the recovery furnace is the reduction of the sodium sulfate content of the black liquor to sodium sulfide.

The smelt, composed largely of sodium carbonate, Na_2CO_3, and sodium sulfide, Na_2S, is tapped from the furnace and dissolved in water in the dissolving tank to form "green liquor." The green liquor is then subjected to a causticizing treatment with lime, $Ca(OH)_2$, to convert the sodium carbonate to sodium hydroxide. In this step the sodium sulfide remains unchanged. The liquor, now known as "white liquor," is then ready for reuse as cooking liquor in the digester. The calcium carbonate sludge reclaimed from the white liquor in the causticizing operation is reburned in a lime kiln, with loss of CO_2, to yield calcium oxide, which is reused in causticizing green liquor to white liquor.

Reclaiming and Concentrating Black Liquor

All of the waste liquor possible must be washed and reclaimed from the brown stock, not only to enhance the purity and quality of the product but also to minimize the loss of the chemicals. The loss of black liquor through leakage, spillage, or foaming must also be minimized in the subsequent handling, all with the aim of returning to the recovery unit the maximum quantity of both the chemical and fuel values. It is also the aim of the mill designer and mill operator to use as little water as possible in the digestion liquor and in washing the pulp. Since this water must be evaporated prior to or in the course of the incineration of the liquor, any avoidable excess means an unnecessary debit in the heat balance. It is for these reasons that black liquor commonly is recycled to the digester when stationary digesters are used. Recycled black liquor is thus used instead of water to supplement the volume of white liquor, so that the chips in the digester are covered with liquid. For the same reasons, multi-stage countercurrent vacuum washers are used to wash the waste liquor from the brown stock with minimum water dilution.

Evaporation of Water in Black Liquor

The waste black liquor normally recovered from the washers has a concentration of 12 to 16% solids. The heating value of the solids, if burned at this stage, would be just about enough to evaporate the water content. It is therefore essential to evaporate as much of the water content as possible in multiple-effect evaporators, where 1 lb of steam will evaporate approximately the quantities of water, in pounds, shown below:

Single-effect	0.85
Double-effect	1.60
Triple-effect	2.30
Quadruple-effect	3.10
Quintuple-effect	3.90
Sextuple-effect	4.70

The majority of modern mills in the United States use quintuple- or sextuple-effect evaporators.

It is also desirable to accomplish further evaporation of the black liquor in a direct-contact evaporator by using the otherwise waste sensible heat of the flue gases discharged from the recovery boiler unit, after the maximum reasonable quantity of heat has been extracted for the direct generation of steam. A certain portion of the evaporation is desirably done in the recovery-unit furnace itself, where the black liquor is finally evaporated to dryness in the process of incineration. This final evaporation helps to keep the furnace temperature low enough to minimize the problems in handling the low-fusion-temperature liquor ash, not only in the furnace but also on the boiler screen and superheater heating surfaces. The softening temperature of this ash ranges from 1500 to 1700 F (ASTM).

To summarize: The maximum quantity of waste liquor solids from the digesters, washers, multiple-effect evaporators, and finally from the direct-contact evaporator should be in solution at optimum concentration at each stage of the process, and as much of the heat from the combustion of the liquor should be utilized as is economically practical. Under normal conditions, the "strong" black liquor comes from the multiple-effect evaporators at a solids concentration of 45 to 55%. It is then ready for further concentration in the direct-contact evaporator. The concentration to "heavy liquor" in the direct-contact evaporator, using hot flue gas, is limited to about 70% because of difficulty in pumping a too viscous fluid, and overconcentration must be avoided on that score. Also, as an aid in controlling furnace temperatures, it is desirable to complete evaporation to dryness in the firing.

Optimum Concentration of Black Liquor

For a range of strong liquor concentrations (from the multiple-effect evaporators) of 40 to 55%, the amounts of water to be evaporated in direct-contact evaporators to obtain a near optimum heavy liquor concentration of 64.5% for spraying are given in Table 1. These values are based on a limiting final exit gas temperature from the direct-contact evaporators of 300 F to avoid corrosion in electrostatic precipitators. To reclaim some of the heat in the

TABLE 1

Optimum Liquor Concentration in the Direct-Contact Evaporator

Liquor Concentration, Per Cent		Water Content, lb/lb Solids		Water Evaporated, lb/lb Solids	Gas Temp To Direct-Contact	Gas Temp From Direct-Contact
Strong	Heavy	Strong	Heavy	From Strong Liquor	Evaporator, F	Evaporator, F
40	64.5	1.50	0.55	0.95	740	300
45	64.5	1.22	0.55	0.67	610	300
50	64.5	1.00	0.55	0.45	510	300
55	64.5	0.82	0.55	0.27	425	300
40	64.5	1.50	0.55	0.95	640	200
45	64.5	1.22	0.55	0.67	510	200
50	64.5	1.00	0.55	0.45	410	200

flue gas leaving a boiler, an economizer and an air heater are frequently installed, designed to leave sufficient heat in the gas to the direct-contact evaporator to obtain the optimum black liquor concentration without reducing the gas temperature below 300 F. Heavy liquor at a concentration of 63 to 65% is easily handled and controlled. If a venturi scrubber (see below) is used in place of an electrostatic precipitator, the exit gas temperature from the direct-contact evaporator may be lowered to about 200 F as a limit.

Salient Features of a Recovery Unit

The functions, objectives, and requirements of the recovery unit and auxiliaries may be listed as follows:

1. The black liquor is dehydrated, and the organic constituents are burned.

2. The ash (inorganic constituents) from the incineration of the char is recovered in molten form with as little contamination as possible.

3. The ash is subjected to active reducing conditions to convert the chemical content of sodium sulfate and other sodium-sulfur-oxygen compounds to sodium sulfide.

4. The furnace floor must be tight against leakage of the molten smelt. The molten sodium compounds are dangerous to handle.

5. The furnace floor must provide positive drainage of smelt to the smelt spout. Under certain conditions and proportions, smelt and water react violently and with explosive force; hence, no pools of smelt should be present to react with water inadvertently admitted.

6. Furnace and char bed temperatures should be kept as low as practicable to minimize fouling of heat-absorbing surfaces and loss of sodium from the furnace through "boiling off" or sublimation of sodium salts.

7. Furnace gas velocities should be kept as low as practical (500 to 800 fpm is a good range) in the char bed and liquor spray zones to minimize the loss of sodium and fuel value through mechanical entrainment and the attendant fouling of heat-absorbing surfaces.

8. Water-cooled furnace walls and widely spaced slag-screen tubes must have adequate surface to absorb sufficient heat from the furnace gas, through radiation, to reduce the temperature of the entrained ash so that it will not be "sticky" or "tacky" as it enters closely spaced tube sections.

9. Laborious hand lancing should be eliminated, first, by minimizing the amount of carry-over and, second, by arranging the boiler unit heating surfaces so that automatic soot blowers are effective in cleaning.

10. The maximum possible quantity of steam should be generated for process use. (Usual practice is to generate the steam in the boiler unit at a pressure and temperature sufficiently above the process pressure that the electrical requirements of the mill may be produced as by-product power in back-pressure turbines.)

11. The black liquor from the multiple-effect evaporators is concentrated, by using the heat in flue gas in a direct-contact evaporator, to the values desired at the furnace spray nozzle.

12. The gas is discharged from the direct-contact evaporator at a temperature suitable for the type of fume collector which follows the recovery unit. (To avoid corrosion, an entering gas temperature of not less than 300 F is required for an electrostatic precipitator. To a venturi scrubber the entering gas temperature may be lower, to 200 F.)

13. Ease of control and operation must be provided.

14. Reliability and continuity of service of the recovery unit and its auxiliaries are essential.

The modern recovery unit, illustrated by Fig. 3, is designed to provide these features. The important components of this design are discussed below.

Characteristics of a B&W Recovery Unit

Spray Nozzle and Oscillator

As previously stated, the black liquor is sprayed

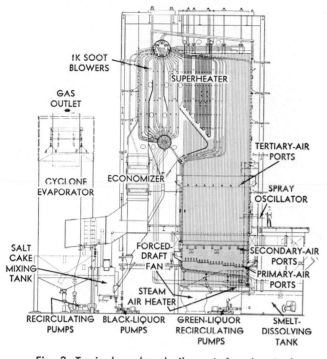

Fig. 3. *Typical modern boiler unit for chemical and heat recovery from black liquor*

onto the walls of the furnace, where it is dehydrated and then falls to the char bed below. The spray nozzle, Fig. 4, located in the center of the front wall, emits a flat or sheet spray and is continuously both rotated and oscillated to cover a wide band of the side and rear walls. The degree of oscillation is adjustable to cover a greater or smaller area of wall surface as required, to compensate for variation in the solids concentration of the atomized liquor and consequently the time needed for dehydration. The

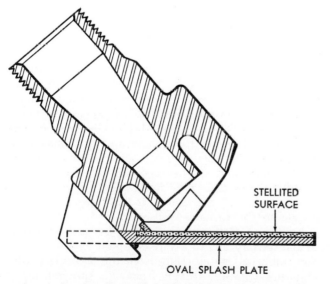

Fig. 4. *Section through a black-liquor spray nozzle*

spray-nozzle actuating mechanism is driven by a fractional horsepower motor.

Floor and Wall Construction of Furnace

The lower half of the furnace, Fig. 3, is actually a chemical retort and is operated as such. Incomplete combustion of the char in the porous bed supplies incandescent carbon and carbon monoxide, which act as reducing agents to convert the sulfate in the smelt to sulfide. All of the smelt filters through the char bed to the furnace floor or hearth, from which it is tapped. To withstand the erosive and penetrating characteristics of the smelt, special construction is used in the lower parts of the furnace walls and the floor to assure that they are leakproof.

For the floor construction, illustrated by Fig. 5, plastic-chrome-ore refractory is packed solidly around studded water-cooled tubes. The thickness of the refractory over the tubes is no greater than can be effectively cooled. An abutting continuous flat-stud arrangement (shown in Fig. 5) at the center line of the tubes is necessary to provide a permanent barrier to chill the smelt and prevent penetration beyond that point.

Refractory-faced water-cooled stud-tube construction is used for all four walls of the furnace in the retort zone. Furnace walls above this zone are bare tubes with the space between tubes closed by flat studs. This construction, shown by Fig. 6, presents to the furnace a fully water-cooled metallic surface. It is upon this surface, at about the center third of the furnace height, that the liquor from the oscillating spray nozzle is deposited.

An outstanding feature of the B&W recovery unit is the absence of expansion joints to compensate for expansion of the furnace. This construction contributes to the reduction of air infiltration and thus helps to obtain maximum steam generation. The modern recovery unit (Fig. 3), including furnace, superheater, boiler, and economizer, is hung from overhead steel. The wall tubes of the furnace, boiler, and economizer support the monolithic refractory, the block insulation, and the steel casing, so that these parts move with the tubes as they expand, thus eliminating the need for special expansion seals. Furnace buckstays are attached directly to, and expand with, the tubes. Buckstays are fitted completely around the unit at each elevation and are fastened together at the corners to form hoops around the unit. The complete assembly of wall tubes, refractory, insulation, buckstays, and casing is free to expand and is, therefore, quite independent of the supporting steel. Details illustrating this construction are shown in Figs. 6 and 12.

Combustion Air to Furnace

Combustion air is admitted to the furnace through three sets of air ports, designated from the hearth

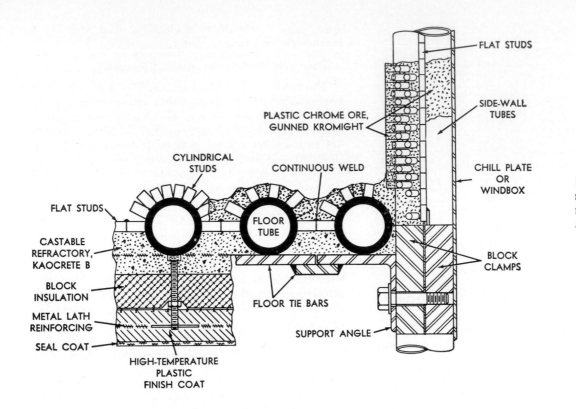

Fig. 5. *Section through recovery-furnace floor and side wall*

Labels in Fig. 5:
FLAT STUDS
SIDE-WALL TUBES
PLASTIC CHROME ORE, GUNNED KROMIGHT
CYLINDRICAL STUDS
CONTINUOUS WELD
CHILL PLATE OR WINDBOX
FLAT STUDS
FLOOR TUBE
CASTABLE REFRACTORY, KAOCRETE B
BLOCK INSULATION
METAL LATH REINFORCING
SEAL COAT
BLOCK CLAMPS
FLOOR TIE BARS
SUPPORT ANGLE
HIGH-TEMPERATURE PLASTIC FINISH COAT

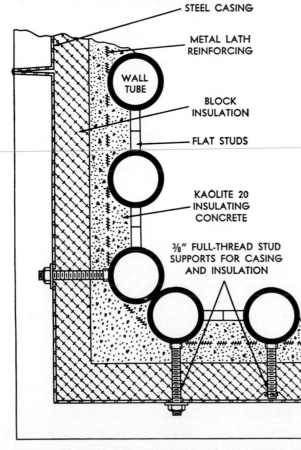

Labels in Fig. 6:
STEEL CASING
METAL LATH REINFORCING
WALL TUBE
BLOCK INSULATION
FLAT STUDS
KAOLITE 20 INSULATING CONCRETE
3/8" FULL-THREAD STUD SUPPORTS FOR CASING AND INSULATION

Fig. 6. *Furnace wall construction above retort zone*

or bottom of the furnace upward (see Fig. 3) as primary, secondary, and tertiary. The primary-air ports are located at an elevation of 36 in. above the hearth and extend around the four walls of the furnace. The secondary-air ports are located in two opposite walls just above the char bed. Tertiary-air ports are located in two opposite walls just above the upper limit of the spray zone.

The primary-air ports, located in every second space between furnace wall tubes, are proportioned to admit about 60% of the total air required at a static pressure of about 2.5 in. of water. Dampers are arranged to control groups of four to six individual primary-air ports.

Approximately one half of the remaining air required is admitted at each of the secondary- and tertiary-air zones. Ports in each zone are individually dampered to permit control of air pressure at about 8 in. of water. The relatively high-velocity secondary air serves to create turbulence and thus intimately mixes with the volatile gases arising from the char bed. Combustion in the secondary-air zone creates a high-temperature zone below the liquor spray to speed drying of the liquor in flight from the spray nozzle to the furnace walls.

Further turbulence is created by the admission of the tertiary air, to assure complete combustion of any unburned gases rising from the secondary zone and any volatiles driven from the sprayed liquor during its flight across the furnace.

Combustion-Air Control

The control of combustion air in early units was essentially manual, with some assistance from monitoring instruments. The operator established the liquor flow to the recovery unit to be consistent with pulping-process requirements. Total-air flow was selected in proportion to liquor flow. A ratio of primary-air to total-air flow was established to provide stable furnace-bed conditions, and automatic controls maintained the selected rates and ratios by adjustment of forced-draft-fan speed or damper and adjustment of primary-air proportioning damper. Such a control system is shown in Fig. 7.

Recently, to insure the maintenance of optimum conditions, a number of installations have been made in which the total-air requirement is determined by continuous analysis of the combustion products. The oxygen and combustibles content of flue gas at the boiler outlet is an accurate measure of combustion efficiency. Using such measurements to automatically adjust or control air flows to the unit enables the operator to gain maximum benefit from the combustion of waste liquors.

Control of Gas Temperature

The arrangement of upper furnace and superheater, shown in Fig. 3, is most important in the performance of a recovery unit. Combustion is completed in the tertiary-air zone, as a result of turbulence and air admitted at this point. Above the tertiary-air zone there is adequate gas travel in the water-cooled furnace to cool the gas to a temperature of about 1600 F before it enters convection surfaces, so that soot blowers can satisfactorily remove ash and fume from these surfaces.

The nose baffle shields the superheater from the radiant heat of the active burning zone of the furnace and causes the gas to enter the screen and superheater at a uniform temperature and velocity. An eddy above and behind the tip of the nose causes the gas to recirculate within the superheater tube bank and thus provides a cool conveying medium for returning material, dropped from or blown off the superheater, to the furnace.

The superheater is arranged for parallel flow of gas and steam. Saturated steam enters the front tubes of the superheater in contact with the hot gas and flows through successive loops, so that the final tube with the hottest steam is in contact with cooler gas. There is a dual advantage with this arrangement. First, cooling of the gas is most rapid at the front of the superheater, where the need for cooling of the ash is greatest. Second, the parallel-flow arrangement results in a lower average tube-metal temperature. This is particularly desirable in recovery units designed for steam temperatures above 700 F. Because of the highly corrosive nature of the

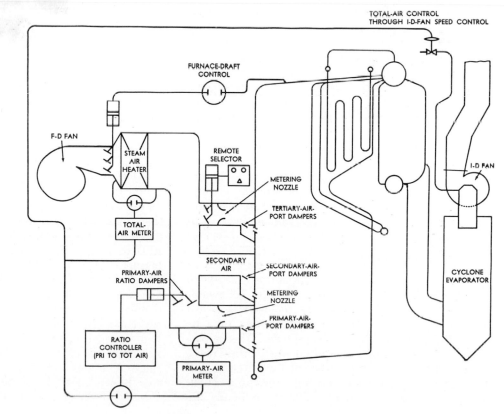

Fig. 7. Schematic arrangement of combustion-air control system

smelt, metal temperatures of carbon-steel tubes in contact with fluid smelt should not exceed 850 F. In zones where there is no fluid smelt, the metal temperatures may be higher. Only careful coordination of superheater metal temperatures, flue gas temperatures, and alloys for superheater tubes permits final steam temperatures up to 900 F.

Maximum Gas Temperatures

Design requirements of the B&W recovery unit are based on maximum gas temperatures of 1600 F and 1450 F (both HVT basis), respectively, entering the widely spaced slag-screen tubes and the more closely spaced tubes. As with other slag-forming fuels, an important objective is to reduce the temperature of the ash particles in suspension below their sticky or tacky temperature before they enter a closely spaced tube bank. This is accomplished by providing a combination of radiant-heat-absorption surface in the open furnace and convection surface in the widely spaced slag-screen tubes. In the design of a modern recovery unit, the radiant heat absorption in the furnace is calculated to drop the gas temperature to about 1600 F, and then, as the gas passes through the widely spaced tubes of the slag screen, it is cooled to about 1450 F.

Slag Screens

In the standard design for usual pressure and superheat, there are as many as six rows of slag-screen tubes in which boiler water at saturated temperature is circulated. The tubes are arranged across the boiler on 10-in. centers. From front to rear the rows of tubes are spaced on 5-in. centers. The tubes in alternate rows are staggered. The closest spacing of the slag-screen tubes is, therefore, about 7½-in. centers on the diagonal. Between the rear slag-screen tubes and the forward superheater tubes a cavity or space is provided for access and accommodation of retractable (type IK) soot blowers. Having reduced the gas temperature to the desirable degree for entry into the superheater surface, the boiler designer's problem is to obtain the required superheat and then provide enough heating surface in boiler, economizer, air heater, and direct-contact evaporator for economical heat utilization.

Superheater Characteristics

For a nominal total steam temperature of 700 to 750 F, depending upon pressure and feedwater temperature, a six-loop superheater with forward and intermediate cavities for soot blowers may be installed following the boiler screen. The superheater is larger than is required with other fuels, because of the low temperature of the entering gas, the need for rather open spacing, and the parallel-flow arrangement. In many units wide bends are

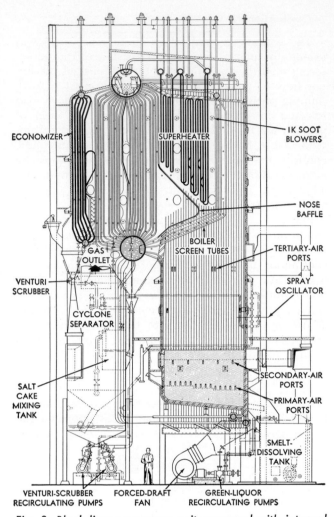

Fig. 8. *Black-liquor recovery unit arranged with integral economizer and venturi evaporator-scrubber*

used for the first, second, and even third loops of the superheater, and the adjacent elements are staggered, simulating slag-screen construction, to reduce to 1450 F the temperature of the gas entering the remaining closely spaced tubes. In thus simulating slag-screen construction within the superheater itself, the number of boiler slag-screen tubes may be reduced, with the result that the gas enters the superheater at a higher temperature. With high gas temperatures entering the superheater, it is possible to reduce the surface required for high steam temperatures. A compromise is necessary between superheater surface receiving hotter gas and an appreciable increase in the over-all size and surface of the superheater. Designing the total superheating surface so that it can be adequately cleaned by two vertical rows of type IK soot blowers is a practical compromise. Effective arrangements of slag-screen and superheater tubes and provisions for soot blowers are shown in Figs. 3, 8, and 9.

Recognition of the need for careful consideration

of gas temperatures at various points in the slag screen and superheater, has led to use of the nose-baffle construction to provide *uniform* temperatures and velocities across the entire slag-screen entrance.

Test Traverse Results. The results of a study of actual temperatures and velocities ahead of the superheater in a 275-ton per day recovery unit, similar to that in Fig. 3, are shown in Fig. 10. During this test the unit was operated at a rating of 273 tons per day, firing liquor at a concentration of 67% solids at the furnace nozzle. The values shown are the averages determined with high-velocity thermocouples and pitot tubes at seven points across the width of the unit and at several elevations. For the traverse shown, the average HVT temperature entering the superheater is 1465 F (note recirculation indicated by lower arrow). Other traverses for different ratings and liquor-firing concentrations have shown similar temperature and velocity patterns.

In addition to creating a favorable pattern of gas flow, the nose baffle shields the bottom of the superheater loops from the radiant heat of the furnace. This shielding reduces heat input to the tubes, thus reducing metal temperatures and slag deposition. Shielding is of special importance at the outlet loops of the superheater, where the steam temperature is highest.

Temperature Leaving Superheater. The temperature of the gas leaving the superheater has been reduced

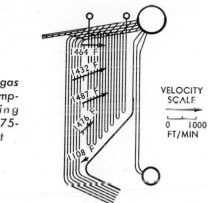

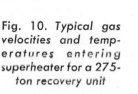

Fig. 10. *Typical gas velocities and temperatures entering superheater for a 275-ton recovery unit*

VELOCITY SCALE

0   1000
FT/MIN

to 1100–1300 F (HVT values), which is well below the temperature at which ash particles in the gas are fluid. Deposits beyond this point are readily blown from the tubes and may be satisfactorily collected in hoppers beneath the boiler for return to the chemical cycle.

When Superheat Is Not Required For Power. Where the generation of electric power is not required because of its availability at low cost or for other reasons, superheaters normally used in recovery units are not installed. Under these conditions the heat absorption by the furnace walls and the standard boiler slag screen is insufficient to reduce the gas temperature to a satisfactory point for entry to the close-spaced tubes of the boiler section. In such cases the standard unit can be modified by bending the first several rows of the boiler section forward into the superheater cavity. By this arrangement, the gas temperature is reduced in the widely spaced tubes within the superheater cavity and above the superheater floor to a suitable point for entry to the remaining closely spaced boiler section. Use of a small superheater to reduce the gas temperature is recommended even when no power generation is desired. When steam at 175 to 200 psi is supplied from a recovery unit for process only, 100 F superheat can be used to advantage in reducing condensation loss in the distribution lines.

Rated Capacity of a Recovery Unit

As the rate of liquor fired and completely burned in a furnace of a given size recovery unit increases, the gas temperatures in the furnace and entering the slag screen increase. The optimum capacity of the furnace of a modern recovery unit has been exceeded when the maximum temperature of the gas entering the screen is so high that fouling of the screen and superheater cannot be controlled with mechanical soot blowers. It may also be said that the peak capacity for that furnace has been exceeded when the gas temperature reaches a level where the fouling of the screen and superheater cannot be controlled with a moderate amount of hand lancing

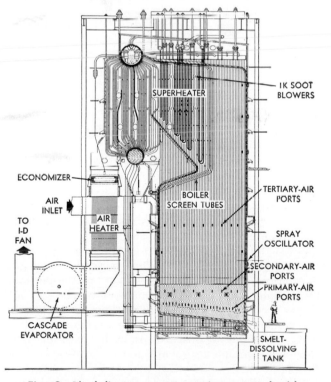

ECONOMIZER

AIR INLET

TO I-D FAN

AIR HEATER

CASCADE EVAPORATOR

SUPERHEATER

IK SOOT BLOWERS

BOILER SCREEN TUBES

TERTIARY-AIR PORTS

SPRAY OSCILLATOR

SECONDARY-AIR PORTS

PRIMARY-AIR PORTS

SMELT-DISSOLVING TANK

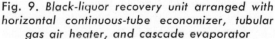

Fig. 9. *Black-liquor recovery unit arranged with horizontal continuous-tube economizer, tubular gas air heater, and cascade evaporator*

in addition to mechanical soot blowing.

The capacity of a paper mill is based on the tons of pulp produced per 24 hr. The object of a recovery unit is to recover the chemicals used and to generate steam by burning the liquor resulting from the production of pulp. The capacity of a recovery unit, within the limitations noted above, should be based on its ability to burn completely, in 24 hr, the dry solids contained in the liquor recovered from the pulp produced in 24 hr. Since the proper measure of the capacity of a recovery unit is the heat released in the furnace, B&W has established as a unit of capacity a heat input of 19,500,000 Btu in 24 hr. This unit, known as the B&W-Btu Ton, corresponds to the heat input from 3000 lb of solids having a heating value of 6500 Btu per lb, which are fair averages for the liquor from a ton of kraft pulp. Recovery units by B&W, sized in accordance with this measure, are designed to handle 15 to 20% overloads.

Nominal Size of a Recovery Unit

The nominal size of a B&W recovery unit for the conditions at a particular mill, where the solids contained in the liquor from an average ton of pulp and the heating value per lb of solids differ from the values used in the unit of measure, will be greater or less in B&W-Btu Tons. The nominal size of a recovery unit for a particular mill will, therefore, be:

$$\text{Nominal Size} = \frac{A \times B \times C}{19,500,000}, \text{ in B\&W-Btu Tons}$$

where:

A = lb of solids recovered from each ton of pulp
B = Btu heating value per lb of solids
C = pulp output of mill in tons per 24 hr

Thus, for a mill producing 200 tons of pulp per 24 hr, where the cook yields 3400 lb solids in the liquor from a ton of pulp at a heating value of 6700 Btu per lb solids, the nominal size of the recovery unit will be $3400 \times 6700 \times 200/19,500,000 = 234$ B&W-Btu Tons.

A B&W recovery unit of nominal capacity as defined above has a margin for overload, as noted, of 15 to 20%, with attendant comparable steam production. Higher overloads are not precluded (some plants run as high as 100% overload), but, if carried much beyond 15 to 20%, the steam production will not keep pace with the liquor feed and will ultimately decrease because of the heat required to evaporate the water in the liquor and to smelt and reduce the chemical ash.

Boiler Section of Recovery Unit

The boiler section of a modern recovery unit is of two-drum vertical-tube design, with two or three gas passes. A two-pass boiler is shown in Fig. 9. Cyclone steam separators (see Chapter 9) are normally used in the steam drum. Gas baffles are arranged to provide generous flow areas at the gas turns where crossflow occurs, and adequate provision is made for the inclusion of soot blowers.

Economizer

When used, the economizer may be either the horizontal continuous-tube type (see Fig. 3) or the two-drum vertical-tube type (see Fig. 8). The former lends itself to high feedwater temperatures of 350 to 450 F normally used with high pressure (1200 psi) application, and the latter to low feedwater temperatures. Feedwater entering the inlet header flows upward through the economizer tubes and through multiple tubular connections to the steam-and-water drum of the boiler. An economizer is used to take advantage of the greater temperature head existing between the gas and feedwater than between the gas and saturated boiler water. The feedwater must be completely deaerated, and, to minimize external corrosion, the feed temperature must be no less than about 260 F (see Chapter 11). This is mandatory because of the high moisture and sulfur content of recovery-unit flue gases. Spacing of the economizer tubes is designed for ease of cleaning with mechanical soot blowers.

Gas Air Heater

The gas air heater, a very efficient means of absorbing "low-head" heat, is a component of recovery units, when practical amounts of boiler and economizer surface cannot reduce the gas temperature to a level suitable for use in the direct-contact evaporator. It is also used when feedwater conditions are below the standards set for safe economizer use. When liquor from the multiple-effect evaporators is delivered at a concentration of 50% solids or higher, the heat balance will frequently require a gas air heater. The trend toward higher steam pressures in pulp-mill operation has increased justification for the use of the gas air heater, since the economic temperature of the exit gas from the boiler-economizer combination increases as the steam pressure increases.

In the gas air heater, shown in Fig. 9, steel tubes are expanded in steel tube sheets. Gas enters the tubes at the top and leaves at the bottom. Air enters at the top and flows downward parallel to the gas in multiple horizontal passes, leaving at the bottom. Steel plate baffles direct the air flow. The gas air heater is cleaned with specially designed soot blowers (see below). The parallel-flow arrangement protects the tubes against corrosion by assuring that tube-metal temperatures are above the dewpoint of the gas.

Where the temperature of the exit gas from the economizer is higher than that required for the direct-contact evaporator and the addition of a gas air heater would lower the gas temperature below that desired, a steam coil air heater may be installed to heat the air to some intermediate temperature before it goes to the gas air heater. By proportioning the steam coil and gas air heater surfaces, the exit gas temperature from the latter can be maintained at the proper temperature for entering the direct-contact evaporator while providing a correct air preheat temperature for the furnace.

Soot Blowing

Prior to 1940, soot blowers were generally ineffective in recovery units. Application was difficult, maintenance was high, and the results were not satisfactory. Consequently hand lancing was a necessary part of recovery-unit operation. Even after mechanical soot blowers of improved design became available for cleaning the rear boiler passes and the economizer, cleaning of the screen, superheater, and front boiler passes still required the constant attendance of hand lancers.

Increasing labor costs and the trend toward larger units forced the development of automatic mechanical cleaning devices to cope with the tenacious deposits that form in the hot-gas regions of the recovery unit. Even with the most effective known cleaning equipment, surfaces must be arranged with due regard to gas temperatures, gas velocities, and tube spacing, in order to achieve a "self-cleaning" recovery unit. First application of modern-type soot blowers in a kraft recovery unit was made in 1946. There has been rapid progress since that time, and at present, when a recovery unit is operated at or near its rated capacity, there is little if any manual labor involved in keeping the gas passages open. As load is increased on a unit, however, mechanical entrainment of ash and sublimation of sodium compounds increase rapidly, and high overloads invariably lead to cleaning problems. In addition to excessive quantities of ash in the flue gas, velocities and temperatures at all points in the unit are increased, and ash deposits become more difficult to remove.

Great care is taken in the design of all recovery-unit heating surfaces to assure that such surfaces are well arranged for mechanical cleaning. Cavities are left at optimum locations in screen, superheater, boiler, and economizer banks to provide for insertion of soot blowers. Gas temperatures are carefully calculated to make certain that velocities and particular tube patterns are compatible with good mechanical cleaning. Even building layout is to a considerable extent dictated by the soot blowers. Nearly all of the soot blowers used on recovery units are of the retractable type, i.e., they retract outside the unit setting when not actually in use, to prevent damage or corrosion by the hot gases. Thus, building clearances and platform elevation are designed to avoid interferences with the retracted blowers. Soot blowers

are generally arranged for automatic sequential operation, controlled from a panel at the main recovery-unit panel board.

Although all soot blowers on a recovery unit are usually of the retractable type, to take advantage of their superior cleaning ability and of the desirability of standardization, the cooler rear portions of the boiler or economizer may be cleaned with fixed-position rotating blowers. Such an arrangement generally is somewhat lower in first cost than the all-retractable installation. Fig. 3 shows a combination retractable and fixed-position installation. Retractable soot blowers are shown in the boiler and superheater in Fig. 8.

In spite of the great dependence upon mechanical soot blowers, lance doors (Fig. 11) should be provided at strategic locations to provide for hand lancing at high overloads or when soot blowers may be out for repairs.

Both air and steam have been used as the cleaning media in hand lances and soot blowers for recovery units. For hand lances, air is generally preferred from both safety and comfort standpoints. In soot blowers, however, steam is more commonly used. Air, being more dense than steam, is theoretically a better cleaning medium. In order to make air competitive, compressors are generally sized to deliver less air than would be the case with steam. Cleaning effectiveness then is about equal. However, limited compressor size is a serious disadvantage when upset furnace conditions or high overloads make it necessary to clean heating surfaces more often than is normal. Under these circumstances, the

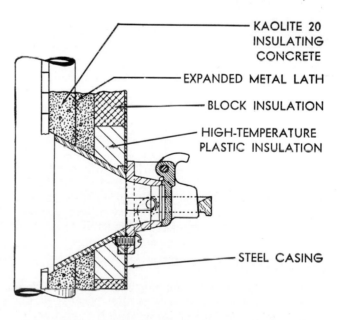

KAOLITE 20 INSULATING CONCRETE

EXPANDED METAL LATH

BLOCK INSULATION

HIGH-TEMPERATURE PLASTIC INSULATION

STEEL CASING

SECTIONAL VIEW

Fig. 11. Lance-port and wall construction

virtually inexhaustible supply of cleaning medium in the steam drum may become most important. Another factor in the almost universal use of steam for soot blowing is that economics generally rules out the use of air for the retractable soot blowers in the hard-to-clean areas of the unit. Such blowers require large quantities of 500 psi air, so that a costly compressor plant is required. With steam virtually necessary for some blowers, few mills find it desirable to install fixed-position air soot blowers at the rear of the recovery unit.

Shot Cleaning

Recently, increasing use has been made of steel shot for the removal of ash deposits, particularly in continuous-tube economizers and tubular gas air heaters. Steel shot of ¼-in. to ½-in. diameter are allowed to fall onto spherical stellited distributors above the tube surface to be cleaned and thus are made to scatter evenly over the top of the surface. They then fall downward over or inside the tubes dislodging ash accumulation. The shot and removed material are separated in a hopper below the cleaned surface, usually by an air blast, with the shot falling into a collecting chamber and the majority of the ash particles being re-entrained in the flue gas for subsequent storage in dust-collection equipment behind the unit. The shot, free of fly-ash particles, are recirculated to the top of the system for another fall through the surface to be cleaned.

Among the advantages in the use of steel shot for cleaning heating surfaces are:

1. Removal of deposits that cannot be removed by steam or air soot blowers.

2. Improved thermal efficiency. Lower average exit gas temperatures are maintained with continuous cleaning or cleaning at more frequent intervals than is the case with soot blowers.

3. Greater latitude in designing for optimum performance. Limitations in tube spacing and arrangement that must be adhered to with soot blowers may be greatly relaxed with shot cleaning.

4. Reduced operating costs. The power used for transporting shot and for air-blast separation of shot from fly-ash is less costly than the steam or air used for soot blowing.

Although shot cleaning of boiler surfaces has not yet been widely used in this country, it offers attractive prospects to the engineer and is likely to become a common feature in future boiler designs.

Optimum Heat Balance

The design of the economizer and air heater is subject to a very practical limitation because of the high moisture and sulfur contents in the products of combustion from kraft black liquor. To prevent rapid corrosion and failure as a result of condensation and formation of dilute sulfurous acid, the metal tempera-

ture of ordinary steel in contact with the gas must not be below the dewpoint of the gas. This means a) that the temperature of the feedwater to the economizer should be above the dewpoint of the gas, and b) that the relative heat transfer rates on the gas and air sides of the air heater tubes should be controlled to keep the tube-metal temperature, at any point, above the dewpoint of the gas. Diminishing returns set an economic limit to the amount of economizer and air heater surface used to decrease the exit gas temperature, and at the same time it becomes more difficult to control tube-metal temperatures to avoid corrosion.

The heat in the flue gas between a practical exit temperature from an economizer (650 F) or air heater (450 F) and the optimum temperature entering the fume collector (300 F for an electrostatic precipitator and 180 F for a venturi scrubber) is generally used in a direct-contact evaporator for further concentration of the black liquor. More heat than that represented by a minimum temperature difference between these points usually can be used for the evaporation of moisture from the liquor after it leaves the multiple-effect evaporators and before it is fired in the furnace. Normally, therefore, a recovery unit can be designed with a heat balance in which all the heat is effectively used.

If the heat available in the gas from the economizer or air heater is greater than that required to evaporate the liquor from the multiple-effect concentration

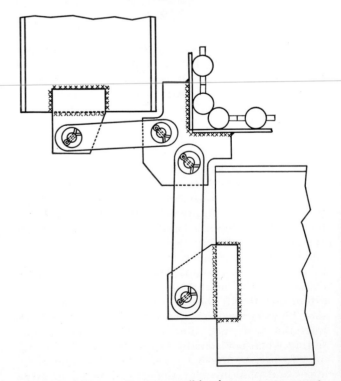

Fig. 12. *Recovery-furnace wall-buckstay arrangement*

to the firing concentration, the excess must be wasted in some manner. This can be done a) through a higher gas temperature to the fume collector, b) by reducing the temperature of the gas through dilution with air, c) by adding water to the direct-contact evaporator to replace the excess evaporation, or d) by reducing evaporation in the multiple-effect evaporators (least objectionable in the loss of thermal efficiency). However, the last method is still undesirable, since multiple-effect evaporation is the most efficient way to remove moisture from the liquor. Thermal efficiency of the recovery unit is at a maximum when the difference between the total heat from combustion of the liquor leaving the multiple-effect evaporators and the total heat in the flue gas entering the fume collector is absorbed in steam or in useful work in processing the chemical ash, without resort to any of the foregoing wasteful procedures. Obviously, it does not matter whether heat is used for final evaporation of the liquor in the furnace or in the direct-contact evaporator. If, however, a low exit gas temperature is attained by diluting the liquor in the direct-contact evaporator, then the exit temperature is no longer a measure of efficiency.

Where the maximum concentration of the black liquor from the multiple-effect evaporators is limited to a rather low figure because of the characteristics of the liquor or other considerations peculiar to a particular mill, the necessary gas temperature for direct-contact evaporation to a concentration suitable for burning in the furnace may be obtained by using only a boiler or boiler-economizer combination. Steam at a pressure of 125 to 150 psi is then used in a steam coil heater to preheat combustion air. In using this steam there is little direct loss in thermal efficiency, since the preheated air becomes an additional source of heat input to the system, resulting in the generation of a correspondingly greater quantity of steam. The losses incident to such a cycle are from unavoidable radiation, leakage, and condensation. On the other hand, if the steam air heater is used in place of the gas air heater when high-concentration liquor is available and the gas air heater is needed to reduce the gas temperature to avoid overconcentration of the liquor, the losses can be appreciable.

Direct-Contact Evaporation

In the direct-contact evaporator the liquor and gas are brought into intimate physical contact, and there is a mass transfer of water vapor from the liquor to the gas across the liquor-gas interface. While there is a decrease in the temperature of the gas in the evaporator, the combined heat of the gas and the evaporated water leaving is nearly the same as the total heat of the gas entering the evaporator. Any difference may be accounted for by radiation loss

from, and air leakage into, the evaporator plus the heat given up or absorbed by the remaining liquor.

In the design of the direct-contact evaporator, adequate surface must be provided for the desired heat and mass transfer. If liquor is splashed or sprayed on hot metal, the quantity must be sufficient for continuous washing. The liquor must be agitated to prevent local overconcentration. A further reason for continuous agitation or movement of the liquor is its acidification by the absorption of CO_2, which decreases the solubility of the dissolved solids. Because of the decreased solubility and the increased concentration, there is a tendency for sludge to precipitate. Gas velocity and flow pattern in the evaporator must be such that liquor entrainment in the exit gas is minimized.

The direct-contact evaporator used in the modern recovery unit is of the cascade (Fig. 9), cyclone (Fig. 13), or venturi (Fig. 14) type.

Cascade Evaporator. In the modern cascade evaporator (Fig. 9) there are from one to four wheels in varying parallel and series configurations. The arrangement and the amount of total contact surface required depend upon the weight and temperature of the gas and the weight of water to be evaporated. Each wheel, made of two circular side plates connected by tubes, is mounted on a heavy shaft, which is rotated at low speed. The wheel is partially submerged in a vat of liquor, so that the tubes alternately dip into the liquor and emerge to present a wetted surface to the gas stream flowing through the wheel above the liquor level. The liquor is constantly agitated by the paddle-wheel action of the rotating bank of tubes. External flow channels are provided for return circulation of the liquor as it is moved toward one end of the vat by the rotation of the wheel. Each wheel is driven by a constant-speed motor through a gear reducer and chain drive. Because of the high starting load, a hydraulic coupling is generally used between the motor and reducer. The concentrated liquor is withdrawn through a screen in a flow box mounted at the side of the evaporator. The screen is equipped with a moving arm for scraping lumps, caused by precipitation or localized liquor drying, into a separate chamber, where they are redissolved with steam.

Cyclone Evaporator. The cyclone evaporator (Fig. 13) is a vertical cylindrical vessel with a conical bottom. The gas is admitted through a tangential inlet near the bottom. It flows in a whirling helical path to the top and leaves the cylinder through a concentric re-entrant outlet. Black liquor is sprayed across the gas inlet. The liquor droplets mix intimately with the high-velocity gas and are then thrown by centrifugal force to the cylinder wall. Recirculated liquor flowing down the wall of the cylinder carries the droplets and any dust or fume thrown from the gas to the conical bottom, out through the

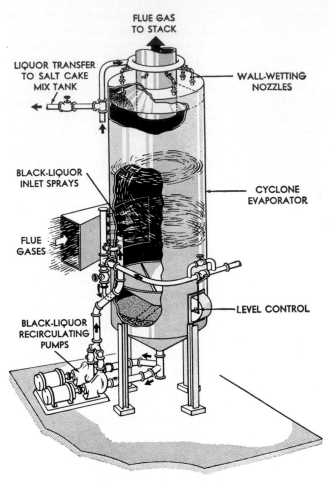

FLUE GAS TO STACK

LIQUOR TRANSFER TO SALT CAKE MIX TANK

WALL-WETTING NOZZLES

BLACK-LIQUOR INLET SPRAYS

CYCLONE EVAPORATOR

FLUE GASES

BLACK-LIQUOR RECIRCULATING PUMPS

LEVEL CONTROL

Fig. 13. *Cyclone evaporator*

drain, and into a sump tank. Sufficient liquor from the sump tank is recirculated to the nozzles at the top of the evaporator to keep the interior wall continuously wet, preventing ash collection or localized drying on this surface. By adjusting the quantity of spray liquor at the inlet, it is possible to control the evaporation to some extent, or, conversely, to control gas temperature drop.

Sodium Fume Particle Recovery

When char is burned in the furnace, an appreciable quantity of sodium is sublimed. As the combustion gases cool, the sodium vapor condenses and is entrained in the gas stream as a very finely dispersed fume. Much of this fume is reclaimed by deposition on the heating surfaces of the recovery unit and on the wetted surfaces of the direct-contact evaporator. The remainder, in suspension in the flue gas as very fine solid particles, passes from the unit. Although some of these particles are as large as 10 microns, collection of the fume from the waste gas must generally be considered in terms of submicron size. The quantity of sodium, largely as sodium sulfate, carried out of the unit in the flue gas depends upon

the service conditions and care in operation, with probable outside limits of 90 to 275 lb and a normal average of about 150 lb per ton of pulp. This is not only a costly chemical loss, which must be replaced with makeup sodium sulfate (salt cake), but it is also an industrial nuisance as an air pollutant. Most alkaline pulping mills are now collecting this fume from the waste gas.

Electrostatic Precipitator

The first equipment successfully used to collect the fume was the electrostatic precipitator. Many installations of this type are now in use, operating at collection efficiencies between 80 and 95%. The equipment operates on the principle that a particle, suspended in a gas subjected to a sufficiently strong electrostatic field, becomes charged electrically and tends to migrate toward an oppositely charged collection electrode, to which it will adhere. The collection electrode is mechanically rapped periodically to shake the particles loose to drop into a hopper or vat of liquor.

To energize the precipitator, potentials of 50,000 to 100,000 volts are used and are adjusted so that a bluish glow may be seen at the discharge electrode. Potentials must be low enough to avoid sparking between discharging and collecting electrodes. Usually the electrical supply is provided by a separate and special unit, which steps up the voltage of the alternating current and then rectifies it to an interrupted but unidirectional current.

The gas temperature, moisture content, velocity, and time of retention within the area subject to the electrical charge are important. Care should be taken that the gas temperature entering a precipitator is not less than 300 F, for otherwise local cold spots result in condensation, fouling, and rapid corrosion.

Venturi Evaporator-Scrubber

Another device for collecting the fume from the waste gas is the venturi evaporator-scrubber (Fig. 14). This scrubber depends upon the collision of fume particles with liquid droplets. In practice, the gas is accelerated in a venturi section, and liquid is admitted through nozzles at the throat in a plane normal to the flow of the gas. The liquid is finely atomized by the high-velocity gas, and intimate mixing results. Most of the fume or dust particles collide with and adhere to the liquid droplets. The mixture of gas and liquid droplets then goes to a cyclone separator, where the droplets with their fume particles are centrifugally removed from the gas stream and drain to the sump tank.

When a water solution is used for scrubbing, it is recirculated from the sump to the throat sprays until the concentration of the solution of water and recovered sodium compounds is about 35% solids. A portion of the solution is then continuously bled off

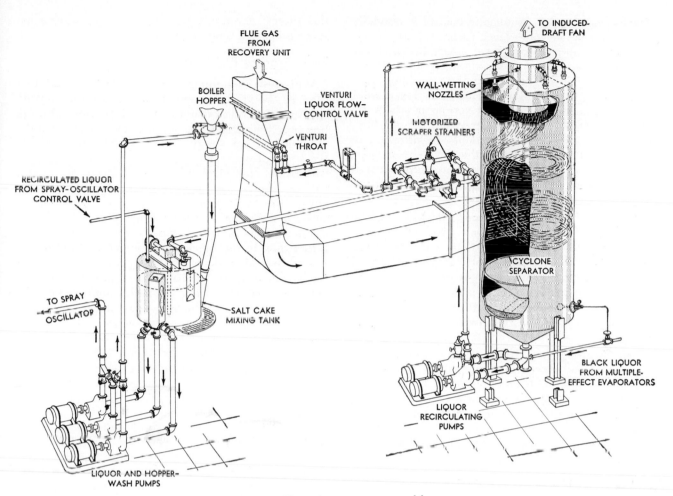

Fig. 14. *Venturi evaporator-scrubber*

and returned with the black liquor to the furnace for smelting and reduction with the ash from the liquor. Makeup water is added to the scrubber system to compensate for that bled off and any evaporation which occurs in the scrubbing process.

When black liquor is used as the scrubbing medium, the venturi scrubber replaces both the direct-contact evaporator and the fume collector. In this application, the liquor is concentrated by cooling of the gas almost to its saturation temperature of about 180 F. The liquor is recirculated from the cyclone-separator sump to the venturi-throat nozzles at a concentration of 60 to 65% solids. Liquor is fed from this system to the furnace for firing, as with the direct-contact evaporators previously described, and makeup liquor from the multiple-effect evaporators is added to the system to compensate for the liquor fired.

The venturi scrubber is a simple piece of equipment, easy to operate and control. Fume collection efficiencies of 85 to 90% are continuously maintained. If a venturi scrubber is used, the recovery unit achieves a higher thermal efficiency, since the termi-

nal gas temperature of the venturi scrubber is about 120 F lower than is permissible with an electrostatic precipitator. When liquor is the scrubbing medium, there is good absorption of SO_2 from the flue gas. SO_2 can also be recovered, when water is the scrubbing medium, by the addition of caustic (NaOH) or soda ash (Na_2CO_3) to the scrubbing solution to maintain alkalinity.

Auxiliaries for Recovery Unit

Successful operation of a recovery unit depends to a large extent upon the performance of its auxiliaries. All the smaller components must be designed and selected with the same care and attention to reliability and continuity of service as the main components. The auxiliaries, preferably and usually supplied as a part of the recovery unit, are described below:

Auxiliary Oil or Gas Burners. These burners, for curing the furnace refractory, preheating at start-up, and emergency use in case of unstable furnace conditions, should be capable of developing full boiler rating and should be designed for insertion quickly and easily when required.

Meters and Controls. Automatic control is normally provided for boiler water level, furnace draft, direct-contact-evaporator liquor level, black-liquor firing temperature, and the various air flows. Instruments should be provided for recording steam flow, total-air flow, primary-air flow, tertiary-air flow, boiler water level, gas temperatures at various points in the system, air preheat temperature, steam temperature, and black-liquor flow. Gages should be provided to indicate draft losses through the different sections of the recovery unit, primary-air pressure, secondary-air pressure, furnace draft, induced-draft-fan suction, and steam pressure.

Forced- and Induced-Draft Fans. Because of the possible unbalance of the rotor caused by deposits from fume-laden gas, the design and selection of the induced-draft fan are particularly important. Speed must be conservative, and straight or nearly straight blades are preferable. A variable-speed drive is often used in the form of a steam turbine, if mill steam balance warrants, or a hydraulic or magnetic coupling.

Smelt-Dissolving Tank. This tank should be of heavy construction and should be equipped for good agitation. One or more side-entering agitators are generally used. The dissolving tank must be vented with a vertical stack of sufficient size to carry off the vapor formed in the tank. Green liquor is recirculated to shatter-nozzles, to disperse the stream of molten smelt before it enters the liquor in the tank. Steam jets are also provided, to help break up the stream of molten smelt and to reduce the noise resulting from the chilling of the hot smelt by the cooler liquor.

Mixing Tank and Salt Cake Feeder. Careful attention to detail is required in the design of this tank and feeder, so that makeup salt cake may be fed at a regular rate and be well mixed with the black liquor. The mixing tank includes a mechanically scraped screen, to assure that all material which passes to the fuel pumps is of small enough size to pass readily through the burner nozzle.

Pumps for Moving the Liquor. Pumps are very important components of the recovery unit. All liquors encountered in the recovery cycle are to some extent corrosive. At concentrations above 65% solids, black liquor becomes increasingly viscous at a rapid rate, and, after salt cake is added at the mixing tank, it also becomes highly abrasive. Centrifugal pumps of special design are used in this service, and due attention must be given to suction heads and liquor concentrations and temperatures for the various pumps.

Black-Liquor Piping and Heaters. Piping, fittings, and heaters must be designed to withstand corrosion and abrasion. Piping sizes must represent a compromise between pressure drops with highly viscous fluids and a tendency for sludge to precipitate when liquor velocities are low. Black liquor heaters should be of the direct steam-injection type, since scaling on surface heaters renders them ineffective.

Soda Process Recovery Unit

With few exceptions, the requirements and features of the kraft recovery unit, as described above, apply to the soda recovery unit. In the soda process the digestion liquor is sodium hydroxide, NaOH, without sodium sulfide, Na_2S, which characterizes the kraft process. The makeup chemical is sodium carbonate, Na_2CO_3 (soda ash), instead of sodium sulfate, Na_2SO_4 (salt cake). Since sulfur is not present in the soda process, there is no reduction of sulfur in the recovery-unit furnace. Therefore, chemical makeup is added to the recovered green liquor rather than to the black liquor ahead of the furnace (as in the kraft process). Consequently, the salt cake feeder and mixing tank are not required. The dust and fume collected from the boiler hoppers and the fume collector are in the form of soda ash, and it can be added directly to the green liquor after the furnace rather than to the black liquor before burning.

In the furnace, the soda liquor does not form a suitable reactive char for burning in a bed, and it is, therefore, finely atomized and sprayed into the furnace. The finely atomized spray dehydrates in flight in the furnace, and combustion takes place largely in suspension. Combustion air is admitted through ports around the furnace periphery, as in the kraft operation, and the hottest part of the furnace is just above the hearth. The ash, sodium carbonate, collects in molten form on the hearth and is tapped through the smelt spout or spouts.

Soda-liquor burning is subject to the same sublimation of chemical and mechanical carry-over of particles as in the kraft process, but the handling of hopper dust and recovered chemical from the fume collector is somewhat different, since it is not necessary to return this material to the furnace. Physically, the design of the recovery unit is the same for soda as for kraft liquors except that the oscillating spray nozzle is replaced by two or more steam-atomizing soda-liquor burners.

Sulfite Process

The sulfite process for wood pulp manufacture differs from the alkaline processes in that an acid liquor is used in the cooking of wood. Chips are prepared in the same fashion as for the alkaline processes and then are cooked in a digester, under steam pressure, to dissolve the lignin binder that holds the cellulose fibers together. Most sulfite mills now use a solution of the bisulfite of calcium or calcium-magnesium, prepared from limestone or dolomite. In recent years, however, increasing interest has been paid to magnesium, ammonia, and sodium as bases for the bisulfite cooking liquor.

Calcium Bisulfite Acid

In the preparation of the calcium bisulfite acid for the sulfite process, SO_2 is first produced by burning either elemental sulfur or pyrites. The quantity of air used for burning is carefully controlled to minimize the formation of SO_3. The SO_2 is then cooled and introduced into the base of a tower packed with limestone. In this tower, known as the strong tower, the SO_2 passes upward in counterflow to a solution of weak acid which flows down over the limestone packing. Within the tower the SO_2 is first absorbed by the water or acid solution to form sulfurous acid, which reacts with the limestone (calcium carbonate) to produce a calcium bisulfite solution with an excess of unreacted sulfurous acid. This solution, which is withdrawn from the strong tower, is known as raw acid. Undissolved SO_2, now at a rather low concentration, is withdrawn from the top of the strong tower and introduced into the base of a second tower, known as the weak tower. The weak tower, like the strong tower, is also packed with limestone. Water is introduced at the top, and the weak acid, formed by the reaction between the SO_2, the water, and the limestone, is withdrawn from the base and fed into the strong tower at the top.

The raw acid withdrawn from the strong tower is fortified under pressure with SO_2, relieved from the digesters during the cook. Various systems are used for fortifying the raw acid. The simplest and least efficient thermally is one in which the SO_2, relieved from the digesters, is cooled in a heat exchanger and then absorbed by cool raw acid at moderate pressure. Also in use are rather involved systems in which the reserve supply of raw acid is kept in high-pressure acid-resistant accumulators and is fortified by receiving the uncooled relieved SO_2 directly from the digesters. Raw acid from the absorption towers contains about 4% total SO_2 by weight, of which 2.75 to 3.0% of the total weight of the solution is SO_2 combined as calcium bisulfite. Corresponding percentages of SO_2 in the cooking liquor range from 5.5 to 6.5 total, with 2 to 3% combined as bisulfite.

It is only for the calcium-base digestion liquor that the base material itself, relatively pure limestone, can be used as packing for the absorption towers of the acid-making system. For other bases (dolomitic limestone, magnesium, ammonia, or sodium) a slurry or solution of the base is used. This slurry or solution passes downward in the tower over chemically inert packing material, and the sulfur dioxide passes upward to form a bisulfite with the base, with an excess of sulfurous acid.

After charging the digester with chips, the cooking acid is added, either hot or cold. The digester is brought up to pressure either by the admission of steam directly or by circulating the liquor through an external heat exchanger, where it is heated and returned to the digester. Because of the release of SO_2 as the temperature increases, the excess gas must be relieved to permit raising the temperature to correspond to the pressure within the digester. Cooking time normally varies from 7 to 10 hr, and, for most of the cook, the pressure and temperature are approximately 90 psi and 300 F. The Mitscherlich process used by a few mills is an indirect low-temperature long-time digestion process.

At the completion of the cook, the gas and vapor are relieved from the top of the digester, and the pressure is reduced to 30 to 40 psi. At this pressure all the contents are discharged to the blowpit through the blow valve at the bottom. The blowpit is an enclosed chamber having approximately $2\frac{1}{2}$ times the volume of a digester. It is equipped with a false bottom of perforated stainless steel plate and a stainless steel target, against which the chips from the digester are blown. A vent, or vomit stack, is provided to relieve the gas and vapor released from the digester charge as it enters the blowpit. The liquor is drained from the pulp through the perforated false bottom, and the pit is then flooded several times with warm water, which also drains through the perforated plate, to wash the pulp. The waste liquor, commonly called red liquor, and the wash water go to the sewer unless the red liquor is to be burned. The pulp is hosed from the blowpit through side doors and, after passing through several refining processes, goes to the paper machine.

Sulfite Waste Liquor

The total pulp production by the three major pulping processes in the United States is divided approximately as follows: the kraft process 70%, the sulfite process 25%, and the soda process 5%. Reclamation of chemicals and the production of steam from waste liquor are well established in the kraft and soda processes. Corresponding progress in using the sulfite waste liquor has lagged, however, for technological and economic reasons. During the past 15 years, pressure for finding a better means for the disposal of waste sulfite liquor has increased, both to improve the over-all economy of the pulping process and to permit compliance with stringent governmental regulations regarding stream pollution. At current fuel costs in the U. S., heat recovery alone from the waste liquors is economically marginal at best, and much effort has gone into development of processes to salvage chemicals, for reuse in cooking, or to obtain salable by-product compounds, such as alcohol, yeast, vanillin, oxalic acid, adhesives, and plastics.

As the cellulose content of the woods used for pulping in the United States may vary from 51 to 65%, the dissolved lignins and other organic constituents of the sulfite waste liquor will roughly equal the cellulose pulp produced. Since individual sulfite pulp mills have production rates from 50 to

600 tons of pulp per day, the disposal problem is of considerable magnitude. The markets for by-product chemical compounds are inadequate to provide more than isolated relief from the problem, and the only universally applicable solution thus far suggested is the use of the sulfite waste liquor as a fuel in the mill where it is produced.

Burning Sulfite Waste Liquor

Through numerous experimental trials, pilot plants, and actual commercial installations, it has been proved beyond any doubt that the sulfite waste liquor can be successfully burned, either alone or in combination with other fuels. The fundamental requirements for satisfactory combustion are now well understood. The optimum arrangement of the equipment for burning sulfite waste liquor will vary somewhat, depending upon the base of the liquor and whether or not there is to be chemical recovery. A brief discussion of the collection, concentration, and burning of sulfite waste liquor follows:

If sulfite waste liquor (red liquor) is to be burned and if any appreciable quantity of steam is to be generated for pulp mill use above the requirement for the multiple-effect evaporators, the pulp must be washed with a minimum of water, so that liquor is recovered at a relatively high concentration. Compared with the multistage vacuum washers commonly used in the alkaline (kraft and soda) pulping mills, a tremendous quantity of water is now used for blowpit washing in most sulfite mills. It is estimated that a recovered weak-red-liquor concentration of 10 to 12½% is economically acceptable. Therefore, with present normal blowpit washing, only liquor from the early part of the washing and draining operation can be accepted for recovery. The remainder of the liquor from the later washing operations is too dilute for economic heat recovery. On this basis only about 50% of the liquor would be collected.

Using a minimum quantity of cooking liquor in the digester and adding previously recovered red liquor to make up the volumetric requirements there and in the blowpit permits increasing liquor-solids recovery up to 75%. To increase recovery further to 90 or 95% of the red liquor would require adapting the blowtank of the kraft process to the sulfite mill or, alternatively, relieving the digesters to atmospheric pressure and dumping the contents into storage tanks. In either case, the pulp and liquor solids would subsequently be separated in multistage vacuum washers.

The importance of collecting the red liquor at the highest possible concentration, in order to reduce the amount of evaporation necessary in preparing the liquor for burning, is illustrated in the following: Based on a 90% recovery, a pulp mill of 100 tons per day capacity would provide about 9000 lb of red-liquor solids per hr. The quantity and concentration of weak red liquor collected and the quantity of water to be evaporated to reach a solids concentration of 50% are given in Table 2. It will be noted that more than double the quantity of water must be evaporated from liquor collected at 8% solids than from liquor collected at 14% solids, thus requiring a much larger, more costly evaporator installation and doubling the steam consumption for evaporation.

TABLE 2

Water Evaporation For 100-Ton Mill

Concentration of Red Liquor as Collected, % Solids	Weak Red Liquor Collected, lb/hr	Water Evaporated for 50% Solids, lb/hr
8	112,500	94,500
10	90,000	72,000
12	75,000	57,000
14	64,280	46,280
16	56,250	38,250

In early commercial installations for evaporating calcium bisulfite waste liquor, the low solubilities of calcium salts and their inverted solubility characteristics led to severe scaling of the evaporator heating surface as the liquor concentration and temperature increased. Thus frequent outages were required for cleaning. Development work during the past ten years has led to a method for evaporating calcium bisulfite waste liquor in the continuous uninterrupted manner essential to a recovery and burning process. In this method the acid condensate produced in multiple-effect evaporation is used to dissolve the scale deposited on heat transfer surfaces. In one application of this method, the so-called channel-switching system, the flow channels for liquor and steam are identical in shape and size. By intermittently switching the liquor from its channel to the steam channel and vice versa, condensate formed on the steam side dissolves the scale previously deposited from the liquor.

With magnesium-base sulfite liquor, calcium enters the system from the wood chips as an impurity in the makeup magnesia, so that evaporator scaling is only slightly less than with calcium-base liquor. With magnesium-base liquors a horizontal submerged-tube forced-circulation evaporation system has been quite successful, using high liquor velocities to discourage the deposition of scale. An added precaution is the use of a spare heater to serve in rotation with the two highest-concentration heaters, so that each heater can be removed from service and washed with acid condensate at regular intervals.

Concentration of Red Liquor

For burning, the red liquor should be concentrated to at least 50% solids. Where heat is recovered in a boiler, some of the heat in the flue gases leaving the boiler unit may be used to evaporate moisture from the liquor in a cyclone or cascade direct-contact evaporator. Liquor concentrations above 50% are desirable and possible.

Experimental trials with existing boilers, pilot-plant operation, and actual commercial installations prove beyond question that burning concentrated sulfite waste red liquor of either calcium, ammonia, or magnesium base is entirely practicable. Few trials have been made using sodium bisulfite red liquor. Only two mills in the United States now use high-cost sodium as a base. However, the possibility of using sodium has been frequently considered, and it is possible to burn sodium-base liquor, either alone or in combination with kraft black liquor, in a kraft recovery furnace. The ash content of the red liquor would, in this case, be recovered as a smelt of sodium carbonate and sodium sulfide, which would be suitable as makeup chemical for an associated or nearby kraft pulp mill. To obtain a regenerative chemical cycle for sodium bisulfite pulping, it would be necessary to convert the recovered sodium sulfide and sodium carbonate to sodium bisulfite. No process for such conversion has yet proved workable and economic.

The fundamental requirements for and the manner of burning the calcium-, ammonia-, and magnesium-base red liquor are much alike and, except for several relatively minor details, may be said to be identical.

Effect of Different Bases

The principal difference in burning the red liquor of the several bases is in the condition of the base itself after combustion. When calcium-base red liquor is burned, the calcium is present largely as calcium sulfate entrained in the flue gas as finely divided dust or fly-ash. When magnesium-base red liquor is burned, the magnesium is present in the flue gas as a fine magnesium oxide dust. When ammonia-base red liquor is burned, the ammonia dissociates to nitrogen and hydrogen, the latter burning to water vapor, so the base is destroyed. Compared with the combustion of the calcium-base liquor, this is an advantage, as the calcium sulfate fly-ash must be collected to avoid air pollution, and some means of disposal must be provided. Compared with the combustion of the magnesium-base liquor, it is a disadvantage, as the MgO ash may be collected, made into a slurry with water, and used to absorb SO_2 from the flue gas to produce magnesium bisulfite raw acid. This, when fortified with makeup SO_2 gas and the digester relief, may be recycled as cooking acid.

Common Requirements in Burning

While red liquor at concentrations of about 45% solids has been successfully burned in all-refractory furnaces, higher concentrations are recommended to assure stable combustion, and in general 50% solids is considered minimum. The liquor must be sprayed into the furnace, in finely atomized form, so that it will quickly absorb radiant heat to complete the evaporation of water from the droplets. Radiation in the furnace may be from hot brickwork or from the flame of another fuel fired simultaneously. When burning red liquor alone, large areas of uncooled brickwork are desirable in that part of the furnace where the liquor spray is introduced. Turbulence of the atomized liquor and air mixture is essential for rapid and complete combustion. Highly preheated combustion air is helpful in maintaining furnace stability.

For the magnesium bisulfite process, high combustion efficiency is required to minimize unburned carbon in the ash. A high degree of turbulence is obtained by using two sets of burners located opposite each other in the side walls of a refractory furnace. The atomized liquor is dried in passing from the spray nozzles into the furnace, and a high turbulence is developed when the two opposing streams of air and liquor particles meet. This design of furnace is also suitable and efficient for burning calcium- or ammonia-base red liquor.

Magnesium Bisulfite Process

Commercial experience has shown that chemicals and heat may be efficiently and easily recovered when magnesium is used as the cooking-liquor base. In the combustion of the waste liquor, the magnesium and sulfur compounds are dissociated to MgO and SO_2, and both are reclaimed and used directly in making fresh cooking acid. Heat from burning the liquor is absorbed by boiler surface before recovery of the chemicals from the flue gases. High recovery efficiencies for both heat and chemicals make the magnesium process commercially profitable, particularly in larger mills. Furthermore, the elimination of stream pollution is an important additional advantage obtainable with the use of magnesium-base cooking.

Certain design features, briefly described below, are necessary to obtain optimum efficiency of heat and chemical recovery from this process.

Cooking and Washing

The digesters must have an acid-resistant lining. Because of the soluble nature of the magnesium base, the porous brick lining commonly used for the calcium base is not suitable. A lining of dense acid-proof brick, alloy steel, or alloy-steel cladding is necessary.

To reduce the quantity of water which must ultimately be evaporated from the red liquor before burning, it is essential that the concentration of the recovered liquor be at a reasonable maximum. This can be assured, first, by circulating the liquor through external heaters to eliminate dilution from heating by direct-steam injection, and, second, by reducing the ratio of the acid charge to the weight of oven-dry wood from 5.1 to 1 used in the calcium-base process to approximately 4 to 1 for magnesium pulping. The reduction in acid charge is possible because the higher solubility of the magnesium base means quicker penetration into, and reaction with, the wood chips and because higher-strength acids may be made with magnesium than with calcium. After a cook of about 7-hr duration and prior to dumping, SO_2 is recovered by first relieving the digester directly to the hot-acid accumulator at a pressure of about 35 psi and then through a heat exchanger to the acid-storage tanks at atmospheric pressure.

The contents of the digester are then dumped. Since the static head of the digester charge prevents the release of all the free SO_2, the cook is washed to large atmospheric dump tanks, where some 5 to 10 lb of sulfur (as SO_2) per ton of pulp may be released. The SO_2 gas released at this stage may be recovered by venting to the recovery-unit flue gas absorption system. The pulp or stock is then pumped to countercurrent vacuum washers, where the liquor is recovered from the stock at a concentration of 14 or 15% solids.

Evaporation of Red Liquor

Evaporation of the red liquor, preparatory to burning, may be accomplished in two successive steps. First, the liquor flows to a cyclone or cascade evaporator, where the concentration is raised slightly by cooling of the flue gases leaving the boiler unit. This evaporator is located in the flue gas stream between the multiclone separators, where MgO is recovered, and the gas-cooling towers. Second, the liquor is pumped to multiple-effect evaporators, where it is concentrated to 55 to 60% solids. External heat exchangers and forced circulation are recommended to provide high velocity and to minimize heating surface. Stainless-steel or stainless-steel-clad construction is required for both direct-contact and multiple-effect evaporator units. The first stage above, evaporation by flue gas, may be omitted under some heat balance conditions.

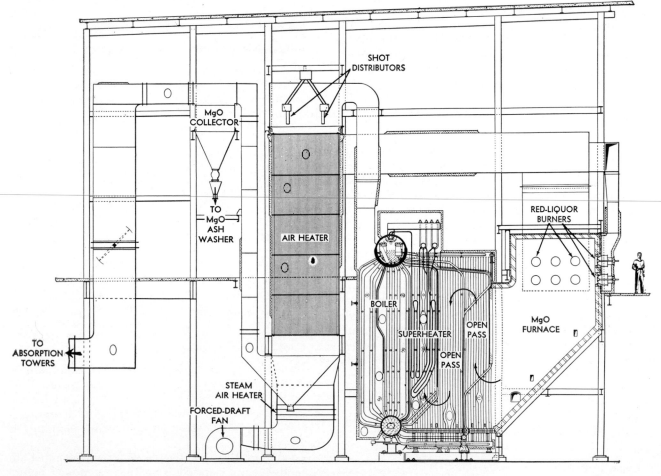

Fig. 15.   B&W MgO chemical- and heat-recovery unit

Burning the Red Liquor

Following evaporation, the concentrated or strong red liquor is ready for burning in the specially designed MgO recovery furnace (Fig. 15). The strong liquor, at 55 to 60% solids, is pumped to steam-atomizing Y-jet burners arranged for opposed firing. The liquor is burned in suspension, under self-sustaining stable combustion conditions, producing a dry MgO ash of high purity and reactivity.

Design Features of the Boiler Unit

The pertinent design features of the boiler unit (Fig. 15) for the peculiar requirements in burning red liquor are:

1. A combustion chamber with large areas of high-alumina refractory.

2. Opposed firing to give highly turbulent furnace conditions.

3. Internal-mix steam-atomizing stationary burners.

4. Open passes (radiant heat absorption) to cool the furnace gases rapidly through the temperature range at which the conversion of SO_2 to SO_3 is high and also to cool them to a temperature below which any sodium and potassium impurities in the ash are in a sticky or tacky state.

5. Wide spacing of boiler and superheater tubes to facilitate cleaning with automatic retractable soot blowers.

6. Large gas air heater with a small "corrosion section" to isolate possible corrosion for easy maintenance.

7. Preheated air at a temperature of approximately 700 F to assist combustion.

Magnesium Oxide Ash

Following the heat recovery unit, it is necessary to separate the MgO ash from the flue gas. The ash is collected in cyclone-type mechanical separators located after the air heater. Following collection of the ash, to minimize evaporator-scaling and boiler-cleaning problems, it is desirable to eliminate the sodium and potassium salts which enter the system with the wood and, as impurities, with the makeup chemicals. These salts are readily soluble in water and may be washed from the MgO slurry on a vacuum type of filter. The collected MgO ash is transported to the filter by a combination screw conveyor and hydraulic flume.

Magnesium Oxide Slurry

The washed MgO cake, free of contaminating salts, is then mixed with the makeup MgO and pumped as a slurry to the MgO slurry tank. The flue gas, relatively free of ash, may pass to the contact evaporator and thence to cooling towers, or directly to cooling towers on its way to the absorption towers.

Magnesium oxide slurry, at a concentration of 10% solids, is pumped from the slurry tank to the absorption tower system, where it is added at the suctions of the recirculating pumps to insure complete mixing with the absorbing liquor. The towers are arranged in series for counterflow of liquor and gas, and vertical pumps are used to recirculate the liquor in each tower. Makeup water is added to the last absorption tower in the gas stream, and transfer of acid from one tower to the next in line is accomplished by gravity overflow.

Theoretically, burning the strong liquor should produce sufficient SO_2 to react with the recovered and added MgO to form magnesium bisulfite, with little or no monosulfite. Actually, magnesium monosulfite is formed and is present in the range of 0 to 0.3%. The formation of low-solubility monosulfite is minimized by controlling the acidity of the liquor in each of the absorption towers to a pH range of 4.0 to 5.0. This control is maintained by adding the MgO slurry to each tower through calibrated weirs in about the following proportions: 58% to the first tower, 25% to the second tower, and 17% to the third tower. Additional pH control in the first tower is obtained by regulating the makeup SO_2 introduced.

Performance of Recovery Unit

Performance of a magnesium bisulfite recovery unit of about 300-ton capacity is indicated in the tabulation below:

Performance, Per Ton of Air-Dry Pulp

Steam generated at 615 psi and 725 F, lb		9000
Energy produced in turbogenerators with this steam, kwhr		400
Steam for process use	(at 125 psi), lb	4000
	(at 35 psi), lb	5000
Sulfur makeup, lb		87
Magnesium oxide makeup, lb		25

An analysis of the cost of chemicals per ton of air-dry pulp produced with various bases, equating the quantities of the base required on a molecular basis to 350 lb of limestone, is given in Table 3. This analysis indicates the range of chemical savings possible in addition to the value of the steam generated, when the base chemical and the SO_2 are recovered by burning the red liquor in a recovery unit for the magnesium bisulfite process, as described above.

Neutral Sulfite Semichemical Process

Semichemical Pulping

"Semichemical" covers pulping processes in which the wood chips are partially cooked and the balance of the pulping is carried out by mechanical means. The aim of the process is to produce pulp at yields approaching those for groundwood but still resembling chemical pulp in its properties. The process

TABLE 3

Cost of Base Chemical and Sulfur Per Ton of Air-Dry Pulp

	Base	Base, lb	$	Sulfur, lb	$	Total Makeup, $
Without Recovery	Calcium carbonate	350	0.74	270	4.38	5.12
	Magnesium oxide	140	2.80	270	4.38	7.18
	Anhydrous ammonia	119	3.57	270	4.38	7.95
	Sodium carbonate	370	3.70	270	4.38	8.08
With Recovery	Magnesium oxide	25	0.50	87	1.41	1.91

was developed to produce high-yield low-cost pulp from wood species not normally suitable for pulping by the kraft or sulfite processes. Hard woods, such as oak, gum, alder, chestnut, aspen, and maple, have been used to produce semichemical pulp. The cooking liquor used may be alkaline or acid, as previously discussed for full chemical pulping, although the term "semichemical pulp" as commonly used generally denotes a pulp produced with a solution of sodium sulfite buffered to a near-neutral pH with sodium carbonate. Thus, the term "NSSC," denoting *neutral sulfite semi chemical* pulping.

Semichemical pulping has been under development for twenty-five years. Early attempts to develop a chemical recovery system utilizing NSSC waste liquor were not successful. As a result of the absence of chemical recovery, advancement of this pulping process has been retarded.

The small amount of heat that can be recovered from NSSC waste liquor per ton of pulp produced limits the economic return and thus has retarded development of recovery processes. As a result of

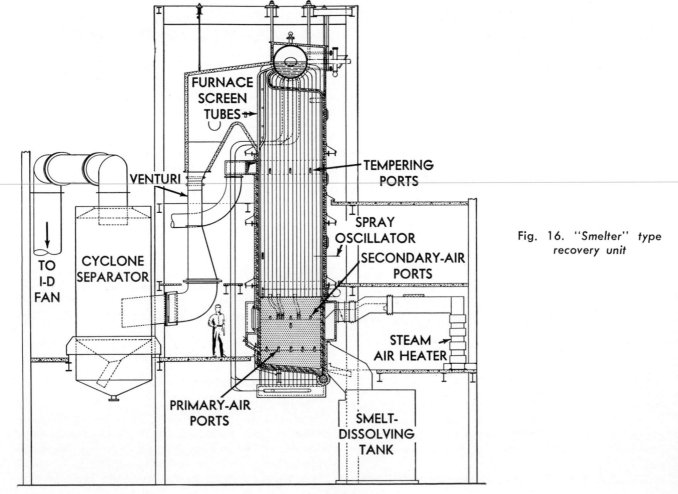

Fig. 16. "Smelter" type recovery unit

the high pulp yield, the organic and total solids in NSSC waste liquor are low—1200 to 2100 lb per pulp ton compared with about 3000 lb per pulp ton in soda and kraft processes. Also the heating value of the solids is relatively low—4300 to 5700 Btu per lb of dry solids—because of the high chemical-to-wood ratio used in the NSSC cook and because of the small amount of wood substances in the waste liquor. The heat in the waste-liquor solids from the manufacture of one ton of NSSC pulp is between 5,500,000 and 12,000,000 Btu, whereas the kraft process averages 19,500,000 Btu per pulp ton. Variations in the heat in the solids produced per ton of pulp depend upon the cooking procedures, type of wood used, yield, and grade of pulp produced. Thus, while NSSC waste liquor can be burned in a conventional kraft recovery unit, the size of unit required for a given pulp-production capacity is generally from one third to one half the size required for the same kraft pulp output.

The "smelter" type recovery unit, designed for economical burning of small quantities of black liquor, is shown in Fig. 16. This type of unit is unconventional in appearance, for it does not include the usual boiler section and other heat traps. The flue gas leaving the furnace passes directly to the venturi evaporator-scrubber. This unit sacrifices some steam flow in favor of lowering first cost, reducing operating labor, and eliminating the problem of cleaning heating surfaces.

Flue gases at between 1000 and 1250 F enter the venturi to evaporate liquor from an entering concentration of between 25 and 30% solids to a burning concentration of about 60% solids. The use of the smelter in the neutral sulfite recovery system is incidental, but it is well suited to this application because of the small amount of heat in the waste liquor. Such smelters may also be applied to small kraft installations.

Neutral Sulfite Recovery Process

The Mead Corporation has developed a process

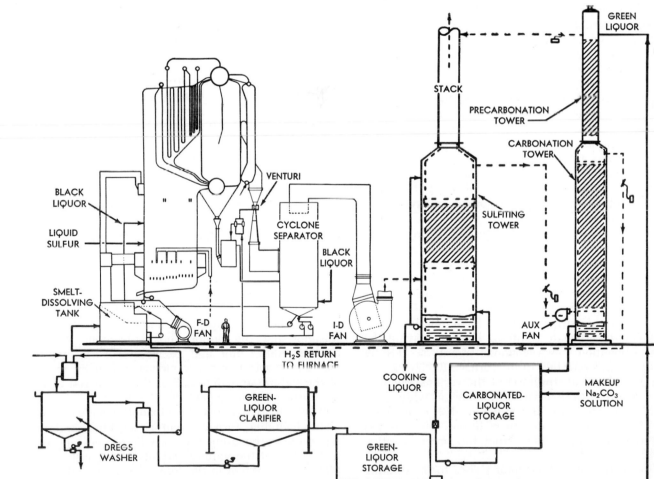

Fig. 17. Schematic diagram of the Mead Recovery System

The operating instruments, supplemented by records or recordings of their indications, needed by an operator vary over a wide range, depending upon the size and type of equipment. With some exceptions, obvious in specific instances, the information which he wants to obtain from the instruments and other sources may be listed in the approximate order of their importance, as follows:

1) Water level.
2) Visual observation of the fire.
3) Pressure of steam and of feedwater.
4) Temperatures of superheated steam leaving the major subdivisions of the superheater and of the reheater.
5) Drafts or pressures of gases and air entering and leaving the principal sections of the equipment traversed.
6) Boiler water conditions, including carry-over.
7) Operation or non-operation of feed pumps, fans, fuel burning and fuel preparation equipment.
8) Relationship of actual combustion air passing through the furnace to that actually needed, as indicated by flue gas analyses, oxygen determinations or other means.
9) Temperatures of water, gas, fuel and air entering and leaving the principal sections of the equipment traversed.
10) Feedwater flow.
11) Fuel flow.
12) Steam flow.
13) Knowledge of what operating functions are interlocked so that they cannot be performed in the improper sequence.
14) Knowledge of what important operating functions are being performed automatically.

Automatic control is virtually inseparable from instruments. The list of functions which should be controlled automatically varies—somewhat as the list of instruments varies—with the size of the plant, the proficiency of the operators, the type of equipment, and therefore with the savings which can be effected. In general, the use of automatic control can be justified in the regulation of all the operating functions which do not require an operator's judgment, and which cannot be performed at less total expense by an operator.

The functions which are to be controlled automatically cannot with safety be limited to some arbitrary number. The selection should cover groups of related operations. For instance, if the coal output from a pulverizer is controlled automatically but the total combustion air is not, the fire may be put out by abnormally high excess air, and be followed by an increase in fuel feed to the fireless furnace. In this example both functions, or neither of the functions, should be automatically controlled. Systems which permit the operator to disconnect one function normally under automatic control should incorporate safeguards to prevent the dangers inherent in temporary partial-hand, partial-automatic control.

The grouping of the instruments and the automatic control on the instrument and control panel, as well as the location of the panel in relation to the boiler, should be given careful consideration.

Grouping of instruments and controls for closely related functions is important not only in time saved for the operators but because a clear overall view of the situation, particularly in an emergency, may impel corrective action which otherwise might not be taken.

Location of the instrument and control panel should be determined from a mental dress rehearsal of the entire plant operation. Bearing in mind that the fullest measure of operator performance will depend on the fewest number of steps required in walking to the panel, its location should be selected after taking into account the anticipated number and qualifications of operators, their preferred location at the time each operation is performed, and the location of the equipment which will be in operation. Some panels are designed for one or more related auxiliaries, some for one complete boiler unit, some for two or more boiler units, and others as master panels for entire generating stations.

In the operation of power plant equipment, gradualness in shifting operations is a primary requisite. If, for instance, an emergency arises, such as a lapse in good combustion, which produces too rich a mixture of combustible in the furnace with a profusion of smoke, it is much more dangerous to shut down and thereby permit the furnace atmosphere to be diluted through the explosive range than to "hold fast" and gradually increase the air for combustion to a normal safe excess. The handling of situations involving low water and other temperature stress conditions should follow the same principle of gradualness.

When a new boiler has been completed a certain procedure should be followed in placing the boiler in operation. The steps in this procedure are: (a) "drying-out" the refractory setting, (b) "boiling-out" with chemically treated water to remove any oil or other deposits accumulated in the pressure parts during fabrication and erection, (c) "initial operation" at moderate loads and (d) "placing on line" in normal high-duty operation. All of these steps may be taken separately but it is common practice to combine (a) and (b) and, recently in many cases (c) has been combined with (b). Acid cleaning, described elsewhere, is sometimes used as a supplement to, or as a substitute for, boiling-out.

Upon completion of major repairs or alterations of old units, some of the procedural steps noted are usually required. Those which should be taken as proper prerequisites in again placing the unit in service will depend upon the extent of the repairs or alterations and are easily recognized.

The following rules, covering the procedure outlined above, are offered for the general guidance of the operator and may be modified to comply with the requirements and preferences at different plants or to meet the demands of the future.

Drying-Out, Boiling-Out, Initial Operation
General

By consultation with the erector of a new boiler or the repair supervisor for an old boiler and by his own inspection, the operator must verify the completeness and fitness of the unit for operation. This will establish that the unit has been thoroughly cleaned internally by mechanical means and that it has been hydrostatically tested with all attendant adjustments as outlined under *Principles and Methods of Installation*, Chapter 25.

The steam drum manhole plates should be removed and the drum internals checked for tightness and inspected, to determine that the boiler is in satisfactory condition for boiling-out. No part or section should be closed until the man responsible for the inspection is certain that all passages to which the part permits access are free and clear of all foreign material except that which can be removed by boiling-out. All parts should be closed immediately after this approval is obtained. The gaskets used for this closure should be those intended for subsequent regular service.

Auxiliary apparatus pertaining to the firing or feeding of the boiler should be tried out as fully as possible, to make certain that it is in proper condition. This procedure should include all fans and dampers and the setting and trial of all interlocks. If an automatic combustion-control system is used, the various regulators should be set for remote hand control and checked to determine that all can function as intended. It is good practice to blow out the superheater and all steam piping when the boiler is first brought up to pressure, to make sure that no foreign material gets into prime movers or process equipment. The furnace and gas passages

Fig. 1. Boiler control room in a Midwestern central station

should be clean and free from all combustible matter.

Valves, Water Level Gages, and Steam Gage

After the boiler is closed, the blowoff valves, water column and water glass drains, and gage cocks should be examined for proper operating condition and closed; the vent valves, the water column shutoff valves, the gage glass shutoff valves, and the valves to the steam pressure gage should be opened; and the economizer and boiler should be filled. The water level showing in the glass should be checked by opening and closing the gage glass drain and noting the movement in the glass. The reasons for any tendency to sluggish movement should be thoroughly investigated, and the difficulty should be corrected.

Water

The unit should be filled through the feed connections to the normal working level with water of the same quality as that of the feedwater to be used for regular service.

To avoid damaging temperature strains and excessive localized heating or chilling of the drum, the difference in temperature of the water and the drum should be not more than 50F. In most cases in regular service the temperature of the boiler drum will be between 100F and 200F and a source of 150F feedwater should be provided. Feedwater of this temperature can be diluted with cold water before feeding when the drum is at a lower temperature than 100F such as may be the case in starting up a new boiler or on other infrequent occasions. If hot water is used to fill the economizer and boiler, extreme care must be taken to feed slowly and vent sufficiently so that no pressure is built up by the attendant flashing into steam.

Care should be taken to use only properly treated and deaerated water so that optimum conditions will be in force from the start in limiting the formation of scale, corrosion, and other difficulties caused by improperly conditioned water.

To avoid excessively high levels when the water swells on firing the unit, the water level should be adjusted (except for Type H boilers noted below) so that only 1 in. shows in the gage. For B&W Type H boilers the water level should be raised to the centerline of the gage glass, in order to keep the temperature of the top rows of steam and water circulators within safe limits during the starting-up period. When raising pressure on the boiler it is also important to establish a steam flow through these circulators by opening the drum vent and superheater drains. This procedure applies to starting-up from cold or bringing the unit up from bank.

To prevent water being carried over into the superheater and the steam line, with the likelihood of undue temperature strains in the superheater and damage to the steam driven equipment, extreme care must be taken to avoid an abnormally high water level. As a precautionary measure, the water level should never be allowed to rise to the top of the glass during the starting-up period, and the boiler should be blown down to one-half glass shortly before line pressure is reached.

Chemicals. Completely dissolve the chemicals to be used for boiling-out in water before placing in the unit. Pump the dissolved chemicals into the boiler through the chemical feed connection, or, as a second choice, through the boiler vent, without passing through a dry pipe, dry pan, or scrubber. For small units, lacking a pumping system for this purpose, the chemical solution may be poured through the upper drum manholes after bringing the water level up to about half-way between the bottom of the drum and the manhole.

With all the water in the unit at the concentration noted below a good cleaning job can be done with any one of the four following combinations of chemicals.

1) Trisodium phosphate ($Na_3PO_4 12H_2O$) 2500 ppm
   Caustic soda (NaOH) 2500 ppm
2) Trisodium phosphate ($Na_3PO_4 12H_2O$) 5000 ppm
   Caustic soda (NaOH) 500 ppm
3) Trisodium phosphate ($Na_3PO_4 12H_2O$) 1500 ppm
   Caustic soda (NaOH) 1500 ppm
   Soda ash (Na_2CO_3) 1500 ppm
4) Caustic soda (NaOH) 3000 ppm
   Soda ash (Na_2CO_3) 3000 ppm

In addition to the above combinations of chemicals some operators use sodium sulfate and sodium sulfite, respectively, as precautionary measures, to prevent caustic embrittlement and oxygen corrosion. However, since the unit is not sufficiently susceptible to attack, from either source, due to the relatively short duration of the boiling-out period, the additional treatment is hardly justified.

Drying-Out the Setting

The refractories in the setting of the unit must be dried out with a slow fire over a period of from about three days to one week depending upon the size of the setting, the thickness of the walls, and the conditions under which the refractories were installed. The fire should be sufficient to hold the water in the boiler at such a temperature that a light vapor is apparent at the open vent on the boiler drum. Water in the boiler should be carried at the normal level and the superheater drains should be wide open.

Block-covered and stud-tube floors of slag-tap furnaces are covered with carefully applied chrome ore of 3 in. or more in thickness. This in turn should be covered with not less than 3 in. of dry granulated slag or stoker ash free from tramp iron. The slag or stoker ash covering is provided chiefly as a protection for the chrome ore surface against traffic during erection and to retard surface drying of the chrome ore.

When boiling-out procedure is combined with the process of drying-out the refractory setting, the fires should be operated for two or three days at an extremely low rate to warm the setting gradually, and then increased to the minimum which will hold the pressure required for boiling-out. The rate of firing must be so regulated that the gas temperature entering the superheater does not exceed 900F.

For small low-pressure jobs it is often convenient to fire with wood thrown on the grates or furnace bottom. For higher-pressure and larger installations it is impracticable to fire with other than the combustion equipment and fuel to be used in regular service.

The fuel-burning equipment should be placed in service in accordance with instructions issued by the manufacturer for the type of system installed, and with rigid observance of all the recognized rules of safety applying to the fuel used. Of special importance, when burning gaseous, liquid, or pulverized fuels, is the necessity of purging the setting before lighting or relighting the first burner, and of using a torch for lighting the individual burners as they are placed in service.

Precautions. To summarize, the following important precautions should be taken before lighting the fire:

1. Remove all structural timber from the furnace and from the gas passages. A glowing ember may ignite explosive gases which can accumulate if the combustion equipment is not operated with care while firing at low rates during boiling-out.

2. Make connections so that all blowoff and drain valves can be used effectively, and without danger to the personnel.

3. See that all dampers are in good working order and so set on the shafts that their positions are correctly indicated.

4. Make sure that the gage glasses and other means of indicating the water level are in good working order.

5. Make sure that the fuel-burning equipment, temporary or otherwise, is in such shape that it can be operated in strict accordance with all recognized rules of safety applying to the particular fuel used.

6. Make sure that the unit is filled with water and chemicals in accordance with the foregoing instructions.

7. Before lighting any fires, completely purge the setting of all combustible gas by circulating air through the setting for at least 5 minutes at the rate of approximately one-fourth of the requirement for maximum capacity of the unit. For units with dampered superheat control, both the superheater and by-pass gas dampers should be wide open during the purging.

Firing

After the fires have been lighted, it is important that they be held continuously at the minimum rates suitable for drying-out and boiling-out, respectively. To avoid puffs or perhaps a serious explosion, it is especially important to maintain stable combustion conditions. Should the fire be accidentally or purposely extinguished, it is absolutely necessary to purge the setting for at least 5 minutes before relighting.

With oil firing at very low rates in furnaces designed for high capacities, vapor leaving the furnace may condense in the colder parts of the setting. To lessen the possibility of the occurrence of this condition, steam or air atomizers should be used, or temporary, relatively small, refractory furnaces should be built around the oil burners in the regular furnace, to aid in supporting ignition and in completing the combustion of the oil before the gases reach the tube surfaces.

When gas firing is used, it is important to make sure that the burners are operated at the gas pressures required to maintain stable ignition. Every precaution should be taken to insure the maintenance of the required gas pressure regulation or control to absolutely prevent even temporary lapses in stable ignition.

It is of critical importance to make sure that all instruments and control equipment are in good working order before the unit is in operation. Instrument accuracy should be checked as completely as possible. All circuits and signals—electrical, air, hydraulic or other types—should be verified. Each of the different pieces of equipment controlled from these circuits should be started up or tried out doubly to confirm that each of the controls is correctly installed.

There have been many instances of serious accidents traceable directly to the failure to delay initial operation until the necessary instruments and control equipment were in proper operating condition.

As a final warning—there is no substitute for a good fireman. Operation of the firing equipment should be entrusted only to experienced operators who are fully familiar with the type of system in use and who are keenly aware of the hazards involved in firing at the low rates required. All too often, the firing during drying-out and boiling-out is looked upon simply as a routine to be endured and completed with minimum inconvenience, and consequently the new equipment is frequently handled by inexperienced operators or men pressed into service from the construction force. If such a course is pursued, not only will the job of drying-out and boiling-out, so important to subsequent successful performance, suffer but the safety of personnel and equipment is seriously endangered.

Pressure and Duration of Boiling-Out

The firing rate should be gradually increased to raise the pressure in the unit slowly to the boiling-out pressure. The recommended pressure for boiling-out is 50 per cent of the normal operating pressure.

Duration of the boiling-out period will vary with the amount of cleaning required. However, experience indicates that a period of 48 hours at the recommended pressure and chemical concentration is usually sufficient to clean a unit. A clear appearance of the blowdown at the end of this time will serve as a guide for ending the process, but the subsequent internal inspection is the final step in determining how thoroughly the boiler has been cleaned, and whether it will be necessary to repeat the process.

Protection of Heat Transfer Components.

Economizers. For economizers with recirculating connections the valves are kept open during the boiling-out and while the pressure is being raised preparatory to initial operation. When such units are on the line and have taken water for approximately 5 minutes, these recirculating valves should be closed. Before feeding water, if there is a possibility of steam forming in the economizer inlet header while the pressure is being raised, the header vent should be kept open until it is certain that the accumulated steam has been blown out. Economizers of this type, designed for the high gas temperature zones, will automatically induce circulation of the boiler water. In economizers, without recirculating connections, suitable for low gas temperature zones, the only flow during boiling-out is from economizer blowdown and the water fed to make up for boiler blowdown. In this type, part of the chemical solution for boiling-out should be introduced into the feed line before the economizer to bring the concentration up to that recommended for the water in the boiler proper.

Superheaters. Before lighting the fire, all superheater drains should be opened wide. For units with dampered steam temperature control the superheater dampers should be closed, except for a slight opening to avoid gas pockets, while the dampers over the by-pass section should be wide-open.

Superheaters, during the boiling-out procedure, should not be flooded; in fact, the object is to keep them clear of water at all times during the various phases of the starting-up procedure in so far as drainability permits, so that the superheater tube metal will be cooled by some flow of steam through the tubes.

For non-drainable units, it may be necessary to open the superheater dampers to provide the heat required to boil any condensate out of the tubes. It may also be necessary to reduce the temperature and increase the overall firing time in order to boil out the water trapped in the tubes. Obviously, there will be no steam flow through a tube partially filled with water until the water has been cleared and those portions of the tube not in contact with the water will be subjected to excessive temperatures and attendant danger unless the entering gas temperature is held to safe limits to boil the water out of superheater elements.

Thermocouples installed in the outlet legs of the superheater tubes where they pass into the unheated vestibule will read at saturation temperature until the tubes are cleared, and there is a flow of steam through them. The temperature of these outlet legs rises sharply immediately after this flow is established to superheated steam temperature which, under normal rate of starting-up, will run 75F or more above saturation. Experience indicates that a thermocouple on each outside tube and on a tube near the center are sufficient for the usual installations to judge the clearing of water from the entire superheater. It may be necessary for large non-drainable superheaters with a relatively large number of loops in series to continue the starting-up firing rates after the boiler is up to line pressure and delivering steam.

Throughout the starting-up period including drying-out, boiling-out, and bringing the unit on the line, the firing should be regulated to keep the temperatures of the superheater tubes within safe limits for the tube metal, and to avoid high stresses due to abnormal temperature differences between one part and another. The tube metal temperatures are normally kept below the temperature usually reached at the maximum design capacity by bleeding steam through the superheater outlet header drains, by-passing gas around the superheater on units with dampered superheater control (for superheaters of the drainable type), and regulating the time of bringing the boiler up to line pressure.

A direct method of determining the time is to use thermocouples to measure the superheater tube temperatures and gradually increase the rate of firing, always keeping the temperature within safe limits. An approximate method is to regulate the firing to limit the temperature of the gas entering the superheater to 900F for steel tubes and 950F for

When the pre
vent, has practic
is a vacuum due
slowly fed to the
and continuing, s
the spill-over. T
erated. The drai
steam stop valve
water getting pas
cumulate on the
should be contin
least 10 psi ag:
watch should be
undue pressure a
leaking feedwate

Boiler connect
and frequent bo
and analyzed.
hydrate alkalinit
water in the dru
operating level,
bring the hydra
boiler should be
added chemicals
age should be c

Even with the
of corrosion mu
boiler should be

F eedwater and
ered general
The problems ii
chemical, but t
interrelated wit
plant operation
the operating a
sential.

Prior to 1900
a recognized 1
treatment was 1
operate for a f
chanical cleanin

As greater d
the formation o
sudden failures
and far too cos
that this early 1

Operation wit

Between 190
ing plants beca

---

case immediately fe
subject to serious t
metal is quenched
feedwater in direct
or thin, may be e
number of such te
veloping incipient
predict accurately
violence may be wi
the metal will occu
unit, safety of the d
sideration of the or
to the drum resultii
capacity and low he
remaining in the fu
compared with the
by feeding water in

The above will ap
fuel, oil, or gas, as
which permits stop
stantly.

In units served b
fuel-burning equipm
not be stopped alm
the furnace tubes a
if the flow of feedw
time after a tube ru

Accordingly, in ca
magnitude to requi
boiler from service,
for the two distinct

1) For units fired by
   a) Shut off the fi
   b) Shut down fo
      fans.
   c) Shut off comp
      the boiler. It
      that this actio
      ble in order
      pressure with
      in temperature
   d) Shut off the su
   e) Adjust the flov
      minimum per
      from water or
      room. This wi
      even chilling o
   f) After the pres
      subsequent or
      low the proce
      shutdown. Th
      until the furna
      at which one
      furnace.
   g) After the unit

---

whether c
connection

Gage g
scratched.
will cause
age at the
cause a l
should be

When
dismantle
the mica
wear thro
but the m
to mainta
cated nea
at an ang
special lig
this type
as a brig
be suffici
at all tim
location (

The di
and vapo
strong c
water- ar
In this h
positione
the gage
the wate
vapor po
gage glas
glass app

Fig. 3. (

---

has dropp
drum-shel
taken, in e

For all v
tancously :
that fall o
$\wedge t$, the dr
within safe
to come cl
large boile
in much le
sible. Mar
up to 1000
tinued pra
experience
expansion
rates help

By assig
100 F for
used to ap
of $\triangle t_o$ for
tensive cal
exact valu
smaller dr
inches.

In cold
drum shell
steam is ge
mum perm
$\triangle t$ will rig
the start-uj
the drum
prevent spi
of a high-l
overflow c
can also b
since there
warm wate
the water i
drum, it sh
by firing tl
ditions. He
sufficient to
mately 150
differential
subsequent

During t
of the oper
of the drum
be extingui:

As previc
stresses fro
always goo
temperature
50 F above

Accelerate
cool down

---

the alloy tubes. When it is impossible to regulate
the firing to the minimum rates required, firing
should be in intermittent periods of 10- to 15-minute
duration at 5- to 10-minute intervals. To avoid
momentarily exceeding the gas temperatures just
noted, it may be necessary to shorten the duration
of, and to lengthen the intervals between, firing
periods.

For both boiling-out and afterward, whenever the
unit is being brought up to pressure for equipment
operation, the vent on the steam drum should be
closed when the boiler pressure has risen to 25 psi.
At this time also, all superheater drains except those
in the outlet section of the outlet header should be
throttled sufficiently to reduce the amount of steam
waste, yet left open enough to keep the header
clear of condensate. However, periodic wide-open
blowing of all superheater drains is assurance against
stoppage of a continuously partially open valve.
The superheater outlet drains should normally be
left wide open until the boiler is on the line, although it may be necessary to throttle these drains
to maintain the desired rate of pressure rise without
exceeding the permissible firing range.

The time required to place a boiler in service depends upon its size and type. Some small low-pressure boilers with superheaters may be placed in service, with comfortable margins of safety, within 1 to
1½ hours. See *Protection of Drums*, below, for large
high-pressure units with superheaters.

To serve as a schedule for the operators in arranging a starting-up program, test measurements
should be carefully translated into terms of available operating indices, such as time as a function of

---

steam pressure, firing-equipment speeds, gas temperatures normally indicated, air pressures, drafts,
and valve openings and closures.

Reheaters. Since they are not connected with any
supply of steam from the boiler, reheaters, which
are in effect superheaters interposed between the
outlet of a high-pressure turbine and the inlet of a
low-pressure turbine, require special consideration
during boiling-out. In some cases a temporary connection is made from the boiler drum or the superheater outlet, so that some steam may be blown
through the reheater drains. If this is done, the reheater should be handled in the same way as the
superheater. In some of the latest installations,
however, the reheaters have been left isolated
during boiling-out and have been given no attention
except that the entering gas temperature has been
limited to 900 F.

Before lighting the fire, all reheater drains should
be opened wide, and care should be taken to see that
the reheater is drained as completely as its design
will permit. For units with dampered steam-temperature control, the reheater dampers should be
closed except for a slight opening to avoid gas
pockets, while the dampers over the by-pass section
should be wide open. If the reheater is nondrainable, the water or condensate that has accumulated in the tubes must be boiled out during the
firing period, and it may be necessary to open the
reheater dampers to provide the heat required for
this purpose. In boiling-out a nondrainable reheater, the procedure outlined above for nondrainable superheaters should be followed except that,

Fig. 2. *Savings in building costs are effected in this Southwestern outdoor installation*

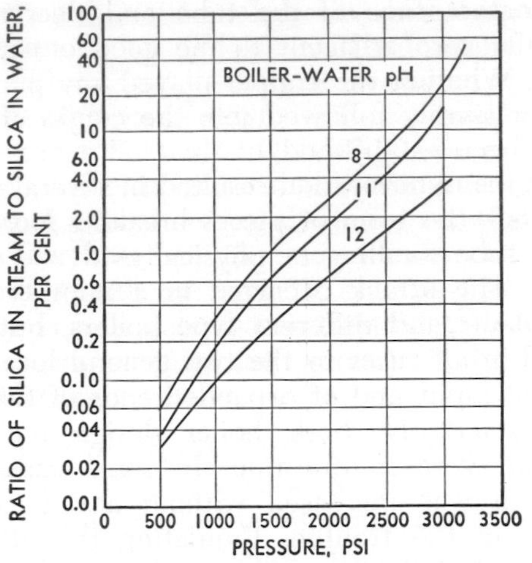

Fig. 10. *Effect of pressure and boiler-water pH on the solubility of silica in steam*

A means for silica reduction by internal treatment, which has been moderately successful in a few cases, is the precipitation of silica by magnesia within the boiler under very carefully controlled conditions. Magnesia, either present naturally or injected as an additive, precipitates the silica as flocculent magnesium silicate if the sodium phosphate residual is kept very low to prevent the magnesia from forming magnesium phosphate.

In some cases, using a practical method developed by water-treating consultants, it has been possible to maintain this delicate balance. The operator is able, day in and day out, to keep the excess sodium phosphate at 1 ppm, high enough to prevent the formation of calcium silicate scale and low enough to allow the silica to precipitate with magnesia as magnesium silicate, leaving a residual silica of 3 to 6 ppm in solution. It must be emphasized that the control of the phosphate residual is critical, since complete depletion of phosphate, unnoticed through analytical errors, can lead to the formation of hard calcium silicate scale and tube failures. In general this method of silica control is not applicable at pressures in excess of 1000 psi, in view of the low silica values which must be maintained in the boiler water.

For some low-pressure installations, where the deposit of silica in the turbine is not a problem, this process has been reversed by adding silica to the boiler water to precipitate magnesia as flocculent magnesium silicate. This produces more turbidity than magnesium phosphate or hydroxide, and it is possible to remove the precipitated particles with the continuous blowdown, thus preventing troublesome sludge accumulation in the boiler.

A recent development which promises to be an important contribution to the prevention of siliceous turbine deposits is the steam washer. The principle of the steam washer involves the intimate contact of the steam with condensate or feedwater of acceptable quality in a countercurrent arrangement.

Early steam washer arrangements suffered from limitations in either capacity or washing efficiency. Extensive research in the field and laboratory has produced a washer capable of reducing the silica at least 50 per cent. This means that the silica in the steam leaving the washer is less than one half of the silica in the steam to the washer. A description of the washer and of its operation is given in Chapter 9, page 12.

Feedwater Conditions—Summary

The broad and general trend in feedwater treatment has been to produce the purest water possible at a cost that can be justified by the conditions at the particular plant to be served, taking into account all of the factors involved. There has been a very active development in external-treatment plants not only in the improvement of the original types of water softeners but also in the application of newer methods of treatment.

The fundamental purpose of feedwater treatment is to remove from the water, outside the boiler, by one means or another and within the cost limitations noted, the maximum amount of foreign matter which is considered potentially detrimental to the pressure parts. Among the impurities to be removed are: scale and sludge-forming materials, soluble salts, oil, dissolved or releasable gases, and all other materials foreign to the water itself which might damage the boiler unit or carry over with the steam.

However, it is now generally the aim in feedwater treatment to make the water suitable for boiler use contingent upon supplementary treatment within the boiler.

Boiler-Water Conditions—Summary

The outstanding development in boiler-water treatment during the late twenties and early thirties, as noted previously, was the almost universal replacement of sodium carbonate with one or more of the various sodium phosphates as water-treating agents for the prevention of scale. With this important exception, the improvements in boiler-water conditioning have been chiefly in the refinement of control and in administration. The steps taken to prevent difficulties from the most common and most fundamental actions or objectionable impurities of the boiler water are summarized below:

Corrosion

Alkalinity. In the early periods of water treatment, alkalinities were considered in terms of grains per gallon. They are now generally thought of and measured in terms of pH values. In using the free-caustic treatment, the most common successful range of pH values is from 11 to 11.5. Those using the controlled phosphate treatment without free caustic maintain pH values of approximately 10.5 to 11.2. Some consultants advocate the same pH range as the preferred practice when using caustic soda.

Dissolved Oxygen. The maximum permissible dissolved oxygen in the water entering the boiler proper dropped from a value of several cc per liter before 1920, through the temporarily recognized figure of 0.2 cc per liter, down to the present final requirement of zero. Mechanical deaeration alone will sometimes produce a zero condition, but in many cases even where this is so, sodium sulfite is maintained, not only as a safeguard against lapses in operation but also as a means of detecting such lapses.

It has usually been impossible to maintain large excesses of sodium sulfite in boilers operating in the higher-pressure ranges. Decomposition of sodium sulfite at the higher pressures and concentrations leads to the liberation of sulfur dioxide and hydrogen sulfide in the steam. Accordingly, sodium sulfite concentrations in boiler water are limited to about 10 ppm at 1400 psi and 3 ppm at 1800 psi.

Hard Scale

For treatment within the boiler of the residual hard-scale-forming materials, such as calcium sulfate and calcium silicate, sodium phosphate has almost completely superseded sodium carbonate.

The phosphate residuals maintained in various plants cover quite a range. Probably good average values, expressed as PO_4, are 20 to 40 ppm at pressures up to 1500 psi and 5 to 20 ppm for pressures above this. Compared with sodium phosphate, it is known that potassium phosphate has superior solubility characteristics at higher temperatures.

The advantage which this could theoretically provide both in the boiler and in the turbine suggests the substitution of potassium salts for the corresponding sodium salts as the internal treatment chemicals, particularly for the higher pressures. The number of installations employing such treatment has been too few for the results to be conclusive.

Sludge

The limiting values of allowable sludge for central station work has undergone little change because, at the end of the earlier period of water treatment, surface condensers and treated evaporated makeup reduced sludge to an almost negligible quantity. With continuing improvement in condensers and evaporators, the problem of sludge in central station boilers has been practically eliminated. While this improvement was important in further increasing the purity of boiler water, no sudden or outstanding change occurred.

In the early thirties, for industrial plants the older allowable limit of sludge-forming materials permissible in boiler feedwaters shifted from 85 ppm to 34 ppm, and a few years later this lesser limit was reduced to a very few ppm. The improved methods of water treatment, the increasing objection to boiler cleaning, and the use of higher steam pressures for industrial work led to the conclusion that any sludge-forming materials are bad and should be kept to an absolute minimum by the best methods of external treatment available.

Even with the very few ppm of total sludge-forming materials entering high-pressure industrial boilers, in some instances it has been found necessary to condition the sludge with organic sludge-dispersal agents to minimize its adherence to boiler surfaces and to permit its removal through the continuous blowdown during operation. There are very successful installations of boilers for pressures up to 1400 psi using 100 per cent treated makeup for feed. Where 100 per cent makeup plants for high-pressure and increased heat-input duty are justified by economics, it is now possible to provide a satisfactorily treated water.

Silica

The amount of silica allowable in the boiler water received increasing attention primarily because of turbine deposits. Because the activity of silica is to some extent a function of other materials in the water, its limits are related to these materials. The important or controlling relationships have not been too clearly developed, but the low limits generally sought in central station work are now less than 5 ppm, and in some of the highest-pressure jobs less than 1 ppm.

Total Solids

The quantity of total solids in a boiler water has always had its primary limit in priming or carry-over. For every combination of water and boiler design, there is some concentration at which the carry-over rises rapidly. It is compulsory to stay below this critical limit. In addition, good practice calls for keeping the total solids just as low as economically possible because, even though the value is below the so-called priming limit, the carry-over ordinarily is some function of the total solids in the water.

The ABAI has established certain arbitrary values for the quantity of total solids in boiler water, which are intended to give the operator all the latitude needed and at the same time set a limit to the boiler manufacturer's responsibility. The ABAI limits range from 3500 ppm for pressures below 300 psi to 1000 ppm for pressures above 1000 psi.

Control of Treatment

The most important factor in water treatment is the rigid and constant control of the chemical limits established as necessary and desirable. The finest system of water treatment becomes dangerously ineffective if the established limits are not maintained vigilantly and consistently. Unsuspected lapses have caused great difficulty as well as great confusion in establishing the causes of the difficulty. The best system is that which reduces these lapses to a minimum or one which is laid out intentionally to make it possible to detect, even by intermittent records, what has taken place between them.

Continuous records for dissolved oxygen are of particular importance in systems not using deaerators under positive pressure, where it is possible for air to enter the feedwater circuit through a leak, when the heater-steam bleed points shift from positive to negative pressure.

The continuous blowdown has been almost universally adopted as indispensable to precise control.

Some companies have operated boilers without any water treatment whatever. One organization associated with a number of inland plants has been able to operate at pressures up to 900 psi without using any water treatment. Where operation without water treatment has been a success, a perfectly tight feedwater system has been maintained to exclude pratically all foreign materials and any access of dissolved oxygen to the feed and boiler water. Experience has shown, however, that even a very small lapse in keeping the system tight against dissolved oxygen will cause far greater damage than would be expected with a highly alkaline water. Notwithstanding the potential and critical danger from leakage into such a system, the effort to produce and maintain perfect purity is a bold step in the constant endeavor throughout boiler history to obtain better quality water for making steam.

The treatment of water for steam boilers has been made a major endeavor by reliable manufacturers of water-treating equipment and by competent water-treating consultants. They are better prepared than the boiler manufacturers to assist the operating companies in the handling of water-treatment projects and water-treating difficulties. The Babcock & Wilcox Company does not seek opportunities to enter this field, but it does intend to continue with whatever analyses and research work it deems necessary to enable its engineers to bring about improvements in the design, manufacture, and operation of its products.

Some Operating Suggestions

The purpose of feedwater and boiler-water treatment is to keep the internal surfaces of the boiler clean—not to keep out of trouble with a dirty boiler. Treating feedwater will not correct circulation deficiencies which cause tube failures.

Oxygen-free feedwater is of utmost importance. Feedwater to the boiler should be deaerated to contain less than 0.005 cc per liter, which is a usual guarantee of deaerator manufacturers. Actual deaerator performance is frequently even better—0.002 cc or 0.003 cc per liter is not unusual.

Chemicals should enter the boiler drum to mix with the high-pH boiler water, and the entering feedwater should mix with the chemical-replenished boiler water. Continuous blowdowns should be located to blow down boiler water which has passed through the boiler circuits and therefore is high in impurities.

Evaporator carry-over is responsible for many feedwater problems, and the importance of pretreatment ahead of the evaporator is now generally recognized. Makeup from the evaportaor should be checked by conductivity equipment. This is just as important as determining any condenser leakage.

Silica should be kept low in high-pressure boilers to prevent (a) silica scale deposits in boiler tubes and (b) carry-over of volatilized silica in the steam to the turbine, where it is deposited as silica scale on the turbine blades. Volatilization of silica increases with temperature, particularly above 500 F, and the danger of silica passing over to the turbine increases as the boiler pressure increases. The ratio of silica in the steam to silica in the boiler water increases with increase in saturation temperature or boiler pressure and decreases as the pH of the boiler water increases (see Fig. 10).

The silica should be kept below 5 ppm for 900 to 1400 psi boilers, not over 3 ppm for pressures between 1400 and 2000 psi, and not over 1 ppm for pressures above 2000 psi.

While high-pressure boilers are being operated with as much as 100 per cent makeup and concentrations in the order of 1500 ppm, most high-pressure boilers operate with only 1 or 2 per cent makeup and concentrations considerably below 500 ppm, where silica content is controlled by per cent of blowdown.

In addition to its effect in reducing the ratio of silica in the steam to silica in the boiler water, a high pH, in the order of 11, will reduce the corrosive effect when small amounts of oxygen are present in the water. The pH value of the feedwater should preferably be maintained at between 8.5 and 9.0.

To protect against corrosion from oxygen which may not have been completely removed, sulfite should be fed to all boilers up to 1800 psi. As boiler pressure increases, the danger of sulfite breakdown increases, and for this reason it is pointless to attempt to maintain a sulfite concentration higher than 10 ppm for 1400 psi boilers or 3 ppm for 1800 psi.

Ammonia and volatile amines are being used to increase the pH of the condensate or feedwater, thereby reducing iron pickup in the preboiler system without increasing its total solids. The few parts per million of ammonia required for this alkalinity control is in contrast to some earlier experiences where relatively heavy concentrations of ammonia (in the order of 100 ppm, originating from sewage or vegetable matter) picked up copper from heaters and other components of the system.

Demineralization of feedwater by the use of cation and anion exchangers, which, if carried to the extreme, can produce water with less than 1 ppm of solids, is now widely recognized as an efficient method of treatment. This method of getting pure makeup and pure feedwater is being used in many instances in place of evaporators.

Lignins are sometimes used in boilers where a high per cent of makeup is required. They aid in keeping the sludge in suspension, so that it may be removed more readily through the continuous blowdown.

Under normal conditions adequate cleaning of a new boiler is possible by a thorough boiling-out. However, some users believe that acid cleaning of a new boiler, followed by a good boiling-out, will give a more uniform oxide protective coating on the tubes. In service, to keep the internal surfaces clean, acid cleaning is recommended. After acid cleaning, it is always necessary to boil-out the boiler, preferably at half the operating pressure. Some operating boilers require frequent acid cleaning, others every 3 or 4 years, the period depending upon the amount of deposits which collect on the tube surfaces. To make the acid cleaning effective where there is oil or organic matter in the deposits, it is necessary to preboil-out and to follow with another boiling-out after the acid cleaning. Iron oxide barnacles from internal corrosion have been successfully removed by a preboil-out, using 25 ppm of sodium sulfite followed by the usual acid cleaning and final boiling-out (see section on *Chemical Cleaning*).

A brief outline of recommendations for the treatment of feedwater and boiler water for high-pressure boilers from 900 to 2500 psi follows:

1. All water going to the boiler should be free of dissolved oxygen.
2. For boilers of 900 to 1800 psi, sulfite should be fed in gradually reduced amounts, according to pressure, from 10 ppm for 900 psi to 3 ppm for 1800 psi.
3. The pH of the feedwater going to the boiler should be maintained at between 8.5 and 9.
4. The pH of the boiler water should be kept between 10.8 and 11.5.
5. Phosphates in the boiler water should be maintained from 15 to 20 ppm for 900 psi with gradual reduction for intervening pressures to 5 to 10 ppm for 2500 psi.
6. Silica in the boiler water should be not over 5 ppm at 900 psi with gradual reduction to not over 1 ppm at 2500 psi.
7. There should be supervisory chemical control of feedwater and boiler water during the day shift, 7 days a week, and supplementary control by operators each night shift.
8. A constant watch should be maintained for condenser leakage and evaporator carry-over by the use of conductivity instruments.

The Present and the Future

Throughout the history of water treatment for steam boilers, alkalinity is the golden thread in the pattern of all successful results. Different type waters, different boiler operating conditions, and different methods of treatment have all permitted some latitude in alkalinity limits, but the existence of alkali in controlled quantities has always been necessary, even when it has been present naturally and unobtrusively with unwanted impurities of waters not artificially treated.

Because of the importance of alkalinity, it has been common practice to provide excess or reserve quantities. In the trend toward perfect purity of boiler water, this excess or reserve is now under scrutiny with the intent of reassessing the amount of excess necessary. The "coordinated phosphate control" system of treatment has been successful in eliminating all excess alkalinity caused by what is termed "free caustic." A rigid control is of course essential. Whether the goal of maximum purity will be served by this system or by the more common systems will be determined by the total chemical used in one as compared with the other, when both are given equal attention in development and control.

The advocates of no-treatment-at-all appear to have made the greatest advance in the direction of purity as well as of low alkalinity. In some of these instances, 10 ppm of total solids have been maintained in the boiler water with pH values of less than 10. However, the value of reserve alkalinity is clearly demonstrated when, in using this system, serious corrosion occurs because of a small inward leak of an active impurity such as dissolved oxygen.

With purity as the goal in water treatment, it would be well, in the light of past experience, to maintain a wholesome respect for excess alkalinity and to reduce it only after reliable assurance that this decrease cannot lead to a difficulty far greater than the saving realized by the increase in purity.

Much attention is now devoted to the solubility at higher temperatures of the various materials found in boiler waters. Reliable data are meager, and the results of the search for accurate information about the solubility of materials alone, as well as in relation to each other, should be of great value. It would be well, in studying these solubilities at higher pressures as well as temperatures, to make certain that the laboratory boilers do not have the circulation defects and the poorly proportioned compartments that have in some instances produced unreliable data because of the critically different concentration in the zone of sampling and in the zone of generation.

Progress toward greater purity will always be accompanied by the discovery of unexpected or previously dormant characteristics of the materials which remain and which perhaps establish an entirely new relationship. Water-treating chemistry research is now approaching the gentler sloping part of the curve representing improvements corresponding to the effort applied. Much effort is necessary to produce small gains. Any claim of a startling improvement which is not the result of a corresponding effort in research and experiment should be received with skepticism. With the purer water, the safeguards against attack will have to be observed with even more vigilance. The use of these safeguards will probably offset part of the gains in purity, but it will be wise always to consider that the ultimate goal is too far away to be reached by any simple improvement.

Steam purity is very close to perfection. The small fraction of 1 ppm of foreign material which remains is responsible for a disproportionate amount of troublesome turbine deposit. This residual impurity is being attacked in two ways. One is to remove it, while the other is to counteract it by additions of other material to the boiler water or to the steam. Since the demand for greater purity is not likely to be less exacting in the future than in the past and also since absolute perfection has not been achieved dependably without chemical help in related fields, such as in the performance of the deaerator, it seems likely that the anticipated improvement in steam purity will be accomplished with the help of some chemical means. Furthermore, the increased purity of the condensate formed from the purer steam can be expected to cause more active dissolution of the condensate return system, unless some chemical escort is provided.

Once-Through Boilers

The gain in cycle efficiency which can be realized by increasing the operating pressure eventually resulted in the utilization of pressures above the so-called critical pressure. Since the two phases, steam and water, do not coexist above the critical pressure, natural circulation cannot be employed, and the boiler design must be of the forced-flow type. Also, since there are no phases to separate, a drum and steam-separating equipment are unnecessary. Since there is no recirculation of a more highly concentrated liquid within the boiler, there is no boiler water as we conventionally regard it, and instead, the feedwater and boiler water are identical.

The once-through principle has also been applied below the critical pressure, and the water requirements for both cases are substantially the same.

Suitability of the feedwater for a once-through boiler requires a more specific definition of the limits of the individual constituents than is required for a natural-circulation boiler. In order to prevent reduction of availability resulting from improper water conditions, the feedwater must be continuously maintained at the highest purity obtainable with the best practices in modern low-makeup central stations. To accomplish this, contamination of the feedwater from all sources must be avoided, and any chemicals added for treatment of the feedwater should be completely volatile in the steam. Makeup must be of the highest purity attainable with well-designed and properly operated modern feedwater-purification equipment.

To avoid contamination of the feedwater from sources exterior to the cycle, condenser leakage must be guarded against by proper condenser design and by provision for sensitive detection of leakage. Contamination of miscellaneous returns must also be avoided.

Contamination from sources within the cycle by the products of corrosion of the materials in the cycle must also be minimized. This can be accomplished by maintaining oxygen and carbon dioxide at very low values and by maintaining the feedwater pH within limits which will provide satisfactory protection to the materials in the cycle. This level of pH usually lies within the range of 8.5 to 9.5 and can be obtained by the addition of an alkaline volatile material such as ammonia or morpholine.

A modern deaerator will reduce dissolved oxygen in feedwater to less than 0.005 cc per liter (0.007 ppm). To achieve even lower values and to provide against upsets in deaerator operation, supplementary chemical deaeration employing hydrazine can be used. Hydrazine, like ammonia and morpholine, is a completely volatile material and does not contribute to the dissolved solids content of the feedwater.

Since the quantities of certain constituents, such as iron and copper, in the feedwater may vary from point to point in the feedwater cycle, the locations at which the desired limits apply must be specific and consistent. The limits which follow apply to the feedwater entering the boiler and hold for all once-through boilers regardless of pressure.

Recommended Limits
Feedwater Entering Boiler

Total dissolved solids	— 0.10 ppm max
Suspended solids	— zero
Hardness	— zero
Free caustic	— zero
Dissolved oxygen	— zero
Carbon dioxide	— minimum, preferably zero
Total silica (as SiO_2)	— 0.01 ppm max
Total iron (as Fe)	— 0.01 ppm max
Total copper (as Cu)	— 0.005 ppm max

pH value — Adjust to obtain 0.01 ppm iron maximum. This will normally require a pH value within the range of 8.5 to 9.5, measured at 77 F.

Chemical Cleaning of Internal Heating Surfaces

CHEMICAL cleaning of internal heating surfaces was first proposed where it was difficult or impossible to clean by other methods. Because of early experience with improper technique and limited knowledge of cleaning solvents, this method was at first subject to certain reservations. With progressive experience and development of materials and procedures, much of the earlier uncertainty concerning chemical cleaning has been resolved, and the process is now widely used with complete confidence as the quickest, cheapest, and most efficient method of cleaning these surfaces in boilers of all sizes. It is, however, extremely important to use a procedure of known reliability under careful control.

The procedure outlined below is recommended with the understanding that the user must depend upon competent chemical supervision of his own choice, supplemented by consultants on boiler-water and scale problems. There are specialist companies equipped to provide complete chemical-cleaning service.

Advantages of Chemical Cleaning

Compared with the removal of scale and deposits from internal heating surfaces by mechanical means, the more important advantages of chemical cleaning may be listed as follows:

1. Outage time is reduced. Usually a boiler can be cleaned in less than 36 hours. More than 18 hours are seldom required.
2. Extensive dismantling of the unit is not required. The solvents can be introduced and discharged through existing connections. The only dismantling necessary is the removal of drum manhole covers and a few header handhole closures for inspection.
3. The total cost is less.
4. Inaccessible areas, such as small tubes, short-radius tube bends, and irregular surfaces, are readily cleaned, since the cleaning medium has access to all locations reached by steam or water. The result is a better cleaning job. The more thorough removal of scale will reduce the rate of subsequent formation of deposits.
5. New equipment can be designed with complete flexibility and simplicity for best economy, efficiency, and over-all cost, since no compromise is required to provide accessibility for cleaning.

General Procedures and Methods

In general, four steps are required in a complete chemical-cleaning process for a boiler:

First. The heating surfaces are washed with an acid solvent containing a proper inhibitor to completely dissolve or to partially dissolve and disintegrate the deposits.

Second. Clean water is used to flush out loose deposits, solvent adhering to the surface, and soluble iron salts. Any corrosive or explosive gases that may have formed in the unit are displaced. The unit is flushed to a positive overflow from the vents.

Third. The unit is boiled-out with soda ash solution to eliminate completely or to neutralize the effect of any acid remaining and to release hydrogen from the metal.

Fourth. The unit is flushed with clean water as a final rinse to remove any remaining loose deposits.

The two generally accepted methods in chemical cleaning are: (a) continuous circulation of the solvent through the parts to be cleaned, and (b) filling the unit with the solvent and allowing it to soak for a prescribed length of time.

Circulation. In the circulation method, after filling the unit the solvent is recirculated until cleaning is completed. Samples of the return solvent are tested periodically during the cleaning. Cleaning is considered complete when the acid strength of the returned solvent reaches equilibrium, indicating that no further reaction with the deposits is taking place. Compared with soaking, since a solvent of lower strength may be used and the solvent is drained from the unit as soon as the reaction is complete, the possibility of damage to the surface cleaned is less in using the circulation method. Also, the cost of chemicals will be somewhat less because of the control testing of solvent strength.

The circulation method is particularly suitable for cleaning forced-flow boilers, superheaters, and economizers with positive liquid flow paths to insure circulation of the solvent through all parts of the unit. A complete cleaning job cannot be anticipated by this method unless the solvent reaches and passes through every circuit of the unit.

Cleaning by the circulation method is aided mechanically by the constant change of solvent which flows over the deposits on the surface. This feature is of particular advantage when foaming may occur, as with deposits of a calcareous nature. The continuously circulating solvent also carries disintegrated undissolved materials through the unit. This is especially helpful in preventing clogging of small tubes.

Soaking. In cleaning by the soaking method, after filling with the solvent the unit is allowed to soak for a length of time, based on deposit conditions, ranging from 4 to 8 hours. To insure complete removal of deposits, the acid strength of the solvent must be somewhat greater than required by the actual conditions, since, unlike the circulation method, control testing during the course of the cleaning is not conclusive, because samples of solvent drawn from convenient locations may not truly rep-

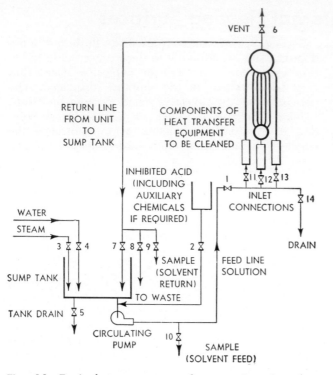

VENT

RETURN LINE
FROM UNIT
TO
SUMP TANK

COMPONENTS OF
HEAT TRANSFER
EQUIPMENT
TO BE CLEANED

INHIBITED ACID
(INCLUDING
AUXILIARY
CHEMICALS
IF REQUIRED)

WATER

STEAM

INLET
CONNECTIONS

DRAIN

SUMP TANK

SAMPLE
(SOLVENT
RETURN)

FEED LINE
SOLUTION

TANK DRAIN

TO WASTE

CIRCULATING
PUMP

SAMPLE
(SOLVENT FEED)

Fig. 11. Typical arrangement of connections in using the circulating method in chemical cleaning of boilers

resent conditions in all parts of the unit.

The soaking method is preferable for cleaning units where definite liquid distribution to all circuits by the circulating method is not possible without the use of many chemical inlet connections or where circulation through all circuits at an appreciable rate cannot be assured except by using a circulating pump of impractical size. These conditions may exist in large natural-circulation units with complex furnace-wall cooling systems.

Advantages of the soaking method compared with the circulating method are: simplicity of piping connections, assurance that all parts are reached by a solvent of adequate acid strength, and less chemical supervision during the cleaning operation.

Solvents, Deposits, Inhibitors

Solvents. For the removal of boiler deposits, various solvents have been suggested or tried, including many acids and a number of alkaline compounds.

In general, the use of alkaline compounds requires considerable time and temperature, and, while the attack on steel is nonexistent or negligible, the surface will not be as clean as with the acid solvents.

On the basis of cost, availability, suitable inhibitors, and rapid removal of deposits, extensive experience indicates that hydrochloric and sulfuric acids are the most practical cleaning agents. Of these two, hydrochloric acid costs less, is more effec-

tive in dissolving a greater number of the usual constituents of boiler deposits, and is more readily available and inhibited. In contrast to the reactions of sulfuric acid, which produce relatively insoluble sulfates, the reactions of hydrochloric acid form readily soluble chlorides.

Pressure parts of alloy steels, particularly those high in chromium, should not be cleaned with acid solvents without competent chemical advice on the type of acid and inhibitor and the conditions of application in each specific case.

For deposits of certain characteristics, the solvent may require additional reagents, such as intensifiers to react with certain constituents or wetting reagents to promote solvent penetration of the deposit. The need for these auxiliary chemicals should be decided by the chemist controlling the specific cleaning operation.

Deposits. Scale deposits formed on the internal heating surfaces of a boiler unit come from the water. In general, the constituents belong to one or more of the following groups: oxides of iron; carbonates, phosphates, and sulfates of calcium and magnesium; silica and silicates. The deposits may also contain various amounts of oil, which are sometimes appreciable in boilers when first placed in service.

For the most efficient and economical scale removal, the deposit should be analyzed, and that acid should be selected for the solvent that will most effectively react with a deposit of this type. The deposit is usually a mixture of several compounds, and the acid that will best dissolve the different major constituents is generally selected as the solvent, since the dissolution of the soluble components will free any insoluble compounds present, which can then be removed by flushing.

To avoid possible redeposition of other iron compounds, hydrochloric acid is usually preferred in removing iron oxide, even though sulfuric acid is theoretically the better solvent. Hydrochloric acid is more effective than sulfuric acid in dissolving calcium and magnesium salts. Neither has any effect on calcium sulfate, although scales containing up to 75 per cent of this compound have been successfully removed by dissolving the soluble constituents.

No universal recommendation can be made for silica or silicates, because some silicates react more readily with hydrochloric acid, some with sulfuric acid, and still others with a combination of strong alkalies and heat. A preboil for several hours with a 5 to 10 per cent soda ash solution, before acid cleaning, has been found effective in changing the silica scale to a more acid-soluble form. In some instances, to remove silica scale hydrofluoric acid has been included in the solvent. Except under expert chemical advice and supervision, this procedure is not recommended.

Small amounts of oil in the deposit are removed when the general deposit is dissolved and disintegrated. For higher percentages of oil contamination, it may be necessary to use a wetting agent in the solvent to promote penetration of the deposit. If the deposit is predominantly oil or grease, boiling-out with alkaline compounds must precede the acid cleaning. In new or repaired boilers with water-soluble lubricants used in tube expanding, boiling-out with alkaline compounds may be omitted.

Inhibitors. The following equations represent the reactions of acids (in this instance hydrochloric) with constituents of boiler deposits:

$$Fe_3O_4 + 8HCl = 2FeCl_3 + FeCl_2 + 4H_2O$$
$$CaCO_3 + 2HCl = CaCl_2 + H_2O + CO_2$$

At the same time, however, the acids will also react with and waste away the metal of the boiler, as represented by the equation:

$$Fe + 2HCl = FeCl_2 + H_2$$

unless means are provided to prevent or retard this reaction without, of course, affecting the attack on the deposits.

For this purpose arsenic compounds, barium salts, starch, quinolin, pyridine, or other products have been added to the acid solvent as inhibitors, to prevent or materially reduce this reaction with the metal. A number of commercial inhibitors are sold under trade names, and still others are made and used by companies furnishing complete acid-cleaning service including the prepared solvents. If the cleaning is done by the operator's own organization rather than by a company specializing in this work, the use of commercial inhibitors offered by reputable chemical concerns is recommended.

The effectiveness of acids in attacking boiler deposits as well as steel increases rapidly with rise in temperature. However, the inhibiting effect decreases as the temperature rises, and at a certain temperature, likely to vary for each inhibitor, the inhibitor may be decomposed into compounds devoid of inhibiting properties. It should also be noted that not all inhibitors are effective with all acids.

Important points in the use of inhibited acid solvent may be summarized as follows: Selection of the acid and auxiliary chemicals should depend upon the type of deposit to be removed. The inhibitor must be suitable for the acid selected. The temperature of the solvent must not exceed that at which the effectiveness of the inhibitor will be reduced or destroyed. The limiting temperatures for the use of the inhibitor should be obtained from the maker.

Determination of Solvent Conditions

Deposit Samples. The preferred type of deposit sample is a small section of tube with adhering deposit. In any case a sample of the deposit, down to the bare metal, representing the worst condition in the unit, should be obtained. Selection of the acid and auxiliary chemicals is then based on an analysis of the sample by chemical, X-ray diffraction, or other methods. After selection of the acid for the solvent and the inhibitor suitable for this acid, it is necessary, to insure complete removal of the deposits, to determine the acid strength of the solvent, the solvent temperature, and the length of time required for the cleaning process.

Acid Strength. Technically, the acid strength would be in proportion to the amount of deposit in the unit to be cleaned. However, since the determination of the amount of deposit cannot be much more than a rough approximation and the general average of conditions observed falls within a fairly narrow range, the acid strength of the solvent usually is set satisfactorily by experience. It is therefore recommended that the acid strength of the solvent, as fed to the unit, should be:

Three per cent when the unit is cleaned by the continuous circulation method, and

Five per cent when the unit is cleaned by the soaking method.

Commercial hydrochloric and sulfuric acids are sold in two grades in carboys of either 13 or 12.7 gal. The principal specifications for each grade and the dilution required for a 3 and a 5 per cent solution, respectively, are noted below:

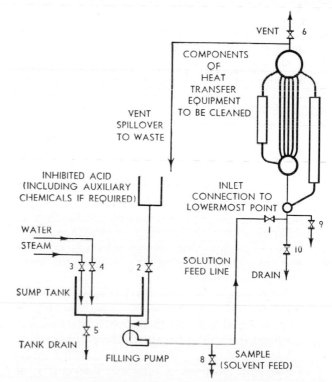

Fig. 12. Typical arrangement of connections in using the soaking method in chemical cleaning of boilers

Commercial Acid	Hydrochloric		Sulfuric	
Degrees Baumé	18	20	60	66
Specific gravity	1.142	1.160	1.706	1.835
Acid strength, %	28.0	31.5	78.0	93.0
Carboy contains, gal	13	13	13	13
Carboy contains, gal	12.7	12.7	12.7	12.7
For a 3% solution, gal H₂O per gal acid	9.5	11.0	42.7	55.1
For a 5% solution, gal H₂O per gal acid	5.3	6.2	24.9	32.3

Solvent Temperature. To aid in the acid attack on the deposits, the temperature of the solvent should be as high as possible without seriously reducing the effectiveness of the inhibitor. Laboratory tests show that most commercial inhibitors break down or lose their effectiveness entirely above 160 F. Experience indicates that as the temperature rises above 140 F the corrosion rate increases. It is therefore recommended that the temperature be limited to 140 F, unless a higher temperature can be tolerated in a particular unit and with an inhibitor safe at the higher temperature.

If a higher temperature is used, care should be taken to inspect the unit thoroughly after the first cleaning and *each subsequent* cleaning. In this way the actual corrosion rate can be determined, and it can be decided either to continue cleaning at this temperature, if the rate is not damaging, or to reduce the temperature for subsequent cleanings. In making up the solvent to the required strength, it should be heated by warm water to 140 F or to the temperature decided upon after all conditions are known. *The temperature of the solvent should not be raised by firing the unit.*

Cleaning Time. When cleaning by the circulation method, completion of the process is determined by analyzing samples of the returned solvent for acid strength and noting when the acidity reaches equilibrium.

In using the soaking method, the length of time the solvent is to be retained in the unit should be decided upon beforehand. While the type and quantity of the deposit and laboratory determination of the reaction rate of the solvent on samples of the deposit should apply in setting the length of time, a practical guide in determining the solvent retention time for the first few cleanings, using the acid strength noted above, is given as follows:

a) For moderate thickness of relatively soft sludges or for conditions that would otherwise require turbining at not less than yearly intervals, the solvent retention time should be a minimum of 4 hours.

b) For thin coatings ("eggshell thickness") of relatively hard scale formation, the solvent retention time should be 6 hours.

c) For deposits such as might result from a severe upset in the feedwater-conditioning system, the solvent retention time should be a maximum of 8 hours.

The periods noted are for the actual retention of the solvent in the unit. The surfaces are, of course, also wholly and partially subjected to the solvent during the time of filling and draining. In establishing permanent schedules, the periods recommended should be extended or shortened on the basis of the results achieved for specific conditions during the first few cleanings, as indicated by: visual inspection; test turbining of selected tubes, before and after cleaning, in areas typical of the worst deposit conditions; or examination of sample sections of tubing cut out of the unit.

Preparation for Cleaning

Heat Transfer Equipment. All parts not to be cleaned should be isolated from the rest of the unit. To do this, connections to these parts may be broken and blanked or plugged with wood or rubber. Where arrangements permit, parts of the unit can be isolated by completely filling with water.

Bronze or brass parts should be removed or replaced temporarily with steel. All valves should be steel or steel alloy. Gage and meter connections should be closed or removed from the unit.

All parts of the unit not otherwise protected by blanking off or by flooding with water should be covered by the inhibited solvent. Vents should be provided wherever vapors might be pocketed, since acid vapors from the cleaning solution do not retain the inhibitor.

Cleaning Equipment. The cleaning equipment should be connected as shown in Fig. 11 if the continuous circulation method is used or as shown in Fig. 12 if the soaking method is used. Continuous circulation requires sufficient inlet connections to insure distribution and to promote circulation through all circuits. It also requires a return line to the sump tank from the highest point of the unit or from the end of a continuous-tube heat transfer apparatus. The soaking method does not require a return line, but means should be provided, such as a rubber hose, to carry the spill-over from the vent to a safe location, and the pump discharge should be connected to the lowermost inlet to the unit. Depending upon the volume of the liquid to be handled, the pump discharge and the return or vent spill-over lines, as the case may be, are usually of 1½-in. to 3-in. pipe size.

The filling or circulating pump should not be fitted with any bronze or brass parts, and it should have the capacity to deliver, in not over 2 hours at 100 psi, a volume of liquid equal to the content of the vessel to be cleaned. For convenience in handling and mixing the solution, the sump tank should be large enough to hold about 5 per cent of the total volume of liquid required to fill completely the vessel to be cleaned. In practice, the capacity should be at least 300 gallons. An adequate supply of clean water and steam for heating the solvent to the desired temperature should be provided. Provision should be made for adding the inhibited acid to the suction side of the filling or circulating pump, as described later in the procedure to be followed for each method.

Cleaning Solutions. To determine the amount of solvent required, an estimate should be made of the content of the vessel to be cleaned, adding 2 per cent to allow for wastage and other contingencies. Commercial acid suitable for the deposit to be removed should be procured in the quantity required, when mixed with water, to make a solvent of the amount and acid strength desired.

An inhibitor suitable for the acid to be used should be procured. In obtaining the manufacturer's recommendation for the amount of inhibitor to be used, care should be taken to make certain that this recommendation is based on full knowledge of the acid strength of the solvent and what it is to be used for, to avoid any possibility of a higher corrosion rate than can be tolerated when cleaning a boiler. The amount of inhibitor specified for each carboy of acid should be completely dissolved or suspended in about 1 gal of acid removed from the carboy, taking care not to let the solution heat. After pouring the mixture of inhibitor and acid back into the carboy, the contents should be thoroughly mixed.

In preparation for the neutralizing process, commercial soda ash should be provided to make up a solution sufficient to fill the unit completely in the proportion of 10 lb of soda ash to 100 gal of water. This will produce a solution strength of about 1 per cent.

If the operator retains an organization specializing in acid cleaning of heat transfer equipment, the latter ordinarily determines and supplies the type of cleaning solvent and handling equipment best suited for the conditions.

Circulating Method Procedure

To reduce to a minimum the time required for cleaning, the preparations indicated in Fig. 11 and as noted above should be carried out as far as possible before the unit is taken off the line. The unit should be removed from service, allowed to cool in the normal manner to about 150 F, and then drained.

Referring to Fig. 11, clean water, 4, with a hydrogen ion value preferably no higher than pH 7, is admitted to the sump tank and heated with steam, 3, to 140 F or to the temperature decided upon. The circulating pump is started, the unit filled, and the water circulated through the system, using the return line, 7, to the sump tank until the return levels off at the desired temperature. Inhibited acid, 2, is then added to the circulating warm water at the pump suction until a sample of the solvent feed, 10, indicates that the solvent has reached an acid strength of 3 per cent, after which the process is carried on in accordance with the schedule indicated in Fig. 13.

The addition of inhibited acid to the solvent is continued during the first period until the acid strength of the returned solvent, sampled at 9, reaches a maximum, as at A in Fig. 13. This sample should also be tested for iron content. Should this test show a rapid rise or an increase of iron content to 1 per cent, which indicates an excessive attack on steel, the solvent should be immediately drained from the unit. While the iron content is not a positive check of the corrosion rate, since it is affected by the amount of iron oxide in the unit, it seems best to use it as a guide. As the volume of the liquid increases and the

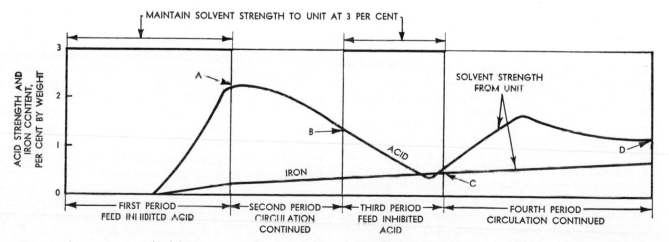

Fig. 13. Approximate schedule for continuous circulation of inhibited acid solvent in chemical cleaning of boilers

level in the sump tank rises because of the addition of acid, it may be necessary from time to time, during this and subsequent operations, to close the return line, 7, and open the waste line, 8. The vent, 6, should be opened now and then to release any acid vapors. Occasionally, for short periods during the circulation of the acid solution and the subsequent circulation of other solutions, the full flow should be circulated alternately through each of the circuits controlled by valves 11, 12, and 13 in Fig. 11. This is to make sure that the solution passes through all circuits.

When the sample tests of the acid strength of the returned solvent indicate the maximum concentration desired, as at A in Fig. 13, addition of the acid should be discontinued, but circulation of the solvent through the system should be continued. The acid strength and iron content of the returned solvent, 9, should be checked periodically at about 10-min intervals. It will be helpful, throughout the course of the solvent application, to plot the actual solvent conditions, as indicated in Fig. 13.

If the tests indicate a reduction in acid strength of the returned solvent exceeding ¾ of 1 per cent and point to a continued sharp decline, as at B in Fig. 13, and there is no evidence of a corresponding sharp increase in iron content or that it exceeds 1 per cent, the solvent should be fortified by adding inhibited acid to bring the acid strength of the solvent, 10, to 3 per cent. The addition of acid should be discontinued when the acid strength of the returned solvent starts to increase, as at C in Fig. 13. Circulation of the solvent through the system should be continued until the acid strength of the returned solvent levels off, as at D in Fig. 13, indicating that the reaction of the solvent with the boiler deposits has been completed.

No additional heat, in any way, should be applied during the acid-cleaning operation.

When the reaction is completed, as indicated by the acid strength of the returned solvent reaching equilibrium, the unit should be flushed by closing the return line, 7, and feeding warm clean water, 4, to the sump tank, with the line, 8, open to waste. Flushing heated water through the unit should be continued until the discharge shows no acid reaction. The presence of acid can be determined by adding a few drops of methyl red indicator to a small sample of the discharged water and to samples from all sampling points and vents on the unit. As long as any acid is present, the samples so treated will turn red. In addition to the test for acid reaction and before any attempt is made to neutralize with soda ash, a pinch of soda ash should be added to a small sample of the discharged flushing water. This will cause a greenish precipitate if soluble iron salts are still present, and the flushing

should be continued. The soda ash solution should not be introduced until repeated tests show that the greenish precipitate is no longer present.

The reason for making sure that soluble iron salts are completely flushed out of the unit is that any soda ash in excess of the requirement for the neutralization of free acid will react with the iron in solution to form gelatinous solids which tend to adhere to metal surfaces.

When the above conditions have been met, the return line, 7, to the sump tank should be opened and the line, 8, to waste should be closed. Circulation of water through the unit should be continued, with the temperature increased to as near 212 F as possible, and soda ash should be added as described below.

To neutralize completely any trace of acid, the surfaces should be washed with a solution in the proportion of 10 lb of soda ash to 100 gal of water by gradually adding enough soda ash to the water in the sump tank to fill the unit with a solution of this strength. The solution should be circulated through the unit until the return shows a strong alkaline reaction, as indicated by a sample turning red on the addition of a few drops of phenolphthalein. The same test should be made with samples from all sampling points and vents, to make sure that the soda ash solution has reached all areas previously reached by the acid.

After the circulation is discontinued and the soda ash solution is lowered to the normal operating level, the unit should be fired to raise the steam pressure and to hold it for 2 hours at 50 to 100 psi. This will aid in cleaning the surfaces and will also drive off hydrogen from the metal. The unit should be vented several times during this period to get rid of the hydrogen liberated. When the pressure has fallen to zero, the line, 8, to waste should be opened, the return line, 7, to the sump tank should be closed, and clean hot water should be flushed through the unit for about 1 hour.

Following completion of the foregoing procedure, the circulating system is shut down and the unit is drained. It is then inspected, carefully observing the precautions noted elsewhere, to determine the effectiveness of the cleaning and any indications of attack on the metal surface. In some cases the acid cleaning may bring down undissolved heavy iron deposits that may lodge in tubes with little slope. These tubes should be cleared, as these deposits may result in overheating and tube failure when the unit is fired. After inspection, on finding conditions satisfactory, the unit is prepared for service.

Soaking Method Procedure

To reduce to a minimum the time required for cleaning, the preparations for using the soaking method, as indicated in Fig. 12 and as previously noted, should be carried out as far as possible before the unit is taken off the line.

The unit should be removed from service, allowed to cool to about 150 F in the normal manner, and then drained. If the unit has not been in service and is cold, it should be filled and refilled with water of not more than 50 F above the boiler temperature for each successive filling until the boiler temperature is 150 F or slightly higher, or the boiler may be fired to this temperature and then drained.

Referring to Fig. 12, clean water, 4, with a hydrogen ion value preferably no higher than pH 7, is admitted to the sump tank. The filling pump is started, and the heating steam, 3, is adjusted to heat the water to the unit to 140 F or to the temperature decided upon for the specific conditions. Inhibited acid, 2, is added to the water entering the pump, the rate of acid feed being adjusted to bring the solution to an acid strength of 5 per cent at the sampling point, 8. The unit is then filled to a positive overflow in the vent spill-over to waste. During the filling operation, frequent checks should be made and conditions adjusted so that the solvent fed to the unit is held at an acid strength of 5 per cent and the maximum temperature desired is maintained (see Fig. 12).

When the unit is full of solvent under the conditions noted, the filling pump is stopped, the shutoff valve, 1, in the filling line is closed, and the vent, 6, is left open. The unit should then be allowed to soak for a period of time suitable for the conditions, as previously outlined. During this period, samples, taken at 10- to 30-min intervals from chemical feed, continuous blowdown, water column or other suitable connection to upper drum, and from any convenient connection to lower drum or headers, 9, should be tested for acid strength and iron content. If the iron content increases to 1 per cent, the unit should be immediately drained for the reason noted above in using the circulating method. The tests for acid strength will indicate the time required.

After having held the solvent in the unit for the prescribed length of time, the unit should be completely drained by opening the drain valve, 10. During this test it is advisable to draw samples of the discharged solvent at frequent intervals. Later analysis of these samples for acid strength and iron content, in conjunction with the original analysis of the deposits, serves as a basis for estimating the quantity of deposits removed and as a guide for maintaining or modifying the solvent conditions for future cleaning operations.

When the solvent has been drained from the unit, the drain line, 10, is closed, the filling-line valve, 1, is opened, the pump is started, and the unit is filled with warm clean water until it overflows through the vent spill-over to waste. Then the unit is drained, and the flushing operation is repeated until there is no acid reaction from the discharged water.

Before any attempt is made to neutralize with soda ash solution, care must be taken to make certain that all soluble iron salts have been flushed out of the unit. This condition should be determined by the tests described above for the circulating method. Flushing should be repeated until there are no indications of soluble iron salts in the discharge water.

When the flushing operation is completed, the surfaces should be neutralized by washing with a soda ash solution. Water is admitted to the sump tank, soda ash is added in the proportion previously noted, and the unit is completely filled with the solution. The water level is then lowered to normal, and the unit is fired and the pressure held at 50 to 100 psi for 2 hours, as outlined above for the circulating method. The neutralizing operation is followed with another flushing, using clean warm water. The unit should then be drained and inspected, following the procedure outlined above for the circulating method and observing the precautions noted below. After inspection, on finding conditions satisfactory, the unit is prepared for service.

Precautions and Measure of Results

Cleaning must not be considered a substitute for proper water treatment. The rigid control maintained in well-operated plants to achieve the best possible water treatment should not be relaxed because of the relative ease of cleaning by the chemical method. Chemical cleaning ordinarily is not necessary more often than once a year. Intervals between cleanings should be extended or reduced as conditions warrant. This is essential, since each time a unit is chemically cleaned the metal surfaces are depacified, or stripped of their protective oxide coating, and, in addition, a slight amount of parent metal is dissolved because none of the known inhibitors is completely effective.

In handling acids, the recognized precautions of using goggles, rubber gloves, and rubber aprons should be observed. Acid should be poured slowly into water; never pour water into acid.

Acid cleaning removes mill scale and products of oxidation. A thorough visual inspection should be made after cleaning to determine whether any parts need replacement.

Undrainable pressure parts, such as pendent-type superheater tube elements, require special attention to make certain that they are cleared of all acid solvent and loose deposits. Usually each individual element must be separately flushed through a tightly fitting hose connection, using a similar arrangement at the discharge end to avoid spilling the flushing discharge over into the other elements. A mixture of compressed air and water as the flushing medium has also been used effectively.

The solvent should be introduced through connections located at the lowest points of the equipment to be cleaned (see Figs. 11 and 12) and should rise gradually in all components of the unit without cascading or undue turbulence.

In riveted joints the solvent may enter seams, and damage can occur without being detected. Therefore, chemical cleaning of riveted drums is usually avoided. This applies particularly to drums calked on the outside.

The possibility of hydrogen gas being generated during the acid cleaning of internal heating surfaces should never be overlooked. The quantity of hydrogen released is a measure of the ineffectiveness of the inhibitor. A portion of the hydrogen will be absorbed by the metal, while the remainder will form part of the atmosphere in the vessel. The portion absorbed by the metal will be liberated gradually, the time required decreasing as the temperature of the metal increases. While the metal wastage indicated by its generation may be inconsequential, the hydrogen is a source of two potentially dangerous conditions—embrittlement of the steel and an explosive atmosphere in the vessel.

On the completion of acid cleaning, because of the possibility of hydrogen embrittlement, the steel should not be cold-worked (tubes rolled, flanges tightened, seams calked, etc.) in any manner for at least four or five days until the pressure boiling-out has been completed or the boiler has been brought up to steam pressure in the normal manner.

In opening a unit for inspection following an acid cleaning, the possibility of an explosion from the presence of free hydrogen in the atmosphere within the unit must be recognized. There have been explosions of hydrogen atmospheres in boilers after acid cleaning, and fatal injuries have resulted. At atmospheric pressure and ordinary temperatures, the values indicated for the inflammability of a mixture of hydrogen in air lie in the range from 6.2 per cent as the lower limit to 71.4 per cent as the upper limit.

The ignition temperature of hydrogen in air, at atmospheric pressure, is between 1076 F and 1094 F.

It is imperative, therefore, because of the possibility of an explosion, to observe the following precautions:

After an acid cleaning, no one should enter the unit or get in the way of any openings to the pressure parts unless the atmosphere within has been cleared of explosive gases. Until this has been done, open flames, flashlights, any other lighting equipment, or anything that might produce a spark of any kind must not be used within or near the openings of pressure parts.

The following steps may be taken to clear the atmosphere of explosive gases within the pressure parts:

Following an acid cleaning, apart from other reasons, the unit should be thoroughly flushed with warm water to a positive overflow from the topmost vent, to make certain that all the atmosphere within has been displaced. To warm the unit and thus accelerate the liberation of hydrogen absorbed in the metal, the temperature of the water should be held as nearly as possible at 212 F by light firing or other means.

After the unit has been opened, air eductors, placed at locations such as open drum manholes, should be used to circulate air through the unit for the removal of hydrogen being liberated from the metal. This procedure should be continued until analysis by a Burrell or other suitable instrument shows that the air within is free of explosive gases.

Measure of Results. Determination of the type and approximate amount of different kinds of scale and impurities removed from a unit at a cleaning will be possible if, at periodic intervals during the operation, the spent cleaning solvent and the solid matter ejected are properly sampled and analyzed and a record is kept of the total amount involved. This information will serve as a valuable guide for further boiler-water treatment and the determination of the required frequency of cleaning.

The Practical Significance of pH Values

THE term "pH" is used to express the degree of acidity or alkalinity of a solution. Acidity is commonly associated with a sour taste, while alkaline or basic materials impart a somewhat bitter taste.

When substances such as acids, bases, or salts are dissolved in water, ions are formed in the solution. These ions consist of electrically charged atoms or groups of atoms which result from the partial or complete dissociation of the solute molecules. The formation of the ions is termed "ionization," and the extent to which it occurs can be expressed by an "ionization constant," which has a fixed value for a given solution at a specified concentration and temperature.

Though many different ions may be formed in solution, the ones which establish whether the solution is acid or alkaline are the hydrogen (H^+) and the hydroxyl (OH^-) ions, respectively. When the hydrogen ions exceed the hydroxyl ions in number, the solution is acid. When they are equal, it is neutral. Alkalinity or basicity denotes that the hydroxyl ions exceed the hydrogen ions.

Acids and alkalies vary in the degree to which they form ions in solution. Those which almost completely ionize are called strong acids or bases. Hydrochloric acid and sodium hydroxide are examples of this type. Other acids and bases ionize to only a small degree and are, therefore, called weak acids or bases. Acetic acid and ammonium hydroxide are typical examples.

Even pure water dissociates to a minute degree into hydrogen and hydroxyl ions. It has been found that pure water at 25 C always contains 1.0×10^{-7} gram equivalents per liter of hydrogen ions and, since pure water is neutral, an equal concentration of hydroxyl ions. The product of these concentrations is a constant equal to 1.0×10^{-14} at 25 C. Thus, if the hydrogen ion concentration of a solution were 1.0×10^{-5} gram equivalents per liter, the hydroxyl ion concentration would be equal to 1.0×10^{-9} gram equivalents per liter. Since, for this case, the hydrogen ion concentration is greater than the hydroxyl ion concentration, the solution is acidic.

In order to express hydrogen ion concentrations more conveniently than by the use of decimals or by negative exponents, the term "pH" was adopted. Expressed mathematically, pH is equal to the negative logarithm to the base 10 of the hydrogen ion concentration. This is expressed as:

Hydrogen ion concentration $= 1 \times 10^{-x}$ where "x" equals the pH. A neutral solution, since it contains 1×10^{-7} gram equivalents of hydrogen ion per liter, has a pH value of 7. Since acid solutions contain more than 1×10^{-7} gram equivalents of hydrogen ion per liter, the pH values of these solutions are less than 7. Conversely, alkaline solutions have pH values greater than 7.

The commonly accepted range within which pH values are expressed covers the scale of 0 to 14. The extremes of this scale correspond to 10^{0} and 10^{-14} gram equivalents of hydrogen ion per liter. Acidities or alkalinities greater than those represented by pH values of 0 and 14, respectively, are more conveniently expressed as per cent concentrations.

The following table is helpful in understanding the relation between hydrogen ion concentration and pH.

Hydrogen Ion Concentration, gram equivalents per liter			pH
1.0		10^{0}	0
0.1		10^{-1}	1
0.01		10^{-2}	2
0.001	ACID	10^{-3}	3
0.0001		10^{-4}	4
0.00001		10^{-5}	5
0.000001		10^{-6}	6
0.0000001	NEUTRAL	10^{-7}	7
0.00000001		10^{-8}	8
0.000000001		10^{-9}	9
0.0000000001		10^{-10}	10
0.00000000001	ALKALINE	10^{-11}	11
0.000000000001		10^{-12}	12
0.0000000000001		10^{-13}	13
0.00000000000001		10^{-14}	14

Examples of acid solutions encountered in everyday life are lemon juice with a pH value of approximately 2.0 and carbonated soft drinks with a pH of about 6.5. On the other hand, a solution of 1 teaspoon of baking soda in a cup of water would be alkaline and have a pH value of nearly 10.

Since the pH value of a solution varies with temperature, it is the usual practice to measure and report all pH values at 25 C. Notwithstanding the scarcity of accurate values at elevated temperatures, such data as are available indicate that pH decreases with increase in temperature, the neutral point decreasing in like manner.

The pH value may be estimated conveniently by the use of specially prepared papers containing dyes which vary in color according to the pH. For feedwater and boiler-water pH determinations, where a higher degree of accuracy is required, it is usual practice to employ an instrument which measures the potential difference established between two suitable electrodes and indicates this reading on a scale graduated in pH units.

BIRTHPLACE OF THE CROLOYS

METALLURGY AND PROPERTIES OF MATERIALS

METALLURGY is concerned with the extraction of metals from ores, and with the combination, treatment and processing of metals into useful engineering materials. As an art, metallurgy has been of great importance to the progress of civilization for at least 6000 years, beginning with the production of the first metal. As a science, metallurgy is only about 50 years old. Important technological developments in modern industry have stimulated its rapid progress and application during the past 25 years. During that period, new theories were advanced, new practices were introduced and new and better alloys were developed. Without these advances in the theory and practice of metallurgy, the present high standards of efficiency, economy and reliability of operation of steam generating equipment would not have been possible.

Main Fields of Metallurgy

Metallurgy is divided into two main fields: the ferrous, which covers iron and iron-base alloys, and the non-ferrous, covering metals and alloys other than iron or iron-base. In accordance with the closeness of its association with other sciences in the study of metals, metallurgy also may be divided into the fields of (1) process or chemical metallurgy and (2) physical and mechanical metallurgy or metallography. Process metallurgy includes the numerous mining and refining processes such as reduction of ores, refining of metals, and the manufacture of metals and alloys. Metallography is devoted to the study of the constitution and structure of metals and alloys, including all the factors and processes which control the physical characteristics and mechanical properties.

The principal pressure parts of a power boiler—the drums, headers and tubes—are made from ferrous alloys. The same is true for most of the other parts of the boiler and its closely related auxiliaries, such as: coal pulverizers, fuel conveying systems, soot blowers, structural supports, economizers, air heaters, casings, ducts, stokers, baffles, hangers, bolting, steam piping, flanges, fittings and valves. Non-ferrous metals are used only to a minor extent in boiler installations; in auxiliary equipment such as water heaters, deaerators and attemperators; in the condensing system beyond the turbines, and in valves and instrumentation. Consequently the following discussion is confined to ferrous metals—their production, fabrication, thermal treatment and application in steam boiler equipment.

It is the purpose of this chapter to present the fundamental metallurgical concepts and practices, and to outline the metallurgical requirements for the selection of materials for boiler construction.

Ores of Iron

Iron was first known in ancient civilization, probably 5000 years ago. Nevertheless, its great usefulness was not fully realized until the characteristics of the metal itself, and its effects when combined with alloying elements were established by the application of the science of metallurgy.

Although iron is one of the most common of metals, metallic iron is very rarely found in nature. It usually occurs in the form of mineral oxides (Fe_2O_3 or Fe_3O_4) and as such it comprises about 6 per cent of the earth's crust. The principal ores of iron in the order of abundance and importance in this country are: hematite (Fe_2O_3), magnetite (Fe_3O_4), limonite ($2Fe_2O_3.3H_2O$) and siderite ($FeCO_3$). Ninety per cent of all the iron ore consumed in this country at the present time is the red oxide of iron—hematite. It is found chiefly in the Lake Superior region, in the states of Minnesota, Michigan and Wisconsin. In a part of this region the ore is economically extracted by open-pit mining methods. In locations where the ore is too far below the surface, shafts are sunk and under-ground mining methods are employed. Some ore is imported, and the amount will increase as the domestic supply diminishes.

Iron ores are classified on the basis of their metallic iron content and the percentage of undesirable impurities (known as "gangue"). The most objectionable of these impurities is phosphorus, because of its harmful effects in steel and, especially, since it cannot be removed in the reduction of the ore. An iron ore containing phosphorus not in excess of 1 part to 1000 parts of iron is classed as a "Bessemer" ore. An ore which contains phosphorus in excess of the 1 : 1000 ratio is classed as a "non-Bessemer" or "basic" ore.

Ores may be shipped as mined or subjected to concentration processes, known as "beneficiation," prior to shipment. Beneficiation of ores includes drying to reduce the water content, roasting to reduce the sulfur content, and washing to remove some of the gangue materials. The iron ore, either as mined or as improved by beneficiation, is shipped by rail and boat to the blast furnaces, where it is smelted.

Manufacture of Iron

The first step in the production of iron and steel is the reduction of the iron ore with coke and limestone in the iron blast furnace. In this process, "reduction" is the removal of the oxygen from the ore, leaving a mixture of iron and carbon and small amounts of other elements as impurities. The coke is the reducing agent and source of heat, and the limestone ($CaCO_3$) is the flux to promote fusion, which, in the molten state, combines with impurities of the ore, floats to the top, and can be removed as slag. A blast furnace is a vertical steel-shell structure 90 to 100 ft high lined from bottom to top with fireclay brick. Carbon block linings are used in some furnaces. The principal components of the blast furnace plant are illustrated in Fig. 1. Its product is pig iron, which is an impure form of iron containing about 4 per cent carbon and varying amounts of silicon, manganese, phosphorus, and sulfur.

The pig iron tapped from the blast furnace may be used directly as hot metal in certain steel-making processes, or it may be taken to pig-casting machines and cast into standard size pigs. It may also be taken to a mixer, where iron from several blast furnaces is mixed to produce more uniform or average analyses.

Cast Iron

Liquid pig iron tapped from the blast furnace is sometimes used directly for metal castings. More often, however, the iron is remelted in a cupola, air furnace, or electric furnace, to adjust its composition before it is used for castings. Pig iron which has been so remelted is known as cast iron, a general term applicable to a group of iron-carbon alloys containing carbon in excess of 2 per cent (usually less than 4.5 per cent) and appreciable amounts of

TABLE 1

General Engineering Grades of Gray Iron—Mechanical and Physical Properties

Class	30	35	40	45	50	60	70	80
Tensile strength, psi (min)	30,000	35,000	40,000	45,000	50,000	60,000	70,000	80,000
Compressive strength, psi	105,000	115,000	125,000	135,000	150,000	175,000	200,000	225,000
Torsional strength, psi	40,000	45,000	54,000	60,000	67,000	76,000	85,000	90,000
Modulus of elasticity[a], psi × 10⁻⁶	14	15	16	17	18	19	20	21
Torsional modulus, psi × 10⁻⁶	—	—	5.5	6.6	7.0	8.0	8.1	—
Impact strength, Izod AB (1.2-in. diam unnotched), ft-lb	23	25	31	36	65	75	120+	120+
Brinell hardness	180	200	220	240	240	260	280	300
Endurance limit, psi:								
Smooth	15,500	17,500	19,500	21,500	25,500	27,500	29,500	31,500
Notched	(13,500)	(15,500)	17,500	(19,500)	21,500	23,500	25,500	27,500
Damping capacity	Excellent	Excellent	Excellent	Good	Good	Good	Fair	Fair
Machinability	Excellent	Excellent	Excellent	Good	Good	Fair	Fair	Fair
Wear resistance	Fair	Fair	Good	Good	Excellent	Excellent	Excellent	Excellent
Pressure tightness	Fair	Fair	Good	Good	Excellent	Excellent	Excellent	Excellent
Specific gravity:								
g per cm³	7.02	7.13	7.25	7.37	7.43	7.48	7.51	7.54
lb per cu in.	0.254	0.258	0.262	0.267	0.269	0.270	0.272	0.273
Thermal coefficient of linear expansion: (in. per in., F) × 10⁻⁶ (50-200 F)	6.5-6.7	—	6.6-6.8	6.4-6.4	—	—	—	—
(50-500 F)	6.9-7.2	—	7.1-7.3	6.8-7.0	—	—	—	—
(50-800 F)	7.4-7.6	—	7.4-7.6	7.0-7.2	—	—	—	—
Magnetic properties	Mag	Mag	Mag	Mag	Mag	Mag	Mag	Mag
Pattern shrinkage, in. per ft	1/10-1/8	1/8	1/8	1/8	1/8	1/8-3/16	1/8-3/16	1/8-3/16
Coef of friction (against steel)	—	—	—	(0.19)	(0.195)	(0.20)	—	—

NOTE: Values in ( ) estimated. [a] At 25 per cent of tensile strength.

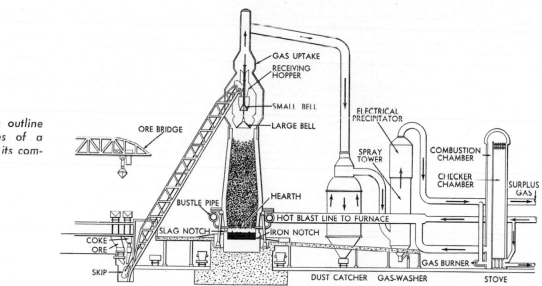

Fig. 1. *Schematic outline —external features of a blast furnace and its components*

silicon. Compared to steel, cast iron is decidedly inferior in malleability, strength, toughness and ductility. On the other hand, cast iron has better fluidity, can be cast satisfactorily into complicated shapes, and is less costly than steel. The most important types of cast iron are the gray and white cast irons.

White Cast Iron

White cast iron is so known because of the silvery luster of its fracture. In this alloy, the carbon is present in combined form as iron carbide (Fe_3C), known metallographically as "cementite." This carbide is chiefly responsible for the hardness, brittleness and poor machinability of white cast iron. These remarks also apply to chilled iron which differs from white cast iron only in the method of manufacture. The latter is cast against metal chills which cause rapid cooling at the adjacent areas, thus promoting the formation of cementite. Consequently, a white or mottled structure is obtained which is characterized by high resistance to wear and abrasion. Elverite, a type of chilled iron casting developed by B&W for use in pulverizers, cement and clinker grinders and in other wear-resistant parts, has long been noted for its uniformity and high quality.

Gray Cast Iron

Gray iron is by far the most widely used of cast metals. In this alloy, the carbon is predominantly in the free state, in the form of graphite flakes, which form a multitude of notches and discontinuities in the iron matrix. The appearance of the fracture of this iron is "gray" since the graphite flakes are exposed. The strength of gray iron depends on the size of the graphite crystals and the amount of cementite formed together with the graphite. The strength of the iron increases as the graphite crystal size decreases and the amount of cementite increases. Gray cast iron is easily machinable because the graphitic carbon acts as a lubricant for the cutting tool and also provides discontinuities which break the chips as they are formed. Modern gray iron having a wide range of tensile strength, from 20,000-30,000 psi to 90,000 psi, can be made by suitable alloying with nickel, chromium, molybdenum, vanadium and copper. Mechanical properties of several engineering grades (ASTM classes) of gray cast iron are given in Table 1.

Malleable cast iron is white cast iron which has been heat treated to change its combined carbon (cementite) into free or "temper" carbon (nodules of graphite). The iron becomes malleable because in this condition the carbon no longer forms planes of weakness.

Ductile Cast Iron

The most recent addition to the cast iron family is the so-called "ductile cast iron." It is a high carbon, magnesium treated ferrous product containing graphite in the form of spheroids or impacted particles. Ductile cast iron is similar to gray cast iron in melting point, fluidity and machinability but possesses superior mechanical properties. This alloy is especially well suited for pressure castings, and by special procedures (casting against a chill) it is possible to obtain a carbide containing abrasion-resistant surface with an interior of good ductility.

The structure of several types of cast iron used in B&W equipment is illustrated in Fig. 2 and Fig. 3.

Cast iron was used to a considerable extent in early steam boilers for both tubes and headers. Presently, this material is no longer used in the pressure parts of modern power boilers but is utilized in related equipment, such as stoker parts,

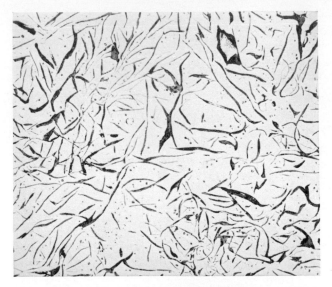

Fig. 2. Gray cast iron—typical microstructure (50x) reduced about ⅔. Note graphite flakes (dark areas)

Bailey metal furnace-wall blocks, grinding rings of coal pulverizers, etc. Typical B&W iron castings are shown in Fig. 4.

Manufacture of Steel

Steel may be simply defined as an alloy of iron and carbon which contains not over 2.0 per cent carbon and is cast in an initially malleable mass. This is by no means a complete definition of steel, but for all practical purposes it is sufficiently adequate. During the past 30 years, an immense variety of steels has been developed for widespread use. All of these steels are basically iron-carbon alloys, but

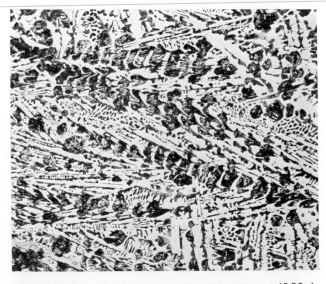

Fig. 3. White cast iron—typical microstructure (250x) reduced about ⅔. Note iron carbide "Fe₃C" (light areas) and tertiary eutectic "Steadite" (mottled areas)

they differ appreciably in carbon content and, in many instances, also in the amount of other alloying elements present. In this way several classes of steels have been produced, with a wide range of physical characteristics and mechanical properties suitable for the specific requirements of many different industrial applications.

All modern processes in the manufacture of steel start with pig iron. Pig iron is transformed into steel by the oxidation of the impurities with air or iron oxide, since these impurities, as compared with iron, have greater affinity for oxygen.

Pig iron may be refined by oxidation alone ("acid" process) or by oxidation in conjunction with a strong basic slag ("basic" process). Carbon, silicon, and manganese are removed by both processes, but phosphorus and some of the sulfur in the pig iron can be removed only in the basic process. When phosphorus is oxidized to a phosphate, it will stay per-

Fig. 4. Typical B&W iron castings of crusher and pulverizer parts in Elverite. Balls are steel (SAE-52100)

sistently with the iron if the slag is strongly acidic (high in silica) and therefore will not be removed. However, if in addition to oxidizing conditions there is also an abundance of a basic constituent (such as calcium or magnesium) in the slag, then the latter will hold the phosphate in combination and prevent it from being again reduced and seized by the metallic iron. The removal of sulfur is similarly facilitated by oxidizing conditions and basic slag.

The principal commercial methods of manufacturing steel in the United States, in the order of tonnage produced by each, are: 1) basic open-hearth, 2) acid Bessemer, 3) basic electric-furnace, and 4) acid open-hearth.

The furnace charge is molten pig iron in the Bessemer process, steel scrap and pig iron in the open-hearth processes, and selected steel scrap in the electric-furnace process. Each of these requires raw materials of particular composition and produces a steel somewhat different in chemical analysis and physical characteristics.

Bessemer Process

Purification of molten pig iron by the oxidation of some of the impurities is the principle of steel-making in the Bessemer process. Air is blown through the charge until the silicon, manganese, and carbon are oxidized. The resulting product is known as blown metal, and the necessary additions, in order to meet steel purification requirements, are made in the ladle. Bessemer steel is characterized by low carbon, high phosphorus and sulfur content, and a considerable amount of nonmetallic inclusions and nitrogen. The major tonnage of steel produced by this process goes into the production of free-cutting screw steels, sheet metal, wire, bolts, nuts, reinforcing bars, and tin plate. Bessemer steel is not used in high-pressure boiler parts, although killed* Bessemer steel is now employed to a considerable extent in the manufacture of seamless steel pipe for ordinary uses.

Open-Hearth Process

a) Basic

By far the greatest tonnage of steel in this country (about 90 per cent) is produced by the basic open-hearth process. The tremendous importance of this method is because of the fact that a uniformly good quality steel can still be produced, even though the furnace charge (pig iron, scrap, iron ore, and limestone) is varied widely to suit economic conditions. For instance, scrap may be at a premium. The ability to control oxidation of carbon in the bath permits use of large quantities of molten pig iron directly from the blast furnace. Some steel plants have used upwards of 70 per cent hot metal in the charge, although about 50 per cent is nearer the average practice. In the open-hearth it is also possible to complete the refinement of partially refined hot metal from the Bessemer converter. Such practice is called duplexing.

The basic open-hearth process is carried out in a large regenerative furnace lined with basic refractories (magnesite, dolomite). Open-hearth furnaces of recent construction have a capacity of at least 200 tons. A diagrammatic section through a typical open-hearth furnace is shown by Fig. 5.

In addition to various types of carbon steel, a considerable quantity of certain grades of alloy steel is produced by the open-hearth process, notably in SAE or AISI types, for engineering uses. In alloy-

*A steel is said to be killed when it has been degassed (mainly deoxidized) prior to pouring, so that the liquid metal lies quiet in the mold without the presence of gas to form porosity in the ingot.

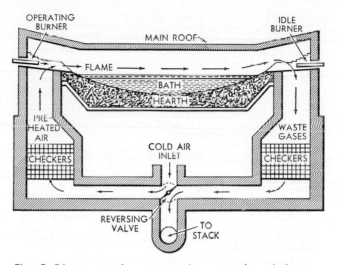

Fig. 5. Diagrammatic cross section, open-hearth furnace

steel boiler materials, carbon-molybdenum steel for boiler plate and superheater tubes or piping, and the low chromium-molybdenum alloy tube materials up to about 1½ per cent chromium can be made by the basic open-hearth process. It is usually preferable, however, to make the chromium-containing tube grades by the electric-furnace process.

b) Acid

The acid open-hearth is essentially a melting process, and, as in all acid processes, the removal of phosphorus and sulfur is impossible. Consequently, it is necessary to use a charge lower in these impurities to produce satisfactory steel. The smaller heats usually made in the acid process and the higher cost restrict the use of the acid open-hearth steel to castings and special products.

Acid open-hearth steels are cleaner than average basic open-hearth steels. Transverse mechanical properties are superior to basic open-hearth steels,

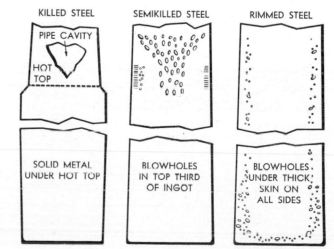

Fig. 6. Schematic sections of ingots—three types of steel

particularly in forgings. Forged seamless steam drums of acid open-hearth steel were used in B&W equipment prior to adoption of the fusion-welding process for drum construction. A very small tonnage of rimmed steel (see Fig. 6) is made by this process; most of the production is killed carbon and alloy steels.

Electric-Furnace Process

Most high-grade alloy steels are manufactured in the electric furnace. For these alloys, the electric-furnace process offers the following important advantages over other steelmaking processes:

1. Any desired temperature can be obtained because the control of temperature conditions is definite with close limits.

2. Either oxidizing, reducing, or neutral conditions may be maintained in the furnace at will. This permits the addition of alloying elements to the bath with assurance of complete deoxidation in the furnace.

3. The bath is not subject to contamination by the source of heat.

4. Sulfur, solid nonmetallic impurities, and occluded gases are significantly eliminated.

Good Control of Composition

The higher temperature generated in the electric furnace increases the fluidity of the metal, permits rapid reaction in removing sulfur and phosphorus, and permits recovery of oxidizable alloying elements from the slag. The control of quality and composition is, therefore, better than in the open-hearth process, but the cost is somewhat higher. An electric-furnace heat is usually from 20 to 50 tons as compared with 100 tons and more in the open-hearth. Steels of intermediate chromium-molybdenum composition, such as those used for superheaters, are generally made in the electric furnace. The basic electric-furnace process is always used for production of stainless, high-alloy, and tool steels. The acid process is used essentially for melting and finds application chiefly in steel foundries.

The rotary piercing process, employed in the manufacture of seamless tubing and pipe, is perhaps the most rigorous hot-forming operation in the entire metalworking industry. It requires, therefore, the highest quality steel, not only to withstand this rigorous forming operation but also to obtain a satisfactory product suitable for the severe conditions encountered in high-temperature service.

Quality Alloy Steel for Tubes—B&W Practice

To insure a uniformly high quality in alloy-steel grades for tube production, an electric alloy-steel plant, to produce high-temperature and corrosion-resistant steels now commonly used by various industries for steam generation, oil refining, chemical processes, and other kindred uses, was erected in 1942 and integrated with the B&W Tubular Products Division's seamless tube mills at Beaver Falls, Pa.

This plant consists of one 75-ton, one 50-ton, and two 15-ton basic electric furnaces of the top-charge type, a battery of soaking and preheat pits, a 1500-ton forging press, and an 8-ton steam hammer which, with a manipulator to handle the ingot, serves as a blooming mill where the ingot is rough-forged into a bloom. The plant is equipped with a 24-inch three-high bar mill with bloom-heating furnace. The 50-ton electric furnace is shown in Fig. 7.

Practically the entire range of ferrous alloys has been melted in these furnaces, from plain low-carbon steel to 25 per cent chromium, 20 per cent nickel stainless alloy, all with double-slag* practice and under rigid technical control. Melt procedures are set up for each grade, and no deviation is permitted after standard procedures have been established. This is important in providing uniform piercing qualities and uniform performance in service. The electric-furnace melt procedures for high-quality alloy tube steel call for thorough degasification of the melt irrespective of composition.

Samples Quickly Analyzed

Only killed (fully deoxidized) steels are made in

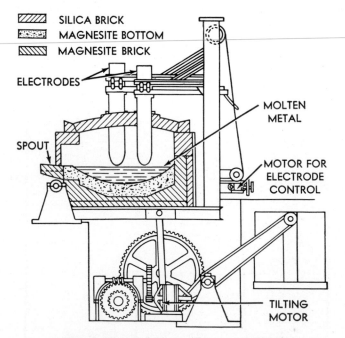

SILICA BRICK
MAGNESITE BOTTOM
MAGNESITE BRICK
ELECTRODES
MOLTEN METAL
SPOUT
MOTOR FOR ELECTRODE CONTROL
TILTING MOTOR

Fig. 7. *Electric furnace (50-ton capacity) used in the production of Croloy steels*

*In double-slag practice, the slag is drawn off twice during the heat. After the first removal of slag fresh fluxing reagents are added, the heat is continued, and the newly formed slag is drawn off before tapping.

the plant. Alloying elements are recovered from the second or finishing slag formed on the completion of the oxidizing period. Samples of the molten steel are taken from the bath and cast into small ingots, which are rushed to the laboratory, about a mile away, by means of a pneumatic tube system. These samples are rapidly analyzed in the laboratory by chemical methods and spectrograph. The results of the analyses are quickly reported to the melter and guide him in making the necessary alloy additions to the bath to bring the steel to the specified composition. To insure high quality, two or more samples are necessary in the course of making the steel.

Ingots are teemed into 19½-in. fluted square molds. The ingot weights are calculated for each specific billet multiple to be produced against the tubing order. Permanent hot-top equipment, a refractory-lined short section fitted over or into the ingot mold, is used with ample cropping to insure freedom from piping.

Special Heating Cycles

To prevent thermal shock or stress-cracking, special heating cycles are maintained for ingots of alloy steel, particularly for the hardenable grades. Each alloy has a certain thermal cycle which must be adhered to in heating ingots for blooming and for bar-mill rolling. To remove all surface defects, blooms are subjected to careful conditioning before bar rolling, with such additional conditioning of bars as may be required to remove any remaining defects. Conditioning is an important operation to remove such surface defects as checks, slivers, etc. It is done by grinding or scarfing, in which the surface where defects appear is removed to sound metal. Superficial scale and loose foreign matter are removed by air jets and hand manipulation. All stainless grades are turned in the round before being sent to the tube plant.

To make a satisfactory seamless tube by the rotary piercing process, the billet must have a dense outer surface free from longitudinal defects or radial planes of weakness. Furthermore, it must have good ductility over a broad enough range of high temperature to permit piercing of hollows of commercial length. Adequate allowance should be made for any temperature build-up from friction during the deformation in piercing. The billet must also be free of pipe or center porosity and other defects that might open up on the inside of the bar in the process.

The Steel Ingot

Molten metal tapped from the steelmaking furnaces is poured from ladles into metal molds and allowed to solidify preparatory to forging and rolling. Such a casting is called an ingot.

All steel used in the production of wrought-steel

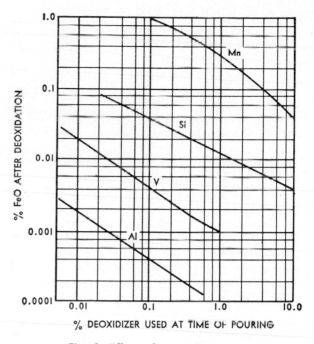

Fig. 8. *Effect of several common deoxidizers in molten steel at 2900 F*

products, such as plate, tubing, and bars for boilers or any other uses, is cast into ingot molds of suitable size and shape. Proper ingot practice is essential to insure a good quality product, free from breaks, internal defects, or excessive segregation.

Ingots are cast in many sizes and shapes, established by the research and experience of the steel producer. The cross section of most ingots approximates a square or rectangle with round corners but may be fluted to give additional hot strength to avoid corner cracks. The greatest dimension is always vertical, and all ingots are tapered. The exact cross section and vertical height are carefully selected for the job at hand. Steel of the rimmed and semikilled types (see Fig. 6) is usually cast in ingots with big end down, while killed steel is commonly cast in ingots with a sink head or hot top, and with big end up. This procedure is employed in the latter case in order properly to feed the so-called "pipe" which forms during cooling and confine it to the hot top, which portion of the ingot is later sheared or cropped in an amount sufficient to give good sound metal. A bottom crop also is taken to ensure sound metal in that area of the ingot.

All steels, irrespective of type, are subject to certain internal variations from natural phenomena which occur as the steel solidifies in the mold. The character and magnitude of such variations and their effects depend upon the size of the ingots and may be generalized as follows:

Primary pipe in the upper portion of the ingot is caused by shrinkage of the metal in passing from the liquid to the solid state during solidification. Since the surface of the cavity becomes oxidized, rolling at a welding heat will not close it. Consequently, the pipe end of the ingot must be cut off and discarded. Under certain conditions, a shrinkage cavity known as secondary pipe is formed below the primary pipe but is not connected with it. Secondary pipe is usually associated with the evolution and entrapment of gases in the ingot during solidification. Due to its nature, however, it will normally weld in the rolling process and does not materially affect the quality of the finished product.

Another phenomenon associated with rate of solidification is segregation or nonuniformity in chemical composition within the ingot. Certain portions of the solidified metal contain either more or less of the elements originally contained in the liquid steel. Segregation in varying degrees is found in all types of steel ingots. The amount of segregation depends chiefly on the type and composition of the steel, the

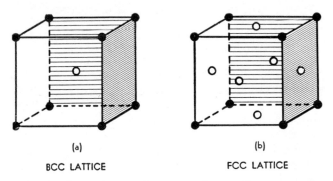

(a)   (b)
BCC LATTICE   FCC LATTICE

Fig. 9. *Space-lattice diagrams of crystalline structure (iron) showing arrangement of atoms in (a) body centered cubic and in (b) face centered cubic*

teeming temperature, the ingot size and the inherent segregating characteristics of the individual elements of the steel. These phenomena have been widely studied and controlled by special practices, proper discard and other measures indicated by the intended end use of the product.

Steel Types

In most steel making processes, the primary reaction is the combination of carbon and oxygen to form a gas. If the oxygen available for this reaction is not removed prior to or during casting by the addition of silicon, aluminum or some other deoxidizing agent, the gaseous products continue to evolve during solidification of the metal in the mold. Proper control of the amount of gas evolved during solidification determines the type of steel. If no gas is evolved and the liquid lies quietly in the mold it is known as killed steel. With increasing degrees of gas evolution the product is known as semi-killed

and rimmed steel. The efficiency of several of the common deoxidizers in molten steel at 2900 F (1600 C) is shown in Fig. 8.

Rimmed Steel

In rimmed steel there is a marked difference in composition across the section and from top to bottom of the ingot. The outer rim is ductile and the amounts of carbon, phosphorus, sulfur and nonmetallic inclusions in this rim are lower than the average composition of the whole ingot, while the amount of these constituents in the inner portion or core is higher than the average in the ingot as a whole. A marked evolution of gas during solidification of the outer rim is responsible for the typical structure of rimmed steel. When solidification begins, concentration of certain elements in the liquid core of the ingot increases; and, at the core there is also some additional segregation toward the upper and central portions.

Rimmed steels normally contain less than 0.25 per cent carbon, under 0.60 per cent manganese and 0.01 per cent silicon maximum. Satisfactory rimmed steels do not retain any significant percentages of highly oxidizable elements such as aluminum, titanium or silicon. Aside from the closing and welding of gas voids (blowholes), the structural pattern of the rimmed steel ingot persists through the rolling process to the final product. Rimmed steel, which costs less to make than killed or semi-killed steels, is widely used as structural plate material. It is used also in strip form for production of electric resistance welded tubing. The rimmed portion is particularly suitable for welding by that process.

Capped Steel

The characteristics of capped steel and rimmed steel are similar, but capped steel represents an intermediate step between rimmed and semikilled steels. A deoxidizer may be added when the ingot is cast to effect a controlled rimming action. Capped steel is generally cast in big-end down bottle-top molds using a heavy metal cap. Capped steel generally has a somewhat thinner rim, and the segregation in the upper central portion of the ingot is less than in rimmed steel. This method is not ordinarily used for steel containing more than 0.15 per cent carbon.

Semikilled Steel

Semikilled steel has a variable degree of uniformity in composition. This type of steel is only partially deoxidized with silicon, aluminum, or both to allow the evolution of sufficient gas to offset, entirely or in part, the shrinkage accompanying solidification. Since pipe cavities are minimized, semikilled steel is usually cast in big-end down molds without hot

"austenite." The temperature exists by itself decreases as along G-S to the so-called " per cent carbon, 1333 F), and increases as the carbon increa is unable to absorb additio higher temperatures.

Critical Points in Steel

Referring again to Fig. 11, steel lie along A_1 correspon 1333 F, and along A_3 corresp temperatures varying with occur in heating and cooling are again subdivided as Ac_1 a Ar_1 and Ar_3 (cooling), respec tions have no place in an equ they are related to time, anot of which is shown later. B of 1333 F, carbon is relatively rite," as alpha iron is known by the addition of other eleme bility of carbon in ferrite as c bility in austenite may be judg Q-P and S-E. This differe carbon in the one as compare the other is the crux of pra treating.

The data in Fig. 11 show possible transformation which never attained short of an infi fabricating steel, however, m time from seconds (spot wel (heat-treating large vessels). pact of these processes on th tion of the steel, it is necessa of time. A typical isothermal trated in the diagram, Fig. 1

Transformation in Steel

This diagram (Fig. 12) c position of steel and indicat for the progress of transforma ferritic constituents at the vari As an example, a hypoeutect a temperature (about 1600 completely austenitic, and it ferred to and held in a furn From Fig. 11 it is evident that carbide should exist at this 12 indicates how long this r jecting the time intervals dur as indicated in the lower po

tops. Most semikilled steels contain between 0.15 per cent and 0.25 per cent carbon, and approximately 0.05 per cent silicon.

Killed Steel

Steel of the killed type is deoxidized almost completely, so that there is essentially no evolution of gas during pouring and solidification. Consequently, a primary shrinkage cavity known as pipe forms during solidification, and this affected part of the ingot is discarded. Killed steel is usually cast in big-end up ingot molds with hot top to supply the shrinkage cavity. There may be a secondary pipe in addition to the primary pipe but this is reduced by the general use of big-end up ingots.

Although killed steel has a more uniform composition than any of the other types, there are some variations in composition from surface to center and from bottom to top. All but a very few compositions of steel can be killed, if sufficient deoxidizing elements may be added to inhibit gas formation. Practically all alloy steels are of the killed type, as are most of the carbon steels containing more than 0.25 per cent carbon. Such steels usually contain 0.10 per cent silicon minimum; for certain uses, however, some steels are killed almost entirely with aluminum. B&W seamless steel boiler tubes are made exclusively of killed steel.

Typical appearance and location of blowholes and pipe in rimmed, semikilled and killed steel are illustrated in Fig. 6.

Atomic Structure of Iron

Pure iron at room temperature is highly ductile and is nearly comparable to copper in hardness. It is strongly magnetic (ferromagnetic), and in this respect differs from all other elements—although nickel and cobalt are magnetic to a milder degree.

Like all other metals, iron is crystalline in structure. All crystalline bodies may be considered as composed of atoms placed at the points of a space-lattice (see Fig. 9). The smallest component unit of this lattice is known as a unit cell and is characterized by a regularity of structure. A crystal is composed of these unit cells, piled upon one another like bricks, and reproducing at their corners the points of the lattice. Different crystals have different types of space lattice. Analysis by X-ray diffraction shows that iron on solidification from a molten state crystallizes in the cubic space lattice.

Iron may exist in one of two forms of cubic space lattice; body-centered or face-centered, so differentiated by the manner in which the atoms are arranged in each of them. Both are illustrated in Fig. 9. The body-centered cubic form has an atom at each corner and one at the center of the cell; the face-centered cubic form has an atom at each corner

and one in the center of each of the six faces.

At room temperature, iron is composed of a body-centered cubic lattice (see Fig. 10). In this form it is known as "alpha" iron or "alpha ferrite," and it is soft, ductile and magnetic. Upon heating above about 1415 F, alpha iron loses its magnetism but retains its body-centered crystalline structure. This structure changes to face-centered cubic at about

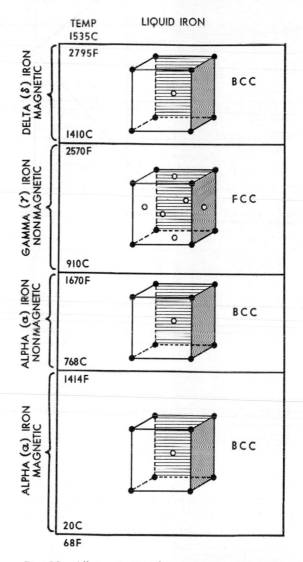

Fig. 10. *Allotropic transformations in pure iron*

1670 F, at which temperature alpha iron is transformed to "gamma iron" and remains non-magnetic. Continuing upward in temperature, another phase change occurs at 2570 F when "delta iron" is formed. The latter is identical in crystal structure (body-centered) to the low temperature alpha iron. It is magnetic and is stable to the melting point. There are no known phase changes in the liquid form (above about 2800 F). On cooling very slowly from

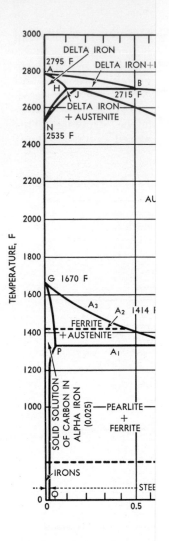

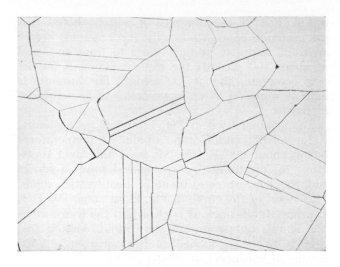

Fig. 13. *Austenite, typical microstructure (500x) reduced about ⅔*

eliminated when the proportion of chromium reaches 13 per cent. The addition of carbon (making a three-component system) changes these values considerably. At about 45 per cent chromium and below about 1500 F, a nonmagnetic compound known as "sigma phase" appears, which renders the alloy brittle.

Nickel acts to widen the region of austenite, so that iron alloys containing more than 25 per cent nickel are practically austenitic at all temperatures. The action of all other alloying elements can be classed as (a) like chromium (ferrite formers), (b) like nickel (austenite formers), or (c) to form compounds.

Microscopic Examination

The microscope is traditionally the tool of the metallurgist for exploring changes in steel from

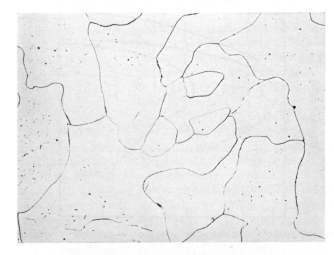

Fig. 14. *Ferrite, typical microstructure (1000x) reduced about ⅔*

the liquid state, the ato[m]
occur again, but in reve[

The modifications of
in iron during heating t
ing point are called "a
peratures at which th
known as "transformati[on
The range of temperat[
mation points is called

Physical Metallurgy o[

The foregoing perta[
difficult to obtain, is co[
in any case does not [
for construction purp[
with carbon and such [
silicon, phosphorus, and[
is an economic mate[
carbon in combination[
in producing desirable[
brought under careful[
ture of steel. Some of[

alloy additions and thermal treatment. The surface of samples is ground flat and then polished to a mirrorlike finish. When the sample is placed under the microscope, the metal reflects light back to the eyepiece, and the discontinuities, which absorb some of the light, appear dark. Customarily, the samples are etched in mild acid solutions to bring out the characteristic appearance of: austenite, Fig. 13; ferrite, Fig. 14; pearlite, Fig. 15; or hard martensite in quenched steel, Fig. 16.

To the metallurgist, the structures shown in these photomicrographs are clear indices to the prior fabrication and to the mechanical properties. For good quality it is obvious, of course, that foreign matter in steel should be reduced to a minimum. The characteristic appearances of the photomicrographs mentioned above may be defined as follows:

Austenite. A solid solution of carbon in gamma iron, containing a maximum of about 2.0 per cent carbon at 2090 F and about 0.80 per cent carbon at 1333 F. It exists in ordinary steels only at elevated temperatures, but it is also found at ordinary temperatures in some stainless steels (18Cr-8Ni type). This structure has high ductility and high impact strength, which it retains even down to minus 320 F.

Ferrite. A commercially pure alpha iron containing a small amount of carbon (0.04-0.05 per cent) in solid solution. This phase is soft, ductile, and relatively weak. Below about 40 F the impact strength is materially reduced. The tensile strength of commercially pure ferrite is of the order of 40,000 psi, the elongation is about 40 per cent, and the hardness is from 90 to 95 Brinell.

Pearlite. A mixture, in laminar form, of iron carbide (cementite) in ferrite, which occurs on slow cooling above the nose of the curve in Fig. 12. This condition is obtained by annealing or normalizing and generally represents an optimum high strength while retaining ductility and some machinability.

Cementite. Iron carbide, Fe_3C (cementite), a compound containing 6.67 per cent carbon, is very hard (about 650 Brinell) and is extremely brittle. The ordinary occurrence of cementite is in slowly cooled hypereutectoid steels (carbon content greater than 0.80 per cent).

Martensite. A very hard constituent obtained by the decomposition of austenite in rapidly cooled steel.

Specific Effect of Alloying Elements

Steel alloys are the chief structural materials of modern engineering because of their wide range in properties to suit almost every specific application. These properties are affected directly not only by the characteristics and the amounts of the elements which, either alone or in combination, enter into the composition of the steel, but also by their reaction as constituents under various conditions of temperature, fabrication and use. For example, chromium increases resistance to corrosion and scaling; molybdenum increases creep strength at elevated temperatures; and nickel (in adequate amounts) renders the steel austenitic. The specific effect of the most important elements found in steel, is outlined in the following.

Carbon. Carbon is not generally regarded as an "alloying" element because steel would not be steel without carbon. Nevertheless, it is appropriate in a discussion of alloying elements to first note the specific effects of carbon on the properties of steel.

In general, an increase in carbon content produces a higher ultimate strength and hardness but lowers the ductility and toughness of steel alloys. The curves in Fig. 17 indicate the general effect of carbon on the mechanical properties of hot-rolled carbon steel. Carbon also increases air hardening tendencies and weld hardness, especially in the presence of chromium. In low alloy steels for high temperature applications, the carbon content is usually restricted to a maximum of about 0.15 per cent in order to assure optimum ductility for welding, expanding and bending operations. To minimize intergranular corrosion caused by carbide precipitation, the carbon content of austenitic (18-8 type) alloys is limited in commercial specifications to a maximum of 0.08 per cent, or even less, i.e., 0.03 per cent in the newer extremely low carbon grades used in corrosion resisting applications.

No generalization is warranted regarding the effect of carbon on the long time, high temperature (creep) properties of low and high alloy steels. In plain carbon steels, in the normalized condition, the resistance to creep at temperatures below 825 F appears to increase with carbon content up to 0.4 per cent carbon; at higher temperatures there is but little variation of creep properties with carbon content.

An increase in carbon content lessens the thermal and electrical conductivity of steel and increases its hardness on quenching (see Fig. 18).

Phosphorus. High phosphorus content has an undesirable effect on the properties of carbon steel—notably on its resistance to shock and ductility when the steel is cold worked. This embrittling effect, generally referred to as "cold shortness," is due to the tendency of phosphorus to enlarge the grain size and cause segregation. The harmful effect of phosphorus increases as the carbon content increases.

Phosphorus is effective in improving the machinability of free cutting steels. This is related to its embrittling effect causing breakage of the chips on machining. In open hearth (carbon) steels phosphorus is limited to a maximum of 0.04 per cent.

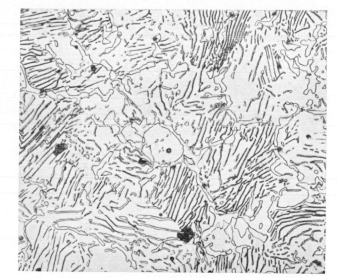

Fig. 15. *Pearlite, typical microstructure (1000x) reduced about ¾*

In alloy steels intended for boiler applications the permissible phosphorus content is still less. Its presence is objectionable for welding. Phosphorus has recently come into prominence as an alloying element (up to 0.15 per cent) in proprietary low alloy, high strength steels, where increased yield strength and resistance to atmospheric corrosion are primary requirements. In certain acids, however, high phosphorus may increase the corrosion rate.

Silicon. The usefulness of silicon is due largely to its qualities as a deoxidizer and degasifier, hence it contributes to the production of sound steel. When added in amounts up to 2.5 per cent, silicon increases the ultimate strength of the steel without decrease in

Fig. 16. *Martensite, typical microstructure in quenched steel (500x) reduced about ¾*

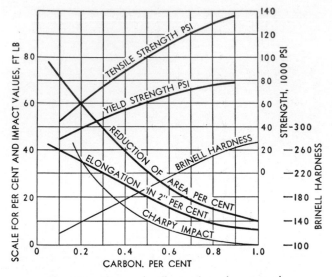

Fig. 17. *General effect of carbon on the mechanical properties of hot-rolled carbon steel*

ductility. Silicon in excess of this amount causes brittleness, and amounts higher than 5 per cent make the steel nonmalleable.

Resistance to oxidation and surface stability of steel are increased by the addition of silicon. These desirable effects partially compensate for the tendency of silicon to lower the creep properties of steel. Silicon increases the electrical resistivity of steel and decreases hysteresis losses. Silicon steels are, therefore, widely used in electrical apparatus.

Manganese. In addition to being an excellent deoxidizer and sulfur neutralizer, manganese improves the mechanical properties of steel, notably the ratio of yield strength to tensile strength at normal temperatures. As an alloying element of steel, manganese serves as an inexpensive means of preventing "red-shortness" (brittleness), and it will improve rolling

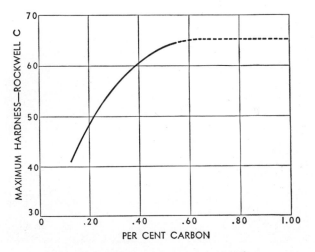

Fig. 18. *Order of maximum hardness attainable in steel with increase in carbon*

properties, hardenability and resistance to wear. However, manganese increases the crack sensitivity of weldments, particularly so with steels of higher carbon content.

Unlike silicon, the effect of manganese is beneficial on the creep properties of steel. It does not appear to have any specific influence on the resistance to oxidation or corrosion of steel.

Chromium. This element is the essential constituent of stainless steel. Chromium has the effect of increasing yield and ultimate strength and hardness and toughness of steel at room temperature. It also contributes somewhat to the strength of steel at high temperatures.

Resistance of the steel to wear or abrasion and increase in cutting ability are two of the outstanding effects of the addition of chromium. A steady improvement is noted in resistance to atmospheric corrosion and to attack by many reagents when the chromium content of steel is increased above 12 per cent. The chemical properties of the steel, however, are affected by the carbon content; and, generally, the higher the chromium and the lower the carbon, the more resistant the alloy will be to certain types of corrosion. Chromium is also instrumental in increasing the resistance to oxidation at elevated temperature, and therefore, is of prime importance in steels intended for high temperature service.

The addition of 1 per cent or more of chromium may cause appreciable air hardening in the steel. Air hardening is a direct function of chromium and carbon content up to about 12 per cent Cr. Low carbon alloy steels containing over 12 per cent chromium tend to become nonhardening but the impact strength is reduced and the ductility is poor. Chromium lessens both thermal and electrical conductivity.

Nickel. Increased toughness, resistance to corrosion and hardenability are the principal benefits when nickel (upwards of 5 per cent) is added to steel. Nickel dissolves in the iron matrix in all proportions and, therefore, it raises the ultimate strength without impairing the ductility of the steel. Nickel is particularly effective in increasing the impact properties—especially at low temperatures. It is a useful element in carburizing steels, and it is used to improve core properties in steels for roller bearings.

Probably the most important use of nickel as an alloying element is in combination with chromium in amounts of 8 per cent Ni or more. By the addition of nickel the high chromium iron-carbon alloys become austenitic in character. The various combinations of these two elements produce alloys (18-8 type) with properties which cannot be obtained with equivalent amounts of any of the elements alone. Such steels are resistant not only to corrosion by the atmosphere and other sources but also

ram forces the tube into the grooves of the rolls, the rotation of which carries it forward over a plug and bar, working the metal between the grooved surfaces of the rolls and the plug (see Fig. 22). Five or six or even more passes with change of plugs may be required in rolling stainless Croloys. To make the wall uniform and to avoid ribs or overfills, the tube is turned 90 degrees after each pass through the rolling mill.

Reeling and Sizing. After rolling, the tube is in a semi-finished condition, that is, of required wall thickness and approximate diameter but with a somewhat rough surface. Directly after rolling, and while the tube is still hot, it is conveyed to a reeling machine (see Fig. 23) where it is forced spirally over a smooth mandrel or "reeler plug" supported by a thrust bar on the outlet side of the mill. In rolling over this plug light overfills and scratches are removed and the tube is smoothed and burnished. The tube is also rounded and expanded a little in diameter, but the wall thickness remains approximately constant, or, depending on the pressure applied, is reduced slightly. After reeling, the tube is taken to a sizing mill.

The function of the sizing mill is to hot-size the tube to its proper diameter. Its main elements are several sets of roll stands with single grooved rolls set in tandem. Following the sizing operation, the tube is annealed or heat treated, if required, and then straightened, cut to length, hydrostatically tested, and finally inspected. Appropriate samples are secured for tensile, hardness and deformation tests, and the length, gage and diameter of the tubes are checked.

To produce smaller tubes in sizes below about 2 in. the tube, after reeling and reheating to a working temperature, is reduced in diameter or increased in length in a reducing mill.

Cold Drawing. Tubes requiring finer finish or closer dimensional tolerances and tubes of smaller or special sizes than can be obtained by the hot-finish process are cold drawn. Tubing to be cold drawn is made in the same manner as hot-finished tubing. The cold drawing is a subsequent additional operation.

The cold drawing is done on a sturdily constructed draw bench fitted at its center with a heavy steel holder for the die through which the tube is drawn. The arrangement of the draw bench, tube die and mandrel is illustrated diagrammatically in Fig. 24. The operation of annealing, pickling, lubricating and drawing is repeated until the tube is of the desired size. Drawing reduces both diameter and wall thickness.

In the final operations, after cold drawing, an appropriate heat treatment is applied to the tubes. Depending on the particular analysis, this may be

Fig. 22.

a full anneal, n[...]
or a quench tr[...]
straightened, c[...]
by inspectors [...]
high-quality pre[...]

Extrusion Proce[...]

Certain sizes [...]
more "refractory[...]
not well suited [...]
process. This m[...]
Ugine-Sejournet [...]

Fig. 23. R[...]

desirable p[...]
hot or cold[...]
forging, pr[...]
ways a hot[...]
in drawing[...]
operation.[...]
metal belo[...]
means at c[...]
is cold wo[...]
the recryst[...]
and the sin[...]
temperatur[...]
satisfactory[...]
above the [...]
which vari[...]

The tem[...]
worked ha[...]
Cold work[...]
and yield [...]
tion and [...]
extent of [...]
elongation[...]
depends o[...]
hardening[...]
tion becom[...]
the metal [...]
to restore[...]

Hot wor[...]
closing blo[...]
its homoge[...]
ture is ref[...]
the ductilit[...]
does not h[...]
process. It[...]
method of [...]
curacy and[...]

Obviousl[...]
ing equipm[...]
ucts used [...]

Fig. 20.
heating fur[...]
heat B&W[...]

BAR

to oxidation at high temperatures, and they possess greatly enhanced creep strength.

Nickel has only a slight beneficial effect on creep properties of low alloy ferritic steels. It reduces the coefficient of thermal expansion and diminishes the electrical conductivity of steel.

Molybdenum and Wolfram (Tungsten). Addition of molybdenum to steel increases its strength, elastic limit, resistance to wear, impact qualities and hardenability. Molybdenum contributes to the "red hardness" of steel, that is, the steel can be heated to a visible degree without materially lowering the hardness. It also adds to the resistance of steel to softening on tempering and restrains grain growth. Making chromium steels less susceptible to temper embrittlement is another beneficial influence of molybdenum.

The principal use of molybdenum in improving resistance to corrosion is in stainless steels of the 18-8 type. It improves the inherent resistance to corrosion of these steels in reducing chemical media and also increases their passivity under mildly oxidizing conditions. Experience indicates that under certain conditions molybdenum effectively reduces the susceptibility of stainless steels to pitting. Molybdenum is the most effective single alloying addition that increases the high temperature creep strength of steel.

Wolfram (also known as tungsten) is similar in behavior to molybdenum. However, of the two molybdenum appears to be more effective in increasing strength for a given cost. Wolfram is an important element in high speed cutting tools and in cemented carbide tools.

Vanadium. While it is to some extent a degasifying and deoxidizing agent, vanadium is seldom used in that capacity because of its high cost. Vanadium, therefore, is applied chiefly as an alloying element in steel. Essentially a carbide-forming element which stabilizes the structure, especially at high temperatures, it increases the strength, toughness and hardness of steel. Vanadium minimizes grain-growth tendencies, thus permitting much higher heat treating temperatures. It also intensifies the individual properties of other elements in alloy steels. In steels containing 0.50 to 1.00 per cent molybdenum, small additions of vanadium (0.1 to 0.5 percent) produce a pronounced improvement in high temperature creep properties if these steels are given certain high-temperature heat treatments. Vanadium improves the cutting properties of tool steels.

Aluminum, Titanium and Niobium (Columbium). Aluminum is an important minor constituent of low alloy steels. It is an efficient deoxidizer and is almost universally used in the production of killed steel. When added to steel in appreciable quantities, aluminum forms tightly adhering refractory oxide

scales, and thus increases resistance to scaling. It is difficult, however, to add appreciable amounts of this element to steel without producing undesirable effects. It is generally agreed that an excessive quantity of aluminum has a detrimental effect on creep properties, particularly in plain carbon steel. This is due to its grain-refining effect and, what is even more serious, to the acceleration which it exerts on spheroidization and graphitization of the carbide phase.

In the amounts that it is customary to add, aluminum does not increase resistance to ordinary forms of corrosion. Actually, due to its avidity for oxygen, steels of high aluminum content generally contain numerous alumina inclusions which tend to produce pitting corrosion under conditions favorable for corrosive attack. Aluminum, however, increases resistance to oxidation when applied to steel as a surface coating, as in the calorizing process.

Titanium and niobium (also known as columbium) are potent carbide-forming elements. In addition, titanium is also a good deoxidizer and denitrider. These elements are most effective in the chromium-nickel austenitic alloys (18-8 type) where they react more readily with carbon than does chromium, allowing the chromium to remain in solid solution and in the concentrations necessary to maintain the "stainlessness" (corrosion resistance) of the steel. Titanium and niobium (or niobium plus tantalum) are sometimes used to reduce air-hardening tendencies and to increase resistance to oxidation in steels containing up to 14 per cent chromium. These elements seem to have a beneficial effect on the long-time, high temperature properties of chromium-nickel stainless steels. Both niobium and titanium have been used in some of the new "super-alloys" to improve high temperature properties.

Copper. Addition of copper in small amounts improves the resistance of steel to atmospheric corrosion and reduces the rate of attack in reducing acids. Copper is not resistant to sulfur compounds at elevated temperatures. Consequently, it is not ordinarily used in low-alloy steels intended for high temperature service. Copper is added (up to 1 per cent) in low-alloy constructional steels to improve yield strength and resistance to atmospheric corrosion, and also in some of the high-alloy steels to increase resistance to corrosion by sulfuric acid. Copper, in amounts between 2.0 and 4.0 per cent, also has been added in certain complex high-alloy austenitic steels in conjunction with molybdenum, titanium and niobium, to cause precipitation hardening, thereby improving the creep and rupture strength properties.

Some specific functions of alloying elements in steel are given in Table A in the Appendix.

Plates are made from ingots of rectangular shape by using a slabbing mill, which performs the same function as a blooming mill but permits rolling the wider sections desired in the initial operation in the production of plates, sheet, and strip. After conditioning and reheating, the rough slabs are rolled to finished plates on either a sheared plate mill or a Universal mill. Some extremely heavy plates may be rolled directly from the ingot. Sheared plate is rolled between straight horizontal rolls only and must be trimmed to the finished size on all edges. Universal mill plates are rolled between horizontal rolls and vertical rolls and are trimmed on the ends only. Mills of various designs are used for rolling plates.

For sheared-mill plates it is customary to roll the ingots or slabs in both directions (cross-rolling) to give uniform physical properties whether the test sample is taken parallel or transverse to the greatest dimension. On the Universal mill, plates are rolled in one direction only; the vertical rolls producing a straight, fairly parallel mill edge. The product of such a mill cannot be expected to have uniform properties in both directions. This metallurgical practice is important in the judicious selection of suitable quality plate material for various parts of the boiler. Drum plate, for instance, must be of higher quality and uniformity than plate used solely for structural purposes.

Tube Manufacturing

Many thousand feet of steel tubes of suitable size, shape and material are required for a large boiler unit. These tubes are used in saturated surfaces including furnace walls and floors, and in superheaters and reheaters, economizers and air heaters. Headers also might be classed as tubes, since the process of manufacture is similar, except the size range (9¾ in. to 14 in.) is beyond that ordinarily associated with tubes.

Seamless steel tubing is the generally used stand-

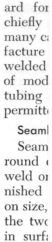

ard for
chiefly
many c
facture
welded
of mod
tubing
permitte

Seaml

Seam
round
weld o
nished
on size,
the two
in surfa
dimensi
close t
special
This p
final he
peratur

The
tools, c
procedu

Cente
may be
ing ro
machin
a some
is first
hole is
of the h
hole m
the bill
to pres

The
40 in. t
is then
ern rot

Pierci
designe
tween t
which
directly
tion an
proper
ameter
point h
is illust
ing, th
tube an
in a su
rolling.

Rollin
lengthe
the ap

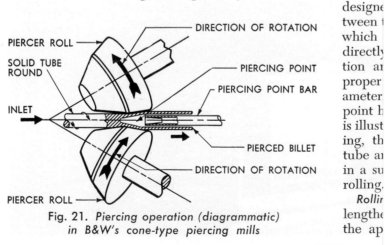

Fig. 21. Piercing operation (diagrammatic) in B&W's cone-type piercing mills

22-18

France, was first used in the United States by B&W. In this process a hollow billet is confined in a container between the ram of the press and the die. A mandrel extending from the ram passes through the billet and the die. As the ram moves forward, the metal is squeezed out between the die and the mandrel, using a special glass lubricant.

Although the billet may be hollowed in the same press, prior to extrusion, by forcing the mandrel through the blank, this method is limited by the strength and stiffness of the mandrel. In an alternate method used by B&W, the billet is first pierced, with an oversize hole, in a separate press. This permits the use of a larger and stiffer mandrel, with less wander at the far end of the pierced billet. Use of a larger diameter mandrel is important because, in some cases, the ratio of extrusion mandrel length to diameter may be about 30 to 1. Use of a separate piercing press improves the concentricity of the final tube since it depends on the concentricity of the pierced billet prior to extrusion.

With present facilities it is possible to produce tube hollows ranging in size from 1½ in. to 3½ in. OD and 0.160 in. to 0.600 in. wall thickness, and from 20 ft maximum length for the heavier wall, to 60 ft maximum length for the lighter wall. These hollows are subsequently reduced by cold drawing to finished tubing of the desired size.

Electric Resistance Welded (ERW) Tubes

Electric resistance welded steel tubing is made by forming flat strip into tubular shape (skelp) and welding the edges together in an electric resistance welding machine. A mill used for the continuous production of electric resistance welded tubing is shown in Fig. 25.

This tubing is widely used in stationary, marine and locomotive boilers. Within the size range in which it is produced it is equal to seamless carbon steel tubing, and in some respects superior. It is, therefore, being used to an increasing extent by manufacturers of steam generating equipment. Com-

pared with seamless tubing, electric resistance welded boiler tubing has a smoother surface, a more uniform wall thickness and less eccentricity. Because of softness and uniformity welded tubes are easily installed.

The pressure tubing produced by electric resistance welding is mainly of carbon steel; and both rimmed and killed steel strip are used. Rimmed steel is used extensively in the lower carbon grades because of its excellent welding characteristics. In rimmed steels, B&W uses single width strip to avoid welding rim to core as would be the case when welding slit strip cut from wide strip. If the additional cost is warranted and killed steel is required by the specifications, slit strip may be used because of its more homogeneous structure.

Electric resistance welded boiler tubing is commonly made in sizes from ¾ in. to 4 in. diam, in gages from 0.049 in. to 0.180 inch.

Hot rolled strip, in coils, is used for most of the tubing produced by this method. The first operation is running the strip through a scale breaker under tension on to a recoiler. After recoiling, following the scale breaking operation, the coil is back-spun to open the individual wraps. The coil is then pickled, rinsed, and conveyed to the cold rolling and sizing mill.

Cold rolling is applied to the hot rolled strip to smooth its surface and to obtain a uniform dimensional accuracy. Close control of the limits of thickness requires the use of a magnetic gage, running on the strip.

After cold rolling, the strip is recoiled and the coil is fed into a leveler for flattening; the ends are then cut square and butt welded to the ends of the preceding and following coils to form an endless strip. Following the butt welding operation, the moving strip is slit to the exact width required for the tube to be made. Width and thickness within close limits are essential for uniformly perfect welding. For strong and sound welds slitting also pro-

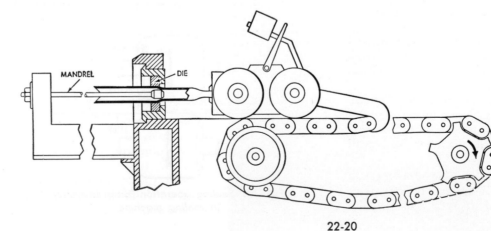

Fig. 24. Cold-draw-bench for producing close-tolerance, fine-surface-finish tubes

22-20

the weld me
porous becau

In the late
for metallic
essentially fr
ing wire wa:
combustible
was shielded
period of he
desirable oxi
weld puddle.

Suitable El
developed tc
in a variety
tions. All o
classified by
American Sc
according to
duced. Class
ing applied 1
position weld
sure work, 1
used with d
trode, used w
type, where t
primarily upc
tion of some
structural as:
is not an e
E-6013 type
larity and a
preferred bec
titanium diox
electrode co:
stabilizer per
positions at 1

In boiler c
in the down]
group of higl
E-6020 and I
trodes of thi
coating, usua
and can be u
duce X-ray-sc

A relatively
electrodes is
reverse polar:
This type of
protection ag
est weld met
of welding.
in boiler con
characteristic:
type, particu]
weld metal ii

Perhaps the
work is a ca1

Fig. 25. B&W Electric-resistance-welded-tube mill for continuous tube-length production

vides fresh edges, eliminating rust and strip-edge damage.

The strip is folded into open tube form (skelp) in a forming mill, preparatory to welding. In the resistance welder, beryllium-copper roll-type electrodes come in contact with the upper surfaces of the formed tube on either side of the seam, while pressure rolls located directly below the electrodes provide the pressure required to bring the edges of the tubing into contact. The outside and inside flashes (or upsets) formed in the welding operation are removed by special tools. The inside weld bead is trimmed within a specified height; the outside bead is cut off. Both of these operations are continuous as the tubing emerges from the welding mill.

On leaving the resistance welder, the tubing is accurately sized and straightened in a three-pass mill. As the welded tubing emerges from the sizing mill it is cut to required length. The transverse welds at coil ends are not allowed as a part of the tube and are cut out. The tubes are then completely normalized in a controlled-atmosphere furnace to a uniform structure throughout, and the surface is given a rust-retardant oxide finish.

The tubes emerging from the normalizing furnace are conveyed through rotary straighteners discharging to the cutoff machines, where each tube is cut exactly to the required length. Coupons cut from the ends of tubes are tested mechanically, according to specifications. One coupon is flattened with the

weld at the flattened edge, another coupon is expanded, and, if required, a third coupon is crushed longitudinally. In these tests, to pass inspection the coupons must not crack or split in the tube metal or open at the weld.

Other machines then perform operations as required in trimming to exact length, chamfering ends inside and outside, and reaming the inside bore at the ends.

Inspection and Testing

All tubes are subjected to hydrostatic pressure from 1000 to 6000 psi or as required by the specifications. Hydrostatic pressure is maintained for several seconds, and a shock stress is induced while under test pressure by striking the tube with mallets.

After hydrostatic testing, the tubing is ready for final inspection, including surface examination, micrometer check of dimensions, and a length check. The finished tubing, stamped with the Company's identification mark and the inspector's symbol, is then stenciled and bundled for shipping.

Quality and Metallurgical Control

To maintain a consistent standard of high quality in electric-resistance-welded tubing, a chemical analysis must be made of each heat of strip received. To preclude mechanical difficulty in forming and welding, camber and strip dimensions are also constantly checked. Etch tests are made to

fully for multipass welding of plate up to and even in excess of 6 in. thick.

Gas Welding. Oxyacetylene gas welding, another fusion-welding process, finds relatively little application in boiler construction in the United States. Compared with metal-arc welding, particularly for thicker materials, this process is expensive and slow. However, there are some applications, such as butt joints in light-gage tubing, where gas welding is used to advantage. In general, the use of gas welding in boiler construction is limited to the plain carbon steels.

Use of the atomic-hydrogen process of fusion welding is limited to light-gage materials, preferably not over ¼ inch. This fact and the inherent slowness of the process have restricted its use.

The inert-gas-arc process of fusion welding, in which helium, argon, or a combination of helium and argon supplies the shielding atmosphere, has somewhat the same limitations as the hydrogen arc and is rarely applied in boiler construction. However, it appears likely that a serious attempt will be made to develop this process, which may open up a new field in welding for boiler construction.

Brazing. The various methods of joining by the brazing process are used rarely in boiler work, since the strength of the joint, particularly at elevated temperatures, is usually too low.

Welding of a Power Boiler

In building a power boiler, thousands of pounds of electrodes of many different types and sizes may be used. The choice of electrode type and size depends primarily upon the composition, thickness, and joint design of the material to be welded. In all cases, welding stresses in a joint must be kept within a safe limit for good practice. Welds in structural members, brackets, supports, casing, and other components, where the finished part is subject to relatively low service stresses, present few complications.

Preheating. Perhaps the most effective way to counteract high stresses in deposited weld metal is to preheat the parts to be welded. The proper preheating temperature depends mainly upon the chemical composition and thickness of the material to be welded and to a lesser extent upon the welding method and type of electrode selected.

A joint in 1-in. thick high-alloy (austenitic) steel, such as 25 per cent Cr and 20 per cent Ni, would not require preheating, while a joint in (ferritic) intermediate Croloy tubing of 2½-in. OD and ¼-in. wall thickness would require a minimum preheat of some 300 F. A 4-in. OD by ⅜-in. wall of SA-106 carbon-steel pipe would be welded without preheat, while a drum plate of SA-212 carbon steel 6 in. thick would be preheated to about 400 F prior

to and during welding. The most severe preheat requirements are for high-carbon (1 per cent) alloy castings containing some chromium, molybdenum, manganese, etc., where preheats as high as 1000 F are used.

Submerged-arc welding, compared with multiple-pass open-arc welding, may be done at some 25 per cent lower preheat temperatures, since the cooling stresses are less severe because the heat input per inch of weld is substantially greater and consequently the rate of cooling of the molten metal is slower. The choice of proper preheat temperature also depends to a marked degree upon the wide variation in the behavior of weld metals deposited with different types of electrodes. Weld metal deposited with lime-coated mild-steel electrodes is practically unaffected by high cooling rates of the weld, while hot rods (E-6020 – E-6030) are very sensitive to variations in cooling rates.

Method of Welding. Automatic welding, using either the submerged-arc or open-arc method, would be selected in preference to manual operation wherever the work can be done under an automatic welding head. However, manual welding must be used for certain types of joints not readily weldable automatically, and, of course, if the work can be positioned to permit its use, downhand welding with the downhand hot rod (E-6020 – E-6030) would be preferable. All other welding has to be done in position, using all-position electrodes of the cellulose type.

The above choice of welding method and operation applies to all carbon steels and carbon-molybdenum steels. While submerged-arc welding has been used in some cases, the majority of welds in joining Croloy steels are made manually with the open-arc method. Stainless steel of the high-Cr-Ni type is welded almost exclusively by the open-arc method, using stainless coated electrodes of the proper composition. However, light-gage tubes formed from strip are welded in large quantities by inert-gas-atmosphere arc welding.

Post-Heat Treatment. The post-heat treatment of weldments is again a function of the composition and thickness of the materials joined and, to a considerable extent, of the complexity of the structure. To avoid cracking, where heavy plates are involved, it is customary, in some cases, to stress-relieve the partially welded joint. Structural welding, on the other hand, is rarely heat treated. Welded joints subject to the internal pressure of the boiler are post-heat treated, except plain carbon-steel or carbon-molybdenum-steel (C equal to or less than 0.20 per cent) tubing or piping of ⅜-in. or less wall thickness and 4-in. or smaller diameter. All Croloy steels of the low-chromium air-hardening grades and most of the high-alloy steels are heat treated after welding. The post-heat-treatment temperatures may vary from 1150 to 1250 F for carbon and carbon-molybdenum steels to as high as 1950 F for some of the high-Cr-Ni austenitic steels.

See Table B in the Appendix for recommended welding rod, preheating, and postweld heat treatment for gas and arc welding of carbon and carbon-molybdenum steels and various ferritic and austenitic Croloy combinations.

Weld Quality. To assure consistently high-quality welds, all welding operators in the plant engaged in boiler work must first prove their ability by proper qualification tests in welding plates or pipes to meet the requirements of the *Welding Qualifications Section* of the ASME *Boiler and Pressure Vessel Code.* As a routine check of the quality of the work, samples of welds made during production should be taken from the job and tested in the laboratory.

To check mechanical properties of the deposited weld metal, all major welding on drums and other critical components is run over to attached test plates, which are cropped and subjected to thorough laboratory tests.

Nondestructive Testing. By Code requirement, after welding and heat treatment, all the main seams and some of the drum attachments must be examined by X ray or radiographed. By the use of powerful X-ray equipment, even very minute flaws or defects in the weld deposit can be detected and can then be cut out and rewelded as required. A 1-million- and a 2-million-volt station are included in the B&W X-ray equipment for shop examination. In the field or where inaccessibility precludes the use of X-ray equipment, examination is made by gamma rays from isotopes or radium. For the detection of flaws and defects open to the surface but too fine to be seen, magnetic particle inspection (Magnaflux) and fluorescent penetrant* inspection (Zyglo) are also used extensively to assure sound welds. The Magnaflux method is used only for magnetic (ferritic) steels, and the Zyglo method is used for non-magnetic steels.

Mechanical Properties and Testing

Specifications standardizing all the conditions relating to the test piece and the method of testing have been formulated by the American Society for Testing Materials and other authorities. Holding to these specifications, it is possible to insure duplication of certain minimum mechanical properties which determine the acceptability of a steel for a particular use.

*In this method a small quantity of fluid, carrying a fluorescent dye, is applied to the surface of the weld and adjacent steel. The liquid is drawn by capillary attraction into any cracks or discontinuities appearing in the surface, and it is made visible by exposure to "black" (near ultraviolet) light.

Tensile Test. The tensile test, a gradually applied unidirectional pull, determines the maximum nominal load that a material can withstand before actually breaking.

The relationship between stress (load per unit area) and the corresponding strain (deformation) in the test piece is illustrated in the stress-strain diagrams (a) and (b) of Fig. 26. The metal begins to stretch as soon as the load is applied, and during the period of the metal's elastic behavior the strain is directly proportional to the stress (Hooke's Law, elongation $\propto$ load $\div$ area). Consequently, if the stress is released at any point along O-A (in either diagram, Fig. 26), the test coupon will return to its initial dimensions. However, if the stress is increased beyond the value A, the metal will no longer continue to be perfectly elastic (there will be a permanent elongation), and the linear relationship (proportionality) between stress and strain ceases. The value A is known as the proportional limit of the material, and in this elementary discussion it may be considered practically the same as the elastic limit, which may be defined as the maximum unit stress that can be developed just before permanent elongation occurs. The exact location of these limits involves laborious techniques and requires extremely sensitive measuring devices.

The unit stress at which a ductile material suddenly continues to elongate without further increase in load is known as its yield point (YP). Since the true yield point for most metals is indefinite and, in common with the proportional and elastic limits, is difficult to determine with accuracy, these terms are being supplanted by "yield strength." Yield strength (YS), which can be readily determined, is the unit stress at which the permanent elongation of the metal reaches an arbitrarily specified value, usually 0.1, 0.2, or 0.5 per cent of the gage length of the test piece.

If the loading is continued after the point of yield strength has been reached, a test piece of homogeneous composition and uniform cross section will be elongated uniformly over its length, with a corresponding reduction in area. Eventually a constriction or "necking down" will occur (in ductile material), usually in the region of the middle third of the test piece (Fig. 27). In other materials the necking down may not be localized but may occur as a more or less uniform reduction in area along the full gage length to instant of rupture. In all cases with ductile materials, however, an appreciable increase in elongation occurs over the portion of reduced area. The elongation before the specimen finally breaks will increase with the ductility of the steel. The maximum applied load in lb required to pull the specimen apart, divided by the area in sq in. of the original cross section of the test

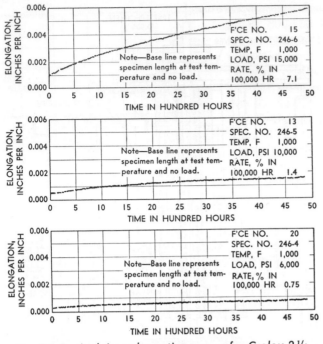

Fig. 34. *Typical time-elongation curves for Croloy 2¼.*
Tested for three loads at 1000 F

of 0.1 per cent per 1000 hr and 0.01 per cent per 1000 hr (see Fig. 35).

The form of the creep curve depends upon the chemical composition and microstructure of the metal as well as upon the applied load and test temperature. The creep behavior of steel is influenced also by various metallurgical factors, as noted below. Tests of long duration provide the most reliable data, both as to the accuracy of the observations and the attainment of structural equilibrium.

Stress-Rupture Test

The stress-rupture test is essentially an overloaded

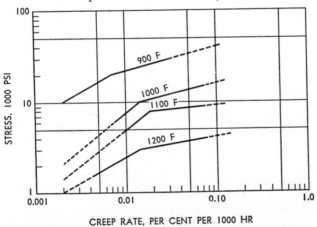

Fig. 35. *Design stress values for 2¼ Croloy at different temperatures for creep rates in the range to 0.1% per 1000 hours*

creep test, continued to actual rupture of the specimen. The more descriptive names "creep-to-rupture" and "creep-rupture" are now frequently used for this test. The time for rupture at any temperature is some function of the applied load. Since the modern concept of this test was first formulated, in 1937 and 1938, it has rapidly gained favor as a necessary supplement to the regular creep test in evaluating the load-carrying ability of metals at elevated temperatures.

Generally, the equipment employed in making the rupture test is the same as that used for the creep test. However, while the elongation of a specimen during a creep test usually varies from 5 to 250 microinches per day, the elongation during a rupture test may be 100 times greater or even more. Consequently, different instruments for measuring the elongation of the specimen are required.

A logarithmic plot of stress versus time for fracture of the specimen generally takes the form of the typical curves shown in Fig. 36. In general, rapid rates of elongation indicate a transgranular (ductile) fracture, and slow rates of elongation indicate an intergranular (brittle) fracture. As a rule, surface oxidation is present when the fracture is transgranular, while visible intercrystalline oxidation may or may not be present when the fracture is intergranular. Because of the discontinuities produced by the presence of intercrystalline oxides, the time to rupture at a given load may be appreciably reduced. The presence of intercrystalline oxidation is indicated in Fig. 36 by the change in slope of the curve for 1200 F.

The duration of the rupture test of a single specimen may be from a few hours to 10,000 hr or longer. A complete creep-rupture test of a given material actually consists of a series of tests at constant temperature with each specimen loaded at a different level. The time for rupture of each specimen is noted. It is customary in the report of test data to give the stress for fracture in 100, 1000, 10,000, and 100,000 hr (see Fig. 37). Since very few tests are carried on for more than 10,000 hr, the values for fracture times longer than this are determined by extrapolation. At the Alliance Research and Development Laboratory, it is the practice to load the specimens so that one or more at each temperature will run for at least 5000 hr, and usually for 10,000 hr or more. The longer testing times give greater assurance that the material has reached structural equilibrium and also materially improve the accuracy of extrapolating the rupture strength for still longer times.

Some Factors Affecting Creep

Creep of metals is a sensitive property and may be profoundly affected by a variety of metallurgical

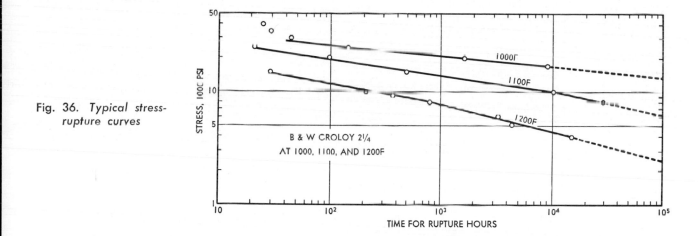

Fig. 36. Typical stress-rupture curves

B & W CROLOY 2¼
AT 1000, 1100, AND 1200F

STRESS, 1000 PSI

TIME FOR RUPTURE HOURS

factors. These factors are difficult to control commercially, and it is almost impossible to isolate any one factor in order to study its specific effects on creep. It is not surprising, therefore, that little progress has been made in establishing general rules regarding the creep behavior of metals.

Composition. It is generally recognized that the most direct way to improve the creep properties of a metal is by adding alloying elements. Carbide forming elements, such as molybdenum, tungsten, and, to a lesser degree, chromium and vanadium effectively enhance the creep resistance of steels. Increased carbon content is beneficial up to a temperature range of approximately 900-1000 F; above this range, however, variations in carbon content in most wrought steels appear to have little influence. Manganese and small additions of silicon have some effect in improving the resistance to creep at the lower temperatures. Aluminum, used as a deoxidizer in plain carbon steel, or as an intentional addition in alloy steels, greatly reduces creep strength at high temperatures. Nickel additions are beneficial when used in sufficient amounts to produce an austenitic structure, which is more creep resistant than ferrite. At the higher temperatures, austenitic stainless steels (18Cr-8Ni type) and certain special alloys have creep properties much superior to low or high-alloy ferritic steels.

Grain Size. At the higher temperatures, experimental evidence strongly indicates that coarse-grained materials usually exhibit greater resistance to creep than fine-grained materials. Conversely, at the lower temperatures, fine-grain structures appear to be slightly superior. However, there are many exceptions to this rule, and no satisfactory explanation has been advanced to account for the specific effect of grain structure on the creep behavior of metals.

Heat Treatment. The creep characteristics of metals are affected by heat treatment, which controls grain size and the stability of structure. When a metal is exposed to elevated temperatures for a long period of time there is a tendency, under the stress and heat to which it is subjected, for the initial structure to attain a more stable state. For instance, lamellar pearlite may revert during service to the more stable spheroidized structure which, in turn, brings about rapid deterioration in the creep strength of steel. Upon prolonged heating in the 900 to 1200 F range, the carbide phase in plain carbon and carbon-molybdenum steels may ultimately change to graphite which, when highly localized, is believed to account for certain failures noted in service. Obviously, therefore, the selection of the

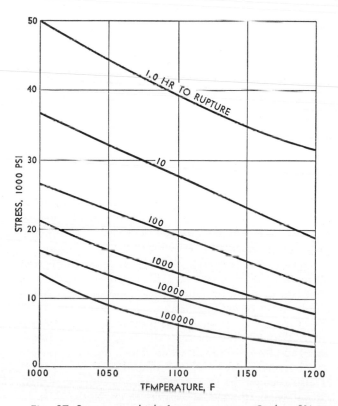

Fig. 37. Stress at which fracture occurs, Croloy 2¼

Table 2

Composition and Properties of Plate Steels

Chemical Composition

ASME Spec	C	Mn	P	S	Si	Cr	Mo
SA-212	0.28-0.35	0.90	0.035-0.04	0.05	0.15-0.30	—	—
SA-285	0.15-0.30	0.80	0.035-0.05	0.05	—	—	—
SA-301	0.18-0.25	0.80	0.035-0.04	0.05	0.15-0.30	0.50-0.70	0.40-0.60

NOTE: Percentages are maximum unless range is given.

Mechanical Properties

	Tensile Strength*	Yield Strength*	Elong in 2 in.†	Elong in 8 in.†
SA-212	65,000-82,000	32,500-41,000	26.9-21.3	24.6-19.5
SA-285	45,000-65,000	22,500-32,500	—	33.3-23.1
SA-301	70,000-82,000	38,500-45,100	23.6-20.1	25.0-21.3

*Pounds per square inch. †In per cent.

NOTE: The chemical composition and mechanical properties given in this table represent a summary of the requirements for the various grades under the specifications noted.

best type of heat treatment for a particular high-temperature application should be based largely on the degree of stability which it would impart to the structure initially and also throughout the service life of the steel at elevated temperatures.

In general, experience has shown that for service above approximately 950 F, annealing (or normalizing) is the most suitable treatment. Age-hardenable alloys, intended for service in which creep resistance is required, are usually subjected to a dual heat treatment. In the initial heat treatment, the precipitating phase is brought into solution; and the final heat treatment is to insure stability of the precipitated phase at the service temperature.

Surface Stability. Creep strength may be seriously impaired by surface reactions at elevated temperatures. By reduction in effective cross section from progressive oxidation or corrosion of the metal, the unit load is increased and the rate of creep is accelerated. Under certain conditions, highly concentrated stresses may greatly accelerate and localize the mechanism of oxidation.

Surface stability may be enhanced by alloying additions of silicon, aluminum, chromium, or nickel. Surface oxidation may also be decreased by applying protective coatings to the metal.

Method of Manufacture. Minor variations in method of manufacture have markedly modified the creep behavior of steel. In general, the investigations made would seem to indicate that steel melted in the electric furnace is somewhat superior to open-hearth steel. This is probably because of less rigid controls and, therefore, wider variations in deoxidation practice usually encountered in the open-hearth process. It is also recognized that killed steel is more creep resistant than rimmed or similar nondeoxidized steel. However, deoxidation per se does not insure superior

long-time high-temperature properties. For example, at 850 F, steels deoxidized only with silicon and having a coarse grain structure are much more resistant to creep than steels deoxidized with large amounts of aluminum and of fine grain size. The detrimental effect of aluminum results from its potency in causing grain refinement and also its acceleration of spheroidization and graphitization of the carbide phase. Both of these characteristics tend to lower creep resistance at elevated temperatures, while a coarse grain size and stability of structure tend to increase resistance to creep.

Steels Used in Boiler Construction

A considerable variety of both carbon and alloy steels is used in boiler construction.

Plate Steels

Since the temperatures do not exceed the saturated steam temperature, the significant mechanical properties of steel for steam drums are the tensile or yield strength, or both, as determined at room temperature, rather than creep-strength properties. Design is based on an allowable stress of ¼ of the minimum ultimate strength to 650 F. For special requirements and the higher temperatures, there are certain advantages in going to higher-tensile-strength carbon-steel plate or to alloy-steel plate. Above 650 F, reduction in working stresses is mandatory for carbon steels and some alloy grades of plate, while certain other alloy plate materials may be used for temperatures to 750 F without reduction in working stress. Use of flange-quality plate is not permitted at temperatures exceeding 850 F nor in thicknesses exceeding 2 inches. When made from plate, manway covers, handhole fittings, lugs, braces, and other parts subject to pressure must be of firebox or flange quality.

Chemical composition and mechanical strength of several plate grades of carbon and low-alloy steels, approved by the ASME for construction of boilers and other pressure vessels, are given in Table 2. For stationary boilers, B&W mainly uses thoroughly deoxidized (killed) carbon steel to SA-212 specification. If required by certain service conditions for saving weight in marine work or because of design requirements, other grades, including alloy-steel plate, may be used. Typical microstructures of several plate steels are shown by Fig. 38.

Tube and Pipe Steels

The principal heat-absorption surfaces of the boiler are the steam-generating tubes, including water-wall furnace tubing and the economizer. Ordinarily, these sections of the boiler are made of hot-rolled low-carbon steel tubing, although small-diameter tubes or special sizes may be cold drawn and an-

nealed. Seamless and electric-resistance-welded tubes are used interchangeably in generating tubes. However, seamless tubes are supplied for high-pressure units requiring a wall thickness difficult to form as skelp. Some of the specifications for ordinary boiler tubes, such as SA-83 and SA-178, do not stipulate whether rimmed or killed steel is to be used. As explained above under tube-manufacturing processes, the current general practice of B&W is to use killed-type steel for seamless tubes and rimmed steel for electric-resistance-welded tubes.

Medium-carbon steel (0.35% C max) finds considerable application for boiler and furnace wall tubes, since this grade will permit higher stress levels in the zone of saturation temperatures from 540 to 685 F encountered in service. The mechanical strength properties are superior to low-carbon steel, and, therefore, lighter-wall tubes may be used for equivalent pressures.

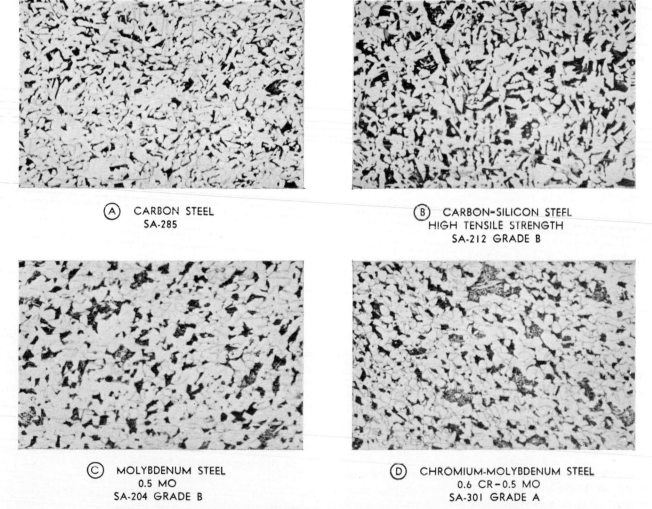

Ⓐ   CARBON STEEL
SA-285

Ⓑ   CARBON–SILICON STEEL
HIGH TENSILE STRENGTH
SA-212 GRADE B

Ⓒ   MOLYBDENUM STEEL
0.5 MO
SA-204 GRADE B

Ⓓ   CHROMIUM-MOLYBDENUM STEEL
0.6 CR–0.5 MO
SA-301 GRADE A

Fig. 38. *Typical structures of plate steels 100x. White matrix, ferrite; dark areas, pearlite; with carbide phase appearing in mottled areas (Widmanstätten pattern) in B, C, & D. Steel shown in A used principally in nonpressure parts. Steels shown in B, C, & D used in pressure parts*

The highest metal temperature of pressure parts in the boiler is in the superheater. Consequently, it must be made of material having superior high-temperature properties and resistance to oxidation. Carbon steel is a suitable and economical material to about 850-950 F metal temperature depending upon pressure. Above this range, alloy steels are required because of the low oxidation resistance and the low allowable stresses of carbon steel. Sometimes two or more alloys may be used in the construction of the superheater. The lower alloy, such as carbon-molybdenum steel, is used toward the inlet section while the better materials, the so-called low and intermediate chromium-alloy steels, are used toward the outlet where the steam and metal temperatures are increasing. Stainless steel tubes are required in the hottest sections of the superheater to meet the operating conditions of modern high-pressure (1800-4500 psi or more) high-temperature (1000-1050 F and even 1150 F) central station boilers.

The B&W Croloy Steels. For many years B&W has been active in the development of tubing alloys for high-temperature applications. A considerable number of the presently accepted ASME standard steels for superheater practice were developed originally by B&W. These steels with the designation "Croloy," meaning chromium-containing alloy, are available in a graded series of intermediate Cr-Mo alloys and also in stainless Cr or Cr-Ni grades.

The intermediate Croloy steels (up to and including Croloy 9M) are complex chromium steels with varying contents of molybdenum. These alloy steels are magnetic and have normal thermal transformations. They may be considered "ferritic" steels in that their microstructure, in the annealed state, is composed mainly of ferrite (alpha iron) and carbides. In general, the behavior of these alloys is somewhat similar to that of high-carbon steel, although they are more ductile for a given strength because of the absence of the equivalent amount of carbide. Heating to or above their transformation temperature, required for forming and after welding, makes these alloys so susceptible to air-hardening that an annealing or stress-relieving (tempering) treatment is necessary to restore toughness and ductility following these operations. Addition of carbide-forming (stabilizing) elements, such as titanium and niobium, tends to restrict air-hardening of the Croloys on heat-treating at temperatures up to about 1700 F. Gradual hardening will take place above these temperatures.

Stainless Croloys are usually classified as of austenitic or ferritic type according to chemical composition and metallurgical characteristics.

Austenitic stainless Croloys are low-carbon chromium-nickel steels containing above 16 per cent

chromium with sufficient nickel to provide an austenitic structure at all temperatures. Moderate amounts of other elements, such as molybdenum, niobium, niobium plus tantalum, titanium, and silicon, may be added for special purposes. Austenitic Croloys are normally nonmagnetic but may become slightly magnetic when cold worked. These steels do not undergo transformations in the usual sense and therefore cannot be hardened by heat treatment. They can be hardened and strengthened materially, however, by cold-working. Included in the austenitic group of stainless Croloys are the widely known 18-8 type steels (18% Cr and 8% Ni).

Ferritic stainless Croloys, usually referred to as "high-chromium irons" or "straight-chromium steels," are iron-chromium alloys containing chromium in excess of 11.5 per cent. Compared with austenitic (chromium-nickel) Croloys, these steels are ferromagnetic, possess less ductility, are notch sensitive, and are subject to excessive grain growth on welding or other treatment at high temperatures. Despite these features, which tend to curtail their utility to some degree, the high-chromium irons occupy an important place in industry in both corrosion- and heat-resisting applications. The 12, 18, and 27 per cent chromium steels are representative of the ferritic group of stainless Croloys.

Applications of Tube and Pipe Steels

The Croloy steels in widest use for superheater tubing in boiler service have been: (a) 2% Cr and 0.5% Mo, (b) 2¼% Cr and 1% Mo, (c) 3% Cr and 0.90% Mo, and (d) 9% Cr and 1% Mo. The most widely used stainless steel is the austenitic 18-8 stabilized with titanium, niobium, or niobium plus tantalum. The chemical composition of these and other grades of carbon and alloy steels for boiler and superheater tubing and steam piping is included in the addenda to Table D in the Appendix.

Creep strength in the intermediate alloy steels is not proportional to chromium content and is somewhat better in those of lowest chromium content. Therefore it becomes necessary, depending upon the anticipated metal temperatures, in choosing the optimum composition to have in mind both strength properties and resistance to oxidation.

The selection of an appropriate and economical material for construction of the superheater is dependent upon a number of factors. Because of the temperature drop caused by the steam film immediately adjacent to the inside surface, the metal of the superheater tube will usually be from 50 to 150 F hotter than the steam in the tube.

Dry steam is delivered to the superheater from the boiler at saturation temperature ranging up to 675 F or more, depending upon the pressure at which the boiler is designed to operate. As the steam passes through the tubes, it may be superheated in some cases to a final temperature of 1050 or 1150 F. Carbon steels are reasonably resistant to scaling in steam and in combustion atmospheres up to about 1000 F but, under high stress, may suffer accelerated oxidation at somewhat lower temperatures. This attack generally takes the form of intergranular penetrations which, since the effective wall thickness of the tube is reduced, increase the unit stress and act as stress-concentration centers. Carbon-steel tubing in the superheater is therefore restricted to the moderate temperatures and pressures, while alloy steels are used for the more severe conditions.

To insure the long life required for satisfactory superheater design, the metal used must meet the following primary requirements at the anticipated operating temperature: (a) resistance to corrosion by steam, (b) resistance to corrosion by flue gas, (c) resistance to creep, and (d) resistance to stress rupture for a reasonable life period. To establish an adequate margin of safety and length of service life, these characteristics of the metal must be given due consideration in design. Economy dictates that the lowest alloy with properties suitable to the conditions should be used, stepping up from carbon steel to carbon-molybdenum steel and to the lower chromium alloy steels as the temperatures increase. For metal temperatures approaching 1125 F, the lower-alloy steels up to and including 3 per cent chromium are usually adequate. Chromium-molybdenum steel (9% Cr) and the stainless steels are used at higher temperatures where conditions require either an increase in resistance to oxidation or higher load-carrying characteristics, or both.

TABLE 3

Safe Maximum Tube-Metal Temperatures
(Oxidation-Resistance Basis)

Material	ASME Specification	Maximum Metal Temp*, F
Carbon steel	SA-210	950
Carbon molybdenum	SA-209 grade T1a	975
Croloy ½	SA-213 (SA-335 P2)	975
Croloy 1¼	SA-213 grade T11	1050
Croloy 2	SA 213 grade T3b	1080
Croloy 2¼	SA-213 grade T22	1100
Croloy 3M	SA-213 grade T21	1125
Croloy 5	SA-213 grade T5	1150
Croloy 9M	SA-213 grade T9	1200
Croloy 18-8 Ti	SA-213 grade TP321	1400†
Croloy 18-8 Cb	SA-213 grade TP347	1400†

*Of surface in contact with flue gases.

†Temperature limit may be modified depending upon character of fuel and other circumstances. It can be 100 to 200 F higher in low-pressure process-steam superheaters fired with low-sulfur fuel, but it should not exceed 1150 F when firing vanadium-bearing oil.

As a general guide, where pressure stresses are not excessively high, the temperatures in Table 3 may be recommended as a safe maximum for various alloy steels. These temperature limits apply to the surface in contact with the flue gas and are based solely on the resistance-to-oxidation characteristics of the metal.

Stresses used for calculation of tube and/or pipe thickness should correspond to those given in Table P-7 of the ASME *Boiler and Pressure Vessel Code* for the respective materials. An abridgment of Table P-7 appears in the Appendix as Table E.

Steam Piping. The steam leads, or piping connecting the boiler and turbine, are highly important components of the power plant. Such piping should be properly designed and erected to accommodate thermal expansion and absorb vibratory stresses, and it should be so supported that it does not produce imposed stress on the boiler proper. While some mechanical joints are still used, it is now common practice to weld most of the joints between the boiler and the turbine. Carbon-steel piping is used for moderate pressures and for steam temperatures up to 800 F.

Carbon-steel pipe has shown a tendency to graphitization in the region of the welds at temperatures over 800 F, and it has been safe and prudent to restrict its use in this service to a temperature limit of this value*. Consequently, at these higher temperatures carbon-molybdenum steel has been commonly used for steam piping in many central stations. Long-time service, however, indicates that piping of this material also graphitizes, with a chain-like formation in the heat-affected area of welds and random formations in the body of the pipe proper. This phenomenon, the effect of which has made it necessary to reweld and replace a considerable amount of piping in the power industry, has been widely investigated. It has been found that the rate and extent of graphitization in piping materials are affected to some degree by steel-manufacturing practice. While it appears that graphitization is more likely to occur in materials which have received a considerable amount of aluminum during deoxidation, recent investigations indicate that, at somewhat longer time, it will also occur (at 900 to 950 F) in coarse-grain normal steel in which little or no aluminum has been used.

For greater resistance to graphitization under prolonged usage, the current trend in steam-piping materials is to use chromium-molybdenum steels. Steels of 0.5% Cr-0.5% Mo and 1% Cr-0.5% Mo are now

---

*Graphitization has been detected in carbon-steel tubes in small amounts, but the experience has been that no failures have occurred, and consequently carbon steel is used for tubing at somewhat higher temperatures (see under *Tube and Pipe Steels*, above) than in the case of piping.

commonly used in the range between 850 and about 1000 F, with a somewhat higher chromium content preferable in the range 950 to 1050 F. Steel of 1¼% Cr-0.5% Mo has also been used to some extent. In several recently designed plants, steels of 2¼% Cr-1% Mo, and 3% Cr-0.90% Mo and, in some, even stainless steels of 18-8 Ti or 18-8 Cb alloy have been used for steam piping.

Steam piping of extreme wall thickness is made by boring solid forgings. Where moderate wall thickness is required, the piping, of seamless type, is made by the rotary piercing process. Precise practices in welding, hot bending, and heat-treating are required in fabricating air-hardening alloys containing chromium, and metallurgical control is a predominant factor in securing the results desired. The steels presently used for steam piping and the corresponding nominal maximum steam temperatures are listed in Table 4. Allowable stress values are specified in Table P-7 of the ASME *Boiler and Pressure Vessel Code* (see Table E in the Appendix, referred to above).

TABLE 4

Suggested Materials for Steam Piping

Material	ASME Specification	Nom Max Steam Temp, F
Carbon steel	SA-106	800
Croloy ½	SA-335 grade P2	950
Croloy 1	SA-335 grade P12	1000
Croloy 1¼	SA-335 grade P11	1050
Croloy 2¼	SA-335 grade P22	1100
Croloy 18-8 Cb	SA-376 type 347	1200
Croloy 16-13-3	SA-376 type 316	1200

Forgings, Castings, Bolting, and Studs

A variety of parts for attachments, fittings, valves, and flanges may be made from carbon- or alloy-steel forgings and castings. While many of these parts are joined integrally to drums, water feed lines, steam lines, etc., by welding, there are also certain attachments which are joined with studs or by bolting. The material for bolts and studs must have high mechanical properties, and it is usually conditioned by normalizing and tempering or quenching and tempering. The tempering temperature is at least 100 F higher than the operating temperature in service. Furthermore, the material must be creep-resisting to minimize the relaxation in service, which would otherwise gradually loosen the fastening and necessitate retightening. Considerable study has been devoted to the subject of stresses and relaxation in

bolts and studs, and a variety of bolting steels suitable for different temperature levels and stresses have been developed and are now in common use.

Heat-Resisting Alloys

High-alloy heat-resisting materials must be used for certain parts in the boiler which are exposed to high temperature and cannot be water cooled. These parts are made from alloys of the oxidation-resistant, relatively high-strength, chromium-nickel-iron type, many of them cast to shape as metallic baffles, supports, and hanger fittings. Oil burner impellers, soot blower clamps, and hangers are also made of heat-resisting alloy steels.

Deterioration of these parts is through conversion of the surface layers to oxides, sulfides, and sulfates, and in this condition they are referred to as burnt or oxidized. Experience indicates that steels containing 25% Cr-12% Ni or 25% Cr-20% Ni give reasonably good service life, depending upon location of the part in the flue gas stream and upon the characteristics of the fuel. Temperatures to which these metal parts are exposed may range from 1000 to 2200 F. Life may be shortened if exposed to flue gases from fuel oil containing vanadium compounds. Sulfur compounds formed from combustion of high-sulfur fuels are also detrimental and will reduce life. These may coreact in the presence of vanadium and cause greatly accelerated rates of attack, especially when the metal temperature of the part exceeds 1300 F. In these circumstances, there may be some ad-

Fig. 39. *Microstructure of metals determined by photography and direct observation*

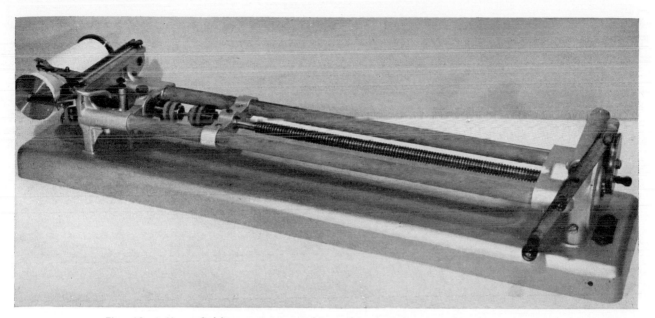

Fig. 40. *A Hounsfield tensometer used in making tensile tests of small specimens*

vantage in using an alloy containing approximately 29% Cr-9% Ni.

Grades of Steel in Boiler Construction

The grades of steel commonly used by builders in boiler construction for tubes, pipe, plates, forgings, castings, and in bolting are covered by ASME specifications as listed in Table F in the Appendix. Other steels in plate form, bars, and in structural shapes, used for nonpressure parts of boilers or for supports, are of usually accepted commercial standards.

Materials used in boiler construction should be obtained from selected vendors with long experience in the manufacture of the specific items required, such as steel plate, tubing and pipe, sheets, forgings, and structural steels.

Research and Development Facilities

For more than 40 years B&W has been actively engaged in the investigation of the behavior of steel under service conditions in the generation of power and in various industrial processes. Extensive laboratory facilities for metallurgical research, development, and control of quality in production are maintained at Alliance, O., Beaver Falls, Pa., and Barberton, O. A brief description of some of the equipment at these laboratories follows.

Metallographic Facilities. A variety of metallographs and microscopes (Fig. 39) are used by trained metallurgists to study the structural characteristics of metals. Microscopically observed characteristics, such as grain size, segregation, mode of occurrence and distribution of nonmetallic inclusions, and other heterogeneous conditions, have considerable bearing on the mechanical properties of the metal. By metallographic examination it is, therefore, possible to predict with some assurance the probable behavior of a metal under specific conditions in service. This method is useful also in determining the reason for failure of metal parts in service, which may lead to improvements or better operating control.

Heat-Treating. Accurately controlled electric furnaces are used for grain-growth studies, carburizing tests, hardenability (Jominy) tests, experimental heat treatments, and for scaling and aging tests of steels at various temperatures.

Melting. The laboratories are equipped with high-frequency induction furnaces for melting experimental heats of any combination of alloying elements

Fig. 41. *Automatic hot-twist test machine for evaluating high-temperature working characteristics of steels*

desired. The melts produced in these units are processed into bars and billets for experimental use in determining the properties of various alloy combinations. To study the suitability of these metals for seamless tubing, sample billets are pierced in a special piercing mill. The final product is subjected to a series of carefully conducted tests designed to supply preliminary information on working characteristics and mechanical properties.

Mechanical Testing. The mechanical-testing laboratories are equipped with Brinell, Rockwell, Vickers, and Tukon hardness testers, and complete facilities for tensile, compression, impact, tensile-impact, and fatigue tests on metals at various temperatures.

A Hounsfield tensometer for tensile tests (Fig. 40) is in operation at the laboratory in Alliance. This unit can be operated by motor or by hand, and it can be used in either the horizontal or vertical position. The load capacity of the tensometer is 4480 lb. Specimens of 0.125-in. diameter and a minimum gage length of 0.447 in. can be tested in this machine (fitted with a suitable heating element) at temperatures up to 1650 F.

At Beaver Falls, an automatic hot-twist test machine (Fig. 41) is used to evaluate high-temperature working characteristics of steels. There are also dilatometers for determining the critical transformation temperatures and the thermal expansion of metals.

Creep and Stress-Rupture Testing. The Research and Development Laboratories in Alliance are equipped with 36 stands for creep tests, 32 stands for creep-rupture tests, and 60 for stress-rupture tests. If desired, the 36 creep-test machines can also be used for creep-rupture tests.

The temperature for 20 of the creep-test machines is regulated by multiple-circuit electronic controls. These controls are actuated by the expansion of the furnace tubes, and the temperature can be regulated to within plus or minus 1 F up to 1550 F. In these units a test bar of 10-in. gage length is used, and it is possible to measure an extension of less than 10 microinches (0.00001 in.). In the other 16 creep-test machines, a temperature up to a maximum of 1800 F can be maintained within plus or minus 2 F. The gage length of the test specimen is 3 in., and an extension of 5 microinches (0.000005 in.) can be measured.

The four stress-rupture furnaces are of annular design, and each contains 12 circular chambers for test specimens. The four multiple units are usually operated at different temperature levels up to 1500 F. Each furnace can be maintained at the desired temperature within plus or minus 3 F. There are

Fig. 43. X-ray equipment for diffraction, spectrometric, and fluorescence analyses of metals for quick results

Fig. 44. *Light spectrograph for quick analysis of a wide variety of metals and other materials*

Fig. 45. *Electron microscope for extremely high magnification (beyond 2000x) in the study of metal structure*

16 additional stress-rupture machines (single-station units) at the Barberton Works.

The creep laboratory is air conditioned, and a constant room temperature of 83 F, plus or minus 1 F, is maintained at all times. A gasoline-driven motor-generator set is available to carry the full load of the creep and stress-rupture equipment in the event of a power outage. A general view of the creep-test section of this laboratory is shown in Fig. 42.

In addition to the creep and stress-rupture tests described above, equipment has been developed and is being used for testing tubular materials in tubular form, which more closely simulates the actual stress conditions encountered in operation. This presents a more realistic picture of the stress combinations prevailing on a tube in service.

Other Testing Facilities. The application of X-ray diffraction to metallurgical research problems and inspection by radiographic methods are standard procedures.

The Barberton Works Control laboratory utilizes the most modern and up-to-date X-ray equipment, including 1-million-volt and 2-million-volt stations, to inspect all the main seams in boiler drums after welding and heat treatment.

X-ray equipment for diffraction, spectrometric, and fluorescence analyses (Fig. 43) is in constant use at Beaver Falls and Alliance. These units provide unique facilities for rapid quantitative and qualitative identification of alloy components and compounds, determination of the mechanism of alloy formation, stress analysis, and related problems.

Two of the Company's laboratories are equipped with light spectrographs for analytical work, while in a third laboratory (Barberton Works) there has recently been installed an electron microscope for special studies of metal structures at extremely high magnifications (see Figs. 44 and 45).

Semioutdoor gas-fired radiant reheat boiler in a southern utility

7. Dust ...
tions.
For a mo...
firing see C

Cyclone F...

Cyclone I...
recent years...
firing. At pr...
method is s...
cannot be ...
boiler. How...
initial and ...
The furnace...
so the addi...
and ash er...
eliminated.
Cyclone Fu...
rently suita...
to more tha...
See Chap...
the Cyclone

Space Limi...

New stea...
stalled in a...
a variety of...
low), and ...
possible arr...
for best ove...
have a dire...
of firing an...
a given ste...
by an older...
for a moder...
steam outpu

Relation of...

If the pe...
existing equ...
steam-produ...
plant, if the...
to accommo...
should have...
to save the...
heaters are ...
nected to t...
drop throug...
the same as...
boiler drum...
laws) are se...
coal pulveri...
to relieve ...
needed stea...
without add...
is to be erec...
limit the al...
frequently b

2, 3, and 20). Of this list, bitumino...
gas, and oil are the most important i...
tion for power, and bituminous coal...
two.

The cost of delivered fuel is con...
because of fluctuations in price an...
seasonal variations in availability of...
temporary shortages of coal or fuel...
a single fuel is possible for some...
pendable and abundant local sourc...
of users, however, particularly ut...
finds it advantageous to plan for ...
than one fuel because of cost fluct...
sure continuity of operation should...
ply be interrupted.

Natural Gas

The operator who has an as...
economical natural gas is fortuna...
only is burned, fuel storage facili...
ashpits, and ash-handling equipm...
sary. Soot blowers can be omitte...
are not needed, and there is nc...
problem. Control of heat input to...
is simple. No consideration of ash...
sary in arranging the heating sur...
heat transfer and draft loss. Th...
volume is at a minimum, and th...
outdoor service is increased. The...
of natural gas fuel is the potenti...
explosive accumulations of gas fro...
fittings or as a result of incorrect...
readily detectable. With well-...
however, adequate safety precauti

Blast-Furnace Gas

Blast-furnace gas, a by-produ...
operation, is usually the princij...
generation at steel mills. Its sto...
because of the large volume per...
(90 Btu per cu ft), and it is eith...
ately or wasted to the atmosph...
ply varies with cycles of blast...
either oil, pulverized coal, or cok...
as a supplementary fuel. When...
are used, it is desirable to water ...
thus avoid excessive maintenan...
be used for combustion to mai...
blast-furnace gas in the water-c...

In most modern plants usin...
precipitators are installed to elir...
lime, and coke particles, which, ...
to deposit on the heating surfa...
difficult to remove during oper...
verized-coal or coke-breeze firi...
in removing these deposits. WI...
of service, the deposits are read...
washing.

---

steam to supply both power and heating requirements is from the utilization of a much larger portion of the heat supplied in the fuel, by reduction or
elimination of the loss to the circulating water in a
condensing plant. This loss can be as much as 60%
of the heat supplied in the fuel, even in a modern
central station.

2. Despite this fundamental thermodynamic advantage, it is usually more economical to buy power
when it is available at reasonable rates from a dependable source, except where:

a) Waste fuels and waste heat such as bagasse,
blast-furnace gas, sawdust or hogged wood, and
hot gases are available at low cost from the plant
process.

b) The steam-heating and power demands are
reasonably parallel and relatively large, i.e.,
50,000 lb of steam per hr or more.

3. Variations in process heat and power demands
usually do not coincide. However, if the process
steam requirement is always the larger, the exhaust
steam from a straight back-pressure machine can be
supplemented with a pressure-reducing and desuper-
heating system. If this is not the case, there are two
possible alternatives:

a) Use of an extraction condensing machine.

b) Generation of a part of the power in a
straight back-pressure machine and purchase of
the remainder of the requirement.

As an example of a by-product power installation
under favorable conditions, the cost of power generated in a plant of 10,000-kw capacity with 12%
fixed charges and fuel cost of 30¢ per million Btu
will be in the order of 4 to 5 mills per kwhr.

The selection of steam pressure and temperature
for by-product power plants requires study. Approximate steam conditions at the turbine or engine
may range from 150 psi and 500 F in one type of
factory application to 1800 psi and 900 F in other
applications.

Power Generation

Steam engines and steam turbines are the alternative prime movers available for the generation of
mechanical or electrical power. Except for the smallest isolated installations (below 500-hp capacity), the
high-speed turbine predominates because of its compactness, efficiency, and low-cost features. However,
since mechanical power in large amounts is seldom
required locally, it is usually more economical to buy
it as electrical energy from a central station. The
present-day central stations can easily deliver a kwhr
for each 9000-10,000 Btu supplied in fuel. The
economy of the central station is evident when this
heat rate is compared with a heat rate in the order
of 50,000 Btu, or more, per kwhr required for a 100-
kw noncondensing engine or turbine-driven generator set. Consequently, the bulk of the mechanical

---

and electrical ...
stationary serv...
steam-driven t...
450,000 kw in s...
pressures, super...
used to obtain ...

To determine ...
give the lowest ...
of a proposed s...
balance plant i...
other operating ...
The optimum m...
for a 5000-kw u...
heat for the larg...
costs of money, ...
dency is to selec...
tures that can be...
materials for sup...
and turbine part...

For optimum ...
practice to maint...
turbine throttle. ...
superheater outle...
the pressure at t...
from the superhe...
pressure drop is ...
pressure at maxim...
allowance for the ...
modern single-boi...
valve between supe...
is not required.

The design pre...
equipment is dete...
items to the turbin...

1. Pressure drop ...
valve at maxim...
2. Pressure drop ...
internals at ma...
3. Ample allowan...
sure at maximu...
valve blowdow...

Item 2 is wholly d...
of the steam-produ...
by the boiler manuf...
should specify that t...
above the maximum...

The steam temp...
heater outlet is take...
required at the turbi...
from one point to th...
mum performance i...
temperature and pr...
loads. Steam tempe...
boilers are discussed...
trolled superheat pr...
30,000 kw. In steel-mi...
nate firing with blast...
breeze tends to produ...

SELECTION OF STEAM-PRODUCING EQUIPMENT

THE boiler designer must produce economically a
steam-generating unit which will satisfy the
needs of his customer. To produce the most
economical steam-generating unit requires close cooperation between the designer and the user's engineering staff or consultants. This community of interest exists whether the unit is small or large.

By coordinating the various components—boilers,
furnaces, fuel burners, fans, and controls—the boiler
manufacturer has produced a limited series of standardized steam-generating units, particularly in the
smaller capacities (up to about 50,000 lb of steam
per hr), burning oil or natural gas. Within the proper
scope of their application, these standardized units
(some sizes shipped assembled) are simple and economical in performance. Beyond these limits, only
partial standardization of some component elements
is possible because of 1) the user's individual requirements and conditions for pressure, temperature,
capacity, and fuel, and 2) the incidence of continual
improvements as a result of the constant search for
better over-all economy. Since the steam plant is to
become the heart of the system it serves, with some
30 years of expected normal useful life, consideration
should be given to every established improvement
applicable to each new design.

The cost of fuel consumed throughout the life of
a steam-generating unit is so great that the savings
from even a slight increase in efficiency can easily
amount to many times the investment required to
obtain this increased efficiency (see *Evaluation* below). The time, effort, and cost to provide proved
features of better operation in keeping with plant
requirements and conditions are economically justified. As long as progress continues, this is why
(generally in the larger-size categories) premature
standardization is contrary to the ultimate best in-
terests of the owner. Each project, therefore, warrants
the attention and expense required to produce a
coordinated steam-generating unit which will insure
a dependable steam supply with maximum economy.

The requirements and conditions that form the
basis for the plant designer's selection of equipment
for a specific case can normally be outlined as
follows:

1. Steam Requirements
   a) Pressure and temperature
      At points of use
      At outlet of steam-generating unit
      Allowable variations
      Predictable future requirements
   b) Rate of heat delivery (or steam flow)
      To points of end use
      To boilerhouse auxiliaries and feedwater
         heating
      To blowdown
      From outlet of steam-generating unit
      Variations — minimum, average, and maxi-
         mum
      Predictable future requirements
2. Boiler Feedwater
   a) Source and analysis
   b) Temperature entering steam-generating unit
3. Geographical Considerations
   a) Available fuels — analyses, costs, and future
      trends
   b) Space limitations
   c) Relation of new equipment to existing boil-
      erhouse equipment
   d) Restrictions of local laws and immediate
      neighborhood, present and predicted
   e) Elevation above sea level
   f) Earthquake possibility
   g) Foundation conditions
   h) Kind and unit cost of energy for driving
      auxiliaries
   i) Climate
   j) Accessibility for service
4. Operating Personnel
   a) Experience level of workmen for operation
      and maintenance

b) Cost of labor
5. Evaluation
   a) Of improved efficiency
   b) Of auxiliary power required
   c) Of various fixed charges
   d) Of many of the above items

Considerable time and effort are required to establish sufficiently accurate basic data with comprehensive consideration of engineering factors, judgment in planning for future expansion or changes, and evaluation of the tangibles and intangibles involved, so that the experience and craftsmanship of the boiler manufacturer can be applied to the full benefit of the plant designer and the owner. The user should, at the outset, decide who is to prepare these data. Lacking adequate and capable personnel, the services of consulting engineers are always available. Before the equipment can be selected, the basis of operation and arrangement of the entire steam plant must be planned, then construction drawings must be prepared for the foundations, building, piping, and walkways. Also the construction work must be coordinated and supervised.

In general, equipment selection cannot be reduced to the application of simple rules or formulas. Through cooperation with the boiler manufacturer, discussion in detail of the items referred to above will help in making intelligent decisions.

Pressure and Temperature

At points of use, the required steam pressure and temperature may be from 2 psi and 215 F (saturated) for heating, to 4500 psi and 1500 F for a large turbine generator. Some general suggestions for establishing the end-use requirements and their effect on the steam-producing equipment seem appropriate.

Steam for Process and Heating

The pressure of saturated steam (no superheat) used for process heating is such that the corresponding condensing steam temperature is somewhat above the required temperature of the materials to be heated. Generally superheat is of no value for this kind of service and is often undesirable because of its interference with temperature control. Reclaiming or devulcanizing rubber, where the rubber in a caustic solution is heated to 400 F by condensing saturated steam at 250 psi (407 F) in the jacket of the devulcanizer, is a typical example of process heating with steam.

Pressures of saturated steam for comfort heating of buildings range from 2 psi to as high as 80 psi in the case of "space heaters." It is seldom economical to distribute steam through long lines at pressures below 150 psi because of piping costs. Furthermore, the usual requirements for steam within the boilerhouse for soot blowers, feed pumps, and other auxiliaries make it desirable to operate boilers at a

peratures for a given steam larly attractive.

For large turbine-generator ity and up—using steam co and 900 F, with a single boile ator, the so-called "reheat" cause of the increased statio the nonreheat cycle (see C is standard practice to locate boiler enclosure. The rehea hausted from an intermedia turbine, raises the temperat turbine-inlet temperature, back to the low-pressure se installations of this type, th sure of the steam leaving ar and the load range over wh of reheat steam is to be m by the plant designer in coc and boiler manufacturers.

Rate of Heat Delivery

To insure prompt fulfilln i.e., the delivery of heat t required rates, it is necessa ing equipment of sufficient and responsiveness. The c in most space-heating sy: widely and rapidly, as in a steam-heating processes, a liquid batch, require high tion. Rapidly changing rat required for a steel-rolling power which fluctuates The steam-flow requiren accurately established fo

Peak flow
Maximum continuou
maximum flow)
Minimum flow
Rate of change in fl

The peak load will, capacity for the steam-p of its auxiliaries. For w advisable to establish th systems, peaks of shorter "storage" of heat.

The range from minin most important factor oil, and gas-burning ec tion and smokeless coi firing, the range from n must also be considere It is of somewhat lesse stokers are used.

The required rate of may materially affect t

Type FF Integral-Furnace Boiler

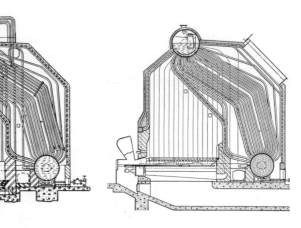
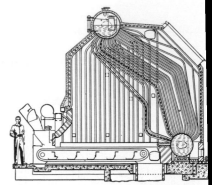

General Description

Standard steel-cased bent-tube unit, with water-cooled furnace and drum cyclones. Smallest size may be shop assembled. The unit is designed in a series of 5 different heights between drums, with provision for superheater. Fans are not integral.

Range in Size, Steam Output
   Lb per hr, to 50,000 in increments
      of 2000 lb per hr, or less
Design Pressure
   Lb per sq in., 160 to 600
Operating Pressure
   Lb per sq in., 15 to safety-valve setting
Steam Temperature
   Saturation to approximately 150 F superheat
Fuel
   Oil and gas; coal with all types of stokers
Operational Control
   Manual, or automatic in varying degree
Furnace
   Water cooled except floor; nonpressure type
Dimensions Outside Setting, Approximate
   Smallest, 7 ft wide × 13 ft high × 15 ft
      front to rear
   Largest, 17 ft wide × 23 ft high × 19 ft
      front to rear

Indicated Field of Application

1. In the production of steam for heating, process, or power needs within the output and specifications noted above, using any of the fuels listed.
2. Where a boiler is needed quickly for either outdoor or housed location.
3. Where space limitations require unusual proportions not met by type FM.
4. Where future conversion to an alternate fuel is

contemplated—because of the simplicity of version with this unit.

5. Where considerable variation in fuel-ash ch acteristics is anticipated.

General Comments

The FF Integral-Furnace boiler is one of the w standardized types widely used in industrial pla With suitable firing methods, oil fuel varying characteristics from bunker C to residual and bitu nous coals of a wide range in per cent ash fusion temperature may be burned successfully. verized-coal firing is not used for this unit.

The range in vertical height of unit (a series 5 standard dimensions between upper and lo drums), which in turn affects the other two dim sions, permits a size selection for comparable formance to suit many existing space conditions headroom and floor area. The space conditions quired for either spreader-stoker or chain-grate ing are comparable.

No major changes in the boiler unit are involv in converting from oil and gas to coal firing or reverse. The "saturated" surface components generally not affected. There are minor alterati to brickwork to suit the new firing equipment, a if a superheater is present, it may be necessary add or remove some surface to meet changed co bustion requirements (chiefly excess air) of the n fuel.

When fuel saving justifies the expenditure, econ mizers and air heaters may be added, as in m boiler types, to utilize low-level heat. However, the more than 1300 type FF boilers placed service in the period 1940-1955, less than 10 per c were equipped with air heaters or economize The proportion of boilers equipped with these ad tional heat traps will tend to increase as fuel pri rise.

Type FP Integral-Furnace Boiler

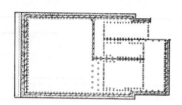

PLAN VIEW

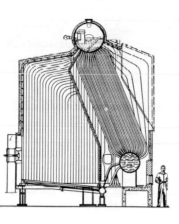

SIDE VIEW THROUGH 3rd PASS,
OIL & GAS FIRED

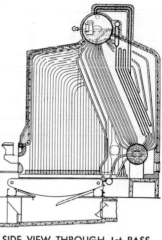

SIDE VIEW THROUGH 1st PASS,
SPREADER-STOKER FIRED

General Description

Standard welded-steel-cased bent-tube unit, with completely water-cooled furnace and drum cyclones. Assembled in the field. The unit is designed in one height (18-ft drum centers) and in 9 widths, with or without superheaters. Fans are not integral.

Range in Size, Steam Output
  Lb per hr, to 80,000 in increments of
    approximately 5000 lb per hr
Design Pressure
  Lb per sq in., 160 to 825
Operating Pressure
  Lb per sq in., 15 to safety-valve setting
Steam Temperature
  Saturation to approximately 850 F
Fuel
  Coal with spreader, underfeed or chain-
    grate stoker; oil and gas
Operational Control
  Manual, or automatic in varying degree
Furnace
  Completely water cooled; nonpressure type
Dimensions Outside Settings, Approximate
  Smallest, 8 ft wide × 28 ft high × 22 ft
    front to rear
  Largest, 17 ft wide × 28 ft high × 22 ft
    front to rear

Indicated Field of Application

1. In the production of steam for heating, process, or power needs within the output and specifications noted above, using any of the fuels listed.

2. Where a boiler is needed quickly for either outdoor or housed location.

3. Where coal ash is particularly abrasive, and stoker firing is preferable, in this size category, to pulverized-coal firing.

4. Where coal ash-fusion characteristics permit little or no uncooled furnace area.

5. Where stoker firing is to be supplemented by simultaneous oil and gas firing with auxiliary burners through the side walls.

General Comments

The FP Integral-Furnace boiler is particularly well suited for stoker firing. With its completely water-cooled furnace, the rates of heat input and heat absorption may be somewhat higher than for the type FF boiler. Travel of the gas through the boiler has been arranged so that the abrasive particles are not concentrated in streams.

Oil and gas firing, either singly or in combination, is entirely suitable and may be used initially as an alternate to stoker firing. Permanent conversion from one fuel to another is as simple as for the type FF boiler. Installation of oil and gas burners in the side walls of a stoker-fired unit permits combination firing, either simultaneously with coal or separately. When firing oil and gas alone, the stoker must be protected with a suitable tile or ash coating. The unit is not designed for pulverized-coal firing. If the fuel saving justifies the expenditure, economizers or air heaters should be installed.

The type FP boiler is well suited for the production of steam for both industrial and power requirements. A highly trained operating staff is not required for its successful operation.

4. Where simplicity of change to accommodate another fuel and method of firing is essential, because of a possible future fuel source.

General Comments

The range in steam output of the Stirling Two-Drum boiler is greater than for any of the other units considered in this series. Because of its range in output and its ready adaptability for burning most fuels, this unit is now widely used. It is particularly suitable for steam production with spreader-stoker firing up to the limit of output possible in using a stoker, in the order of 250,000 lb of steam per hr. In this application, the single-pass gas flow (no turns) helps to prevent concentration of abrasive particles and consequent tube damage.

All tubes can be entered from the two drums for inspection and cleaning.

Where the additional cost is warranted to maintain a constant steam temperature at reduced loads, the superheater is designed for control of temperature by an attemperator of either the submerged-surface type installed in the lower drum or the spray type.

The water-cooled tubes in the side, front, and rear walls of the furnace are variously spaced, as required by the fuel characteristics, on from 6-in. centers to touching.

Hopper bottoms are usually fitted for pulverized-coal firing. A somewhat lesser height is required for Cyclone Furnace firing and slag-tap ash removal than for pulverized-coal firing and dry-ash removal. In the larger units, particularly with Cyclone Furnace or pulverized-coal firing, additional furnace surface is frequently provided by installing an intermediate or furnace division wall, as in the RB type of boiler (see below).

An economizer or an air heater, or both, may be installed if justified by an evaluation of the fuel saving and performance.

Open-Pass (OP) Boiler

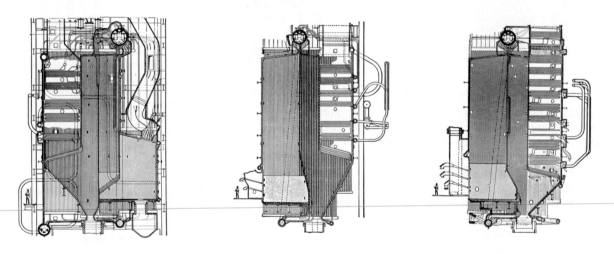

General Description

The Open-Pass boiler is almost always designed in the larger sizes and in the higher-pressure range, for field assembly, to meet specific requirements of function and space. While some of the components and arrangements are standard, the assembly as a whole is specially designed to satisfy the requirements of each job. A single drum serves the entire unit. The boiler is top supported from the drum elevation. Furnace walls are usually of touching-tube construction. Ash removal is by slag-tap only. In some cases, slag-tap may be combined with a short dry-ash hopper.

There is little or no convection boiler surface. Steam is produced in the furnace walls and sometimes, in a small amount, in a steaming economizer. In the usual application requiring high superheat, as much as ⅛ of the total heat absorption takes place in the superheater, which is relatively large. An air heater is always necessary, and some steam reheater convection surface may be installed as required by the plant heat cycle. Attemperators are usually specified to maintain constant steam temperature at less than full load.

Range in Size, Steam Output
   Lb per hr, about 300,000 to 2,000,000 at no fixed incremental amounts
Design Pressure
   Lb per sq in., 675 and above
Operating Pressure
   Lb per sq in., to safety-valve setting
Design Temperature
   To 1100 F, and reheat to 1100 F
Draft Loss at Maximum Output
   In. of water, designed for the conditions; usually about 8 through all components

single-boiler single-
larger industrial pla
erate size.

Refinements in c
of the user are simil
as for the Open-Pa
specially designed
precisely to the tra
user.

To obtain the re
ture in a unit of thi
tional furnace surfa

Evaluati

Costs related to t
tics of equipn
concern to the engi
attractive initial cost
by low efficiency or
pensive over the p
increase in initial or
run only if the valt
is worth the extra
justifiable expenditi
calculated for the pe
tics of the equipme
for *evaluations* or c

Principal items ol
usually considered f
boiler units and rel

Fig. 1. Capitalizat
per million Btu (M
per hr for changes
ciency. Base conc
hr per year; fuel c
MkB; capitalization
per year. Use eq
text for condition
base

Fuel
Coal, pulverized; oil and gas as primary or
supplemental fuels
Operational Control
Usually completely automatic, including feedwater flow, combustion, and steam temperature
Furnace, Pressure or Nonpressure
All surfaces water cooled, including slag-tap floor
Dimensions Outside Setting, Approximate
Commensurate with output. A 1,400,000 lb steam
per hr unit is typically 56 ft wide × 117 ft
high above basement floor × 75 ft front to
rear. Additional space required for air heater
depending upon type and arrangement

Indicated Field of Application

1. Where the requirements in size and function
preclude the selection of one of the more
standardized assemblies. For requirements of
large output with very high temperature (over
950 F), the selection should be based on the
results of a study of the Stirling Two-Drum, the
Open-Pass (OP), and the Radiant (RB) (see
below) types.
2. Where consideration is not to be given to dry-
ash removal.
3. Where a study indicates that the evaluated cost,
to meet the required conditions, is lower for
the OP than for the RB design.
4. Where, with load schedules requiring frequent
starts, the draining type is more desirable than
the nondraining type of superheater.

General Comments

The name of the Open-Pass boiler is derived from
its characteristic gas flow in two or more successive
directions in open areas bounded by heat-absorbing
surface. This unit and its companion design in the
same size range, the Radiant (RB) boiler (see
below), are well suited for single-boiler single-turbine operation in the public utility field, where electrical energy must be produced at the lowest possible
cost. Refinement in functional design of the turbine
and the boiler unit is justified, and every apparatus
that can show a sound evaluated saving in heat re-

covery, labor, and fuel should be considered. An
optimum plant heat balance, for instance, may call
for a relatively high feedwater temperature (550 F)
from the last stage heater and a very low exit gas
temperature (250-300 F). To meet these requirements, a large amount of both economizer and air
heater surface is necessary.

In boiler units of this type, variations in design
to meet rigid specifications are almost endless. It
may be economically desirable, for example, to
maintain high steam temperature from full load to
a substantially reduced load (75 or 50%). More
superheater surface, occupying greater space, will be
required than if the characteristic superheat drop
with reduced load were allowable; also some means
of temperature control, such as gas by-pass, gas recirculation, or attemperator, must be provided—all
affecting the disposition of various components.

The "custom-built" boiler units in this series, the
Stirling Two-Drum, the OP, and the RB (see below),
are designed to suit the specific characteristics of
the fuel and ash. The furnace surface must be adequate in extent and arrangement to absorb the
correct amount of heat to give a desired gas temperature entering the convection surface. This must
be done without harmful effect on many other conditions, such as fluidity of slag, proximity of flame
to furnace boundaries, and operational procedure.

Dry-ash removal is not used for the OP boiler
unit, chiefly because a hopper under the furnace
would increase the over-all height, which might
limit its suitability for the space available. In the
same service where coal-ash properties permit slag-
tap ash removal, the OP unit is usually of somewhat
less height than the RB type with ash hopper and
dry-ash removal.

Although simplicity of support is a distinct advantage of the pendent (nondraining) superheater,
conservative start-up procedure requires the evaporation of the accumulated condensate to avoid damage
to the tubes. For this reason, to shorten the start-
up period the "drainable" superheater is sometimes
preferred (see Chapter 21 on required time for
start-up). Because of its horizontal superheater arrangement, the OP boiler is well suited for the drainable type.

cost of *up to* 1.0 per cent is justified, in each case, for improved performance of the order indicated in the first four items listed above. Building space may be similarly evaluated in the general range of from $1.00 to $2.00 per cu ft.

Superheater and economizer pressure drops should be considered on the basis of power required to operate feed pumps. The rough evaluation frequently made of this item (which includes a demand charge) is approximately $1.50 per 1000 lb steam per hr of unit output, per 1 psi pressure drop.

More precise calculations for the evaluation of efficiency and auxiliary power are demonstrated in the examples below.

Data Needed for Evaluation

Capitalization Rate

Capital evaluation of performance (i.e., what expenditure is justified to avoid a penalty or to obtain an advantage) is based on an acceptable capitalization rate set by the user's management. This rate, for instance, might vary from a low of 10% to a high of 30%.

To make these capital evaluations for various conditions of operation, it is necessary to know:

1. Fuel Cost per suitable unit, ¢ per million Btu (MkB).
2. Heat Rate per kwhr, Btu/kwhr generated.
3. Purchased Power Cost, ¢ per kwhr.
4. Demand Charge, usually $ per installed kw.

Fuel Cost

Fuel cost is the cost of fuel delivered to point of use. This cost is used in evaluations of efficiency. It is also used in evaluations of power for the auxiliaries, when the power is produced within the plant.

Heat Rate

The heat rate of the plant is the fuel heat input required to generate a kwhr. It is used in evaluations of power for the auxiliaries, when the power is produced within the plant. When back-pressure turbines are used where the quantity of low-pressure steam for heating and processing is well above that required to generate the power for the auxiliaries, or when turbine-driven auxiliaries are used to provide exhaust steam, the thermal cycle is very efficient, the heat rate is low (4000-5000 Btu per kwhr, see Chapter 10), and the cost of auxiliary power is correspondingly low.

Purchased Power Cost

Purchased power cost is the cost of power required to operate the auxiliaries when the power is bought from outside sources.

Demand Charge

Demand charge represents the capitalized cost of any additional capacity in boilers, turbines, and generators necessary to generate the power required for the auxiliaries. The demand charge is not always used, but in many cases, especially in public utilities, its application is common practice. Where two or more different types of firing are used, the demand charge is based on the firing with the largest ratio of gas weight to heat input, since the maximum installed kilowatts to provide the greater fan power are required for this condition.

Efficiency and Fan-Power Evaluation

Capital evaluation curves for the unit and for fan power, over a range in efficiency at average present-day high-load-factor and three-shift operation with expensive coal or oil fuels, are presented in Figs. 1 and 2, respectively. The basic conditions applying to these curves are noted below in each case. For all other conditions, the evaluation of unit efficiency and fan power is established by use of the pertinent equations listed.

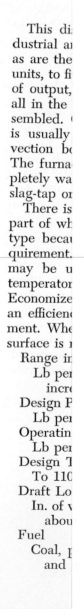

This di...
dustrial a...
as are the
units, to fi
of output,
all in the
sembled. (
is usually
vection b(
The furna...
pletely wa...
slag-tap or
There is
part of wh...
type becau...
quirement.
may be u...
temperatur...
Economizer
an efficienc
ment. Whe...
surface is ...
Range in
Lb per
incre...
Design P...
Lb per
Operatin...
Lb per
Design T...
To 110...
Draft Lo...
In. of v...
abou...
Fuel
Coal, p...
and

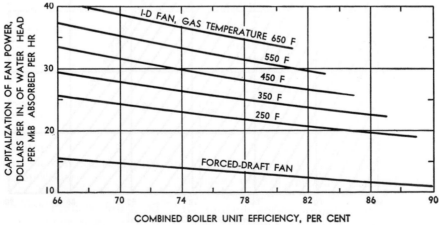

Fig. 2. Fan-power capitalization, in dollars per in. of water head per million Btu (MkB) absorbed per hr by boiler unit, for different gas temperatures and values of boiler unit efficiency. Base conditions are given in text preceding equation (2). Use equations (2) to (7) for conditions other than base

Calculation of Eval

EXAM

Evaluation fo

Fuel cost, natural gas, oil

Capitalization rate, % per

Demand charge, $ per in

Heat rate, Btu per kwhr

Building space evaluatior

Average steam flow, lb p

Peak steam flow, lb per h

Operating time at avg ste

Barometric pressure, in. I

Heat absorbed by steam,

Total heat absorbed at av

Total heat absorbed at pe

Boiler efficiency at avg rate, gas fired, %

Draft loss at avg steam flow, gas fired, in. of wate

Air resistance at avg steam flow, gas fired, in. of w

Draft loss, at peak steam flow, oil fired, in. of wat

Air resistance at peak steam flow, oil fired, in. of v

Boiler exit gas temperature, F

Excess air leaving boiler, gas fired, %

Excess air leaving boiler, oil fired, %

Stated price of unit, $

Capitalization, in $, for:
Difference in efficiency (0.5%)

Fuel cost for I-D fan

Fuel cost for F-D fan

Demand charge for I-D fan

Demand charge for F-D fan

Difference in building volume

Evaluated price (net)

In this example, under the conditions established for fuel cost, capitalization rate, demand charge, heat rate, and building space evaluation,

Capitalization of Boiler Unit Efficiency

For Base Conditions (Fig. 1)
(1 MkB = 1,000,000 Btu)

Factors	Base
N = heat absorbed in MkB per hr (avg)	1
T = operating time, hr per yr	8,000
C = fuel cost, ¢ per MkB	30
Y = capitalization rate, % per yr	10

Capitalization of Boiler Unit Efficiency in Dollars

For Conditions Other than Base

$$\text{Capitalization} = \text{Value from Fig. 1} \times \frac{N}{1} \times \frac{T}{8,000} \times \frac{C}{30} \times \frac{10}{Y} \qquad (1)$$

Capitalization of Fan Power

For Base Conditions (Fig. 2)
(1 MkB = 1,000,000 Btu)

Factors	Base
X = I-D fan head, in. of water at 1,000,000 Btu absorbed per hr	1
V = F-D fan head, in. of water at 1,000,000 Btu absorbed per hr	1
C = gas weight, lb per 10,000 Btu input	10
A = air weight, lb per 10,000 Btu input	8
N = heat absorbed in MkB per hr (avg)	1
M = heat absorbed in MkB per hr (peak)	1
B = barometric pressure, in. Hg	30
T = hr per yr at N input	8,000
R = heat rate, Btu per kwhr	12,000
C = fuel cost, ¢ per MkB	30
Y = capitalization rate, % per yr	10
P = power cost, ¢ per kwhr	0.36
D = demand charge, $ per installed kw	150

Gas and Air Weights
(lb per 10,000 Btu input)

Firing	G	A
Natural gas	8.8	7.5
Fuel oil	9.1	7.8
Cyclone	9.4	7.9
Pulverized coal	10.1	8.0
Stokers	11.3	9.0
Blast-furnace gas	16.0	6.6

When fuel cost applies:

$$= \text{I-D fan base value} \times X \times \frac{M}{1} \times \frac{C}{1}$$

$$= \text{F-D fan base value} \times V \times \frac{M}{1} \times \frac{A}{8}$$

When power cost applies:

$$= \text{I-D fan base value} \times X \times \frac{M}{1} \times \frac{G}{10}$$

$$= \text{F-D fan base value} \times V \times \frac{M}{1} \times \frac{A}{8}$$

When demand charge applies: (add to either

$$= \frac{\text{I-D fan base value}}{1.3} \times X \times \frac{M}{1} \times \frac{G}{10}$$

$$= \frac{\text{F-D fan base value}}{1.3} \times V \times \frac{M}{1} \times \frac{A}{8}$$

Feed-Pump Power Evaluation

Formulas for capital evaluation of fe

Capitaliz

Fac

$$FW_{avg} = \text{lb fluid pum}$$
$$FW_{peak} = \text{lb fluid pum}$$
$$\Delta P = \text{superheater}$$
$$T = \text{hr per yr at}$$
$$R = \text{heat rate, Bt}$$
$$C = \text{fuel cost, } \cancel{c} \text{ } $$
$$Y = \text{capitalizatio}$$
$$P = \text{power cost,}$$
$$D = \text{demand cha}$$

Capitalizatior

When fuel cost applies:

$$= 0.5 \times \Delta P \times \frac{FW_{peak}}{1,000} \times \frac{T}{8,000} \times \frac{P}{12,0}$$

When power cost applies:

$$= 0.5 \times \Delta P \times \frac{FW_{peak}}{1,000} \times \frac{T}{8,000} \times \frac{P}{0.36}$$

When demand charge applies:

$$= 0.4 \times \Delta P \times \frac{FW_{peak}}{1,000} \times \frac{D}{150} \times \left\{ \frac{FW}{FW} \right.$$

Detailed Evaluation of Items Capitalized in Example No. 1

Difference in efficiency:

Value from Fig. 1 for gain of 1% in eff (from 81 to 82%) = $350/N

Value for loss of 0.5% in eff (from 82 to 81.5%) = $175/N

To correct for conditions of Example No. 1, use equation (1)

$$\text{Capitalization for difference in eff} = 175 \times 560.5 \times \frac{12}{30} = \$39,240$$

Fuel cost for operating fans:

Value from Fig. 2 for I-D fan at 320 F & 82% boiler eff = $23.0

Value from Fig. 2 for I-D fan at 340 F & 81.5% boiler eff = $23.5

To correct for conditions of Example No. 1, use equation (2)

$$\text{For I-D fan, Unit No. } 1 = 23.0 \times 4.5 \times 785.0 \times \frac{8.8}{10} \times \frac{12,500}{12,000} \times \frac{12}{30} = \$29,800$$

$$\text{For I-D fan, Unit No. } 2 = 23.5 \times 5.5 \times 785.0 \times \frac{8.8}{10} \times \frac{12,500}{12,000} \times \frac{12}{30} = \underline{\$37,200}$$

Additional capitalization required for Unit No. 2 = $7,400

Value from Fig. 2 for F-D fan at 81.5 or 82% boiler eff = $12.5

To correct for conditions of Example No. 1, use equation (3)

$$\text{For F-D fan, Unit No. } 1 = 12.5 \times 4.7 \times 785.0 \times \frac{7.5}{8} \times \frac{12,500}{12,000} \times \frac{12}{30} = \$18,100$$

$$\text{For F-D fan, Unit No. } 2 = 12.5 \times 5.6 \times 785.0 \times \frac{7.5}{8} \times \frac{12,500}{12,000} \times \frac{12}{30} = \underline{\$21,460}$$

Additional capitalization required for Unit No. 2 = $3,360

Demand charges for fans: (Based on oil firing)

Use Fig. 2, as before, and equations (6) & (7) to establish values

$$\text{For I-D fan, Unit No. } 1 = \frac{23.0}{1.3} \times 9.5 \times 785.0 \times \frac{9.1}{10} \times \frac{150}{150} \times \left\{ \frac{785.0}{560.5} \right\}^2 = \$235,300$$

$$\text{For I-D fan, Unit No. } 2 = \frac{23.5}{1.3} \times 11.5 \times 785.0 \times \frac{9.1}{10} \times \frac{150}{150} \times \left\{ \frac{785.0}{560.5} \right\}^2 = \$291,000$$

Additional capitalization required for Unit No. 2 = $55,700

$$\text{For F-D fan, Unit No. } 1 = \frac{12.5}{1.3} \times 10.0 \times 785.0 \times \frac{7.8}{8} \times \frac{150}{150} \times \left\{ \frac{785.0}{560.5} \right\}^2 = \$144,300$$

$$\text{For F-D fan, Unit No. } 2 = \frac{12.5}{1.3} \times 11.9 \times 785.0 \times \frac{7.8}{8} \times \frac{150}{150} \times \left\{ \frac{785.0}{560.5} \right\}^2 = \$171,600$$

Additional capitalization required for Unit No. 2 = $27,300

EXAMPLE No. 2

Evaluation of a Pulverized-Coal-Fired Unit—Arrangements A, B, C

(Base and Two Alternates)

Fuel cost, bituminous coal, ¢ per MkB	34.6
Capitalization rate, % per yr	18
Demand charge, $ per installed kw	160
Heat rate, Btu per kwhr	13,000
Average steam flow, lb per hr	100,000
Peak steam flow, lb per hr	125,000
Operating time at avg steam flow, hr per yr	7,500
Barometric pressure, in. Hg	27.0
Heat absorbed by steam, Btu per lb	1,200
Total heat absorbed at avg rate, MkB per hr	120.0
Total heat absorbed at peak rate, MkB per hr	150.0

	A Base No Air Heater or Economizer	B Alternate Air Heater only	C Alternate Air Heater and Economizer
Boiler efficiency at avg rate, %	77.5	82.0	83.5
Draft loss at avg steam flow, in. of water	6.8	9.6	10.0
Air resistance at avg steam flow, in. of water	5.0	7.3	7.3
Boiler exit gas temperature, F	550	400	350
Economizer pressure drop, psi	—	—	10.0
Capitalization in $ for:			
Increase in efficiency	Base	131,190 (credit)	173,360 (credit)
Fuel cost, I-D fan	Base	2,900	1,900
Fuel cost, F-D fan	Base	2,740 (debit)	2,500
Demand charge, I-D fan	Base	5,700	3,800
Demand charge, F-D fan	Base	5,400	4,930 (debit)
Fuel cost, feed pump	Base	Base	406
Demand charge, feed pump	Base	Base	834
Evaluated worth (net)	Base	$114,450	$158,990

A clear understanding of the net results in the above example is important: With A at base cost, alternate B at $114,450 additional cost over A, and alternate C at $158,990 additional cost over A, all three arrangements offer investments of equal financial return, and no definite choice is indicated on such grounds alone.

However, the selection of an alternate over the base arrangement is economically justified if the increase in bid price, attributable to the additional equipment of the alternate, is less than its evaluated net worth: The greater the difference, the greater will be the return on the investment.

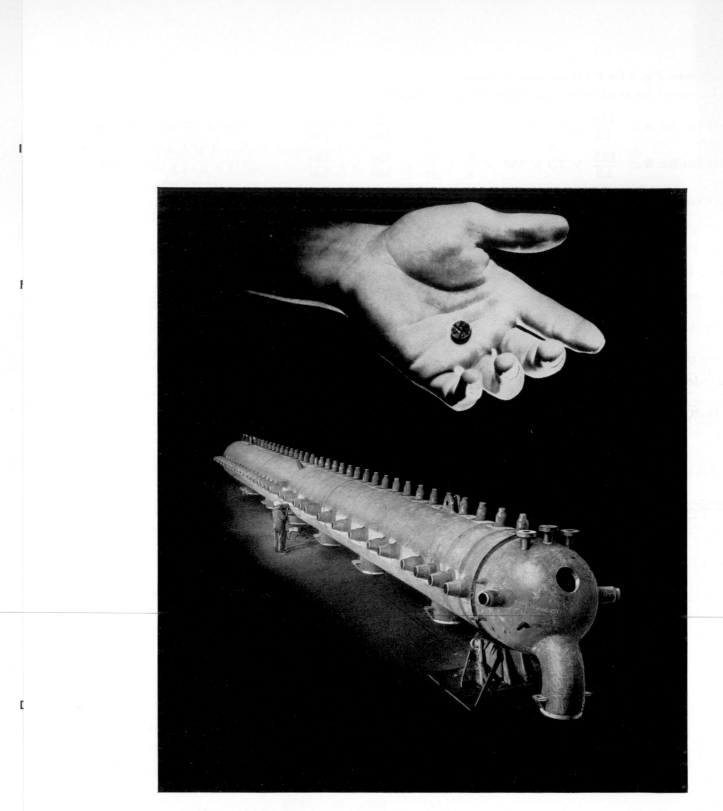

BOILER SHOPS ARE CALLED UPON TO MANUFACTURE PARTS
AS SMALL AS AN OIL BURNER SPRAYER PLATE AND AS
LARGE AS A 104-FT 230-TON DRUM

the edge of the head is ma
welding to the shell. Ther
machined edges of the fini
drum assembly bay, Fig. 1

The formed drumhead i
die by a ram operating fron
in Fig. 8). For heavy-plat
circular shape, is machined
thin-plate heads, the manh
the original hot-forming of

Edges Prepared for Weldir

Only very small drums v
6500-ton press and 1200-tor
in. OD, as noted above) ca
drical piece. In preparing

Fig. 8. *Start of operatio*
from heavy plate (h

end of the shell and one
cumferential connecting s
length required, must be
this size (almost always
from shell and head com
machined at longitudinal a
and fitted together prepara

A half-cylindrical drum
on a large planer. The lo
chined to a definite contou
machined in the edges of
groove of the proper size
of the weld metal when t
bled. In a later operation t
cylinders are similarly pre
weld and any intermediate

PRINCIPLES AND METHODS OF MANUFACTURE

A T the turn of the century, 25,000 lb steam per hr at 200 psi working pressure and saturation temperature was considered top production for any steam boiler unit. At the present time there are units of capacities far above 2,500,000 lb steam per hr, pressures of 4500 psi and above, and steam temperatures above 1100 F.

In the production of modern steam boilers and their auxiliary equipment, there are many difficult engineering and manufacturing problems in design, fabrication, and the use of materials. The rapid progress in the solution of these problems is the result of research, experimentation, and the application of operating experience made possible by close cooperation between user and manufacturer.

It was early recognized that manufacturing facilities must keep pace with improvements in the design of boilers. Special personnel is employed, whose exclusive duty it is to study and provide the best possible manufacturing methods, tools, and equipment. Mass production is applicable to only a part of the many components of a complete boiler unit. A large percentage of skilled workmen is required.

The organization must have a corps of experienced engineers, designers, and calculators to check all the parts and assemblies of a unit to make sure of proper performance and to meet applicable codes, laws, and regulations. Inspectors also check all parts for correspondence to orders and drawings and workmanship for compliance with permissible tolerances. An essential feature is a fully equipped physical and chemical laboratory for testing materials and products as required. Practically all parts and assemblies of the equipment designed and sold by B&W are manufactured at its own works.

General Requirements

In general, the user of a steam boiler unit will expect the equipment he purchases to meet the following requirements:

1. To be permanently strong enough in all its parts.
2. To have satisfactory length of life.
3. To be as tight as necessary against air, gas, or water pressure.
4. To provide adequate means to take care of expansion from thermal or other causes of change in shape or dimension.
5. All parts to be accessible, inspectable, and repairable.
6. Components to be of suitable size and weight for handling and installation.
7. To present pleasing appearance and workmanlike finish.
8. The manufacturer should be able to command material supply and fabrication.
9. The manufacturer should be able to supply replacements promptly.

The *Boiler and Pressure Vessel Code* of the ASME is the basic Code for the construction of stationary boilers. All designs, materials, and workmanship must fully comply with its requirements. Supplementing this Code are items of desirable features based upon knowledge attained by the user or manufacturer through previous experience.

Acceptance of Welding

No single feature in the construction of boiler drums and other pressure vessels has contributed more to the removal of size and functional limitations than the development and acceptance of welding.

Based on extensive research during the years 1926 and 1928, a welding process was developed by The Babcock & Wilcox Co. that would consistently produce a weld at least as good as the parent plate, physically as well as chemically. A practical nondestructive method of testing to prove the weld was also developed. On Sept. 17, 1929, a proposed specification for electric-arc welding of pressure vessels

Fig. 6. As shown, thir
drum section, thus r

diameter and wall
permissible length.

The hollow forg
variety of OD and
for pipe, headers,
range of diameter
mandrels is betwe
34¾-in. OD with 3½
dimensions may be
special mandrels.

Lengths of the
weight of the ing
Standard lengths v
and thinner wall t
and heavier wall.

Standard toleran
ness are as follows

Outside Diame
inches

8¾ to 18
18 to 24

Minimum wall
not more than 1
wall thickness s
Cut lengths are
¼ in.

Ingots are poured
arc melting furnace
is possible in this p

The Drum, a Majc

Drums are fabri
see below) rolled
chemical specificati
spected for defect:

Fig. 11. One of the drum assembly and finishing bays. Preheating and automatic welding of circumferential seams may be noted in foreground

(visible) is continuously fed to the arc area, completely covered by a granular flux which excludes air from the weld metal. In the operation shown, the electrode carriage moves steadily along the seam from end to end. Several passes are required, the number depending on thickness of plate, plate material, and form of welding groove. Weld metal deposited in previous passes is indicated in the groove ahead of the moving carriage.

Circumferential welds are made with automatic equipment in a manner similar to the longitudinal welds except that the drum is rotated under a stationary electrode and flux carrier. This operation may be noted in the foreground of the drum assembly bay illustration, Fig. 11. To avoid excessive stresses and detrimental metallurgical transformations, preheat, generally with gas burners as indicated, is applied to keep the drum welding area at an even temperature.

External connections to a drum, such as various nozzles for steam exit, sometimes connections for steam or water circulators, safety valves, gage glass fittings, chemical connections, and blowdowns, do not lend themselves well to automatic welding and are done by hand.

One of the Bays in the Drum Shops

A partial view of one of five bays in the drum shops at Barberton for assembling and finishing boiler drums is shown in Fig. 11. Each of the bays is specially equipped for a certain range in size and pressure of drums.

Many operations are underway in this view. In a large drum (right foreground) assembled preparatory to making circumferential welds, the areas in way of the welds are being preheated. An automatic

submerged arc welder is shown in operation at the near end (drum head being welded to shell). The drum is rotated continuously under the electrode. At the extreme right, a reel of filler wire is shown above another automatic welder in operation on a circumferential seam near the drum center. At left center, drum heads and shell sections are shown extending into the background.

Stress Relief After Welding

Stress relief after all welding has been completed is an indispensible requirement of Code welding. This operation follows prescribed schedules of temperature rate of increase, time at the temperature required, and cooling rate. These criteria depend on the kind of material, its shape, and the dimension of the weld section. The end result of this operation (stress relief) is the elimination of any stresses set up during welding.

Fig. 12. Two of several stress relieving furnaces. They are gas-fired and the atmosphere is controlled as required

Two of the many stress-relieving furnaces at Barberton are shown in Fig. 12. The largest of these furnaces (in capacity) can accommodate in a single heat a charge that does not exceed a hot length of 116 ft and a hot width of 14 ft 6 inches.

A great number of inlet and outlet gas ports provide an even distribution of heat throughout the furnaces. The elevated structures at the open end of the furnaces house door closures. The furnaces were designed and built at the Barberton Works.

After stress-relief has been completed, the inside and outside surfaces of the welds are chipped and ground flush with the surface of the plate. Fillet welds are ground to smooth radial contours. This simplifies the taking and interpretation of X-ray pictures, and the finished surface at all welds eliminates stress-raisers.

Testing and Radiographic Examination

After stress-relief and the finish of the weld surface by chipping and grinding, pressure vessels are subjected to important shop tests. The principal tests are:

1. Coupons prepared from metal deposited during the welding operation are strength tested, chemically analyzed, and microscopically examined.
2. The vessel is tested under hydraulic pressure to Code requirements.
3. All welds are given a careful radiographic examination in accordance with the Code and the Company's own rigorous manufacturing requirements.

Routine tensile, bending, and impact strength tests are made on coupons prepared from areas representative of the welding. Samples from the coupons are also used for chemical analysis and microscopic examination. To provide these coupons, weld metal is deposited on an extended tab beyond the weld proper, as shown in Fig. 10.

In accordance with the Code, the vessel is subjected to a hydraulic pressure test (with temporary closure of all openings) at 1½ times the design pressure specification.

For the radiographic examination of the welds, extensive X-ray equipment of a wide range of power, as listed above, is used in the shops and in the separate X-ray building.

Registering the 2,000,000-volt X-ray machine (located in a separate building) on a sector of the weld of a head to a large drum is shown in Fig. 13. The entire length of all welds, circumferential and longitudinal, is X-rayed section by section. The films, in cassettes, are successively positioned on the inside surface of the vessel.

Where gamma rays are used in weld examination, the active source of radiation may be placed inside the vessel if the distance (d) from source to weld and the wall thickness (t) relationship is favorable. The ratio, d/t, should not be less than 4 and in general should lie between 4 and 7. Sometimes, when the source of radiation must be placed outside, both walls of the vessel will appear in the radiograph and must be differentially appraised.

In the case of defective welds, a radiographic examination usually gives clear evidence of slag, porosity, cracks, and lack of fusion. A good radiograph will reveal the presence or absence of a defect

Fig. 13. Registering 2,000,-000-volt X-ray machine on circumferential seam of drum for radiographic examination of the weld. Film cassette is held in place on inner surface

Fig. 14. Tubeholes in large drum drilled with a battery of single-spindle machines

or discontinuity, and if a defect is present it will portray its shape and extent. Experience is essential in the correct evaluation of defects or discontinuities. The effect on the intended service of the weld of any discontinuities that may be present is again primarily a matter of judgment and experience. Defects inimical to performance must be cut out and the area rewelded.

For indicating fine surface cracks or defects not more than ⅛ in. below the surface, the magnetic particle method of inspection is very effective (see Chapter 25). This method has been adopted by B&W as a standard test to supplement examination by X rays or gamma rays. It is now also required by some of the local codes.

Drilling Tubeholes in Drums

After completion of all tests and inspection, the drum is marked for the tubeholes required. A large drum so marked, for tubeholes at various pitches, is shown in Fig. 14 under a battery of single-spindle

drills. Special milling cutters or twist drills are used, depending on the diameter and depth of hole. Circular grooves are milled in the tube seats to increase the holding power and tightness of the expanded

Fig. 16. Square header stock formed into the sinuous shape characteristic of the B&W sectional-header boiler

tube joint. The number of grooves depends on the depth of the tube seat. The grooves are machined with a specially designed tool mounted in the press used in drilling the holes.

For standard boilers with holes at a definite pitch, the drill heads are set to the required pitch on a multiple-spindle press (as shown in Fig. 15). The plate of the drum shown in this illustration is comparatively thin for small low-pressure boilers. Small-diameter holes at close pitch are drilled with several individual drills powered from a single spindle through a special multiple-drill head.

When all tubeholes have been drilled and grooved,

Fig. 15. Multiple-spindle drill press used for rapid drilling of tubeholes on standard spacing

Fig. 17. *Several types and sizes of round headers on layout benches, where they are marked as required for tubeholes and attachments*

the holes are checked for size, inspected, cleaned, and the burrs and sharp corners are removed. Careful chocking and steel lashing are required to secure large and small finished drums on railroad cars for shipment. The necessity for this precaution is apparent because of the great damage possible should one of these heavy components (from 1 to 250 tons in weight and from 5 to more than 120 ft long) come adrift in transit.

Headers as Terminal Pressure Vessels

Sinuous Headers of Square Section

One of the distinctive B&W boilers of the past, still quite extensively used in its modern form, is the sectional-header ("staggered") type. The forming of the sinuous component is still admired as a particularly ingenious operation in manufacture.

Square header stock is heated to the required temperature and is then hot forged with suitable outer forming dies working against articulated (and separable) inner mandrels (see Fig. 16). The undulating or offset intervals permit a staggered arrangement of tubes (well shown in Fig. 6, Chapter 29) which improves heat absorption. Another important result, since the extent of flat areas is much reduced, is the strengthening of the structure.

Straight tubes extend between front and rear headers of a section. The handholes opposite each tubehole provide access for expanding tube ends in the headers.

The thickness of square-header-stock steel commonly varies in the range from about ⅜ in. to 1¼ inches. The side dimension varies from about 6⅝ in. to 8 in., and the maximum length is about 11 feet.

The basic form of the sinuous header is used in the cross-drum boiler and in some boilers for marine service. Despite the development of many other basic boiler types, use of the sinuous-header boiler in the production of steam will continue.

Headers of Round Section

There are innumerable instances, in the many types of boilers illustrated in this book, of arrangements where headers are used as junction or terminal pressure vessels at either or both ends of a system of tubes. Furnace water-wall tubes and one or both ends of superheater and economizer tube banks are usually connected to headers (drums also may form terminals). In Fig. 6, Chapter 28, the end views of no less than seven headers are indicated by reference to the inlets and outlets for the superheater and economizer.

Carbon- or alloy-steel headers range from 6 in. to 30 in. in diameter and from ⅜ in. to 4 in. in wall thickness. Headers are made from seamless or forged and bored tubular stock. The 6500-ton piercing press and the 1200-ton drawbench (see above) have proved very useful in producing suitable seamless stock, particularly of high-alloy

Fig. 18. *A long (42-ft) superheater header in the final stage of fabrication*

Fig. 19. A bay used for the fabrication of superheater and economizer sections, in which the production of short-radius bends is an important operation

steels. As with all boiler pressure components, headers must conform to the Code requirements.

In Fig. 17 several examples of headers are shown on the layout benches. The ends have been closed in by a spinning operation. In this operation the seamless tube is heated to forging temperature and placed in a specially designed spinning machine. After the header has been clamped into position, a rotating contour-forming roll is brought up against the heated end by hydraulic pressure. The rotation of this forming roll gradually causes the end to form the required shape. The smoothly rounded contour of

Fig. 21. An automatic machine used to make butt welds in a continuous-tube superheater section. Note newly made weld and other welds in the completed portion

the header ends, visible in the illustration, suggests the satisfactory result possible with this method.

Tubeholes, handholes, and other openings as required are scribed on the coated surface of the header. Guide lines are center punched preparatory to drilling, reaming, and grooving tubeholes, and profiling noncircular holes. Locations of outside attachments are established.

A special milling cutter, guided from a template, is used to mill elliptical handhole openings and the internal counterbore required to seat handhole caps with gasket (see Fig. 12, Chapter 25).

Nozzles or branch connections are welded to prepared openings in a manner identical with this operation for drums.

The finished header shown in Fig. 18 is a good

Fig. 20. Welding support and spacing lugs of the pin-and-clevis type to a superheater section

Fig. 22. *Tube-bending machine to form easy-radius bends required in some long circuits*

example of the extent of the operations performed on a long, 42-ft, superheater header. A steam outlet at each end, tubeholes, support hangers, and casing seal plates are shown.

Tubes as Heat-Absorbing Surface

Tubes, in an almost endless variety of arrangements, serve as the heat-absorbing surface and provide flow circuits in today's steam production, as the boiler units displayed throughout this book clearly show. Tube material may be carbon or alloy steel, of definite specification to suit the pressure and temperature conditions of service.

Tubes may be small (1 in.) to large (4½ in. or more), plain, or fitted with extended surface as in some cases of furnace walls. As heat-absorbing surface, tubes are used in the furnace, boiler convection components, superheaters, reheaters, attemperators, economizers, and air heaters.

An array of tubes in various stages of production

is shown in one of the shop bays where superheater and economizer sections are made (see Fig. 19). Short-radius bends are produced by special machinery developed for their manufacture (see right foreground).

A completed superheater section, with short-radius bends, is shown in Fig. 20 being fitted with articulated pin-and-clevis hangers (mentioned in Chapter 12). The butt welds indicated in this section were made by the automatic resistance-butt-welding equipment shown in Fig. 21. In this operation the tube ends, milled to the proper shape, are brought together, resistance welded (in a matter of seconds), and heat treated, all in one continuous operation. The finished weld can be produced virtually without inside projection. Thus, the finished section shown in Fig. 20 is one continuous-loop circuit made by butt welding commercial lengths of straight tubing.

Very short radius bends (such as 2½-in. tubes on 1½-in. radius) are made in a hot die forge operation, where the diameter, roundness, and required wall thickness of the tube section are maintained.

Easy-radius bends are common in furnace walls, boiler convection surface, and outside tubing in riser and downcomer circuits. Such bends are produced as indicated in Fig. 22 for a long tube. It will be noted that there are a number of bends in different planes.

The extended surface (round studs), visible at the near end of the long tube in Fig. 22, is applied before bending by special automatic resistance-welding machines. Flat-stud extended surface is also frequently used in furnace wall construction (see Fig. 14, Chapter 14).

Forge Shop

Forgings are used extensively for pressure parts as well as nonpressure parts in the various components of a steam-producing unit. The flanging of drum-

Fig. 23. *Wrought-steel flanged nozzle hot forged in one operation with this press and suitable dies*

Fig. 24. *Manipulator and furnace for heating billets used to forge flanged nozzles, pulverizer balls, and other parts*

Fig. 25. *Press used to forge pulverizer balls from alloy-steel billet cut to proper length*

Fig. 27. *A large number of molding machines and receiving racks for completed molds in a bay of the foundry*

heads, the forging of specially shaped headers, and the spinning in of the ends of round headers have been illustrated and mentioned above.

A wrought-steel flanged nozzle, forged from a solid billet in one operation, is shown in Fig. 23. The forging is next machined to dimensions and then welded to a drum as an external connection.

The grinding balls used in coal pulverizers are forged from alloy steel. The raw material is in the form of billets cut to the proper length to give the material required for one ball. The billet being placed in the heating furnace is shown in Fig. 24. A cropped portion of the heated billet (of the proper length) is placed in the press. The forging operation completed for one ball and a second ball (after having been stripped of the forging flash) rolling in transit to the heat-treating furnace are shown in Fig. 25.

Foundry

Boiler pressure parts (drums, headers, and tubes) are made almost entirely from steel plate, forgings, or prepared billet sections (tube-rounds). On the other hand, castings are used economically for a very considerable part of the weight of many of the associated nonpressure components of a complete boiler unit, such as stokers, pulverizers, fuel feeders, and burning equipment. These castings are of a wide variety and are made of gray iron, alloy iron, carbon steel, and alloy steel to suit service requirements.

Extensive facilities are provided at Barberton for pattern making and storage, molding, melting, pouring, handling, and finishing operations. The prompt supply of castings for older designs, as replacements to equipment still in service after many years, is an inescapable responsibility.

In Figs. 26 and 27 are shown rows of modern small

Fig. 26. *Squeeze-molding machines in the foundry used to make molds for casting many small parts*

Fig. 28. *Mechanical sandslinger in operation in the foundry. This equipment is useful for filling large molds*

Fig. 29. Arrangement of chill pieces on patterns preparatory to use in molds for casting pulverizer grinding rings

Fig. 31. Cutting duplicate irregular shapes from a thick steel plate with an automatically guided four-unit acetylene torch

squeeze-molding machines and racks for receiving the completed molds. These facilitate the mass production of duplicate castings.

How molds for large castings are made is indicated in Fig. 28, which shows a sandslinger impacting molding-sand into a flask around the pattern of a large pulverizer grinding ring. By this method uniform molds are produced with a minimum of handwork. Large ladles are used to supply the metal required to fill molds of this order.

A somewhat specialized molding practice is required to produce chilled castings with specially hardened surface desirable for certain pulverizer parts, as in grinding rings. The hardened surface is obtained by the presence of a mass of metal in a selected portion of the mold, which serves to chill

quickly the molten metal and so give the desired characteristic. In Fig. 29 the chill components are shown placed on the patterns of three sizes of grinding rings, preparatory to filling the molds with sand. When the pattern is removed from the mold, the mass of metal is still in place to chill quickly the poured metal in the desired areas.

In the production of steel castings at Barberton, induction-type electric furnaces are used to melt higher-alloy steels under closely controlled conditions. Carbon and low-alloy steels are melted in an electric-arc furnace. Parts to withstand high temperature, such as superheater spacers and support castings, are examples of the use of higher-alloy steels. The electric-arc furnace is used in melting the metal for a wide variety of castings, where close control of

Fig. 30. Typical arrangement of stock and various machine tools in a structural steel fabrication bay

Fig. 32. *Radial drill used to cut tube-holes in a large air heater tube sheet*

and some pulverizer parts. As a class, these items are made from plate and sheet of the required thickness and from rolled shapes.

One of four bays devoted to structural fabrication is shown in Fig. 30, where sheets and plates are laid out and cut by shear or by single or multiple acetylene torch equipment. In Fig. 31 a four-unit acetylene torch is shown cutting duplicate irregular shapes from a thick plate.

Plate is variously straightened or bent in large horizontal bulldozers fitted with suitable edges. Appropriate use is made of radial drills with long radius of action in drilling tubeholes in large air heater tube sheets. A radial drill used for this purpose is shown in Fig. 32.

In the structural shop, rotating jigs are provided to facilitate the welding of such items as pulverizer housings, some types of supports, some conical shapes, and cyclone separators for drums.

properties is essential.

The foundry at Barberton is also equipped to dip-calorize (coat with aluminum) steel plates and castings.

Structural Fabrication

There is a wide variety of fabricated steel structure, to function as nonpressure parts, associated with a boiler unit. In this category may be listed casings, built-up supports of standard steel shapes, air heater components (exclusive of tubes), flues and ducts, dust hoppers, drum baffles, cyclone separators,

Machine Shop

In machining the various parts of the component assemblies required for a complete boiler unit, an ex-tensive machine shop fully equipped with modern tools, such as the one at Barberton, is essential for efficient production. The equipment consists mainly of standard machine tools: various types and sizes of lathes, horizontal and vertical boring mills, planers, shapers, drill presses, and grinders. Parts which have been assembled and welded, cast, or forged in other departments are usually finished in the machine shop, as are special tools and equipment for use in the

Fig. 33. *General view of a machine shop bay for the fabrication of pulverizer parts*

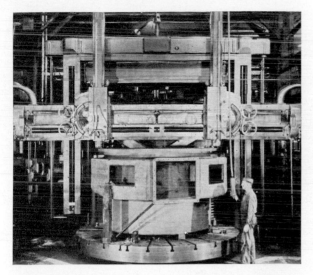

Fig. 34. *Vertical boring mill used to machine the main flange of a pulverizer housing*

plant and in erection.

One of the four bays of the machine shop, where the principal parts and assemblies of pulverizers are machined, is shown in Fig. 33. A pulverizer gear housing similar to the one shown in Fig. 15, Chapter 17, may be seen in the vertical boring mill, at left center. Other gear housings are shown inverted on the floor, at center. At right center, flanges are shown being machined in two horizontal boring mills. Two upper grinding rings for a Type B (Fig. 14, Chapter 17) pulverizer are shown stacked, at left foreground. Several intermediate rings for Type B double-row pulverizers appear at left beyond the vertical boring mill.

Finished components are assembled at the far background, in Fig. 33. The pulverizers range in size and weight from the E-17 of the E series, 7 ft high and about 4 tons, to the B 282 of the B series, about 15 ft high and 54 tons. The crane shown at the top background has a capacity of 30 tons.

Many Items in Mass Production

An endless variety of machined parts is required for the wide range of products of the power plant equipment manufacturer. Such parts can be made with standard commercial and special machine tools, using mass-production methods. Typical items in this category are: drum and header nozzles, tube nipples, manhole and handhole plates, a wide size range of studs and bolts, stoker parts such as shafts and gear-drive components, flanges for pipes, tubes, and mechanical drives, gear blanks, various dampers, and many others.

Machining Top Sections of Pulverizers

Top housings for pulverizers, fabricated of plate steel, are welded, annealed, and then machined.

The windbox air-inlet flange of the top housing for an E-series pulverizer, shown in a large (146-in. capacity) vertical boring mill (Fig. 34), has already been faced on another machine. In the operation shown, the main lower flange for assembly to the gear housing is being faced. This component weighs about 9 tons, and the flange diameter is 9 feet. In spite of the large size and weight, precision machining is required for dust- and gastight final assembly. No gasket is necessary for joints of this excellence.

With suitable cutting tools, grinding-ring material of 700 Brinell hardness can be turned in this mill.

Driving-Gear Sets for Pulverizers

The teeth of the main spiral bevel drive-gear sets (gear and pinion) for coal pulverizers are precision cut in forged blanks in a gear-tooth-generating machine. The tooth generation of the alloy-steel gear (67 in. in diameter, 70-in. maximum capacity), shown mounted in the machine in Fig. 35, has just been completed. Significant tooth form dimensions are held to ± 0.0005-in. tolerance.

After the tooth generation is completed, the gear is moved to the hardening bench, where the bearing surface of each tooth is heated successively by a carefully controlled gas flame, followed at a timed interval with quenching sprays of a suitable coolant. Tooth surface-hardness of 500 to 600 Brinell is customary. The gear and its mating pinion are then meshed in true working position and lapped by running contact.

An important final step in gear performance is a

Fig. 35. *Teeth in the spiral bevel gears used in B&W pulverizers are cut to close tolerances in special machine tools of the type shown*

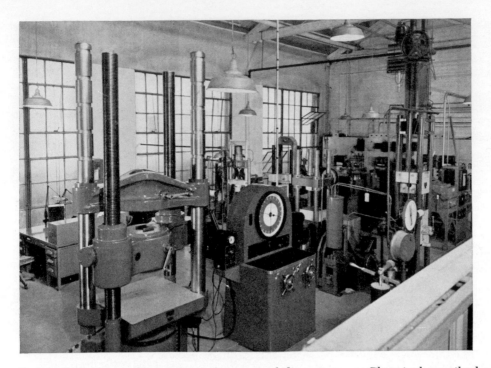

Fig. 36. *Some of the physical test equipment in the Works Control Laboratory at Barberton. Specimen-heating furnaces, tensile and impact machines are in constant use*

"run-in," after assembly of the pulverizer, of the gear and pinion on the test floor for several hours. This run-in is equally important for all the moving parts of the pulverizer.

Works Control Laboratory

The works control laboratory (Figs. 36 and 37) is equipped and maintained principally to provide the laboratory service required in the performance of the work of the various manufacturing and engineering departments. The services of the laboratory may be outlined as follows:

1. Supply information for the preparation of specifications required in the purchase of proper materials for the various components.
2. Make the tests required by the *Boiler and Pressure Vessel Code* of the ASME, the federal, state, and municipal laws and ordinances, the purchaser's specifications, and the manufacturer's own specifications and standards.
3. Instruct the departments in the use of proper procedure and temperature for a manufacturing operation.
4. Take actual readings and make other checks as the work is underway to ascertain that it is done within the permissible limitations.
5. Establish all welding procedures throughout the plant and maintain check controls on the work.
6. Conduct experiments and tests in connection with new welding problems.
7. Supervise the welding school conducted by the Company as well as the qualification tests of operators and procedures.

Chemical, tensile, bend, impact, and other tests are required to fulfill the responsibilities implicit in the above list. Radiographic, magnetic-particle, fluorescent, and micrographic analyses are required. A portion of the laboratory devoted to heat treating and physical testing of specimens is shown in Fig. 36. Adequate facilities for the prompt chemical analysis of metals are provided in another section of the laboratory. Some equipment for the micrographic examination of metal specimens is shown in Fig. 37.

Works Contract Engineering Department

Preparation of the design details and specifications, for manufacture in the shops or for purchase of the various parts and assemblies necessary to fulfill the

Fig. 37. *A corner of the photographic laboratory for the micrographic examination of metallurgical materials*

Fig. 38. *Section of the Works Contract Engineering Department for the preparation of design layouts, purchase and manufacturing specifications, and general working drawings*

contracts entered into by the Company, is the responsibility of the works contract engineering department. For small standardized boilers, drawings on hand are generally available, and shop manufacture can begin promptly. A modern large boiler unit, on the other hand, is usually nonstandard and is assembled from several thousand different pieces, each of which must be designed and detailed.

Layouts, calculations, and drawings must be prepared to determine and define all pieces and assemblies. The information in drawings and memoranda must be arranged so that it will convey to the various manufacturing departments, in a complete, clear, and proper manner, what is to be produced, and to the erection department how all parts are to

be assembled in the field.

One division of the works contract engineering department is shown in Fig. 38. All Code requirements, federal, state, and municipal laws, purchaser's specifications, and the Company's own rules and standards must be observed in the designs prepared.

The works contract engineering department is equipped with a complete electronic computer system, as shown in Fig. 39, to obtain quick and accurate calculations of intricate stress analysis problems such as piping flexibility.

Complete records of existing installations are maintained in this department, and orders for replacement parts are given immediate attention as received.

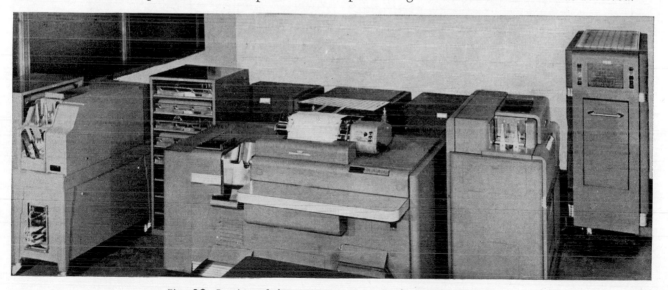

Fig. 39. *Portion of the computer room in the Works Contract Engineering Department, stress analysis division*

POSITIONING A FURNACE TUBE DURING ERECTION OF A
WATER-COOLED FURNACE

PRINCIPLES AND METHODS OF INSTALLATION

A FEW boiler types are small enough to permit shipment completely assembled. Some marine boilers are in this class and may be loaded on a single freight car. To ship all of the materials for a large central station unit a hundred cars may be necessary, and economic construction requires careful scheduling and planning.

To achieve the highest standards of workmanship and inspection in the erection of a large modern water-tube boiler with its auxiliaries and instruments, to assure safe and successful operation, requires a well trained, fully equipped organization and the skillful use of specially designed tools. Furthermore, the work must be done to meet shipping and erection schedules set up with the view of completing the job quickly so that the unit may be placed in useful production as soon as possible.

Material Storage and Handling

After the sale of the boiler and following a study of the arrangement drawings an erection schedule, outlining in some detail the sequence of erection, is submitted to the factory as a basis for shop fabrication and shipment. In preparing shipping and erection schedules it is necessary to know the actual conditions for material storage, handling and erection. Adverse conditions increase erection time and cost and, therefore, affect estimates. The most troublesome conditions are: a) lack of storage space near the site which would necessitate double handling of the material, b) restricted or difficult access to the site proper, so that many items usually shop assembled must be shipped knocked down, and c) extremely close quarters for actual erection where the optimum sequence cannot be followed.

Before shipment begins details of storage, handling and erection are thoroughly reviewed on the job site with the customer and his general contractor in order to arrange for:

1) Adequate storage space near the site, varying from a few hundred sq ft to 5 acres according to the size of the boiler. Large areas should be served by a railroad spur and a truck road with another spur and road to the boiler site (see Fig. 1).

2) An erecting field office, a tool and material room and a change room for the workmen (see Fig. 2 and Fig. 3).

3) Construction facilities such as compressed air and electric power, suitably located at the boiler site.

4) Banks of welding machines (for large jobs) located at several floor elevations to avoid unsafe working conditions by haphazard runs of electric lines and welding leads.

5) Stairways and floors to permit safe access and working conditions on all sides and at every elevation around the boiler.

6) Setting derrick (if required) on the roof for raising material (see Fig. 4).

7) Leaving out or removing structural members

Fig. 1. Boiler unit components in field storage convenient for assembly at boiler site

Fig. 2. *Typical temporary field office used by the erection force during assembly of boiler unit*

as required to permit erection of large components such as heavy drums, headers, and long tubes.

8) Openings in buildings such as hatchways in the roof and large doors in the sides at ground level.

Where the building is new it is preferable not to start erection of the boiler until the building is far enough advanced to provide protection from the weather. In an existing plant the time to start erection of the boiler is after all old equipment has been removed and sufficient access has been provided. Before erection is started enough material should be available at the site for continuous prosecution of the work.

Materials arriving before the required date must be carefully protected. Machined surfaces and uncapped tube ends should be heavily greased. Light gage metals require cover. Welding rod, valves, fittings, instruments, and gages should be stored indoors and refractories should be protected from moisture.

For large units a systematic arrangement of the storage yard is essential (see Fig. 1). Loose parts and boxes should be located and marked for ready identification. Yard areas should be numbered and notation made on drawings or bills of material indicating locations.

Tool Division and Specialists

An effective erection organization must have an efficient tool division, which, at B&W is divided into three groups: (1) design and analytical; (2) maintenance and shipping; (3) testing and research. From this division the erection supervisor will receive a list of tools, expanding equipment, welding machines, rigging, hoists and cranes selected for his job after careful study of the job drawings and field conditions. Designers are constantly improving tools and machines. For lifting heavy components such as drums it is usually necessary to design special rigs to suit the particular conditions in the field.

Although operations of the B&W Erection Depart-

ment are directed from headquarters at Barberton, O., a district erection supervisor and staff of erectors are located at most branch offices of the Company. A supply of tools and equipment for maintenance repairs is also available in the districts. The nature of these tools and supplies is indicated in Fig. 5.

As the work progresses specialists in the erection organization may be called on by the erection supervisor in the field for advice and assistance. Specialists in welding, preheating, stress relieving and radiographic examination of welds visit the job at specified times. The erector submits weekly progress reports, with the percentage of completion of each component, as a check against the original schedules.

Suggestions and ideas from erectors and others in the field for improvement of methods, design details or equipment are encouraged. Every member of the erection forces should constantly bear in mind that all the vision, research and experience in design and manufacture will produce a successful steam generating unit only if the assembly and erection on the site of the customer are correctly and carefully accomplished.

Foundations

Foundations for boilers and auxiliary equipment are usually designed and constructed by the customer or for him by an engineering firm, specializing in this type of work. Drawings indicating size and location of anchor bolts, conduits and other openings and the loads to be carried are supplied by the equipment manufacturers. For pulverizers, fans and other auxiliaries these drawings usually note the quantity of concrete required in the foundation.

To avoid costly delays and interferences all foundations should be completed and centerlines, to-

Fig. 3. *Tools, gear, and materials in current use should be stored in orderly fashion in clean quarters at erection site*

Fig. 4. Stiff-leg derrick on roof raising section of duct from cars for lowering into building

Erection Procedure

A typical steam generating unit consists of a boiler, often with water-cooled furnace walls which may or may not be an integral part; and other components, variously required, such as superheater, economizer, sootblowers, and air heater. Fuel preparation and burning equipment, fans, flues and ducts, and metering and control apparatus are also required, and their installation must be closely related to the over-all erection procedure. Before erection begins the design of structural supports, walkways, stairways and grating has been carefully coordinated with the requirements of the boiler unit. The procedure and sequence of erection will vary with the type of boiler, the space available, and the means of access to the site. With two or more entries on different sides the sequence of erection naturally will be much simpler than if all the material must be brought in from one direction and through one opening.

Apart from limited space conditions the sequence of assembly may be governed by the design arrangement of boiler tubes and supports. Though in some cases tubes may be erected in any sequence, usually a definite relative position of the tubes requires their erection in a predetermined sequence. Because of these variations the sequence of erection can be outlined only in general terms.

As a rule structural supports (see Fig. 6), also walkways and stairways are erected first, taking care to maintain the strength of the structure by suitable means when members are temporarily omitted to make room for the erection of large components of the boiler.

gether with datum marks locating the base plate elevations of the equipment, should be established by the customer's engineer before arrival of the boiler erection force. Immediately on arrival the erector will check the centerlines, anchor bolt locations and elevation datum marks, and if there is any discrepancy corrective measures should be determined with the customer's engineer. The erector will make a general inspection of the foundations to determine if any required features have been overlooked. This is a rational precautionary measure and no criticism is implied.

Fig. 5. Portion of main tool and supply storage at B & W Barberton Works erection headquarters

Fig. 6. *A virtually completed steel structure as shown is required to support a large boiler. The steam drum is here hung from above in U shaped members*

Alignment of Structural Supports

All structural supports for a boiler must be aligned with the utmost care due to the many attachments on the boiler which are secured to the supporting steel and because of the assembly of pressure parts which are difficult to alter if they do not fit properly. Accurate alignment of the supporting steel will save many man-hours in the erection of a boiler.

For most types of boilers, where the steam drum is the anchor point for all expansion, the longitudinal and transverse centerlines of the drum serve as base lines to determine the alignment of structural members and pressure parts.

The supporting structure is aligned by cable and turnbuckle guy lines or wooden shores in conjunction with its own diagonal bracing. With a safe minimum of bolting to hold it in place the structure is then completely bolted or riveted as indicated on the drawings. The structure for smaller boilers is generally bolted throughout, while for larger boilers the load-bearing members are usually riveted and secondary members are bolted. Welding is rarely used for structural connections made in the field because of difficulty in maintaining accurate alignment of the structure.

In many designs of small boilers the vertical columns of the structural frame are not braced diagonally and are ultimately held in alignment by the brickwork of the boiler setting. In this case all guy wires, shores and temporary bracing, arranged to avoid interference, must remain in place until the brickwork is well advanced.

Column footings are grouted as soon as possible after the steel structure is completely bolted and riveted.

Drums, Headers and Tubes

After completion of the structure the boiler drums, large and heavy, are usually erected first. Once in position and accurately aligned to the base lines they are blocked or braced to prevent movement when the tubes are installed and expanded. The furnace wall headers, superheater headers and economizer headers are erected next, and are located in relation to the steam drum rather than the structural steel to avoid an accumulation of dimensional errors.

Tubes between drums and headers are erected in the sequence required by the arrangement and are usually held in place temporarily by enlarging or locally flaring the projecting tube ends. When all the tubes in one wall or one component of the unit are in place they are aligned for correct spacing, proper projection of ends in drums and headers and with the faces in line before they are expanded. Tubes must enter the holes fairly, with the tube wall parallel to the axis of the hole.

Accuracy of alignment is governed in general by clearance requirements. For instance, spacing of tubes must be maintained within the specified tolerances to permit the withdrawal of other tubes, to allow clearance for soot blowers with lanes of proper width for the blowing mechanism, and to provide room for spacers, supports or other attachments. The position of the tubes at the outer perimeter of the

Fig. 7. *Typical equipment, rolls, mandrel, and drive motor used to expand and flare tubes in steam drum (54 in. drum shown)*

boiler must be maintained to allow for expansion clearances and proper space for brickwork, insulation, and casing. Tube alignment is maintained by temporary wooden spacers and blocking or permanent spacer attachments, or both, until the tubes are permanently connected to the drums and headers.

Tubes Connected to Headers and Drums

Normally tubes are connected to headers and drums by the simple and effective operation of expanding the tube ends into holes. In this operation, sometimes referred to as "rolling" (see Fig. 7), a tool called an expander is employed to press the tube wall against the solid metal of the hole (the hole is usually grooved), setting up an elastic reaction of sufficient force to hold the tube in place (see Fig. 8). This type of connection, the expanded joint, has great inherent strength and is widely used. However, there may be conditions where an expanded joint cannot be made, due to inaccessibility or where, by itself, it is inadequate because of insufficient holding power to resist externally imposed loads or the stresses caused by temperature differentials. Also, there are cases where the tube walls are too thick to be expanded by practical tools or where the header is too thin to provide adequate support for the expanded joint. Consequently, where the simple expanded joint is inadequate or cannot be used, welding, under properly controlled procedures, is in order either in place of or as a supplement to expanding.

Where the expanded joint is precluded by a lack of access, tubes may be secured by welding to stubs or nozzles already welded to the drums or headers in the shop and stress-relieved there. The same construction can be used when the tube walls are too thick to expand or when the header plate is too thin to provide enough seat at the joint.

Use of Seal Welding

In general, a properly expanded joint will develop the full strength of a tube in straight tension. However, where a joint is in torsion, subject to rapid temperature changes, or under bending loads, the simple

Fig. 9. Erection of boiler pressure parts completed, and all openings closed ready for the hydrostatic test

expanded joint alone is not sufficient, and seal welding is customary in addition to expanding. Tubes acting as major support members may also be welded as a supplement to expanding. Because of the trend in recent years to high pressure and high capital investment, particularly for large units, welded tube joints are more generally used in all pressure components. Recommended practice for pressures of 1800 psi and above is to seal weld all expanded joints or, alternately, to use shop-welded and annealed stubs.

For economizers at any pressure, it is usual practice, in addition to expanding, to seal weld tube ends at both inlet and outlet headers to prevent possible leaks caused by rapidly changing water temperature, which produces temperature differentials between tubes and header.

For superheaters at any pressure, the outlet header tube ends should be expanded and then seal welded, when the design steam outlet temperature exceeds 850 F. Expanding only is usually considered sufficient for temperatures below 850 F. Some inlet superheater header tube seats are seal welded, particularly in boiler units designed to operate at pressures above 1050 psi.

Field welding should be undertaken only where it is required by the design and where it is specifically

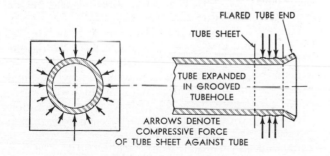

Fig. 8. Elastic radial forces, between walls of tubehole and tube, grip the tube in an expanded joint

Fig. 10. *Circular manhole in lower drum, 960 psi design pressure, and handholes in lower water-wall header (extreme left) provide access during erection and subsequent inspection and maintenance*

are installed. Openings provided for equipment not installed are blanked off. The hydrostatic test should be completed before brickwork and insulation are started. However, where this is not possible because of the time element, especially on large units, expanded joints and field welds are left bare for inspection during the hydrostatic test. Internal fixtures in drums and the safety valves are generally installed after the test is completed.

Erection of the boiler casing is started as soon as the brickwork and insulation are sufficiently advanced. Soot blower heads and piping and all permanent drain piping are installed during erection of the casing.

Handhole Fittings and Gasketed Joints

Handholes and manholes are provided in boiler components for access to tubes which must be expanded during erection, and for subsequent inspection, maintenance, cleaning and repairs (see Fig. 10).

Manhole openings in drums are either circular or elliptical depending mainly on manufacturing practice. Manholes for B&W boilers have an inside gasket surface and an outside yoke. Woven gaskets are used for boilers with design pressures up to 500 psi. For higher pressures the use of metallic gaskets is general. Before installing the gasket and closing the manhole opening the gasket face is thoroughly cleaned, burrs are removed and the cover is tried in place to make sure that it fits evenly. Manhole covers are generally interchangeable but if they are attached to the drum by hinge bars (see Fig. 11) they are match marked with the drum. Yoke bars on plates for manhole covers are fitted to the contour of the drum head and are also match marked for position.

No jointing compound is used on metallic gaskets or their seats. Woven asbestos gaskets are coated lightly with a mixture of graphite and kerosene. The threads on manhole studs and nuts are coated with a powdered graphite and kerosene mixture. Studs on manhole covers are usually 1½ in. in diameter with 8 threads per inch. They are tightened evenly on initial assembly using a torque of 400 lb ft. When the hydrostatic test is applied they should be retightened using the same torque.

Handhole openings are of various sizes as required for expanding and inspecting the tubes. Inside gasketed fittings are used in water-wall headers for pressures up to 1200 psi and, at somewhat lower pressures, for superheaters with steam temperatures up to 850F (see Fig. 12). Where these limitations are exceeded or if subject to rapid variations in temperature, the handhole fittings are of either an expanded and welded, or all-welded type.

After cleaning the gasket face and removing the

called for on the working drawings. Furthermore, since improper and indiscriminate field welding of pressure parts may result in actual damage, particularly with an increasing use of many different types of steels and alloys, field welding should not be done without a specific procedure from the designer.

Boiler tubes are forwarded in one piece unless restricted by space limitations in shipping or erection. If received in two or more pieces these are joined together at the job site by welding as they are erected or temporarily aligned and finally welded after all tubes are in place.

External Attachments Installed

When all the tubes in a section of furnace wall or boiler have been expanded, external attachments including doors, soot blower wall boxes, tie-bars for furnace wall alignment, buckstays and supports for brickwork, insulation and casing are installed. These attachments, usually made by welding, must be installed before the hydrostatic test.

Preparations for the hydrostatic test of the unit are made as the tube expanding and welding nears completion (see Fig. 9). Tubes are probed to remove any obstructions, headers and drums are cleared of all foreign matter, and handhole and manhole fittings

burrs, a gasketed handhole fitting should fit freely into the opening. The stud in the fitting should be lubricated in the same manner as the manhole stud. A hardened washer is installed between the nut and the yoke. Handhole studs, except for special fittings, are 1 in. in diameter with 8 threads per inch. In tightening initially to a torque of 300 lb-ft, a torque wrench should be used. One type of wrench is fitted with a graduated dial to register the torque developed in lb-ft. The fittings should be tightened again, using the same torque, when the full hydrostatic pressure is applied.

As noted above, when operating pressures or temperatures exceed the practical limits for gasketed handhole fittings, an expanded or welded type fitting is used. In this case the handhole is similar to a tube seat in which a forged fitting is installed by either method to close the opening. Because of the shoulder required on the part of the fitting that is inside of the header, the diameter at this point is larger than the handhole opening, and it is therefore necessary to provide a master handhole through which the fitting can be entered. The master handhole, in turn, is closed with a special shouldered fitting by welding.

To remove an expanded handhole fitting, the wall of the fitting is grooved at three points and collapsed slightly inward so that it may be driven from the opening. The grooving may be done with a pneumatic chisel, by careful use of an acetylene torch, or by a special drilling device.

Fig. 11. Hinged manhole cover in 1475 psi design pressure, 60-in. steam drum

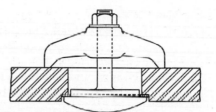

Fig. 12. Gasketed handhole fitting used to close header openings under moderate conditions of pressure and temperature

Assembly of Flanged Joints

The general precautions taken in the installation of handhole and manhole fittings are followed in the assembly of flanged joints, except that nothing is gained by tightening such joints under pressure. Sufficient and uniform tightening of flange studs is of primary importance.

A stress of 30,000 psi in all studs is the optimum degree of tightening and may be determined by the elongation of the stud, using 0.001 in. per in. of stud length measured between centers of nuts. Increase in stud length may be measured with a micrometer or with a dial indicator. Comparative measurements are made of all studs before tightening, and measurements are taken again as the nuts are tightened.

If the threads of the studs and nuts and the bearing surfaces of the nuts have a good machine finish and are properly lubricated, uniform results are also obtainable by using a torque wrench. Under average conditions of surface finish and lubrication, the following torque values have been found to give 30,000 psi stress in studs:

Stud Diameter, inches	Threads, per inch	Torque, lb-ft
⅝	11	89
¾	10	107
⅞	9	162
1	8	244
1⅛	8	322
1¼	8	410
1⅜	8	510
1½	8	615

Cleaning and Hydrostatic Test

Cleaning Pressure Parts

During erection or repair of a boiler, precautions must be observed so that no foreign matter is lodged in the unit when completed. Some variation in the inspection and cleaning procedure may be required for different designs of boilers.

It is essential (normally before the hydrostatic test) to probe all tubes, clean out all headers and drums, and clean and inspect those sections of pressure parts that must be closed, before the test, by permanent welded fittings. At this time all tubes that are clear of obstructions should be plugged or covered to prevent the entry of foreign matter during the installation of drum internals. The drum, however, must be finally cleaned and inspected after the hydrostatic test and after all baffles and other internal connections are in place.

A weight or ball should be passed through each tube, where its shape and location permit, to prove that there is no obstruction. If a ball will not roll in a tube by gravity, compressed air is blown through, using a nozzle with a reasonably tight connection at the entering end. Minor obstructions usually can be removed by first thoroughly wetting the tube and inserting a soaked sponge of full fit which, on being blown through the tube with compressed air, will carry with it any loose foreign matter.

Obstructions are sometimes encountered in bent tubes between an upper and lower drum (pieces of wood or perhaps an expander mandrel), which entered the tube at the upper drum and fell downward to lodge at a bend. The armored hose of a tube cleaner pushed up the tube from the lower end will often dislodge the obstruction and return it to the upper drum. Where a wire cable or a plumber's snake can be passed down the tube beyond the obstruction to emerge at the lower end, a suitable ball or plug may be fastened to the cable or snake, which, on being pulled upward, will remove the obstruction. To dislodge a tightly wedged obstruction in a tube may require much patience and ingenuity. If the obstruction cannot be removed by the methods outlined, the tube must be cut and replaced. No tube is passed for service even if only partially obstructed.

Where there are large pipes running horizontally, a ball of canvas is pulled through with a rope. After all tubes have been probed, all dirt and mill scale is brushed from headers and drums.

On jobs where turbo-driven tube cleaners are provided, the cleaner is passed through at least one tube of each size.

Hydrostatic Test

Safety valves are usually mounted after the hydrostatic test to avoid both the danger of loose dirt floating into the valve seats and the necessity of gagging the valves against test pressure. Water column gage glasses are removed before the test to prevent the entry of surface scum when the boiler is first filled for testing.

Water for the hydrostatic test must be clean and of a temperature not less than 70 F nor more than 90 F. At less than room temperature condensation makes inspection of the outside surfaces of tubes and drums more difficult, and if the temperature is over 90 F minor leaks may not show. One type of pump commonly used in hydrostatic testing is shown in Fig. 13.

To save time in pumping the boiler to the test pressure, the volume of unfilled air space must be at a minimum. Consequently, in filling the boiler with water, a procedure should be followed that will reduce the volume of air space as much as possible. Since it is usually difficult completely to fill the superheater and economizer, the general practice is to fill these sections through drain connections farthest removed from the boiler vent and, when time permits, to fill the entire boiler through the same connections.

When the test pressure is in excess of 500 psi, no one except those actually engaged in inspecting the unit should be allowed in the vicinity of the boiler. This may necessitate making the test outside of regular working hours. The unit must remain under full pressure for not less than 8 hours, so that any leaks which may develop due to creep strain may be detected. This period need not be continuous and may be interrupted for re-expanding where leaks appear or to suit working hours.

The pressure gage used in making the test should be checked for accuracy against a master gage.

When making hydrostatic tests in cold weather, precautions must be taken to prevent damage to the water-filled piping and fittings from freezing. The same precautions must be taken on completion of erection if the boiler is not to go into operation immediately and may, in the interval, be exposed to freezing weather.

Test Pressure After Repairs

On completing repairs to any pressure part of a boiler, a hydrostatic test is required. If it is the renewal of a tube either by expanding or welding or other work not involving changes in design, the test pressure should be 10 per cent below the steam line operating pressure. When the work involves design changes including the drilling of drum or headers, a test pressure of 1½ times the working pressure must be applied. However, if only isolated holes are drilled, the test pressure may be limited to 10 per cent below the line pressure at the discretion of the insurance inspector.

Whenever repairs or alterations such as adding nozzles, superheaters, or other pressure parts are made to an old boiler, the hydrostatic test pressure should never exceed 1½ times the allowable working pressure at the time the work is completed. In testing at 1½ times the working pressure, all safety valves must be removed and the nozzles must be blanked. To make certain that no water will enter the steam line, a check should be made to see that a drain valve is open between the boiler nonreturn valve and the second stop valve at the header. Where a single boiler is connected to a prime mover, the Code permits the omission of stop and nonreturn valves provided the prime-mover throttle valve can with-

Fig. 13. One type of portable air driven pump used for hydrostatic test. The air pressure for driving the pump is usually in the range of 80 to 100 psi

stand the required hydrostatic test pressure. In such cases, the steam line is, of course, full of water during a hydrostatic test.

Checking the Water Level

For a new boiler, after the hydrostatic test is completed and the gage glass is installed, the water level in the gage glass should be checked with the actual water level in the drum. The centerline of the gage glass may be on, above, or below the centerline of the drum. The exact relation is established on the job drawings. When the boiler is filled to the level of the open manhole in the drum, measurements are taken from the water level in the drum to the drum centerline, and from the water level in the gage to the gage centerline. Agreement of these measurements with the dimensions from the drawings is the final proof that the gage glass is located at the correct elevation. Piping to the gage glass should be checked to see that it is free and clear by opening and closing the gage glass drain. The water should flow freely and should come back promptly to its previous level in the gage to indicate that there are no restrictions in the line.

In some high-pressure boilers, the length of the glass in the water gage may be so short that the water is not visible in the glass when the boiler is filled to the bottom of the open manhole in the drum. In this case the gage is removed from its fittings, and the boiler is filled until water appears in the lower gage fitting. After taking the necessary measurements, the gage is replaced, the manhole cover is installed and the boiler is filled to normal level. The gage glass drain is then opened and closed to prove that there are no restrictions in the gage glass piping.

Welding in the Field

For the majority of all field welds the metal-arc process is used and direct current welding machines are employed in nearly all cases. Other types of arc or resistance stud welding, and occasionally the submerged arc process, are also used. Oxyacetylene and inert gas welding are used to a much lesser extent for special applications. The alternating current type of welding machine is not extensively used in field work.

In direct current welding either straight polarity (electrode positive) or reverse polarity (electrode negative) may be used. Where good physical properties are required in the deposited weld metal, including all welding of boiler pressure parts and primary structural members, electrodes made for reverse polarity are used almost exclusively. Where high rates of weld deposits and good appearance are more important than physical properties, electrodes made for straight polarity are used. The boiler casing and minor structural parts are frequently welded with straight polarity electrodes.

Oxyacetylene welding is used for thin wall tubes of small diameter and in locations inaccessible for metal arc welding. Gas welding is used quite extensively in repair work because it can be applied in confined spaces, especially where mirrors are necessary for viewing the point of weld deposit.

No particular problems are involved in welding the boiler casing and the duct work. The prime requisite is neat appearance and that the welds are free from cracks and pinholes and are of sufficient cross-section for structural strength. Where absolute gas or airtightness is required, the enclosure is tested under air pressure and the welded joints are checked for leaks by applying a soap solution. When the boiler operates under negative pressure minor leaks are rarely of enough importance to make an air pressure test necessary. When the entire boiler and furnace operate under positive pressure the casing, usually installed in close proximity to the furnace and the boiler tubes, is designed for zero air leakage. For testing welds to meet this requirement, blanks are fitted at the air inlet and at the air heater gas outlet and an air pressure of 1½ times the design pressure is applied.

Code Rules Must be Followed

Welding together of boiler pressure parts and welding attachments to these parts must be done according to the rules of Section I of the Boiler and Pressure Vessel Code of the ASME (see below). The Code states the limitations of welds that may be made to power boilers and specifies the requirements for radiographic examination and heat treatment of such welds.

All welds for power boilers must be made by qualified welding operators in accordance with qualified welding processes. A process qualification is essentially demonstrable proof that a certain material prepared in a specific way can be welded with specified electrodes by using a specified technique. An operator qualification is proof that the operator can deposit sound weld metal in various positions following an established procedure. Section IX of the Code covers welding qualifications for procedures and operators and lists the variables involved.

While the number of process qualifications for every conceivable type of welding is almost unlimited, in actual practice the number required is not so extensive. Procedure specifications are generally established for various groups of base or parent metals and for various weld positions. Other variables such as filler metal, welding currents and heat treatment are usually limited within each procedure specification. The Code requires that each manufacturer or contractor set up his procedure specifications and make the tests specified by the Code to qualify these procedures. The number of process qualifications set up by the manufacturer or contractor, therefore, depends largely on the versatility of his operations. The process qualifications are usually made at the manufacturer's plant, not in the field, and the field erector is given an attested list of those that have been made, to show to the authorized inspectors as required.

Operator Qualification Tests

Tests actually required for operator qualifications for most of the field work are relatively few. The operator tests for any order of base metal need be made only in horizontal and vertical positions for groove welds and in vertical and overhead positions for fillet welds. The following operator qualification tests will cover almost all welding required in field erection:

1) Groove weld on carbon steel pipe in fixed horizontal position, using carbon steel filler metal.
2) Groove weld on carbon steel pipe in fixed vertical position, using carbon steel filler metal.

Operator qualification tests for gas welding duplicate those for arc welding.

It is frequently desirable to qualify different operators for different types of welds. For welding on the higher alloys an operator qualification test should be made on the actual material to be welded.

The responsibility of the manufacturer and the prerogatives of an authorized inspector with reference to the proper qualification of welding operators on power boilers are specifically covered in Section IX of the Code.

Operator qualification test samples are usually welded at the field erection job site, and are forwarded to the manufacturer's plant or to a competent laboratory for testing. If the results of the tests are satisfactory, the manufacturer issues a certificate of operator qualification for each test completed.

Rules for Repairs to Boilers by Welding

Since repairs to boilers are not specifically covered by the ASME Code, work of this nature is done under the guidance of *Recommended Rules for Repairs by Fusion Welding to Power Boilers and Unfired Pressure Vessels*, formulated and issued by the National Board of Boiler and Pressure Vessel Inspectors, Columbus, O.

No repairs by welding are to be made to a boiler without the approval of an authorized inspector. Where the strength of the structure depends on the strength of the weld the repair must be made by a qualified operator. For repair work the welding operator need not be qualified by the manufacturer, the only requirement being that the inspector is satisfied that the operator is properly qualified. Frequently, however, the power station operator will request that welding operators in his maintenance force be qualified by the manufacturer.

For certain repairs where the strength of the structure does not depend on the strength of the weld, as in building up corroded surfaces the National Board rules permit the use of an "approved operator." The requirements for an approved operator, as outlined in the rules, are somewhat less rigid than those for a qualified operator.

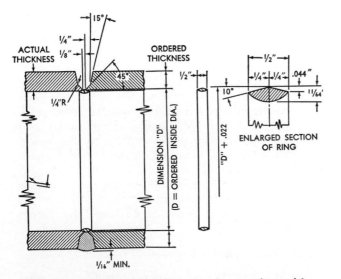

Fig. 14. *One form of backing ring frequently used for butt welds in tubes, pipe, and round header sections*

Work of a Qualified Welder

In boiler erection the work done by qualified welding operators falls into two broad categories. The first and more important of these is the welding together of tubes and other connections which form part of the boiler circulating system. The other is welding attachments to tubes for boiler structural supports and for refractory, insulation and casing supports. The work may be divided into butt welds, socket welds and seal welds for the first category—pressure part connections, and into fillet welds and stud welds for the second category—structural attachments.

Field butt welds are necessary in tubes and other connections of the average large central station boiler primarily because of dimensional limitations in shipping. The large downcomers, connecting upper and lower drums, and attemperator and circulator connections also always require field welded butt joints. Butt welded joints made in the field vary from ½ in. OD for #16 gage tubes to 35 in. OD for 3½ in. thick downcomers.

To simplify the tasks of both erector and inspector in making certain that all welds are properly made, the erector is usually given a schedule prepared by the manufacturer's engineering department, listing all field pressure part welds and including the following information:

1) Name and description of parts to be joined by welding.
2) Material specification of base metal.
3) Diameter and thickness of material.
4) Type and position of welds.
5) Quantity of welds.
6) Welding process.
7) Type of electrode or wire.
8) Diameter of electrode or wire.
9) Preheat temperature.
10) Radiographic or other inspection requirements.
11) Stress relief (temperature and time).
12) Welding procedure specification and welding process qualification references.

Welding Butt Joints

Butt joints for field welding are usually prepared in the shops, and cleaning and buffing the welding edges are the only field preparations required. At present backing rings are widely used for butt welds and a ring with 20 degrees included bevel is usual (one type shown in Fig. 14). Special tools are provided (see Fig. 15) for preparing the joint in the field if, due to alterations or errors, it is necessary to remachine the welding groove and the seat for the backing ring. Butt welds, acceptable under the Code, may be made without backing rings, and a more extensive use of this simplified type of junction may be expected.

Fig. 15. *Typical special tools used in the field to prepare backing ring seats and welding grooves for butt welds*

In fitting the joint together for welding extreme care must be taken properly to seat the backing ring in each half of the connection. If the welded joint is larger than 6 in. ID the backing ring is generally tack-welded to one side of the connection. The tack welds are ground smooth and to the contour of the pipe and ring.

Fitting for welding butt joints in smaller sizes of tubes and piping is facilitated by the use of an alignment jig (see Fig. 16). For larger connections the attachment of pull lugs (see Fig. 17), will usually serve the purpose. Where there are several welded joints in a connection, bridge bars are often installed to hold all parts in alignment until the welds can be made.

Preheating and stress relieving as required by the welding procedure specification must be done during the welding. The methods employed and also the inspections required are described later in this chapter.

Fig. 16. *Simple form of jig used to align ends of tubes and pipe accurately for butt welds*

25-11

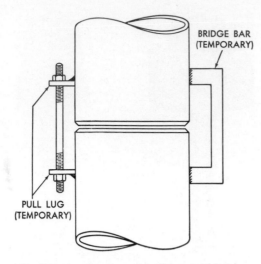

Fig. 17. *Application of pull lug and bridge bar to draw together pipe ends and to hold them in position for butt weld*

Socket and Seal Welds

Socket welds are not used extensively in boiler erection except in the attachment of the smaller sizes of valves and fittings where not in contact with furnace gases. To allow for weld shrinkage, the pipe should not bottom in the socket within $\frac{1}{16}$ inch. The procedure specification must be followed and the operator must be qualified for fillet welding. A typical

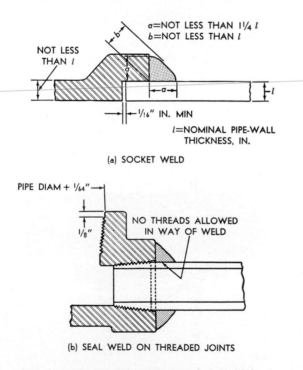

(a) SOCKET WELD

(b) SEAL WELD ON THREADED JOINTS

Fig. 18. *Sketch (a), typical socket weld for pipe 3 in. and under in size. Sketch (b), typical seal weld for threaded connection*

socket weld is illustrated in sketch (a), Fig. 18.

Seal welding, a continuous weld at the joint of connecting parts, is used to secure fluid tightness where other means, such as expanding or threaded connection, provide the mechanical strength. Seal welding, where required, should be so noted on the job erection drawings.

In a seal-welded threaded connection, sometimes used for smaller fittings, no weld metal should be deposited on the threaded section of the pipe. A satisfactory way to prevent such deposit is to counterbore the threaded fitting to a depth of $\frac{1}{8}$ in. at a diameter of $\frac{1}{64}$ in. larger than the OD of the pipe (see sketch (b), Fig. 18).

An expanded joint subject to sudden temperature changes and to certain limited bending or torsional stresses may require seal welding, and the drawing or other engineering order will authorize its use accordingly. A seal weld must be deposited, by an operator qualified for fillet welding, in a minimum of two layers of two to four beads of weld metal and in all other respects in accordance with the procedure specification. Preheating is applied according to the type of material being welded, but stress-relieving is done by re-expanding rather than by heat. The throat of a seal weld is limited to $\frac{3}{16}$ in. minimum and $\frac{3}{8}$ in. maximum according to the Code.

Other Types of Welds

Fillet welding used for attachment to the tubes of supports for the boiler, insulation, refractories, and casing comes under the second of the two categories, noted above, that require a qualified operator. The size of weld for adequate strength or heat transfer is indicated on the job drawings. If the throat exceeds $\frac{3}{8}$ in., these welds are stress-relieved by heat treatment. Except for those carrying primary loads, they are made with a straight-polarity electrode.

Temporary attachments for aligning purposes and support bracing should not be welded to drums or headers. For supporting such pressure parts from the building structure during the initial stages of erection, there usually are shop-welded attachments to which the bracing may be field welded or, lacking these, the bracing can be welded to brackets bolted to handhole or nozzle openings.

Under the rules of the Code, carbon-steel headers may be welded where the carbon content does not exceed 0.35 per cent and the throat of the weld does not exceed $\frac{1}{4}$ in. if the welds are not over 3 in. long, are not closer than 6-in. centers, and each segment is peened before additional segments are welded. Such welds should be made only on advice of the designers.

A stud gun is used in welding studs up to ½-in. diameter for holding insulation and refractories in place. The method of operation depends largely on the type of stud and equipment selected, and procedure qualification for stud welding has not been fully established. It is essential that stud welds be free from undercutting, and a complete fillet at the junction with the base metal is preferred. Studs with exposed edges at the weld line will develop little strength and will break off easily. Before proceeding with the work, the erector should try out the equipment under actual welding conditions on components identical to those on which the studs are to be welded and then examine the results for strength, and, in the case of tubes, to establish that the internal surface has not been upset.

Inspection Requirements

Inspection of welding on pressure parts is required to the extent necessary (a) to assure the manufacturer or contractor that all workmanship meets his standards of quality, and (b) for the authorized inspectors representing the state, municipality, or insurance company to certify that all welding complies with the rules of the *Boiler and Pressure Vessel Code* of the ASME. For the latter, the number, time, and duration of inspections are usually determined by mutual agreement between the inspection agency and the manufacturer before the job is started. The inspections made by the erecting organization are usually done by the erector in charge, as delegated to welding technicians, foremen, and the welding operators.

The general inspection requirements are:

1. To determine that each operator is qualified, in accordance with the Code, for the welds he makes.
2. That the procedure specifications are followed in every respect.
3. Examination of the joint for proper fit-up and alignment before the weld is started.
4. Routine checks as welding progresses of (a) preheat and welding current, and (b) technique of operator in cleaning each weld bead of slag and in keeping the weld free from slag, porosity, and undercutting.
5. Visual examination of the finished weld (a) for undercutting or overlapping, (b) for satisfactory general appearance, and (c) for reinforcement at the center of groove ($\frac{1}{16}$ in. above surface of tube).

Where the material is of a critical nature, though not a requirement of the Code the weld is frequently examined by the magnetic particle method used extensively in checking welds in alloys and in heavy weld sections. This method is commonly used as a preliminary step in eliminating surface defects on welds which are to be radiographed.

Nondestructive Examination

Magnetic Particle Inspection

Inspection of field welds by passing an electric current through the area to be examined and dusting the surface with magnetic powder (any finely divided iron particles will do) is a convenient method of detecting cracks or other defects. The electric current sets up a magnetic field at right angles to its path, and, if the metal is uniform and free from cracks, the magnetic field will also be uniform, and consequently the magnetic powder will assume a uniform pattern. If the magnetic field is interrupted by a defect on or near the surface, the lines of the powder will also be interrupted at this point and thus indicate the defect.

The magnetizing current may be either alternating or direct. For a given magnetizing strength, less current is required if alternating, since it causes a

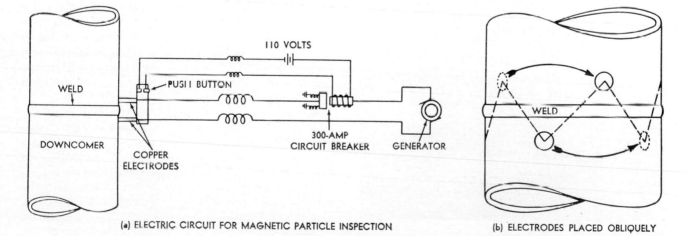

(a) ELECTRIC CIRCUIT FOR MAGNETIC PARTICLE INSPECTION

(b) ELECTRODES PLACED OBLIQUELY

Fig. 19. Sketch (a), typical electric circuit for magnetic particle inspection to detect weld defects on or near the surface. Sketch (b), optimum position of electrodes in relation to weld for satisfactory results

concentration close to the metal surface known as "skin effect." A supply of 300-amp alternating current produced by a transformer such as is used in the field for stress-relieving will be quite suitable. The amount of current required will vary, of course, with the size of the material under test. If too much current is used, the magnetic powder will stand out in streamers and lead to false observations; and if the current is too weak, the powder will not bridge the gaps formed by defects. In testing overhead welds, it is important to make certain that there is enough magnetizing strength to hold the powder to the weld.

In its simplest form, the equipment required to examine a weld by the magnetic particle method consists of a source of electric current, two conductors, two copper electrodes, and some magnetic powder. To prevent arc burns, a circuit breaker is installed as indicated in sketch (a), Fig. 19.

The weld surface should be dry, and it should be ground and polished clean and free of all loose scale before beginning the test. The copper electrodes should then be placed in good contact with the metal, one on each side of weld. The circuit is then closed by using the push button mounted on the wooden handle, which also holds the electrodes as indicated in sketch (a), Fig. 19.

Since the magnetic field is at right angles to the path of the electric current and defects in a welded joint are always either parallel or transverse to the weld, a satisfactory inspection can be made by staggering the electrodes obliquely, as indicated in sketch (b) of Fig. 19. Marking the polished weld surface by the current-carrying electrodes is also avoided by this setting.

Magnetic powder is dusted or sprinkled on the magnetized metal surface between the electrodes. Dusting the powder from a coarse cloth bag is recommended for field tests. A minimum quantity of powder should be used to make one uniform layer on the area under test, and any excess powder should be gently blown off. It will be easy to note any defects by the concentration of powder in which they are outlined.

The location of a defect should be marked so that repairs can be made after the test. To prevent arc

burns, before removing a copper electrode care must be taken to shut off the current by releasing the push button, thus opening the circuit breaker. The entire weld, taking 6 sq in. at a time, must be examined in this manner. With the electrodes in staggered position, only one electrode need be moved for each step around the weld.

For optimum results in magnetic particle inspection, the operator must be trained by conducting tests on specimen welds of known defects, using a procedure that can be duplicated in the examination of production welds.

Radiographic Inspection

Under the rules of the Code, fusion-welded circumferential joints of pipe, tubes, superheater headers, water-wall headers, or economizer headers must be radiographed when their dimensions exceed those given in 1, 2, and 3 below, and the results must meet the standards set by the Code for acceptability of such welds.

1. When the parts to contain steam exceed 16-in. nominal pipe size or 1⅜-in. wall thickness, or the parts to contain water exceed 10-in. nominal pipe size or 1⅛-in. wall thickness. In each case the welds shall not be in contact with furnace gases.
2. Pipe or tubes exceeding 6-in. nominal pipe size or ¾-in. wall thickness, when the welds are to be in contact with furnace gases but not subject to radiation from the furnace.
3. Pipe or tubes exceeding 4-in. OD or ½-in. wall thickness, when the welds are to be in contact with furnace gases and subject to radiation from the furnace.
4. The diameter and thickness limitations shall apply independently.

Welds requiring this inspection in the field are radiographed with gamma rays. These are a direct product of a radioactive substance, and their wavelength is shorter than that of X rays, although at 1,000,000 volts the wavelength of X rays begins to approach that of gamma rays. Because of this and their ability to penetrate opaque substances, gamma rays are used in the radiographic examination of welded joints.

The amount of radiation given off depends on the weight and material of the radiating source. Capsules containing a given weight of radium sulfate or a radioactive isotope are used as the source of radiation. In the field, use of a 100 to 400-mg equivalent capsule is customary. When not in use, the capsule must be kept in a special lead container. The operator must be careful to follow instructions in handling the capsule and must not use it any longer or oftener than necessary. To protect the operator and others working in the vicinity when

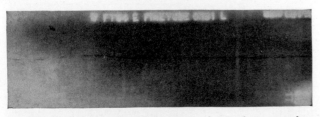

Fig. 20. *Radiograph by X rays reveals crack in metal as a dark line shadow in this case. Similar results are obtained with gamma rays*

using the capsule, lead shields are set up as required, and warning signals are posted.

The degree of darkening of the photographic film from a very light gray to opaque black depends on the amount of radiation that strikes it. A defect in the weld, being less dense than the steel, will permit more radiation to pass through and thus cause a dark area to appear on the film at that point. The photograph obtained by the use of gamma rays, as it would be with X rays, is, in effect, a shadow picture (see Fig. 20). It is helpful to imagine the gamma rays as light and the film as a screen located to show a projected shadow. In making exposures with gamma rays, two films are generally used in a single film holder or cassette. The two pictures are jointly evaluated to distinguish between the irrelevant film-process markings and the actual shadow picture of the weld.

The Code requires the use of penetrameters or "thickness gages" in radiographic inspection to prove that the radiation is effective throughout the full thickness of the material. A penetrameter is a small strip of metal of substantially the same material as, and of a thickness equal to 2 per cent of the thickness of, the plate under examination. It is placed on the side of the material facing the source of radiation. The image of the penetrameter on the exposed film will indicate the effectiveness of the penetration of the radiation and consequently the reliability of the radiograph.

Field gamma-ray inspection may be divided into two groups, depending on the thickness of the plate:

1. For plate thickness of ¼ in. to and including 1¼ inch:
   a) If focal distance is 9 in. or above, use one setup, as shown in sketch (A), Fig. 21.
   b) If focal distance is less than 9 in. use three or more setups, as shown in sketch (B), Fig. 21.
2. For plate thickness of 1⁵⁄₁₆ in. and above:
   a) If focal distance is 14 in. or above, use one setup.
   b) If focal distance is less than 14 in., use three or more setups.

Note: Focal distance is measured from the radium capsule to the film.

The following table gives the approximate time of exposure for a 200-mg gamma-ray capsule.

Pipe, 12-in. OD		Pipe, 30-in. OD	
Wall Thickness, inches	Time, minutes	Wall Thickness, inches	Time, minutes
½	27	½	45
1	30	1	75
2	75	2	150
3	120	3	330
		4	720

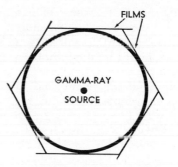

(A) IF FOCAL DISTANCE IS 9 IN. OR ABOVE

SOURCE OF RADIATION PLACED IN GEOMETRIC CENTER OF OBJECT. FILMS PLACED AROUND THE OUTSIDE. IN ACTUAL PRACTICE FILMS FIT CURVATURE.

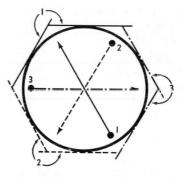

(B) IF FOCAL DISTANCE IS LESS THAN 9 IN.

SOURCE OF RADIATION PLACED ON FAR SIDE OF OBJECT. ONE THIRD RADIOGRAPHED AT EACH SETUP. NUMBERS SHOW LOCATION OF FILMS FOR THREE SETUPS AND POSITION OF SOURCE OF RADIATION FOR EACH.

Fig. 21. *Relative position of gamma-ray source to film and material to be examined for a range of focal distances*

Thermal Stress Relieving

The Code requires that all welds shall be stress-relieved by heating, except in carbon steel and carbon-molybdenum steel where the wall thickness does not exceed ⅜ inch. It is also specified that the weld shall be heated to 1100 F, or higher if the material characteristics so require, and held at that temperature for one hr per in. of thickness and allowed to cool in still air. In stress-relieving welds in pipes or tubes, the material must be heated to a uniform temperature on each side of the weld for a distance of 6 times the thickness of the weld.

The time required to satisfy the proviso in the Code that heating and cooling shall be done "slowly" will depend upon the size and wall thickness of the pipe or tube being stress-relieved. Two extreme examples may be cited: For a 20-in. OD pipe with a wall thickness of 2 in., a heating and cooling rate of 200 F per hr would be in order, while for a 4-in.

OD tube with a wall thickness of ½ in. a rate of 1000F would be considered satisfactory. The temperature for stress relieving will vary with the materials used and should be noted in the welding procedure specification.

To avoid cracks in the weld, and to reduce the cooling rate of the deposited metal, the base metal is usually preheated before welding. The preheating temperature will vary with the type of material and thickness, and should be noted in the procedure specification.

Flame heating, electrical resistance heating, and electrical induction heating are used for preheating and stress relieving.

Flame Heating

The simplest means of stress relieving by heat is flame heating but it is also the least exact as far as temperature is concerned. Reasonably small pipes and tubes may be adequately stress relieved by using two or more oxyacetylene torches if care is taken to heat the metal uniformly and to avoid local overheating.

Use of a muffle furnace, illustrated in Fig. 22, fired with various gas fuels or kerosene, is a simple,

convenient and economical method of flame heating under certain conditions. Such furnaces are widely used where natural gas is readily available. The disadvantages of this method are, (a) space required around the pipe, (b) lack of flexibility in clearing external connections on the pipe, and (c) the careful operation required to obtain uniform heating.

For alloy materials, where very close control of temperature is desired, the use of flame heating is not recommended. However, in the absence of sufficient power for stress relieving by electrical heat, a satisfactory job can be done with the muffle furnace.

Electrical Resistance Heating

Various types of electrical resistance heaters are used for preheating and stress relief where a large number of identical tubes are involved. In one type, the heating elements (commercially available) bent to the required shape, are fitted into cannisters (see Fig. 23).

One of the resistance heaters of wide application for use on large pipe is the wrap around type, of spiral wound wire covered with short porcelain insulators. Heaters of this type usually operate on 220 volts and are made in sizes from 3 to 24 kw. One or more such heaters may be used for stress relieving a welded joint. To reduce heat loss sufficient insulation must be applied outside the coils, and the coils must be properly supported to maintain continuous contact with the surface about the joint. Plastic insulation is particularly suitable as it will also aid in supporting the coils.

This type of heater can be used for both preheating and stress relieving. The initial cost is not excessive and the electrical connections are simple. However, under certain conditions and on very large, thick pipe the deterioration of the resistance coils and porcelain beads may be excessive.

Electrical Induction Heating

In induction heating, also employed extensively for stress relief in the field, alternating current at 60 cycles and in the range of 20 to 90 volts is generally used for reasons of safety, convenience of application and ease of control. In this method the pipe is wrapped with a number of turns of conductor attached to the source of current. The currents induced in the pipe, acting as a secondary circuit of a transformer system, are dissipated in the form of heat. Prior to stress relieving by this method the welded joint and adjacent area are insulated. The conductor is of copper, covered with woven asbestos sleeving. In some cases water-cooled copper conductors are used. No thermal insulation is applied over the induction coil. The amount of heat can be varied by means of the voltage transformer. The

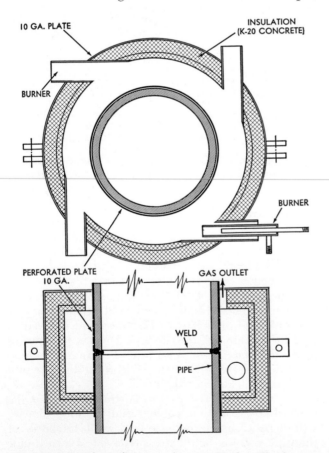

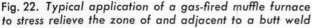

Fig. 22. *Typical application of a gas-fired muffle furnace to stress relieve the zone of and adjacent to a butt weld*

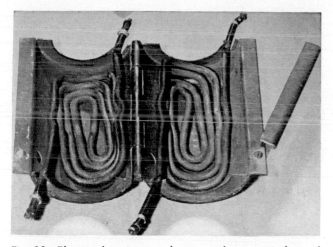

Fig. 23. *Electrical resistance heating elements in hinged cannister for quick application to stress relief and preheat*

weld joint can be preheated and stress relieved with the same coil if the coil and the insulation on the pipe are spaced to allow room for welding.

Equipment (see Fig. 24) required for induction heating includes the transformer, rubber covered leads for both primary and secondary current, and copper cable for the induction coil. The initial cost is quite high and under certain conditions the electrical problems may be rather complex. The equipment, however, is very rugged, extremely flexible in application to various sizes of pipe, and it will give uniform heating which is particlarly valuable in large thick-walled pipe.

Determination of Temperature

In preheating and stress relieving the temperature is usually measured with thermocouples and a potentiometer. Recording potentiometers can be used if permanent records of preheat and stress relieving temperatures are required. In the use of both resistance and induction heating, commercial equipment is available for controlling the rate of increase or decrease in temperature.

A simple method of determining the temperature of heated metal is the use of special crayons or low fusion "sticks." Each crayon or stick is marked for the temperature at or above which it will leave a liquid smear on the heated surface. Crayons are available for temperatures in the range of 125 to 2000F in increments of 50F.

Installation of Auxiliary Equipment

In the field installation of fans, pumps, motors, turbines, pulverizers and chain grate stokers standard methods are used for setting and alignment. Foundations are designed to support the weight and to absorb dynamic forces which tend to set up vibration. For rotating equipment, separate or integral base

plates are used to distribute the loads over the support surfaces and to the foundations. The sequence of installation is as follows: Base plates are placed on the foundations and adjusted to correct elevation for all integral components; the equipment is set on the base plates; space between bottom of plates and top of foundations is grouted; after the grout sets the shims are removed and the base plates are pulled down tight on the grout surface; alignment of all integral components is rechecked and adjusted as required.

Rigid or flexible couplings usually connect the drive and driven components of rotating equipment. For low speed machines, disconnected only occasionally, and not subject to temperature differential, the rigid coupling is customary. Flexible couplings will compensate for slight misalignment during the rise to operating temperatures, absorb shock, dampen vibration, provide free end float of the shafts, and will to some extent compensate for unequal bearing wear. Since the flange faces may not be perfectly true in relation to the axis of either the driven or driving unit, alignment of the coupling, whether rigid or flexible, should be carefully checked and adjusted as

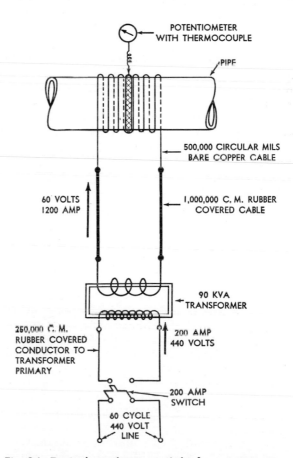

Fig. 24. *Typical application of high capacity electrical induction heating equipment for stress relief and preheat of large thick-walled pipe*

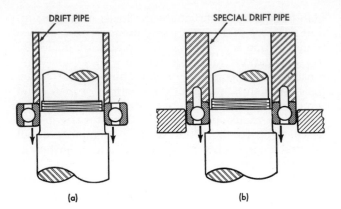

Fig. 25. *Typical use of drift pipes in lightly pressing or driving ball bearings on shaft*

required using a method recommended by the equipment vendor. During preliminary alignment of the shafts of direct connected machines some allowance is made for difference in temperature. A final check, however, is made under operating conditions.

Grouting of Bases

Proper grouting of bases for rotating machines is essential and requires close supervision. In operation the equipment will develop vibration and noise if the grout job is not well done. Thickness of grout will vary with the design of the base and the weight to be supported. The least thickness is limited to that which will allow free flow of the grout mixture under all surfaces. There is no absolute maximum thickness of grout, but allowance must be made for the amount of shrinkage which varies with thickness. Shrinkage may be troublesome in grouting for machines with base surfaces at irregular elevations unless the concrete foundation or the machine has been designed to allow for the shrinkage corresponding to the thickness at these irregularities. Grout should be made of one part cement and two parts of medium coarse sand mixed dry, adding water until the mixture has a consistency of thick cream.

Before grouting, the top of the foundation is cleaned, roughened and moistened. The grout is poured with as high a head as possible and from one side only so that as it flows under the base all air is forced out. A dam of lumber built around the base to a height of 3 to 4 in. above the final level will insure that the grout completely fills all of the space intended. The pour should be made as quickly as possible. A piece of cable pulled back and forth under the base or constant "puddling" with a heavy wire will help the flow and eliminate possible air pockets.

In freezing weather care must be taken to free the foundation of any frost before pouring the grout and after pouring to protect it from frost until the grout has fully hardened. When the initial set has taken place, but before the grout hardens, the wooden dam is removed and the excess grout material is sliced off until the surface is flush with the bottom edges of the base. A few days later all leveling shims, wedges or jack bolts must be removed and the gaps filled with a stiff plug grout. If regular portland cement is used, the grout will normally set fully in 28 days. If equipment is to be operated in less than 28 days, high early strength portland cement should be used for grouting. When fully set, all fundation bolts are retightened to pull the base down firmly in contact with the surface of the hardened grout bed. The alignment of the equipment is then rechecked and necessary adjustments made before doweling the drives and shaft bearings to base plates and pedestals.

Balancing of Rotating Machines

The balancing of rotating machinery is given careful attention by the manufacturer and therefore field balancing is seldom necessary. It is sometimes impracticable dynamically to balance rotors for field assembled fans in the manufacturer's shop. They are, therefore, made with very close tolerances for uniformity of section and are statically balanced with care, which is usually sufficient. However, should a fan under operating conditions set up vibrations greater than the foundation can absorb it will be necessary to balance the rotor in the field.

Ball Bearings

During the storage and field assembly of ball bearings care must be taken to prevent the entrance of dirt, which according to the manufacturers, is the cause of 90 per cent of the failures of bearings of this type. A ball bearing is not removed from its shipping container until immediately before installation, when it should be laid on a clean sheet of paper and covered. It is not customary to wash off the factory lubricant. Clean rags should be used to wipe bearings; cotton waste should not be used.

Either excessive looseness or tightness in shaft fit is objectionable and should be checked against specific recommendations of the bearing manufacturer. The allowable tightness of the shaft fit for a ball bearing depends largely on the initial clearance between the balls and races, which is .0002 to .0003 in. in common practice. This will require a light tap or light press fit of .0001 to .0002 in. between the shaft and the inner race.

Ball bearings are usually assembled on shafts by pressing them on with a hand or light power press or by driving them on with a drift pipe and hammer. Sketches (a) and (b), Fig. 25 illustrate the installation of ball bearings as described above.

If the hot oil method is used in preparing a bearing for assembly, overheating must be avoided.

About 225F is the highest permissible temperature. The shaft size should be checked to determine the tightness of fit. The bearing must be held against the shaft shoulder until it cools enough to grip the shaft tightly, or, if there is a lock nut it should be pulled down before the bearing cools. The bearing should be greased directly after assembly.

The same general precautions should be observed in removing a bearing (if it is to be used again) as when installing it. Correct methods of removal are illustrated in sketches (a), (b), and (c), Fig. 26. When a gear or some other part on the shaft abuts the inner ring, the bearing can be forced off ahead of the part, without injury, by tapping it lightly.

In arc welding on machinery having ball bearings, welders must be cautioned to attach the ground connection so that the current will *not* pass through the bearing. If this precaution is not observed, possible arcing between the bearing races and the balls may not only cause pitting but may also reduce the hardness of the courses with consequent quicker wear of the bearing.

After installation or repairs and before operation it is the erector's responsibility to make certain that all bearings of pulverizers, fans, feeders, pump motors and other rotating equipment are properly lubricated in accordance with approved practice.

Protection of bearings before erection is very important. For instance, immediately on arrival at the storage area of the job site, a heavy coat of good grease should be applied at the junction of bearings and shaft of fans. These parts should then be covered with burlap and tar paper to protect them from the weather. The shafting, where it can be readily cleaned, may be coated with a tallow and white lead mixture. Machined surfaces of all parts should receive similar care. Cup grease holes, oil holes and other holes in journal or bearing housings should be closed with wooden plugs until the equipment is installed. If possible equipment of this kind should be stored under cover.

B&W Pulverizers

Unless conditions and facilities at the job site permit placing pulverizers directly on the foundations, the larger sizes, some of which weigh 30 tons, are not shipped completely assembled. As shipped for field assembly, parts of the pulverizer are: (1) base or gear housing complete with gears, driving yoke, rotating table and lower grinding ring; (2) other grinding elements; (3) rotating classifier; (4) upper section or pulverizing chamber housing. The gear housing should be protected by tarpaulins or otherwise in the storage yard.

Pulverizers are usually installed at ground floor level. However, because of the floor above, there is rarely enough headroom to permit assembly of the upper section if the gear housing is first placed in position on the foundation. Therefore, as a rule, skids placed on the foundation are extended out to a point where the headroom is sufficient to assemble the upper section on the gear housing. Then, after assembly, the pulverizer is skidded into position over the foundation and lowered by jacks to the desired elevation. To joint the upper section to the gear housing a light coating of sealing compound that will remain flexible at moderate temperatures is recommended.

In leveling the pulverizer, before grouting, the top of the upper section may be used as a reference surface since it is machined parallel to the bottom flange which is bolted to the gear housing. Shims and wedges should not be used in leveling a B&W Type E pulverizer. It is set and leveled by jack bolts tapped through the base flange. After the grout has fully hardened the jack bolts are removed and the nuts on the foundation bolts are sledged tight. The jack bolt holes are then filled with a stiff grout mixture. If the driving motor is placed and aligned before the nuts on the pulverizer foundation are sledged, its shaft center line should be .002 to .003 in. lower than the center line of the pulverizer shaft. After the

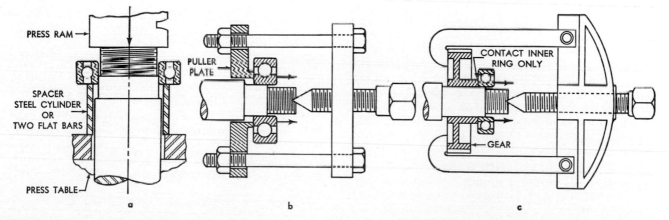

Fig. 26. *Two general methods used for the safe removal of ball bearings. Sketch (a) shows use of arbor press and spacer. Sketches (b) and (c) show two types of conventional gear pullers adapted for this light service*

sledging and bedding down of the pulverizer, the two halves of the connecting coupling should then be level.

Pulverizer balls are forged and heat treated. The tolerance in diameter is ⅛ in., and in operation all the balls must rotate and spiral. The balls are arranged in the course according to size, the largest ball, or balls, if more than one of the same diameter, is installed first and then flanked by the next largest, and so on until the set is closed by the smallest ball or balls. Graduation in this manner will prolong the working life of the balls and is essential for best production from the pulverizer.

Fig. 27. *Plastic chrome ore applied during erection to full-studded wall tubes of a slag-tap furnace*

Brickwork, Refractories, Insulation

Whatever the size or type of boiler unit, the brickwork setting is designed to exclude air from the furnace and boiler passes (or completely to contain combustion gases in pressure-fired settings), to retain most of the heat generated, and to withstand the expansion due to temperature differentials. The brickwork setting should also resist any chemical or mechanical reaction of fuel slag and ash which may grind against it, run over it in molten form or be blown against it in fine particles.

Properties of refractory materials and some general principles of application are given in Chapter 14. Care must be taken to use the type and quality of refractory specified by the boiler manufacturer, bear-

ing in mind that the choice is made only after careful consideration of the type of fuel to be used, the firing equipment, and the type of load or operation anticipated. Furthermore, to obtain the full benefit of the materials specified they should be properly installed by a reliable contractor who specializes in refractory work.

Plastic Chrome Ore

Plastic chrome ore is used in many types of boiler furnaces, particularly for slag-type units designed for molten ash removal. It is used for the refractory coating in stud-tube construction and for the hearth covering at the bottom of a slag-tap furnace. It is frequently used for the refractory areas around burners and furnace inspection openings or doors (see Fig. 27).

Plastic chrome ore should always be applied in lumps large enough to give the required thickness. It should be heavily pounded into place with wooden mallets. On a fully studded wall (see Fig. 15, Chapter 14) it should first be applied between the tubes on the outside of the furnace to a thickness just covering the first row of studs and then be backed up by a heavy wooden (oak) form shaped to the final contour of the surface. To complete the wall, the plastic is then driven in from the furnace side to the thickness shown on the drawing. Each section should be completed as the work progresses. The two applications must be made in immediate sequence as described.

Where the plastic chrome ore is to be applied between the tubes only and not to their faces all of it should be driven in from the outside against a heavy wood form giving the exact thickness on the furnace side. If for any reason this method is not feasible the procedure used for the fully studded tubes should be followed.

To consolidate and bond plastic chrome ore vigorous pounding is required. Light pounding, slicking or troweling bring the plasticizing liquid to the surface where it hardens into a sheath of film which prevents the plastic from drying since the contained moisture cannot escape. Finishing the still plastic surface with a stiff wire brush is recommended. Where this plastic is applied to floor tubes, the considerable mass above and between the tubes should be vented by pricking with a grid of nails to a depth of 1½ to 2 inches. Since the plastic chrome ore can be deformed even after surface setting has occurred if weight is placed on it, a newly constructed floor should not be walked on or subjected to any other pressure until it has been fired.

Storage and Handling of Plastic Chrome Ore

As shipped from the factory, in steel containers holding 200 lb the plastic chrome ore is of the correct consistency and no water or other liquid should be added in the field. On delivery at the job site each container is examined for any damage which may have destroyed the effectiveness of the rubber gasket seal. The containers are stored in a dry, warm place, with the lid down so that any leakage through the lid seal may be detected. No container should be opened unless its contents are to be used immediately. When workmen applying the plastic stop for any reason it should be covered with burlap bags which have been wrung out after dipping in water.

In preparing the plastic chrome ore for application it is dumped from the containers onto a clean surface, preferably a steel plate, or into a liquid-tight mixing box. Some of the liquid may have separated from the ore but must not be discarded as it is needed not only to make the ore plastic but also as an air-setting binder. To remix the material it is cut with a spade or hoe into pieces about a cu. in. or smaller so that the liquid is distributed throughout the mass. In this way, using the contents of two or more containers it is also possible to mix the somewhat dry with more plastic material. After mixing, the material is kneaded by hand into the lump size required for application.

Application in Freezing Temperature

Plastic chrome ore should not be applied in freezing temperatures until the surface has been warmed with salamanders or other heaters. A better method is to circulate warm water through the tubes of the wall. A temperature of 60 to 100F is sufficient. If freezing weather continues after the application is completed the temperature of the circulating water in the tubes should be raised to 150-200F and held at this temperature until the plastic chrome ore is thoroughly dry. If exposed to freezing temperature while drying, the material will crack and disintegrate when the boiler is placed in service.

Moldable Plastic Refractory

Moldable plastic refractory other than plastic chrome ore is sometimes used and, in general, is applied by the same methods. It is shipped in drums and should be of the proper consistency for application when received. If too dry, however, it may be dampened slightly with clean water. With the correct amount of moisture the material, if rolled into a ball, will barely moisten the hands. The mixture is difficult to apply and will slump away from the tubes if too much water is added. If too moist it should be air dried or mixed with some of the drier moldable. If not contaminated, reclaimed plastic moldable may be mixed with water and used over again.

Plastic moldable is generally more difficult to finish to shape than plastic chrome ore, and forming

trowels are required. In applying plastic moldable to walls of either partly or full-studded tubes the same method is used as in applying plastic chrome ore to walls of the latter type. After application, for even drying and to prevent shrinkage cracks, the surface should be roughened with a coarse wire brush. Where a thick mass is applied it is vented by punching ⅛ to 3⁄16 in. holes on 1½ in. centers over the entire surface. To secure proper bonding, before adding new material to partly dried moldable after an interruption, clean water is sprinkled on and is allowed to soak into the first layer.

Plastic Insulation

To obtain full insulating value and to avoid cracks, high-temperature plastic insulation must be mixed with the correct quantity of water. Because of the slow absorption of the fibers and because the material handles easier when quite wet the tendency is to use too much water. Instructions from vendors giving the exact quantity of water to be used should be closely followed. After mixing, since the insulation absorbs water slowly, it should be allowed to stand several hours, preferably overnight, covered with a tarpaulin to prevent drying out.

The insulation is applied by impacting or throwing against the surface and then smoothing by hand or trowel to the correct thickness. A warm surface is

Fig. 28. *Plastic insulation applied to steel mesh over block insulation*

preferable. If the surface is cold, the insulation is applied in thin layers. Each layer is allowed to dry and all cracks must be filled before applying the next layer. A thin coating troweled over the existing surface will aid adhesion. If the layers are too thick, the insulation will slump away from the surface. The number of layers required for a given thickness of insulation is, therefore, determined by the maximum permissible thickness of each layer for proper adhesion.

Block Insulation and Casing

When applied over plastic insulation, block insulation can be fitted while the last plastic layer is still wet. This will help to produce an airtight job if the block insulation is properly pounded into place. Asbestos cement is used to point up the block insulation and to fill the voids.

To avoid looseness in the finished insulation, wire mesh (see Fig. 28) applied as specified must be securely anchored. A complete metal casing over the insulation, for a 75,000 lb steam per hr boiler unit, is shown in Fig. 29.

Metering Equipment, Gages, Mountings

Installation

Metering and control equipment is installed in accordance with instructions usually issued by the manufacturer. From these instructions, those in charge of the equipment installation will determine the location of any boiler connection required, if it is not already given on the job drawings. While the manufacturer will generally call for tubing to be run to the equipment as directly as possible, this does not mean at the sacrifice of proper pitch, good workmanship in forming well-rounded bends, and first-class appearance throughout.

For the various types of meter installations, copper tubing is furnished in two degrees of hardness, soft annealed and half-hard. The soft annealed comes in coils of about 35 ft and the half-hard in straight lengths of about 20 ft. The soft annealed, as received, may be easily bent and flared, while the half-hard must be annealed to cherry red and cooled quickly in water before bending or flaring. The tubing is annealed only at bends and at the ends where flaring is required. Tools for bending and flaring tubing are shipped to the job site before installation of equipment begins.

The coiled soft-annealed copper tubing is straightened before installing and rebending as required. It must be supported by clips or other means at intervals of from 3 to 5 ft to prevent sagging. Where clips are not suitable for this purpose, the tubing may be run through iron pipe or concealed in chan-

Fig. 29. Complete metal casing for a 75,000 lb per hr steam boiler in a pharmaceutical plant

nel members. The pitch of the tubing should be not less than 1 in. per ft, and there must be no loops or pockets where air may be trapped.

Unpacking

All metering equipment is carefully packed for shipment to prevent damage in transit. The utmost care must be taken in unpacking the equipment, since rough handling may disturb the correct alignment of the mechanism and affect its accuracy in operation. All meters are mounted level and in a rigid manner, so that they will not be affected by vibration.

Piping and Tubing

Connecting piping to multipointer gage units should not be branched to any other gages or apparatus. Draft gages or other elements should not be connected to the piping used for Boiler Meter airflow recorders.

Capillary tubing for temperature recorders must be uncoiled with extreme caution to avoid sharp bends or kinks. While this tubing is run as directly as possible from the bulb to the helical coil at the recorder, care should be taken to prevent damage to it by keeping it out of the way of plant maintenance

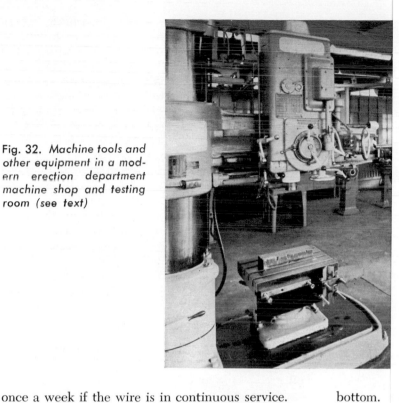

Fig. 32. *Machine tools and other equipment in a modern erection department machine shop and testing room (see text)*

once a week if the wire is in continuous service.

Slings should be given frequent and thorough inspection. When attached they should be protected at sharp bends at the corners of the load by inserting pieces of wood for wire rope or burlap pads for manila rope.

To uncoil wire rope the coil is kept upright and rolled like a hoop paying out the cable in a straight line until the other end is reached.

General rules for the care of wire rope are: 1) keep well oiled; 2) do not overload; 3) prevent kinking; 4) watch clamps for looseness due to wire stretching; 5) do not leave cable lying on the ground; 6) before cutting serve on each side of cut to prevent fraying; 7) see that sheaves are in good condition.

Care of Manila Rope

When not in use manila rope should always be hung to permit air to circulate through the loose coils. The storage place, rigging shanty or other location, should be neither damp nor too hot. Wet, dirty rope should be washed and dried. Wet rope should never be laid on hot steam pipes to dry. After such treatment its strength has been seriously affected even though there is no visible sign that it has been burned. Frozen rope has only about 60 per cent of normal strength and should not be used. A load should never be put on a kinked rope, since a kink will often cause a rope, which appears in good condition, to break.

To avoid kinks in uncoiling new manila rope the coil is laid on the floor with the inside end at the

bottom.
from the
counter
This end
and the
starting
should n
from the

Codes a

In con
The Bab
built in th
Pressure
this Code
no legal
pality. T
ministere
Pressure
are the c
ties that

The N
for the r
*Rules for
ers and
ordinance
ing, repa
recomme
have no
municipa
both by
througho

25-25

---

operations and, if necessary, it should be enclosed, protected and concealed by channels or moldings.

Tools and Equipment

From a study of the drawings for any job a list can be made of every tool, every expander and mandrel and all rigging or heavy equipment required for that job. Every tube end on the job is accounted for in making the list so that the erector on the job will know exactly what expander and mandrel are correct for use in any tube at any location in the unit. A complete tool list will cover everything from hand tools to air motors, pneumatic hammers, chain hoists, welding machines and major items such as electric hoisting engines, steam and diesel railroad cranes, and truck-mounted motor cranes.

Many special tools, not available in the open market, must be designed and made by the erection organization. For example, because of steam cuts or other operational damage it is sometimes necessary to reface handhole and manhole seats in the field. Special machines have been designed for this purpose. One type of manhole refacing machine is shown in Fig. 30.

Tube Expanders and Expanding*

Most of the special tool work is in connection with tube expanders and expanding equipment because of the wide range in tube diameters and thickness and in the thickness of the drums and headers into which these tubes are expanded. Diameters of the principal tubes range from 1 in. to 6 in., with wall thickness from ⅛ in. to ¾ in. Some minor control tubing will range from ¼ in. to ½ in. in diameter, with wall thickness of about ¹⁄₁₆ in. or a little more. Drums and headers range from ½ in. to 8½ in. in thickness of plate.

Aside from the tool problems due to this wide range in dimensions there are also the different methods of expanding used for particular conditions such as:

1) Ball drifting, in the erection of marine boilers.
2) Retractive ball drifting, as in heat exchanger erection.
3) Standard propulsive expanding, in the erection of standard boilers up to about 1000 psi.
4) Retractive expanding in higher pressure boilers where the drum plate thickness is over 2 inches.
5) Incremental propulsive expanding for tubes into headers on boilers of over 2000 psi.

Temporary Overhead Steel and Lifting Lugs

For heavy rigging, the arrangement of the temporary overhead steel from which the rig is to be

---

* By custom in the trade, the word "expanding" is used interchangeably as a noun and as a verb.

---

hung, must be established, and the lifting lugs must be designed for attachment to drums of such size and weight that handling with cable lashings is not considered safe (see Fig. 31).

Stress Relieving Equipment

The type of stress relieving equipment to be used on each job is determined, and the erector is fully informed about the method selected. Development of a recirculated gas-fired furnace for stress relieving a 14 ft diameter 100 ft high bubble tower, after erection, may be cited as an instance of the work required along these lines.

Maintenance and Shipping

The maintenance and shipping group of the tool division is located in the building where the tools are stored, classified and protected. This group is responsible for wrapping machined tools in oil paper for domestic delivery and in self-sealing waterproof fabric for export, ordering the necessary crates or cases of suitable size and properly closing and marking them for shipment.

On the completion of a job the maintenance section of this group checks the tools returned against the list shipped to that job. The condition of each item is noted and those in first-class order are returned to storage for the next job; others are repaired or discarded according to their condition.

Erection Tool Department

New tools, appliances or equipment designed for a specific job are constantly being developed. Not

Fig. 30. *Manhole refacing machine in operation as it might be viewed from inside drum*

25-23

only are tests made to prove that the new tool is mechanically sound, but its actual performance is supported by tabulated data, as, for instance, in the case of new expanding equipment.

A complete combination machine shop and testing room is a necessary part of an erection organization. The arrangement of the machine shop and testing room at B&W Barberton Works, shown in Fig. 32, has been found satisfactory. Among the principal items of equipment are: a 16 in. lathe, bench lathe, small drill press, sensitive drill press, radial drill press, universal milling machine, tool and cutter grinders, surface grinder, shaper, band saw, 30,000 psi hydrostatic test pump, 200-ton press, power cut-off machine, and power hack saws.

Rigging, with Emphasis on Safety

Improper care and use of wire or manila rope and ignorance of safe knots and hitches when slinging loads are likely to cause serious injuries to workmen and damage to material. The erector should make certain that a dependable rigger who will not take chances is in direct charge of each gang handling or raising materials.

The erector in charge must check any rigging selected for a given purpose against tables of safe lifting capacities for wire or manila rope tackles and slings. There is a simple rule for approximate safe load in tons corresponding to the diameter of the rope. For plow steel wire rope the formula is $8D^2$, that is: $4\frac{1}{2}$ tons for $\frac{3}{4}$ in. dia.; 8 tons for 1 in. dia.; $12\frac{1}{2}$ tons for $1\frac{1}{4}$ in. dia. For manila rope the formula is D^2, that is: $\frac{1}{2}$ ton for $\frac{3}{4}$ in. dia.; 1 ton for 1 in. dia.; $1\frac{1}{2}$ tons for $1\frac{1}{4}$ in. diameter.

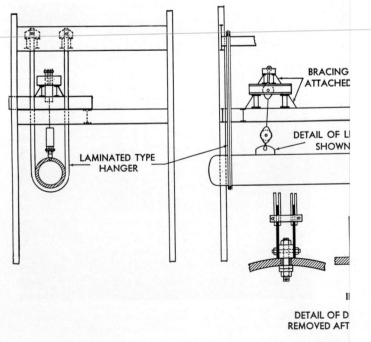

BRACING
ATTACHED

DETAIL OF L
SHOWN

LAMINATED TYPE
HANGER

DETAIL OF D
REMOVED AFT

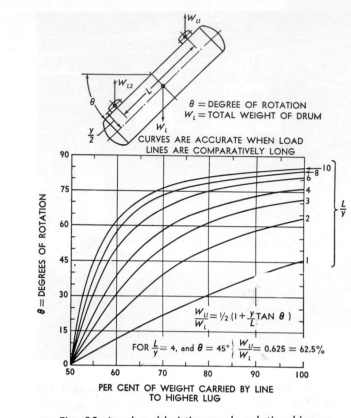

θ = DEGREE OF ROTATION
W_L = TOTAL WEIGHT OF DRUM

CURVES ARE ACCURATE WHEN LOAD
LINES ARE COMPARATIVELY LONG

$$\frac{W_{U}}{W_L} = \frac{1}{2}\left(1 + \frac{y}{L}\text{TAN }\theta\right)$$

FOR $\frac{L}{y}$ = 4, and θ = 45° $\left\{\frac{W_{U}}{W_L} = 0.625 = 62.5\%\right.$

Fig. 33. *Load and hoisting-angle relationship as applied to lifting symmetrically supported drum*

stances, the Code and the National Board rules are now the basis for all legal requirements.

The National Bureau of Casualty and Surety Underwriters, New York, issues a booklet, *Synopsis of Boiler Rules and Regulations*, listing the states, cities, and communities that have laws in effect governing the installation and operation of steam boilers. Other pertinent information includes names of administrative officials, fees, licenses, and inspections required.

Boilers complying with the Code must be erected by or under the supervision of an organization authorized to use the ASME Power Boiler stamp or the ASME assembler's stamp. The requirements for authority to use these stamps are given in the ASME Code.

Each boiler erector should have at hand the latest issue of the *Boiler and Pressure Vessel Code* of the ASME, section I, *Rules for Construction of Power Boilers*, section II, *Material Specifications*, and section VI, *Rules for Inspection of Power Boilers* together with the current addenda sheets issued between editions.

A boiler manufactured and erected in accordance with the Code must be inspected at certain stages by an authorized inspector, who, if satisfied, signs data sheets and witnesses the stamping of the boiler pressure parts. All stamping required by the Code is usually done in the shops, and the portion of the data sheets signed by the inspector pertains to shop inspection. Before signing the portion of the data sheets that applies to field assembly, the field inspector will determine that the boiler has been assembled in accordance with the Code and that it complies with all local regulations. He will also do any stamping required by a state or municipality.

The term "authorized inspector" refers to a person licensed by the state or municipality in which the boiler is erected and who has a National Board commission. Much of the inspection work is done by insurance companies whose inspectors comply with the requirements noted.

While repairs to boilers are not specifically covered by the Code, the National Board rules are generally accepted as a guide for permissible repairs by welding. The approval of an authorized inspector, however, should be obtained before repairs or alterations are made to a boiler.

In the erection of new boilers where field welding of pressure parts is not involved, the inspector is usually called only to witness the final hydrostatic test. When welding of pressure parts is required, the inspector must be given an opportunity to assure himself that the welding operators and welding procedures have been properly qualified and to inspect the welding in progress. The number of such inspections required on any given job is usually determined by arrangement with the inspector.

RESEARCH AND DEVELOPMENT

RESEARCH in one form or another, actively applied in varying degree, appears always to have been practiced by man. Its wide acceptance and application today as an essential factor in progress is merely an indication of the accelerated pace in the development of practically all phases of human endeavor. Invention, the ultimate goal of essentially all research, has been and always will be the basis on which the development of useful attainments for the benefit of mankind is predicated. Research, as it is now known, represents the concentration of intellectual and practical creative ability to the solution of specific problems.

In the early days of development, man utilized his inventive genius primarily to simplify the labor of winning a livelihood from nature. Examples of fundamental importance among the early inventions are the wheel and the plow. As civilization advanced as a result of invention, the needs of man increased, and consequently inventions became more numerous and more complex.

The product of inventive genius, as originally conceived and subsequently improved upon as the result of keen observation and insight into natural phenomena, is the basis, either directly or indirectly, for practically every important attainment of current benefit to mankind. Most worthwhile inventions have been developed to practical usefulness only after diligent effort, frequently involving time-consuming trial-and-error experiments. Often this development has been pursued at considerable cost to those with faith in the ultimate outcome and successfully completed only because of the determination to overcome the many obstacles always present.

Engineering Research

Engineering research originated as the development and application of inventions for military pur-poses. It was not until about the middle of the eighteenth century that attention was diverted to the more specifically peaceful applications. Since then, the technical advances of industry have exerted an increasing influence on social development. Today, throughout the world, technological progress continues to affect the welfare and destiny of mankind at an accelerated pace.

Research may be defined as "Critical and exhaustive investigation or experimentation, having for its aims the discovery of new facts and their correct interpretation, the revision of accepted conclusions, theories, or laws in the light of newly discovered facts, and the practical application of such new or revised conclusions."

It has been suggested that research may be divided into three broad categories:

1. Pure research
2. Background research
3. Applied research and development

The boundaries between these classifications are neither simple nor sharply defined. Study, however, reveals that each category has a definite function and requires different treatment for maximum results.

Pure research, without any specific practical goal, advances general knowledge and understanding of natural laws. The results, when subsequently applied to research and development, provide the basis for the improvement of existing industries and the possible creation of new processes.

In background research, accurate data on scientific development are prepared and compiled for general reference. This information is used extensively in both pure and applied research in correlating data previously collected pertinent to the particular field under investigation.

Fig. 1. *A row of stress-rupture machines in the creep and stress-rupture laboratory for determining, under uniaxial stress and controlled temperature conditions, the long-time load-carrying ability of metals at high temperature. To keep the load on the test specimen constant over the duration of the test, it is applied with a weighted lever arm.*

The specimen is placed in one of the cylindrical, insulated, high-temperature furnaces (shown), and a constant temperature (within a range of plus or minus 2 F) is maintained by means of a magnetic temperature control at the base of the machine. The temperature control, very reliable and of sturdy construction, can operate for tens of thousands of hours without repair or loss of accuracy. No electronic tubes or moving parts are used. To insure high accuracy of temperature control and to keep all of the sensitive equipment clean and in good operating condition, the laboratory space is air-conditioned and the temperature is held at 83 F plus or minus 1 F throughout the year

Industry is primarily interested in applied research and development. This differs from pure research in several important respects. The aims of applied research are normally immediate and practical. Frequently the work can be specifically planned and organized. Usually none of these characteristics applies to pure research. The expense involved in applied research and development is heavy. Since industry in general must, of necessity, measure the expense in terms of results, the economic justification for continuing the effort in any particular field should be recognized at all times.

Purposes of Industrial Research

The principal purposes of industrial research may be broadly outlined as follows:
1. To improve the quality of products.
2. To develop new materials, processes, or devices for existing or new markets.
3. To develop new uses for existing materials, processes, or devices.
4. To effect savings in costs of production or use.
5. To abate dangers or nuisances.
6. To prevent or cure troubles of production or use.
7. To assist in standardization.
8. To improve customer or public relations.
9. To conserve natural resources.
10. To render special or unique service to the country in time of national crisis.

In the case of steam generation, the field for ap-

plied research and development covers all phases of the utilization of fuels for the production of thermal energy; the containment and flow of fuels; the transfer of heat to working media at high pressures and temperatures; the discovery of new materials; the improvement of existing materials of construction and manufacturing methods; and the effect of the interdependence of the sciences of chemistry, physics, metallurgy, and ceramics.

The frontiers of this field of endeavor are constantly expanding, and each progressive forward step brings on new and more difficult problems previously considered unimportant because of the then less-exacting demands upon performance. To solve these problems requires skillful use of the tools of science and technical knowledge in coordinated efforts by qualified personnel of widely varied training. Adequate facilities and instrumentation must be provided for successful results.

Projects Proposed for Research

There is no dearth of ideas in this growing field of activity. Proposals for projects emanate from all departments of the Company, from customer organizations, and from related industries, as well as from fields of basic science, all of which have attractive aspects for investigation. The economic potentialities of all such projects and the ability, with available facilities and personnel, to handle them satisfactorily must be evaluated. For those projects selected for research investigation, some measure of organization and control is necessary. In this way the most productive procedure is followed in pursuing the over-all Company aims and welfare. However, the control of the investigation must be carefully applied so that there is no serious restriction on individual enterprise and imagination.

Many of the proposals can be appraised by analytical study and calculation, bringing to bear previous experience and the background of references to existing literature. Sometimes the idea can be tested by a small-scale laboratory demonstration to prove or disprove the validity of its essential features. Where promising results are obtained, a further trial in pilot-scale equipment may be justified to integrate the additional factors of size, timing, and practical implementation.

It is important, in any research investigation, to make systematic observations and to keep careful records. Through the correlation of such data, the ultimate value of the project or possibly constructive ideas for the solution of some of the difficulties may be revealed. Furthermore, new avenues of approach to other methods or apparatus may be suggested, which may prove to be equivalent or superior to

the initial project. Even negative results, when evaluated, can be of material value in avoiding an expensive large-scale application of an intriguing but erroneous idea.

Unit Cost of Power Reduced

During the past half century, the phenomenal development and growth of the electrical industry have resulted in a consistently lower cost of power to the consumer. The reduction in the cost of power can be attributed almost entirely to improvements in the technology associated with its generation, in which the boiler industry has made many important contributions. One outstanding development in steam generation, described elsewhere in this book, was the invention, by Stephen Wilcox in 1867, of the header-type water-tube boiler, which supplanted the hazardous shell-type boiler of limited application. Other major developments include the mechanical firing of fuel to eliminate hand labor, suspension burning of pulverized coal, which extended the range of capacity of units, and the introduction of water-cooled furnace walls to reduce maintenance and to overcome unit size limitations. Supplementing these developments, meters and automatic control equip-

Fig. 2. A well-lighted testing area at the Research Center. Facilities for the study of heat transfer and steam generation are shown at the right. Various test arrangements for the study of the feeding and combustion of fuels appear at the left. Supercritical pressure heat transfer and flow are under study in right foreground. A 2-ft Cyclone Furnace (see Fig. 3 for more detail) is shown in the left foreground. Equipment for oil burner testing is located in center background. Planned and orderly procedure, well-trained personnel, adequate facilities, and suitable working space are all essential for optimum results in research and development work

Fig. 3. Cyclone Furnace (2-ft diameter) used for experiments to determine the suitability of fuels for this method of firing and to study the effect of design modifications prior to more extensive tests with larger-diameter units. An experimental unit of 5-ft diameter (first of the commercial sizes, 5, 6, 7, 8, 9, and 10 ft) is also used in regular test work at the Research Center. For making tests under regular field conditions, use is made of a 5-ft Cyclone-Furnace-fired boiler which supplies steam for the Company's Main Works at Barberton. See Chapter 28 for a description of Cyclone Furnace operation

Fig. 4. A view of the chemical laboratory and of the microchemical facilities in particular at the Research Center. This equipment is specifically designed for the study of the chemical behavior of substances when only very small samples are available, such as inclusions in metals, very thin corrosion films, and traces of gases in metals or liquids.

The apparatus in the foreground is a combination of equipment for investigating the reactions in microcombustion (at the left) with high-vacuum inorganic-reaction techniques under the protection of highly purified inert gas atmospheres (at the right). In the apparatus shown in the background, quantities of gas mixtures as small as a thimbleful can be analyzed with good accuracy.

This laboratory space is carefully air-conditioned. In operations of this kind, a very high degree of cleanliness and good housekeeping must be maintained, not only during working hours but at all times

Fig. 5. Locomotive boiler test. Prototype of a water-tube natural-circulation stoker-fired steam generator, operated with forced draft and designed for 51,400 lb of steam per hr at 600 psi and 900 F, for a 1500-hp atmospheric-exhaust steam turbine-electric locomotive in the largest size category. Design and developmental tests were conducted at the Research Center prior to assembly in the locomotive and road testing

ment have had a considerable effect on performance because of the resulting great improvement in the efficient use of fuels.

During this same period, progressive steps were made in the use of superheated steam. As a result of the knowledge from previous experience and the progress made in developing new materials of construction, welding methods, steam purification, and control of water chemistry, steam pressures and temperatures have steadily increased. Through the development of the metallurgical art, the materials for many critical components of boilers and prime movers have successfully advanced from cast iron to steel to high-strength alloys. At present, alloy materials are being developed for superstrength construction, which will further extend the limits of operating pressures and temperatures with resulting improvement in steam-cycle efficiency and consequent reduction in the unit cost of power production.

All of these steps, now accepted as logical procedure, were fraught with difficult and, at times, frustrating problems during their development. The then current prejudices and misconceptions, largely from lack of knowledge and experience, frequently resulted in the employment of obstructive or abortive modifications. But the great gains, based on fundamentally sound ideas, have survived the rigorous test of utility and, in perspective, point the way to further advancement.

Continuous Research Necessary

There is still much to be learned concerning the constitution and strength of all materials of construction, particularly metals; of the effect of trace amounts of certain elements in alloy compositions; and of the changes brought about by temperature, stress, and contacting fluids, over long periods of time. Direct measurement of creep and stress-rupture properties of existing materials and more rigorous analysis and measurement of stress distribution in pressure vessels and other structures help to reduce the "ignorance factor" of design and to establish more exact use limits. Active research, now under way in the production and testing of experimental superstrength alloys, forecasts a new era of superior performance of power-generating equipment.

It is anticipated, in the foreseeable future, that dependence upon coal and its derivatives as the source of energy will steadily increase, with the probability that the quality of the coal available, as defined by per cent of ash content and ash-fusing properties, will deteriorate. With such characteristics of coal ash, difficulties are experienced in all methods of firing and in the transfer of heat to the absorbing media. The comparatively recent development of the cyclone principle in burning crushed coal represents a definite advance in the utilization of low-grade coal and is a notable example of the fruits of engineering research.

Other products of recent engineering research may be cited, such as improvements in devices for obtaining and measuring steam purity; new processes for coal gasification; recovery of pulp-mill chemicals and heat values; pebble heaters for heating gases or

vapors t
heaters;
their fue
ing the c
ment by
within th
by curre

Applica

No st
it pertai
without
amounts
reactors
utility g
tions pow
with eq
tensive
tions ar
propulsi
Nautilus
strated
the use
dustrial
present
The tin
fission h
power c

ASSEMBLING FUEL ELEMENTS TO SIMULATE A POWER
REACTOR CORE AT B&W'S CRITICAL EXPERIMENT LABORATORY

NUCLEAR REACTORS AND STEAM-GENERATING EQUIPMENT

THE discovery of a practical method for the release of nuclear, or atomic, energy has disclosed a new power source of tremendous importance. The device in which this energy is produced is called a nuclear reactor, which is, in effect, a furnace that generates heat by the interaction of nuclear particles rather than by chemical combustion. At present the only nuclear reaction capable of sustained and large-scale production of heat is fission, or the splitting apart of a heavy nucleus upon absorption of a neutron.

A nuclear reactor is currently defined, therefore, as an apparatus in which fission can be initiated and maintained at a controlled rate in a self-supporting chain reaction. It includes, among other things: fissionable material (fuel), such as uranium-235, uranium-233, and plutonium-239; a coolant to remove heat; a control system; and usually a moderating material to slow down neutrons. It often includes a reflector to conserve escaping neutrons. The terms *pile* and *reactor* have been used interchangeably, with *reactor* now becoming more common.

The heat generated by a nuclear reactor may be transferred to a working fluid for use in conventional heat-power plant equipment. Steam is of such dominating significance in these operations that the boiler manufacturer is uniquely qualified to design and build reactors and their accompanying steam-generating apparatus.

Characteristics of Atomic Nuclei

The operation of nuclear reactors depends upon various types of interaction of neutrons with atomic nuclei. An atom consists of a positively charged nucleus surrounded by a number of negatively charged electrons, so that the atom as a whole is electrically neutral. Chemical energy, such as that obtained from the combustion of coal or oil, results from a rearrangement of the atoms caused by a redistribution of the electrons. In the processes taking place in a reactor, leading to the release of atomic energy, it is only the atomic nuclei which are involved; the electrons may be neglected. For this reason, the term nuclear energy is frequently used as a more precise alternative to the historic name, atomic energy.

Atomic nuclei are composed of two kinds of primary particles—protons and neutrons. These particles are often referred to by the general term *nucleon*. Both protons and neutrons can be obtained in the free state, i.e., outside atomic nuclei, and their individual properties can be studied experimentally. The *proton* carries a single unit positive charge, equal in magnitude to the electron charge. This particle is identical with the nucleus of the hydrogen atom. The *neutron*, which is of fundamental importance in connection with the release of nuclear energy, is electrically neutral. Consequently, it does not suffer electrical repulsion when it approaches an atomic (positively charged) nucleus from outside, as does a charged particle, such as a proton.

The term *nuclide* is used to describe an atomic species characterized by the composition of its nucleus, i.e., by the numbers of protons and neutrons it contains. An *isotope* is one of a group of two or more nuclides having the same number of protons (the same atomic number) but different numbers of neutrons. Most elements exist as mixtures of isotopes. Uranium as found in nature is comprised of several isotopes, the most abundant being U-238 (99% plus) and the fissionable isotope U-235 (about 0.7%).

Nuclear Reactions

Fission. At the heart of the reactor is a small mass of fissionable material, the nuclei of which split apart upon absorption of neutrons. The fission products, or fragments, emerge from this reaction at very high speeds and carry most of the energy in kinetic form, which, in turn, is rapidly converted to the heat form. After the self-sustaining reaction has begun in an assembly containing sufficient fuel (more than a "critical mass"), it continues because two or three neutrons are emitted by each fissioning nucleus and these are made to fission one neighboring nucleus. The result is a chain reaction, feeding on its own neutron yield, which continues indefinitely as long as the critical mass of fuel is maintained.

Neutron Capture. Only a fraction of the neutrons released at the moment of fission remains available to cause further fission and maintain a chain reaction. Some of the neutrons may be captured by the fertile material (e.g., U-238 or thorium-232) to generate new fissionable nuclei (e.g., plutonium-239 or U-233); some leak out of the reactor or are captured parasitically by the structural material, coolant, fission products, and other materials in the reactor system. Neutron leakage and parasitic-capture losses are the main problems of the reactor designer because they can reduce the neutron multiplication factor below unity. When the multiplication factor is less than unity, the chain reaction cannot be sustained.

The usual way of expressing the probability that a nucleus can absorb a bombarding neutron is to quote the "capture cross section" for a particular reaction. A reaction cross section is the effective area presented by a target nucleus to a bombarding neutron under defined conditions and for a given result. In general, the capture cross sections are relatively large for neutrons of low energy (thermal neutrons) and are appreciably less for neutrons of high energy (fast neutrons).

Reactor Components

Reactors are usually composed of fuel, moderator, coolant, control system, structural material, and shielding.

Fuel. The fuel for a nuclear reactor is limited to one of the three fissionable isotopes: U-235, U-233, and Pu-239. It is contained in the core of the reactor, where the major portion of the heat is generated. Fuel elements must be protected with a suitable jacket or cladding because uranium and plutonium are very active chemically and are readily attacked by air, water, and liquid metals, which are the coolants commonly used. Cladding also prevents the escape of fission products and other toxic materials from the fuel element.

Moderator. The energy of most of the neutrons emitted by a fissioning nucleus is extremely high, approximately 200 million electron volts (1 Mev = 1.52×10^{-16} Btu). Since neutrons are electrically neutral they are very penetrating, especially at high velocities, and the fast neutrons can easily escape from the reactor. Those that do escape are lost and useless. For this reason the speed of the neutrons is often reduced by a "moderator," which is a material containing nuclei of low mass number, such as hydrogen or carbon. When neutrons strike the nuclei of the moderator there is an elastic collision; they give part of their energy to the moderator and bounce off at a reduced speed. At this lower velocity the probability of neutron capture by uranium atoms (resulting in fission) increases, and the chain reaction is more readily sustained.

Coolant. The heat generated in a reactor of any appreciable power level must be carried outside the core to prevent serious overheating and to be of use in the generation of mechanical power. This is the function of the reactor coolant. In a nuclear power plant, therefore, the coolant is the essential link between the reactor itself and the conventional power-generating equipment, such as a steam turbine. Ordinary (light) water, heavy water, carbon dioxide, and liquid sodium are among the more frequently used reactor coolants.

Control System. A fission chain reaction is not difficult to control. Some core configurations are self-regulating. Usually, however, a separate control system is incorporated in the reactor structure. This often takes the form of rods or sheets of neutron-absorbing material, mounted in the core so that they can be moved in and out quickly and precisely. Boron, hafnium, and cadmium, which have high neutron-absorption cross sections, are frequently used as control materials.

Structural Material. The fuel and moderator are held in place within the flowing coolant by means of structural materials. These materials should have good mechanical properties at high temperature and substantial corrosion resistance. In addition, the structural materials in the core and reflector of a thermal reactor should have low neutron-capture cross sections. Magnesium, aluminum, and zirconium have low cross sections, but stainless steel with a slightly higher cross section is a frequently used reactor structural material because of its outstanding mechanical and corrosion properties.

Shielding. One additional feature is essential to every nuclear reactor, although not an actual working part. This is the massive shielding that must completely surround the reactor to protect operating personnel from the penetrating lethal neutrons and gamma rays. Neutrons are attenuated best by water or other hydrogenous materials; gamma rays by very dense materials. Ordinary concrete is an inexpensive material that combines these requirements and is widely used, in conjunction with water or sheets of steel, lead, or other metals, for shielding purposes. It is the shield that makes even a small reactor look impressively large. The shielding, which must be heavy, is therefore economical only in large installations.

Reactor Types

At present the building or planning of reactors is directed towards one of the following objectives: 1) the production of heat and power, 2) the production of plutonium, uranium-233, or radio-isotopes, 3) the production of neutrons for research, or 4) the experimental development of reactors.

Reactors can also be classified (a) according to type of fuel used: 1) natural uranium, which contains 0.7% U-235, 2) enriched uranium, which contains a higher percentage of U-235, 3) plutonium-239, or 4) U-233; or (b) according to the energy of the neutrons at the time they are captured by the fuel to induce fission: 1) fast, 2) thermal, or 3) intermediate.

In fast reactors, which have no moderator, neutrons are captured by the fuel immediately after they are generated. This reactor has certain advantages in neutron economy but requires a large amount of fuel.

Thermal reactors contain sufficient moderator to slow down the neutrons, so that they are in thermal equilibrium with their surroundings when captured. Since the probability of capture by fissionable material is high in the thermal range, thermal reactors generally require less fuel for a critical mass than do other reactors of the same output. Intermediate reactors contain a reduced amount of moderator and, therefore, an increased amount of fuel.

A further classification of reactors can be made according to the physical condition of the fuel: 1) heterogeneous, or 2) homogeneous. Heterogeneous reactors have solid fuel elements separated from moderator and coolant in definite geometric patterns. The fuel in homogeneous reactors may be: 1) aqueous solutions of uranium salts, 2) slurries of uranium salts in water, 3) fused salt mixtures containing uranium, or 4) solutions of uranium in molten metals.

Another reactor classification distinguishes between the *breeder* and the *converter*, depending upon the amount of new fissionable fuel produced by the absorption of neutrons in the fertile materials, uranium-238 or thorium-232. A breeder reactor produces more fissionable material than it consumes.

Many other classifications of reactors follow from the numerous design parameters shown in Table 1.

TABLE 1

Reactor Design Parameters

Neutron Energy
    Fast, thermal, or intermediate
Geometry
    Heterogeneous or homogeneous
Fuel
    U-235, U-233, or Pu-239

Fertile Material
    Uranium, thorium, or none
Fuel Regeneration
    Less than consumption (converter), more than consumption (breeder), or no regeneration (burner)
Coolant
    Pressurized water (H_2O), pressurized heavy water (D_2O), boiling H_2O, boiling D_2O, air, carbon dioxide, helium, nitrogen, sodium, NaK, diphenyl, terphenyl, lead, bismuth, or fluid fuel
Moderator
    H_2O, D_2O, graphite, diphenyl, terphenyl, beryllium, or beryllium oxide
Structural Material
    Aluminum, zirconium, stainless steel, or carbon steel

Activities of The Babcock & Wilcox Company

Many major components of a nuclear power plant are quite similar to those which a boiler manufacturer is tooled and manned to fabricate. These include boilers, superheaters, economizers, heat exchangers, pressure vessels, containment vessels, tanks, pressurizers, supporting structures, reactor grids, thermal shields, and piping.

The Company is currently engaged in designing and manufacturing equipment for many nuclear systems. It was the first private firm to build a fabrication plant specifically for the production of fuel elements for nuclear reactors. This plant, located near Lynchburg, Virginia, went into operation in April of 1956 and began shipping metallic plate-type fuel elements in July of the same year. These first elements were for the Material Testing Reactor at the National Reactor Testing Station (NRTS) in Idaho. The manufacturing procedure is illustrated by Fig. 1.

The Nuclear Facilities Plant at Lynchburg has manufactured fuel elements for the Engineering Test Reactor, also located at NRTS in Idaho, and for several other research reactors in different parts of the world. The fuel elements for the power reactors that B&W has contracted to design, fabricate, and erect will also be made at the Lynchburg plant.

From 1943 through 1952 the Company's work in atomic energy consisted primarily of several fabrication assignments for the Manhattan Project; basic research in materials and methods of fabrication for the U.S. Navy, Atomic Energy Commission, and other governmental agencies; development, design, and/or manufacture of reactor pressure vessels, heat exchangers, and other components for the Submarine Thermal Reactor and the Submarine Intermediate Reactor projects, the Brookhaven Research Reactor, and the Materials Testing Reactor; and loan of technical manpower to reactor design groups in the various National Laboratories.

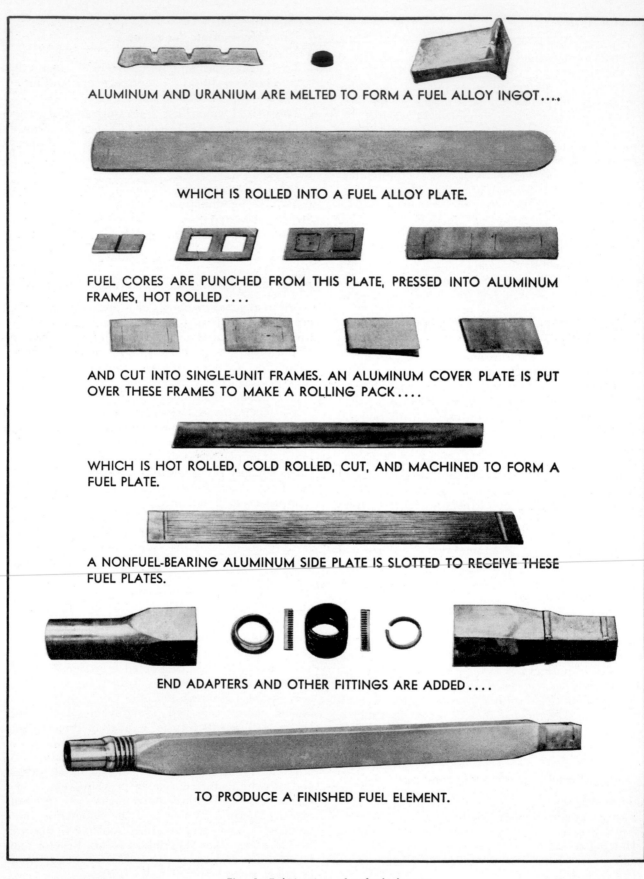

ALUMINUM AND URANIUM ARE MELTED TO FORM A FUEL ALLOY INGOT....

WHICH IS ROLLED INTO A FUEL ALLOY PLATE.

FUEL CORES ARE PUNCHED FROM THIS PLATE, PRESSED INTO ALUMINUM FRAMES, HOT ROLLED....

AND CUT INTO SINGLE-UNIT FRAMES. AN ALUMINUM COVER PLATE IS PUT OVER THESE FRAMES TO MAKE A ROLLING PACK....

WHICH IS HOT ROLLED, COLD ROLLED, CUT, AND MACHINED TO FORM A FUEL PLATE.

A NONFUEL-BEARING ALUMINUM SIDE PLATE IS SLOTTED TO RECEIVE THESE FUEL PLATES.

END ADAPTERS AND OTHER FITTINGS ARE ADDED....

TO PRODUCE A FINISHED FUEL ELEMENT.

Fig. 1. *Fabrication of a fuel element*

In 1953 B&W established a separate Atomic Energy Division and announced its intention to build complete nuclear steam boilers just as it builds complete conventional boilers. The nuclear activities of the Company expanded considerably in the ensuing years, and today there is a large backlog of work in this field on the Company's books.

Many new reactor concepts have been proposed, using selected fuels, moderators, coolants, and other elements in various combinations (see Table 1). The Company has supplied equipment components for most of the reactor concepts that have reached the prototype construction stage. The reactor pressure vessel which B&W fabricated for the Experimental Boiling-Water Reactor is shown by Fig. 2.

Space does not permit a complete discussion of all the reactor types in which the Company is interested. However, a brief description of four important projects — the Consolidated Edison Thorium Reactor, the Nuclear Merchant-Ship Reactor, the Liquid-Metal Fuel Reactor Experiment, and the Swimming-Pool Research Reactor — may serve to give a broad picture of these diverse activities.

Consolidated Edison Thorium Reactor

The Atomic Energy Act of 1954 encouraged private industry to develop, design, construct, and operate central station power plants fired by nuclear fuels. Shortly after the Act was signed, the Consolidated Edison Company of New York, Inc. contracted with The Babcock & Wilcox Company to design and build a nuclear boiler plant for a proposed power station at Indian Point. This station is designed for an ultimate generating capacity of 275 megawatts, but the initial operation will probably be limited to 236 megawatts.

The Indian Point Station will be located on the east bank of the Hudson River about 24 miles north of New York City on a site of approximately 350 acres. The general arrangement of the plant is shown by Fig. 3.

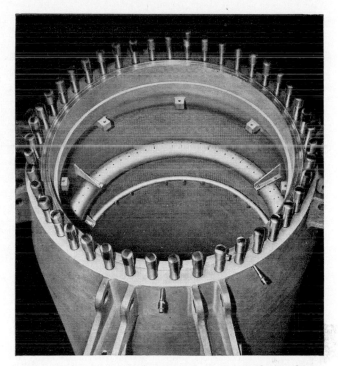

Fig. 2. Stainless-clad pressure vessel, 7 ft ID, for Experimental Boiling-Water Reactor

The heat balance diagram is shown by Fig. 4. Dry saturated steam will leave the boiler drum at 420 psia, enter the superheater, where it will be heated by conventional oil firing, and arrive at the turbine throttle at 370 psia and 1000 F. The exhaust to the condenser will be at 1.5 in. of Hg with approximately 6% moisture. The condensate will be returned to the boiler after 4 stages of extraction heating — 3 closed heaters and one deaerator. The feedwater will be delivered to the boiler at 332 F.

The flow path of the reactor system is also shown in Fig. 4. Water at a pressure of 1500 psia will enter the reactor at 481.5 F and leave at 510 F, at which temperature it will enter the boiler, where its heat will be transferred to make steam.

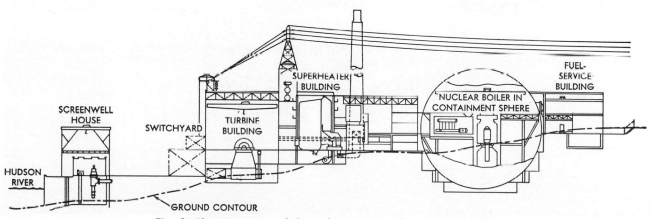

Fig. 3. Elevation view of the Indian Point nuclear power plant

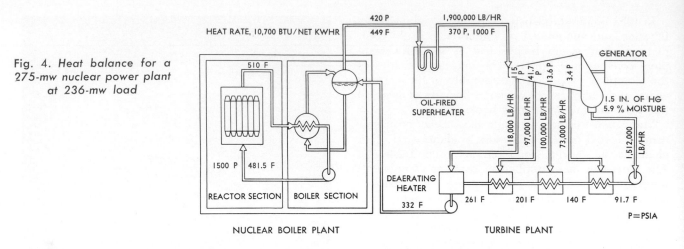

Fig. 4. Heat balance for a 275-mw nuclear power plant at 236-mw load

NUCLEAR BOILER PLANT   TURBINE PLANT

The nuclear portion of the plant, Fig. 5, will consist of a 160-ft-diam steel sphere containing the reactor, the high-pressure high-temperature plant systems, and shielding; a reactor service building housing the low-pressure auxiliary equipment; a fuel-handling building, where the spent fuel elements from the reactor will be stored and prepared for shipment to a reprocessing site; and a contaminated-water process area, where the radio-active liquid wastes discharged from the reactor systems will be disposed of through concentration and ion exchange.

The reactor vessel will be surrounded by a neutron-shield tank filled with water. Four primary-piping loops, each including 24-in.-diam piping, one boiler, two vertical centrifugal canned-motor pumps, two check valves, and two stop valves, will be in the sphere. The pressurizer, located just above the primary piping, will maintain a pressure of 1500

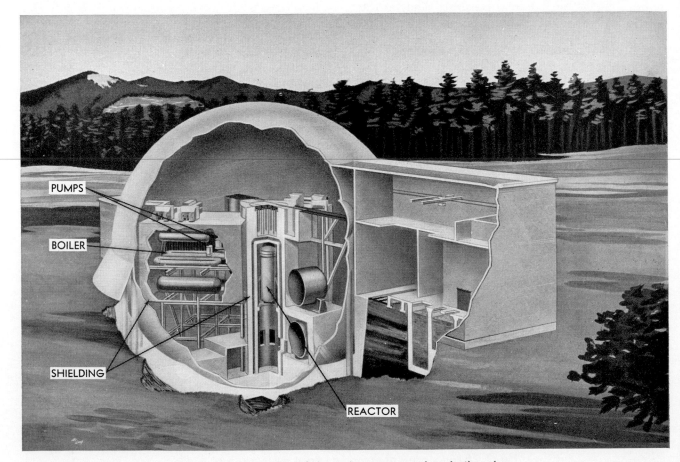

Fig. 5. Cutaway view of the Indian Point nuclear boiler plant

psia on the primary system and accommodate the expansion of the water caused by temperature changes. A crane in the upper portion of the sphere will facilitate equipment removal and fuel-element transfer. Various blowdown tanks for pressure relief and purification will be in the lower section of the sphere. The entire weight of equipment, concrete shielding, and structural steel (80,000 tons) will be supported on a concrete pad, poured both inside and outside the bottom portion of the containment sphere, which supports only its own weight.

Reactor Core

The reactor will be a thermal thorium internal converter, fueled with highly enriched uranium. A high percentage of the neutrons produced will transmute some of the thorium to U-233, which will partially fission in situ, thus prolonging the life of the core. The core will be a right circular cylinder about 6 ft in diam and 8 ft high. It will consist of 120 fuel elements, one of which is shown by Fig. 6. The fuel elements will be assemblies of stainless tubes containing a mixture of thorium and uranium oxides.

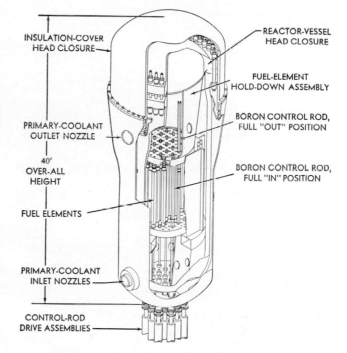

Fig. 7. Pressure vessel for a thorium reactor

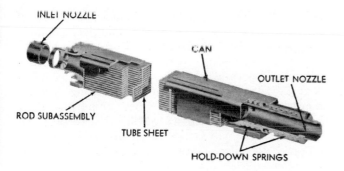

Fig. 6. Cutaway view of a rod-type fuel element

Reactor Pressure Vessel

The reactor pressure vessel, Fig. 7, will be a cylindrical shell of carbon steel about 10 ft in diam and 30 ft high with hemispherical heads. The walls of this vessel will be about 7 in. thick, providing for a design pressure of 1800 psi, and clad on the inside with type-304 stainless steel. There will be four 24-in. inlet nozzles on the bottom head of the vessel and four 24 in. outlet nozzles on the upper section. The upper head will be gasketed and may be seal welded; it must be removable for the replacement of fuel elements. The lower head will contain the nozzles through which the control rods will be driven. This vessel will weigh approximately 280 tons.

Boilers

Each of the four boilers will consist of a U-tube heat exchanger, where the heat from the primary water, flowing through the tubes, will be transferred to lower-pressure water to form steam in the shell (see Fig. 8). This steam will circulate through a system of risers to the upper drum, where it will separate from the water and pass to the superheater. The water will return to the heat exchanger through a system of downcomers. All the material in contact with the primary water will be type-304 stainless steel, the remainder carbon steel. The heat exchangers will be similar to the one shown in Fig. 9.

Primary-Coolant Pumps

A total of eight vertically mounted centrifugal canned-motor pumps will be installed, two in each of the four coolant loops. Each unit will deliver 16,000 gpm against a pressure differential of 125 psi. All the material in contact with the primary water will be type-304 stainless steel.

Primary-Coolant Piping

The primary-coolant piping will be manufactured of type 304 stainless steel and will have an outside diam of 24 in. and an inside diam of 20⅛ in. The total weight of this piping will be approximately 100 tons.

Shielding

The shielding will consist of 1) a water shield above and around the reactor, 2) a concrete shield

Fig. 8. *Cutaway view of boiler for a pressurized-water reactor (Shippingport)*

Fig. 9. *B&W heat exchanger for Shippingport boiler installation*

around the primary-loop equipment, and 3) a concrete shield wall outside the spherical containment vessel. The water shield will protect personnel during fuel-changing operations. Although personnel will not normally be allowed within the containment vessel while the plant is operating, certain emergency situations may arise requiring their presence in limited areas within the vessel. The concrete shield within the vessel, therefore, will be designed to allow access to certain portions of the sphere during operation. The concrete wall outside the containment vessel will be designed to protect personnel in the area from fission-product activity within the sphere, in the unlikely event of a simultaneous mechanical failure of the high-pressure system and rupture of the cladding of one or more fuel elements.

Containment Vessel

Should a simultaneous failure of pressure parts and fuel elements occur, radioactive fission products might be released to the atmosphere were it not for the 160-ft-diam containment sphere, which surrounds the high-pressure equipment. It has been calculated that, if the entire volume of primary and secondary water within the sphere were released instantaneously, the air-steam mixture would pressurize the sphere to 18 psi. The sphere has been designed for 23 psi, which is adequate to contain the maximum accident considered credible for this plant. The sphere will be fabricated from 1-in. carbon-steel plate.

Nuclear Merchant-Ship Reactor

The construction of the world's first nuclear-powered merchant ship is expected to begin in 1958. In view of the Company's extensive experience in marine boilers, the U.S. Atomic Energy Commission has awarded a contract to B&W for the nuclear reactor, the steam-generating equipment, and the main propulsion machinery of this passenger-cargo vessel.

The reactor will be of the pressurized-water type, but it will differ from the Consolidated Edison reactor in that it will be fueled with slightly enriched uranium oxide clad in stainless steel. The cooling system will consist of two parallel loops, each with two circulating pumps and one boiler.

The following table contains the basic data for the proposed reactor and may be altered as the detailed design is perfected:

Reactor power ....233 $\times$ 10^6 Btu/hr
(68.3 mw)
Shaft power (maximum) ....22,000 shp
Shaft power (normal) ....20,000 shp
Reactor mean temperature......508 F
Reactor operating pressure......1,750 psi
Coolant flow................8,000,000 lb/hr
Reactor fuel inventory, U-235...560 lb (250 kg)
Total uranium................19,000 lb (8,600 kg)
Total uranium as uranium dioxide 22,000 lb (10,000 kg)
Dimensions of active reactor core
(equivalent cylinder) ......66-in. diam, 66 in. high
Core lifetime ....2-3 yr
Steam conditions at turbine
throttle (normal power) .....240,000 lb/hr @
465 psi sat.
Condenser pressure............1.5 in. of Hg

At full power, the core inlet and outlet temperatures will be 495 F and 521 F, respectively. Saturated steam at 470 psi will be generated (450 psi at turbine throttle) when operating at maximum load. The reactor will be so controlled that, when the load on the system is reduced, the mean reactor temperature will remain constant, resulting in a steam pressure rise to about 700 psi for zero load. These conditions should result in an over-all efficiency of 20 to 25%.

Liquid-Metal Fuel Reactor Experiment

Development work on the Liquid-Metal Fuel Reactor (LMFR) concept has been proceeding at Brookhaven National Laboratory since 1947, comprising, in the main, theoretical and experimental work on the nuclear, metallurgical, and chemical aspects of molten uranium-bismuth, including preliminary reactor design and economic studies. In order to evaluate the work that had been done and determine what future research and development would be required before a large scale reactor of this type could be built, a study group consisting of engineers and scientists from seventeen industrial organizations was formed in 1954. This group, under the direction of the Company, worked at Brookhaven for six months during 1955 and later that year submitted a report which concluded that the LMFR could be proved technically feasible in the near future and appeared to offer an attractive outlook for economic nuclear power.

In 1956 a contract to develop, design, construct, and operate a Liquid-Metal Fuel Reactor Experiment (LMFRE) was given to B&W by the AEC. The design of the LMFRE has not yet been established, but a review of the long-range reference design for a full-scale power plant that was developed by the study group will help to demonstrate the attractiveness of this reactor type.

This design consists of a reactor utilizing a circulating liquid-metal fuel solution and a circulating breeder slurry, a heat-transport and steam-generating system, a conventional turbogenerator plant, and chemical processing facilities for treating both fuel and breeder fluids. The fuel solution for the reactor is U-233 dissolved in liquid bismuth, and the breeder fluid in the blanket is a suspension, or slurry, of particles of thorium bismuthide in liquid bismuth. The heat produced in the core is 500 mw (1,700 million Btu/hr) and in the blanket 50 mw. This heat is transferred to a lead-bismuth intermediate heat-transport system, which delivers it to boiler, superheater, and reheater equipment to produce 2000 psi, 975 F steam. The gross output of the turbogenerator plant is 240 mw, netting 226 mw of salable electricity, see Fig. 10.

The details of the reactor are shown by Fig. 11. The steel vessel, 18 ft high and 12½ ft in diam, contains a cylindrical graphite core, 5 ft in both diam and height, drilled with 2-in. flow channels for the fuel solution. The blanket region is 3 ft thick and consists of graphite with 2-in. flow channels for the breeder slurry. A 5/16-in.-thick Croloy vessel supports the core graphite and separates the core and blanket regions, preventing mixing of the fuel and breeder fluids.

The fuel, at a flow rate of 36,000 gpm (1.76 $\times$ 10^6 lb/hr), enters the reactor at 752 F and passes up through the core into a degassing vessel, where volatile fission products are removed. Flow velocities are uniform in all channels of the core, but exit temperatures vary from 1290 F at the center to 842 F at the outer periphery because of the radial neutron

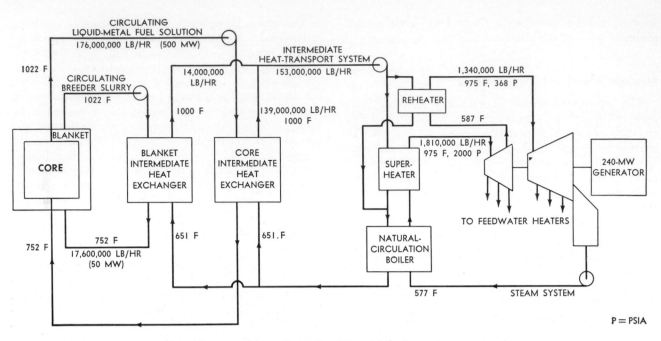

Fig. 10. *Reference design for a liquid-metal fuel reactor power plant*

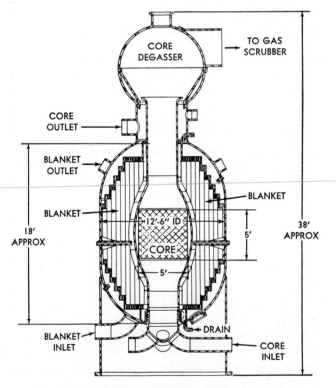

Fig. 11. *Design for a liquid-metal fuel reactor*

flux distribution. The high degree of turbulence in the upper section results in sufficient mixing to produce an average fluid exit temperature of 1022 F.

Operating pressure in the reactor is low and depends upon the static head of the fuel solution and the pumping pressure losses, since the vapor pressure of liquid bismuth is negligible. The pressure drop from the inlet manifold to the degasser is 18.6 psi; the maximum pressure in the reactor is about 120 psi at the reactor inlet.

The breeder fluid contains 25% by volume of thorium bismuthide solids, average particle size being 100 microns. This percentage of solids is about the highest practical to maintain moderate pumping power. The flow circuit is similar to that of the fuel, but the velocity is 1/10 that of the fuel flow rate.

Swimming-Pool Reactor

Although only a limited number of nuclear power reactor projects are under way, many research reactors have been or are being built. The "swimming-pool" reactor, featured by B&W, is a versatile tool readily adaptable to a multipurpose nuclear research program.

This reactor, shown by Fig. 12, is a thermal heterogeneous unit, consisting of a cubical array of vertical aluminum-clad fuel elements placed near the bottom of a large pool of ordinary water that acts as both moderator and coolant.

The unit built for the University of Michigan, Fig. 13, is one of many possible variations. The Company has completed a 5,000-kw research reactor in Sao Paulo, Brazil, and is building another for installation in Hamburg, Germany. The Michigan design utilizes fuel elements containing uranium enriched to about 93% U-235, with graphite reflector elements in the periphery of the core. The other two reactors will operate with fuel elements fabricated with uranium enriched to 20% U-235. Beryllium oxide reflector elements can be used in place of graphite, if it is desired to minimize the fissionable material required.

The University of Michigan reactor pool is about 10 ft wide, 20 ft long, and 25 ft deep. Its walls are made of high-density concrete 6 ft thick up to a height of about 15 ft. Above this height standard concrete of lesser thickness is utilized. At full power the shielding walls reduce the radiation level to 1/10 of the safe tolerance.

Control is accomplished with boron-steel rods, which are actuated vertically by top-mounted drive mechanisms. The neutron flux is continuously monitored by means of fission and ionization chambers; electronic circuits relay the resulting signals to the rod drives. Should preset limits be reached in these readings, the reactor will shut itself down promptly. This is known as a "scram."

Twelve aluminum beam ports penetrate the pool walls, providing access adjacent to the reactor core for the irradiation of samples. A graphite-filled thermal column about 6 ft square is built into a side wall. A pneumatic tube system for fast "rabbit" experiments is also provided. These experimental facilities can, of course, be varied.

At full power the core is cooled by pumping pool water downward through the fuel-element passages to a header and then through a heat exchanger at a rate of 1000 gpm. Build-up of radioactive corrosion products is controlled by continuously passing a portion of the flow through an ion exchanger.

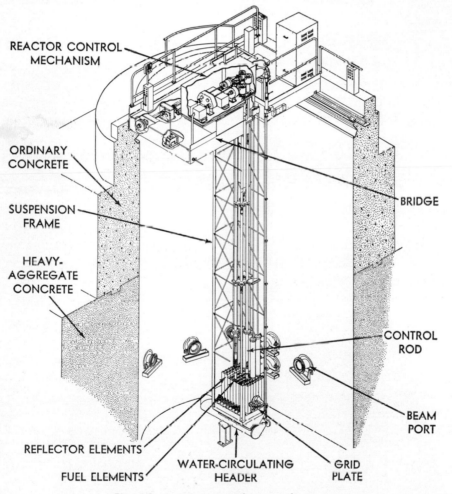

Fig. 12. *Swimming-pool research reactor*

The Role of Steam in Nuclear Power

Reactors that are now being designed for the generation of steam use water, gas, or liquid-metal coolants. These designs have limitations that restrict the steam temperatures and pressures to levels which are low when judged by the conventional heat-power standards. This and other features make reactors complex and expensive. The Atomic Energy Commission, electric utility companies, and heat-power-equipment suppliers are investigating various types of reactors and nuclear fuels in a concerted effort to reduce both investment and operating costs. There is no real reason to believe that these efforts will not be ultimately successful. In any event, steam will continue to play a dominant role in the production of power.

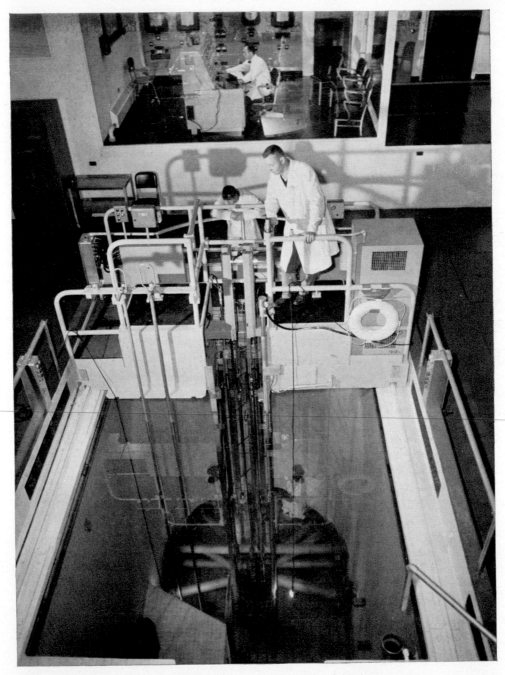

Fig. 13. *Pool reactor at University of Michigan*

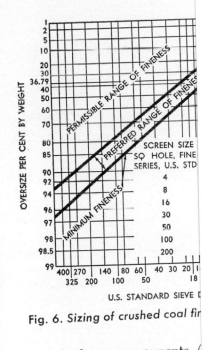

Fig. 6. Sizing of crushed coal fir[...]

and feeding arrangements (
and the bin or storage system
for most bituminous coals
permits. With this system co[a]
preparation plant to a sizing
the crushed coal is deliver[ed]
range of sizing of crushed c[oal]
system is given in Fig. 6. B[...]
is relatively large in partic[le]
sociated with pulverized-coa[l]
exist. The only precaution
adequate venting of the bu[...]
of the small amounts of co[...]
from freshly crushed coal o[f]
bin system the amount of
room is reduced, and short
accommodated without inter[...]

The second method of
direct system, which has
crusher located between th[e]
of each Cyclone Furnace.
system is that the intimate
air in the crusher helps to
proves crusher performance
moisture coals, such as lign[ite]
to accommodate the direct
where the coal-handling e[...]
be adapted to the bin syste[m]

Coal Feeders

The coal feeder normal[ly]
shown in Fig. 7. A distri[b...]
coal discharge from the f[...]
uniform rate of feed. This
coal is burned almost instan[t...]
the Cyclone Furnace, and

---

tion insures the high temperatures necessary to complete combustion and to provide the desired liquid
slag covering of the surface.

The gaseous products of combustion are discharged
through the water-cooled re-entrant throat into the
gas-cooling boiler furnace. Molten slag in excess of
the thin layer retained on the walls continually
drains toward the rear and discharges through the
tap hole (shown in Fig. 1) to the boiler furnace,
from which it is tapped into a slag tank and disposed
of in conventional manner.

The results of this method of combustion are that
the fuel is burned quickly and completely in the
small cyclone chamber and the boiler furnace is used
only for cooling the flue gases. Most of the ash is
retained as a liquid slag and tapped into the slag
tank under the boiler furnace. Thus, the quantity
of fly-ash is low and its particle size so fine that
erosion of boiler heating surfaces has never been
experienced even at high gas velocities.

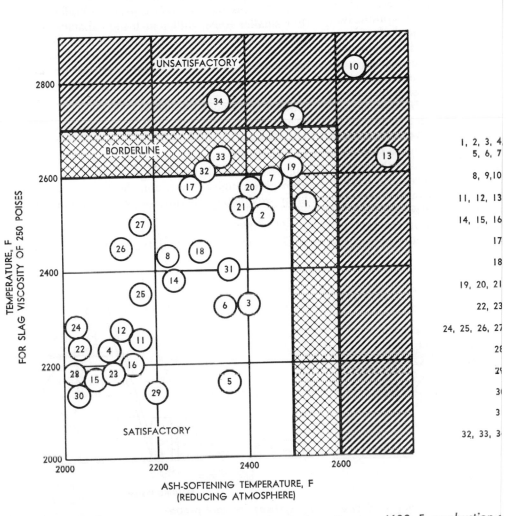

Fig. 3. Tests of coal suitability for the Cyclone Furnace (600 F combustion-[...]

Suitability of Fuels for the C[...]

In the production of pow[er]
burning fuel has proved suit[...]
tions of fuels under all condi[...]
Furnace is no exception; how[...]
of fuels is relatively broad.
500,000 tons of bituminous a[...]
in this country in 1950, app[...]
sidered suitable for use. Fu[...]
cheaper grades of coal gener[...]
teristics which are well suite[d]
considerable economic impo[r...]
tion of power. In buying fue[l]
boilers, there are fewer restr[...]
of coal, and full advantage ca[n]
petitive fuel market and the
area of the plant. Fuel oils
many other by-products from
wood, are suitable for firing (

THE CYCLONE FURNACE

OVER the years continued advances have been
made in the methods of burning coal. The
motivating factors were mainly economics,
growth of industry, and higher standards of living.
Economics demanded the efficient use of the cheapest
coals available. Growth of industry and higher living
standards required more steam-generating units of
higher capacities than those attainable with the older
types of equipment. In the early 1920's intensive
work on pulverized-coal firing was started to overcome the limitations of the stokers available at that
time. The advantages that pulverized-coal firing
offered were:

1. The use of the most economical size of coal
   available.
2. The removal of capacity limitations imposed by
   stokers.
3. Improvement in response to load.
4. The ability to burn all ranks of coal from lignite
   through anthracite.
5. Ease of combination firing of oil and gas with
   coal.
6. An increase in thermal efficiency because of
   lower excess air for combustion and lower carbon loss than that with stoker firing.
7. A reduction in operating labor requirements.

Today, pulverized-coal firing is highly developed
and is considered an excellent way to burn many
types of coal, particularly the higher grades and
ranks; however, in its development and application,
experience has shown this method of firing to have
certain limitations and undesirable features, such as:

1. Large power consumption required for driving
   pulverizers.
2. High maintenance costs for pulverizers.
3. Excessive fly-ash discharge from the stack (approximately 80% for dry-ash-removal furnaces
   without dust collectors).
4. Erosion of boiler pressure parts by fly-ash entrained in the flue gases (unless low gas velocities are maintained).

5. Erosion of induced-draft fan blades and scrolls,
   even when the fans are located after dust collectors.
6. Lower availability and increased maintenance
   because of eroded components.
7. Relatively large furnace volumes required for
   good combustion.

To understand the latter, a brief review of combustion and the functions of a furnace may be helpful. Very simply, combustion of coal is a chemical
reaction in which carbon combines with oxygen to
form CO_2. This gas tends to blanket the coal particles and retard further combustion. To maintain
rapid combustion the CO_2 must be scrubbed away
and every particle of coal brought rapidly into intimate contact with additional oxygen.

Pulverized-coal firing requires that the coal be reduced from 1- or 2-in. diam lumps to a powder, so
fine that approximately 70% will pass a 200-mesh
screen, which requires a large amount of power. The
finely pulverized coal is then very intimately mixed
with combustion air in the burner; however, after
this initial mixing the tiny coal particles are merely
carried along in the air stream, and very little additional scrubbing by the air occurs. Thus, further
contact of oxygen with the coal must be largely by
diffusion. The furnace consequently has to be relatively large to give the necessary retention time for
oxygen to diffuse through the blanketing CO_2 layer
to reach the coal particles, and, at the same time,
temperatures must be sufficiently high to complete
combustion. After combustion, since the residual ash
particles are much smaller than even the original
tiny pulverized-coal particles, the former are easily
carried along with the flue gases from the furnace
and through the boiler setting.

At the same time the pulverized-coal-fired boiler
furnace also has the function of cooling the combustion gases, so that when they enter the convection
surfaces they are below the temperature at which
slagging occurs. This function conflicts with that of
maintaining the high temperatures necessary to com-

plete combustion. It would therefore be preferable to separate these functions and use the boiler furnace for cooling only. This would require a separate small combustion chamber where high turbulence and temperature may be maintained.

For many years engineers recognized this need and actively explored basic changes in the design of furnaces and fuel-burning equipment to improve combustion and furnace performance. In addition, significant changes in the availability and use of coal further increased the need for new designs. For example, demands for the higher grades of coal have depleted many seams, and many others have been reserved for metallurgical and other uses. Mechanization in coal mining has increased the ash content of mined coal. Washing is widely used to lower ash and sulfur contents; however, this is an added expense (see Chapter 15). The industrial growth of the Western portion of the country, rich in reserves of subbituminous and lignitic coal, is rapidly increasing the consumption of these lower ranks of coal. This has furthered the need for equipment fully suitable for the lower grades and ranks of high-ash low-fusion-temperature coal.

The Cyclone Furnace is an outgrowth of efforts by many engineers to meet these needs and to overcome some of the difficulties encountered with other firing methods. It is a significant step in improving the methods of firing fuels and bettering the functional, design, and performance characteristics of boilers and related equipment.

Principle of Operation

The Cyclone Furnace (Fig. 1) is a water-cooled horizontal cylinder in which fuel is fired, heat is released at extremely high rates, and combustion is completed. Its water-cooled surfaces are studded and covered with refractory chrome ore. Coal crushed in a simple crusher, so that approximately 95% will pass a 4-mesh screen, is introduced into the burner end of the cyclone. About 15% of the combustion air also tangentially enters the burner and imparts a whirling motion to the incoming coal. Secondary air with a velocity of approximately 300 fps is admitted in the same direction tangentially at the roof of the main barrel of the cyclone and imparts a further whirling or centrifugal action to the coal particles. The combustible is burned from the fuel at heat release rates of 500,000 to 900,000 Btu/cu ft, hr, and gas temperatures exceeding 3000 F are developed. These temperatures are sufficiently high to melt the ash into a liquid slag, which forms a layer on the walls of the cyclone. The incoming coal particles (except for a few fines which are burned in suspension) are thrown to the walls by centrifugal force, held in the slag, and scrubbed by the high-velocity tangential secondary air. Thus the air

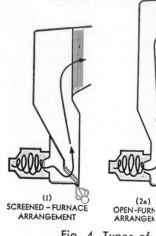

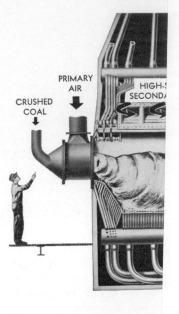

Fig. 1. The Cyclone Furnace, cylinder, is completely wat the main boiler circulation. through the re-entrant thro drains from the bottom at th ing into the adja

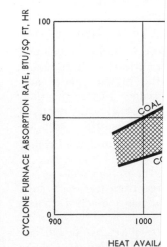

Fig. 2. Heat absorption

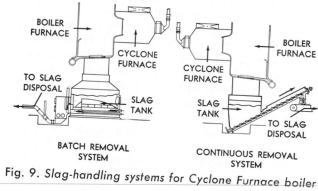

Fig. 4. Types of with Cycl

The suitability of m upon the amount of m and the quantity and ty ence with both commer it has been found that, of solid fuel, the ash m in the cyclone and the r in the slag layer must bustion. With a norma of 600 F, it has been fo istics will be suitable (from the coal ash has less at 2600 F. Also, th should exceed 15% on the required high comb high moisture content to limit the coal ash-s viscosity. There is c these characteristics, a ature of the combustio

required to burn the coa the products of combus Even though the release Cyclone Furnace is very heat actually absorbed is cause of the small amou and the insulating prop layer. Heat absorption 100,000 Btu/sq ft, hr, as bination of high heat re

compared with 15% for coal firing. With the lower air pressure, atomizing oil burners are used.

Slag-Handling Equipment

Slag-handling equipment for a Cyclone Furnace boiler is similar to that for a pulverized-coal slag-tap boiler, except that since the per cent of ash recovered in the Cyclone Furnace is higher the capacity of the slag-handling equipment must be correspondingly greater. There are two principal types of handling in use, as shown in Fig. 9. The first consists of one or more large storage tanks located under the furnace floor, into which slag is continuously tapped, quenched, and allowed to accumulate. It is withdrawn at intervals and discharged to a storage area, where it is recovered for sale or other use. The second type of slag handling is similar with the exception that a smaller storage volume is provided under the furnace floor, and the slag is removed continuously as it discharges into the water-quench tank. The advantages of the continuous handling system are that less space is required under the boiler furnace for the slag tanks and that no routine operating labor is required.

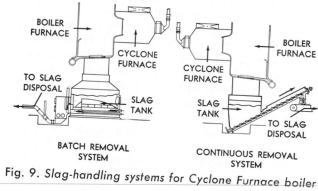

Fig. 9. Slag-handling systems for Cyclone Furnace boiler

Combustion Controls

Automatic combustion controls for Cyclone Furnace boilers are generally based on maintaining equal feeder speeds (feeders are calibrated to give equal volumetric flows for equal speed) and equal total air flows to individual Cyclone Furnaces. The air flows are measured by venturi meters in the air ducts to each furnace. In this way, equal coal rates and air flows are maintained to each cyclone, and the over-all excess air is controlled with a boiler meter based on steam flow-air flow in the usual manner. Often oxygen recorders are used as operating guides to monitor the controls.

Operating Results

Fuels Burned

The first commercial Cyclone Furnace boiler was

designed to burn Central Illinois coal and was installed at the Calumet Station of the Commonwealth Edison Co., Chicago, in 1944. Since then this method of burning has been incorporated in many units throughout the United States and Europe. In this country coals of the following range of constituents have been burned in commercial Cyclone Furnace boilers:

Moisture, %	2 to 40
Volatile matter (dry), %	18 to 45
Fixed carbon (dry), %	35 to 75
Ash (dry), %	35 to 75

As mentioned previously under *Suitability*, a number of by-products from petroleum and many waste fuels, such as bark, can be successfully burned. The petroleum products (coke and pitch) range in volatile matter from as low as 5% for some petroleum coke to as high as 60% for pitch. Because of the very low ash content of these petroleum by-products, it is usually necessary to add a slag-forming material or to also burn coal with suitable ash characteristics to provide the necessary slag coating of the cyclone barrel. For the 5% volatile coke it is also necessary to burn 5 to 10% auxiliary oil or gas to stabilize ignition.

Coal chars resulting from the low-temperature carbonization of bituminous or lignitic coals have

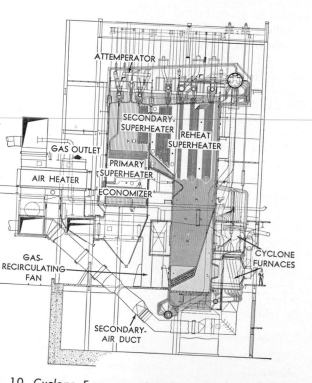

Fig. 10. Cyclone Furnace unit with screened boiler furnace. Maximum continuous steam output 1,523,000 lb per hr, 1050 F, 2400 psi design pressure. Five 9-ft-diameter Cyclone Furnaces per boiler

sufficient ash and volatile matter and are suitable for firing, provided the ash viscosity characteristics are suitable. Fig. 10 shows one of three units designed for burning coal char of 15% volatile matter content and bituminous coal.

Two units designed to burn bark and bituminous coal in amounts up to approximately 50% by weight of each are in operation in a large Southern paper mill. To burn the bark successfully, it is necessary to fire sufficient coal to supply the slag coating in the cyclone and to maintain sufficiently high temperatures to provide the necessary fluidity of the slag. Preparation and feeding of bark are discussed in Chapter 19.

Power Requirements

Since the only coal preparation is crushing, the power required is low compared with that for pulverized-coal firing. To offset this, the forced-draft-fan power required is relatively high, the Cyclone Furnace air pressure drop being in the range of 20 to 40 in. of water compared with 2 to 10 in. of water for pulverized-coal burners. The net result is that power requirements for a Cyclone Furnace boiler are of the same order as for pulverized-coal firing. Fig. 11 shows the comparative power re-

quirements for a wide range of coals. It will be seen that, for the low-grindability low-heating-value bituminous and lignitic coals, the power required is substantially less than that for a pulverized-coal-fired unit. However, for high-heating-value high-grindability bituminous coal, the power is greater.

Combustion Efficiency

The excess air required for satisfactory combustion is less than 10%. However, where automatic controls are used and particularly where there are several Cyclone Furnaces for one boiler, excess air is usually maintained between 10 and 15% to insure that no individual cyclone is operating with insufficient air. When operating with coal of suitable sizing and with 10% excess air, the loss in efficiency from unburned combustible has been found to be less than 0.1% with most coals.

Ash Recovery and Dust Collectors

The results of dust-loading tests from a number of operating Cyclone Furnace units are given in Fig. 12. The dust loading of the flue gas is in the range of 5 to 15% of the ash in the coal, compared with about 80% for a dry-ash pulverized-coal-fired unit. For many installations the dust loading for the

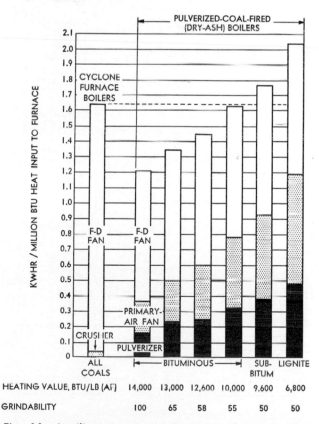

Fig. 11. *Auxiliary power requirements of typical high-capacity pressure-fired Cyclone Furnace and pulverized-coal units*

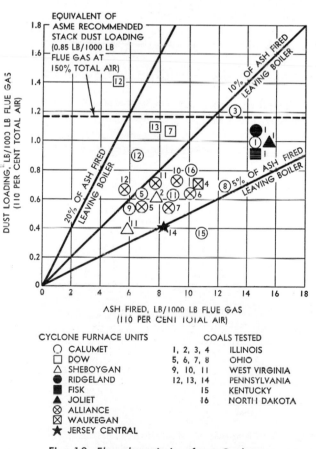

Fig. 12. *Fly-ash emission from Cyclone Furnace units (test results)*

Cyclone Furnace without a dust collector is within the ASME recommendation of 0.85 lb per 1000 lb of flue gas at 150% total combustion air. This lower dust loading is important not only from the standpoint of reduced dust nuisance but also because of the reduction in boiler cleaning requirements and the elimination of erosion of convection heating surface and induced-draft fans. Low dust loading also permits the boiler to be designed for higher gas velocities through the convection banks, resulting in better heat transfer.

It is common practice to equip pulverized-coal-fired boilers with high-efficiency dust collectors to eliminate the dust nuisance. This, however, does not change the amount of fly-ash passing through the boiler. The dust loading of a pulverized-coal-fired unit with a dust collector is but little lower than that of a Cyclone Furnace boiler operating without benefit of dust collector. This comparison is illustrated in Fig. 13 for a large central station Cyclone Furnace unit and a pulverized-coal-fired unit arranged for dry-ash removal. Both units are of 200-megawatt capacity, each consuming approximately 1800 tons of coal per day and producing 360 tons of ash. With pulverized-coal firing approximately 290 tons per day of fly-ash passes through the boiler to the dust collector. The latter traps approximately 260 tons of fly-ash per day, allowing 30 tons, or approximately 8% of the ash in the coal, to discharge to the atmosphere. Under similar operating conditions with the Cyclone Furnace, only about 36 tons of fly-ash per day, or approximately 10% of the ash in the coal, passes through the boiler to the atmosphere. If a smaller dust collector of only 80% efficiency were added to the Cyclone Furnace unit, the amount of dust discharged to the atmosphere would be 7 tons per day, or 2% of the original ash in the coal. The

dust from the collector may be returned to the Cyclone Furnace and recovered as slag, thus effecting a complete elimination of fly-ash handling and the near elimination of dust emission from the stack.

Typical Installations

Although Cyclone Furnace units were first used in central stations, their use has been extended to a wide variety of industries. Fig. 14 shows a unit installed in a large Northern industrial plant. The unit incorporates the direct-firing system, and for maximum ash recovery, the boiler furnace is of the screen type. Slag is collected in a large quench tank with batch discharge to storage.

Fig. 15 shows a smaller unit installed in a Southern chemical plant. This unit incorporates the bin

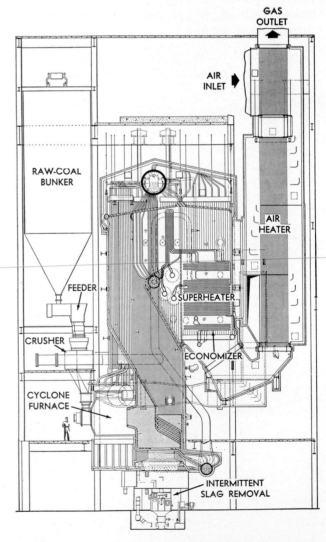

Fig. 14. Cyclone Furnace unit with screened boiler furnace, direct-firing system, and intermittent slag removal

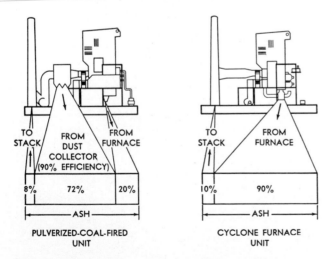

Fig. 13. Comparison of fly-ash emission from typical large dry-ash-removal pulverized-coal-fired unit and Cyclone Furnace unit

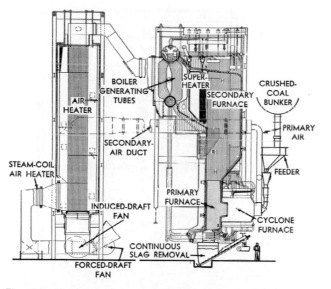

Fig. 15. Cyclone Furnace unit with open boiler furnace, bin-firing system, and continuous slag removal

system for firing and the open boiler-furnace arrangement. Slag is handled by a continuous removal system. Both this and the preceding unit are designed for pressure operation (without induced-draft fan).

The designs of Cyclone Furnace units have followed the general trend of the power industry to higher steam temperatures and pressures and larger capacities. Fig. 16 shows a 450-megawatt-capacity unit, one of the largest in the world. It has the open boiler-furnace arrangement with Cyclone Furnaces located in both the front and the rear boiler-furnace walls. The boiler is a Universal-Pressure once-through type designed for 4500 psi. The high-pressure superheater and the medium- and lower-pressure reheaters are all designed for 1050 F steam temperature. Flue gas is recirculated from the economizer to the boiler furnace, where it is introduced above the Cyclone Furnaces for the purpose of tempering the combustion gases without interference with superheat and reheat absorption requirements.

Operation

Start-Up

The Cyclone Furnace can be started by the continuous firing of coal, oil, or gas. Coal is ignited by a permanently installed gas-lighting torch or a retractable oil-lighting torch inserted into the front secondary-air port. With coal firing, the usual load range for good operation of an individual furnace is from 100 to 50% of rated capacity, depending upon the ash characteristics; however, for short periods, such as start-up, loads of 20 to 25% can be carried with some increase in unburned combustible. The load range for continuous operation of the entire

Cyclone Furnace unit is from full to approximately half load, again depending upon the ash characteristics and the furnace arrangement. For short periods, such as overnight load drops, lower ratings can be carried by allowing the slag tapped from the Cyclone Furnace to accumulate and solidify on the boiler-furnace floor. When the load is increased, this slag will melt and tap in the usual manner.

Operating Labor

Typical operating-labor requirements for a large

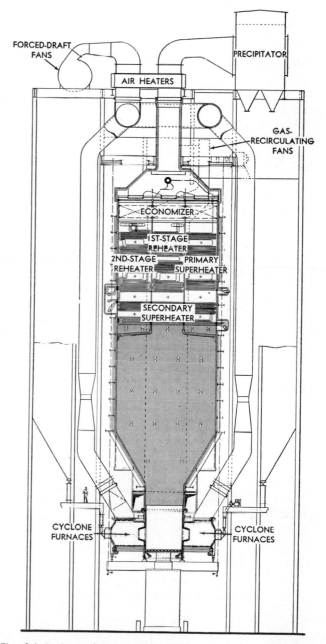

Fig. 16. Universal-Pressure once-through boiler with open boiler furnace and opposed Cyclone Furnaces

In 1895 two units of the *Reverie* design, after some changes in arrangement of the protected side walls and tube sizes had been made (see Fig. 2), were installed in the S. S. *Zenith City* (on the Great Lakes) for the Zenith Transit Co., now known as the Pittsburgh Steamship Co. These units were fitted with economizers. However, since at that time no satisfactory feedwater treatment had been developed, the water fed to the units contained high oxygen concentrations, and the economizers soon failed because of corrosion and were never replaced. A year later, boilers of this design were installed in the United States naval vessels *Marietta, Annapolis,* and *Chicago.*

Although the *Reverie* design was an outstanding success and proved to be far more satisfactory in service than other boilers previously used by the Navy, combustion was not entirely satisfactory. The boiler was fired at the uptake end, which made it necessary to slope the grates down toward the rear to gain furnace volume. At high ratings this form of furnace was not suitable for good combustion because of the difficulties in firing and ash handling. Further, the shallow ashpit at the rear had a tendency to overheat the grate bars. The fittings and water gages were not readily accessible from the firing aisle because of the location of the steam drum.

To overcome these difficulties, the design was modified to permit firing from the downtake end. This led to improved combustion conditions, since the furnace was enlarged in the direction in which combustion took place. The grates were properly located, and the accessibility of the tubes for cleaning from the fireroom floor was greatly improved. The steam drum was now at the firing end of the boiler, where the water gage could be easily seen and where all fittings were more accessible. These

modifications, patented in 1897 by William D. Hoxie, although seemingly very simple, revolutionized marine water-tube boiler practice.

The boiler was further improved by lengthening the tubes to increase furnace volume and to reduce the weight for a given heating surface. Performance was also considerably improved by the installation of baffles to provide three gas passes. The first boiler with these revisions was installed in 1899 in the Navy cruiser *Alert* and became known as the *Alert* design (see Fig. 3).

The first installation of the *Alert* design in a merchant vessel was in the *Asuncion,* on the Great Lakes, in 1900. In this unit the clusters of 2-in. tubes were replaced by single 4-in. tubes, which were easier to clean—an important item with water-treatment practice prevailing at that time. The design proved successful in the Merchant Marine, and many installations soon followed. This type of boiler, fitted with 4-in. tubes and equipped to burn oil, was widely used in the emergency fleet vessels of World War I. The same type fitted with 2-in. tubes was used in all the Liberty ships of World War II.

In the Navy the torpedo boat was developed in the middle seventies, and the destroyer first appeared in the early nineties. Vessels of these types required boilers of the lightest and most compact design, and several different drum-type boilers had been developed to save weight and space. Recognizing the advantages of this general design for the naval service, B&W investigated the various boilers of this type then available and acquired the rights to the White-Foster boiler which had been patented in 1897. This boiler was of the three-drum type, with the tubes inclined and bent so that each tube, without disturbing the others, could be removed by

PRIMARY
B

SECTI
(COAL IN

Fig. 1. Early B&W cross-drum sinuous-header marine boiler (1889) for yacht *Reverie*

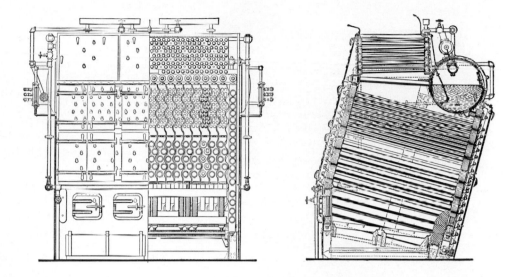

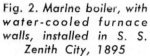

Fig. 2. Marine boiler, with water-cooled furnace walls, installed in S. S. Zenith City, 1895

passing it through the manhole opening in the steam drum. The design was modified by B&W to meet Navy requirements, and the first boilers of this type were installed in the destroyer *Mayrant* in 1909.

The advantages of superheated steam had been recognized as early as 1859, and several installations were made with claims of economy gains ranging from 25 to 50 per cent. However, lubrication difficulties in the prime mover and lack of suitable materials and methods of lubrication prevented any general use of superheated steam in those early days. The first B&W marine boiler equipped with a superheater was installed in a Great Lakes ore carrier, the *James C. Wallace*, in 1904. In this header-type boiler unit designed for 85 F superheat, the superheater was located above the first and second gas passes of the boiler. By a simple alteration in baffling, the gases could be made to by-pass the superheater so that comparative results could be obtained for operation with either saturated or superheated steam. Operating results indicated a saving of 9 per cent in fuel (coal) when using superheated steam and a 17 per cent saving in fuel when compared with a typical Scotch marine boiler on the

Great Lakes using saturated steam.

In 1904 B&W water-tube boilers equipped with superheaters were installed in the S. S. *Creole*, while Scotch (cylindrical fire-tube) boilers delivering saturated steam were installed in two sister ships. The over-all performance records of the machinery plants of all three were closely checked, and it was found that the ship with B&W boilers fitted with superheaters again showed a saving of 17 per cent as compared with Scotch boiler installations in the two sister ships. This marked the successful revival of the use of superheated steam on board ship although the superheat temperature was still modest. With the gradual development of higher-alloy steels, steam temperatures have been increased, and turbine-driven ships are now operating with steam temperatures up to 1050 F.

The many advantages of oil over coal for firing marine boilers was generally recognized about the same time, and the use of oil increased greatly during the years 1905 to 1915. Currently, most sea-going ships are fitted with oil-fired boilers.

Steam pressures and temperatures were increased gradually during the period from 1920 to 1930, and

U. S. S. MISSOURI, BATTLESHIP

Fig. 3. Marine boiler of the "Alert" design. First unit of this type installed (1899) in the U. S. cruiser Alert

in the latter year the ocean liners *Manhattan* and *Washington*, each rated at 30,000 shp, were placed in service. The B&W three-drum express-type boilers, similar to the White-Foster design, installed in these ships delivered steam at 400 psi and 675 F at the superheater outlet (see Fig. 4).

Following the first World War, the Navy's building program was concentrated on major ships, and

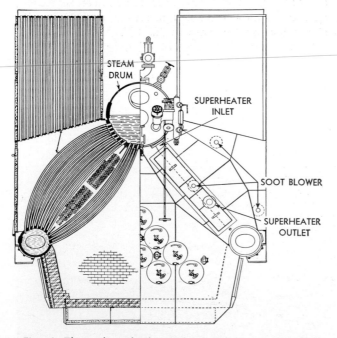

Fig. 4. Three-drum boiler with air heater as installed (1930) in S. S. Manhattan and S. S. Washington

construction was actually started on 12 battleships and 16 cruisers. Of this program, a considerable tonnage later was scrapped in accordance with the terms of the treaty, based on the Washington Disarmament Conference, which became effective in August 1923. However, the so-called treaty cruisers (permitted under the terms of the treaty) were designed and built. The first few of these cruisers were of the *Salt Lake City* class, named after the first ship in this group. These vessels were fitted with oil-fired B&W three-drum boilers to deliver saturated steam at a pressure of 300 psi. Several other classes of vessels were also constructed during the treaty period, which ended Dec. 31, 1936.

The weight limitations set by the treaty necessitated the use of the lightest possible equipment, so that the weight savings might be used to enhance fighting efficiency. The Navy considered the possibility of using higher steam pressures and temperatures to reduce the quantity of steam required per shaft horsepower and thus save weight. This posed a difficult problem for the boiler designer, since the efficiency of any boiler decreases with an increase in pressure unless the heat can be recovered in some manner, as by air heaters or economizers. The use of these heat-reclaiming devices was not acceptable to the Navy at that time because of space limitations, air pressure requirements, and the lack of available means for deaerating feedwater to the degree required for the economizer. Furthermore, large tube ligaments were necessary in the steam drum because of the nonradial drilling of the White-Foster design and the limitation in drum-shell thickness required by the riveted construction used prior to 1930. Therefore the tube pitch could not be reduced, and there was no apparent way of increasing the heat absorption in the boiler bank.

The sectional-express (SX) type of boiler was one of two types designed to overcome these difficulties. In the SX boiler some of the features of the sectional-header type of boiler were used, but the headers were cylindrical and connected by curved tubes of relatively small diameter. High heat transfer rates were obtained by arranging the tube bank to provide a decreasing gas flow area through the boiler. Since the tubeholes were in small forged headers, it was possible to reduce the pitch of the tubeholes and thus greatly improve the effectiveness of the boiler bank.

Research in fusion welding was started by the B&W Co. about 1923, and this effort culminated in the development of a process that produced a weld which was ductile and equal to, or better than, the parent drum metal in all respects. Consequently it was possible to produce drums without the buttstraps required for riveted construction, and the weight saving was appreciable. Satisfactory welds were assured by X-ray control of all welded seams and physical tests of test coupons.

The Navy was actively interested in the B&W research, since the development of successful welds would permit the use of lighter weight boilers and eliminate troubles resulting from caustic embrittlement and corrosion fatigue. After reviewing the B&W welding techniques and the results of tests conducted under the direction of Prof. H. F. Moore of the University of Illinois (presented before the semiannual meeting of the ASME in Detroit, June 1930), the Navy, in August 1930, approved a B&W proposal and specification for the use of fusion-welded boiler drums.

Consequently, SX-type boilers (see Fig. 5) designed for improved efficiency and the use of fusion-welded steam drums were ordered in 1930 for the Navy's scout cruisers *New Orleans, Minneapolis,* and *Astoria,* and the aircraft carrier *Ranger.* These boilers were designed to deliver steam at a pressure of 300 psi and a temperature of 572 F, and on the official trials the boilers developed an efficiency of 82.1 per cent at the full-power firing rate (1.10 lb of oil per sq ft of boiler heating surface per hr).

Subsequent to these installations, all Navy boilers were fitted with welded drums, and further, the important decision by the Navy to use welded drums was quickly followed by ASME approval of fusion-welded drums and the use of welded instead of riveted drums on practically all types of stationary boilers.

At about the same time, the sinuous-header type of boiler was also greatly improved and found wide application in the merchant service. The heating surface per unit of volume of the boiler was increased by the reduction in tube size, as was being done in the SX type for naval service, and by arranging nine 1¼-in. or fourteen 1-in. tubes in clusters it was

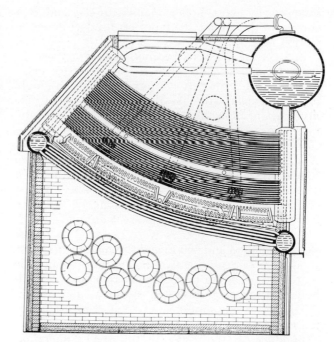

Fig. 5. Express boiler for U. S. cruisers and aircraft carrier (1930) following Navy approval of welded drums

possible to obtain a more efficient tube bank. Further, since the gas baffles were eliminated, the draft loss through the boiler was reduced. Compared with the 2-in. and 4-in. tube header-type boilers, there is a very considerable saving in weight and space per sq ft of heating surface. The front and rear headers remained vertical. This modified sinuous-header type of boiler was first installed in the lighthouse tender *Violet* in 1929, followed by installations in the sea train *New York* and the sea train *Havana* in 1932. This design proved so successful that it has been

S. S. AMERICA, TRANSATLANTIC LINER

followed by most boiler manufacturers, and it is currently the standard type of header boiler in marine service.

In 1933 the Navy's construction program was increased with the authorization for 20 destroyers, 4 cruisers, and 2 aircraft carriers. Three-drum single-furnace boilers were installed in these ships. The drums were of welded construction, and the tube-holes were drilled radially permitting a smaller tube pitch than in the White-Foster design. Although the feature of independent removal of each tube was sacrificed, the closer spacing of the tubes resulted in a reduction in the weight, size, and cost of the boiler, and the radial drilling of the tube-holes permitted a better tube-seat arrangement. In the destroyers the boilers were designed to deliver steam at 400 psi and 650 F, and the superheaters were located in one of the two boiler tube banks. The cruisers and aircraft carriers were equipped with boilers generating saturated steam at 450 psi and separately fired superheaters delivering steam to the turbines at 400 psi and 650 F.

Building up the Navy to full treaty limitations was first authorized by Congress in 1934, and the contracts for the *Somer* class destroyers were issued in that year. These vessels were equipped with a new design of B&W two-furnace double-uptake type of boiler and a convection superheater located in one of the boiler tube banks. This was the first boiler of the type with superheat control. Moreover, steam

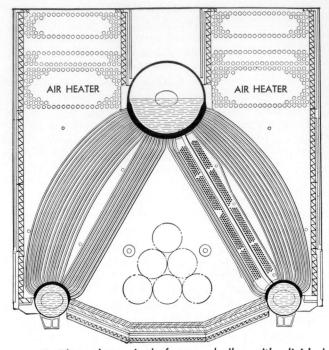

Fig. 7. Three-drum single-furnace boiler with divided air heater, as installed (1939) in S. S. America

pressures and temperatures were substantially increased to 565 psi and 700 F. The required superheat was obtained by varying the firing rate in the furnace on the superheater side. By providing, in a single unit, direct steam temperature control without dampers and without a separately fired superheater, a considerable saving was made in weight and space. Weight was also saved by the use of a special light-weight alloy casing—a development which called for new special skills in fabrication and design. Another important feature of these boilers was the introduction of air casings, thus eliminating the cumbersome and vulnerable closed-fireroom system previously used in naval service.

Further improvements were made in 1938 in the design of the boilers for the *Gleaves* class of destroyer. To meet the increasingly congested space conditions aboard destroyers and still retain the advantages of superheat control, a two-furnace single-uptake type of boiler, designed to operate at a pressure of 580 psi and a temperature of 825 F, was developed for this class. This general design (see Fig. 9) was widely used for all subsequent combat vessels, with an increase in steam temperature to 850 F.

Most of the combatant vessels in the Navy's World War II fleets were fitted with boilers operating at steam pressures of approximately 565 psi and temperatures of 850 F. Naval designs developed subsequent to World War II cover a pressure range of 875 to 1200 psi and temperatures of 950 to 1050 F.

Header-type boilers, designed for 625 psi and a

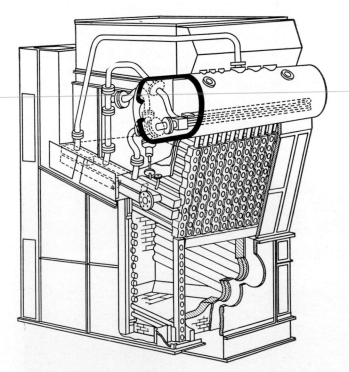

Fig. 6. Header-type boiler, 625 psi and 835 F controlled steam temperature, installed (1936) in tanker Van Dyke

supply, some of th
to oil firing.

Boiler design is
of fuel used. For
heavy fuel oils has
mum clearances w
the oil burners an
to prevent flame
deterioration. How
these clearances n
creasing the size c
does not violate o

Most modern c
with stokers, alth
pacities, are hand
are more compac
signed for hand f
higher efficiencies.
however, they are
verized coal is
limitations.

Although some
still continue to
units are now fitt
fans, or a combin
weight. Some ea
forced-draft syster

In one of the fi
fans forced cold
water into a close
be exceeded witl
to the fireroom. T
to provide protect
the air-encased bc
vessels. This boil
high-pressure air
In this system an
carried within th

ing, some of this
the boiler with
under these cond
servative rates of
Although difficult
oil in the boiler
outages can be re

On the other h
ture may be use
except that for t
bines the steam
some conditions
800 to 900 F
blading.

When designin
ments, space lin
Limitations usua
sions—length, wi
dition to specify
requirements su
pressure, steam t
efficiency, and al
naval architect
that the most
"High" boilers,
to minimum wei
necessitating wi
is the most serie
length is also qu
since additional
make up the to

controlled steam temperature of 835 F, were installed in 1936 in the tanker *Van Dyke* and were followed in 1938 by a similar installation in the tanker *Henry*, designed for a steam temperature of 910 F. These units were equipped with an attemperator in the steam drum to control superheat, air heaters to improve efficiency, stud-tube water-cooled walls to reduce furnace maintenance, and feedwater and combustion-control equipment to facilitate operation and enhance economy. Many of the design features used for the power plant of the *Van Dyke* have been adopted in the current installations of header-type boilers. This type of boiler unit has proved unusually rugged, reliable, and economical over years of extended service (see Fig. 6).

Construction of the ocean liner *America*, the largest merchant ship to be built in the United States up to that time, was started in 1938 and completed in 1940. This vessel is equipped with six B&W three-drum single-furnace boilers fitted with superheaters and air heaters (see Figs. 7 and 12). These boilers deliver steam at 425 psi and 725 F. War curtailed her peacetime activities, and as the troop transport *West Point* she carried more than 350,000 troops to and from the war zones all over the world. Reconditioned at the end of the war, she returned to the North Atlantic passenger service of the United States Lines to become again the S. S. *America*.

The S. S. *Independence* and the S. S. *Constitution*, built by the Bethlehem Shipbuilding Division of the Bethlehem Steel Co. at Quincy, Mass., for the American Export Lines, entered service at the end of 1950 and the beginning of 1951. Each ship is equipped with four B&W two-drum single-furnace boilers fitted with air heaters. The boilers deliver steam at 600 psi and 840 F. These ships, now engaged in service between New York and Mediterranean

ports, are capable of carrying 1000 passengers each.

The superliner *United States*, designed by Gibbs & Cox, Inc., built by the Newport News Shipbuilding & Dry Dock Co. at Newport News, Va., for the United States Lines, is equipped with boilers designed by B&W. On entering the North Atlantic service as Queen of the American Merchant Marine, she immediately established a new speed record. On her maiden voyage from New York, July 3, 1952, the *United States* made the crossing from Ambrose Lightship, outside New York, to Bishop Rock, off Lands End, England, covering 2942 nautical miles in 3 days 10 hours 40 minutes, at an average speed of 35.59 knots. The previous eastward record established in August 1938, over approximately the same course, covering 2938 nautical miles in 3 days 20 hours 42 minutes, at an average speed of 31.69 knots, is held by the Cunard liner *Queen Mary*. Westward on her maiden voyage the *United States* passed Ambrose Lightship at 4:29 p.m. July 14, having covered the 2902 nautical miles from Bishop Rock in 3 days 12 hours 12 minutes, at an average speed of 34.47 knots, thus breaking, by 9 hours 36 minutes, the previous record of 3 days 21 hours 48 minutes for the westward crossing, established by the *Queen Mary* in 1938. On the last leg of the eastward crossing (17 hours 16 minutes) in a high wind, the *United States* covered 631 nautical miles at an average of 36.5 knots, by far the fastest speed of any merchant ship over a sustained period of time.

George Horne, in concluding his report to the New York Times of the record Atlantic crossing eastward, said:

"Officers, passengers, and company officials are somewhat awed by the magnitude of the ship's achievement and agree that the sea lanes between America and Europe, coursed through the centuries

S. S. INDEPENDENCE, PASSENGER LINER, NEW YORK TO MEDITERRANEAN PORTS

by vesse
have thi
engineer
Durin
fitted wi
psi and
tions o
mately 8
the war
both ste
been ma
850 F,
in the 6

Genera

Based
operatir
the sect
commor
particul
stallatio
to estab
ship, th
skill ar
availabl
general

The
advanta
of a fev
be carr

Fig. 10.
B&W—s

Operat
the servi
ships usi
steady p
quiremer
operatior
designed
the same
oil-drillin

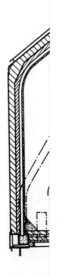

Fig. 11.
This ge

Fig. 8.

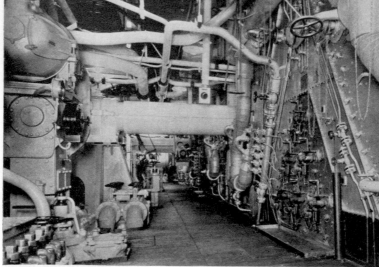

Fig. 12. *Afterfireroom of the S. S. America, showing three of the six B&W boilers installed*

understood and recognized. Among the criteria most frequently used are certain rates:

1. The heat release per cu ft of furnace volume per hr.

2. The heat release per sq ft of radiant heat-absorbing surface per hr.

3. The heat release per sq ft of boiler, water, or total heating surfaces per hr.

4. Evaporative ratings per sq ft of boiler heating surface.

5. The heat absorption per sq ft of radiant heat-absorbing surface per hr.

A discussion of the use of these criteria, in the order listed, follows.

The Btu release per cu ft of furnace volume per hr is not an important design criterion and has value only when used to compare firing rates for similar designs. Actually this figure serves only to indicate for this comparison, in a very general way, the time required for the products of combustion to leave the furnace. It is important to realize that two boilers may be designed for identical heat release rates per cu ft of furnace volume and yet have such entirely different furnace contours and arrangements that the respective heat-absorbing surfaces may be in the ratio of 2 to 1, or almost any ratio. It is surface, not volume, that absorbs heat. Furnace temperatures and furnace tube temperatures are more closely related to surface than to volume. The only limitation on the furnace heat release rates per cu ft should be that

imposed by the ability of the firing equipment to maintain satisfactory combustion conditions over the entire operating range of the boiler. Satisfying this important condition will permit the installation of high-capacity light-weight boiler units in a minimum space.

Another misleading aspect of this criterion is the custom of using the calorific heat content of the fuel in establishing the furnace volume heat release rates. In doing so, the effect of an air heater, if installed, is completely overlooked. Air may be supplied to the burners at a temperature of 350 F, which would add to the total heat available about 1000 Btu per lb of oil fired. Heated combustion air raises the adiabatic flame temperature an amount equal to approximately 75 per cent of the air temperature rise in the air heater and will increase the furnace temperature by an amount equal to approximately 25 per cent of the air temperature rise in the air heater. Therefore, for identical boiler units reporting the same furnace volume heat release rates, the unit equipped with an air heater will operate with a higher furnace temperature and a higher heat absorption per sq ft of furnace surface.

The heat release rate in Btu per hr per sq ft of radiant heat-absorbing surface is somewhat more significant, since it indicates to some degree the absorption rate in the furnace. Unfortunately, however, this criterion does not indicate the approximate furnace tube temperatures, since these are affected by the boiler operating pressure. Neither are the size

After having est
the furnace requi
burners, the furnac
and absorption rat
years most boiler
saturated steam, a
were conservative,
furnace temperatu
the introduction of
where superheaters
and with higher f
came necessary to
perature accurately
superheater design
absorption by the f
quate circulation m
selection of riser an

Furnace gas tem
from formulas base
that the heat absorl
to the difference be
absolute temperatu
the receiving surface
mination of radiant
naces is a very con
many variable facto
the combustion cha
the heat content of
of the products of c
air, furnace size ar
the cold surfaces ar
furnace envelope, t
air, latent heat loss
emissivity of the var
and the flame lumin

Furnace exit gas t

and arrangement of tubes, which greatly affect the heat absorption rates, taken into account. Further, this criterion does not indicate the increase in the absorption of radiant heat when preheated air is used for combustion. Therefore, while this criterion has some value, it also has some serious limitations in application to design and is more suitable for comparing similar designs of boilers to operate at the same pressure.

The heat release rate per sq ft of heating surfaces is rather meaningless. It is possible in two boiler units, designed for the same specified heat release rates per sq ft of heating surface, to have appreciable differences in heat absorption, circulation, draft loss, and efficiency characteristics, because of widely different arrangements of tube banks. A specified maximum heat release in these terms merely places a minimum limit on the amount of boiler heating surface, or possibly the total water surface (boiler and economizer), or the total surface in the unit (boiler, superheater, economizer, and air heater), without indicating any arrangement of component surface or taking into account the heat absorption rates.

The evaporative rating per sq ft of steam-generating surface is one of the most common and oldest of the criteria used and at one time was quite indicative of boiler performance. However, with the introduction of a wider range of pressures and temperatures, the equivalent evaporation rate has generally been substituted for the actual evaporation rate. This rate is established by considering the heat absorption in the boiler in terms of units equal to 970.3 Btu per lb of steam. However, it is based on the over-all *average* performance and in no way indicates conditions where maximum absorption rates and maximum tube temperatures occur in the steam-generating surfaces. It has little value except in comparing similar units operating under similar conditions.

The heat absorption rate per sq ft of radiant heat-absorbing surface has become the most important factor in boiler design. This criterion is especially valuable since it takes into account the arrangement of surfaces in the furnace, the relationships between absorbing and radiating surfaces, and the effect of heated combustion air. The designer is concerned with furnace heat absorption. Radiation to the furnace wall tubes and radiation and convection to the furnace rows of the boiler bank must be established in order to determine tube temperatures and thermal stresses and provide a satisfactory operating margin against possible internal scale from feedwater contamination. All of these determinations are directly related to the heat absorption rate per sq ft of radiant heat-absorbing surface. The diagrams in Fig. 13 indicate the practical use of this criterion in boiler design.

Marine Boiler Design

The design procedures outlined below, while generally applicable for any fuel and method of firing, are based more particularly on the use of oil. It should be noted, moreover, that the average rates of firing with oil are likely to correspond to near the maximum for stoker-fired coal units and usually cannot be maintained at all with hand-fired coal boilers.

Before starting the design, the required steam temperature and pressure, temperature of feedwater, efficiency, and capacity when operating at the normal and overload rates must be established to determine the amounts of oil to be fired. Then, assuming the type of burners to be used, the possible allowable draft loss through the burners, satisfactory combustion conditions, and allowable furnace heat absorption rates, the size

U. S. S. BALTIMORE, CRUISER

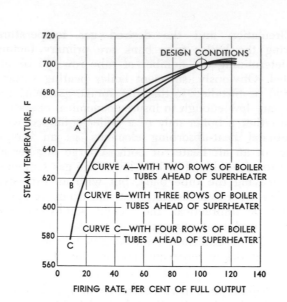

Fig. 17. *Typical curves showing effect of super-heater location and firing rate on superheat*

ment efficiencies. Therefore it is sometimes economically desirable to increase the ligament efficiency by increasing the tube spacing, in order to keep the thickness of the drum tube sheet within reasonable limits.

Single-pass header boilers are usually designed with 2-in. screen tubes and 1¼- or 1-in. bank tubes. By using 1-in. instead of 1¼-in. tubes in the boiler bank, the heating surface for a given size boiler can be increased about 25 per cent. However, the advantages of increased heating surface may be balanced by the adverse effect of using small-diameter tubes with inferior feedwater conditions.

Since it is customary in this country to use integral superheaters, the boiler unit should be con-

sidered as being of two sections. In the design of the section between the furnace and the superheater, due consideration must be given to its effect on the desired steam temperature and the maximum allowable tube-metal temperature. Behind the superheater, the goal should be to supply the most economical combination of tube bank and economizer or air heater, or both, to obtain the required uptake temperature. In conservatively designed units, the gas temperatures leaving the boiler tube bank at full power may be 100 to 150 F above saturation temperature.

The number of tube rows and the spacing of the tubes in the saturated surface ahead of the superheater will greatly affect the design. It is customary in the preliminary design of marine boilers to establish the tentative number of rows and the spacing of these tubes, so that the gas temperature entering the superheater will be sufficient to obtain the desired steam temperature with a superheater of reasonable size and arrangement. A wide spacing of the tubes in the screen or tubes ahead of the superheater will allow the penetration of considerable furnace radiation to the superheater. A superheater located behind a shallow screen (two or three rows), where it is subject to furnace radiation, will have the characteristics of both a straight convection and a radiant superheater, the steam temperatures will be relatively constant over a wide range of operation, and the amount of surface required will be reduced. Conversely, a superheater located behind a relatively deep water screen (four or five rows) will require more surface than one located nearer the furnace and will have a steeper rising steam temperature characteristic from low to full load.

Design of the tube bank behind the superheater is relatively simple, once the drum ligament has been determined. The number of rows in the saturated bank is usually determined following an analysis of the economic advantages of economizers and air heaters as compared with boiler surface. Knowing the efficiency desired, it is relatively easy to select the proper proportions of boiler surface and additional heat-reclaiming surface beyond the boiler bank.

Superheater Design

The heat absorption is the product of the heat-absorbing surface, the mean temperature difference, and the heat transfer rate. To reduce the size and weight of the superheater and thereby the boiler unit as a whole, it is always desirable that a superheater for marine service should have a minimum amount of heating surface. It is therefore usually advisable to maintain the highest possible tempera-

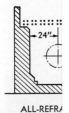

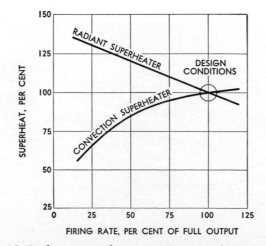

Fig. 18. *Performance of a convection superheater and a contemplated radiant superheater to give the desired temperature at the same design point*

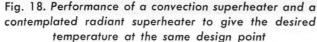

ture difference between the gas and the steam by locating the superheater (see Fig. 17) as near the furnace as is practicable and to use the allowable heat transfer rates commensurate with acceptable draft loss. The steam pressure drop through the superheater should be sufficient to insure proper steam distribution. However, the steam pressure drop in the superheater directly affects the boiler design pressure and consequently the weight, space, and cost of the unit.

In general there are two types of superheaters, radiant and convection. The former receives heat principally by radiant and the latter principally by convection heat transfer. In a radiant-type superheater the steam temperature decreases with increased steam output, since the quantity of heat absorbed by radiation does not increase in the same proportion as the steam flow. Conversely, in most convection-type superheaters the steam temperature generally increases with load, since the heat absorption of the superheater by convection increases at a faster rate than the steam output (see Fig. 18). However, in some highly rated boilers with superheaters normally considered to be convection type, the steam temperature decreases at high ratings.

In marine practice most superheaters are of the convection type, and the heating surface usually consists of "hairpin" or U-shaped tubes connecting the headers. With this arrangement the superheater can be vented, drained, and easily cleaned by mechanical means. Complete draining and venting, however, are possible only when the vessel is on an even keel.

It is customary to select an appropriate number of steam passes in keeping with a reasonable pressure drop. This assures reasonable tube temperatures and proper steam distribution through the superheater. The steam passes in the superheater are generally separated by diaphragms located in the headers. Since there are thermal stresses if the temperature difference across the diaphragm exceeds about 175 F, it is advisable to use separate headers. When separate headers are used for this purpose, there are somewhat wider lanes in the tube bank, where the headers meet end to end, through which the gas mass flow will be higher than across other sections of the superheater bank. With this arrangement, the temperatures of the tubes adjacent to the lane may be excessive on the gas entrance side of the bank. To alleviate this condition the lane should be, if possible, on the back side of the superheater in a zone of lower gas temperatures. If, however, the lane must be located in a zone of hot gas, it is usually necessary to provide crossover tubes connecting adjacent headers. Since the path of travel is shorter, the steam flow through the crossover tubes is increased. Consequently, the steam film transfer rate in these tubes is higher, and they are, therefore, maintained at a cooler temperature than would otherwise be possible.

It is the intention of all boiler manufacturers to eliminate by design, so far as possible, all gas and steam maldistribution (or "upset," as it is called) in the superheater. However, with various fuels and operating demands it is almost impossible to maintain in practice the conditions for perfect dis-

U. S. S. ANDERSON, DESTROYER

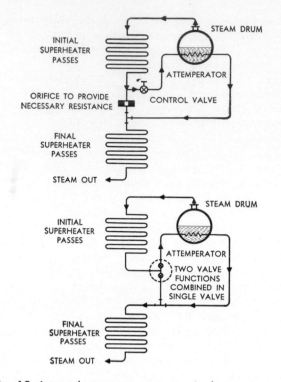

INITIAL
SUPERHEATER
PASSES

STEAM DRUM

ATTEMPERATOR

ORIFICE TO PROVIDE
NECESSARY RESISTANCE

CONTROL VALVE

FINAL
SUPERHEATER
PASSES

STEAM OUT

INITIAL
SUPERHEATER
PASSES

STEAM DRUM

ATTEMPERATOR

TWO VALVE
FUNCTIONS
COMBINED IN
SINGLE VALVE

FINAL
SUPERHEATER
PASSES

STEAM OUT

Fig. 19. *Internal attemperators—typical arrangements*

tribution. It is therefore good practice, when calculating steam and tube temperatures, to assume a maldistribution of 20 per cent for gas and 15 per cent for steam. With this assumption, the highest steam and tube-metal temperatures will occur in a tube having 92.5 per cent of the average steam flow and receiving 110 per cent of the average gas flow.

For merchant boilers it is usual practice to expand the tubes into the headers of a superheater when the steam temperatures are not in excess of 800 F. For steam temperatures above 800 F, the superheater tubes are usually expanded into the headers and then seal welded. For naval vessels, the tubes are usually expanded for steam temperatures up to 850 F, since it is essential on these vessels to be able to renew superheater tubes quickly and easily.

Where dissimilar metals are used for tubes and headers, the tubes are generally "safe-ended" at the place of manufacture with a short length of tubing, identical with the header material, which is welded to the superheater tubes under closely controlled shop-welding procedures.

In addition to being supported by the headers, superheater tubes are also supported at one or more points by a number of alloy plates, which in turn are fastened to water-cooled tubes acting as supports. These alloy plates or brackets are frequently used under conditions where the metal temperatures are in excess of 1700 F, and the alloys used for this purpose must be selected to withstand considerably higher temperatures, which may result

from maldistribution of gas and steam flows. It is also customary to use alloy plates to protect from the hot gases the exposed steam and water drum surfaces as well as the superheater headers. In many recent designs, the drum protection plates have been eliminated by arranging the boiler tubes in the zone of the superheater to enter the drums at a spacing close enough to assure adequate cooling of the tube sheet. This method of protection is of special value when high pressures, which require thick tube sheets, are used, since failure of a drum protection plate could cause high thermal stresses in the drum.

In drum-type boilers the superheater headers are located either at the front or rear of the boiler, depending upon superheater design and space available for tube renewal. In header-type boilers the superheater headers are generally installed at the boiler side, and the aisle between the boilers should be large enough to permit tube renewal.

Slagging

In recent years superheater slagging, a serious problem in some installations, has become a matter of increasing concern to the designer and operator, and much attention has been devoted to finding a satisfactory remedy. Superheater slagging, it is believed, is caused mainly by burning fuel oil with an ash content high in sodium plus sulfur or vanadium in boilers which have a combination of high gas and heat-receiving-surface temperatures. The presence of salt water in the fuel oil aggravates this condition. Experience supports the validity of this theory of high gas and surface temperatures, since considerable slag forms in the front portion of the superheater where the temperatures of the gas and heat-receiving surface are both high, and less slag forms in the rear portion where the gas temperatures are much lower, although the receiving surface temperatures are practically unchanged.

In boilers of high rating operating at full power, the gas temperature entering the saturated-tube screen ahead of the superheater may be nearly 500 F higher than the gas temperature entering the superheater, and there is no material difference in the gas velocities in either case. The receiving-surface temperatures in the water screen are about 400 F lower than the receiving-surface temperatures in the superheater. The importance of receiving-surface temperatures as well as gas temperature is apparent, since very little slag forms in the water screen of these boilers, whereas the superheaters are heavily slagged.

To reduce boiler size and weight, it has long been the custom in oil-fired units to use the minimum practical spacing for boiler and superheater tubes. To obtain the maximum rate of heat transfer, it has also been common practice to use a staggered tube arrangement. Consequently, with increased firing and evaporative ratings and deterioration of fuel oil quality, the accumulation of slag, particularly in the superheater, has become a major problem of design and maintenance. While some slag accumulations can be removed by soot blowing and manual cleaning of external surface, lack of time makes such cleaning practically impossible in many services. Slagging of superheaters and the time required for external cleaning have been reduced by the development of designs to permit relocation to lower the entering gas temperature, by the use of "in-line" in place of "staggered" tube arrangement and by increased spacing of tubes. Also, to facilitate manual cleaning and washing, the superheater should be designed to permit ready access to the portion where slag accumulates. In this way maintenance and outages are reduced.

Control of Temperatures

The arrangement of the superheater, the depth of the saturated screen ahead of the superheater, and the rating of the boiler affect the steam temperature. For high-rating units with shallow screens, steam temperatures have a tendency to remain relatively constant over a wide range of operation. With the ratings common in merchant service, however, the steam temperature generally increases with boiler rating, and it is often desirable to provide some means of temperature control.

This can be done in several ways. Limited control of steam temperature is possible by varying the position of the superheater in relation to the burner flame center. For instance, in many single-pass header-type boilers the superheater tubes do not extend along the entire boiler depth, thus leaving a gas cavity at the front of the superheater. With this arrangement a portion of the gases entering the cavity can be made to by-pass the superheater by retracting the burners, and the steam temperature is lowered. The steam temperature may also be reduced by using wide-angle sprayer plates, which give a broader and shorter flame. Proximity of the burner to the saturated screen also has a definite effect on steam temperature. In drum-type boilers having two rows of burners, 40 F higher steam temperature has been obtained by using the row adjacent to the screen instead of the other row of burners, other conditions remaining the same.

Steam temperature may also be controlled by allowing a portion of the saturated steam to by-pass the superheater or by the use of dampers to regulate the gas flow across the superheater. These methods, however, are seldom used. The by-passed steam is not readily utilized. If too much steam is by-passed, superheater failure may occur because of excessive steam and tube-metal temperatures, especially during maneuvering. With the damper arrangement there is always a possibility of warpage and breakdown. Further, the size of the boiler is increased, and there is usually a greater draft loss through the unit.

Attemperators of both internal and external types are very effective in the control of steam temperature. Internal types are generally installed in the steam or water drums, and the boiler water is used as the coolant (see Fig. 19). In the external types (spray attemperators) good quality feedwater (not more than 2 ppm total solids), in direct contact with the steam, is used as the coolant. Both types are usually installed between steam passes rather than at the superheater outlet, in order to reduce the tube-metal temperature in the last steam pass of the superheater and thus permit the use of less-costly alloys. With this method of steam temperature control, the over-all steam pressure drop will increase, the superheater surface must be increased,

S. S. Cimarron, Tanker

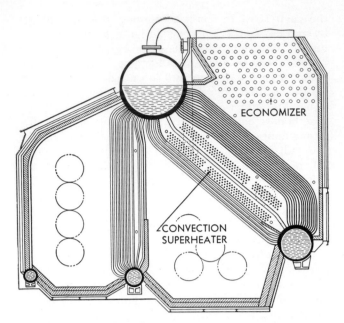

Fig. 20. *Controlled-superheat marine boiler with superheater located in uptake tube bank*

and additional valves, piping, and fittings will be required.

Where large steam capacities are required, it is generally simpler and more economical to control steam temperature by the use of two-furnace boilers. The steam temperature is controlled by varying the quantity and temperature of the gas flowing across the superheater by adjustment of the amount of oil fired in each furnace. Two designs are in general

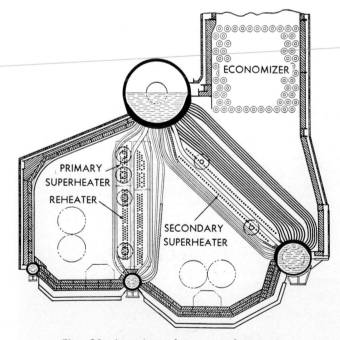

Fig. 21. *Location of steam reheater in two-furnace single-uptake marine boiler*

use, the single- and the double-uptake types of two-furnace boilers. Although both permit a close control of steam temperature over a wide operating range, the two-furnace single-uptake boiler is by far the more widely used. This is primarily because of the reduced number of uptakes in the fireroom, permitting a simpler and more convenient system of ducts through the decks above. At present over 90 per cent of the Navy's major fighting ships are powered by B&W boilers of the two-furnace single-uptake design. In two-furnace single-uptake boilers, convection superheaters may be installed either in the bank of tubes separating the furnace, as in Fig. 9, or in the uptake boiler tube bank, as in Fig. 20.

Reheaters

In spite of the increased cycle efficiencies possible with reheated steam, reheaters are seldom used in marine boilers, since the advantages are usually more than offset by the increase in boiler size and weight and the added complexity of the operation.

To maintain a high cycle efficiency it is necessary to design reheaters with a low steam pressure drop. Therefore particular attention must be given to steam distribution and tube temperatures. Since a low steam pressure drop adversely affects steam distribution and tends to cause excessive tube-metal temperatures, a careful balance must be established between the desired efficiency and the steam pressure drop.

For reheaters, either steam or gas may be used as the heating medium. When steam is the heating medium, the maximum reheat temperature is usually limited to 550–600 F, since condensing steam is generally used because of its higher heat transfer characteristics. When gas is used as the heating medium, higher steam reheat temperatures can be obtained, and the cycle efficiencies are correspondingly higher. In a two-furnace design that includes a gas reheater, the reheater is usually installed in the setting with the boiler tube bank and the superheater. One arrangement is shown in Fig. 21. Separately fired gas reheaters have been built, but they have not been used extensively because of the additional space required for installation.

Air Heaters and Economizers

Air heaters or economizers, and in some instances both, are necessary for high boiler efficiency, and the initial and maintenance costs are usually economically justified. Whether either or both are used will depend upon the design of the power plant and the required performance characteristics.

The temperature of the feedwater to most marine economizers ranges between 220 and 250 F, and low-pressure (10 to 15 psi) exhaust steam is used for feed heating. With these inlet water temperatures, economizers can be economically designed to give uptake gas temperatures of about 300 F, corresponding to 88 per cent efficiency at normal rating.

If the feedwater temperatures to the economizer are high, the maximum efficiency is limited, since the gas temperature leaving the economizer cannot be lower than the inlet feedwater temperature. Consequently, if through regenerative feed heating (turbine bleeding) the inlet feedwater reaches temperatures of 300 to 450 F, it would generally not be economical to use an economizer unless it was followed by an air heater.

Plant efficiency can be increased about 1 per cent for each 100 F rise in feedwater temperature by regenerative feed heating. The attractiveness of the air heater stems in large measure from the additional plant efficiency contributed by it, when using feedwater raised to 300 to 450 F by regenerative feed heating. At normal operating rates, inlet air temperatures of 80 to 100 F, exit air temperatures of 300 to 450 F, and exit gas temperatures of 300 to 350 F are common and are required to obtain a boiler efficiency of 88 to 87 per cent.

Air Heaters

The use of air heaters and regenerative feed heating results in high plant efficiency and over-all economy. Since the air heater, unlike the economizer, is not a pressure vessel, it can be relatively simple in design. An important additional advantage is the improvement in furnace combustion with preheated air, particularly at both the high and low rates of firing. This will reduce soot accumulation and lessen the likelihood of ignition loss.

For marine service, air heaters are almost always of the tubular type; the plate and regenerative types (see Chapter 11) are seldom used. Tubular air heaters in marine service are generally of the horizontal type, so designated from the position of the longitudinal axis of the tubes. The vertical type (tubes in vertical position), although used, is not too well suited to marine service because of large surface and space (height) requirements. In the horizontal type (to avoid lodgment of deposits inside the tubes), the air to be heated passes through the inside of the tubes, and the hot gases pass over the outside of the tubes; the reverse is true of the vertical type.

The tube arrangement is usually in line, which makes external cleaning easier. This more than offsets the slight advantage in heat transfer with staggered tubes. Obviously, increased air pressure must be provided when an air heater is installed, to overcome the additional resistance to air flow through the air heater, air ducts, and oil burners. For boilers of the same size, operating at similar firing rates, a higher total air pressure will usually be needed for an air heater installation than for an economizer installation, and where both an economizer and an air heater are installed, air pressure requirements are still higher.

Air heater tubes are generally 1½-in. to 2½-in. OD, and the 1½-in. tubes are used in most installations. Tube diameters must be selected with due consideration for both draft loss and heat absorption. To reduce internal flow resistance, which for the same mass flow varies inversely as the ID, the larger tubes should be used. Conversely, to provide the greatest surface in the limited space available, small tubes should be used. Furthermore, at any given gas mass flow the heat transfer rate will increase as the tube diameter is reduced, since the heat transfer rates

U. S. S. ATLANTA, CRUISER

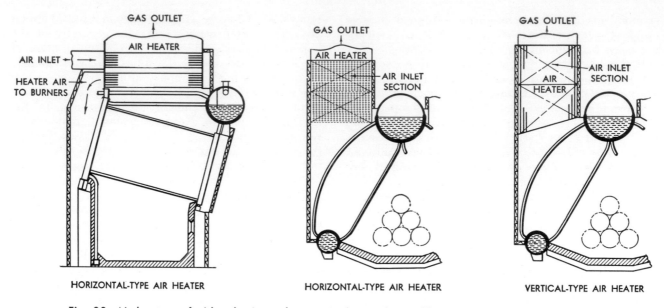

HORIZONTAL-TYPE AIR HEATER   HORIZONTAL-TYPE AIR HEATER   VERTICAL-TYPE AIR HEATER

Fig. 22. *Air heaters of either horizontal or vertical type fit readily into marine boiler contours*

of the gases flowing across and through the tubes, respectively, vary inversely as about the 0.39 and 0.20 powers of the tube diameter. To obtain maximum heat absorption with minimum fan horsepower, the effect of tube size and spacing must be carefully analyzed.

The temperatures of the inlet air to the air heater range from 80 to 100 F, and, at normal operating rates, the exit air temperatures range from 300 to 350 F. Any variation in the inlet air temperature will affect air pressure, efficiency, and external tube corrosion and, therefore, must be considered in the design. Exit gas temperatures leaving the air heater are generally reduced to 300 to 350 F, required for boiler efficiencies of 88 to 87 per cent, respectively. Because of the lesser weight and the lower specific heat of the air as compared with the products of combustion, the reduction in the temperature of the hot gases passing through the air heater, when using 15 per cent excess air and firing oil, is about 13 per cent less than the difference between the exit and inlet air temperatures.

For the same heat absorption, since the heat

transfer coefficients of the gas and air films on their respective sides of the tube are of the same magnitude and relatively quite low, air heaters require more heating surface than boilers, economizers, or superheaters. In an air heater tube the heat must traverse an air as well as a gas film, while in a boiler, economizer, or superheater tube the heat, after traversing the gas film, traverses a water or steam film which has a much higher transfer coefficient than the air film of the air heater.

Air heaters usually fit easily into the contour of marine boilers. In the single-pass header-type boiler, an air heater with two air passes and one gas pass is usually installed with both air inlet and outlet at the rear of the boiler (see Fig. 22). The hot air flows through a duct down the rear of the boiler and then under the furnace floor into the burner double front. For drum-type boilers a similar arrangement can be used, but it is preferable to discharge the air at the front of the air heater and to utilize the insulated double front (usually fitted) as a hot-air duct. Where the boiler is double cased and insulated on all sides, the air flow from the air heater may be through the rear or the front to meet the preference of the customer.

Corrosion in the zone of low tube-metal temperature is of primary concern in the design and operation of air heaters. Much effort has been devoted to the development of practical means to overcome this difficulty, and experience indicates that the best preventive is to design the air heater so that dangerously low tube-metal temperatures cannot occur at any stage throughout the entire range of operation.

The tube-metal temperature at any point in an air heater is approximately equal to the average

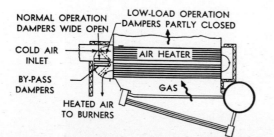

Fig. 23. *Air inlet by-pass dampers arranged for control of air heater tube-metal temperature*

of the adjacent gas and air temperatures, since the gas and air heat transfer rates are about equal. In a counterflow air heater the lowest tube-metal temperatures occur in the air inlet and gas exit zone, where both the air and the gas are at their lowest temperatures. When operating with inlet air of 100 F and uptake gas temperatures of 300 to 350 F, the tube-metal temperature in the coolest zone will be about 200 to 225 F. Under normal conditions, when firing fuel oil of low sulfur content, the dewpoint of the products of combustion will be about 50 F below the tube-metal temperatures in the coolest zone. This margin of safety, however, may be lost if the inlet air temperature or the evaporative rating decreases, allowing the tube-metal temperatures to fall below the dewpoint. Under such conditions sulfur corrosion will take place. Also, as recent observations indicate, the dewpoint may be increased appreciably by constituents such as vanadium and sodium compounds, in addition to sulfur, in some fuel oils and by possible catalytic action as the products of combustion pass across the superheater tubes. Dewpoints up to 100 F have been noted.

Air heater corrosion can be reduced or practically eliminated in several ways:

The air heater tube-metal temperatures can be increased by designing the boiler for higher exit gas temperatures. However, this will reduce boiler efficiency.

By using parallel flow instead of counterflow arrangements, the inlet air enters the air heater in a hotter zone. The tube-metal temperatures will increase, but the over-all mean temperature difference between the air and gas will be lower, thus reducing the heat absorption in the air heater and consequently the boiler efficiency.

Use of air by-pass dampers for tube-temperature control provides a good reserve margin against corrosion, with loss of boiler efficiency only when operating at low load (see Fig. 23). By operating the dampers so that part of the combustion air by-passes the air heater during lighting-off and low-load operation, the tube temperatures will approach the surrounding gas temperature.

The tube-metal temperatures may be increased by recirculating a part of the exit (hot) air through the entering air pass to raise the inlet air temperature. The loss in efficiency is negligible, but some increase in air pressure (fan power) is required.

The temperature of the inlet air may also be increased by installing steam air heaters. By this method the heat balance may be improved, especially if exhaust steam is used for heating. A fleet of 28,000-ton tankers equipped with this arrangement has been particularly economical in operation.

To reduce or eliminate tube corrosion, some consideration has been given to the use of steel alloys for air heater tubes, but the possible advantages are usually offset by the additional cost.

The life of the air heater can be lengthened considerably by the use of thicker-wall tubes, if the conditions affecting corrosion cannot be corrected.

If soot is allowed to accumulate on air heater surface, there is some danger of fire. Experience proves, however, that soot fires in air heaters are caused by maloperation. No such fires will occur if proper operating procedures are followed. Thorough investigations indicate that air heater soot fires have occurred almost without exception while lighting

S. S. Leon Fraser, Ore Carrier, Great Lakes

off, operating in port at low rating or in bringing up the rating after extended periods of port operation, and, in most cases, under intermittent firing of the burners with insufficient air for combustion.

Economizers

Two general classes of economizers, the bare-tube and the extended-surface types, are used for marine service. Both are nonsteaming and are usually arranged for counterflow of the water and the gases to obtain a higher mean temperature difference and consequently greater heat absorption. In using counterflow the maximum possible efficiency is greater, since the exit gas temperature can approach the inlet water temperature.

The bare-tube economizer is usually made of ½-in. to 2-in. tubes arranged in hairpin loops or continuous loops. In the hairpin type, single or multiple rows of U-bent tubes are welded or expanded into two or more headers. In the continuous-loop type, the number of tube joints is greatly reduced, since several runs of straight tubing are connected by a series of U bends and only two headers are required.

Concentration of heating surface, comparatively few tube joints, and the use of only two main headers are the distinctive features of all the many types of extended-surface economizers. The most common of the various types have: (a) circumferential fins of aluminum, steel, or cast iron; (b) vertical longitudinal fins of steel; (c) oval-shaped studs; or (d) a combination of vertical longitudinal steel fins and oval-shaped studs.

To establish the economizer size, knowing the anticipated resistance to the flow of water and gas, an approximate tube length is selected, and then the number of elements in width is estimated from experience. The required heat absorption can be calculated from the temperature of the gas entering the economizer and the specified or assigned gas temperature at the outlet. Having established the tentative length and width of the economizer, it is possible to determine the gas mass flow rate and thus the heat transfer rate. The amount of heating surface required can then be established by dividing the necessary heat absorption by the product of the heat transfer rate and the log mean temperature difference between the gas and water temperatures. The over-all dimensions of the economizer may be readjusted as necessary to give an acceptable resistance to flow of gas and water and to satisfy space limitations.

Heat absorption and resistance to flow are true measures of economizer performance. The amount of heating surface is not a true measure of economizer performance, since, for an equal amount of heating surface, heat absorption will vary considerably be-cause of the many different types and arrangements of surfaces. The desired increase in the temperature of the feedwater, rather than the amount of heating surface, should be the controlling factor in the specifications. For the same heat absorption and resistance to flow, certain fin-tube types require twice the amount of heating surface needed for a bare-tube economizer of small-diameter tubes. This is because of (a) the increase in heat transfer rate, at a given mass flow, with decrease in tube diameter, and (b) reduced heat absorption and high resistance to heat flow of the fin-tube type caused, respectively, by the high tip temperatures of the extended surface and the contact between this surface and the tube. However, since the surface is concentrated, the space required for the extended-surface type will not be greater, and it will in many instances be even less, than that required for the bare-tube economizer.

The arrangement of the economizer has a very considerable effect on the resistance to gas or water flow. Varying the width of the economizer will change the resistance to gas flow. Since heating surface varies directly with width and the gas heat transfer rate in crossflow varies as the 0.61 power of the gas mass flow rate, the height must be rechecked if the width is changed. The height can usually be reduced if the width is increased. To prevent recirculation, the water pressure drop at about 25 per cent of normal operating rate should be equal to, or greater than, the static water head when the economizer is arranged for downflow water and upflow gas. Multiple water passes are often used in hairpin-type economizers to obtain satisfactory water velocities and pressure drops. In this arrangement calculation of heat transfer is based on average flow, since the water and the gas have both counter- and parallel-flow relations. A single water pass counterflow to the gas is used in most continuous-loop and extended-surface economizers.

Limiting the temperature of the feedwater entering the economizer to a minimum of 220 F will prevent, or greatly reduce, internal oxygen corrosion, since this temperature is sufficiently high for deaeration of the water; nor should external corrosion of tube metal occur when burning low-sulfur bunker C fuel oil, because this temperature is usually about 50 F above the dewpoint of the products of combustion with this fuel. For meeting conditions when burning less favorable fuel oils with high content of sulfur, vanadium, and sodium compounds, see above.

To prevent steaming, water hammer, and thermal shock, the temperature of the exit water from the economizer should be maintained at not less than 75 F below the saturated steam temperature, especially when operating at overload rating or during maneuvering. Economizers arranged for parallel flow or a combination of parallel flow and counterflow must be used if the exit temperature is to approach the saturation temperature. A parallel-flow section at the outlet end is also required for steaming economizers. The steaming economizer, however, is seldom used in marine service because of size limitations and the difficulty in effectively arranging the necessary heating surface.

Economizers are generally designed to reduce gas temperatures by 200 to 300 F. Since, for oil-fired boilers, the rise in temperature of the water in passing through the economizer is about ⅓ of the drop in temperature of the gas passing across the economizer, the rise in the temperature of the water varies between 70 and 100 F. If the inlet water temperature is 240 F, the exit water temperatures will, therefore, range from 310 to 340 F, which is more than 100 F lower than saturation temperature corresponding to a pressure of 450 psi.

The tube-metal temperature in bare-tube economizers is assumed to be the same as the temperature of the water within the tube, since the temperature drop across the tube wall is small. This is also true for the tube metal of the extended-surface elements in economizers, but the tip temperatures of the elements are considerably higher.

If practicable, economizers should be located entirely below the normal water level in the steam drum. Where it is necessary to place the economizer above the level of the water in the steam drum, as is often the case, a loop should be provided in the piping between the economizer and the drum,

with the highest point of the loop above the economizer to make certain that it is filled with water when starting the boiler.

Since the resistance to gas flow through the economizer is usually quite high compared with that of other components, it is customary, when an economizer is to be installed, to fit a complete air casing or a combination of air casing and a single welded casing around the boiler unit. Since it is usually necessary, after reaching steaming pressure, to tighten or take up on the fittings of the economizer headers, easy access should be provided to the headers through closed vestibules subject to the full static air pressure but with limited air flow, so that, in opening the doors in the vestibules while the boiler is in service, only a small amount of combustion air will be lost.

To prevent loss of steam pressure should the economizer be inoperative, a check valve is often fitted in the piping connecting the economizer and the steam drum. Since a head of several feet of water is usually required to lift the valve, it will also help in filling the economizer, especially if the economizer is located above the normal water level in the drum. Because of the cost and the complicated piping required, a by-pass line, for the express purpose of permitting operation during an outage of the economizer, is seldom fitted.

However, if a by-pass line is fitted for operation of the boiler with the economizer out of service, it will be necessary to fire more fuel to maintain the required evaporative rating (because of decreased

U. S. S. Tranquillity, U. S. Navy Hospital Ship

efficiency), and proportionally more air must be supplied at an increased static pressure. When the economizer is by-passed, more heat is transferred to the steam because of the increase in the ratio of gas to steam weight with the increased gas flow. This increase in steam temperature is of primary importance and requires more attemperation (if an attemperator is provided) or even a reduction in rating to prevent overheating superheater tubes or turbine beyond the allowable contemplated in design.

There should be no danger of metal oxidation in the economizer during by-pass operation, since the gas temperatures entering the economizer are usually less than 900 F.

Rapid fluctuations in water temperature during maneuvering may subject economizers to thermal shocks. The temperature will tend to increase to the steaming point if the water flow is momentarily stopped, and then on the sudden resumption of water flow, as the load increases, the economizer may be subjected to water hammer and high thermal stresses. Consequently, to prevent leakage of joints and fittings, the tubes are usually welded to the headers, and soft sheet gaskets are used in all fittings.

When using economizers, deaeration heaters should be installed to remove all traces of oxygen from the feedwater. If the feedwater contains dissolved oxygen, internal corrosion of tubes and headers may be expected, since oxygen is released within the economizer as heat is applied.

Practically all marine economizers are designed to be "drainable and ventable" and, until recently, "cleanable" both internally and externally by mechanical means. With the successful application in recent years of chemical cleaning for internal surfaces of boilers and superheaters (see Chapter 21), it has been possible to use attractive design features that, however, do not permit mechanical cleaning internally. This simplified design, suitable for chemical cleaning internally, has been applied to marine economizers with gratifying results in reduced cost, size, and maintenance. Continuous-loop economizers, without cleanout fittings and intended for chemical cleaning internally, are now finding some use on shipboard.

Care must be taken to prevent soot fires in economizers by reducing the deposit of soot through correct operating procedure and by providing efficient equipment for removing the soot that does collect. Soot fires in economizers, like those in air heaters, occur almost invariably during or just after lighting-off and during operation in port, when excessive soot deposits are liable to form on the external surfaces because of low and intermittent firing rates and insufficient combustion air. After such operations, any soot deposits in the economizer may easily

ignite when the firing rate or the excess air is increased or torching occurs through the unit.

Efficiency and Air Pressure

Unless conservative ratings are used, high air pressures are generally required for high efficiency. The saying that an increase in efficiency requires an increase in resistance to flow applies only to the design stage of a boiler unit for a given firing rate or steam output. Obviously, if the firing rate of a boiler of any given design is increased, the gas flow rate must also increase. This will, of course, require greater air pressure, but the efficiency will decrease in accordance with its own characteristic curve of efficiency versus output.

Steam Drums—Swash Plates

The steam drums of header-type boilers are usually about 42 in. in diameter. For small-capacity and low-rating boilers of this type, drums 36 in. in diameter or less may be used, but the moisture carry-over, although satisfactory, may be somewhat greater than that obtained from larger-diameter drums. For header-type boilers installed in dredges, drill barges, and vessels fitted with reciprocating engines, where wide fluctuations in load are required and the maintenance of a large water reserve is desirable, steam drums about 48 in. in diameter are frequently used. The usual range of steam drum diameters for drum-type boilers is from 27 to 50 inches. Generally, steam drum diameters in drum-type boilers range from 42 to 48 in. for merchant vessels and from 46 to 50 in. for naval service.

To reduce the effect on circulation of the vessel's roll by damping the motion of the water, swash plates are fitted in the steam drums of header-type boilers, usually located with the longitudinal axes of the drums athwartship. Swash plates are not necessary for drum-type boilers, since the longitudinal axes of the drums are positioned fore and aft.

Circulators, Baffles, Water Walls

After having established the various heating surface arrangements, it is necessary to determine the circulation characteristics of the boiler and the effect on the circulatory system of the type of baffling to be used in the steam drum. In marine boilers the steam drum baffling is usually simple in construction and arrangement.

"Vertical baffles" (see Fig. 24), separating the dry pipe from the discharge of the circulator tubes, are commonly present in most header-type boilers. However, it may be necessary in some designs to slope the baffle or increase the size of the steam drum in order to maintain steam velocities, behind and around the ends of the baffle, below the critical velocity at which steam picks up water.

V-type baffles using single, double, and triple

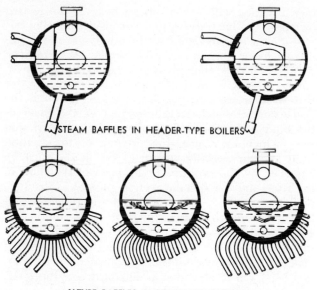

STEAM BAFFLES IN HEADER-TYPE BOILERS

V-TYPE BAFFLES IN DRUM-TYPE BOILERS

Fig. 24. *Simple arrangements of steam drum baffling in header- and drum-type marine boilers*

perforated steel plates, all of similar contour, are generally used in drum-type boilers (see Fig. 24). The single V-plate baffle is used for steam release rates up to about 35 cfm per sq ft of drum water-releasing area. The double and triple V-type plate baffles, with relatively small clearance between the plates, will break up the steam and water jets more effectively than the single V-type plate baffles and are, therefore, used for the higher release rates, ranging between 35 and 80 cfm per sq ft of drum releasing area. The use of cyclone steam separators (see Fig. 25) is recommended for drum-type boilers of high rating and when fluctuating water levels or high solids concentrations are encountered (see also Chapter 9). While the resistance to flow is greater when using cyclone steam separators, the circulation is not impeded, since the circulating head is increased because of the practically "steam-free" water discharge from the cyclone separators as compared with the "frothy" water-steam mixture discharged from plate baffles.

A single horizontal row of 4-in. circulator tubes (Fig. 3) is generally used with header-type boilers. However, for boilers of high capacity or low pressure, 4½-in. circulator tubes or two rows of 4-in. or 4½-in. tubes are sometimes used (Fig. 5) to reduce the steam velocity through the circulators. Single-pass header-type boilers, operating at pressures of 400 to 600 psi and steam and feedwater temperatures of about 750 and 230 F, respectively, can generate about 4,000 lb of steam per boiler section per hr without exceeding the desirable maximum steam velocity through the circulators. As the pressure decreases, the amount of steam generated per boiler section must be reduced because of the rapidly increasing

specific volume of saturated steam, even though the permissible steam velocity through the circulators can be increased. By way of definition, boiler components known as sections are indicated in Fig. 6.

Either inclined tubes (parallel to the boiler tubes, see Fig. 26) or vertical tubes are used in the two most common arrangements of furnace side walls for header-type boilers. In the inclined arrangement all the tubes are of the same length, which facilitates fabrication and replacement and also reduces the number of spares required. In the vertical arrangement the tubes are usually of different lengths, and, unless they can be cut to length and bent to shape on board ship, additional spares must be carried. While the circulating head is usually considerably greater with the vertical arrangement, the number and size of downcomers and risers are not ordinarily reduced.

In header-type boilers with water-cooled furnace side walls, external downcomers and risers are generally used to connect the steam drum with the supply and uptake headers of the side walls, respectively. With this arrangement the circulatory systems of the water walls and the boiler tube banks are separated, and the circulation, especially during rapid changes in load, is improved. For good steam distribution behind the drum baffles, the riser tubes should enter the drum along its length. To provide prompt circulation in the furnace wall tubes when starting-up, the risers should enter the drum at or below water level. However, this is usually not convenient. If there are two rows of circulators and certain risers must enter well above the water level, all of the risers are usually joined to a junction box, from which one or more of the risers discharge into the steam drum at or below water level.

The downcomers for the supply headers of the water walls should enter the steam drum at the lower central zone, so that the variations in the water head caused by fluctuations in water level, rolling,

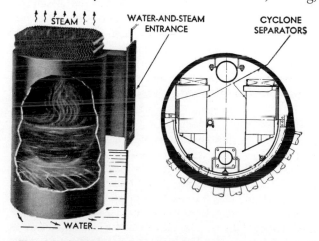

Fig. 25. *Cyclone steam separators—recommended for high-rating drum-type marine boilers*

and pitching of the ship may be minimized. Theoretically, because of the greater volume of the water-steam mixture, the risers should be larger than the downcomers. However, both are made the same size to reduce the number and variety of spare parts and tool sizes carried on board. A satisfactory water-steam ratio must be provided in the wall tubes by the downcomers and risers, and the latter must be properly located to relieve the steam generated.

Vertical tubes are generally used in the rear furnace water walls of header-type boilers. Water is received directly from the steam drum, and the steam-water mixture is discharged into the boiler uptake headers. This is a satisfactory arrangement, since the increased steam loading is distributed among all of the uptake headers of the boiler.

In drum-type boilers, furnace water-wall supply headers receive water from the steam drum through

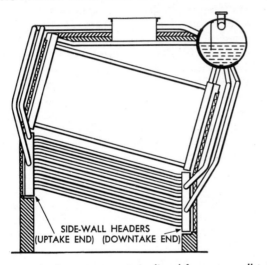

Fig. 26. *Typical arrangement, inclined furnace wall tubes*

external downcomers or from the water drum through horizontal supply tubes located below the furnace floor. Furnace side-wall tubes usually discharge directly into the steam drum, since the tubes are often arranged to form the furnace roof. When furnace front and rear water walls are used, the tubes can either terminate in headers which are connected to the steam drum by a number of riser connections or terminate directly in the steam drum.

Circulation

The circulation characteristics of boiler tube banks and furnace water walls are determined (see below), and, since the ratio of water to steam decreases with increased rating, these characteristics must be established for the intended overload rating.

Each circuit in the circulation system is, in effect, a U tube. The riser section of the U tube will be those tubes in the bank in which steam and water flow upward as heat is applied, while the down-

comer section will be the tubes which are not heated or where the heat absorption is considerably lower.

With the U-tube analogy in mind, the net available head for circulation in the simple system may be determined thus: The pressure exerted on the downcomer side of a vertical plane in the lower water drums or headers by the fluid flowing through the downcomers, which is the product of the head of the fluid and its specific weight minus the friction loss (which in turn is the product of the friction head and the specific weight of the fluid) must be balanced by the product of the head of the fluid in the risers and its specific weight plus the resistance to flow (which is the product of the resistance-to-flow head and the specific weight of the fluid). By equating these two quantities and dividing by 62.4 lb (the weight of one cu ft of water at standard conditions), it is evident that the downcomer friction-loss head (in ft of water at standard conditions) is equal to the product of the head in ft (difference in elevation of top and bottom of U tube) and the difference of the specific gravities of the contents of the downcomers and the risers minus the resistance-to-flow head in the risers (in ft of water at standard conditions). This is the available head, in ft of water at standard conditions, for circulation.

For algebraic treatment and examples, see *Principles of Natural Circulation*, Chapter 9, pp 5-8, inc.

In analyzing circulation it is customary to calculate the steam generated in the riser sections. For various ratios of water to steam, the water-steam flows and the net available heads are then determined. The water-steam mixture flow required to balance the circulatory system is the flow at which the net available head minus the resistance to flow through the steam baffles equals the resistance to downcomer flow.

To prevent overheating of tubes, the percentage of steam by volume in the tops of the risers must be limited to a satisfactory maximum. If it is excessive, the resistance to flow must be reduced by changing the size and contour of the downcomers or by providing additional downcomers. It may also be necessary to redistribute heat absorption and reduce flow resistance by changing the size, contour, and location of the boiler tubes. The allowable percentage of steam by volume at the top of the riser tubes will vary as an inverse function of pressure.

No circulatory system is satisfactory unless sufficient water is supplied for each pound of steam generated. For adequate circulation it is customary to use water-steam ratios ranging from 5 to 10 in some circuits in certain types of service to 15 to 20 in other situations. The purpose of lower ratios for certain kinds of service is to reduce the downcomer requirements, so that boiler size and weight may be less.

Analysis of circulation in header-type boilers is extremely difficult because of the many flow circuits, all with different circulating heads. Therefore most analyses are usually limited to the determination of the maximum steam velocity through the circulator tubes and a comparison of the contemplated design with similar boilers of approximately the same capacity and duty.

Effect of Drum Baffles

Since a flow change in any one circuit affects the flow through, and hence the resistance of, the steam drum baffles, such a change will cause changes in flow in all other circuits. If the flow through a circuit is increased by additional downcomers, the flow through the steam drum baffles will also increase. This imposes a greater resistance in the other flow circuits, decreasing the flow in them. The over-all resistance in the boiler circuits can be reduced by decreasing the resistance in the steam drum baffling beyond the minimum requirements by enlarging the baffles or by installing more cyclone separators. This may be difficult because of space limitations within the steam drum, but, where the design permits a decrease in steam baffle resistance, it will be possible to reduce the downcomer area without a decrease in the water-steam ratio.

Downcomers for Drum-Type Boilers

In drum-type boilers operating at conservative ratings with gas temperatures of about 850 F or less leaving the boiler, the first several rows of tubes will act as risers, and the remaining tubes will serve as heated downcomers. With increased firing rate, the high-temperature gas zone moves deeper into the tube bank, and the number of tubes acting as risers increases, with a corresponding decrease in the number of heated downcomer tubes. Excessive firing rates or rates beyond those contemplated in the design may reduce the number of downcomers below the minimum requirements. Tube failure from such overfiring generally occurs in the zone of transition between riser and downcomer tubes and not in the furnace row tubes as might be expected. For units operating at high rating, the transition zone can be located by design in the lower-temperature gas region, through the use of larger-diameter tubes in the rear bank to act as heated downcomers or by arranging the steam drum baffles to give a definite transition zone. More frequently, for highly rated units it is necessary to install external or internal unheated downcomers, to be sure that the transition zone is back far enough in the low-temperature region. Circulation tends to benefit by interposing a convection superheater in the boiler bank, because of the heat absorbed by the superheater and the resulting reduction in temperature of the gas flowing over the boiler tubes beyond the superheater and at the transition zone. In this way the transition zone is clearly defined, and certain boiler tubes will

act as risers or downcomers over a wide operating range.

External downcomers are required in conservatively rated drum-type boilers only in those parts where the tubes cannot perform this function. A single tube row forming a furnace boundary, a shallow tube bank between two furnaces, or tube banks screening a superheater from two furnaces will require external downcomers. When downcomers are required to maintain adequate circulation in the boiler tube banks, it is customary to locate them externally. Unheated internal downcomers can also be used, but the external location is preferable even though longer boiler drums may be needed for this arrangement. Moreover, unheated internal downcomers usually enter the steam drum at comparatively high levels, and, while their use will keep the drum length at a minimum and tubes can be eliminated in the main boiler bank, they may lose water during heavy rolls or if the water level is low; also the tube bank arrangements are complicated, resistance to gas flow is increased, and boiler heat-absorbing surface is reduced.

When external downcomers are located in the air casings, as is frequently done, they can be finned for heating the combustion air before it enters the oil burners, thus improving combustion.

Review of Boiler Components

After satisfactory circulation characteristics have been developed, the estimated performance of all boiler components is reviewed and correlated, and the design as a whole is tentatively established. It is at this time, while assessing the performance of the various components, that it may be possible to reduce the size and weight of the boiler, to increase reliability and efficiency, and to reduce maintenance by making readjustments. From the various component analyses, having made these changes, it will be possible to develop final design details and to prepare optimum and accurate final performance estimates.

Location of Boilers

Header-type boilers may be installed with the longitudinal axis of the steam drum positioned either fore and aft or athwartship. However, drum-type boilers are almost always installed with the longitudinal axis of the steam drum in a fore-and-aft position. During heavy rolling or pitching, all of the boiler sections in a header-type boiler can be supplied with water, since the common mud drum is connected to all of the downtake headers. Further, the water flow to the furnace tube rows would not be impeded or restricted should a water level be established in the top rows of generating tubes. At certain periods of heavy roll, the boiler tubes of header-type boilers, having the longitudinal axis of the drum in fore-and-aft direction, may be in a horizontal plane or even inclined downward toward the uptake boiler headers. At conservative ratings, however, this condition will not appreciably affect circulation, since inertia will cause the circulation to persist in the direction already established.

Drum-type boilers should not be located with the longitudinal axis of the drums athwartship, since tube failure may result if a water level is established in the side generator tubes during a roll. While this difficulty is alleviated by locating the drums fore and aft, even in this position, when the ship is rolling, water levels may be established in the top ends of rear boiler tubes. In this instance boiler circulation may be affected to some extent, since it is the function of these tubes to act as downcomers. Under conditions of a heavy roll, conservative evaporation ratings should be maintained if possible, even though there is a considerable margin of reserve in the design.

Cooperation of Operator and Designer

The operator of a ship will consider a marine boiler successful if it meets the following conditions: (a) delivers the required amount of steam at the pressures and temperatures desired, when a specified quantity of fuel is fired; (b) is pleasing in appearance and arranged to facilitate operation and upkeep; (c) is efficient in operation and with the capacity and flexibility to satisfy all routine, maneuvering, and emergency demands of service at sea and in port; and (d) has a good record of minimum outage and maintenance. If the boiler meets these requirements, the designer has performed his function well.

To produce the best possible design for each installation, the designer should be free, within the limiting conditions imposed by the intended service, fully to apply the knowledge and accumulated experience of the art. To develop an all-round truly economical boiler unit for any particular installation, the operator's naval architect and the boiler designer should have a complete and mutual understanding

A UNITED STATES NAVY TASK FORCE

of all the problems involved.

Conclusion

Installed in all types of ships, B&W marine boilers have established a reputation for dependability and efficiency. The history of these boilers during the last 75 years reflects sound principles of design and fine workmanship in fabrication. Since the first installation in the *Monroe,* B&W boilers have been installed in more than 4,000 ships of the Navy and the Merchant Marine.

During the first World War, B&W boilers were installed in 50 minesweepers, 100 destroyers, and 500 Shipping Board vessels. In the second World War, B&W boilers were furnished to the Navy for all but two of the battleships; all the cruisers, both heavy and light; all the aircraft carriers, except some of the small escort class; 90 per cent of the destroyers; 33 per cent of the destroyer escorts; and numerous miscellaneous small craft. The Company also manufactured the boilers for 30 per cent of all the merchant vessels, developed the boiler design for all, and fabricated a good proportion of the units installed in the 2,500 Liberty ships that were built.

The record of this vast fleet of ships of all types is history. The high order of operating reliability and economy of the boilers is indicated by the long distances steamed and the long periods in service without overhaul. Boilers manufactured by the Company, backed by a completely integrated organization including design, manufacturing, erection, and service facilities, have made and are making excellent operating records in the Navy and Merchant Marine.

Chapter 2. Sources of Heat Energy — Coal

The following ASTM standards for testing coal, specifications, and definitions of terms are generally used and should be followed in detail to produce comparable results.

ASTM Standards for Testing Coal

D492-48	Sampling Coals Classed According to Ash Content
D271-48	Laboratory Sampling and Analysis of Coal and Coke
D197-30	Sampling and Fineness Test of Powdered Coal
D409-51	Test for Grindability of Coal by the Hardgrove Machine Method
D440-49	Drop Shatter Test for Coal
D441-45	Tumbler Test for Coal
D410-38	Test for Screen Analysis of Coal
D431-44	Designating the Size of Coal from its Screen Analysis
D310-34	Test for Size of Anthracite
D311-30	Test for Sieve Analysis of Crushed Bituminous Coal
D291-29	Test for Cubic Foot Weight of Crushed Bituminous Coal
D547-41	Test for Index of Dustiness of Coal and Coke
D720-46	Test for Free-Swelling Index of Coal Test for Agglutinating Value of Coal (Proposed Draft)
D980-48T	Sampling and Analysis of Coal for Volatile Matter in Connection with Smoke Ordinances

Specifications

D388-38	Classification of Coals by Rank
D389-37	Classification of Coals by Grade
D166-24	Gas and Coking Coals
E11-39	Sieves for Testing Purposes (Wire Cloth Sieves, Round-hole and Square-hole Screens or Sieves)

Definitions of Terms

D121-30	Terms Relating to Coal and Coke
D407-44	Terms Gross Calorific Value and Net Calorific Value of Fuels
D493-39	Commercial Varieties of Bituminous and Subbituminous Coals

Chapter 3. Sources of Heat Energy — Other than Coal

Analyses of Natural Gas from United States Fields

Column No.*		1	2	3	4	5
Analyses						
Constituents, % by vol						
H_2	Hydrogen	—	—	1.82	—	—
CH_4	Methane	83.40	84.00	93.33	90.00	84.10
C_2H_4	Ethylene	—	—	0.25	—	—
C_2H_6	Ethane	15.80	14.80	—	5.00	6.70
CO	Carbon monoxid.	—	—	0.45	—	—
CO_2	Carbon dioxide	—	0.70	0.22	—	0.80
N_2	Nitrogen	0.80	0.50	3.40	5.00	8.40
O_2	Oxygen	—	—	0.35	—	—
H_2S	Hydrogen sulfide	—	—	0.18	—	—
Ultimate, % wt						
S	Sulfur	—	—	0.34	—	—
H_2	Hydrogen	23.53	23.30	23.20	22.68	20.85
C	Carbon	75.25	74.72	69.12	69.26	64.84
N_2	Nitrogen	1.22	0.76	5.76	8.06	12.90
O_2	Oxygen	—	1.22	1.58	—	1.41
Specific gravity (rel to air)		0.636	0.636	0.567	0.600	0.630
Higher heat value						
Btu/cu ft @ 60 F & 30 in. Hg		1,129	1,116	964	1,002	974
Btu/lb of fuel		23,170	22,904	22,077	21,824	20,160

*Col No.	Source of Gas
1	Pennsylvania
2	So. California
3	Ohio
4	Louisiana
5	Oklahoma

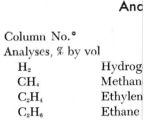

Fig. 2. Enthalpy o

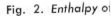
Fig.

And

Column No.°
Analyses, % by vol
H₂ .... Hydrog
CH₄ .... Methan
C₂H₄ ...... Ethylen
C₂H₆ ...... Ethane
CO .... Carbon
CO₂ .... Carbon
N₂ .... Nitroge
O₂ .... Oxygen
C₆H₆ ...... Benzen
H₂O .... Water

Specific gravity (rel to a

Higher heat value
Btu/cu ft, gross @ 60
Btu/cu ft, sat. @ 80 F

Detailed Requirements for Fuel Oils[a]

Commercial Standard, CS12—48, U.S. Dept. of Commerce

Grade of fuel oil b (No.)°	1c	2	4	5	6
Flash point (min), F	100 or legal	100 or legal	130 or legal	130 or legal	150 or legal
Pour point (max), F	0	20d	20	—	—
Water and sediment (max), %	trace	0.10	0.50	1.00	2.00 f
Carbon residue on 10 % residuum (max), %	0.15	0.35	—	—	—
Ash (max), %	—	—	0.10	0.10	—
Distillation temp (max), F					
10% point	420	e	—	—	—
90% point	—	675	—	—	—
End point	625	—	—	—	—
Viscosity					
Saybolt					
Universal @ 100 F (max)	—	40	125	—	—
Universal @ 100 F (min)	—	—	45	150	—
Furol @ 122 F (max)	—	—	—	40	300
Furol @ 122 F (min)	—	—	—	—	45
Kinematic centistokes					
At 100 F (max)	2.2	(4.3)	(26.4)	—	—
At 100 F (min)	1.4	—	(5.8)	(32.1)	—
At 122 F (max)	—	—	—	(81)	(638)
At 122 F (min)	—	—	—	—	(92)
Gravity, deg API (min)	35	26	—	—	—

°Grade of Fuel Oil

No. 1. Distillate oil intended for vaporizing pot-type burners requiring this grade.

No. 2. Distillate oil for general-purpose domestic heating for use in burners not requiring No. 1.

No. 4. Oil for burner installations not equipped with preheating facilities.

No. 5. Residual-type oil for burner installations equipped with preheating facilities.

No. 6. Oil for use in burners equipped with preheaters permitting a high-viscosity oil.

Notes
(See reference to these notes in Table)

a. Recognizing the necessity for low-sulfur fuel oils used in connection with heat-treatment, nonferrous-metal, glass, and ceramic furnaces, and other special uses, a sulfur requirement may be specified in accordance with the following table:

Grade of fuel oil	Sulfur, max, %
No. 1	0.5
No. 2	1.0
Nos. 4, 5, and 6	No limit

Other sulfur limits may be specified only by mutual agreement between buyer and seller.

b. It is the intent of these classifications that failure to meet any requirement of a given grade does not automatically place an oil in the next lower grade unless in fact it meets all requirements of the lower grade.

c. Number 1 oil shall be tested for corrosion in accordance with Par. 15 for 3 hours at 122 F. The exposed copper strip shall show no gray or black deposit.

d. Lower or higher pour points may be specified whenever required by conditions of storage or use. However, these specifications shall not require a pour point lower than zero F under any conditions.

e. The 10% point may be specified at 440 F. Maximum for use in other than atomizing burners.

f. The amount of water by distillation plus the sediment by extraction shall not exceed 2.00%. The amount of sediment by extraction shall not exceed 0.50%. A deduction in quantity shall be made for all water and sediment in excess of 1.00%.

Column No.°
Analyses (Dry
 Proximate
  Volatile m
  Fixed carb
  Ash
 Ultimate
  H₂   H
  C   C
  S   S
  N₂+O₂   N
  A   A
Heating value,
Ash analysis, %
  Silica
  Iron
  Titanium
  Aluminum
  Manganes
  Calcium
  Magnesiu
  Alkalies
  Sulfate
  Chloride
  Carbonate
  Undeterm

Ash-fusion tem

°Col No.
  1   S
  2   C
  3   V
  4   V
  5   S
  6   F

Chapte

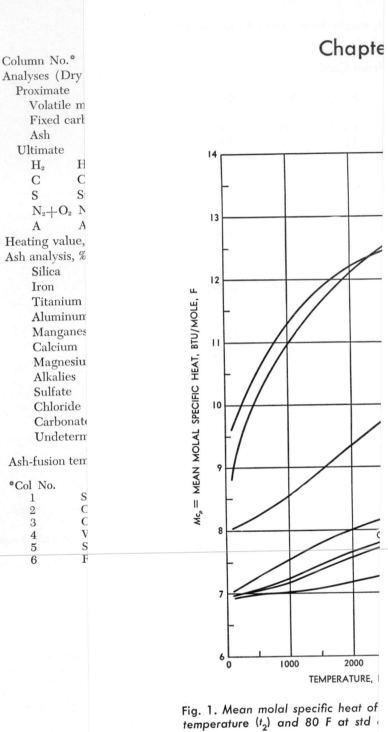

Fig. 1. Mean molal specific heat of
temperature (t_2) and 80 F at std

Mc_p = MEAN MOLAL SPECIFIC HEAT, BTU/MOLE, F

TEMPERATURE,

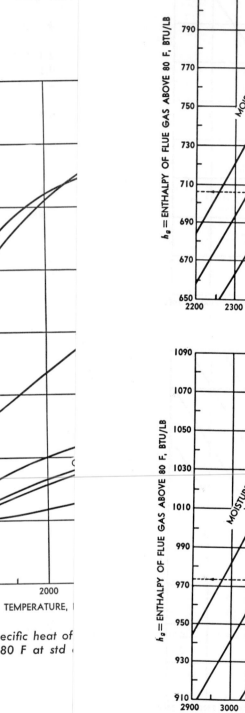

h_g = ENTHALPY OF FLUE GAS ABOVE 80 F, BTU/LB

MOISTURE, % BY WT

FLUE GAS

Fig. 2

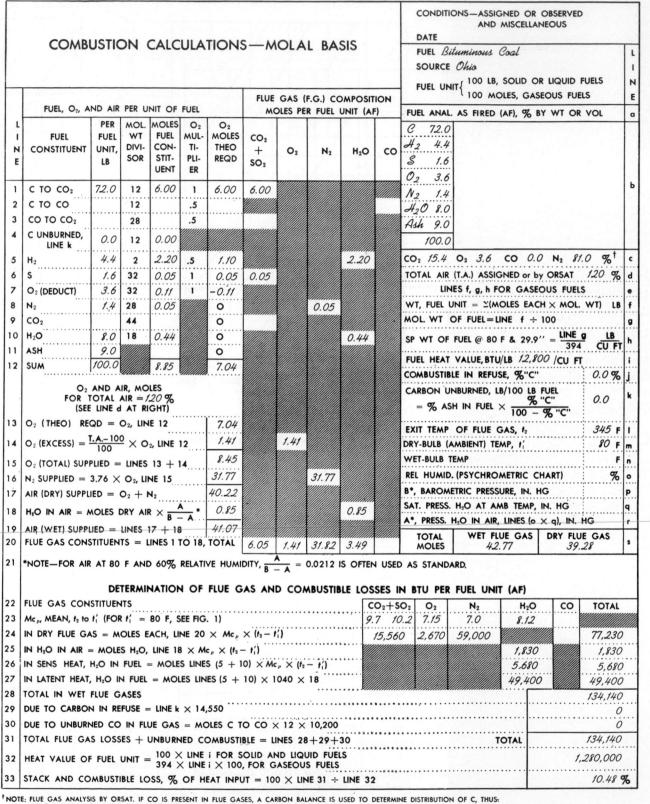

COMBUSTION CALCULATIONS—MOLAL BASIS

CONDITIONS—ASSIGNED OR OBSERVED AND MISCELLANEOUS

DATE
FUEL *Bituminous Coal*
SOURCE *Ohio*
FUEL UNIT { 100 LB, SOLID OR LIQUID FUELS / 100 MOLES, GASEOUS FUELS

LINE	FUEL CONSTITUENT	PER FUEL UNIT, LB	MOL. WT DIVISOR	MOLES FUEL CONSTITUENT	O₂ MULTIPLIER	O₂ MOLES THEO REQD	CO₂+SO₂	O₂	N₂	H₂O	CO
1	C TO CO₂	72.0	12	6.00	1	6.00	6.00				
2	C TO CO		12		.5						
3	CO TO CO₂		28		.5						
4	C UNBURNED, LINE k	0.0	12	0.00							
5	H₂	4.4	2	2.20	.5	1.10				2.20	
6	S	1.6	32	0.05	1	0.05	0.05				
7	O₂ (DEDUCT)	3.6	32	0.11	1	−0.11					
8	N₂	1.4	28	0.05		0			0.05		
9	CO₂		44			0					
10	H₂O	8.0	18	0.44		0				0.44	
11	ASH	9.0				0					
12	SUM	100.0		8.85		7.04					

O₂ AND AIR, MOLES FOR TOTAL AIR = 120% (SEE LINE d AT RIGHT)

LINE				
13	O₂ (THEO) REQD = O₂, LINE 12	7.04		
14	O₂ (EXCESS) = $\frac{T.A.-100}{100}$ × O₂, LINE 12	1.41	(O₂) 1.41	
15	O₂ (TOTAL) SUPPLIED = LINES 13 + 14	8.45		
16	N₂ SUPPLIED = 3.76 × O₂, LINE 15	31.77	(N₂) 31.77	
17	AIR (DRY) SUPPLIED = O₂ + N₂	40.22		
18	H₂O IN AIR = MOLES DRY AIR × $\frac{A}{B-A}$*	0.85	(H₂O) 0.85	
19	AIR (WET) SUPPLIED = LINES 17 + 18	41.07		
20	FLUE GAS CONSTITUENTS = LINES 1 TO 18, TOTAL	CO₂+SO₂ 6.05	O₂ 1.41	N₂ 31.82	H₂O 3.49

TOTAL MOLES — WET FLUE GAS 42.77 — DRY FLUE GAS 39.28

21 *NOTE—FOR AIR AT 80 F AND 60% RELATIVE HUMIDITY, $\frac{A}{B-A}$ = 0.0212 IS OFTEN USED AS STANDARD.

Right-hand conditions column (lines a–s):

Line	
a	FUEL ANAL. AS FIRED (AF), % BY WT OR VOL
b	C 72.0 / H₂ 4.4 / S 1.6 / O₂ 3.6 / N₂ 1.4 / H₂O 8.0 / Ash 9.0 / 100.0
c	CO₂ 15.4 O₂ 3.6 CO 0.0 N₂ 81.0 %†
d	TOTAL AIR (T.A.) ASSIGNED or by ORSAT 120 %
	LINES f, g, h FOR GASEOUS FUELS
e	WT, FUEL UNIT = Σ(MOLES EACH × MOL. WT) LB
f	MOL WT OF FUEL = LINE f ÷ 100
g	SP WT OF FUEL @ 80 F & 29.9″ = $\frac{\text{LINE } g}{394}$ LB/CU FT
h	
i	FUEL HEAT VALUE, BTU/LB 12,800 /CU FT
j	COMBUSTIBLE IN REFUSE, %"C" 0.0 %
k	CARBON UNBURNED, LB/100 LB FUEL = % ASH IN FUEL × $\frac{\%\,"C"}{100-\%\,"C"}$ 0.0
l	EXIT TEMP OF FLUE GAS, t_2 345 F
m	DRY-BULB (AMBIENT) TEMP, t_1' 80 F
n	WET-BULB TEMP F
o	REL HUMID. (PSYCHROMETRIC CHART) %
p	B*, BAROMETRIC PRESSURE, IN. HG
q	SAT. PRESS. H₂O AT AMB TEMP, IN. HG
r	A*, PRESS. H₂O IN AIR, LINES (o × q), IN. HG

DETERMINATION OF FLUE GAS AND COMBUSTIBLE LOSSES IN BTU PER FUEL UNIT (AF)

LINE		CO₂+SO₂	O₂	N₂	H₂O	CO	TOTAL
22	FLUE GAS CONSTITUENTS						
23	Mc_p, MEAN, t_2 to t_1' (FOR t_1' = 80 F, SEE FIG. 1)	9.7	10.2	7.15	7.0	8.12	
24	IN DRY FLUE GAS = MOLES EACH, LINE 20 × Mc_p × ($t_2 - t_1'$)	15,560	2,670	59,000			77,230
25	IN H₂O IN AIR = MOLES H₂O, LINE 18 × Mc_p × ($t_2 - t_1'$)				1,830		1,830
26	IN SENS HEAT, H₂O IN FUEL = MOLES LINES (5 + 10) × Mc_p × ($t_2 - t_1'$)				5,680		5,680
27	IN LATENT HEAT, H₂O IN FUEL = MOLES LINES (5 + 10) × 1040 × 18				49,400		49,400
28	TOTAL IN WET FLUE GASES						134,140
29	DUE TO CARBON IN REFUSE = LINE k × 14,550						0
30	DUE TO UNBURNED CO IN FLUE GAS = MOLES C TO CO × 12 × 10,200						0
31	TOTAL FLUE GAS LOSSES + UNBURNED COMBUSTIBLE = LINES 28+29+30 TOTAL						134,140
32	HEAT VALUE OF FUEL UNIT = 100 × LINE i FOR SOLID AND LIQUID FUELS / 394 × LINE i × 100, FOR GASEOUS FUELS						1,280,000
33	STACK AND COMBUSTIBLE LOSS, % OF HEAT INPUT = 100 × LINE 31 ÷ LINE 32						10.48 %

†NOTE: FLUE GAS ANALYSIS BY ORSAT. IF CO IS PRESENT IN FLUE GASES, A CARBON BALANCE IS USED TO DETERMINE DISTRIBUTION OF C, THUS:
ALL C IN FUEL = C IN FLUE GAS CONSTITUENTS + C IN REFUSE. MOLES C IN FUEL = % C BY ANAL. ÷ 12.
MOLES C IN REFUSE = LINE k ÷ 12. MOLES C IN CO₂ = (MOLES C IN FUEL − MOLES C IN REFUSE) × % CO₂ BY ORSAT ÷ % CO₂ + CO BY ORSAT.
MOLES C IN CO = MOLES C IN FUEL − MOLES C IN REFUSE − MOLES C IN CO₂.

Conversion from Molal to Pound Units

SINCE the weight of a mole in lb is equal to the molecular weight of the element or compound, and the volume in cu ft of a mole of any gas under the same condition of temperature and pressure is approximately constant, the combustion calculations on the molal basis can be readily converted to lb units.

An example of conversion to lb units for the combustion calculations on the opposite page is given below. Reference in this form to gaseous fuels applies to combustion calculations for natural and blast-furnace gases on following pages.

LINE	MOLAL QUANTITIES — CONVERTED TO LB UNITS SEE COMBUSTION CALCULATIONS—MOLAL BASIS FOR LINE REFERENCES							LINE
a^1	AIR (DRY) SUPPLIED PER UNIT OF FUEL = MOLES AIR, LINE 17 $\times$ 29, (MOL. WT AIR)					*1166.4*	LB	a^1
b^1	H_2O IN AIR SUPPLIED PER UNIT OF FUEL = MOLES H_2O, LINE 18 $\times$ 18, (MOL. WT H_2O)					*15.3*	LB	b^1
c^1	WET AIR SUPPLIED PER UNIT OF FUEL = LINES a^1 + b^1					*1181.7*	LB	c^1
d^1	WET AIR SUPPLIED PER LB OF FUEL {LINE c^1 ÷ 100 FOR SOLID OR LIQUID FUELS / LINE c^1 ÷ LINE f FOR GASEOUS FUELS					*11.82* /	LB / LB	d^1
e^1	FLUE GAS CONSTITUENT AND MOL. WT	CO_2 + SO_2 44 64	O_2 32	N_2 28	H_2O 18	CO 28		e^1
f^1	WET F.G., % BY VOL = 100 $\times$ LINE 20 ÷ LINE s (WET)*	*14.14*	*3.30*	*74.40*	*8.16*			f^1
g^1	DRY F.G., % BY VOL = 100 $\times$ LINE 20 ÷ LINE s (DRY)*	*15.40*	*3.59*	*81.01*	////////			g^1
h^1	WT OF EACH CONSTIT = LINE 20 $\times$ MOL. WT OF EACH, LB	*264.0* *3.2*	*45.1*	*891.0*	*62.8*			h^1
i^1	TOTAL WT FLUE GAS = Σ (LINE h^1 WET) AND Σ (LINE h^1 DRY) WET WT *1,266.1* LB DRY WT *1,203.3* LB							i^1
j^1	WET FLUE GAS PER LB FUEL {WET WT, LINE i^1 ÷ 100, SOLID AND LIQUID FUELS / WET WT, LINE i^1 ÷ LINE f, GASEOUS FUELS					*12.66* /	LB / LB	j^1
k^1	DRY FLUE GAS PER LB FUEL {DRY WT, LINE i^1 ÷ 100, SOLID AND LIQUID FUELS / DRY WT, LINE i^1 ÷ LINE f, GASEOUS FUELS					*12.03* /	LB / LB	k^1
l^1	MOLECULAR WT OF WET FLUE GAS = WET WT, LINE i^1 ÷ WET MOLES, LINE s					*29.60*		l^1
m^1	MOLECULAR WT OF DRY FLUE GAS = DRY WT, LINE i^1 ÷ DRY MOLES, LINE s					*30.63*		m^1
n^1	SP WT OF WET FLUE GAS = LINE l^1 ÷ 394 † (AT 80 F AND 29.92 IN. HG)					*0.0751*	LB/CU FT	n^1
o^1	SP WT OF DRY FLUE GAS = LINE m^1 ÷ 394 † (AT 80 F AND 29.92 IN. HG)					*0.0778*	LB/CU FT	o^1

* FLUE GAS ANALYSIS AS CALCULATED, BASED ON TOTAL AIR, LINE d, ASSIGNED OR OBSERVED.
THE CALCULATED VALUES, LINE g^1, SHOULD AGREE SUBSTANTIALLY WITH ORSAT ANALYSIS WHEN FLUE GAS IS ANALYZED.

† VOLUME OF 1 MOLE OF ANY GAS AT 80 F AND 29.92 IN. HG = 394 CU FT.

COMBUSTION CALCULATIONS—MOLAL BASIS

CONDITIONS—ASSIGNED OR OBSERVED AND MISCELLANEOUS

		LINE
DATE		
FUEL	*Natural Gas*	
SOURCE	*California*	
FUEL UNIT {	100 LB, SOLID OR LIQUID FUELS	
	100 MOLES, GASEOUS FUELS	

FUEL, O₂, AND AIR PER UNIT OF FUEL / FLUE GAS (F.G.) COMPOSITION MOLES PER FUEL UNIT (AF)

LINE	FUEL CONSTITUENT	PER FUEL UNIT, LB	MOL. WT DIVISOR	MOLES FUEL CONSTITUENT	O₂ MULTIPLIER	O₂ MOLES THEO REQD	CO₂ + SO₂	O₂	N₂	H₂O	CO
1	C TO CO₂	1326.0	12	110.5	1	110.5	110.5				
2	C TO CO		12		.5						
3	CO TO CO₂		28		.5						
4	C UNBURNED, LINE k		12								
5	H₂	416.8	2	208.4	.5	104.2				208.4	
6	S		32		1						
7	O₂ (DEDUCT)	9.6	32	0.3	1	− 0.3					
8	N₂	47.6	28	1.7		O			1.7		
9	CO₂	4.4	44	0.1		O	0.1				
10	H₂O		18			O					
11	ASH					O					
12	SUM	1804.4		321.0		214.4					

FUEL ANAL. AS FIRED (AF), % BY WT OR VOL   a

CH₄ 85.3
C₂H₆ 12.6
O₂ 0.3
N₂ 1.7
CO₂ 0.1

Moles C & H₂/100 Moles fuel

	C	H₂
In CH₄	85.3	170.6
In C₂H₆	25.2	37.8
Totals	110.5	208.4

No unburned fuel

100.0

CO₂	O₂	CO	N₂	%† c

TOTAL AIR (T.A.) ASSIGNED or by ORSAT	114 %	d

LINES f, g, h FOR GASEOUS FUELS   e

WT, FUEL UNIT = Σ(MOLES EACH × MOL. WT) LB		f
MOL. WT OF FUEL = LINE f ÷ 100	18.04	g
SP WT OF FUEL @ 80 F & 29.9″ = $\frac{LINE\ g}{394}\ \frac{LB}{CU\ FT}$	/CU FT	h
FUEL HEAT VALUE, BTU/LB	1092	i
COMBUSTIBLE IN REFUSE, %"C"	0.0 %	j
CARBON UNBURNED, LB/100 LB FUEL = % ASH IN FUEL × $\frac{\%\ "C"}{100 - \%\ "C"}$	0.0	k

O₂ AND AIR, MOLES FOR TOTAL AIR = 114 % (SEE LINE d AT RIGHT)

LINE		O₂ MOLES THEO REQD	O₂	N₂	H₂O
13	O₂ (THEO) REQD = O₂, LINE 12	214.4			
14	O₂ (EXCESS) = $\frac{T.A.-100}{100}$ × O₂, LINE 12	30.0	30.0		
15	O₂ (TOTAL) SUPPLIED = LINES 13 + 14	244.4			
16	N₂ SUPPLIED = 3.76 × O₂, LINE 15	918.9		918.9	
17	AIR (DRY) SUPPLIED = O₂ + N₂	1163.3			
18	H₂O IN AIR = MOLES DRY AIR × $\frac{A}{B-A}$*	24.7			24.7
19	AIR (WET) SUPPLIED = LINES 17 + 18	1188.0			
20	FLUE GAS CONSTITUENTS = LINES 1 TO 18, TOTAL		110.6	30.0	9.20.6	233.1

EXIT TEMP OF FLUE GAS, t₂	304 F	l
DRY-BULB (AMBIENT) TEMP, t₁′	80 F	m
WET-BULB TEMP	F	n
REL HUMID. (PSYCHROMETRIC CHART)	%	o
B*, BAROMETRIC PRESSURE, IN. HG		p
SAT. PRESS. H₂O AT AMB TEMP, IN. HG		q
A*, PRESS. H₂O IN AIR, LINES (o × q), IN. HG		r

TOTAL MOLES	WET FLUE GAS	DRY FLUE GAS	s
	1294.3	1061.2	

21 *NOTE—FOR AIR AT 80 F AND 60% RELATIVE HUMIDITY, $\frac{A}{B-A}$ = 0.0212 IS OFTEN USED AS STANDARD.

DETERMINATION OF FLUE GAS AND COMBUSTIBLE LOSSES IN BTU PER FUEL UNIT (AF)

LINE	FLUE GAS CONSTITUENTS	CO₂+SO₂	O₂	N₂	H₂O	CO	TOTAL
22							
23	Mc_p, MEAN, t₂ TO t₁′ (FOR t₁′ = 80 F, SEE FIG. 1)	9.55	7.12	7.0	8.1		
24	IN DRY FLUE GAS = MOLES EACH LINE 20 × Mc_p × (t₂ − t₁′)	236,600	47,800	1,443,500			1,727,900
25	IN H₂O IN AIR = MOLES H₂O, LINE 18 × Mc_p × (t₂ − t₁′)				44,800		44,800
26	IN SENS HEAT, H₂O IN FUEL = MOLES LINES (5 + 10) × Mc_p × (t₂ − t₁′)				378,100		378,100
27	IN LATENT HEAT, H₂O IN FUEL = MOLES LINES (5 + 10) × 1040 × 18				3,901,300		3,901,300
28	TOTAL IN WET FLUE GASES						6,052,100
29	DUE TO CARBON IN REFUSE = LINE k × 14,550						0
30	DUE TO UNBURNED CO IN FLUE GAS = MOLES C TO CO × 12 × 10,200						0
31	TOTAL FLUE GAS LOSSES + UNBURNED COMBUSTIBLE = LINES 28+29+30					TOTAL	6,052,100
32	HEAT VALUE OF FUEL UNIT = 100 × LINE i FOR SOLID AND LIQUID FUELS / 394 × LINE i × 100, FOR GASEOUS FUELS						43,024,800
33	STACK AND COMBUSTIBLE LOSS, % OF HEAT INPUT = 100 × LINE 31 ÷ LINE 32						14.07 %

†NOTE: FLUE GAS ANALYSIS BY ORSAT. IF CO IS PRESENT IN FLUE GASES, A CARBON BALANCE IS USED TO DETERMINE DISTRIBUTION OF C, THUS:
ALL C IN FUEL = C IN FLUE GAS CONSTITUENTS + C IN REFUSE. MOLES C IN FUEL = % C BY ANAL. ÷ 12.
MOLES C IN REFUSE = LINE k ÷ 12. MOLES C IN CO₂ = (MOLES C IN FUEL − MOLES C IN REFUSE) × % CO₂ BY ORSAT ÷ % CO₂ + CO BY ORSAT.
MOLES C IN CO = MOLES C IN FUEL − MOLES C IN REFUSE − MOLES C IN CO₂.

COMBUSTION CALCULAT...
BASED ON QUANTITIES PER 10,000 BTU

LINE		
1	FUEL— *Fuel Oil, Texas, Heavy*	
2	ANALYSIS AS FIRED	BY
3	ULTIMATE, % BY WT PROXIMATE, % BY WT	TOTAL AIR
4	C MOISTURE	AIR TEMPERATUR...
5	H₂ VOLATILE	AIR TEMPERATUR...
6	S } *Unknown* FIXED CARBON	FLUE GAS TEMPE...
7	O₂ ASH	H₂O PER LB DRY...
8	N₂	
9	H₂O	UNBURNED FUEL
10	ASH	UNACCOUNTED
11		RADIATION LOSS
12	BTU PER LB, AS FIRED, *18,500*	
13	**QUANTITIES PER 10,000 BTU FU...**	
14	FUEL BURNED, 10,000 ÷ LINE 12	
15	TOTAL AIR REQUIRED, LINE b ÷ 100 × VALUE FROM FIG. 4 OR TABLE 5	
16	H₂O IN AIR, LINE 15 × LINE f = 9.14 x 0.0132	
17	WET GAS, TOTAL, LINES (14 + 15 + 16)	
18	H₂O IN FUEL, (LINE 5 ÷ 100) × LINE 14 × 8.94 + (LINE 9 ÷ 100) × LIN...	
19	H₂O IN FLUE GAS, TOTAL, LINE 16 + LINE 18	
20	H₂O IN FLUE GAS, TOTAL, IN PER CENT, (LINE 19 ÷ LINE 17) × 100	
21	DRY GAS, TOTAL, LINE 17—LINE 19	
22	**LOSSES PER 10,000 BTU FUEL**	
23	UNBURNED FUEL, 10,000 × LINE h ÷ 100	
24	UNACCOUNTED, 10,000 × LINE i ÷ 100	
25	RADIATION, 10,000 × LINE j ÷ 100	
26	LATENT HEAT, H₂O IN FUEL, 1040 × LINE 18	
27	SENSIBLE HEAT, FLUE GAS, LINE 17 × BTU FROM FIG. 2 @ LINE e AND LIN...	
28	TOTAL LOSSES, LINES (23 + 24 + 25 + 26 + 27)	
29	TOTAL LOSSES IN PER CENT, LINE (28 ÷ 10,000) × 100	
30	EFFICIENCY, BY DIFFERENCE, 100—LINE 29	
31	**QUANTITIES PER 10,000 BTU FUE...** **COMBUSTION TEMPERATURE, ADI...**	
32	HEAT INPUT FROM FUEL	
33	HEAT INPUT FROM AIR, LINES (15 + 16) × BTU FROM FIG. 3 @ LINE d TE...	
34	HEAT INPUT, TOTAL, LINES (32 + 33)	
35	LESS LATENT HEAT LOSS, H₂O IN FUEL, LINE 26	
36	HEAT AVAILABLE, MAXIMUM	
37	LESS LINES (24 + 25) × 0.5*	
38	HEAT AVAILABLE, LINE 36—LINE 37	
39	HEAT AVAILABLE PER LB OF FLUE GAS, LINE 38 ÷ LINE 17	
40	ADIABATIC TEMPERATURE, FROM FIG. 2 FOR LINES 20 & 39	

* NOTE: IT IS CUSTOMARY TO REDUCE THE MAXIMUM HEAT AVAILABLE, LINE 36, BY FROM ⅓ TO ½
ON THE ASSUMPTION THAT A PORTION OF THESE LOSSES OCCURS IN THE COMBUSTI...

COMBUSTION CALCULATIONS—MOLAL BASIS

CONDITIONS—ASSIGNED OR OBSERVED AND MISCELLANEOUS

DATE
FUEL *Blast Furnace Gas*
SOURCE *Wharton, W. Va.*
FUEL UNIT { 100 LB , SOLID OR LIQUID FUELS / 100 MOLES, GASEOUS FUELS }

	FUEL, O₂, AND AIR PER UNIT OF FUEL					FLUE GAS (F.G.) COMPOSITION MOLES PER FUEL UNIT (AF)					
LINE	FUEL CONSTITUENT	PER FUEL UNIT, LB	MOL. WT DIVI-SOR	MOLES FUEL CON-STIT-UENT	O₂ MUL-TI-PLI-ER	O₂ MOLES THEO REQD	CO₂ + SO₂	O₂	N₂	H₂O	CO
1	C TO CO₂		12		1						
2	C TO CO		12		.5						
3	CO TO CO₂	714	28	25.5	.5	12.75	25.5				
4	C UNBURNED, LINE k		12								
5	H₂	6	2	3.0	.5	1.50				3.0	
6	S		32		1						
7	O₂ (DEDUCT)		32		1	—					
8	N₂	1596	28	57.0	O				57.0		
9	CO₂	638	44	14.5	O		14.5				
10	H₂O		18		O						
11	ASH										
12	SUM	2954		100.0		14.25					

FUEL ANAL. AS FIRED (AF), % BY WT OR VOL — a

		b
H₂	3.0	
CO	25.5	
CO₂	14.5	
N₂	57.0	
	100.0	

	CO₂	O₂	CO	N₂	%†	c
TOTAL AIR (T.A.) ASSIGNED or by ORSAT					125 %	d
LINES f, g, h FOR GASEOUS FUELS						e
WT, FUEL UNIT = Σ(MOLES EACH × MOL. WT)				954 LB		f
MOL. WT OF FUEL = LINE f ÷ 100				29.54		g
SP WT OF FUEL @ 80 F & 29.9" = LINE g ÷ 394				.075 LB /CU FT		h
FUEL HEAT VALUE, BTU/LB /CU FT				90.0		i
COMBUSTIBLE IN REFUSE, %"C"				0.0 %		j
CARBON UNBURNED, LB/100 LB FUEL = % ASH IN FUEL × %"C" ÷ (100 − %"C")				0.0		k
EXIT TEMP OF FLUE GAS, t_2				525 F		l
DRY-BULB (AMBIENT) TEMP, t_1'				80 F		m
WET-BULB TEMP				F		n
REL HUMID. (PSYCHROMETRIC CHART)				%		o
B* BAROMETRIC PRESSURE, IN. HG						p
SAT. PRESS. H₂O AT AMB TEMP, IN. HG						q
A* PRESS. H₂O IN AIR, LINES (o × q), IN. HG						r

O₂ AND AIR, MOLES FOR TOTAL AIR = 125 %
(SEE LINE d AT RIGHT)

		CO₂+SO₂	O₂	N₂	H₂O	CO
13	O₂ (THEO) REQD = O₂, LINE 12	14.25				
14	O₂ (EXCESS) = $\frac{T.A. - 100}{100}$ × O₂, LINE 12	3.56	3.56			
15	O₂ (TOTAL) SUPPLIED = LINES 13 + 14	17.81				
16	N₂ SUPPLIED = 3.76 × O₂, LINE 15	66.97		67.0		
17	AIR (DRY) SUPPLIED = O₂ + N₂	84.78				
18	H₂O IN AIR = MOLES DRY AIR × $\frac{A}{B-A}$ *	1.80			1.80	
19	AIR (WET) SUPPLIED = LINES 17 + 18	86.58				
20	FLUE GAS CONSTITUENTS = LINES 1 TO 18, TOTAL	40.0	3.56	124.0	4.80	

TOTAL MOLES	WET FLUE GAS	DRY FLUE GAS	s
172.36	167.56		

21 *NOTE—FOR AIR AT 80 F AND 60% RELATIVE HUMIDITY, $\frac{A}{B-A}$ = 0.0212 IS OFTEN USED AS STANDARD.

DETERMINATION OF FLUE GAS AND COMBUSTIBLE LOSSES IN BTU PER FUEL UNIT (AF)

		CO₂+SO₂	O₂	N₂	H₂O	CO	TOTAL
22	FLUE GAS CONSTITUENTS						
23	Mc_p, MEAN, t_2 TO t_1' (FOR t_1' = 80 F, SEE FIG. 1)	10.1	7.22	7.05	8.20		
24	IN DRY FLUE GAS = MOLES EACH, LINE 20 × Mc_p × ($t_2 - t_1'$)	179,800	11,400	389,000			580,200
25	IN H₂O IN AIR = MOLES H₂O, LINE 18 × Mc_p × ($t_2 - t_1'$)				6,570		6,570
26	IN SENS HEAT, H₂O IN FUEL = MOLES LINES (5 + 10) × Mc_p × ($t_2 - t_1'$)				10,950		10,950
27	IN LATENT HEAT, H₂O IN FUEL = MOLES LINES (5 + 10) × 1040 × 18				56,160		56,160
28	TOTAL IN WET FLUE GASES						653,880
29	DUE TO CARBON IN REFUSE = LINE k × 14,550						0
30	DUE TO UNBURNED CO IN FLUE GAS = MOLES C TO CO × 12 × 10,200						0
31	TOTAL FLUE GAS LOSSES + UNBURNED COMBUSTIBLE = LINES 28+29+30 TOTAL						653,880
32	HEAT VALUE OF FUEL UNIT = 100 × LINE i FOR SOLID AND LIQUID FUELS / 394 × LINE i × 100, FOR GASEOUS FUELS						3,546,000
33	STACK AND COMBUSTIBLE LOSS, % OF HEAT INPUT = 100 × LINE 31 ÷ LINE 32						18.44 %

†NOTE: FLUE GAS ANALYSIS BY ORSAT. IF CO IS PRESENT IN FLUE GASES, A CARBON BALANCE IS USED TO DETERMINE DISTRIBUTION OF C, THUS:
ALL C IN FUEL − C IN FLUE GAS CONSTITUENTS + C IN REFUSE. MOLES C IN FUEL = % C BY ANAL. ÷ 12.
MOLES C IN REFUSE = LINE k ÷ 12. MOLES C IN CO₂ = (MOLES C IN FUEL − MOLES C IN REFUSE) × % CO₂ BY ORSAT ÷ % CO₂ + CO BY ORSAT.
MOLES C IN CO = MOLES C IN FUEL − MOLES C IN REFUSE − MOLES C IN CO₂.

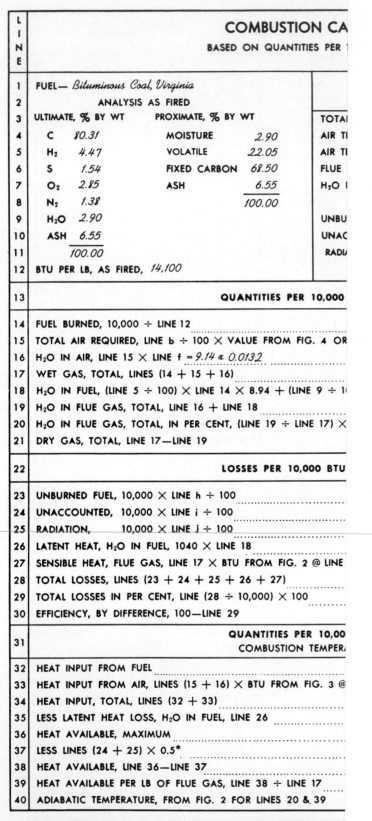

L I N E	
	COMBUSTION CA
	BASED ON QUANTITIES PER 1
1	FUEL— *Bituminous Coal, Virginia*
2	ANALYSIS AS FIRED
3	ULTIMATE, % BY WT PROXIMATE, % BY WT
4	C 80.31 MOISTURE 2.90
5	H_2 4.47 VOLATILE 22.05
6	S 1.54 FIXED CARBON 68.50
7	O_2 2.85 ASH 6.55
8	N_2 1.38 100.00
9	H_2O 2.90
10	ASH 6.55
11	100.00
12	BTU PER LB, AS FIRED, *14,100*
13	QUANTITIES PER 10,000
14	FUEL BURNED, 10,000 ÷ LINE 12
15	TOTAL AIR REQUIRED, LINE b ÷ 100 × VALUE FROM FIG. 4 OR
16	H_2O IN AIR, LINE 15 × LINE f = 9.14 × 0.0132
17	WET GAS, TOTAL, LINES (14 + 15 + 16)
18	H_2O IN FUEL, (LINE 5 ÷ 100) × LINE 14 × 8.94 + (LINE 9 ÷ 10
19	H_2O IN FLUE GAS, TOTAL, LINE 16 + LINE 18
20	H_2O IN FLUE GAS, TOTAL, IN PER CENT, (LINE 19 ÷ LINE 17) ×
21	DRY GAS, TOTAL, LINE 17—LINE 19
22	LOSSES PER 10,000 BTU
23	UNBURNED FUEL, 10,000 × LINE h ÷ 100
24	UNACCOUNTED, 10,000 × LINE i ÷ 100
25	RADIATION, 10,000 × LINE j ÷ 100
26	LATENT HEAT, H_2O IN FUEL, 1040 × LINE 18
27	SENSIBLE HEAT, FLUE GAS, LINE 17 × BTU FROM FIG. 2 @ LINE
28	TOTAL LOSSES, LINES (23 + 24 + 25 + 26 + 27)
29	TOTAL LOSSES IN PER CENT, LINE (28 ÷ 10,000) × 100
30	EFFICIENCY, BY DIFFERENCE, 100—LINE 29
31	QUANTITIES PER 10,00 COMBUSTION TEMPERA
32	HEAT INPUT FROM FUEL
33	HEAT INPUT FROM AIR, LINES (15 + 16) × BTU FROM FIG. 3 @
34	HEAT INPUT, TOTAL, LINES (32 + 33)
35	LESS LATENT HEAT LOSS, H_2O IN FUEL, LINE 26
36	HEAT AVAILABLE, MAXIMUM
37	LESS LINES (24 + 25) × 0.5*
38	HEAT AVAILABLE, LINE 36—LINE 37
39	HEAT AVAILABLE PER LB OF FLUE GAS, LINE 38 ÷ LINE 17
40	ADIABATIC TEMPERATURE, FROM FIG. 2 FOR LINES 20 & 39

* NOTE: IT IS CUSTOMARY TO REDUCE THE MAXIMUM HEAT AVAILABLE, LINE 36, BY FRO
ON THE ASSUMPTION THAT A PORTION OF THESE LOSSES OCCURS IN THE

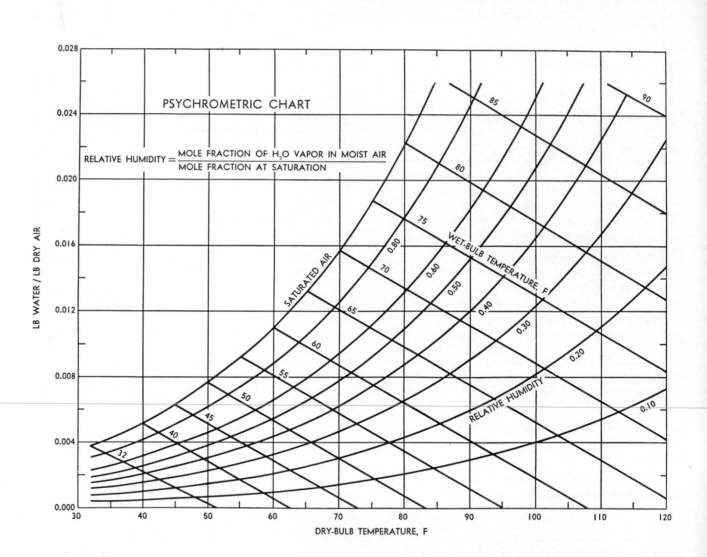

PSYCHROMETRIC CHART

$$\text{RELATIVE HUMIDITY} = \frac{\text{MOLE FRACTION OF } H_2O \text{ VAPOR IN MOIST AIR}}{\text{MOLE FRACTION AT SATURATION}}$$

LB WATER / LB DRY AIR

DRY-BULB TEMPERATURE, F

Chapter 6. Temperature Measurement

Temperature-emf relationship of standardized thermocouple
wires as established by Leeds & Northrup for four thermocouple pairs

90% Plat.-10% Rhodium (+) to Platinum (−) Thermocouple

Degrees F   Reference Junction, Zero F

F	0	100	200	300	400	500	600	700	800	900	1000	1100	1200	1300	1400	1500
								Millivolts								
0	0.000	0.313	0.687	1.108	1.565	2.048	2.549	3.067	3.597	4.136	4.686	5.247	5.817	5.399	6.990	7.592
5	0.014	0.331	0.707	1.130	1.589	2.072	2.574	3.093	3.624	4.163	4.713	5.275	5.846	6.428	7.020	7.622
10	0.028	0.349	0.727	1.152	1.613	2.097	2.600	3.120	3.651	4.190	4.741	5.303	5.875	6.458	7.050	7.653
15	0.043	0.366	0.747	1.174	1.636	2.122	2.626	3.146	3.677	4.217	4.769	5.331	5.904	6.487	7.079	7.683
20	0.057	0.384	0.768	1.197	1.660	2.147	2.652	3.173	3.704	4.245	4.797	5.360	5.933	6.516	7.109	7.713
25	0.071	0.402	0.788	1.219	1.684	2.172	2.677	3.199	3.731	4.272	4.825	5.388	5.961	6.545	7.139	7.743
30	0.086	0.420	0.809	1.242	1.708	2.197	2.703	3.225	3.759	4.300	4.853	5.416	5.990	6.575	7.169	7.774
35	0.101	0.438	0.829	1.265	1.732	2.222	2.729	3.251	3.786	4.327	4.881	5.444	6.019	6.604	7.199	7.805
40	0.116	0.457	0.850	1.288	1.756	2.247	2.755	3.278	3.812	4.355	4.909	5.473	6.048	6.634	7.229	7.836
45	0.132	0.475	0.871	1.310	1.780	2.272	2.781	3.304	3.839	4.382	4.937	5.501	6.077	6.663	7.259	7.866
50	0.148	0.493	0.892	1.333	1.804	2.297	2.807	3.331	3.866	4.410	4.965	5.530	6.107	6.693	7.290	7.897
55	0.164	0.512	0.913	1.356	1.828	2.322	2.833	3.358	3.893	4.437	4.993	5.558	6.136	6.722	7.320	7.927
60	0.180	0.531	0.935	1.379	1.852	2.347	2.859	3.385	3.920	4.465	5.021	5.587	6.165	6.752	7.350	7.958
65	0.196	0.550	0.956	1.402	1.876	2.372	2.885	3.411	3.947	4.492	5.049	5.616	6.194	6.782	7.380	7.989
70	0.212	0.569	0.978	1.425	1.900	2.397	2.911	3.438	3.974	4.520	5.077	5.645	6.224	6.812	7.410	8.020
75	0.229	0.588	0.999	1.448	1.924	2.422	2.937	3.464	4.001	4.547	5.105	5.673	6.263	6.841	7.440	8.050
80	0.245	0.608	1.021	1.472	1.949	2.448	2.963	3.491	4.028	4.575	5.134	5.702	6.282	6.871	7.471	8.081
85	0.262	0.627	1.042	1.495	1.973	2.473	2.989	3.517	4.055	4.603	5.162	5.730	6.311	6.900	7.501	8.112
90	0.279	0.647	1.064	1.518	1.998	2.498	3.015	3.544	4.082	4.631	5.190	5.759	6.341	6.930	7.531	8.143
95	0.296	0.667	1.086	1.541	2.023	2.523	3.041	3.570	4.109	4.658	5.218	5.788	6.370	6.960	7.561	8.173
100	0.313	0.687	1.108	1.565	2.048	2.549	3.067	3.597	4.136	4.686	5.247	5.817	6.399	6.990	7.592	8.204
*	0.00313	0.00374	0.00421	0.00457	0.00483	0.00501	0.00518	0.00530	0.00539	0.00550	0.00561	0.00570	0.00582	0.00591	0.00602	0.00612

F	1600	1700	1800	1900	2000	2100	2200	2300	2400	2500	2600	2700	2800	2900	3000	3100
								Millivolts								
0	8.204	8.826	9.457	10.099	10.749	11.408	12.069	12.734	13.397	14.060	14.721	15.380	16.035	16.688	17.339	17.984
5	8.235	8.857	9.489	10.131	10.782	11.441	12.102	12.767	13.431	14.093	14.754	15.413	16.068	16.721	17.371	18.017
10	8.266	8.888	9.521	10.163	10.815	11.474	12.135	12.800	13.464	14.126	14.787	15.445	16.101	16.753	17.403	18.049
15	8.297	8.919	9.553	10.195	10.848	11.507	12.168	12.833	13.497	14.159	14.820	15.478	16.133	16.786	17.436	18.081
20	8.328	8.951	9.585	10.228	10.881	11.540	12.202	12.867	13.530	14.192	14.853	15.510	16.166	16.818	17.468	18.113
25	8.359	8.982	9.617	10.260	10.914	11.573	12.235	12.900	13.564	14.225	14.886	15.543	16.199	16.851	17.500	—
30	8.390	9.014	9.649	10.293	10.947	11.606	12.269	12.933	13.597	14.258	14.918	15.576	16.231	16.883	17.532	—
35	8.421	9.045	9.681	10.325	10.979	11.639	12.302	12.966	13.630	14.292	14.951	15.609	16.264	16.916	17.565	—
40	8.452	9.077	9.713	10.358	11.012	11.672	12.335	12.999	13.663	14.325	14.984	15.642	16.297	16.948	17.597	—
45	8.483	9.108	9.745	10.390	11.045	11.705	12.368	13.033	13.696	14.358	15.017	15.675	16.329	16.981	17.630	—
50	8.514	9.140	9.777	10.423	11.078	11.738	12.402	13.066	13.729	14.391	15.050	15.707	16.362	17.014	17.662	—
55	8.545	9.171	9.809	10.455	11.111	11.771	12.435	13.099	13.762	14.424	15.083	15.740	16.395	17.047	17.694	—
60	8.576	9.203	9.841	10.488	11.144	11.804	12.468	13.132	13.795	14.457	15.116	15.772	16.427	17.079	17.726	—
65	8.607	9.235	9.873	10.520	11.177	11.837	12.501	13.166	13.829	14.490	15.149	15.805	16.460	17.112	17.759	—
70	8.638	9.267	9.905	10.553	11.210	11.870	12.534	13.199	13.862	14.523	15.182	15.838	16.493	17.144	17.791	—
75	8.660	9.208	9.037	10.585	11.243	11.903	12.567	13.232	13.895	14.556	15.215	15.871	16.525	17.177	17.823	—
80	8.701	9.330	9.969	10.618	11.276	11.936	12.601	13.265	13.928	14.589	15.248	15.904	16.558	17.209	17.855	—
85	8.732	9.362	10.002	10.650	11.309	11.969	12.634	13.298	13.961	14.622	15.281	15.937	16.590	17.242	17.888	—
90	8.763	9.394	10.034	10.683	11.342	12.003	12.667	13.331	13.994	14.655	15.314	15.970	16.623	17.274	17.920	—
95	8.794	9.425	10.066	10.716	11.375	12.036	12.700	13.364	14.027	14.688	15.347	16.003	16.656	17.307	17.952	—
100	8.826	9.457	10.099	10.749	11.408	12.069	12.734	13.397	14.060	14.721	15.380	16.035	16.688	17.339	17.984	—
*	0.00622	0.00631	0.00642	0.00650	0.00659	0.00661	0.00665	0.00663	0.00663	0.00661	0.00659	0.00655	0.00653	0.00651	0.00645	0.00645

*Average millivolts per degree F.

Copper (+) to Constantan (−) Thermocouple

Degrees F   Reference Junction, Zero F

F	mv	F	mv	F	mv	F	mv	F	mv	F	mv	F	mv
0	0.00	100	2.19	200	4.64	300	7.31	400	10.19	500	13.24	600	16.44
2	0.04	102	2.23	202	4.69	302	7.37	402	10.25	502	13.30	602	16.50
4	0.08	104	2.28	204	4.74	304	7.43	404	10.31	504	13.37	604	16.57
6	0.12	106	2.33	206	4.79	306	7.48	406	10.37	506	13.43	606	16.63
8	0.16	108	2.37	208	4.84	308	7.54	408	10.43	508	13.49	608	16.70
10	0.21	110	2.42	210	4.89	310	7.59	410	10.49	510	13.56	610	16.77
12	0.25	112	2.47	212	4.95	312	7.65	412	10.55	512	13.62	612	16.83
14	0.29	114	2.51	214	5.00	314	7.71	414	10.61	514	13.68	614	16.90
16	0.33	116	2.56	216	5.05	316	7.76	416	10.67	516	13.74	616	16.96
18	0.37	118	2.61	218	5.10	318	7.82	418	10.73	518	13.81	618	17.03
20	0.42	120	2.66	220	5.15	320	7.88	420	10.79	520	13.87	620	17.09
22	0.46	122	2.70	222	5.21	322	7.93	422	10.85	522	13.93	622	17.16
24	0.50	124	2.75	224	5.26	324	7.99	424	10.91	524	14.00	624	17.23
26	0.54	126	2.80	226	5.31	326	8.05	426	10.97	526	14.06	626	17.29
28	0.58	128	2.85	228	5.36	328	8.10	428	11.03	528	14.12	628	17.36
30	0.63	130	2.90	230	5.42	330	8.16	430	11.09	530	14.19	630	17.42
32	0.67	132	2.94	232	5.47	332	8.22	432	11.15	532	14.25	632	17.49
34	0.71	134	2.99	234	5.52	334	8.27	434	11.21	534	14.31	634	17.56
36	0.76	136	3.04	236	5.58	336	8.33	436	11.27	536	14.38	636	17.62
38	0.80	138	3.09	238	5.63	338	8.39	438	11.33	538	14.44	638	17.69
40	0.84	140	3.14	240	5.68	340	8.44	440	11.39	540	14.50	640	17.75
42	0.89	142	3.19	242	5.74	342	8.50	442	11.45	542	14.57	642	17.82
44	0.93	144	3.23	244	5.79	344	8.56	444	11.51	544	14.63	644	17.89
46	0.97	146	3.28	246	5.84	346	8.62	446	11.57	546	14.69	646	17.95
48	1.02	148	3.33	248	5.90	348	8.67	448	11.64	548	14.76	648	18.02
50	1.06	150	3.38	250	5.95	350	8.73	450	11.70	550	14.82	650	18.09
52	1.10	152	3.43	252	6.00	352	8.79	452	11.76	552	14.89	652	18.15
54	1.15	154	3.48	254	6.06	354	8.85	454	11.82	554	14.95	654	18.22
56	1.19	156	3.53	256	6.11	356	8.90	456	11.88	556	15.01	656	18.29
58	1.24	158	3.58	258	6.16	358	8.96	458	11.94	558	15.08	658	18.35
60	1.28	160	3.63	260	6.22	360	9.02	460	12.00	560	15.14	660	18.42
62	1.32	162	3.68	262	6.27	362	9.08	462	12.06	562	15.21	662	18.49
64	1.37	164	3.73	264	6.33	364	9.14	464	12.12	564	15.27	664	18.55
66	1.41	166	3.78	266	6.38	366	9.19	466	12.19	566	15.33	666	18.62
68	1.46	168	3.83	268	6.43	368	9.25	468	12.25	568	15.40	668	18.69
70	1.50	170	3.88	270	6.49	370	9.31	470	12.31	570	15.46	670	18.75
72	1.55	172	3.93	272	6.54	372	9.37	472	12.37	572	15.53	672	18.82
74	1.59	174	3.98	274	6.60	374	9.43	474	12.43	574	15.59	674	18.89
76	1.64	176	4.03	276	6.65	376	9.48	476	12.49	576	15.66	676	18.95
78	1.68	178	4.08	278	6.71	378	9.54	478	12.56	578	15.72	678	19.02
80	1.73	180	4.13	280	6.76	380	9.60	480	12.62	580	15.79	680	19.09
82	1.77	182	4.18	282	6.82	382	9.66	482	12.68	582	15.85	682	19.16
84	1.82	184	4.23	284	6.87	384	9.72	484	12.74	584	15.92	684	19.22
86	1.86	186	4.28	286	6.93	386	9.78	486	12.80	586	15.98	686	19.29
88	1.91	188	4.33	288	6.98	388	9.84	488	12.87	588	16.05	688	19.36
90	1.96	190	4.38	290	7.04	390	9.90	490	12.93	590	16.11	690	19.42
92	2.00	192	4.43	292	7.09	392	9.96	492	12.99	592	16.18	692	19.49
94	2.05	194	4.48	294	7.15	394	10.01	494	13.05	594	16.24	694	19.56
96	2.09	196	4.53	296	7.20	396	10.07	496	13.12	596	16.31	696	19.63
98	2.14	198	4.58	298	7.26	398	10.13	498	13.18	598	16.37	698	19.69
100	2.19	200	4.64	300	7.31	400	10.19	500	13.24	600	16.44	700	19.76
*	0.022		0.025		0.027		0.029		0.031		0.032		0.033

*Average millivolts per degree F.

Chapter 10. S[...]

Note: The following steam tab[...]
Properties of Steam (Copyright, [...]
Reference to this book is necessa[...]

TABLE [...]

Temp	Abs Press.	Specific Vol[...]	
	Lb	Sat.	
F	Sq In.	Liquid	Evap
t	*p*	v_f	v_{fg}
32	0.08854	0.01602	3306
35	0.09995	0.01602	2947
40	0.12170	0.01602	2444
45	0.14752	0.01602	2036.4
50	0.17811	0.01603	1703.2
60	0.2563	0.01604	1206.6
70	0.3631	0.01606	867.8
80	0.5069	0.01608	633.1
90	0.6982	0.01610	468.0
100	0.9492	0.01613	350.3
110	1.2748	0.01617	265.3
120	1.6924	0.01620	203.25
130	2.2225	0.01625	157.32
140	2.8886	0.01629	122.99
150	3.718	0.01634	97.06
160	4.741	0.01639	77.27
170	5.992	0.01645	62.04
180	7.510	0.01651	50.21
190	9.339	0.01657	40.94
200	11.526	0.01663	33.62
210	14.123	0.01670	27.80
212	14.696	0.01672	26.78
220	17.186	0.01677	23.13
230	20.780	0.01684	19.365
240	24.969	0.01692	16.306
250	29.825	0.01700	13.804
260	35.429	0.01709	11.746
270	41.858	0.01717	10.044
280	49.203	0.01726	8.628
290	57.556	0.01735	7.444
300	67.013	0.01745	6.449
320	89.66	0.01765	4.896
340	118.01	0.01787	3.770
360	153.04	0.01811	2.939
380	195.77	0.01836	2.317
400	247.31	0.01864	1.8447
420	308.83	0.01894	1.4811
440	381.59	0.01926	1.1979
460	466.9	0.0196	0.9748
480	566.1	0.0200	0.7972
500	680.8	0.0204	0.6545
520	812.4	0.0209	0.5385
540	962.5	0.0215	0.4434
560	1133.1	0.0221	0.3647
580	1325.8	0.0228	0.2989
600	1542.9	0.0236	0.2432
620	1786.6	0.0247	0.1955
640	2059.7	0.0260	0.1538
660	2365.4	0.0278	0.1165
680	2708.1	0.0305	0.0810
700	3093.7	0.0369	0.0392
705.4	3206.2	0.0503	0

Chromel (+) to Alumel (−) Thermocouple

Degrees F   Reference Junction, Zero F

F	0	100	200	300	400	500	600	700	800	900	1000	1100	1200
						Millivolts							
0	0.00	2.20	4.50	6.77	8.99	11.24	13.53	15.86	18.20	20.56	22.93	25.30	27.66
5	0.10	2.31	4.61	6.88	9.10	11.35	13.64	15.97	18.31	20.68	23.05	25.42	27.78
10	0.21	2.42	4.73	6.99	9.21	11.47	13.76	16.09	18.43	20.80	23.17	25.53	27.89
15	0.31	2.53	4.84	7.10	9.32	11.58	13.87	16.20	18.55	20.92	23.28	25.65	28.01
20	0.42	2.65	4.96	7.21	9.44	11.70	13.99	16.32	18.67	21.04	23.40	25.77	28.13
25	0.53	2.76	5.07	7.32	9.55	11.81	14.11	16.44	18.78	21.15	23.52	25.89	28.25
30	0.64	2.88	5.19	7.43	9.66	11.93	14.23	16.56	18.90	21.27	23.64	26.01	28.36
35	0.75	2.99	5.30	7.54	9.77	12.04	14.35	16.68	19.02	21.39	23.76	26.13	28.48
40	0.86	3.11	5.42	7.66	9.88	12.15	14.46	16.79	19.14	21.51	23.88	26.25	28.60
45	0.97	3.22	5.55	7.77	9.99	12.26	14.57	16.91	19.26	21.63	24.00	26.37	28.72
50	1.08	3.34	5.65	7.88	10.11	12.38	14.69	17.03	19.38	21.75	24.11	26.48	28.83
55	1.19	3.45	5.76	7.99	10.23	12.49	14.80	17.15	19.49	21.85	24.23	26.60	28.95
60	1.30	3.57	5.87	8.10	10.34	12.61	14.92	17.26	19.61	21.98	24.35	26.72	29.07
65	1.41	3.68	5.98	8.21	10.45	12.72	15.04	17.38	19.73	22.10	24.47	26.84	29.19
70	1.52	3.80	6.10	8.32	10.56	12.84	15.16	17.50	19.85	22.22	24.59	26.95	29.30
75	1.63	3.92	6.21	8.43	10.67	12.95	15.28	17.61	19.97	22.34	24.70	27.07	29.42
80	1.74	4.04	6.32	8.55	10.79	13.07	15.39	17.73	20.09	22.46	24.82	27.19	29.54
85	1.85	4.16	6.43	8.66	10.90	13.18	15.51	17.85	20.20	22.57	24.94	27.31	29.66
90	1.97	4.27	6.55	8.77	11.01	13.30	15.62	17.97	20.32	22.69	25.06	27.42	29.77
95	2.08	4.38	6.66	8.88	11.12	13.41	15.74	18.08	20.44	22.81	25.18	27.54	29.89
100	2.20	4.50	6.77	8.99	11.24	13.53	15.80	18.20	20.56	22.93	25.30	27.66	30.01
*	0.022	0.023	0.0227	0.0222	0.0225	0.0229	0.0233	0.0234	0.0236	0.0237	0.0237	0.0236	0.0235

F	1300	1400	1500	1600	1700	1800	1900	2000	2100	2200	2300	2400
						Millivolts						
0	30.01	32.33	34.62	36.88	39.11	41.30	43.45	45.57	47.65	49.69	51.68	53.63
5	30.13	32.45	34.74	36.99	39.22	41.41	43.56	45.68	47.76	49.79	51.78	53.73
10	30.24	32.56	34.85	37.10	39.33	41.51	43.66	45.78	47.86	49.89	51.88	53.82
15	30.36	32.68	34.97	37.22	39.44	41.62	43.77	45.88	47.96	49.99	51.98	53.92
20	30.47	32.79	35.08	37.33	39.55	41.73	43.88	45.99	48.06	50.09	52.07	54.01
25	30.59	32.91	35.19	37.44	39.66	41.84	43.99	46.09	48.17	50.19	52.17	54.11
30	30.70	33.02	35.30	37.55	39.77	41.95	44.09	46.20	48.27	50.29	52.27	54.20
35	30.82	33.14	35.42	37.67	39.88	42.06	44.20	46.30	48.37	50.39	52.37	54.30
40	30.94	33.25	35.53	37.78	39.99	42.16	44.30	46.41	48.47	50.49	52.46	54.39
45	31.06	33.37	35.65	37.89	40.10	42.27	44.41	46.51	48.57	50.59	52.56	54.49
50	31.17	33.48	35.76	38.00	40.21	42.38	44.51	44.61	48.67	50.69	52.66	54.58
55	31.29	33.60	35.87	38.11	40.32	42.49	44.62	46.72	48.78	50.79	52.76	54.68
60	31.40	33.71	35.98	38.22	40.43	42.59	44.72	46.82	48.88	50.89	52.85	54.77
65	31.52	33.83	36.10	38.33	40.54	42.70	44.83	46.93	48.98	50.99	52.95	54.87
70	31.64	33.94	36.21	38.44	40.64	42.81	44.94	47.03	49.08	51.09	53.05	54.96
75	31.76	34.06	36.32	38.56	40.75	42.92	45.05	47.14	49.19	51.19	53.15	55.06
80	31.87	34.17	35.43	38.67	40.86	43.02	45.15	47.24	49.29	51.29	53.24	55.15
85	31.99	34.28	36.55	38.78	40.97	43.13	45.26	47.34	49.39	51.39	53.34	55.25
90	32.10	34.39	36.66	38.89	41.08	43.24	45.36	47.44	49.49	51.48	53.43	55.34
95	32.22	34.51	36.77	39.00	41.19	43.35	45.47	47.55	49.59	51.58	53.53	55.44
100	32.33	34.62	36.88	39.11	41.30	43.45	45.57	47.65	49.69	51.68	53.63	55.53
*	0.0232	0.0229	0.0226	0.0223	0.0219	0.0215	0.0212	0.0208	0.0204	0.0199	0.0195	0.0190

*Average millivolts per degree F.

Iron (+)

De...

F	0	100	200	
0	0.000	2.88	5.84	
5	0.144	3.03	5.99	
10	0.288	3.18	6.14	
15	0.432	3.32	6.29	
20	0.576	3.47	6.45	
25	0.720	3.62	6.60	
30	0.864	3.77	6.75	
35	1.01	3.92	6.90	
40	1.15	4.06	7.05	1
45	1.30	4.21	7.20	1
50	1.44	4.36	7.36	1
55	1.58	4.51	7.50	1
60	1.73	4.66	7.66	1
65	1.87	4.80	7.81	1
70	2.02	4.95	7.96	1
75	2.16	5.10	8.11	1
80	2.30	5.25	8.26	1
85	2.45	5.40	8.42	1
90	2.59	5.54	8.57	1
95	2.74	5.69	8.72	1
100	2.88	5.84	8.87	1
*	0.0288	0.0296	0.0303	0.

F	1200	1300	1400
0	36.96	40.38	43.88
5	37.13	40.56	44.06
10	37.30	40.73	44.23
15	37.47	40.90	44.41
20	37.64	41.08	44.58
25	37.81	41.26	44.76
30	37.99	41.43	44.94
35	38.16	41.60	45.11
40	38.33	41.78	45.29
45	38.50	41.95	45.46
50	38.67	42.13	45.64
55	38.84	42.30	45.82
60	39.01	42.48	45.99
65	39.18	42.65	46.17
70	39.35	42.83	46.34
75	39.52	43.00	46.52
80	39.70	43.18	46.70
85	39.87	43.35	46.87
90	40.04	43.53	47.05
95	40.21	43.70	47.22
100	40.38	43.88	47.40
*	0.0342	0.0350	0.0352

*Average millivolts per degree F.

TABLE 2. SATURATION: PRESSURES

Abs Press. Lb Sq In. p	Temp F t	Specific Volume		Enthalpy			Entropy			Internal Energy			Abs Press. Lb Sq In. p
		Sat. Liquid v_f	Sat. Vapor v_g	Sat. Liquid h_f	Evap h_{fg}	Sat. Vapor h_g	Sat. Liquid s_f	Evap s_{fg}	Sat. Vapor s_g	Sat. Liquid u_f	Evap u_{fg}	Sat. Vapor u_g	
1.0	101.74	0.01614	333.6	69.70	1036.3	1106.0	0.1326	1.8456	1.9782	69.70	974.6	1044.3	1.0
2.0	126.08	0.01623	173.73	93.99	1022.2	1116.2	0.1749	1.7451	1.9200	93.98	957.9	1051.9	2.0
3.0	141.48	0.01630	118.71	109.37	1013.2	1122.6	0.2008	1.6855	1.8863	109.36	947.3	1056.7	3.0
4.0	152.97	0.01636	90.63	120.86	1006.4	1127.3	0.2198	1.6427	1.8625	120.85	939.3	1060.2	4.0
5.0	162.24	0.01640	73.52	130.13	1001.0	1131.1	0.2347	1.6094	1.8441	130.12	933.0	1063.1	5.0
6.0	170.06	0.01645	61.98	137.96	996.2	1134.2	0.2472	1.5820	1.8292	137.94	927.5	1065.4	6.0
7.0	176.85	0.01649	53.64	144.76	992.1	1136.9	0.2581	1.5586	1.8167	144.74	922.7	1067.4	7.0
8.0	182.86	0.01653	47.34	150.79	988.5	1139.3	0.2674	1.5383	1.8057	150.77	918.4	1069.2	8.0
9.0	188.28	0.01656	42.40	156.22	985.2	1141.4	0.2759	1.5203	1.7962	156.19	914.6	1070.8	9.0
10	193.21	0.01659	38.42	161.17	982.1	1143.3	0.2835	1.5041	1.7876	161.14	911.1	1072.2	10
14.696	212.00	0.01672	26.80	180.07	970.3	1150.4	0.3120	1.4446	1.7566	180.02	897.5	1077.5	14.696
15	213.03	0.01672	26.29	181.11	969.7	1150.8	0.3135	1.4415	1.7549	181.06	896.7	1077.8	15
20	227.96	0.01683	20.089	196.16	960.1	1156.3	0.3356	1.3962	1.7319	196.10	885.8	1081.9	20
30	250.33	0.01701	13.746	218.82	945.3	1164.1	0.3680	1.3313	1.6993	218.73	869.1	1087.8	30
40	267.25	0.01715	10.498	236.03	933.7	1169.7	0.3919	1.2844	1.6763	235.90	856.1	1092.0	40
50	281.01	0.01727	8.515	250.09	924.0	1174.1	0.4110	1.2474	1.6585	249.93	845.4	1095.3	50
60	292.71	0.01738	7.175	262.09	915.5	1177.6	0.4270	1.2168	1.6438	261.90	836.0	1097.9	60
70	302.92	0.01748	6.206	272.61	907.9	1180.6	0.4409	1.1906	1.6315	272.38	827.8	1100.2	70
80	312.03	0.01757	5.472	282.02	901.1	1183.1	0.4531	1.1676	1.6207	281.76	820.3	1102.1	80
90	320.27	0.01766	4.896	290.56	894.7	1185.3	0.4641	1.1471	1.6112	290.27	813.4	1103.7	90
100	327.81	0.01774	4.432	298.40	888.8	1187.2	0.4740	1.1286	1.6026	298.08	807.1	1105.2	100
120	341.25	0.01789	3.728	312.44	877.9	1190.4	0.4916	1.0962	1.5878	312.05	795.6	1107.6	120
140	353.02	0.01802	3.220	324.82	868.2	1193.0	0.5069	1.0682	1.5751	324.35	785.2	1109.6	140
160	363.53	0.01815	2.834	335.93	859.2	1195.1	0.5204	1.0436	1.5640	335.39	775.8	1111.2	160
180	373.06	0.01827	2.532	346.03	850.8	1196.9	0.5325	1.0217	1.5542	345.42	767.1	1112.5	180
200	381.79	0.01839	2.288	355.36	843.0	1198.4	0.5435	1.0018	1.5453	354.68	759.0	1113.7	200
250	400.95	0.01865	1.8438	376.00	825.1	1201.1	0.5675	0.9588	1.5263	375.14	740.7	1115.8	250
300	417.33	0.01890	1.5433	393.84	809.0	1202.8	0.5879	0.9225	1.5104	392.79	724.3	1117.1	300
350	431.72	0.01913	1.3260	409.69	794.2	1203.9	0.6056	0.8910	1.4966	408.45	709.6	1118.0	350
400	444.59	0.0193	1.1613	424.0	780.5	1204.5	0.6214	0.8630	1.4844	422.6	695.9	1118.5	400
450	456.28	0.0195	1.0320	437.2	767.4	1204.6	0.6356	0.8378	1.4734	435.5	683.2	1118.7	450
500	467.01	0.0197	0.9278	449.4	755.0	1204.4	0.6487	0.8147	1.4634	447.6	671.0	1118.6	500
550	476.93	0.0199	0.8424	460.8	743.1	1203.9	0.6608	0.7934	1.4542	458.8	659.4	1118.2	550
600	486.21	0.0201	0.7698	471.6	731.6	1203.2	0.6720	0.7734	1.4454	469.4	648.3	1117.7	600
700	503.10	0.0205	0.6554	491.5	709.7	1201.2	0.6925	0.7371	1.4296	488.8	627.5	1116.3	700
800	518.23	0.0209	0.5687	509.7	688.9	1198.6	0.7108	0.7045	1.4153	506.6	607.8	1114.4	800
900	531.98	0.0212	0.5006	526.6	668.8	1195.4	0.7275	0.6744	1.4020	523.1	589.0	1112.1	900
1000	544.61	0.0216	0.4456	542.4	649.4	1191.8	0.7430	0.6467	1.3897	538.4	571.0	1109.4	1000
1100	556.31	0.0220	0.4001	557.4	630.4	1187.8	0.7575	0.6205	1.3780	552.9	553.5	1106.4	1100
1200	567.22	0.0223	0.3619	571.7	611.7	1183.4	0.7711	0.5956	1.3667	566.7	536.3	1103.0	1200
1300	577.46	0.0227	0.3293	585.4	593.2	1178.6	0.7840	0.5719	1.3559	580.0	519.4	1099.4	1300
1400	587.10	0.0231	0.3012	598.7	574.7	1173.4	0.7963	0.5491	1.3454	592.7	502.7	1095.4	1400
1500	596.23	0.0235	0.2765	611.6	556.3	1167.9	0.8082	0.5269	1.3351	605.1	486.1	1091.2	1500
2000	635.82	0.0257	0.1878	671.7	463.4	1135.1	0.8619	0.4230	1.2849	662.2	403.4	1065.6	2000
2500	668.13	0.0287	0.1307	730.6	360.5	1091.1	0.9126	0.3197	1.2322	717.3	313.3	1030.6	2500
3000	695.36	0.0346	0.0858	802.5	217.8	1020.3	0.9731	0.1885	1.1615	783.4	189.3	972.7	3000
3206.2	705.40	0.0503	0.0503	902.7	0	902.7	1.0580	0	1.0580	872.9	0	872.9	3206.2

APPENDIX

TABLE 3. SUPERHEATED VAPOR

Abs Press. Lb/Sq In. (Sat. Temp)		200	300	400	500	600	700	800	900	1000	1200	1400	1600
1 (101.74)	v	392.6	452.3	512.0	571.6	631.2	690.8	750.4	809.9	869.5	988.7	1107.8	1227.0
	h	1150.4	1195.8	1241.7	1288.3	1335.7	1383.8	1432.8	1482.7	1533.5	1637.7	1745.7	1857.5
	s	2.0512	2.1153	2.1720	2.2233	2.2702	2.3137	2.3542	2.3923	2.4283	2.4952	2.5566	2.6137
5 (162.24)	v	78.16	90.25	102.26	114.22	126.16	138.10	150.03	161.95	173.87	197.71	221.6	245.5
	h	1148.8	1195.0	1241.2	1288.0	1335.4	1383.6	1432.7	1482.6	1533.4	1637.7	1745.7	1857.4
	s	1.8718	1.9370	1.9942	2.0456	2.0927	2.1361	2.1767	2.2148	2.2509	2.3178	2.3792	2.4363
10 (193.21)	v	38.85	45.00	51.04	57.05	63.03	69.01	74.98	80.95	86.92	98.84	110.77	122.69
	h	1146.6	1193.9	1240.6	1287.5	1335.1	1383.4	1432.5	1482.4	1533.2	1637.6	1745.6	1857.3
	s	1.7927	1.8595	1.9172	1.9689	2.0160	2.0596	2.1002	2.1383	2.1744	2.2413	2.3028	2.3598
14.696 (212.00)	v		30.53	34.68	38.78	42.86	46.94	51.00	55.07	59.13	67.25	75.37	83.48
	h		1192.8	1239.9	1287.1	1334.8	1383.2	1432.3	1482.3	1533.1	1637.5	1745.5	1857.3
	s		1.8160	1.8743	1.9261	1.9734	2.0170	2.0576	2.0958	2.1319	2.1989	2.2603	2.3174
20 (227.96)	v		22.36	25.43	28.46	31.47	34.47	37.46	40.45	43.44	49.41	55.37	61.34
	h		1191.6	1239.2	1286.6	1334.4	1382.9	1432.1	1482.1	1533.0	1637.4	1745.4	1857.2
	s		1.7808	1.8396	1.8918	1.9392	1.9829	2.0235	2.0618	2.0978	2.1648	2.2263	2.2834
40 (267.25)	v		11.040	12.628	14.168	15.688	17.198	18.702	20.20	21.70	24.69	27.68	30.66
	h		1186.8	1236.5	1284.8	1333.1	1381.9	1431.3	1481.4	1532.4	1637.0	1745.1	1857.0
	s		1.6994	1.7608	1.8140	1.8619	1.9058	1.9467	1.9850	2.0212	2.0883	2.1498	2.2069
60 (292.71)	v		7.259	8.357	9.403	10.427	11.441	12.449	13.452	14.454	16.451	18.446	20.44
	h		1181.6	1233.6	1283.0	1331.8	1380.9	1430.5	1480.8	1531.9	1636.6	1744.8	1856.7
	s		1.6492	1.7135	1.7678	1.8162	1.8605	1.9015	1.9400	1.9762	2.0434	2.1049	2.1621
80 (312.03)	v			6.220	7.020	7.797	8.562	9.322	10.077	10.830	12.332	13.830	15.325
	h			1230.7	1281.1	1330.5	1379.9	1429.7	1480.1	1531.3	1636.2	1744.5	1856.5
	s			1.6791	1.7340	1.7836	1.8281	1.8694	1.9079	1.9442	2.0115	2.0731	2.1303
100 (327.81)	v			4.937	5.589	6.218	6.835	7.446	8.052	8.656	9.860	11.060	12.258
	h			1227.6	1279.1	1329.1	1378.9	1428.9	1479.5	1530.8	1635.7	1744.2	1856.2
	s			1.6518	1.7085	1.7581	1.8029	1.8443	1.8829	1.9193	1.9867	2.0484	2.1056
120 (341.25)	v			4.081	4.636	5.165	5.683	6.195	6.702	7.207	8.212	9.214	10.213
	h			1224.4	1277.2	1327.7	1377.8	1428.1	1478.8	1530.2	1635.3	1743.9	1856.0
	s			1.6287	1.6869	1.7370	1.7822	1.8237	1.8625	1.8990	1.9664	2.0281	2.0854
140 (353.02)	v			3.468	3.954	4.413	4.861	5.301	5.738	6.172	7.035	7.895	8.752
	h			1221.1	1275.2	1326.4	1376.8	1427.3	1478.2	1529.7	1634.9	1743.5	1855.7
	s			1.6087	1.6683	1.7190	1.7645	1.8063	1.8451	1.8817	1.9493	2.0110	2.0683
160 (363.53)	v			3.008	3.443	3.849	4.244	4.631	5.015	5.396	6.152	6.906	7.656
	h			1217.6	1273.1	1325.0	1375.7	1426.4	1477.5	1529.1	1634.5	1743.2	1855.5
	s			1.5908	1.6519	1.7033	1.7491	1.7911	1.8301	1.8667	1.9344	1.9962	2.0535
180 (373.00)	v			2.649	3.044	3.411	3.764	4.110	4.452	4.792	5.466	6.136	6.804
	h			1214.0	1271.0	1323.5	1374.7	1426.4	1477.5	1529.1	1634.5	1743.2	1855.5
	s			1.5745	1.6373	1.6894	1.7355	1.7776	1.8167	1.8534	1.9212	1.9831	2.0404
200 (381.79)	v			2.361	2.726	3.060	3.380	3.693	4.002	4.309	4.917	5.521	6.123
	h			1210.3	1268.9	1322.1	1373.6	1424.8	1476.2	1528.0	1633.7	1742.6	1855.0
	s			1.5594	1.6240	1.6767	1.7232	1.7655	1.8048	1.8415	1.9094	1.9713	2.0287
220 (389.86)	v			2.125	2.465	2.772	3.066	3.352	3.634	3.913	4.467	5.017	5.565
	h			1206.5	1266.7	1320.7	1372.6	1424.0	1475.5	1527.5	1633.3	1742.3	1854.7
	s			1.5453	1.6117	1.6652	1.7120	1.7545	1.7939	1.8308	1.8987	1.9607	2.0181
240 (397.37)	v			1.9276	2.247	2.533	2.804	3.068	3.327	3.584	4.093	4.597	5.100
	h			1202.5	1264.5	1319.2	1371.5	1423.2	1474.8	1526.9	1632.9	1742.0	1854.5
	s			1.5319	1.6003	1.6546	1.7017	1.7444	1.7839	1.8209	1.8889	1.9510	2.0084

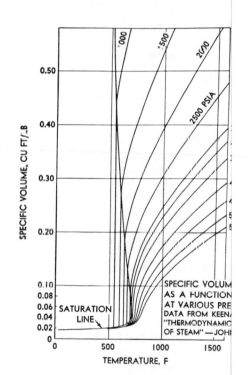

SATURATION LINE

SPECIFIC VOLUME AS A FUNCTION AT VARIOUS PRE DATA FROM KEEN "THERMODYNAMIC OF STEAM" —JOH

Some T in the Su

Heat, Work, and Power (Cont'd)

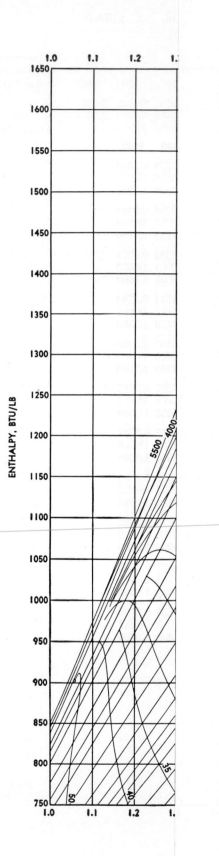

1 Btu/hr, sq ft, F/in.	= 0.1240 Cal/hr, sq m, C/m
1 therm	= 100,000 Btu
1 Calorie (Cal)	= 3088 foot-pounds
	= 427 kilogram-meters
	= 3.968 Btu
1 Cal per kilogram	= 1.8 Btu per pound
1 Cal per cu meter	= 0.1124 Btu per cubic foot
1 Cal per sq meter	= 0.3687 Btu per square foot
1 Cal/sq meter, C	= 0.2048 Btu/sq ft, F
1 Cal/hr, sq m, C/m	= 0.672 Btu/hr, sq ft, F/ft
	= 8.06 Btu/hr, sq ft, F/in.
1 electrical unit	= 1 kilowatthour
1 foot-pound (ft-lb)	= 0.1383 kilogram-meter
1 kilogram-meter (kg-m)	= 7.23 foot-pounds
1 kilowatt (kw)	= 738 foot-pounds per sec
	= 102 kilogram-meters per sec
	= 1.341 horsepower
	= 1.360 metric horsepower
1 horsepower (hp)	= 33,000 foot-pounds per min
	= 550 foot-pounds per sec
	= 76.04 kilogram-meters per sec
	= 0.746 kilowatt
	= 1.014 metric horsepower
1 metric horsepower	= 32,550 foot-pounds per min
	= 542 foot-pounds per sec
	= 75 kilogram-meters per sec
	= 0.735 kilowatt
	= 0.986 horsepower
1 kilowatthour (kwhr)	= 3412.75 Btu (3413)
	= 860 Calories
1 horsepower-hour	= 2545.1 Btu (2545)
1 metric horsepower-hour	= 632 Calories
1 lb per horsepower-hour	= 0.447 kg per metric hp-hr
1 kg per metric hp-hour	= 2.235 lb per horsepower-hr
1 boiler horsepower	= 10 sq ft of boiler heat-ing surface
	= 34.5 lb per hour evapo-ration from and at 212 F
100% boiler rating	= 3348 Btu (i.e., 3.45 lb evaporation from and at 212 F) per sq ft heating surface per hour

Table D

Creep Stress Data* for Tubular Materials in High-Temperature Service

Material

1. E-6010 (
2. E-6015 (
3. E-7010 (
4. E-7015 (
5. Croloy 1A
6. Croloy 2A
7. Croloy 2¼
8. Croloy 5,
9. Croloy 5S

° Should cont
† Croloy "A"
Champion R
carbon comm

Electrodes

Commerci
½ to 9M in
"15" type co

Preheating

The prehe
materials to
blies welded
400 F or hi

Postwelding

(1) The
times the w
any case no
within plus
1 hr per in
less than 30
uniform rat
applied to t

Chapter 22. Me

Specific

Element	Solid Solu In Alpha Iron
Al	30% ±
Cr	Unlimited
Co	80% ±
Mn	15 to 18%
Mo	32% (Less with lowered temperature)
Ni	25% ± (Irrespective of C)
P	2.5% (Irrespective of C)
Si	18.5% (Not much changed by carbon)
Ti	6% ± (Less with lowered temperature)
W	32% (Less with lowered temperature)
V	Unlimited

Chapter 18. Fuel Ash Related to Boiler Design and Operation

Determination of Ash-Fusion Temperatures

The standard laboratory procedure for the determination of the fusibility of ash, quoted below, appears in Standards On Coal and Coke (D271-48), issue of 1952, published by the American Society for Testing Materials:

Apparatus

27. The apparatus shall consist of the following:

(a) FURNACE—Any gas or electric furnace conforming to the following requirements may be used:

1) Capable of maintaining a zone of uniform temperature in which to heat the ash cones,

2) Capable of maintaining a reducing atmosphere surrounding the ash cones during heating, in which the ratio by volume of reducing gases to oxidizing gases is as specified in Section 30, (A mildly reducing atmosphere shall be maintained surrounding the cones during the heating. The ratio by volume of reducing gases to oxidizing gases in this atmosphere shall be between the limits 20 to 80 and 80 to 20. Hydrogen, hydrocarbons, and carbon monoxide shall be considered as reducing gases, and oxygen, carbon dioxide, and water vapor shall be considered oxidizing gases. Nitrogen is inert. For information concerning the effect of various atmospheres, see U. S. Bureau of Mines *Bulletin 129*, 1918).

3) Capable of regulation, so that the rate of temperature rise shall not be less than 5 and not more than 10 C per min, and

4) Provided with means of observing the ash cones during heating.

(b) CONE MOLD—The cone mold shall be suitable for making ash cones ¾ in. in height and ¼ in. in width at each side of the base, which is an equilateral triangle. A suitable mold, made from metal, is shown in Fig. A.

(c) PYROMETER—Temperature measurements shall be made with a thermocouple of platinum and platinum-rhodium used in conjunction with a high-resistance millivoltmeter or potentiometer; or with an optical pyrometer of the disappearing filament type, which has been calibrated to be accurate to 10 C up to 1400 C and to 15 C from 1400 to 1600 C. If a thermocouple is used, it shall be protected from the furnace gases by a glazed porcelain tube and so placed in the furnace that the hot junction is in the immediate vicinity of the cones. The pyrometer equipment shall be checked frequently by mounting small pieces of pure gold and nickel in the same manner as the cones. With a strong reducing atmos-

phere, 1452 C shall be obtained for the melting point of nickel and 1063 C for gold. The pyrometer equipment shall also be standardized, from time to time, through the temperature range for which it is used, by a suitably equipped standardizing laboratory, such as that of the National Bureau of Standards.

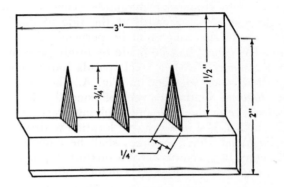

Fig. A. Brass cone mold

If temperature measurements are made by sighting an optical pyrometer through the glass window of the observation tube, the following corrections shall be added to the observed temperatures to correct for absorption of light by the glass window:

Observed Temperature, C	Correction, Deg C To be Added
800	5
1000	8
1200	10
1400	13
1600	16

Preparation of Ash

28. A 50- to 100-g portion of the coal or coke sample passing a 250-micron (No. 60) sieve shall be spread out on a 6-in. fireclay roasting dish. The sample shall be completely converted to ash in a muffle furnace at a temperature of 800 to 900 C. A 5- to 10-g portion of this ash shall be transferred to an agate mortar and ground so that it will pass a 74-micron (No. 200) sieve. The ash shall then be placed in a silica or porcelain capsule, ⅜ in. in depth and 1¾ in. in diameter, and ignited for a period of 2 hr in a current of oxygen at a temperature of 800 to 850 C to insure complete and uniform oxidization of the ash.

Preparation of Cones

29. (a) The ignited ash...
a solution of dextrin (10%)...
(0.1%) as a preservative a...
mass with a spatula. The...
molded into triangular py...
height and ¼ in. in width...
One side of the cone shall...
base. The cones shall be ma...
plastic material with a stee...
the dimensions specified in...
the material shall be stru...
removed from the mold by...
base, and placed in a suitab...

(b) When dry, the cone...
refractory base composed o...
by weight of kaolin and...
kaolin and alundum cemen...
tory brick. In using a mixtu...
alumina or of kaolin and a...
ture shall be moistened to...
the mixture shall be spread...
the cones mounted to no...
vertical positions in small...
and the base material press...
the bottom of the cones to...
make the cones stand firm...
cones may be mounted in...
Fig. B. When a piece of r...
the base, a layer of wet alu...

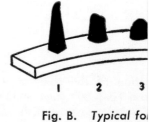

Fig. B. *Typical fo...*

TABLE E
Maximum Allowable Stress Values, Pounds per Square Inch

ASME Spec	Grade	Nominal Composition	Notes	Spec Min Tensile	−20 to 100	300	−20 to 400	400	500	650	700	800	900	1000	1100	1200	1300	1400	1500
PLATE STEELS																			
Carbon Steel																			
SA-30	Flange	—	(1)	55,000			13,750		13,750		13,250	10,200	—	—					
SA-30	Firebox A	—	(1)	55,000			13,750		13,750		13,250	10,200	5,000	—					
SA-30	Firebox B	—	(1)	48,000			12,000		12,000		11,650	9,000	5,000	—					
SA-129	A, B, C	—	—	44,000			11,000		11,000	11,000	—	—	—	—					
SA-201	A	C-Si	(1)	55,000			13,750		13,750		13,250	10,200	5,000	1,500					
SA-201	B	C-Si	(1)	60,000			15,000		15,000		14,350	10,800	5,000	1,500					
SA-212	A	C-Si	(1)	65,000			16,250		16,250		15,500	11,400	5,000	1,500					
SA-212	B	C-Si	(1)	70,000			17,500		17,500		16,600	12,000	5,000	1,500					
SA-285	A	—	(1)(6)	45,000			11,250		11,250		10,900	8,300	5,000	—					
SA-285	B	—	(1)(6)	50,000			12,500		12,500		12,100	9,400	5,000	—					
SA-285	C	—	(1)(6)	55,000			13,750		13,750		13,250	10,200	5,000	—					
SA-299		C-Mn-Si	(1)	75,000			18,750		18,750		17,700	12,000	5,000	1,500					
Low-Alloy Steel																			
SA-202	A	Cr-Mn-Si	—	75,000			18,750		18,750	18,750	17,700	12,000	5,000	1,500					
SA-202	B	Cr-Mn-Si	—	85,000			21,250		21,250	21,250	19,800	12,000	5,000	1,500					
SA-203	A, D	2½ & 3½Ni	—	65,000			16,250		16,250	16,250	15,500	11,400	5,000	1,500					
SA-203	B, E	2½ & 3½Ni	—	70,000			17,500		17,500	17,500	16,600	12,000	5,000	1,500					
SA-203	C	2½Ni	—	75,000			18,750		18,750	18,750	17,700	12,000	5,000	1,500					
SA-204	A	C-½Mo	(2)	65,000			16,250		16,250	16,250	16,250	15,650	12,500	5,500					
SA-204	B	C-½Mo	(2)	70,000			17,500		17,500	17,500	17,500	16,900	12,750	5,500					
SA-204	C	C-½Mo	(2)	75,000			18,750		18,750	18,750	18,750	18,000	13,000	5,500					
SA-225	A	Mn-V	(1)	70,000			17,500		17,500	17,500	16,600	12,000	5,000	1,500					
SA-225	B	Mn-V	(1)	75,000			18,750		18,750	18,750	17,700	12,000	5,000	1,500					
SA-301	A	½Cr-½Mo	—	65,000			16,250		16,250	16,250	16,250	15,650	12,500	6,250	2,800				
SA-301	B	1Cr-½Mo	—	60,000			15,000		15,000	15,000	15,000	14,750	13,100	7,500	1,000				
SA-302	A	Mn-½Mo	(2)	75,000			18,750		18,750	18,750	18,750	18,000	13,000	5,500					
SA-302	B	Mn-½Mo	(2)	80,000			20,000		20,000	20,000	20,000	19,100	13,250	5,500					
SA-357		5Cr-½Mo	—	60,000			15,000		14,500	14,500	13,400	12,800	11,500	7,300	3,300	1,500			
High-Alloy Steel																			
SA-240	S	18Cr-8Ni	(7)	75,000	18,750	16,000		15,450	15,100	14,850	14,800	14,550	14,000	14,000	7,500	4,500	2,450	1,400	750
SA-240	S	18Cr-8Ni	—	75,000	18,750	15,000		13,650	12,500	11,200	10,800	10,000	8,800	8,800	7,500	4,500	2,450	1,400	750
SA-240	M	18Cr-10Ni-2Mo	—	75,000	18,750	17,900		17,500	17,200	17,050	17,000	16,750	16,000	14,000	10,400	6,800	4,000	2,200	1,000
SA-240	T	18Cr-8Ni-Ti	—	75,000	18,750	17,000		15,800	15,200	14,850	14,800	14,550	14,350	13,500	10,300	5,000	2,200	1,200	750
SA-240	C	18Cr-8Ni-Cb	—	75,000	18,750	17,000		15,800	15,200	14,850	14,800	14,550	14,100	13,500	10,300	5,000	2,200	1,200	750
PIPE & TUBES																			
Seamless Carbon Steel																			
SA-53	A	—	(1)(3)	48,000			12,000		12,000		11,650	9,000	5,000	—					
SA-53	B	—	(1)(3)(12)	60,000			15,000		15,000		14,350	10,800	5,000	—					
SA-83	A	—	(12)	(47,000)			11,750		11,750		11,450	9,000	—	1,500					
SA-83	B	—	(12)	(40,000)			10,000		10,000		9,700	—	—	—					
SA-106	A	—	(1)	48,000			12,000		12,000		11,650	9,000	5,000	1,500					
SA-106	B	—	(1)	60,000			15,000		15,000		14,350	10,800	5,000	1,500					
SA-192	A	—	(1)(12)	(47,000)			11,750		11,750		11,450	9,000	5,000	1,500					
SA-210	A	—	(1)	60,000			15,000		15,000		14,350	10,800	5,000	—					

For metal temperatures not exceeding deg F

TABLE E (Continued)

Maximum Allowable Stress Values, Pounds per Square Inch

ASME Spec	Grade	Nominal Composition	Spec Min Tensile	Notes	-20 to 100	300	400	For metal temperatures not exceeding deg F -20 to 400	500	650	700	800	900	1000	1100	1200	1300	1400	1500
Seamless Alloy Steel																			
SA-209	T1	C-½Mo	55,000	(2)	—	—	—	13,750	13,750	13,750	13,750	13,450	12,500	5,500	—	—	—	—	—
SA-209	T1a	C-½Mo	60,000	(2)	—	—	—	15,000	15,000	15,000	15,000	14,400	12,500	5,500	—	—	—	—	—
SA-209	T1b	C-½Mo	53,000	(2)	—	—	—	13,250	13,250	13,250	13,250	13,000	12,500	5,500	—	—	—	—	—
SA-213	T5	5Cr-½Mo	60,000		—	—	—	15,000	14,500	13,700	13,400	12,800	11,500	7,300	3,300	1,500	—	—	—
SA-213	T7	7Cr-½Mo	60,000		—	—	—	15,000	14,500	13,700	13,400	12,500	9,500	5,000	2,500	1,200	—	—	—
SA-213	T9	9Cr-1Mo	60,000		—	—	—	15,000	14,500	13,700	13,400	12,800	12,000	8,500	3,300	1,560	—	—	—
SA-213	T11	1¼Cr-½Mo	60,000		—	—	—	15,000	15,000	15,000	15,000	15,000	13,100	7,800	4,300	1,200	—	—	—
SA-213	T12	1Cr-½Mo	60,000		—	—	—	15,000	15,000	15,000	15,000	14,750	13,100	7,500	2,300	1,000	—	—	—
SA-213	T5b	5Cr-½Mo-Si	60,000		—	—	—	15,000	14,500	13,700	13,400	12,800	10,900	5,500	2,500	1,200	—	—	—
SA-213	T3b	2Cr-½Mo	60,000		—	—	—	15,000	15,000	15,000	15,000	14,700	12,500	6,200	2,750	1,200	—	—	—
SA-213	T21	3Cr-1Mo	60,200		—	—	—	15,000	15,000	15,000	14,800	13,900	12,000	7,000	4,000	1,500	—	—	—
SA-213	T22	2¼Cr-1Mo	60,300		—	—	—	15,000	15,000	15,000	15,000	15,000	13,100	7,800	4,200	2,000	—	—	—
SA-213	TP304	18Cr-8Ni	75,000	(7)	18,750	16,000	15,450		15,100	14,850	14,800	14,550	14,000	12,500	7,500	4,500	2,450	1,400	750
SA-213	TP304	18Cr-8Ni	75,000		18,750	15,000	13,350		12,500	11,200	10,800	10,000	9,400	8,890	7,500	4,500	2,450	1,400	750
SA-213	TP316	16Cr-13Ni-3Mo	75,000		18,750	17,900	17,530		17,200	17,050	17,000	16,750	16,000	14,000	10,400	6,800	4,000	2,000	1,000
SA-213	TP321	18Cr-8Ni-Ti	75,000		18,750	17,000	15,830		15,200	14,850	14,800	14,550	14,100	13,500	10,300	5,000	2,200	1,200	750
SA-213	TP347	18Cr-8Ni-Cb	75,000		18,750	17,000	15,800		15,200	14,850	14,800	14,550	14,100	13,500	10,300	5,000	2,200	1,200	750
SA-312	TP304	18Cr-8Ni	75,000	(7)	18,750	16,000	15,450		15,100	14,850	14,800	14,530	14,000	12,500	7,500	4,500	2,450	1,400	750
SA-312	TP304	18Cr-8Ni	75,000		18,750	15,000	13,650		12,500	11,200	10,800	10,030	9,400	8,800	7,500	4,500	2,450	1,400	750
SA-312	TP316	16Cr-13Ni-3Mo	75,000		18,750	17,900	17,500		17,200	17,050	17,000	16,750	16,000	14,000	10,400	6,800	4,000	2,000	1,000
SA-312	TP321	18Cr-8Ni-Ti	75,000		18,750	17,000	15,200		15,200	14,850	14,800	14,550	14,100	13,500	10,300	5,000	2,200	1,200	750
SA-312	TP347	18Cr-8Ni-Cb	75,000		18,750	17,000	15,800		15,200	14,850	14,800	14,550	14,100	13,500	10,300	5,000	2,200	1,200	750
SA-335	P1	C-½Mo	55,000	(2)	—	—	—		13,750	13,750	13,750	13,450	12,500	5,500	—	—	—	—	—
SA-335	P2	½Cr-½Mo	55,000		—	—	—		13,750	13,750	13,750	13,450	12,500	6,250	—	—	—	—	—
SA-335	P3b	2Cr-½Mo	60,000		—	—	—		15,000	15,000	15,000	14,700	12,500	6,200	2,750	1,200	—	—	—
SA-335	P5	5Cr-½Mo	60,000		—	—	—		14,500	13,700	13,400	12,800	11,500	7,300	3,300	1,500	—	—	—
SA-335	P5b	5Cr-½Mo-Si	60,000		—	—	—		14,500	13,700	13,400	12,800	10,900	5,500	2,500	1,200	—	—	—
SA-335	P11	1¼Cr-½Mo	60,000		—	—	—	15,000	15,000	15,000	15,000	15,000	13,100	7,800	4,000	1,200	—	—	—
SA-335	P12	1Cr-½Mo	60,000		—	—	—	15,000	15,000	15,000	15,000	14,750	13,100	7,500	2,800	1,000	—	—	—
SA-335	P7	7Cr-½Mo	60,000		—	—	—	15,000	14,500	13,700	13,400	12,500	9,500	5,000	2,500	1,000	—	—	—
SA-335	P9	9Cr-1Mo	60,000		—	—	—	15,000	14,500	13,700	13,400	12,800	12,000	8,500	3,300	1,500	—	—	—
SA-335	P21	3Cr-1Mo	60,000		—	—	—	15,000	15,000	15,000	14,800	13,900	12,000	7,000	4,000	1,500	—	—	—
SA-335	P22	2¼Cr-1Mo	60,000		—	—	—	15,000	15,000	15,000	15,000	15,000	13,100	7,800	4,200	2,000	—	—	—
Electric-Resistance-Welded Carbon Steel																			
SA-53	A	—	48,000	(1) (8)	—	—	—	13,200	12,850	10,200	9,900	7,650	4,250	—	—	—	—	—	—
SA-53	B	—	60,000	(1) (8)	—	—	—	12,750	12,750	12,750	12,200	9,200	4,250	—	—	—	—	—	—
SA-135	A	—	48,000	(1) (8)	—	—	—	10,200	10,200	10,200	9,900	7,650	4,250	—	—	—	—	—	—
SA-135	B	—	60,000	(1) (8)	—	—	—	12,750	12,750	12,750	12,200	9,200	4,250	—	—	—	—	—	—
SA-178	A	—	(47,000)	(1) (3) (11) (12)	—	—	—	11,750	11,750	11,750	11,450	7,650	4,250	1,300	—	—	—	—	—
SA-178	B	—	40,000	(3) (11)	—	—	—	8,500	8,500	8,500	8,200	—	—	—	—	—	—	—	—
SA-178	C	—	60,000	(3) (11)	—	—	—	-5,000	15,000	15,000	14,350	9,200	4,250	1,300	—	—	—	—	—
SA-226	—	—	(47,000)	(1) (11) (12)	—	—	—	11,750	11,750	11,750	11,450	7,650	4,250	1,300	—	—	—	—	—
Electric-Resistance-Welded Alloy Steel																			
SA-249	TP304	18Cr-8Ni	75,000	(7) (8)	15,950	13,600	13,150		12,850	12,600	12,550	12,350	11,900	10,650	6,400	3,850	2,100	1,200	650
SA-249	TP304	18Cr-8Ni	75,000	(3)	15,950	12,750	11,600		10,650	9,500	9,200	8,500	8,000	7,500	6,400	3,850	2,100	1,200	650
SA-249	TP316	16Cr-13Ni-3Mo	75,000	(8)	15,950	15,200	14,900		14,600	14,500	14,450	14,250	14,450	11,900	8,350	5,800	3,400	1,700	850
SA-249	TP321	18Cr-8Ni-Ti	75,000	(8)	15,950	14,450	13,450		12,900	12,600	12,550	12,350	12,000	11,500	8,750	4,250	1,850	1,000	650
SA-249	TP347	18Cr-8Ni-Cb	75,000	(8)	15,950	14,450	13,450		12,900	12,600	12,550	12,350	12,000	11,500	8,750	4,250	1,850	1,000	650

TABLE E (Continued)

Maximum Allowable Stress Values, Pounds per Square Inch

ASME Spec	Grade	Nominal Composition	Spec Min Tensile	Notes	For metal temperatures not exceeding deg F														
					−20 to 100	300	400	−20 to 400	500	650	700	800	900	1000	1100	1200	1300	1400	1500
Electric-Resistance-Welded Alloy Steel																			
SA-250	T1	C-½Mo	55,000	(2)(8)	—	—	—	—	13,750	13,750	13,750	13,450	12,500	*5,500*	—	—	—	—	—
SA-250	T1a	C-½Mo	60,000	(2)(8)	—	—	—	—	15,000	15,000	15,000	14,400	12,500	*5,500*	—	—	—	—	—
SA-250	T1b	C-½Mo	53,000	(2)(8)	—	—	—	—	13,250	13,250	13,250	13,000	12,500	*5,500*	—	—	—	—	—
Lap Welded																			
SA-53	steel	—	45,000	(9)	—	—	—	9,000	9,000	9,000	8,750	—	—	—	—	—	—	—	—
SA-72	wrought iron	—	40,000	(9)	—	—	—	8,000	8,000	8,000	7,800	—	—	—	—	—	—	—	—
SA-83	steel	—	(45,000)	(9)(12)	—	—	—	9,000	9,000	9,000	8,750	—	—	—	—	—	—	—	—
SA-83	iron	—	—	(9)	—	—	—	8,000	8,000	8,000	7,800	—	—	—	—	—	—	—	—
Butt Welded																			
SA-53	steel	—	45,000	(10)	—	—	—	6,750	6,750	6,750	6,500	—	—	—	—	—	—	—	—
SA-72	wrought iron	—	40,000	(10)	—	—	—	6,000	6,000	6,000	5,800	—	—	—	—	—	—	—	—
Automatically Welded Austenitic Stainless Steel																			
SA-312	TP304	18Cr-8Ni	75,000	(7)(8)	15,950	13,600	13,150	—	12,850	12,600	12,550	12,350	11,900	10,650	6,400	3,850	2,100	1,200	650
SA-312	TP304	18Cr-8Ni	75,000	(8)	15,950	12,750	11,600	—	10,650	9,500	9,200	8,500	8,000	7,500	6,400	3,850	2,100	1,200	650
SA-312	TP316	16Cr-13Ni-3Mo	75,900	(8)	15,950	15,200	14,900	—	14,600	14,600	14,450	14,250	13,600	11,900	8,850	5,800	3,400	1,700	850
SA-312	TP321	18Cr-8Ni-Ti	75,000	(8)	15,950	14,450	13,450	—	12,900	12,600	12,550	12,350	12,000	11,500	8,750	4,250	1,850	1,000	650
SA-312	TP347	18Cr-8Ni-Cb	75,000	(8)	15,950	14,450	13,450	—	12,900	12,600	12,550	12,350	12,000	11,500	8,750	4,250	1,850	1,000	650
FORGINGS — Carbon Steel																			
SA-105	I	—	60,000	(1)(3)	—	—	—	15,000	15,000	15,000	14,350	10,800	*5,000*	*1,500*	—	—	—	—	—
SA-105	II	—	70,000	(1)(3)	—	—	—	17,500	17,500	17,500	16,600	12,000	*5,000*	*1,500*	—	—	—	—	—
SA-181	I	—	60,000	(1)(3)	—	—	—	15,000	15,000	15,000	14,350	10,800	*5,000*	*1,500*	—	—	—	—	—
SA-181	II	—	70,000	(1)(3)	—	—	—	17,500	17,500	17,500	16,600	12,000	*5,000*	*1,500*	—	—	—	—	—
SA-266	I	—	60,000	(1)	—	—	—	15,000	15,000	15,000	14,350	10,800	*5,000*	*1,500*	—	—	—	—	—
SA-266	II	—	70,000	(1)	—	—	—	17,500	17,500	17,500	16,600	12,000	*5,000*	*1,500*	—	—	—	—	—
SA-266	III	—	75,000	(1)	—	—	—	18,750	18,750	18,750	17,700	12,000	*5,000*	*1,500*	—	—	—	—	—
Alloy Steel																			
SA-182	F1	C-½Mo	70,000	(2)	—	—	—	17,500	17,500	17,500	17,500	16,900	*12,750*	*5,500*	—	*1,000*	—	—	—
SA-182	F12	1Cr-½Mo	70,000	—	—	—	—	17,500	17,500	16,800	16,150	14,850	13,100	7,500	2,800	1,500	—	—	—
SA-182	F5	5Cr-½Mo	90,000	—	—	—	—	22,500	21,600	19,000	17,500	14,500	11,500	7,300	3,300	*1,800*	—	—	—
SA-182	F11	1¼Cr-½Mo	70,000	—	—	—	—	17,500	17,500	16,800	16,150	15,000	13,100	7,800	3,300	1,500	—	—	—
SA-182	F9	9Cr-1Mo	100,000	—	—	—	—	25,000	24,000	22,000	21,200	17,700	13,100	8,500	3,300	1,500	—	—	—
SA-182	F22	2¼Cr-1Mo	70,000	(7)	—	—	—	17,500	17,500	17,500	17,500	14,000	14,000	7,800	4,200	2,000	—	—	—
SA-182	F304	18Cr-8Ni	75,000	—	—	—	—	—	15,100	14,850	14,550	14,550	14,000	12,500	7,500	4,500	2,450	1,400	750
SA-182	F304	18Cr-8Ni	75,000	—	—	—	—	—	12,500	11,200	10,800	10,000	9,400	8,800	7,500	4,500	2,450	1,400	750
SA-182	F316	18Cr-8Ni-Mo	75,000	—	—	—	—	—	17,200	17,050	17,000	16,750	16,000	14,000	10,400	6,800	4,000	2,000	1,000
SA-182	F321	18Cr-8Ni-Ti	75,000	—	—	—	—	—	15,200	14,850	14,800	14,550	14,100	13,500	10,300	5,000	2,200	1,200	750
SA-182	F347	18Cr-8Ni-Cb	75,000	—	—	—	—	—	15,200	14,850	14,800	14,550	14,100	13,500	10,300	5,000	2,200	1,200	750
SA-336	F1	C-½Mo	70,000	(2)	—	—	—	17,500	17,500	17,500	17,500	16,900	*12,750*	*5,500*	—	*1,000*	—	—	—
SA-336	F2	1Cr-½Mo	70,000	—	—	—	—	17,500	17,500	16,800	16,150	14,850	13,100	7,500	2,800	1,500	—	—	—
SA-336	F5	5Cr-½Mo	80,000	—	—	—	—	20,000	19,200	17,300	17,300	14,500	11,500	7,300	3,300	2,000	—	—	—
SA-336	F22	2¼Cr-1Mo	80,000	(7)	—	—	—	20,000	20,000	20,000	20,000	14,550	14,000	7,800	4,200	2,000	—	—	—
SA-336	F8	18Cr-8Ni	75,000	—	—	—	—	—	15,100	14,850	14,800	14,550	14,000	12,500	7,500	4,500	2,450	1,400	750
SA-336	F8	18Cr-8Ni	75,000	—	—	—	—	—	12,500	11,200	10,800	10,000	9,400	8,800	7,500	4,500	2,450	1,400	750
SA-336	F8m	18Cr-8Ni-Mo	75,000	—	—	—	—	—	17,200	17,050	17,000	16,750	16,000	14,000	10,400	6,800	4,000	2,000	1,000
SA-336	F8t	18Cr-8Ni-Ti	75,000	—	—	—	—	—	15,200	14,850	14,800	14,550	14,100	13,500	10,300	5,000	2,200	1,200	750
SA-336	F8c	18Cr-8Ni-Cb	75,000	—	—	—	—	—	15,200	14,850	14,800	14,550	14,100	13,500	10,300	5,000	2,200	1,200	750

TABLE E (Concluded)

Maximum Allowable Stress Values, Pounds per Square Inch

ASME Spec	Grade	Nominal Composition	Spec Min Tensile	Notes	-20 to 100	300	400	-20 to 400	500	650	700	800	900	1000	1100	1200	1300	1400	1500
CASTINGS Carbon Steel																			
SA-95	—	—	70,000	(1) (5)	—	—	—	17,500	17,500	17,500	16,600	12,000	5,000	1,500	—	—	—	—	—
SA-216	WCA	—	60,000	(1) (5)	—	—	—	15,000	15,000	15,000	14,350	10,800	5,000	1,500	—	—	—	—	—
SA-216	WCB	—	70,000	(1) (5)	—	—	—	17,500	17,500	17,500	16,600	12,000	5,000	1,500	—	—	—	—	—
Alloy Steel																			
SA-157	C9a	18Cr-8Ni	70,000	(5) (7)	17,500	15,600	15,000	—	14,600	14,200	14,050	13,600	13,000	12,100	7,500	4,500	2,450	1,400	750
SA-157	C9a	18Cr-8Ni	70,000	(5)	17,500	14,250	13,100	—	12,200	11,500	11,300	10,900	10,400	9,850	7,500	4,500	2,450	1,400	750
SA-217	WC1	C-½Mo	65,000	(2) (4) (5)	—	—	16,250	16,250	16,250	16,250	16,250	15,650	12,500	5,500	—	—	—	—	—
SA-217	WC4	Ni-Cr-½Mo	70,000	(4) (5)	—	—	17,500	17,500	17,500	17,500	17,500	17,000	14,000	6,250	—	—	—	—	—
SA-217	WC5	Ni-Cr-1Mo	70,000	(4) (5)	—	—	17,500	17,500	17,500	17,500	17,500	17,000	14,000	7,800	—	—	—	—	—
SA-217	WC6	1¼Cr-½Mo	70,000	(4) (5)	—	—	17,500	17,500	17,500	17,500	17,500	17,000	14,000	7,800	—	—	—	—	—
SA-217	WC9	2¼Cr-1Mo	70,000	(4) (5)	—	—	17,500	17,500	17,500	17,500	17,500	17,000	14,000	7,800	—	—	—	—	—
SA-217	C5	5Cr-½Mo	90,000	(4) (5)	—	—	22,500	22,500	22,500	22,500	21,600	19,000	13,600	7,300	3,300	1,500	—	—	—
SA-217	C12	9Cr-1Mo	90,000	(4) (5)	—	—	22,500	22,500	22,500	22,500	22,900	19,400	15,000	8,500	3,300	1,500	—	—	—
SA-351	CF8	18Cr-8Ni	70,000	(5) (7)	17,500	15,600	15,000	—	14,600	14,200	14,050	13,600	13,000	12,100	7,500	4,500	2,450	1,400	750
SA-351	CF8	18Cr-8Ni	70,000	(5)	17,500	14,250	13,100	—	12,200	11,500	11,300	10,900	10,400	9,850	7,500	4,500	2,450	1,430	750

GENERAL NOTE: Stress values shown in italic are permissible, but use of these materials at these temperatures is not current practice.

NOTES:

(1) Upon prolonged exposure to temperatures above about 800 F, the carbide phase of carbon steel may be converted to graphite.

(2) Upon prolonged exposure to temperatures above about 875 F, the carbide phase of carbon-molybdenum steel may be converted to graphite.

(3) Only killed steel shall be used above 900 F.

(4) These stress values apply to normalized and tempered material only.

(5) To these stress values a casting quality factor as specified in paragraph P-27, ASME Code, shall be applied.

(6) Flange quality in this specification not permitted above 850 F.

(7) See note 7, Table P-7, ASME Code.

(8) These stress values include a joint efficiency factor of 0.85.

(9) These stress values include a joint efficiency factor of 0.80.

(10) These stress values include a joint efficiency factor of 0.60.

(11) Above 700 F these stress values include a joint efficiency factor of 0.85. When material to this specification is used for pipe, multiply the stress values up to and including 700 F by a factor of 0.85. When material to this specification is used for boiler, water-wall, superheater, and economizer tubes that are enclosed within a setting, the stress values above 700 F up to and including 850 F may be divided by a factor of 0.85.

(12) Tensile value in parentheses is expected minimum.

Table F
Index of Specifications for Ferrous Boiler Materials

Boiler Tubes

ASME Spec	Material	OD Min	OD Max	Wall Thk Min	Wall Thk Max
SA-83	Lap-welded steel	½″	6″	0.035″	0.320″
SA-83	Seamless steel	½″	6″	0.035″	0.320″
SA-83	Lap-welded iron	½″	6″	0.035″	0.320″
SA-178	ERW steel	½″	5″	0.035″	0.320″
SA-178	Open-hearth iron	½″	5″	0.035″	0.320″
SA-192	Seamless (h-p)	½″	7″	0.085″	1.000″

Boiler and Superheater Tubes

ASME Spec	Material	OD Min	OD Max	Wall Thk Min	Wall Thk Max
SA-210	Seamless C-Mo	½″	5″	0.035″	0.500″
SA-209	Med-C seamless	½″	5″	0.035″	0.500″
SA-213*	Seamless alloy	½″	5″	0.035″	0.500″
SA-226	ERW (h-p service)	½″	5″	0.085″	0.360″
SA-249	Welded alloy	½″	5″	0.035″	0.320″
SA-250	ERW C-Mo alloy	½″	5″	0.035″	0.320″

ASME Grade	Corresponding B&W Grade
T12	Croloy 1
T11	Croloy 1¼
T14	Croloy 2
T22	Croloy 2¼
T21	Croloy 3M
T5	Croloy 5
*T13	Croloy 5Si
T7	Croloy 7
T9	Croloy 9
TP304	Croloy 18-8S
TP321	Croloy 18-8Ti
TP347	Croloy 18-8Cb
TP316	Croloy 16-13-3

Pipe

ASME Spec	Material	Nom Size Min	Nom Size Max	Wall Thk Min	Wall Thk Max
SA-53	Welded & seamless	⅛″	8″	0.068″	0.875″
		—	12″	—	0.500″
SA-106	Seamless carbon (h-t)	⅛″	24″	0.068″	1.750″
SA-135	ERW steel	⅛″	30″	0.068″	—
SA-158*	Seamless alloy (h-t)	⅛″	24″	0.068″	1.750″
SA-206	Seamless				
	C-Mo alloy (h-t)	⅛″	24″	0.068″	1.750″
SA-280†	Seamless				
	Cr-Mo alloy (h-t)	½″	6″	0.187″	1.562″
SA-312	Austenitic stainless	⅛″	12″	0.049″	0.500″
SA-315‡	Seamless				
	Cr-Mo alloy (h-t)	½″	16″	0.187″	1.562″
SA-335	Seamless ferritic (h-t)	½″	16″	0.187″	1.593″

ASME Grade	Corresponding B&W Grade
P11	Croloy 1¼
P3a	Croloy 1¾
P3b	Croloy 2
*P5a	Croloy 5
P5c	Croloy 5 (Ti or Cb)
P8a	Croloy 18-8S
P8b	Croloy 18-8Ti
† —	Croloy ½
‡ —	Croloy 1

Plates—Boilers & Other Pressure Vessels

ASME Spec	Material	Quality & Grade	Max Thk
SA-201	C-Si steel fusion welded, usual tensile range	Flange, A, B	2″
		Firebox, A	12″
		Firebox, B	8″
SA-202	Cr-Mn-Si alloy	Firebox, all grades	2″
SA-203	Nickel steel	Flange, all grades	2″
		Firebox, A, B	
		Firebox, C, D, E	4″
SA-204	Molybdenum steel	Flange, all grades	2″
		Firebox, A, B	6″
		Firebox, C	4″
SA-212	High-tensile C-Si	Flange, all grades	2″
		Firebox, all grades	6″
SA-285	Carbon steel, low & inter tensile	Flange, Firebox, all grades	2″
SA-299	High-tensile C-Mn-Si	Flange, Firebox	2″
SA-301	Cr-molybdenum	Flange, all grades	2″
		Firebox, all grades	6″
SA-302	Mn-molybdenum	Flange, A, B	2″
		Firebox, A, B	4″

Castings

ASME Spec	Material	Used For
SA-48	Gray iron	Iron castings
SA-95	Carbon steel	Valves, flanges, and fittings in h-t service
SA-157	Alloy steel	Valves, flanges, and fittings in h-t service
SA-216	Carbon steel	Fusion welding in high-temp service
SA-217	Alloy steel	Fusion welding in high-temp service
SA-351	Stainless steel	Stainless steel castings

Forgings

ASME Spec	Material	Used For
SA-105	Steel	Forged or rolled pipe flanges, forged fittings, valves, & parts for h-t
SA-182	Alloy steel	Forged or rolled pipe flanges, forged fittings, valves, & parts for h-t
SA-266	Carbon steel	Seamless drum forgings
SA-336	Alloy steel	Seamless drum forgings

Bolting and Nuts

ASME Spec	Material	Used For
SA-193	Alloy steel	Bolting in h-t service
SA-194	Carbon & alloy steel	Nuts for bolts in high-press. & temp service
SA-306	Med-carbon steel	Bars subject to mechanical property requirements

INDEX